14.99 T
574

advanced

BIOLOGY

principles
&
applications

STUDY GUIDE

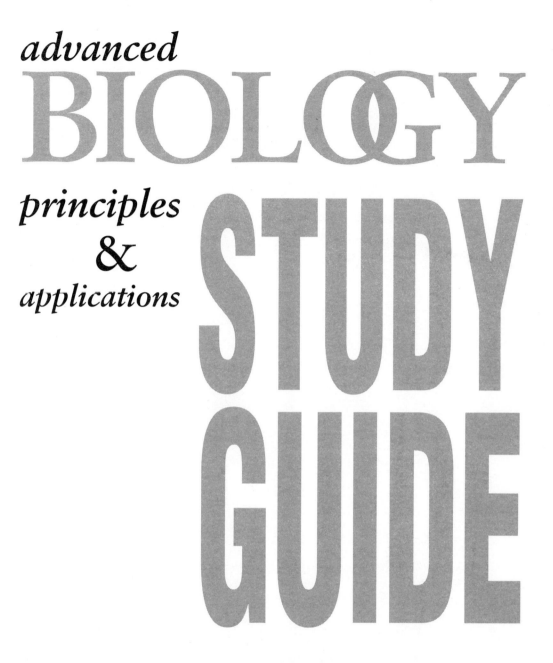

advanced

BIOLOGY

principles
&
applications

STUDY GUIDE

C J CLEGG with D G Mackean
P H Openshaw and R C Reynolds

JOHN MURRAY

© 1996 C J Clegg with D G Mackean, P H Openshaw and R C Reynolds

First published in 1996
by John Murray (Publishers) Ltd
50 Albemarle Street
London W1X 4BD

Illustrations by Don Mackean. Additional illustrations by Barking Dog Art.
Layouts by Eric Drewery.

Typeset in 9.5/11pt Sabon and Helvetica Condensed by Wearset, Boldon, Tyne and Wear.
Printed and bound in Great Britain by Butler and Tanner, Frome and London.

A CIP catalogue record for this book is available from the British Library.

ISBN 0-7195-5358-X

Contents

CONTENTS

Introduction

Advanced Biology Study Guide is not a course, it's a resource!

The contents of each chapter are potentially very useful to the study of biology at this level, but you will not have time to try all the projects or even all of the practicals.

Make a careful selection (see below) based on the syllabus you are working to, the resources available and on your particular interests and needs.

Each chapter provides:
- a **Summary** of the concepts and key terms;
- **Practicals** (and other Activities) for laboratory, classroom or field studies;

The practicals are of four types:

1 **skills and techniques** practicals essential or useful to investigations at this level;

2 **data-generating** practicals on important issues which, suitably reported, are ideal as teacher-assessed course work (Statistical methods are introduced in appropriate situations.);

3 **demonstrations**, which may raise questions and enhance understanding;

4 **investigations**, longer practicals with greater opportunities for experimental design.

The activities make use of IT developments (simulation software, spreadsheets, CD-ROM, the Internet, for example) and other audio-visual aid resources. They help you extend your skills of data handling and develop your understanding, your own thinking, and your communication skills.

- **Projects** are 'starter' ideas for extended fieldwork or longer-term laboratory experiments. Many of the practicals that are described as 'Investigations' may serve the same role.
- **Problems** (and Assignments) are for group work or individual, structured private study. Items may require you to recall, interpret, apply, explain or summarise. Others raise issues of experimental design, and require the processing of second-hand data and the interpretation of results. Some examine scientific achievements from social, environmental and commercial perspectives, in order to consider the consequences of science. Some items further the acquisition of communication skills. Appropriate answers to the Problems are suggested at the back of the book.

At the end of the book there are useful reference resources – a **Glossary** and **Appendices** on Equipment and materials, Experimental design and the evaluation of data, and on Study techniques, revision and examinations. In addition there are **Answers to questions** (those raised in the Problems).

Being selective over the Practicals, Projects and Problems used

The Biology syllabus you are working to may be modular or 'straight through'. Either way, it lists rather a lot of subject matter, much of which will need to be studied in detail and understood. Some syllabuses suggest practicals, too, and all courses involve assessments of practical, investigational skills. The added challenge comes from the time factor; you will almost certainly have only five terms of full-time teaching and study for all this!

When your syllabus is organised into a sequence of topics to be covered each term, this organisation provides a **scheme of work**. Often, a copy of the 'scheme of work' is as useful to you as a copy of the syllabus, or more so. For example, it may help you to see the links that can be developed between topics. By checking your scheme of work regularly, you get a sense of the progress you are making.

As you progress through your course, you develop your knowledge, extend your skills and acquire new skills, too. The items of this *Study Guide* are designed to help you in this.

For example, you might select some of the following:

1 **To acquire knowledge of key concepts**, tackle Practical and Problem items, for example:

classification of living things	Problem 2.1, p. 15
water as a biologically important molecule	Problem 6.2, p. 92
cell structure	Practical 7.4, p. 100–1; Problem 7.4, p. 104
DNA and protein synthesis	Problem 9.3, p. 125
water potential	Practical 11.2, p. 133; Problem 11.2, p. 136
leaf structure and photosynthesis	Practicals 12.1, p. 140, and 12.4, p. 145; Problems 12.1 and 12.2, pp. 150–1
heterotrophic nutrition	Problem 14.1, p. 176
digestion in the gut	Problem 13.5, p. 170
stages of tissues respiration	Problem 15.4, p. 190–1
mineral nutrient requirement	Practical 16.3, p. 195–6
translocation of elaborated food	Problem 16.3, p. 201
blood circulation	Problems 17.1 and 17.2, pp. 209–10
kidney structure and function	Practical 18.3, p. 213–5; Problem 18.2, p. 220
growth and development	Practicals 19.1, 19.2 and 19.3, pp. 224–7, 19.5, 19.6 and 19.7, pp. 228–30; Problems 19.2 and 19.3, pp. 233–5
response and sensitivity	Practicals 21.4, 21.5, 21.6, 21.7 and 21.8, pp. 249–55; Problems 21.1, 21.2 and 21.3, pp. 258–9
locomotion	Practicals 22.4 and 22.5, pp. 262–4; Problem 22.1, p. 265
homeostasis	Practicals 23.1, 23.2, 23.3 and 23.4 pp. 266–9; Problems 23.1 and 23.2, pp. 275–6
life-cycles and reproduction	Practicals 26.3, 26.4, 26.5, 26.6, 26.7 and 26.8, pp. 305–11, 27.1, p. 320–1; Problems 27.1, 27.2 and 27.3, pp. 328–39
Mendelian genetics	Practicals 28.1, 28.2 and 28.3, pp. 333–8; Problem 28.3, p. 347

2 To develop essential practical skills, tackle Practicals, for example:

making and using keys	Practicals 2.1, and 2.2, p. 8–10; Problems 2.2, p. 15–17, and 26.7, p. 317–18
ecological investigations	Practical 3.2, p. 28–31; Problem 3.3, p. 43–4
microscopy	Practicals 7.1, 7.2, 7.3 and 7.4, pp. 94–101
handling enzymes	Practicals 8.1, 8.2, 8.3, 8.4 and 8.5, pp. 107–11
chromatography	Practicals 8.8 p. 113–14, 12.2 p. 141–3, and 12.6, p. 147
manometry	Practicals 15.1 and 15.2, pp. 178–80
exercise physiology	Practical 17.3, p. 206–7
studying 'behaviour'	Practicals 23.5, 23.6, 23.7, 23.8 and 23.9, pp. 269–73; Project 27.6, p. 327
bacteriology	Practicals 5.2, p. 69, 7.5, p. 101, 25.1, 25.2 and 25.3, pp. 284–8
handling *Drosophila*	Practical 28.4, p. 338

3 To appreciate the economic significance of biology, tackle Practical and Problem items, for example:

disposal of nuclear waste	Practical 4.8, p. 58
organic farming	Problem 4.5, p. 63
water treatment	Practical 5.1, p. 67–9
industrial use of enzymes	Practical 5.5, p. 72–3, and 5.8, p. 76
yoghurt production	Practical 5.6, p. 73–4
fermenter technology	Practical 5.7, p. 74–5; Problem 5.6, p. 81
use of bovine somatotrophin	Problem 5.3, p. 79
photosynthesis	Problems 12.5 and 12.6, pp. 152–3
pesticides	Problem 20.3, p. 243–5
health and disease	Problems 24.1, 24.2, 24.3, pp. 280–2; 25.2, p. 298, and 27.5, p. 330
contraception and fertility	Problems 27.4, p. 329, and 27.6, p. 330–1
human embryo research	Problem 27.7, p. 332
genetic engineering	Problems 29.2, 29.3, 29.4 and 29.5, pp. 356–63

4 To develop investigational/problem solving skills, tackle Practicals, for example:

a small-scale scientific investigation	Practical 1.2, p. 4–5 or select Problems (or adapt 'Investigation' Practicals) from those in each chapter

5 To develop mathematical skills, tackle Practicals or Problem items, for example:

handling of data from field (or lab) studies	Practical 3.4, p. 38–40
statistical tests	
– Standard deviation	Problem 3.7, p. 47–8
– *t*-test	Problem 3.8, p. 48–9
– Mann-Whitney *U* test	Problem 3.9, p. 50
– χ^2 test	Problem 28.1, p. 346

6 To develop communication skills, tackle Practicals or Problem items, for example:

pesticides	Problem 5.4, p. 79–80
smoking and health	Problem 15.6, p. 191–2
summarising evidence	Problem 24.1, p. 280–1
ethical issues	Problem 29.5, p. 359

7 To develop IT skills, tackle Practicals or Problem items, for example:

interfacing of micros with apparatus	Practicals 8.1, p. 107–8, and 15.4, p. 182–4, Figure 3.7, p. 24
exploiting the Internet	Practical 29.5, p. 354–5

The issue of safety at work

Safety issues arise in all practical work, whether laboratory-based or field studies. In science laboratories there are all sorts of **potential hazards**. Thinking about them, you soon realise that a lab can be a dangerous place. Many common circumstances might trigger an accident, and in biology there are specific additional sources of danger:

- water spilt on the floor from taps, sinks, tubing or beakers, causes you to slip or skid and fall;
- the Bunsen, used with an almost invisible flame, may cause a burn;
- dangerously hot glassware and tripods stands, left to cool, yet looking exactly like cold ones;
- the microorganisms you culture and some chemicals used may be dangerous if they get into or onto your body.

Yet the record of accidents in school laboratories shows that serious incidents are rare. This record of safety in school and college science laboratories is achieved and maintained by:

- **eternal vigilance** – accidents are prevented by 'thinking safety' at all times;
- **training** – by being shown and carefully learning, how to do practical things the right, safe way;
- the practice of **Risk assessment** during the planning of practical and project work.

■ Making a Risk assessment

The Management of Health and Safety (COSHH) Regulations (1994) require us to carry out a risk assessment before conducting practical work.

The Health and Safety Executive pamphlet suggests there are *Five Steps to Risk Assessment*, as follows:

1 **Look for hazards** as you gather information about the substances and the work. Take account of the environment of the experiment (e.g. size and ventilation of the laboratory) and the age and capabilities of the students. Consider substitution if there is a less hazardous alternative, or reduce the quantities to be used.

2 **Think about who might be harmed,** including students, teachers, technicians and all who may enter the laboratory (e.g. cleaners), arising from the laboratory technique, and also the risk from the substances used and the chemical products of reactions. Establish the procedures for the routine disposal of substances and for the cleaning of contaminated apparatus.

3 **Evaluate the risk** arising from the hazards, and decide whether existing precautions are adequate or whether more should be done. Consider the properties of substances, and

the extent to which those involved will be exposed (through the skin, by ingestion or via the eyes). What steps are necessary to minimise exposure (via use of fume cupboard, by reduction in quantities used and by use of personal protective equipment such as goggles, lab coat or gloves). Establish the procedures to adopt in the case of an accident.

4 **Record your findings as a Risk assessment,** so that everyone at risk can know about the risks and the precautions. Hold the assessments in an accessible position. You may refer to other documents that already list hazards and precautions, which do not need to be repeated, e.g. the CLEAPSS haz-cards or *Safeguards in the School Laboratory*. These sources must then be available for consultation, along with the assessments.

5 **Review the assessments regularly,** and revise when necessary. Revision must occur when substances or work methods are changed. Review assessments with students new to the practical work.

■ A form for routinely conducting Risk assessments

A suitable form for routinely conducting Risk assessments and keeping appropriate records is given below:

Assessment dated:　　　　　　School/Laboratory:　　　　　　　　Teacher/lecturer:

Title of experiment/procedure:

Information source (e.g. CLEAPSS hazcards):

Do quantities and solutions make 'Good laboratory practice' sufficient to take account of any hazards and avoid significant risk? If so, no further action is required.

In other cases, proceed with the Risk assessment:

Substances/equipment to be used:　　　　　　　　　　Hazards identified:

Control measure

(i) Eye protection　　　(ii) Gloves　　　(iii) Fume cupboard　　　(iv) Good ventilation　　　(v) Others

Disposal procedure:

Emergency procedure:

If any substance/procedure above poses a special hazard, then identify the necessary actions:

(i) First Aid　　　　　　　(ii) Spillage　　　　　　　(iii) Fire fighting equipment

---

■ The Practicals in this book carry Risk assessments

With the Risk assessment is an icon, 'flagging' potential hazards. These icons are explained below:

 Corrosive　　 Highly flammable　　Risk of electric shock　　 Biohazard　　Danger　　 Oxidising　　 Harmful or irritant　　 Toxic　　Eye protection must be worn　　Gloves should be worn

■ Safety with living organisms, inside and outside the laboratory

Biology practical experiences may involve work with living things (including the human animal!), studying them in organised scientific investigations. Safe work with living organisms requires that we:
- minimise their use to conserve natural resources;
- handle living animals in a way that avoids pain or distress;
- take note of the special hazards of working with living things.

Working with microorganisms The essential precautions in microbiological investigation are detailed on p. 70 and pp. 284–5.

Working with the human animal The essential precautions in working with the human organism (the pupil/student) as 'guinea pig' in experiments are detailed on p. 206.

Working in the field and on ecology expeditions The essential precautions in fieldwork are detailed on pp. 19 and 30.

■ References useful or essential to safety in laboratory and fieldwork

Institute of Biology *Safety in Biological Fieldwork – Guidance Notes for Codes of Practice*

Department for Education and Employment (1986) *Safety in Science Laboratories*. HMSO

ASE Laboratory Safeguards Sub-committee (1996) *Safeguards in the School Laboratory*. Association for Science Education

AMMA (1987) *AMMA Briefing: Safety in Schools*. Association of Teachers and Lecturers

School Science Service (constantly updated) *Laboratory Handbook*. CLEAPSS

M O'Connor (1987) *Out and About; A Teacher's Guide to Safe Practice Out of School*. Methuen

Department for Education and Employment (1989) *Safety in Outdoor Education*. HMSO

C Warn (1985) *The Ordnance Survey Map Skills Book*. Arnold-Wheaton and Ordnance Survey

A Watts (1971) *Instant Weather Forecasting*. Hart-Davis

Sources of the References in this book

This book has many useful cross-references. These help to make links, and encourage research and wider reading. Articles published in journals like the *School Science Review* (SSR) and the *Journal of Biological Education* (*J. Biol. Ed.*) are identified as sources for practical ideas. If your school or college has back copies of these journals, you can look up the articles easily. If you cannot put your hands on back copies, then you should note that the Association for Science Education (publishers of the *SSR*) and the Institute of Biology (publishers of *J. Biol. Ed.*) will supply copies of specific articles. The details of these schemes are as follows.

■ School Science Review

If you do not have back copies of the *SSR*, write for photocopies of articles to: The Secretary, Association for Science Education, College Lane, Hatfield, Hertfordshire AL10 9AA or Fax on (01707) 266532. This service is free to members on receipt of a membership number (single copies of articles only) and 50p per article to non-members, payable in stamps, postal orders or cheques (made payable to ASE).

■ Journal of Biological Education

If you do not have back copies of the journal, please write for photocopies of articles to: The Executive Editor, Journal of Biological Education, Institute of Biology, 20–22 Queensberry Place, London SW7 2DZ. Price: 20p per article; seven articles for £1 (Please make cheques/postal orders payable to the Institute of Biology.) (Payment from overseas must be in sterling only.)

Acknowledgements

To the many known and unknown experimental scientists, naturalists and observers, teachers, illustrators and writers who have influenced our own understanding we gladly acknowledge our debt. Where we have used copyright materials we have sought to obtain permission and we have acknowledged our sources. However, if we have inadvertently overlooked an existing copyright and used materials that are the intellectual property of another, without acknowledgement, then we ask that John Murray (Publishers) Ltd, 50 Albemarle Street, London, are contacted so that correction can be made.

We would like to specially thank **Peter Openshaw** and **Roger Reynolds** for their helpful advice and their many suggestions for practical work. In particular we would like to thank Peter for his contributions to the practical work, techniques and investigations in Ecology and in Humans and the environment. Peter also advised on biotechnology and biochemical practicals, and contributed his specialist knowledge of interfacing and exploiting the Internet. Roger contributed practical work in cell biology, plant structure and function, and to the chapter on the Life cycles of green plants. He also contributed to the presentation of statistics.

We sought advice on specific issues in ecology and field studies from **Professor Charles Gimingham** of the Plant and Soil Science Department of the University of Aberdeen. Professor Gimingham kindly consented to read this part of our manuscript, and then made very many valuable observations on the contents, and on the presentation of ideas.

We have also sought opportunities to take advice and suggestions on specific issues from biologists experienced in school teaching, laboratory work, field studies or the commercial applications of biology. Those who have been consulted in these ways are:

Mr John Bebbington	Warden, Juniper Hall Field Centre;
Ms Alison Bilsborough	Marketing Manager, Philip Harris;
Dr Iain Boulton	Environmental Sciences, University of Greenwich;
Dr Arthur Berg	Department of Plant and Soil Science, University of Aberdeen;
Mr Philip Bunyon	Newark, Nottingham (and ASE Safety Committee);
Miss Judith Clegg	Ranger Service, Bracknell Forest Council;
Dr Enrico Cohen	John Innes Centre, Norwich;
Professor John Dodge	Royal Holloway College, University of London;
Professor Richard Doll	Radcliffe Infirmary, Oxford;
Dr Margaret Frayne	James Allen's Girls' School, Dulwich;
Mr Martin Gardner	Conifer Conservation, Royal Botanic Gardens, Edinburgh;
Mr David Jeffreys	Biological Education Laboratory, University of Greenwich;
Dr Richard Johnson	Aberdeen University;
Professor Neil Jones	University College of Wales, Aberystwyth;
Dr Nigel Monkton	Nirex UK;
Ms Gillian Rhinds	Inveralmond Community High School, Livingston;
Mrs Isle Towler	Chemical Education Laboratories, University of Greenwich;
Ms Lesley Wood	Trinity Academy, Edinburgh.

Certain Practicals were specifically tried and tested by students training for secondary science teaching. In this connection we would like to thank those involved, especially the work of Mark Legg, Mark Jordan and John Taylor.

Nevertheless, the faults that remain are the sole responsibility of the authors. It is hoped that our readers will write to point out any errors and omissions they find.

At John Murray's the skill and patience of Nikki Taylor (Science Desk Editor) working with Helen Townson (Design Manager), Jean Macqueen (Editor), and Katie Mackenzie Stuart (Commissioning Editor) have brought together text, drawings, and photographs exactly as we have wished, and we are most grateful to them.

C J Clegg, Salisbury, Wiltshire
D G Mackean, Welwyn Garden City, Hertfordshire
May 1996

The following have provided photos or given permission for copyright photos to be reproduced:

p. 3 Fig. 1.2 Gene Cox, Fig. 1.3a and b Gene Cox; **p. 11** Fig 2.2 The Flora Project, University of Devon; **p. 22** Fig. 3.4 Philip Harris; **p. 24** Fig. 3.7a Philip Harris; **p. 26** Fig. 3.11b Penlon Ltd; **p. 28** Fig. 3.13a Mrs A Gillespie, Fig. 3.13b John Bebbington; **p. 33** Fig. 3.16a Chris Westwood/The Environmental Picture Library; **p. 35** Fig. 3.17 Biophoto Associates; **p. 44** Fig. 3.21a G I Bernard/Oxford Scientific Films, Fig 3.21b Colin Milkins/Oxford Scientific Films, Fig. 3.21c Biophoto Associates, Fig. 3.21d Oxwich, Gower/Planet Earth Pictures, Fig. 3.21e and f Biophoto Associates, Fig. 3.21g G I Bernard/Oxford Scientific Films, Fig. 3.21h Dr Jeremy Burgess/ Science Photo Library; **p. 45** Fig. 3.22b C J Clegg; **p. 53** Fig. 4.1a Martin Jones/Ecoscene, Fig. 4.1b Julie Meech/Ecoscene; **p. 67** Fig. 5.1 Thames Water Plc; **p. 71** Fig. 5.3a Martin Bond/Science Photo Library, Fig. 5.3b Nigel Cattlin/Holt Studios International; **p. 95** Fig. 7.2a Last Resort Picture Library; **p. 101** Fig. 7.7 Moredun Animal Health Ltd/Science Photo Library; **p. 103** Fig. 7.9 (top) Biophoto Associates, (bottom) Dr Jeremy Burgess/Science Photo Library; **p. 104** Fig. 7.11 (left) Institut Pasteur/CNRI/Science Photo Library, (right) R P C Johnson, Department of Botany, Aberdeen University; **p. 105** Fig. 7.13 Biophoto Associates; **p. 115** Fig. 8.6a and b C J Clegg; **p. 122** Fig. 9.1 A Barrington Brown/Science Photo Library; **p. 124** Fig. 9.2 Biophoto Associates; **p. 129** Fig. 10.2a Biophoto Associates, Fig. 10.2b Manfred Kage/Science Photo Library, Fig. 10.2c Biophoto Associates, Fig. 10.3a and b Biophoto Associates; **pp. 130** Fig. 10.4 (top) Biophoto Associates, (bottom) M I Walker/Science Photo Library; **p. 131** Fig. 10.5 Biophoto Associates; **p. 151** Fig. 12.6c Gene Cox, Fig. 12.6d R P C Johnson, Department of Botany, Aberdeen University; **p. 158** Fig. 13.1 Kathie Atkinson/Oxford Scientific Films; **p. 174** Fig. 14.1 C J Clegg; **p. 201** Fig. 16.5 R P C Johnson, Department of Botany, Aberdeen University; **p. 217** Fig. 18.4 Dr David Patterson/Science Photo Library; **p. 226** Fig. 19.3 Gene Cox **p. 238** Fig. 20.2 D G Mackean; **p. 287** Fig. 25.3 Geoff Tomkinson/ Science Photo Library; **p. 292** Fig. 25.6 Gene Cox; **p. 293** Fig. 25.7 Andrew Syred/Science Photo Library; **p. 294** Fig. 25.8 Biophoto Associates; **p. 307** Fig. 26.6 Biophoto Associates; **p. 317** Fig. 26.13 Mrs K Novosel; **p. 320** Fig. 27.1 F Bunker; **p. 327** Fig. 27.8 (top and bottom) P H Openshaw; **p. 329** Fig. 27.11 Andrew McClenaghan/Science Photo Library; **p. 333** Fig. 28.1 G A Mackean/Oxford Scientific Films; **p. 339** Fig. 28.5 Dr Jeremy Burgess/Science Photo Library; **p. 353** Fig. 29.2 M P Fuller & F M Fuller; **p. 365** Fig. 30.1 Neville Hollingworth, NERC, Swindon; **p. 366** Fig. 30.2 C J Clegg; **p. 368** Fig. 30.3 (clockwise from top left) John Heseltine/Science Photo Library, Biophoto Associates, John McCammon/Oxford Scientific Films, Planet Earth Pictures, John McCammon/Oxford Scientific Pictures, Professor Neil Jones, Nigel Cattlin/Holt Studios International.

The following are sources from which artwork, data or text extracts have been adapted, redrawn or reproduced with permission:

p. 6   Panel 1.1 Philip Allan Publishers Ltd

p. 22   Table 3.2. Data adapted from G R Clarke (1957) *The Study of Soil in the Field*. Oxford University Press, and Professor Joseph Tinsley (1970) *A Manual of Experiments for Students of Soil Science*. Department of Soil Science, University of Aberdeen

p. 47–8   Tables 3.11 and 3.12 The Ecological Society of America. Data adapted from S Utida 'Cyclic fluctuations of population density intrinsic to the host–parasite system', *Ecology* **38**, pp. 462–9 and H N Southern (1970) 'The natural control of a population of tawny owls (*Strix aluco*), *J. Zool.* **62**, pp. 197–285

p. 46   Fig. 3.23 Liverpool University Press

p. 60   Fig. 4.3 The United Nations is the author of the original materials

p. 61   Panel 4.1 The Benjamin/Cummings Publishing Company and Daniel D Chiras

p. 62   Panel 4.2 The Institute of Biology, Fig. 4.4 *Scientific American*

p. 63   Panel 4.3 Ecoropa Ltd

p. 64   Fig. 4.5 from RA Houghton and GM Woodwell (1989) 'Global climatic change' *Scientific American* **260**(4), pp. 18–26

p. 65   Fig. 4.6 from I Woodward (1989) 'Plants in the greenhouse world', *New Scientist* (6 May 1989). Fig. 4.7 data from New *Scientist* (12 November 1987), p. 53

p. 67   Table 5.1. Data adapted from B Finch (ed.) (1982) *Fertilisers*. ICI Educational Publications

p. 80   Panel 5.1 *Craven Herald*

p. 92   Panel 6.1 E J Wood and W R Pickering

p. 103   Panel 7.1 Cambridge University Press

p. 105   Panel 7.2 Professor Robert Freedman

p. 137   Data in Questions 4 and 5 (from Problem 11.3) adapted from A G Smithers and K Wilson (1968) 'Laboratory investigations in plant physiology I. Metabolic absorption of mineral salts', *J. Biol. Ed* **2**(3), pp. 239–57, published by the Institute of Biology

p. 152   Panel 12.1 Institute of Biology

p. 153   Panel 12.2 Reprinted by permission from *Nature* **367**, pp. 322–3. Copyright © 1994 Macmillan Magazines Ltd

p. 159   Fig. 13.2. Steps based on H G Q Rowett (1962) *Guide to Dissection*. John Murray and drawings based on the video *Vertebrate Dissection Guides – The Rat*, by the University of Portsmouth in association with the Institute of Biology

p. 160   Fig. 13.3 based on both H G Q Rowett and video (see above)

p. 165   Fig. 13.5 based on H G Q Rowett (see opposite)
p. 168   Panel 13.1 The Peters, Fraser & Dunlop Group Ltd
p. 169   Panel 13.2 Elsevier Science Ltd
p. 170   Fig. 13.7 adapted from HJ Leese (1984) 'The digestion and absorption of carbohydrates and protein: role of the small intestine' *J. Biol. Ed.* **18**(4), pp. 286–8, published by the Institute of Biology
p. 181   Fig. 15.3. First and final drawings based on W M Clarke and M M Richards (1976) *The Locust as a Typical Insect*. John Murray
p. 191   Panel 15.1 Sir Richard Doll
p. 202   Fig. 16.6. Data from RM Jackson and PA Mason (1984) *Mycorrhiza*. Arnold Studies in Biology no 159. Cambridge University Press
p. 244   Panel 20.1 the *Guardian*, Panel 20.2 HarperCollins Publishers Ltd
p. 245   Panel 20.3 *Scientific American*
p. 247   Fig. 21.1 based on H G Q Rowett (see opposite)
p. 248   Fig. 21.2 based on both H G Q Rowett and video (see opposite)
p. 281   Panel 24.1 Reprinted by permission from *Nature* 375, p. 365. Copyright © 1995 Macmillan Magazines Ltd
p. 298   Panel 25.1 Cambridge University Press, Panel 25.2 *Scientific American*
p. 323   Fig. 27.5 based on both H G Q Rowett and video (see opposite)
p. 324   Fig. 27.6 based on the video (see opposite), Fig. 27.7 based on both H G Q Rowett and video (see opposite)
p. 330   Panel 27.1 *New Scientist*
p. 331   Panel 27.2 *New Scientist*
p. 351   Practical 29.2 adapted from *Plant Protoplast: Practical Biotechnology – a Guide for Schools and Colleges* (1993), NCBE, University of Reading
p. 365   Panel 30.1 *New Scientist*
p. 372   Fig. 30.6. Data taken from C Wriedt (1930) *Heredity in Livestock*. Macmillan Publishers Ltd
p. 374   Panel 30.2 *New Scientist*.

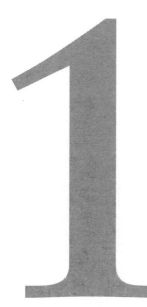

Biology Today: Environmental Biology

1 Biology, the science of life

Summary

Biology is the scientific study of living things. By 'life' we mean the sum of all the characteristic activities that are exhibited by living things, but absent from non-living things. These characteristics are: feeding (**nutrition**), release of energy (**respiration**), **metabolism**, **excretion**, responsiveness (**sensitivity**), locomotion (**movement**), **reproduction**, and **growth** and development.

Another characteristic shown by nearly all living things is that they consist of cells; some organisms are **unicellular** and others are **multicellular**. The cell, consisting of **nucleus** and **cytoplasm** contained within a cell membrane, is the basic unit of structure of living things.

By biological science we mean the processes by which biological information is obtained, and the resulting understanding or knowledge. The processes of biology involve the originating of ideas and explanations (hypotheses), and testing these by observations and experiments.

In experimental work, one condition of the experiment is changed systematically (the independent variable), and the effect of these changes on the dependent variable is carefully observed and measured. Meanwhile, we arrange for all other factors (the controlled variables) to be unchanged. The control experiment, when this is set up, is one value of the independent variable.

Nevertheless, the methods by which biological knowledge is established are various; there is certainly no one scientific method. As a result, very often the ways by which information has been established are as important as the results themselves. And however carefully experiments or observations are conducted, all scientific studies have limitations.

Modern biology is divided into many distinct disciplines. Some disciplines are concerned with structure and function (for example, morphology, anatomy, histology, cytology, physiology, biochemistry); others deal with the range of life and its classification (botany, zoology, mycology, bacteriology, virology, taxonomy) and with the change of life with time (palaeontology, evolution, genetics, embryology). Certain disciplines make up applied biology (which includes biotechnology, medicine, veterinary science, agriculture, soil science, forestry and fishery science), while others are environmental in focus (such as ecology, biogeography and ethology).

Biology is an invaluable component of our general education. The results of biological research tend to be published in a growing array of rather technical and inaccessible scientific journals, but some local natural history societies publish much more readable periodicals. Developments in science are also frequently discussed in general 'review' journals such as *New Scientist* and *Scientific American*. These are available in most large public libraries. Becoming a biologist may involve studying biology and other science, to the highest levels one can master. This opens a range of job opportunities; the work that biologists do to earn a living is almost as varied as work itself.

Practicals and activities

1.1 Levels of organisation in biology: an introduction to microscopy
(Skills and techniques, Data generating)

Living things are made of cells and exist as a range of different levels of organisation, from unicellular to elaborate multicellular structures. Cells are extremely small. They are examined by means of the compound microscope, in which the magnifying powers of two convex lenses (the eyepiece and the objective lens) are used to produce a much magnified image. Multicellular organisation shows a great range of structural complexity, from multicellular colonies with little or no co-ordination of component cells to multicellular organisms consisting of vast numbers of cells showing marked division of labour. The specialised cells of multicellular organisms make up the tissues (cells of a similar structure that perform a particular function) and organs (collections of tissues).

■ Aim

To develop compound microscopy skills; to develop the associated skills of preparing biological materials for examination, together with the examination of different levels of biological organisation.

■ Risk assessment

- Compound microscopes must be handled with great care, for they are precision instruments, expensive to replace (they cost £300–400).
- Direct sunlight must not be used to illuminate the mirror/condenser lens of the microscope, since sunlight when focused on to the retina may damage your eyes.
- When using the slides, coverslips, laboratory tools (forceps, mounted needles and so on), stains, solvents and mounting materials in normal (bright field) transmitted light microscopy at this level, good laboratory practice is sufficient to take account of any hazards and avoid significant risks.

■ Method

1 To set up the microscope, follow the instructions in Chapter 7, Practicals and activities (pp. 94–6).
2 Use your microscope to observe the different levels of biological organisation as follows:
   a *Unicellular organisms:* Use a culture of *Paramecium* (living), or unicellular members of the phytoplankton (living) in pond water. Make a temporary mount by placing a drop of the culture in the centre of a clean microscope slide using a teat pipette and then lower a coverslip over (Figure 1.1), carefully avoiding trapping too many air bubbles.

   Living, moving unicellular organisms may need to be slowed down to be observed microscopically. Introducing

Figure 1.1 Making a temporary mount

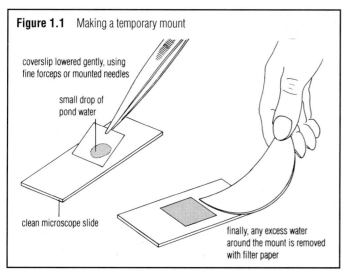

coverslip lowered gently, using fine forceps or mounted needles

small drop of pond water

clean microscope slide

finally, any excess water around the mount is removed with filter paper

a few fine strands of cotton wool into the medium before positioning the coverslip achieves this effectively without mechanical or chemical harm to the organisms.

b *Multicellular, colonial organisation:*

i Using *Spirogyra* (living). Make a temporary mount by transferring filaments of *Spirogyra* to a little water on a slide by means of forceps, and then covering with a coverslip. To the fingers, *Spirogyra* feels incredibly slippery. Why? To what extent do the cells of the filament differ?

ii Using *Obelia* (preserved). A prepared, stained slide of *Obelia* (a permanent mount) should be examined (Figure 1.2). *Obelia* is a colony of 'hydroid' individuals (i.e. like *Hydra* in their construction), interconnected by a hollow tube. There is a continuous cavity running through the entire colony.

Figure 1.2 *Obelia*

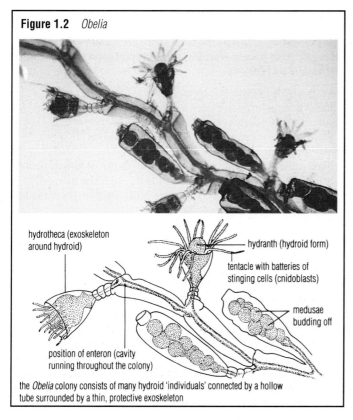

hydrotheca (exoskeleton around hydroid)

hydranth (hydroid form)

tentacle with batteries of stinging cells (cnidoblasts)

medusae budding off

position of enteron (cavity running throughout the colony)

the *Obelia* colony consists of many hydroid 'individuals' connected by a hollow tube surrounded by a thin, protective exoskeleton

c *Multicellular organism showing division of labour:* Multicellular organisation of this type can be observed using prepared stained slides of thin sections taken from a plant stem and mammalian stomach (Figure 1.3). These are called permanent mounted or prepared slides. Examine the slides carefully to identify regions of the sections occupied by cells of a similar type (tissues).

Figure 1.3 a Part of a buttercup (*Ranunculus*) stem (TS); b section through mammalian stomach wall, with representative tissue maps

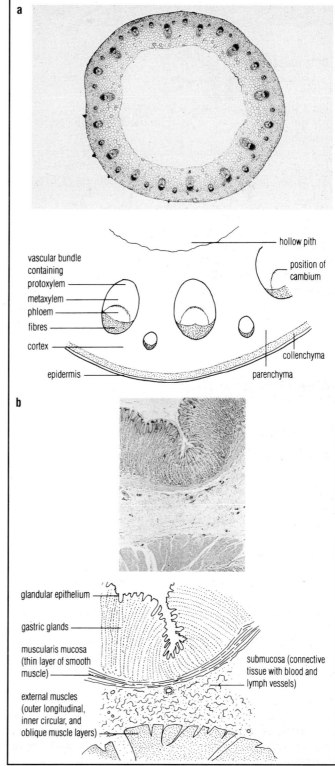

a

hollow pith

vascular bundle containing

protoxylem

metaxylem

phloem

fibres

cortex

position of cambium

collenchyma

parenchyma

epidermis

b

glandular epithelium

gastric glands

muscularis mucosa (thin layer of smooth muscle)

external muscles (outer longitudinal, inner circular, and oblique muscle layers)

submucosa (connective tissue with blood and lymph vessels)

■ Data presentation

In making a record of what you see by means of clear, simple drawings, it is important to:
- use a sharp HB pencil and a clean eraser;
- use unlined paper, and a separate sheet for each species you record;
- draw clear, sharp outlines, avoiding shading or colouring;
- label each sheet/drawing with the species, condition – living or stained (which stains?), whole or sectioned (TS or LS), and so forth;
- label your drawing fully, with labels in a column or line, well clear of the structures shown, remembering that label lines should not cross;
- annotate (add notes about function/role/development), if appropriate;
- include a statement of the magnification under which the specimen has been observed (for example, the magnification given by a ×10 eyepiece lens used with an objective lens of ×40 = ×400).

■ Conclusion

List the three levels of organisation observed. Suggest other organisms that fit the three levels of organisation observed? What organisms (if any) do not fit this simple classification?

■ Evaluation

What makes a good temporary mount?

In a good mount the material is well displayed, without excess liquid, and with very few tiny air bubbles trapped. (Remember, during initial focusing of a temporary slide an occasional small air bubble may help!)

Make sure you understand the difference between magnification and resolution (*Advanced Biology*, p. 147).

1.2 A small-scale scientific investigation
(Investigation)

This introductory project is a short practical investigation. It provides an introduction to independent enquiry as an early component of your course at Advanced level.

■ Aim

To provide experience of testing a hypothesis of your own devising, as a component of the processes of practical science (*Advanced Biology*, pp. 12–13).

■ Risk assessment

Good laboratory practice will be sufficient to take account of any hazards and avoid significant risks.

■ Method

You are required to choose a small-scale investigation that you can carry to a successful conclusion in the limited time available, working on your own.

This is not the sort of course work where you look things up in books and encyclopaedias, and then write about them. Some possible practical investigations are suggested below, to help you to start thinking.

Your investigation must involve observing and measuring, so keep this in mind when you are planning what you will investigate. You must find all the equipment yourself, so choose a project based on a hobby interest that you have, or for which you will require only the sort of equipment found in your home or in a garden.

Do not make plans to use laboratory equipment which would require you to be supervised while you use it. You will record your observations and measurements at the time you do the practical work, so plan the record keeping before you start, bearing in mind how you will later present the results to others. The steps you must take are as follows:

1 Decide what you will investigate.
2 Predict what the outcome may be.
3 Select the method to be used.
4 Decide what you will allow to vary or change (independent variable).
5 Decide what variables must be controlled to make it a fair test (controlled variables).
6 Decide what to observe and/or measure and how often (dependent variable).
7 Pay special attention to making your measurements as accurate as possible.
8 After this round of planning you must check with your tutor:
  a that your idea is viable (that is, it is likely to yield an interesting result in the time available), and
  b that your plan is entirely safe for you and anyone else it might involve.

Some possible investigations include the following:
- How does your pulse vary with different exercise tasks you commonly undertake?
- Design an experiment involving observations of a pet animal's behaviour.
- How quick are your reactions, and those of other people (catching a 0.5 metre rule as it falls through the fingers)?
- How do the number and type of birds seen in your garden vary at different times of the day?
- What evidence suggests the presence of larger animals in a wood or hedge, using tracks and signs left?
- The nocturnal behaviour of woodlice (*Advanced Biology*, p. 523).
- Was the past growing season better or worse than the same period a year earlier, for the annual growth in length of twigs of a particular species of tree?
- How much does your body temperature vary during a 48-hour period?
- Is there a connection between length of index finger and arm length? Or between arm length and body height?
- What are the most common 'weed' seeds in the soil in your garden? How common are they?

- What variation of type and number of 'minibeast' can be found in pitfall (jam jar) traps placed in different positions in the garden?
- How do the temperatures of bare soil and the soil of a lawn vary, in comparison to air temperature?
- How many of the garden's 'minibeasts', found under a damp brick, return to the same shelter each day?
- Which type of wind-dispersed seeds travel best?
- Do people show a connection between left/right-handedness and their dominant eye?
- How common are different types of leaf parasites (galls, for example) on oak leaves?
- Find the number and types of weed species that grow in mud dredged from a local pond, and compare them with those growing from pond bank soil.

■ Data presentation

This will be a concise, written and illustrated report, covering two sides of A4 paper at most, following these headings:
- title, your name and the date;
- aim;
- prediction or hypothesis;
- equipment, listed, but only draw items specially made or constructed;
- method;
- results, first tabulated and then (if appropriate) presented as a graph or histogram to facilitate comparison;
- interpretation of the results;
- conclusions.

In this form the reports can be displayed on a notice board (as a poster or wall paper). You can talk about your study to your group before you hand it in for assessment.

■ Evaluation

At the end of the study you should be able to criticise your methods constructively, and then suggest what sorts of further work would be possible and illuminating.

Projects

This introductory chapter does not raise issues in sufficient detail to lead to longer-term investigations. The characteristics of living things and cell structure and function are all discussed in much more detail in later chapters, and project suggestions are made in these chapters.

Problems and assignments

1.1 Characteristics of living things

■ Reading for understanding and for note-taking

First, scan through the article to assess its main 'direction'. Scanning an article involves reading the new material quickly just to pick up the general approach, broad content and an impression of the main ideas.

Then, by reading more carefully and, at the same time, highlighting or underlining the key words and phrases (this has been done for you in Panel 1.1, overleaf), you are able to make an appraisal of the content.

Now make accurate and concise written notes of the key points, using your own words. Finally, scan again to check that nothing important has been overlooked from your record.

■ Assignment

Answer the following questions about the article in Panel 1.1.

1 The article talks about different sorts of 'germs' and mentions a few examples. Take bacteria first. What features of bacteria are mentioned that we will agree are 'characteristics of living things'? List them.

2 What features of virus particles allow us to question whether these are living?

3 You may know the way in which some crystals can be 'grown', as when you hang a starter crystal in a saturated solution of copper(II) sulphate in a beaker, and a much larger crystal forms about it. Make a table listing (and contrasting) the differences between growth shown by the crystal, a bacterium and a virus.

4 Read the article again. To fully understand it you need to know what is meant by several technical terms. Check that you know what they mean, or look them up in the glossary. Refer to the relevant chapters in *Advanced Biology* for more information, if necessary:
- gene (Chapter 9);
- protein (Chapter 6);
- pathogens (Chapter 24);
- light microscope (Chapter 7);
- inoculation (of plates) (Chapter 4);
- electron microscope (Chapter 7);
- nanometres (nm) (Chapter 7);
- genome (Chapter 29);
- nucleic acids, RNA and DNA (Chapter 6);
- parasite (Chapter 14);
- vaccination (Chapter 17).

1.2 Experimental situation analysis

The drainage properties of a soil may influence the flora and fauna present. The apparatus shown in Figure 1.4 (p. 7) is used to make a comparison of the rates at which water (rain water, for example) may drain through soils.

The two soil samples used had been collected from around the roots of plants; one was a clay soil, and the other a sandy soil. These samples were then air-dried to a constant mass. Then identical quantities of the soils (about 200 g) were weighed out and placed in the funnels (a plug of glass wool was first placed at the neck of the funnels to retain the soil).

Panel 1.1 Viruses; protein-wrapped genes doing a takeover!

The man or woman in the street usually thinks that germs, microbes, bacteria and viruses are all very small, nasty creatures that cause colds, influenza, food poisoning or other afflictions. Since none of these organisms has ever been seen without the aid of a powerful microscope, they certainly fall into the 'very small' category of things. Their invisibility combined with their disease-causing activity also gives them an air of mystery. But is a virus the same as a bacterium? Do they function in the same way? Can the 'afflictions' they cause be treated equally easily? To get answers to these questions, one good starting point is to consider the size of the organisms.

VIRUSES – HOW BIG ARE THEY?
The size of disease-causing agents (pathogens) was something that exercised the minds of early scientists working in the field of infectious diseases and by the 1890s it was possible to divide pathogens into two broad groups. The first contained organisms that could be viewed clearly with the microscopes available at that time. Most of these organisms, mainly bacteria, could be cultivated in the laboratory in simple nutrient media such as beef broth.

The second group was made up of agents of unknown identity that could be shown to cause disease when they were transferred from a diseased individual to a healthy one. The mosaic disease of the tobacco plant, for example, could be induced in healthy plants by inoculating them with the sap from diseased plants. Similarly, foot-and-mouth disease of cattle could be transmitted by using the saliva of diseased animals.

Examining the disease-carrying fluids under the microscope failed to show the presence of cells (or any other particulate bodies) such as could be seen in suspensions of bacteria. Furthermore, a nutrient medium that would support the growth of bacteria failed to show signs of anything growing on it when it was inoculated with fluids containing these unknown agents. It was quite a puzzle because these results appeared to rule out the idea that the unknown agents were extremely minute bacteria, beyond the reach of available microscopes (although it was still possible that the agents were so fastidious in their nutrient requirements that the standard beef broth was inadequate).

Experiments with bacterial filters added to the puzzle. Bacterial filters are small discs which contain tiny pores. When fluids containing bacteria are filtered through them, the bacteria are trapped on the filter so the filtrate is sterile (i.e. pathogen-free). However, it was found that sap which transmitted tobacco mosaic disease could be filtered through bacterial filters and still remain capable of transmitting the disease. A number of other pathogens were also shown to be filterable, impossible to cultivate on laboratory nutrient media and too small to see, and eventually (by the turn of the century) they became known as the 'filterable viruses'.

THE STRUCTURE OF VIRUSES
When the electron microscope was introduced in the 1930s, viruses finally came into view and it soon became clear why they were able to pass through the filters that held back bacteria. The smallest viruses are approximately 20 nm across, the largest 300 nm – by comparison, the well-known bacterium, *Escherichia coli*, is 2000 nm long.

Viruses turned out to have a variety of shapes. Some are long and thin (helical), some have a geometrical appearance (icosahedral), some have an irregular, squarish appearance, some have spikes protruding from the surface, some have envelopes and some phages have tails. Regardless of appearance, all viruses are essentially a piece of genetic information (a genome) wrapped up in a protein coat. The protein coat, or 'capsid', protects the nucleic acid as the virus travels between host cells.

The virus particle (often referred to as the virion) usually contains less nucleic acid than protein and is never more than 50% nucleic acid. This means that most viruses have very few genes, and that none of the genes are very large. The protein coat of the virus is therefore not a single large molecule (which would have to be coded in a large gene, but consists of many copies of a much smaller molecule, thus ingeniously reducing the amount of genetic information required. The small capsid proteins are arranged around the viral nucleic acid in regular patterns, which give many viruses a geometric shape.

THE UNIQUENESS OF VIRUSES
The animal, plant and bacterial cells taken over (parasitised) by viruses contain both RNA and DNA. The cells are reproduced from pre-existing cells, which have grown by increasing the amounts of all their constituent parts, using their own biosynthetic machinery, organelles, etc.

In contrast, a given virus contains only one type of nucleic acid, either DNA or RNA, never both. (RNA viruses have mastered the secret of using RNA as genetic material.) A new virus particle never arises directly from a pre-existing virus particle: a virus particle outside a cell is inert. New viruses can only be formed inside cells and, once a single virus has entered a cell, the cell is coerced into producing more virus particles so that it is the infected cell that is replicating the virus.

The total simplicity of viruses – they merely contain the genetic information required to persuade a cell to replicate them, together with a protective coat – separates them from all other living creatures. Indeed, many biologists deny that viruses are alive. It certainly means that viruses cannot be accommodated in the standard classification of living things.

The intimate relationship between any virus and the cells it is parasitising makes treatment of virus diseases difficult. Chemicals that might disrupt the virus in some way are almost certain to disrupt the cells as well. So substances akin to the antibiotics used against bacteria have been slow to appear in our doctors' surgeries or chemists' shops, and those that have appeared are relatively inefficient. So far, vaccination is the most effective way of preventing many virus infections. However, as we learn more about the chemistry of viral replication, it is becoming clear that viruses do have certain unique properties. Eventually these might lead to the discovery of agents that will kill the viruses but save the cells. ■

From: Biological Sciences Review *(November 1990)* **3**(2), pp. 6–10

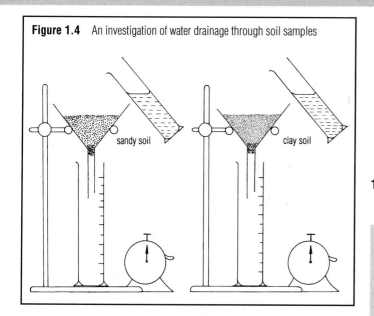

Figure 1.4 An investigation of water drainage through soil samples

Next, the funnels with their samples were gently immersed in water for 60 minutes in order to hydrate the soil, then carefully lifted out and allowed to drain. As a result, the soils were then at 'field capacity', and were ready for the experiment.

The experiment was set up as shown in Figure 1.4. Simultaneously, 100 cm^3 of water was added to each of the two funnels and allowed to drain through the soil. The volume of water that collected below each soil sample was recorded at frequent, regular intervals over an appropriate period. The results are given in Table 1.1.

Table 1.1 Readings from the experiment shown in Figure 1.4

Time (min)	Soil type	
	Sandy soil	Clay soil
0.5	18	
1.0	36	10
1.5	54	
2.0	71	19
2.5	89	
3.0	99	27
3.5	99	
4.0	100	35
5.0		43
6.0		52
7.0		60
8.0		67
9.0		75
10.0		82
11.0		90
12.0		96
13.0		99
14.0		100

1 What term do we use to describe the soil layer in which plant roots normally grow?
2 Why were soil samples air-dried to constant mass before similar quantities were weighed out?
3 Why was it necessary to bring the soils to 'field capacity' at the outset?
4 In science, how do we refer to general, descriptive observations, such as 'water drained more slowly through clay soil and more quickly through sandy soil'?

5 Plot a histogram to compare the drainage of water at one-minute intervals through the soil samples, over the period of the experiment.
6 In science, how are numerical data of this sort generally described or referred to?
7 What explanation might you propose to explain the slower drainage of clay soil?
8 In science, how are tentative explanations of this sort best described?
9 In this experiment, which was the dependent variable and which the independent variable?
10 Identify one controlled variable. Suggest why, in this experiment, no one controlled variable was selected as a 'control'.

1.3 Quick test

1 Distinguish between the following pairs:

  a tissue respiration and gaseous exchange;
  b autotrophic and heterotrophic nutrition;
  c inorganic and organic nutrients;
  d anabolism and catabolism;
  e growth and development;
  f sexual and asexual reproduction;
  g tissues and organs;
  h qualitative and quantitative data;
  i hypothesis and inference;
  j dependent and independent variable;
  k cytology and anatomy;
  l ecology and ethology;
  m mycology and bacteriology;
  n genetics and embryology;
  o physiology and biochemistry.

2 Identify the steps we may take in science between making an initial observation and arriving at accepted knowledge about a living thing.

3 What characteristics of living organisms enable us to identify them as distinctly different from non-living things?

4 Make labelled drawings of sections through plant and animal cells to highlight both their common features and the differences between them.

5 By reference to a simple biology experiment with which you are familiar, explain the differences between the 'control' and the 'experiment'.

1.4 Essay assignment

Select one of the following:

• Discuss the extent to which the characteristics of living things manifested by a unicellular organism like *Amoeba* and by the human animal are very similar. What, if any, are the significant differences?

or:

• You are asked to assess whether a commercial herbicide changed the community of the most commonly encountered minibeasts in the topsoil around a crop plant. Outline a simple experiment and control you would have to set up. State the independent and dependent variables in your experiment, and suggest some of the controlled variables you would identify.

2 The range of living things: systematics

Summary

There are vast numbers of species: a very great diversity of organisms, in fact. A **species** is defined as a group of individuals of common ancestry that closely resemble each other, and are normally capable of interbreeding to produce fertile offspring. **Systematics** is the science of classification of species, and is central to biology. The majority of plant species belong to the flowering plants, and the majority of animal species to the insects. These two groups are the largest.

The application of the electron microscope to cytology has led to the discovery of the three distinctly different levels of biological organisation: **viruses**, **prokaryotes** and **eukaryotes**. Viruses are not made of cells and are not considered to be alive outside their host cell. The prokaryotes and eukaryotes are cellular, but their cells are fundamentally different in size and complexity. Prokaryotes (the bacteria and cyanobacteria) are extremely small, no bigger than some of the organelles found in eukaryotic cells, in fact. Within the eukaryotes are four separate kingdoms of living things: the Plants, Animals, Protoctista and Fungi. Representative members of many of the phyla of these kingdoms are studied at Advanced level, and are listed in the Check-list of organisms in *Advanced Biology*, pp. 27–41.

All organisms are named by the **binomial system** (**genus** and **species**), designed by Linnaeus, and classified in a **hierarchical classification system**, which comprises **family**, **order**, **class**, **phylum** and **kingdom**. Our classification systems aim to reflect natural relationships (evolutionary relationship, p. 369) as far as these are known. The phenomenon of organisms with similar structures due to common ancestry is known as homology, and the structures are said to be **homologous**. Structures that carry out the same function but are not related are **analogous**. Relationships based on a common ancestry (relatedness) are said to be **phylogenetic**, whereas relationships based on similarity of appearance are known as **phenetic**.

The process of naming unknown organisms is important but time-consuming. We often attempt this by comparisons or by the use of dichotomous **keys**. Biologists undertaking investigations involving whole communities of organisms frequently select a representative few species to study, rather than seeking to identify and name the complete range of different types of organisms present.

Practicals and activities

2.1 Classification for beginners!
(Skills and techniques)

Biological classification schemes are the inventions of biologists, based upon the best evidence available at the time. In biology, the process of classification of organisms involves:
- the identification of each organism, normally by means of a name;
- the arrangement of the organisms into groupings of apparently related organisms (as far as these relationships are understood).

A successful classification scheme must be flexible enough to allow new organisms to be classified as they are discovered. In fact, biological schemes use principles that change as our understanding changes. So, classification schemes are frequently changed, and classification as a process is often controversial, as you may discover!

■ Aim
To discover the process by which 'organisms' may be classified.

■ Risk assessment
Good laboratory practice will be sufficient to take account of any hazards and avoid significant risks.

■ Method
Dr Joseph Camin of Kansas University created a whole family of animals in order to introduce the principles of classification in a practical way. He called these animals 'caminacules' (Figure 2.1)! You need a copy of Figure 2.1 for this exercise.

1 Using the scissors provided, cut up your sheet of paper showing the 'caminacules' so that each organism (with its number) is freed from the others.
2 Organise the 'caminacules' on the bench in front of you into groups of similar (related?) organisms. Note down the type of criteria you use to group them, so that you can compare your decisions with those of other students later.
3 Now look for relationships between the groups. Perhaps you will sort those with fins separately from those with hands and feet? One group may have bodies divided into thorax and abdomen, whilst others may have an undivided body.
4 Can you now construct a family tree that shows how closely each group of animals is related? If your tree does not look like your neighbour's tree, stick to your own ideas. It may turn out that, whilst there is no one answer, your plan makes more sense than others.

NOTE TO TECHNICIAN

Each student requires:
- a copy of the drawings of 'caminacules' (Figure 2.1);
- a pair of scissors for cutting paper;
- a large sheet of paper (lining paper or a sheet of A2 paper);
- a glue stick.

Figure 2.1 A selection of Camin's 'caminacules'

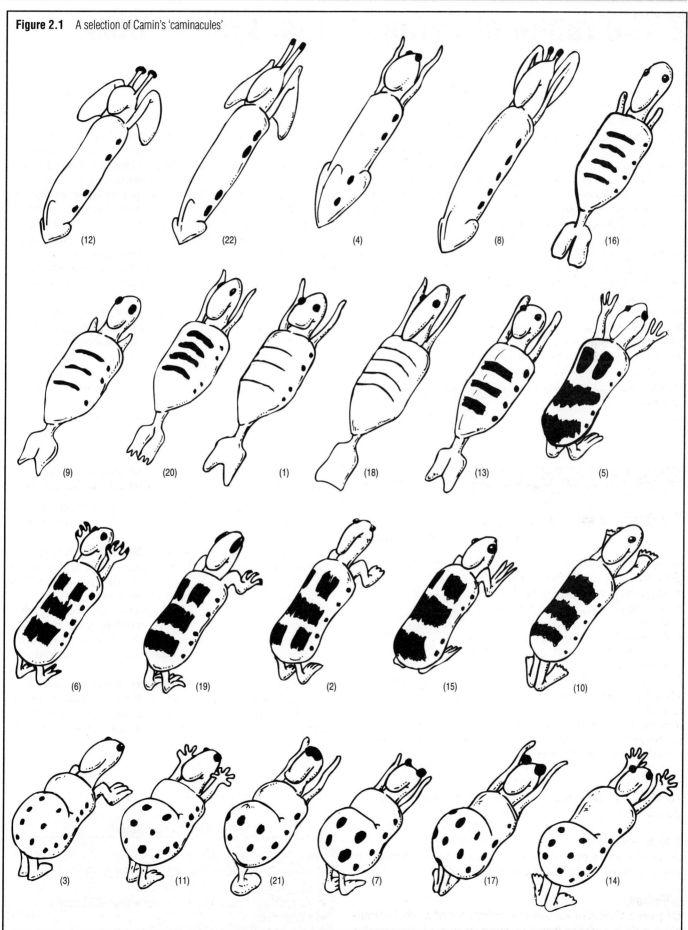

9

■ Data presentation

Lay out your 'tree' as a flow diagram, using the large sheet of paper provided.

You may need to give a name to each of the groups you create.

Can you give reasons for each division within your flow diagram? Write them down at this stage.

Will it help you to communicate your ideas better if you give (descriptive) names to the individual organisms, too?

■ Discussion

You should be able to present your family tree to your peers, justifying your scheme.

You should be able to use your ideas to criticise constructively the other schemes presented.

■ Conclusions

• What are the difficulties you have experienced in trying to decide upon relationships between organisms?

• What additional information would have helped you most?

■ Evaluation

How would you attempt this exercise again, knowing the sort of difficulties you have experienced?

2.2 The construction of a dichotomous key
(Skills and techniques)

Keys may assist us in the identification of unknown organisms. The advantage of using a key is that it demands very careful observation. We learn a lot about the biology of a group of organisms when we construct a key, and we learn a great deal about individual specimens when a good key is used to identify them.

Keys typically have a single access point with alternative, mutually exclusive characteristics at each step; that is, they are **dichotomous** keys.

■ Aim

To construct a dichotomous key for a small group of biological objects, such as leaves or twigs, that can subsequently be used by other people working with the same range of organisms (possibly from the same habitat).

■ Risk assessment

Good laboratory practice will be sufficient to take account of any hazards and avoid significant risks.

■ Method

1 Make a collection of (say) eight different, yet related objects such as typical leaves from eight different tree species. As you sample, note how representative your sample is. For example, do the leaves vary only in size, or are their shapes quite variable, too? (If no one shape of leaf is representative of most leaves of that species – rare, but not unknown – then the leaf of that species is an unsuitable organ for identification purposes.)

2 Make a careful, detailed examination of the specimen for features of shape and external appearance that are shown by one or more specimens, but not present in all. For example, ignore the fact that all the leaves were green, or that all had waxy upper surfaces (if they did). Look for characteristics

Table 2.1 A typical matrix of characteristics

	A	B	C	D	E	F	G	H
leaf entire (not divided into leaflets)	✓	✗	✓	✓	✗	✗	✓	✗
serrated edge to leaf margin (not smooth-edged)	✗	✗	✓	✗	✗	✓	✓	✓
etc.								

shown by some leaves only, such as the presence of a serrated margin (as opposed to a smooth margin).

3 Construct a matrix showing the eight different organs identified by capital letter along the horizontal axis, and the observable characteristic shown by one or more of the organs listed down the vertical axis. Against each organ place a ✓ or ✗. Table 2.1 shows an example.

4 From the matrix select a characteristic shown by exactly half the specimens only. This divides the specimens into two groups. Make a dichotomous flow diagram, progressively dividing the specimens into smaller, equal groups. Label each divide point with the diagnostic characteristic:

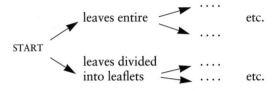

Your flow chart will probably take up about one page of A4 paper.

5 Now construct your key, reducing the dichotomy points of your flow chart to alternative statements to which the answer is either 'yes' or 'no'. To each alternative give a number to which the reader must refer to carry on the identification.

Dichotomous key to eight leaves

Go to:

1 Leaves entire (not divided into separate leaflets)......   2
  Leaves divided into leaflets.....................................   5
2 Margin of leaves .... (etc.)

NOTE TO TECHNICIAN

It may be necessary to make the collection of objects for this exercise in advance of the work.

    Students will require a hand lens.

■ Data presentation

Retain your matrix and flow diagram with the dichotomous key produced. If the biological objects used were leaves, you could press-dry them and later mount them as part of your record.

■ Conclusion

What are the characteristics of a feature of a living organism that would be reliable if used in a dichotomous key?

■ Evaluation

Read about the methods of specimen identification generally available to biologists (*Advanced Biology*, pp. 41–2).

2.3 Microcomputers and identification

(Demonstration)

Microcomputer programs can store a vast number of details about common (and not-so-common) species in a way that may be accessed to identify unknown organisms found in the field. They can be especially useful on 'lap-top' microcomputers, in use in the field. Two such programs are currently available:

- *A random access guide to the sedges of the British Isles using a microcomputer (IBM or BBC)*, produced for the Field Studies Council by C Legg (1992).
- *FLORA (IBM)*, produced by the Flora Project Team, Seal Hayne Faculty, University of Plymouth, Newton Abbot, Devon, and sponsored by Rhône Poulenc Agriculture Ltd.

FLORA is a computerised key which uses a multiaccess approach to identification. You have to answer questions about the unknown plant you observe, and then FLORA comes up with a short list of possible names. A copy of the Character menus summary screen of this program, by which a description of the plant to be identified is built up, is shown in Figure 2.2. Once you have completed the description with as many features as you can define (there is no need to select a feature for every characteristic), the 'search' is begun. A list of the most likely plants comes up as the Results screen. You can then make and confirm the final identification, perhaps with the help of identification books.

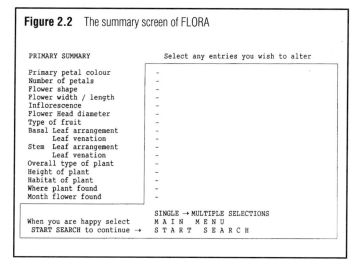

Figure 2.2 The summary screen of FLORA

```
PRIMARY SUMMARY              Select any entries you wish to alter

Primary petal colour          -
Number of petals              -
Flower shape                  -
Flower width / length         -
Inflorescence                 -
Flower Head diameter          -
Type of fruit                 -
Basal Leaf arrangement        -
        Leaf venation         -
Stem  Leaf arrangement        -
        Leaf venation         -
Overall type of plant         -
Height of plant               -
Habitat of plant              -
Where plant found             -
Month flower found            -

                              SINGLE → MULTIPLE SELECTIONS
When you are happy select     M A I N   M E N U
START SEARCH to continue →    S T A R T   S E A R C H
```

2.4 Directory of useful identification books

(Skills and techniques)

Useful published resources are listed firstly according to habitat, and secondly according to broad taxonomic groupings. Where several texts are mentioned, they are listed in order of increasing technicality.

■ By habitat

Seashore

D Ovenden and J Barrett (1981) *Handguide to the Sea Coast*. Collins

J Cremona (1983) *A Field Atlas of the Sea Shore*. Cambridge University Press

A C Campbell (1979) *The Seashore and Shallow Seas of Britain and Europe*. Hamlyn

J Barrett and C M Yonge (1974) *Pocket Guide to the Sea Shore*. Collins

Freshwater

J Clegg (1980) *The Observer's Book of Pond Life*. Warne

J Clegg (1974) *Freshwater Life*. Warne

J G Needham and P R Needham (1964) *A Guide to the Study of Freshwater Biology*. Constable

A M Leadley Brown (1970) *Key to Pond Organisms*. Nuffield Advanced Science/Penguin

Soils

S Trudgill (1989) *Soil Types: a Field Identification Guide*. AIDGAP/Field Studies Council Publications

Land surface

P Bang and P Dahlstron (1974) *Guide to Animal Tracks and Signs*. Collins

Gardens

M Chinery (1977) *The Natural History of the Garden*. Collins

Buildings and homes

H Mourier and O Winding (1975) *Guide to Wild Life in the Home*. Collins

A Darlington (1981) *The Ecology of Walls*. Heinemann

■ By groups of organisms

Non-vertebrate animals

D Nichols and J Cooke (1979) *The Oxford Book of Invertebrates*. Oxford University Press

S M Tilling (1987) *A Key to the Major Groups of British Terrestrial Invertebrates*. AIDGAP/Field Studies Council Publications

P S Croft (1986) *A Key to the Major Groups of British Freshwater Invertebrates*. AIDGAP/Field Studies Council Publications

T T Macan (1959) *A Guide to Freshwater Invertebrate Animals*. Longman

P Willmer (1985) *Bees, Ants and Wasps – the British Aculeates*. AIDGAP/Field Studies Council Publications

S Hopkin (1991) *A Key to the Woodlice of Britain and Ireland*. AIDGAP/Field Studies Council Publications

S L Sutton (1972) *Woodlice*. Ginn

J Burton (1981) *The Oxford Book of Insects*. Oxford University Press

M Chinery (1979) *A Field Guide to the Insects of Britain and Northern Europe*. Collins

P Skidmore (1991) *Insects of the British Cow-dung Community*. AIDGAP/Field Studies Council Publications

L M Jones-Walters (1989) *A Key to the Families of British Spiders*. AIDGAP/Field Studies Council Publications

M P Kerny, R A D Cameron and G Riley (1979) *A Field Guide to the Land Snails of Britain and Northern Europe*. Collins

R A D Cameron, B Evesham and N Jackson (1983) *A Field Guide to the Slugs of the British Isles*. AIDGAP/Field Studies Council Publications

G E Beedham (1972) *Identification of British Mollusca*. Hulton

Vertebrate animals

R Phillips (1985) *Fishes of Britain and Europe*. Pan

E N Arnold and J A Burton (1980) *A Field Guide to the Reptiles and Amphibians of Britain and Europe*. Collins

Royal Society for the Protection of Birds (1975) *Looking at Birds*. Macmillan

H Heinzel and M Woodcock (1978) *A Handguide to the Birds of Britain and Europe*. Collins

B Brunn, H Delin and L Svensson (1987) *Guide to Birds of Britain and Europe*. Hamlyn

P Hyman (1980) *The Mitchell Beazley Birdwatcher's Pocket Guide*. Royal Society for the Protection of Birds

G Corbet and D Ovenden (1980) *A Field Guide to the Mammals of Britain and Europe*. Collins

Plants

J H Belcher and E M F Swale (1976) *A Beginner's Guide to Freshwater Algae*. HMSO

S Haslam, C Sinker and P Worsley (1975) *British Water Plants*. Field Studies Council

F H Brightman (1979) *The Oxford Book of Flowerless Plants*. Oxford University Press

R Phillips (1981) *Mushrooms and other Fungi of Great Britain and Europe*. Pan

M Lange and F B Hora (1963) *A Field Guide to Mushrooms and Toadstools*. Collins

R Phillips (1977) *Wild Flowers of Britain*. Pan

R Fitter, A Fitter and M Blamey (1974) *A Field Guide to the Wild Flowers of Britain and Northern Europe*. Collins

J Hayward (1986) *A New Key to Wild Flowers*. Cambridge University Press

R Phillips (1978) *Trees in Britain, Europe and North America*. Pan

J Wilkinson and A Mitchell (1978) *Handguide to the Trees of Britain and Northern Europe*. Collins

K A Kershaw and K L Alvin (1980) *The Observer's Book of Lichens*. Warne

R Phillips (1980) *Grasses, Ferns, Mosses and Lichens of Great Britain and Ireland*. Pan

E V Watson (1981) *British Mosses and Liverworts*. Cambridge University Press

R J Pankhurst and J Allen (1985) *British Grasses: a Punch Card Key to Grasses in the Vegetative State*. AIDGAP/Field Studies Council Publications

J Merryweather and M Hill (1992) *The Fern Guide: an Introductory Guide to the Ferns, Clubmosses, Quillworts and Horsetails of the British Isles*. AIDGAP/Field Studies Council Publications

Economically important organisms

E Hvass (1966) *Plants that Feed and Serve us*. Blandford

R J Chancellor (1966) *The Identification of Weed Seedlings of Farm and Garden*. Blackwell

A Darlington and M J D Hirons (1968) *The Pocket Encyclopaedia of Plant Galls*. Blandford

H Belcher and E Swale (1978) *A Beginner's Guide to Freshwater Algae*. HMSO

H Belcher and E Swale (1979) *An Illustrated Guide to River Phytoplankton*. HMSO

G E and R C Newell (1963) *Marine Plankton. A Practical Guide, 1st edn*. Hutchinson

2.5 Classification quiz

(Data generating)

Acquiring familiarity with the main groups of organisms and the principles upon which they are classified is an essential step in the understanding of the relationships between structure and function in the living world.

■ Aim

To test the ability to identify animals and plant groups using the fundamental group characteristics listed in the Check-list of organisms in *Advanced Biology*, pp. 27–41.

■ Risk assessment

- Specimens preserved in formalin (10% solution of methanal) or ethanol should be handled with forceps. Methanal is harmful to the eyes at this concentration. Eye protection must be worn. It is an irritant to the nose, throat and skin. Ethanol is poisonous and highly flammable.
- Otherwise, good laboratory practice will be sufficient to take account of any hazards and avoid significant risks.

■ Method

1 For each of the specimens A, B, C and D state:
  a the major group to which it belongs;
  b two visible features which are characteristic of the group.
2 Specimens E, F and G belong to the same major group. State:
  a the major group to which they belong;
  b the class to which E, F and G each belong;
  c one visible feature which is characteristic of that class.
3 For specimens A, B, C and D suggest:
  a a habitat they might be found in;
  b a likely feeding relationship that might exist between them.

NOTE TO TECHNICIAN

A = *Spirogyra*, B = *Asellus* (woodlouse), C = *Gasterosteus* (stickleback), D = *Rana* (frog), E = *Lithobius* (centipede), F = *Locusta* (adult locust) and G = *Araneus* (spider).

■ Data presentation

The responses should be presented as a table.

■ Discussion and conclusion

Which of these organisms would be impossible or difficult to identify if the juvenile or larval forms only were available?

■ Evaluation

Think of other species, possibly involving different phyla, that could be substituted in this quiz.

2.6 Non-vertebrates ('minibeasts') in the soil

(Skills and techniques)

Living organisms in the soil comprise bacteria, fungi and non-vertebrates (*Advanced Biology*, p. 43). One way of investigating the population of non-vertebrates is to drive them out of a soil sample by slowly drying it out from above. Mobile organisms retreat from the heat and dryness and are collected in a preserving fluid. The apparatus used is the Tullgren funnel (p. 27).

■ Aim
To obtain and analyse a sample of non-vertebrates from the soil using the Tullgren funnel

■ Risk assessment
- Check that the lamp housing is tested by a competent person if home-made versions of the Tullgren funnel are used.
- Otherwise, good laboratory practice will be sufficient to take account of any hazards and avoid significant risks.

■ Method
Commercial models of the Tullgren funnel are available, but home-made versions are relatively easily assembled (see below). In the latter case, many Tullgren funnels can be set up at low cost, permitting comparisons to be made of different samples.

1 Collect the soil sample(s) with a hand sampler or modified tin can, and place in labelled polythene bags for transport to the laboratory.
2 Transfer the soil to the Tullgren funnel metal gauze. Break up the soil into natural crumbs, but do not compress it or smear the crumbs..
3 Place preserving liquid in the minibeast collecting dish and assemble the apparatus (for example, as shown in Figure 2.3).
4 Connect the lamp-house to the electricity supply and switch on the current. Leave in position for at least five days.
5 After five to seven days, search the dish for animals under the lowest-power objective of the microscope.

NOTE TO TECHNICIAN

Collecting fluid
Equal volumes of glycerine and 2.5% formalin.
Allow 4 cm^3 for each collecting dish if a Petri dish is used.

Apparatus
Commercial Tullgren funnels (or home-made, as in D G Mackean (1983) *Experimental Work in Biology.* pp. 96–7. John Murray). If constructing home-made equipment, the security of all electrical wiring must be inspected and tested by a suitably experienced person.

Collecting the samples and identifying the animals
The soil population will vary with the time of the year, the degree of moisture, the depth and the type of soil. All these variables can be exploited in taking the samples. Only broad categories of animals can be identified with any ease, such as collembolans, mites, nematodes, worms, but in any population it might be possible to isolate smaller groups, for example red mites.

■ Data presentation
Make a list of the organisms collected and their numbers. It is unlikely that you will be able to identify the species but springtails, mites, millipedes, centipedes and insect larvae should be fairly easy to recognise. If possible, draw representative organisms.

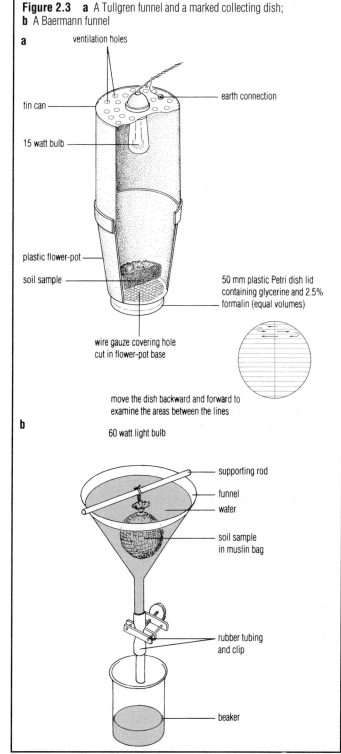

Figure 2.3 **a** A Tullgren funnel and a marked collecting dish; **b** A Baermann funnel

a
- ventilation holes
- tin can
- earth connection
- 15 watt bulb
- plastic flower-pot
- soil sample
- 50 mm plastic Petri dish lid containing glycerine and 2.5% formalin (equal volumes)
- wire gauze covering hole cut in flower-pot base

move the dish backward and forward to examine the areas between the lines

b
- 60 watt light bulb
- supporting rod
- funnel
- water
- soil sample in muslin bag
- rubber tubing and clip
- beaker

■ Conclusion
Although extracting and observing the organisms is interesting, the results will be more useful if you compare two samples of soil from contrasting areas and see if you can offer an explanation of the differences observed.

■ Evaluation
How representative of the non-vertebrate soil population do you think your sample is? What types of organisms are likely to be under-represented in the sample?

Projects

2.1 Investigations of ant hills in the field

A comparison between the plant distribution on mounds built by *Lasius flavus* (yellow hill ant) with that typical of the surrounding, undisturbed soils in meadows and pasture land may illustrate the profound effect an organism has on its environment. The percentage cover of vegetation (p. 24) of whole ant hills and of meadow land sampled by quadrats provides the essential data. Analysis of the results will suggest subsequent enquiries to be pursued. One abiotic factor that can be compared accurately in ant hills and surrounding soil is the temperature.

References

J M Pawson (1975) 'Ant hills in school ecology', *J. Biol. Ed.* 9(2), pp. 75–9

J Sankey (1975) 'Ant hill vegetation and rabbits', *J. Biol Ed.* 9(3/4), p. 183

T J King and R J Woodell (1975) 'The use of the mounds of *Lasius flavus* in teaching some principles of ecological investigation', *J. Biol. Ed.* 9(3/4), pp. 109–23

G J Skinner (1987) *Shire Natural History: Ants of the British Isles.* Shire Publications, Aylesbury

2.2 Ant behaviour observed using a formicarium

Ants can be kept in a laboratory in artificial nests, known as formicaria. In this condition feeding behaviour and aspects of the social life of an ant colony can be investigated.

References

M Archer (1969) 'Keeping and studying the behaviour of some arthropods in the laboratory', *School Science Review* 51(175), pp. 349–52

C J Bulloch and M L Street (1978) 'Keeping ants in the laboratory', *School Science Review* 59(208), pp. 481–6

M V Brian (1977) *Ants.* Collins New Naturalist, Chapter 10, pp. 191–200

Dr E Evesham (1995) 'The collection, maintenance and behaviour of ants'. This resource (video and booklet) is available from Biology Department, Mill Hill School, The Ridgeway, Mill Hill, London NW7 1QS

2.3 Earthworms and soil use

Hand-sorting soil samples may be the most accurate method of estimating earthworm populations, but the necessary digging can cause habitat destruction. Instead, the relatively harmless substance, culinary mustard (ready-mixed emulsion $15\,cm^3\,l^{-1}$ using 10 litres per m^2 quadrat), can be applied to bring worms to the surface; about 90% of the worm population will surface within five minutes or so. This technique can be used to investigate whether there is a correlation between the size of the earthworm population and various forms of soil treatment (such as compost *v.* chemical fertiliser, or trampling *v.* minimal disturbance) applied to comparable soils.

Earthworms can also be collected by exploiting their response to light ground vibrations (as when birds search for food).* Applying heel–toe rocking movements to the soil surface of meadow land has been found to yield more organisms than the alternative hand-sorting approach.

References

A Gunn (1991) 'Estimating earthworm populations', *School Science Review* 72(261), pp. 86–8

*M P Hill-Cottingham (1981) 'Collecting earthworms', *J. Biol. Ed.* 15(3), p. 185–6

Problems and assignments

2.1 Living things classified into five kingdoms

Examine the classification flow chart in Figure 2.4, and then answer the questions below.

1 In the five-kingdom classification represented below, the first division (X) was correctly established after the electron microscope became available and was used in biology. Why is this so?
2 What is the characteristic size range of the organisms typical to Kingdom 1?
3 The organisms of Kingdom 1 are described as prokaryotes. What feature of their cells does this name refer to?

4 The organisms of Kingdom 2 have hyphae with walls of distinctive composition. Exactly what is distinctive about the chemistry of their walls?
5 Saprotrophic nutrition is typical of most organisms of Kingdom 2. What does this mean?
6 Kingdom 3 consists of the protozoa and algae. What characteristics do organisms of these two sub-kingdoms have in common?
7 What features of the protozoa and algae can be used to separate them?
8 What are the common structural features of the nuclei of the cells of Kingdoms 2, 3, 4 and 5?
9 The life-histories of members of Kingdom 4 show alternation of generations. What does this mean?
10 What are the fundamental differences in the nutrition of members of Kingdoms 4 and 5?
11 Give the names of Kingdoms 1, 2, 3, 4 and 5.

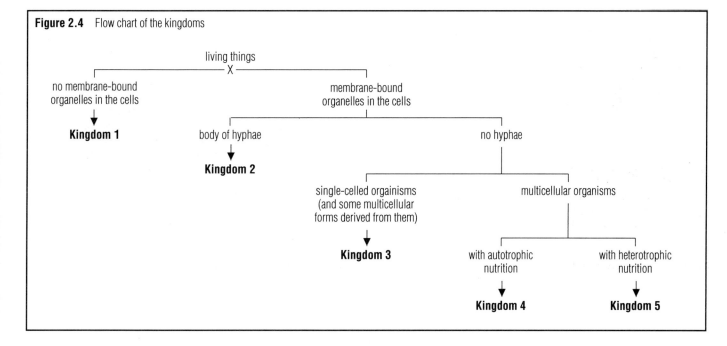

Figure 2.4 Flow chart of the kingdoms

living things — X

no membrane-bound organelles in the cells → **Kingdom 1**

membrane-bound organelles in the cells

body of hyphae → **Kingdom 2**

no hyphae

single-celled orgainisms (and some multicellular forms derived from them) → **Kingdom 3**

multicellular organisms

with autotrophic nutrition → **Kingdom 4**

with heterotrophic nutrition → **Kingdom 5**

2.2 Identification with a key

Figure 2.5 (p. 16) shows drawings of eight animals which are often represented in biology books, illustrating points of structure, function and behaviour.

1 Use the identification key provided in Figure 2.6, together with your general knowledge of these organisms, to identify each animal by one of the letters given in the key (A to H).
2 For each of the eight animals illustrated, state the phylum to which it belongs, and give three specific features by which the animal is identified as a member of the phylum.
3 The identification key provided is neither a dichotomous key, nor is it a 'natural' key. Explain what these terms mean.

Figure 2.6 Identification key

1	Multicellular organism, without significant division of labour among the cells, e.g. no nervous system present	**A**
	Multicellular organism, with pronounced division of labour among the cells. A nervous system present	2
2	Radially symmetrical animal	3
	Bilaterally symmetrical animal	4
3	Two-layered body, with special stinging cells present	**B**
	More than two layers of cells to the body wall, and with a complex water vascular system present	**C**
4	Body with some form of external skeleton present (an exoskeleton)	5
	Soft and pliable body, without a hard skeleton system	6
5	Body enclosed by jointed exoskeleton, with distinctive jointed appendages	**D**
	External skeleton in the form of a shell into which the animal can withdraw if necessary	**E**
6	Body flattened dorsiventrally	**F**
	Body tubular, elongated and worm-like	7
7	Tubular body with pronounced divisions into many segments	**G**
	Narrow, tubular body, sharply pointed at both ends	**H**

Figure 2.5 Eight common animals

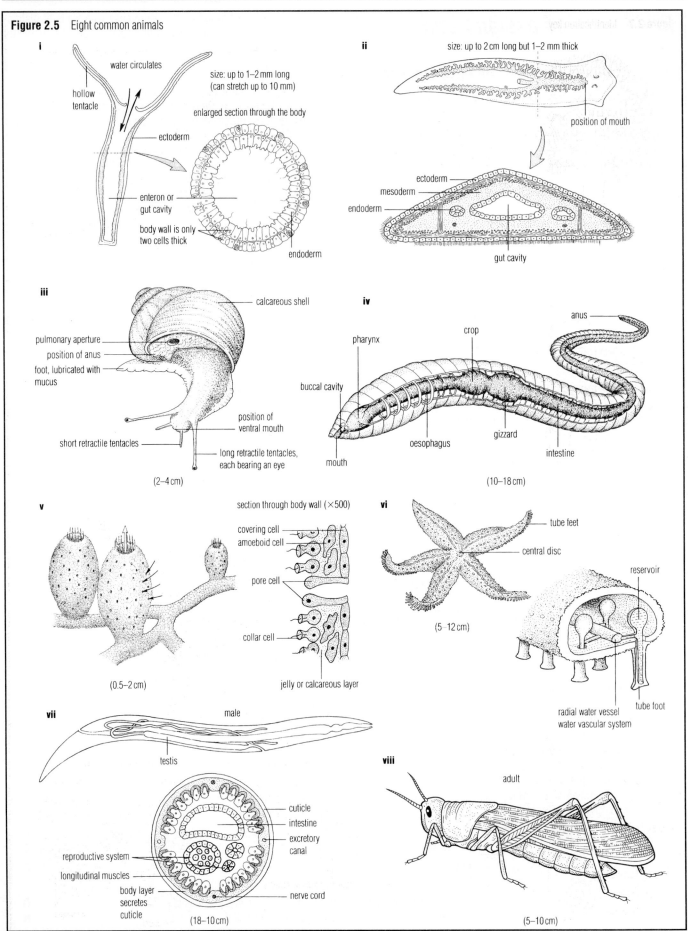

i

water circulates

hollow tentacle

size: up to 1–2 mm long (can stretch up to 10 mm)

enlarged section through the body

ectoderm

enteron or gut cavity

body wall is only two cells thick

endoderm

ii

size: up to 2 cm long but 1–2 mm thick

position of mouth

ectoderm

mesoderm

endoderm

gut cavity

iii

calcareous shell

pulmonary aperture

position of anus

foot, lubricated with mucus

position of ventral mouth

short retractile tentacles

long retractile tentacles, each bearing an eye

(2–4 cm)

iv

anus

crop

pharynx

buccal cavity

mouth

oesophagus

gizzard

intestine

(10–18 cm)

v

section through body wall (×500)

covering cell

amoeboid cell

pore cell

collar cell

jelly or calcareous layer

(0.5–2 cm)

vi

tube feet

central disc

reservoir

radial water vessel

tube foot

water vascular system

(5–12 cm)

vii

male

testis

cuticle

intestine

excretory canal

reproductive system

longitudinal muscles

body layer secretes cuticle

nerve cord

(18–10 cm)

viii

adult

(5–10 cm)

Figure 2.7 Identification key

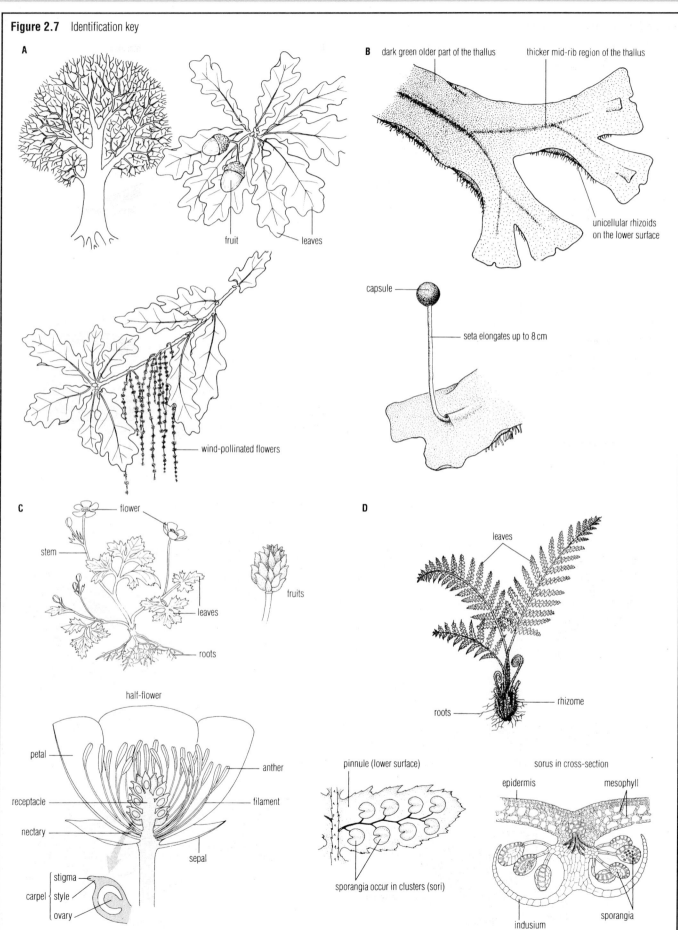

A

fruit

leaves

wind-pollinated flowers

B dark green older part of the thallus   thicker mid-rib region of the thallus

unicellular rhizoids on the lower surface

capsule

seta elongates up to 8 cm

C flower

stem

leaves

roots

fruits

half-flower

petal

receptacle

nectary

anther

filament

sepal

carpel { stigma / style / ovary }

D leaves

rhizome

roots

pinnule (lower surface)

sporangia occur in clusters (sori)

sorus in cross-section

epidermis   mesophyll

sporangia

indusium

2.3 'Design a key' exercise

1 Draw up and complete a table comparing features of the four plants represented in the drawings in Figure 2.7. Use features visible in the drawings, together with your knowledge of plant physiology and reproduction.
2 Now construct a dichotomous key to distinguish plants A to D, using the information in the table you have drawn up. (The steps to designing and drawing up a dichotomous key are presented in Activity 2.2, 'The construction of a dichotomous key', p. 10.)
3 How could you test for the presence of the strengthening substance lignin in cell walls of thin sections of tissue of these plants?
4 Which of the plants A to D contain lignin? In which tissues does lignin occur?

2.4 Quick test

1 Distinguish between the following pairs:

   a homologous and analogous structures;
   b systematics and taxonomy;
   c artificial and natural classifications;
   d fungi and green plants;
   e bryophytes and ferns;
   f dicotyledons and monocotyledons;
   g diploblastic and triploblastic organisms;
   h flatworms and tapeworms;
   i bilateral symmetry and radial symmetry;
   j coelom and enteron;
   k exoskeleton and endoskeleton;
   l cnidoblast and cnidocil;
   m open and closed circulatory systems;
   n nerve cord and notochord;
   o vertebral column and cranium.

2 What do you understand by the following:

   a the binomial system of nomenclature;
   b the five-kingdom scheme of classification;
   c the hierarchical taxa by which organisms are classified;
   d the main difficulties in defining the term 'species';
   e metameric segmentation?

2.5 Essay assignment

Select one of the following:

• What do we mean by the following terms:
   a diploblastic;
   b coelom;
   b metameric segmentation?
   In your answer give examples from the Animal Kingdom which show the importance of these terms in systematics.

or:

• Bacteria, fungi and green plants are classified in separate kingdoms. Justify this decision of taxonomists by reference to the more significant characteristics consistently shown by members of these kingdoms.
   What features of viruses have caused some biologists to question whether they can be described as 'living things' in the usual sense?

3 Introduction to ecology

Summary

Ecology is the study of the relationships between living things and the environment. It is one of the most important component disciplines of modern biology, for living things can be fully understood only in the context of their interactions with their environment.

Only a relatively tiny part of planet Earth and its atmosphere is habitable, and this part is called the **biosphere**. An **ecosystem** is a natural ecological unit, consisting of living things and their physical environment. The chief energy source of an ecosystem is the Sun. Green plants use energy from the Sun to manufacture their own organic foods from inorganic substances. Consequently, we say that green plants are the **primary producers**, and the animals and other organisms that feed on them (directly or indirectly) are **consumers**. Organisms that feed on dead plants and animals are **detritivores** and **decomposers**. They play a key part in the **recycling of nutrients** on which all living things depend. The transfer of food energy from its source in green plants through a series of organisms that eat and are eaten is known as a **food chain**. In nature, food chains are interconnected as **food webs**, illustrating the interdependence of all living things.

The seashore is an example of an ecosystem. Lakes, woodlands and forests are the major terrestrial ecosystems. The physical factors of the environment that affect the distribution of living things are known as **abiotic factors**. These are classified as **climatic, topographic** and **edaphic** (soil) factors, and, in the case of the seashore, the effects of the **tides** and **waves**. The interactions of the living things in an ecosystem, known as the **biotic factors**, also play a key part in determining the distribution of organisms. The biotic factors include competition for resources between members of the same species (**intraspecific competition**) and different species (**interspecific competition**), **predation** (and browsing on vegetation) by animals, and **symbiosis**. Symbiotic relationships range from harmless feeding associations (**commensalism**), to organisms living together to their mutual benefit (**mutualism**), and to **parasitic relationships**, where one organism is harmed.

Organisms can be seen as occurring in **populations** of the same species and in **communities** of different species, present in an ecosystem. The density of a population may change, but population density change tends to be self-regulating by **negative feedback**. Communities of organisms often exist as a stable **climax community**, provided the community is diverse and sufficiently rich in species to withstand any temporary damage to one of its components. When new habitats arise or a climax community is destroyed, a **succession** of changes leads to a relatively stable climax again.

Within the biosphere energy enters as sunlight and is reflected away, or converted to chemical energy or heat energy, but ultimately all energy is lost to space as heat. Whilst energy flows through the biosphere in this way nutrients are recycled and endlessly re-used. The proportion of incoming energy that is used to build up biological tissues and thus become available to other organisms as food represents the **productivity** of the ecosystem. Natural ecosystems show variable productivity; some are very low, others are relatively high. The productivity of human agriculture may exceed that of the most productive natural systems because of energy 'subsidies' from fossil fuels.

Practicals and activities

3.1 Ecological techniques

(Skills and techniques)

Ecological investigations are often more complex than laboratory investigations because of the numerous variables involved, which are frequently difficult or impossible to control. For example, you may have put some pitfall traps out at noon one day and examined them at dusk and in the morning, hoping to look for correlations between the small non-vertebrate animals ('minibeasts') you catch and the time of day or night. But during the course of a 24-hour period there might be significant, abrupt changes in temperature, humidity or rainfall, over which you have no control. It is essential, therefore, to combine selected measurements of abiotic factors with measurements of biotic factors. Even then, the handling of the data produced by ecological investigations almost invariably presents challenges. Careful planning is the essential first step to any investigation.

The ecological techniques you select will vary according to the issues you are investigating, the accuracy needed, and the ability of the technique to work in the demanding experimental situation of the environment – for example, rain can ruin delicate electronic equipment. The apparatus or approach adopted must fit the particular circumstances. Accurate measurements from carefully calibrated equipment are vital. If you are comparing two or more habitats or microhabitats, however, then accurate comparisons, using identical techniques, may be even more important.

■ Risk assessment

- Some of the methods described below involve the use of chemicals. Where these are particularly hazardous, a further warning is included. It is not always possible to wear protective clothing other than eye protection during fieldwork, but you should nevertheless take sensible precautions. Always carry chemicals in well-padded, large plastic containers.
- In any investigation involving the handling of wild animals (especially wild mammals), you must follow Local Education Authority or school or college guidelines.
- If faecal pellets are to be collected place your hand inside a plastic bag, pick up the faecal pellets and then turn the bag inside out and secure.
- Wash your hands with soap and water after completing fieldwork.

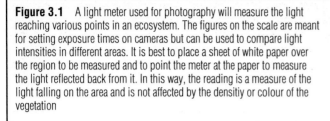

Figure 3.1 A light meter used for photography will measure the light reaching various points in an ecosystem. The figures on the scale are meant for setting exposure times on cameras but can be used to compare light intensities in different areas. It is best to place a sheet of white paper over the region to be measured and to point the meter at the paper to measure the light reflected back from it. In this way, the reading is a measure of the light falling on the area and is not affected by the densitiy or colour of the vegetation

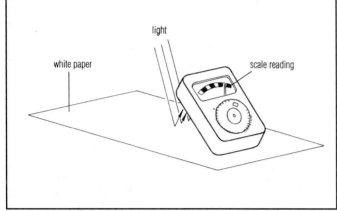

Figure 3.2 Types of hygrometer

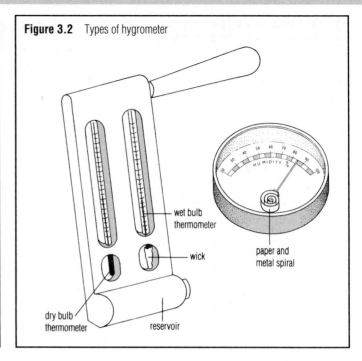

Abiotic techniques

■ Light

Light varies in intensity, duration and wavelength, and so the measurement of light presents problems. Single measurements of light intensity are probably meaningless, since intensity can change rapidly – with varying cloud cover, for example. Using a photographic exposure meter, the incident light at a particular (shaded) location can be compared with the value at other locations, or can be expressed as a percentage of the incident light in a similar, exposed (unshaded) location nearby (*Advanced Biology*, pp. 56–7) (Figure 3.1).

Equipment: Photographic light meter.

■ Temperature

The ordinary mercury thermometer is too fragile for use in fieldwork, and is also usually difficult or impossible to read in the location where the data are required. It may be useful to monitor daily fluctuations in temperature, obtained over an extended period from two or more locations (microhabitats) within a particular habitat, using a maximum and minimum thermometer. Using an electronic field thermometer or environmental comparator with probes sensitive over the range 0–40 °C, temperatures may be simultaneously measured in air, in water and at different depths in soil.

Equipment: Maximum and minimum thermometer, electronic thermometer or environmental comparator with suitable probes.

■ Rainfall

Rainfall is collected and measured in a rain gauge consisting of a funnel and collecting cylinder. The gauge must be appropriately supported, and must be checked and emptied frequently, particularly in hot weather.

Equipment: Rain gauge.

■ Humidity

Relative humidity (the amount of water vapour in the air expressed as a percentage of what would be held in saturated air at that temperature) can be measured with a whirling hygrometer, which consists of wet and dry bulb thermometers mounted in a frame so that it can be swung around like a rattle. You do this until the temperature readings are constant. These thermometer readings are converted into relative humidity readings using given tables or slide-rule. Alternatively, a (less accurate) hair hygrometer may be used (Figure 3.2).

Filter paper strips, immersed in 25% cobalt chloride solution and dried (pp. 194–5), may also be used. These papers change from blue in low humidity to pink in high humidity. Placed in a microhabitat, colour changes can be timed to get comparative data on the humidity.

These last two methods are applicable to restricted working spaces typical of microhabitats.

Equipment: Whirling hygrometer, or hair hygrometer, or 25% cobalt chloride paper strips (in desiccator).

■ Wind

Wind speeds can be judged subjectively by applying the criteria of the Beaufort scale of wind speed (Table 3.1), which uses movements of leaves or branches. Precise measurements can be made at particular microhabitats, with a hand-held flowmeter or a digital anemometer.

Equipment: Wind speed meter or digital anemometer.

■ Edaphic (soil) factors

Soil profile

Unless it will cause disturbance to a valuable habitat, select a typical area of the site and dig a pit down to the bedrock, keeping one side as a clean, vertical face (the profile). You can then observe, measure and draw (or photograph) the various soil horizons (*Advanced Biology*, p. 61). Take separate samples from each horizon for laboratory analysis. If this is not possible, take core samples of soils with a soil augur or corer (Figure 3.3) and lay them in a length of plastic guttering in order to examine the soil profile. You can make a finger smear of each layer on the drawing, in order to have a record of the colour and texture of the horizons. Record the position from which the core was taken on a map of the site. As soils may vary even over quite short distances, it is unwise to rely on a single sample, so take several replicate samples. If it is desirable to gain an indication of range and variability in a given soil property, these samples should be analysed separately; if only a general value is required they can be bulked for analysis.

Table 3.1   Beaufort scale of wind force

Beaufort number	General description		Approximate velocity /km h^{-1}
0	calm	calm; smoke rises vertically	<2
1	light air	direction of wind shown by smoke drift but not by wind vanes	2–5
2	light breeze	wind felt on face; leaves rustle; ordinary vane moved by wind	6–11
3	gentle breeze	leaves and small twigs in constant motion; wind extends light flags	12–19
4	moderate breeze	raises dust and loose paper; small branches are moved	20–30
5	fresh breeze	small trees in leaf begin to sway; crested wavelets form on inland waters	31–40
6	strong breeze	large branches in motion; whistling in telegraph wires; umbrellas used with difficulty	40–50
7	near gale	whole trees in motion; inconvenience felt when walking against the wind	51–61
8	gale	breaks twigs off trees; generally impedes progress	62–74
9	strong gale	slight structural damage occurs (chimney pots and slates removed)	75–87
10	storm	seldom experienced inland; trees uprooted; considerable structural damage occurs	>88

Safety note: Never use an augur or corer where there is any risk of contact with electricity cables (for instance, near buildings). Always return the core to the hole when measurements are complete.

Equipment: Spade, and/or an augur or corer with similar length of plastic gutter.

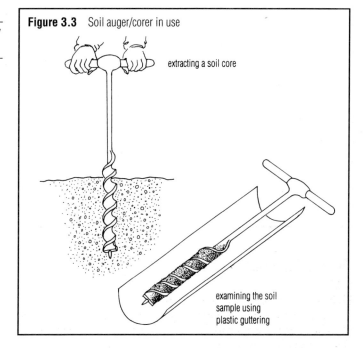

Figure 3.3   Soil auger/corer in use

extracting a soil core

examining the soil sample using plastic guttering

Soil texture

The relative proportions of different-sized particles in soil determines its texture. Soil texture can be assessed manually, by examination of a sample with a hand lens and by 'feel' (Table 3.2).

Mechanical analysis

The separation of soil into its constituent particle fractions in order to find the ratio of coarse particles (sand) to fine particles (silt and clay) allows the soil to be designated clay, loam or sandy soil. The separation may be carried out:

- accurately, by sieving a known mass of dried soil through a nest of sieves, and weighing the portions that are trapped at each particle size (designated sand, silt or clay by the Soil Survey, *Advanced Biology*, p. 59);
- approximately, by shaking a soil sample with water in a measuring cylinder until all the particles are mobile. Then allow the sample to stand (larger particles settle first, fine clays settle last, and most humus particles float). Use the cylinder's markings to gauge the heights of the particles of each different size-class, and hence the proportions of each size-class in the soil as a whole.

Equipment: soil sieves, top-pan balance, measuring cylinder.

Mineral salt (ion) content

Commercial soil-testing kits, based largely upon Horticultural Research International methods, are available to assess the concentrations of nitrate, phosphate and potassium ions in soils. The techniques involve adding a fixed amount of distilled water to the soil and using test strips.

Equipment: Portable soil-testing kit.

Table 3.2 Assessing soil texture

1 Examine soil samples 'dry' using a hand lens.
2 Handle the dry soil; does it feel gritty or non-gritty?
3 Moisten the soil to the point of stickiness and knead it with your fingers. Is it cohesive or plastic? Does it feel gritty?
4 Roll it into long threads (if possible). Will these threads bend into rings?

Now use the table to judge the texture.

Appearance under lens	Feel between fingers		Rolling between fingers	Texture
	Wet or dry	Wet		
large grains absent or very few in number	smooth and non-gritty, or slightly gritty	generally very sticky, plastic	gives long threads which will bend into rings	clay, silty clay, sandy clay
many sand grains present	slightly gritty	moderately plastic	gives threads with difficulty, which will NOT easily bend into rings	silty clay loam, clay loam, sandy clay loam
sand grains present but silt predominating	smooth	smooth	forms threads with broken appearance	silt, silty loam
comparable portions of sand, silt and clay	gritty	slightly plastic	gives threads with great difficulty	loam
sand grains predominate	more gritty	not plastic, only slight cohesion	gives threads with very great difficulty	fine sandy loam, sandy loam
mostly sand	very gritty	forms flowing mass	does not give threads	loamy sand, sand

Soil pH

The pH of soils can be measured colorimetrically by adding an indicator solution from a soil test kit to a small sample, and comparing the colour developed with a colour chart. If the solution is cloudy, remove suspended particles with a flocculating agent (such as barium sulphate) before carrying out the colour test. Soil test kits are effective, reliable and accurate. Alternatively, commercially available pH test papers (or sticks) can be used. Use a pH paper sensitive to a wide range of pH to gauge pH approximately, and then choose a pH paper sensitive to the appropriate narrow range, to measure accurately.

Soil pH can also be measured electrometrically with a battery-operated pH kit equipped with a hydrogen-ion sensitive probe (electrode). You have to calibrate the electrode against a standard buffer solution before use. The electrode is fitted with a plastic guard with spear point, so it can be inserted into the soil without damage (Figure 3.4).

Equipment: soil test kit, or soil pH meter with probe.

Soil air

Soil air is measured in representative samples of known volume. Use a corer to remove an undisturbed soil sample. Calculate the volume of the soil sample (length × cross-sectional area), and then add the soil to a known volume of water in a measuring cylinder. When water has penetrated the air spaces of the soil sample, the total volume of soil sample and water will be reduced by the volume of air displaced. This volume is expressed as a percentage of the sample volume. An alternative method of collecting the sample is to use a can or tube of known volume, with many small holes bored in the wall. This is forced into the earth and then carefully dug out.

Equipment: Corer and measuring cylinder.

Soil water and humus content

Soil water and humus content are measured by driving off the water and later burning out the humus from weighed samples

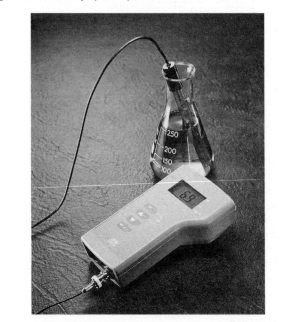

Figure 3.4 A battery-operated pH meter

of soil. Using a small preweighed iron tray, weigh a sample of soil and then dry it in an electric oven at 110 °C for 24 hours. Weigh the cooled tray with dry soil, and then reheat it, cool, and reweigh it. Repeat this process until the dry soil is at constant mass. Then calculate the mass loss as a percentage of the oven-dry mass of the soil sample.

Alternatively, you can use a moisture meter to obtain quick and direct measurements that are useful for comparisons – when sampling along a transect line, for example.

Strong heating of the dried soil on the iron tray, using a high, hot Bunsen flame in a fume cupboard, will burn off the humus. Then the sample may be cooled and weighed. Repeat the process until the soil mineral skeleton (remaining) is at constant mass. (The results will not be valid if chalk is present in the soil, since chalk is decomposed by heat.)

Equipment: Small iron tray, top-pan balance, drying oven, bunsen/tripod/gauze/heat pad, and desiccator.

Soil temperature

See the methods for measuring air temperature (above).

■ Water analysis

The simplest method of sampling water (for measuring pH, ion content or Biological Oxygen Demand (BOD), for example) at given depths in a river or lake is to fix a weight to a plastic drinks bottle, very lightly insert the stopper and lower it into the water. When the stopper is removed the water will enter (Figure 3.5).

pH and temperature

The pH and temperature of water samples can be measured in the same ways as for soil (see above).

Conductivity

Conductivity meters, which measure the amount of electrical current that will flow through a sample of water, give a quick and useful guide to the amount of dissolved material in a river. The readings do not tell us which solutes are present, however. Conductivity is temperature-dependent, so care is needed with readings that have been taken at different times. Biological equipment suppliers offer various portable meters (water test meters and specific conductivity meters) with probes that are sensitive over the ranges typical of fresh and seawater. Readings obtained may be compared with the conductivity of distilled water and that of tap water. Conductivity readings are specially important for testing salinity in estuaries and rockpools.

Equipment: Water test meter or conductivity meter with probe.

Dissolved substances/ions

Commercially available water-testing kits allow accurate field determinations of a range of substances, including ammonium, nitrate, nitrite, phosphate, potassium, sulphate, chloride, chlorine and iron ions, and the general 'hardness' of water. Tests are mostly performed by immersing a test strip or dipstick in a water sample (or adding a reagent pack to a sample) and comparing the colour developed with a given scale.

Equipment: Merck, Hach, Hanna or Palintest field kits, or similar.

Dissolved oxygen

Dissolved oxygen can be measured accurately by the Winkler method, which involves a titration and many reagents. Each determination is time-consuming (although the Winkler method is available as a 'dissolved oxygen test kit' for field use). Various oxygen meters are also commercially available, some of questionable reliability or limited 'life expectancy', or both.

The BOD of water is a measure of organic pollution of water. Comparison of BOD values obtained by means of the methylene blue test (pp. 71–2) is a sound, safe comparative method that yields valuable results.

Equipment: Oxygen test kit.

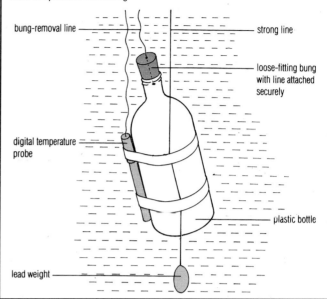

Figure 3.5 Apparatus for sampling water, including a digital probe for water temperature monitoring

bung-removal line

strong line

loose-fitting bung with line attached securely

digital temperature probe

plastic bottle

lead weight

Light penetration/turbidity

The clarity of water is important, since cloudy water reduces the light available for photosynthesis (and may harm fish gills). A Secchi disc (a 20 cm wide circular disc painted black and white and suspended horizontally), lowered into water on a graduated line until it just disappears, gives an approximate method for quantifying turbidity. The length of string paid out is inversely proportional to the turbidity.

Equipment: Secchi disc.

Water speed

Current meters can be used to measure water flow, but they are expensive. Where the flow rate is quite high a Pitot tube with manometer is effective (Figure 3.6). Alternatively a 'Pooh

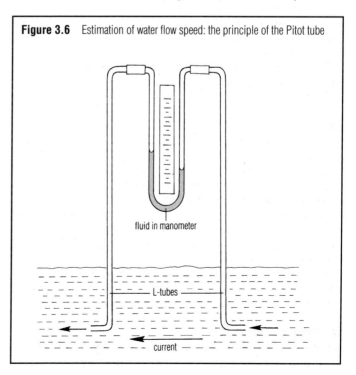

Figure 3.6 Estimation of water flow speed: the principle of the Pitot tube

fluid in manometer

L-tubes

current

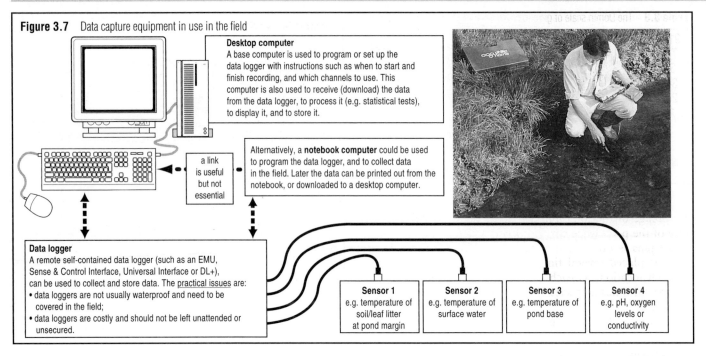

Figure 3.7 Data capture equipment in use in the field

Desktop computer
A base computer is used to program or set up the data logger with instructions such as when to start and finish recording, and which channels to use. This computer is also used to receive (download) the data from the data logger, to process it (e.g. statistical tests), to display it, and to store it.

a link is useful but not essential

Alternatively, a **notebook computer** could be used to program the data logger, and to collect data in the field. Later the data can be printed out from the notebook, or downloaded to a desktop computer.

Data logger
A remote self-contained data logger (such as an EMU, Sense & Control Interface, Universal Interface or DL+), can be used to collect and store data. The practical issues are:
• data loggers are not usually waterproof and need to be covered in the field;
• data loggers are costly and should not be left unattended or unsecured.

Sensor 1
e.g. temperature of soil/leaf litter at pond margin

Sensor 2
e.g. temperature of surface water

Sensor 3
e.g. temperature of pond base

Sensor 4
e.g. pH, oxygen levels or conductivity

---

stick' float (traditionally, an orange) can be placed in the current and its passage timed over, say, 50 metres. Water speed should be given as distance/time.

Using data capture techniques in fieldwork

The term **data capture technique** refers to the automatic collection of data using sensors attached to a multichannel data memory system, such as Vela or DL Plus (Figure 3.7). These units are invaluable when data need to be collected over a long period of time. For example, data on diurnal changes in air and water temperature, dissolved oxygen, light intensity or pH in an aquatic environment, detected by portable meters and probes, reveal a lot more about change in the environment than do a few measurements over a limited time span.

On return to the laboratory, the recorded data are downloaded on to a microcomputer and processed and displayed, using appropriate software (Figure 3.7). It is necessary to incorporate a buffer box as protection between the sensor device and the logger or computer (to ensure the output voltage of the device does not exceed the permitted input voltage on the data logger/microcomputer).

Biotic techniques

We cannot analyse the totality of habitats like woods or ponds because of their size and the huge numbers of organisms they contain, and because of our limited resources, including that of time. Instead, we adopt a **sampling** approach. Normally this is done by investigating sample areas, remembering that there is always a question as to whether the sample is representative.

■ Quadrats

A **quadrat** is a frame which outlines a known area for the purpose of sampling. The choice of size and number of quadrats used depends upon:
• the nature of the community of organisms present (a 10 cm^2 quadrat is useful for assessing epiphytic *Pleurococcus* on trees, but 10 km^2 quadrats are more useful for estimating the population of lions in a game reserve);

• the type of data required, which may be either the species composition of the community, or the relative abundance of the species present, or both.

For 'species composition' alone, one relatively large quadrat placed in a representative position may be sufficient. For a quantitative analysis it is essential to take random samples. Random quadrats are placed according to random numbers after the area has been divided into a grid of numbered sampling squares. This may be necessary to overcome a bias obtained by the alternative technique of quadrats being positioned by dropping or 'throwing' them over the left shoulder.

Assessing occurrence within a quadrat

The following quantitative assessments may be made:
• **density** – the number of individuals per unit area; it is not always possible to count individuals in a quadrat, and sometimes the assessments have to be made in a different way;
• **abundance** – a subjective assessment of abundance that can be translated into a numerical scale and entered on to a spreadsheet; one frequently used abundance scale is the five-point DAFOR scale:
  5 = Dominant; 4 = Abundant; 3 = Frequent; 2 = Occasional; 1 = Rare
  (if the same observer makes 'abundance' judgements of two or more habitats, then the resulting comparison may be objective);
• **frequency** – the number of quadrats (expressed as a percentage) in which a species is found;
• **cover** – the percentage ground area within a quadrat covered by sedentary or fixed species; this is a useful measure for a species where separate individuals cannot be differentiated.

The cover contributed by the species present in a quadrat is often estimated according to a scale such as the Domin scale (Table 3.3).

To avoid errors due to subjective estimations of cover, an objective assessment may be made using the point method. If a large number of points ('pins') are lowered on to vegetation, the number of times a given species is hit (expressed as a

Table 3.3 The Domin scale of ground cover

91–100%	cover is recorded as	10
76–90%		9
51–75%		8
34–50%		7
26–33%		6
11–25%		5
4–10%		4
<4%:	many individuals	3
	several individuals	2
	few individuals	1

percentage of the total number of points recorded) is a measure of the percentage cover of that species. A standing frame of 10 pins is often used (Figure 3.8). The whole frame can then be placed several times in randomly selected positions. At each location, as each pin is lowered to the ground, the number of times a species is touched by one of the 10 pins is recorded.

Equipment: Quadrats, point frame.

■ Transects

Whereas some communities are relatively uniform over a given area and are suitable for random analysis, others show a trend of variation in a particular direction. Examples include a seashore, pond margin, saltmarsh or even a change from dry soil to wet. The appropriate technique to study such a trend of variation is the transect.

Transects are a means of sampling biotic (and abiotic) data at right angles to the impact of unidirectional physical forces. Although often there is time to study only one transect in detail, and this may be sufficient as a demonstration of the zonation of communities, a single transect does not provide an adequate sample or give an indication of differences or variations from place to place. Transects should therefore preferably be replicated several times.

Line transect

A tape or rope is laid in a straight line across an apparently representative part of a habitat, and the position of every organism (normally plant), or those at regular intervals, covered or touched by the line is noted.

Belt transect

This is a broad transect, usually a half-metre wide. To produce it, a tape measure or rope is laid as for a line transect, but this time the organisms in a series of quadrats of half-metre width are sampled at metre intervals. If the community changes little along the transect, then quadrats can be placed at 5 m or 10 m intervals.

Profile transect

When transects are carried out across a habitat where the land changes in height and where level is an important factor (such as a seashore or a saltmarsh), then the changes in level along the transect line can be measured and recorded as a profile transect. The techniques for working out the height of the next station in relation to the last are shown in Figure 3.9 on p. 49 of *Advanced Biology.*

Equipment: Rope or tape measure, survey poles, Abney level, metre rules, spirit level.

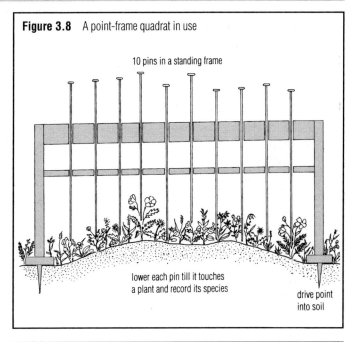

Figure 3.8 A point-frame quadrat in use

10 pins in a standing frame

lower each pin till it touches a plant and record its species

drive point into soil

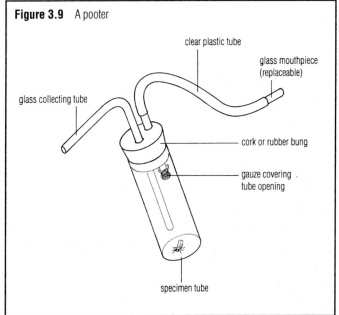

Figure 3.9 A pooter

clear plastic tube

glass mouthpiece (replaceable)

glass collecting tube

cork or rubber bung

gauze covering tube opening

specimen tube

■ Sampling techniques for animal communities

Nets (See Figure 3.10, p. 26, for a selection of nets).

Sweeping air nets Nets such as butterfly nets can be used to catch insects on the wing. When swept through tall vegetation such as lank grass in a controlled, reproducible manner, stationary insects may be dislodged and trapped also. A pooter (Figure 3.9) can be used to 'harvest' delicate animals. Identification can be limited to class or order unless greater precision is required.

Aquatic nets A useful pond net can be constructed from a metal kitchen sieve fixed to a broom pole with jubilee clips. Purchased 'D'-shaped nets are useful for quantitative sampling. For aquatic catches, sort the organisms in a white tray. After the plant species have been identified, shake them over the tray (to release trapped animals) and return them to the river or pond. Then identify and count the animals before

Figure 3.10 Different types of collecting nets

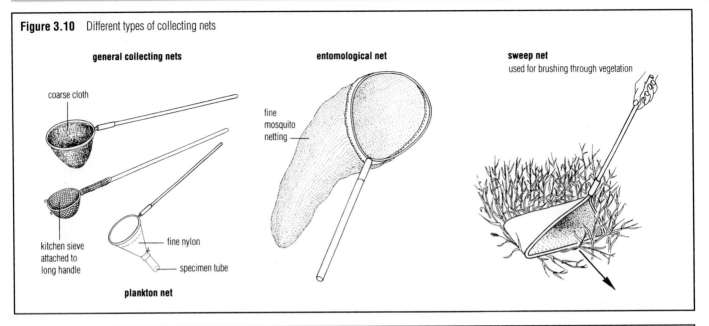

general collecting nets

coarse cloth

kitchen sieve attached to long handle

fine nylon

specimen tube

plankton net

entomological net

fine mosquito netting

sweep net
used for brushing through vegetation

Figure 3.11 **a** A pitfall trap *in situ*; **b** a Longworth small-mammal trap

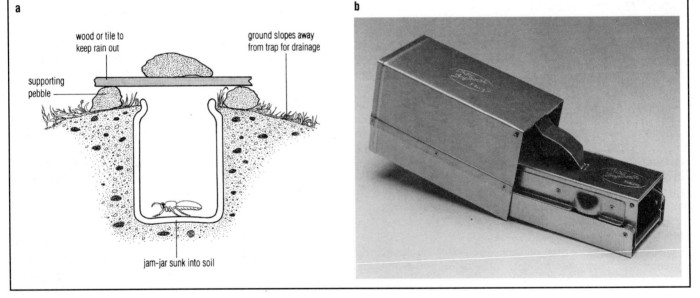

a

wood or tile to keep rain out

ground slopes away from trap for drainage

supporting pebble

jam-jar sunk into soil

b

releasing them too. Identification should only be as far as is needed for the particular study purpose.

Plankton nets These require a very fine mesh, together with a transparent plastic sample tube secured at the net apex. The contents of the tube may be transferred to jars or other tubes, prior to microscopic examination of the catch.

Equipment: Air (insect) nets, pond nets, plankton nets.

Traps

Pitfall trap These are for the fauna active on the soil surface or in leaf litter. The trap consists of a plastic pot, tin can or similar container, buried in the soil so the top is flush with the surface. A lid (such as a Petri dish with a stone on top) is balanced on three stones and keeps out the rain (Figure 3.11a). Pitfall traps can be baited, or contain alcohol. You should visit baited traps regularly, as there is a risk that carnivores may eat the other animals trapped.

Sticky traps These are for flying insects. The trap can consist of a plastic tube or card, coated with black treacle. Hang it out or support it on sticks where insects pass.

Longworth small-mammal trap Small rodents and insectivores can be trapped in Longworth traps (Figure 3.11b), baited with grains of wheat and with bedding of hay. Set the traps in the evening and examine them the following morning.

Equipment: pitfall traps, tube or card, black treacle.

Estimating population size by trapping Populations of animals such as small mammals, woodlice or insects can be estimated by sampling for mark–release–recapture (MRR, *Advanced Biology*, pp. 66–7). The captured sample of animals is labelled (ringed/tagged/marked with coloured paint). MRR may be trialled on populations of woodlice discovered sheltering under stones or flower-pots in a garden. You can mark your 'captured' samples with 'Tipp-Ex' or coloured nail varnish. If you merely need to establish the accuracy of MRR, however, you can do this by modelling the method on surrogate 'animals' without loss of rigour or accuracy.

The population of organisms may be represented by a large batch of about 500 dried peas, held within a confined space (such as an opaque polythene bag). You have to be able to withdraw samples at random, without viewing the whole population.

1 Withdraw a random sample of the whole population of peas (say 25).
2 Replace this sample by the same number of eosin-coloured peas (equivalent to 'marking' the first sample before returning them to the whole population).
3 Shake the bag so as to mix the contents thoroughly (equivalent to allowing the marked sample to disperse themselves among the whole population).
4 Withdraw a second sample (of a similar number as the original sample), and record the number of recaptured 'organisms' (pink-stained peas).
5 Calculate the size of the whole population using the Lincoln Index according to the formula:

$$N = \frac{n_1 \times n_2}{n_3}$$

where N = the population being estimated
n_1 = number captured, marked and released
n_2 = total number captured on the second occasion
and n_3 = number of marked individuals recaptured.

6 Repeat this procedure with captured samples of 50 or 100 'organisms', having added 25 or 75 more coloured peas, and allowed for these in the total.
7 Finally, count the total population to check the accuracy of the estimate.

NOTE TO TECHNICIAN

Each group will require:
- about 500 dried peas (they can be counted by weighing a known number);
- a black plastic bag (= the habitat);
- a sample of 100 dried peas previously stained red with eosin and dried.

Comparable studies of the Lincoln Index applied to model populations have been published:
J A Bishop and J S Bradley (1972) 'Taxi cabs as subjects for a population study', *J. Biol. Ed.* **6**(4), pp. 227–31
E C Gilhooley (1985) 'Using shopping trolleys to teach animal population estimating techniques', *J. Biol. Ed.* **19**(3), p. 184
M C Calver, B D Porter and J S Bradley (1990) 'A simple simulation for teaching capture–recapture methods of population estimation', *J. Biol. Ed.* **24**(4), pp. 267–72

Habitat disturbance

Beating tray The beating tray device consists of a white linen platform which you hold below overhanging vegetation. As you shake the vegetation by strong beating movements with a stick, the small animals within it fall on to the tray. You can collect and store the catch for later identification, by means of a pooter. Comparative results are obtained from a standardised technique.
Equipment: Beating tray with stick, pooter.

Kick sampling Benthic animals of flowing streams can be dislodged when you disturb their stony habitat by sudden deliberate movements made with toe or heel of your Wellington boot (provided you can do this without losing your footing). Scoop up the dislodged organisms in a net held downstream of the disturbed microhabitat.

Repulsion techniques

Earthworms Earthworms may be driven from below ground by the application of a suspension of culinary mustard to the soil surface (p. 14).

Driving soil organisms from soil samples Soil samples can be brought to the laboratory and subjected to conditions that dislodge or drive out the fauna.

1 The Tullgren funnel (Figure 2.3a, p. 13) drives animals out of the air spaces. The technique depends on the soil animals moving down as the soil is dried out by the heat from the bulb suspended above. The animals eventually fall into a container of alcohol. This system works very well provided the light bulb is not too hot.
2 The Baermann funnel (Figure 2.3b, p. 13) is useful for collecting animals of the soil water. A soil sample, wrapped up in muslin, is suspended in water and illuminated from above (60 W bulb). The resulting heat gradient causes very small animals to pass through the muslin bag and collect at the bottom of the funnel, from where they can be extracted.
Equipment: Tullgren and Baermann funnels.

Animal tracks and signs
Rather than catch the animals themselves, you can study their activities by their tracks left behind in soft earth or mud (specimen footprints can be 'captured' for identification by plaster casting), and by the signs of foraging and feeding (by nut-eating animals, for example). Other identifiable mementoes left behind are pellets and faeces.

Owl pellets Owls' pellets can be found on the ground below roosts or nests, typically in large trees, barns or old walls (Figure 3.12). The pellets are grey in colour. Soak them in warm water in a dish under a binocular microscope. Using a mounted needle and a pair of fine forceps, tease the pellets apart to release any recognisable animal remains. Place these on a wad of filter paper to dry out before examining and identifying them. From fragments of mammal jaw bones and insect cuticles, you may be able to identify the diet of the owl.
Equipment: Petri dish, binocular microscope, mounted needles and fine forceps.

Faecal pellets Fresh pellets, such as rabbit droppings, are preferable, so that bacterial decomposition is limited. Collected pellets may be stored in alcohol. Remove a small part of the centre of a pellet, cover it with household bleach (4% sodium chlorate(I) (hypochlorite) – care! Wear eye protection.) and keep it for 6–12 hours at room temperature. Then wash the debris in a fine sieve, using tap water. Stain the plant debris retained by the sieve and examine it by the high power of the microscope. The epidermal cells of monocotyledons are long, narrow and cuboidal, whereas those of dicotyledons are irregularly shaped.
Equipment: storage tubes with 70% ethanol (highly flammable), forceps, domestic bleach, fine mesh sieve, microscope slides, coverslips, plant tissue stains, microscope.

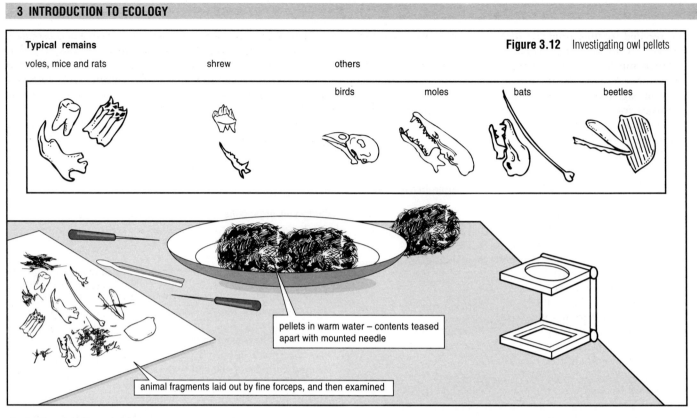

Typical remains

voles, mice and rats   shrew   others

birds   moles   bats   beetles

Figure 3.12   Investigating owl pellets

pellets in warm water – contents teased apart with mounted needle

animal fragments laid out by fine forceps, and then examined

3.2 Analysing a habit

(Data generating)

When we examine a habitat such as a wood, pond or seashore, we see a distinctive pattern in the form of zonations or stratifications in the living things (biota). The precise pattern is characteristic of the particular type of habitat, but is always a product of interactions between specific abiotic factors and the biota. Biotic and abiotic components influence each other in significant ways. Moreover, several distinct microhabitats may be present within the larger habitat. Ecologists analyse ecosystems in order to identify the precise nature of the interactions within them. This is an important first step in understanding our environment.

Firstly we need to remind ourselves of the salient features of these habitats as we find them today, together with a little about their origins (historical ecology).

■ Types of habitat

Woodlands

Woodland is the climax community for the greater part of the UK, given altitude, soil types and climate (*Advanced Biology*, p. 68). Woods and forests were established here after the last

Figure 3.13   Working in the field: analysing soil samples and measuring tree heights

ice receded; of this original 'wildwood', however, very little remains. Clearance has gone on at an accelerating pace through much of human history; by the start of the 1990s, only about 9% of Britain was still wooded. Now there are hopeful signs of significant deliberate replanting of trees. Evidence for the existence of remaining patches of the wildwood (known as 'relict' woodland) is the presence of certain species in the herb layer.

Most of our remaining original woodlands have been 'managed' by coppicing or pollarding, at some stage in their history. In coppicing, the trees are cut at ground level, leaving a stump (stool) from which many smaller stems sprout. These are then harvested at intervals of about 8–12 years. In pollarding (applied in woods where deer or cattle roamed) the trees are cut about 3 m above the ground level, so that the new branches grow out of the reach of the browsing animals.

Today we study woodland as a precious natural resource that we seek to conserve. A wood can be divided into several different layers at different levels above the ground (*Advanced Biology*, p. 56). Within a wood, the distribution of species can be related most directly to light intensity, soil type and drainage. The overall characteristics of the habitat, however, relate to the dominant tree species (Figure 3.13).

Hedgerows

A hedge is a haven for wildlife, and an effective corridor along which wildlife can travel. Although in Britain thousands of kilometres of hedgerows are lost each year, about 75% of our farms still have hedges, and the area of hedges remaining exceeds 200 000 hectares. This is about twice the size of all our recognised nature reserves! Indeed, hedges constitute the longest nature reserve in the world. Nearly a thousand species of our native plants have been recorded in hedges, and about 250 species are confined to them. Many birds use hedges for nesting, cover and food, and over half our mammals are to be found in hedgerows. Hedges tend to maintain a high species diversity long after any surrounding woodland has been cleared. As an ecosystem, a hedge is of special ecological interest because in a small distance there are rapid and important changes of both abiotic and biotic factors (Figure 3.14).

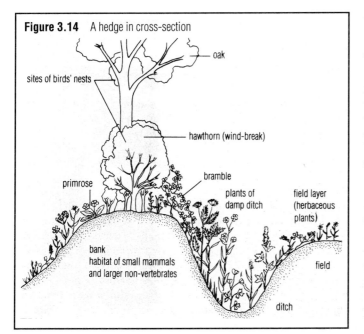

Figure 3.14 A hedge in cross-section

oak

sites of birds' nests

hawthorn (wind-break)

bramble

primrose

plants of damp ditch

field layer (herbaceous plants)

bank habitat of small mammals and larger non-vertebrates

field

ditch

Many hedgerows have a history which goes back centuries. As woodland was cleared to provide space for crops, hedges were needed to keep stock under control. Many new hedges were created in Britain between the sixteenth and nineteenth centuries, as part of the switch to crop cultivation on hitherto unenclosed strips of land, a process referred to by historians as the Great Enclosures. Ecologists have devised ways of estimating the age of a hedge, based upon the numbers of trees and shrubs present in a given length. These methods work well, except where a hedge was originally planted with many species.

Fresh water

Freshwater habitats, such as rivers and streams, canals, shallow lakes, deep lakes, puddles and ditches, are all worthy of study. But freshwater sites remaining in crowded islands, like the British Isles, have been profoundly influenced by human activities. Long-standing ponds are quite rare, partly because ponds often silt up and become woodland (*Advanced Biology*, p. 69), but partly because many ponds are deliberately drained. An increasing number of urban ponds in gardens provide support for wildlife, however.

Rivers and canals make an interesting comparison. Canals are usually deep, rectangular in cross-section, and with few water weeds along the margins. The bottom of the canal is made of non-porous clay. Boat traffic disturbs floating plant life; if the boats travel fast enough they cause wave erosion, which destroys plant life at the margins. On the other hand, non-navigable canals silt up, and then fill with rooted aquatic 'weeds' as part of a succession that leads eventually to woodland. A river community depends on the speed of the water flow. In fast, eroding rivers, the bottom is rocky or stony, and the river has a high species diversity and density. In slow, depositing rivers silt accumulates and the water is low in dissolved oxygen, a condition which many animals cannot tolerate. The nature of the rocks in which some rivers originate, and the characteristics of the soil over which they flow, also affect their composition and their communities. 'Chalk' rivers have a high calcium content (over 20 ppm), and are rich in molluscs and crustaceans. 'Acid' rivers have a low pH, usually rise on moorland, and have few, if any, molluscs or crustaceans.

Seashore

Tides dominate our shore, but in a few parts of Europe (including the Mediterranean) the tidal range is relatively insignificant. Seashores are ideal for studying adaptations to the environment, for with constantly changing abiotic factors the selection pressures at work on the fauna and flora are often severe (*Advanced Biology*, p. 51). The chief abiotic and biotic factors which bring about the clear zonation of the shore are:

- wave action – some seashores are exposed to long wind fetches resulting in severe wave action, whereas others are sheltered by islands or headlands;
- alternating emersion and desiccation – the possible loss of water will be greater on the more exposed upper part of the seashore;
- light – this is one of the most important factors controlling the zonation of the algae: light at the blue-green end of the visible spectrum penetrates deepest into seawater and the red pigment (phycoerythrin) of red seaweed is more efficient at absorbing this blue-green light;

- competition for food and space – there is a constant battle on most parts of the seashore, and some species crowd out nearly everything else (for example, barnacles and mussels, or heavy layers of brown algae).

■ Aim

To investigate the ecology of a chosen habitat (woodland, hedgerow, freshwater site or seashore), and to study the effects of abiotic and biotic factors on the fauna and flora there, and within the various microhabitats present.

■ Risk assessment

- Never work alone, but in responsible groups. Leave a record of when and where you will be for others (teacher, tutor or parent) to consult if necessary. Report in by phone as soon as possible if your plans have to be changed.
- All aquatic sites are especially hazardous. Take special care and extra precautions at all times when working:

  a at deep water sites, and at fast-flowing water, and rivers or canals with steep sides;
  b on seashores, marshes and mudflats where the land slope is shallow and the tide comes in quickly;
  c on exposed rocky shores, for here there may be a danger from unpredictable and infrequent, very large waves.

- For marine habitats, study the tide tables beforehand, so that you will be working on the beach around low water. Admiralty tide tables and *Reed's Almanack* are available from most libraries.
- Be concerned about hygiene. Cover any cuts or abrasions on your hands with waterproof plasters. Wash your hands after working at aquatic sites. Although the chance of catching Weil's disease (leptospirosis) is very low, the causative organisms are now common in many mainland European rivers and canals. Should you get influenza-like symptoms after aquatic fieldwork, tell your doctor about your fieldwork site.
- When pushing through undergrowth or low-growing trees and shrubs, take care to avoid damage to your eyes and to those of your colleagues.
- Do not damage stone walls, hedges and any type of fence by making holes in them. Close all gates.
- Conserve the countryside. Careless trampling as well as over-zealous sampling and collecting can destroy a habitat very quickly.
- The 'Country Code' asks us to 'Take nothing but pictures. Leave nothing but footprints. Kill nothing but time!'.

■ Method

1 An action plan

Practical fieldwork requires careful preparations in the form of an **action plan**, covering the following points:

- What is the aim or hypothesis for this investigation, and how does this fieldwork fit into your overall study of the environment? Why has this site been chosen?
- Do you need permission from the landowner (or the riparian owner, if it is a river study)?
- What sampling methods will you use? Make a list of the biotic measurements that need to be made, and list the abiotic measurements. You will also require an equipment list.

- The logistics of the team work needs planning, too. What will be the job of each member of the group?
- Have you estimated the time needed to carry out the data collection? If it is too long, now is the time to make adjustments to the plan.
- Data collection and presentation should also be planned in advance. Have you decided exactly how you are going to present the data to aid analysis?
- Safety issues must be addressed: have you checked the risk assessment statement?
- Are you clear about the conservation factors that need to be kept in mind?

2 An initial survey

Record the type of locality (including its name and Ordnance Survey reference), together with an annotated sketch of the area where the detailed study will be undertaken. Note the positions of nearby industrial sites, dwellings, farms, paths and roadways. Comment on the general use of the area by humans. Add, to your sketch, notes on the nature of the soil (pp. 20–3) and the variety of microhabitats offered. Note down significant, abnormal or unusual features, such as fallen trees or evidence of human interference.

3 Transect analysis

Make an initial analysis of your habitat by means of transects. Your investigations should focus on the range of microhabitats and the flora and fauna typical of the chosen ecosystem. Transect analyses are a good method of detecting information about a representative part of the whole habitat, and conditions at distinct transitions within a habitat. To create your transect, lay a tape measure across or through what appears to be a representative part (biotic techniques, p. 25), as far as this is possible. Then measure and record data on the relevant abiotic factors for the particular habitat (pp. 20–4), and also the biota present (pp. 24–8) at regular intervals along the transect line. Adapt your sampling positions to the conditions of the habitat. For example, if the conditions change abruptly, sample every metre or more often, but if there is a long way between changes in conditions then sampling every 5 to 10 m may be more appropriate. Measure and record the distance between sampling stations carefully. If possible, use a data logger (p. 24) to record over a 24-hour period the factors that appear to determine the biota present (for instance, temperature, humidity and light).

The study of one site alone may provide an introduction only. It may be useful at an early stage to make a comparison of two related but different sites within the same locality. Compare, for example, a clearing in a wood with an area of mature woodland, the opposite sides of a hedge, a fast river with a slow canal, a river above and below a sewage effluent outfall, or an exposed part of a shore with a nearby sheltered part.

4 Quadrat analysis

Then, if possible and appropriate (often not so in hedge or pond habitats), use quadrats to convert your transect line into a belt transect by using half-metre quadrats at suitable intervals along a transect line. Measure and record details of the most important abiotic factors in each quadrat. Quadrats will allow you to survey the biota in appropriate detail. For example, what are the chief plant species present, and what is their percentage cover in each quadrat (p. 24)? What is the composition of the animal community, as shown by various sampling methods? You may use pond-dipping nets (p. 25) in aquatic habitats, tree shaking (p. 27), pooters to collect small animals in terrestrial microhabitats (p. 25), sweep nets to collect flying insects, and insects in long grass (p. 26), Longworth mammal traps and pitfall traps buried in different habitats (p. 26). You will need good identification books too (p.11–12).

NOTE TO TECHNICIAN

Since student teams will plan the analyses to be undertaken in any particular habitat, using the methods listed in Section 3.1 above, they will be required to provide the list of equipment

---

■ Data presentation
Your first step is to produce a table of data (p. 38). Design the table so that comparable data are shown side by side and can easily be analysed. To help you analyse your data, display them in the form of a line graph or kite histograms (p. 39), to show changes (if any) along the transect line.

Data can be presented and analysed using a microcomputer and printer via an Ecology program (p. 40).

■ Conclusions
Use the table of data and the display of data to produce a concise written summary of the effects of abiotic factors on the biota. Look for patterns and correlations (p. 39). For example, what is the dominant abiotic factor?

Share information with other groups of students working in the same area or on the same investigation by means of presentations. Seek to discover how the data of each group fit together to furnish an emerging ecological pattern of the habitat you have studied.

Draw conclusions about the differences between the habitats you have studied, where you choose to make a comparison. Add a final paragraph to your conclusion which sets your investigation in the context of the whole habitat.

From your observations, together with the work of other members of your team, piece together a food web for your chosen habitat. Compare it with published food webs (for example, *Advanced Biology*, pp. 54 and 64).

Then, working on the assumption that the fauna and flora of your habitat might have important commercial and leisure values, draw up future management (conservation) plans for both uses of the area. What might be the impact of such usage on the ecology of the area?

■ Evaluation
Some issues to be thinking about include:
- Was the part of the habitat you sampled representative of the whole?
- How could your investigation have been improved? For example, what further investigative fieldwork might help to clarify your discoveries?
- Is it worth enquiring of holders of local records (secretary to the local Natural History Society, or firms or companies with an interest in the area) to discover whether your conclusions tie in with other observations and records for the area?
- What evidence did you find of significant human influence on the environment?

3.3 Ecological investigations

(Data generating)

From the initial survey of a habitat, certain ecological issues that require further exploration will become clear. A small-scale enquiry into one (or more) of these issues provides a next step in the analysis of the habitat.

■ Aim
To conduct an individual (or small-team) investigation, involving a given idea (or your own suggestion) and some guiding questions and instructions, formulated into a hypothesis, to be tested by independent work (an element of open enquiry/research).

■ Risk assessment
The risk assessments relating to 'Analysing a habitat' (p. 19) and to 'Ecological techniques' (p. 30) apply here too.

■ Method
Design an investigation of your own or select one of the topics described below. Your investigation should include experimental work and data collection in the field, and must be completed in the time available. Check each stage of the process with your teacher/tutor.

Investigations in woodland or hedgerow habitats

■ The effects of light on flora and fauna
Where the intensity of shading imposed by tree canopies changes, the flora and fauna at ground, herb/field (and sometimes shrub) layers may be found to differ too. This may occur within a wood (for example, where a mature tree has fallen down, or where a broad path or ride crosses woodland, or where a part of the wood has recently been coppiced), as well as at the boundary of the wood and the surrounding habitat.

The general features of the zone of transition (ecotone) from light to shade may be detected by means of a transect, with the results presented as a profile drawing of the transect. Detailed information on the abiotic factors (most importantly, the incident light, of course) of shaded and exposed zones and on the flora and fauna must be obtained. Abiotic factors may be measured along the transect line, and in the randomly placed quadrats used to estimate the percentage cover and the relative abundance of herbaceous plants in the two zones. The community of larger fauna and minibeasts may be detected and populations estimated approximately by analysis of the catches obtained by the use of sweep nets and by frequently examined pitfall traps, and the minibeasts of the lower canopy can be sampled using a beating tray. The variations in the leaf litter and topsoil and the communities they support should also be examined, comparing shaded and exposed positions.

To what extent can the differences in the two communities be attributed to the differences in solar flux?

■ How old is the hedge?
In the United Kingdom hedges have been planted at different times, and so the remaining hedges are of enormously different ages. There are remains of Roman field systems, and a few older hedges date back to Iron and Bronze Age times. In the twelfth and thirteenth centuries, when woodland was cleared

in much of England to provide space for crops, new hedges were grown for stock control. Between the sixteenth and the nineteenth centuries, unenclosed common land was replaced by fields in the Great Enclosure movements. Hedge formation, and hedge destruction, have continued subsequently.

Hedges may be dated from old maps and other historical archives, or with the help of local natural historians. In 1974, a group of ecologists, working for the Nature Conservancy Research Centre in Monks Wood, Cambridgeshire, published a formula for the dating of a hedge, based on the number of different woody species (shrubs and trees) contained in a 30 yard (27 m) stretch. Their observation, that a hedge typically acquires a new woody species every 100 years, is known as the Hooper Index.

Hooper Index:

$$\text{age of hedge (years)} = \text{number of species of trees/shrubs per } 27\,\text{m} \times 100$$

Study the ecology of hedges in your locality, in order to establish how representative a randomly selected 27 m stretch is of the whole hedge, in respect of the species contained. Apply the Hooper Index to hedges about which you have information of age (and to some of which do not). Thus seek to check out the reliability of the Index for your area.

References

E Pollard, M D Hooper and N W Moore (1974) *Hedges.* Collins, New Naturalist no 58

W H Dowdeswell (1987) *Hedgerows and Verges.* Allen and Unwin

■ The effects on fauna and flora of conifers and broad-leaf trees

Deciduous and evergreen woods support very different communities. A study of two such woods growing on similar soils and with similar aspects, if you can find them in your locality, may enable you to measure the extent of the differences and suggest many of the reasons for them. Consider ways of collecting or sampling the birds, mammals, smaller fauna and minibeasts in a selected area of pine trees or a coniferous plantation, and the same area of broad-leaf woodland. Record other biotic and abiotic factors such as the density of trees, depth of leaf litter, light intensity, soil moisture and temperature. Look for significant differences in the abiotic conditions, the fauna and the plants (which are the primary producers). Try to show any interrelationships between these differences.

References

R J Putman (1984) 'Practical exercises for the study of community ecology at Advanced level', *J. Biol. Ed.* **18**(3), pp. 229–38

D Kemp (1983) 'Epiphyte distribution on tree bark,' *J. Biol. Ed.* **17**(2), pp. 93–7

■ Fauna and microflora in woodland decomposition

The recycling of nutrients from dead organic matter is essential for all life. More than 80% of all green leaves (primary producers) is recycled as dead matter. Decay is carried out by decomposers or detritivore animals like earthworms and slugs, and by the soil microflora, mainly fungi and bacteria.

The behaviour of slugs may be observed after dark, particularly on damp nights and during rainy periods, using a torch, although where there is dense vegetation they are often hidden. The size of populations of slugs can be estimated by slow, progressive immersion of samples of soil or leaf litter in cold water, thus driving the slugs to the surface without drowning them. The dispersal of slugs (and the application of mark–release–recapture population size, p. 26, perhaps) can be analysed by feeding slugs with agar jelly stained with neutral red, which will show through the gut and foot.

Cellulose digestion is catalysed by cellulase, an enzyme produced by many saprotrophic microorganisms. The cellulose-digesting ability of soil samples can be assayed by incubating soil with a cellulose suspension (biocide-free wallpaper paste), and measuring the degree of cellulose degradation by the speed with which the liquid flows through the nozzle of a syringe barrel. The cellulose-digesting potential of the gut and gut contents of slugs could also be assayed, if the slugs are first killed.

References

J Napier (1988) 'Woodland decomposition', *School Science Review* **69**(248), pp. 469–76

D Pallant (1967) 'Slugs in school biology', *School Science Review* **48**(166), pp. 782–6

NCBE (1993) *Practical Biotechnology: a Guide for Schools and Colleges*, pp. 50–1. Department of Biotechnology, University of Reading, Reading RG6 2AJ

■ Biomass pyramid for a bryophyte community

Moss communities are more or less self-contained microhabitats with a characteristic fauna of non-vertebrates. They can be used to produce a biomass pyramid for a community with a minimum of destructive damage to the environment. A moss community occupying a known area (for example, the base of a Petri dish = 60 cm^2) is harvested and analysed in the laboratory, dividing individual moss plants and the non-vertebrates living there into separate dishes. The minibeasts should be killed by trapping on filter paper soaked with methanal (take care!, p. 12). The separated organisms are then classified into the trophic levels: producers (moss plants), primary consumers (herbivores such as fly larvae and *Collembola*) and secondary consumers (spiders), and the total numbers and masses of all three categories measured. From the results, ecological pyramids of numbers and of biomass can be constructed.

Reference

M Negus (1974) 'A biomass pyramid from a bryophyte community', *School Science Review* **56**(195), pp. 303–4

■ Holly leaf parasites

Many holly trees may be heavily parasitised by the leaf-mining fly (*Phytomyza ilicis*). The adult fly lays eggs on the underside of leaves in June. The larva penetrates and feeds in the midrib until late autumn. Then it migrates into the mesophyll tissue, and there creates a large mine by feeding on the cells there. By March the following year the larva is ready to pupate. Before doing so, it forms a triangular 'escape hatch' in the epidermis, and arranges an escape patch on the pupa case to line up. The pupal stage lasts from late March until early July, when adults emerge. The life cycle is then repeated. Meanwhile, in the vacated mines, fresh mesophyll cells form by divisions of existing cells, leading to bright green, irregularly shaped patches on the leaves. The incidence of parasitism of leaves on different aspects of the tree, at different heights above the ground, on

Figure 3.15 *Phytomyza* parasite of a holly leaf, and the life cycles of its own parasites

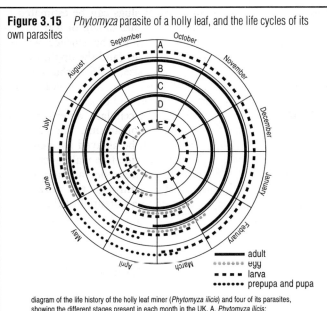

diagram of the life history of the holly leaf miner (*Phytomyza ilicis*) and four of its parasites, showing the different stages present in each month in the UK. A, *Phytomyza ilicis*; B, *Chrysocharis gemma*; C, *Chrysocharis syma*; D, *Sphegigaster flavicornis*; E, *Pleurotropis amyntas*

—— adult
········· egg
– – – larva
•••••• prepupa and pupa

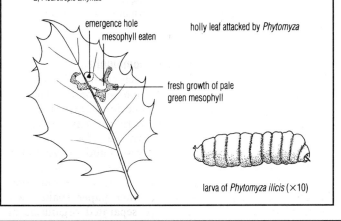

emergence hole
mesophyll eaten
holly leaf attacked by *Phytomyza*
fresh growth of pale green mesophyll

larva of *Phytomyza ilicis* (×10)

leaves of different ages, and on trees exposed to different levels of pollution may be investigated.

Of particular interest is the fact that the *Phytomyza* larva itself may be parasitised by several species of wasp. The life cycles of the common ones, together with stages in the *Phytomyza* life cycle, are illustrated in Figure 3.15. The incidence of this level of parasitism may also be researched.

Reference
T Lewis and L R Taylor (1972) *Introduction to Experimental Ecology*, pp. 202–8. Academic Press

Investigations in freshwater habitats

■ Aquatic pollution assessed by a biotic index
Freshwater pollution may be measured by chemical means (i.e. by measuring the concentration of specific pollutants), or assessed by its effect on living organisms (a bioassay), because the species of animals present are influenced by the quality of the water. In general, the greater the number of species, the better is the water quality. The Trent Biotic Index uses the number of different species or families to calculate a value for water quality.

The first step is to count the number of species or families present in a stretch of water and enter the number in Table 3.4. For example, if you find *Polycelis nigra* and one of another species of *Polycelis*, you enter 2 in Table 3.4 in the space for 'Flatworms'. If you find a caddis larva with a tube made of snail shells it is probably in the family Limnophilidae. A larva with a case of vegetation might be in the family Phryganidae. These would score 2 in the table. Add up all the scores to produce a total called the 'group score'.

The second step is to use key indicator species (such as stonefly nymphs) to provide an overall picture of the quality of the water. The group score provides a more detailed analysis

Figure 3.16 Investigating in freshwater habitats

within the quality range indicated by the key species. For example, stonefly nymphs are found in clean water, but there are 10 subdivisions of that clean water (6 to 15). If the range of species is low, say 5, then the biotic index will be just 7 instead of the maximum 15.

To convert your group score to an index of water quality, use Table 3.5. On the top line select the range of figures which includes your group score. Look down the column beneath these figures till you come to an animal which was present in your sample.

For example, if your group score was 23 and included one or more caddis larvae, the index would be 9. If your sample included a stonefly nymph, the index would be 11. If none of the first three insects was present but you found some *Gammarus*, the index would be 8.

The seven animals in Table 3.5 are the ones that are most sensitive to pollutants. The biotic index therefore depends on the range of species and the presence of a few 'key' species. An index of 15 implies very good water quality.

Reference

National Water Council (1981) *River Quality – the 1980 Survey and Future Outlook*. HMSO

Table 3.4   The Trent River Board Biotic Index: range of species

Scoring	Animal group	Score
Score one point for each of these animal species found in the river	flatworms	
	annelid worms	
	leeches	
	mollusca	
	crustacea	
	stonefly nymphs	
	mayfly nymphs	
	alder fly larvae	
	beetles and beetle larvae	
	water mites	
Score one point for each family	caddis fly larvae	
	chironomid larvae	
	Simulium larvae	
	total number of points =	

Table 3.5   Calculating the biotic index

Group score total	0–1	2–5	6–10	11–15	16–20	21–25	26–30	31–35	36–40	41–45
Key species	Biotic index									
stonefly nymph (Plecoptera)	6	7	8	9	10	11	12	13	14	15
mayfly nymph (Ephemeroptera)	5	6	7	8	9	10	11	12	13	14
caddis fly larva (Trichoptera)	4	5	6	7	8	9	10	11	12	13
Gammarus, but none of the above	3	4	5	6	7	8	9	10	11	12
Asellus, but none of the above	2	3	4	5	6	7	8	9	10	11
Tubifex and *Chironomus*	1	2	3	4	5	6	7	8	9	10
none of the above animals	0	1	2	–	–	–	–	–	–	–

■ Microhabitats

In aquatic environments such as ponds, lakes and rivers there are numerous microhabitats, each with its own fauna and flora. In some of these organisms at least, there are adaptations that reflect demands of the microhabitat. Typical microhabitats include the mid-river open water zone, the surface film of the water, the benthic zone (under the stones and in the mud on the bottom), and the quiet water around the water weeds. Select two such microhabitats with contrasting abiotic features, for example, in speed of water, depth, light intensity, or type of substrate. Compare the fauna and flora of these habitats. Measure physical factors that you judge may be significant. Take particular care to observe the smallest detail that might affect survival in these microhabitats, such as adaptations to hanging on, or to low oxygen availability. Another potentially critical feature is the laminar flow of water closest to the surface of a boulder (a thin, slow-flowing layer, in which certain small animals can survive).

Present your data in a way that will aid relating the biota to abiotic characteristics, and the comparison of microhabitats. You may also be able to compare microhabitats using the biotic index (above).

■ Plankton and drift

Plankton consists of tiny animals and plants, many unicellular, that are carried by water currents and are unable to control their general movement. **Drift** is the community of larger aquatic non-vertebrate organisms and larval forms of larger animals that often occur with plankton.

Plankton is found in all bodies of water, stationary and flowing. The composition of the planktonic community may vary vertically (in species present and the density of the community) and horizontally (as a community travels down a river, for example). As a consequence, any sampling programme needs careful planning. Sample the area of water you are studying in at least two places, but avoid sampling at too many different places. Samples will not survive out of their habitat for long, so work quickly. Ideally, aim to collect a sample every three hours. If you move your net too fast then a wave will build up in front of the net and sampling will be inefficient. Observe and identify plankton and drift species using either a binocular microscope or a compound microscope with a low-power objective. Your aim is not the accurate identification of all the types found, but the comparison of samples using selected types which can be readily identified. An assessment of relative quantities of plankton in different sites is relevant too. The following issues may also help you analyse and compare the catches.

- Is there a dominating group or species? Do plants or animal species dominate?
- Are there any species present which could indicate important environmental factors (the presence of bacteria-eating protozoans might indicate the presence of bacteria from sewage pollution)?
- Are unnatural blooms present, indicating nutrient-enriched waters (such as those contaminated by phosphate and/or nitrate fertilisers)? These are especially common when the weather is hot.

Investigations of the seashore (and related habitats)

■ Algal dehydration

Investigate the water loss from hydrated samples of different species of algal fronds, of approximately equal area, hung on a line in the laboratory to dry. Include algal species which are found high up on the shore, such as channel wrack (*Pelvetia caniculata*), since this species can survive exposure for several days during neap tides. Weigh the different fronds every hour, or as frequently as possible, over a 24-hour period.

The differing rates of water loss may be related to the cell wall thickness. (Typical wall measurements are: *Fucus spiralis* 1.47 μm; *Ascophyllum nodosum* 1.02 μm; *F. vesiculosus* 0.69 μm; *F. Serratus* 0.42 μm. 1 μm = 1×10^{-6} m.)

Cut a thin section of the frond of *Pelvetia*, mount on a slide, and use a micrometer eyepiece to measure the cell wall thickness (p. 97).

Those species which rapidly lose water may also be able to take up water more quickly when covered by the tide. The validity of this idea could be checked. What other adaptations are found in algae that will reduce water loss?

■ Rates of growth in *Mytilus*

Mussels (*Mytilus* spp.) are filter feeders, exploiting the plankton in the seawater around them. The growth lines on mussel shells (numerous small ones and a few larger ones) reflect the rate at which new shell is laid down at different times of the year. Growth is obviously slower during the winter months.

Figure 3.17 Belt transect analysis on a rocky shore

Using the larger growth lines and the size (length or mass) of the mussel, construct scatter diagrams (p. 39). Look for a relationship between size and age, and follow up some or all of the following issues:

- On which parts of the shore do mussels live the longest or shortest?
- Where is the best place for rapid growth?
- Suggest reasons or explanations for any significant differences; these may include the effects of both abiotic factors (wave crash, dehydration) and biotic factors (food supply, predation, competition for space).
- Work out a population age structure by using a quadrat to count the individuals, and then work out the size of the age groups.

Another mollusc that can be used in this study is the top shell *Monodonta*.

■ The size of populations

The mark–release–recapture (MRR, p. 26) technique can be used on the sea slater (*Ligia oceanica*), a large isopod found in crevices at the top of rocky seashores, and on the sand hopper (*Talitrus saltator*), a fast-moving amphipod found under stones along the strand line on sandy seashores. Both animals explore the beach at night. Mark the cuticle with spots of waterproof paint or varnish.

Check this population estimation technique by using a quadrat to sample the chosen area and counting the individuals (Figure 3.17). If there is a significant discrepancy, suggest reasons why. Which technique is the best to use for these two crustaceans?

■ The elasticity of seaweeds

Most algae need to float near the surface, but the movement of waves will stress the structure of the frond. There are several competing factors, chiefly the tensile strength (the force required to break a frond per unit area per standardised length, such as 10 or 20 cm), and the elasticity of the frond (if stretched, will the frond return to its original length?)

Clamp a standard length (10 or 20 cm) of algal frond to a retort stand, and apply increasing tension to the frond by adding masses to the free end. Record the increase in length with additional masses, until the frond breaks. If you measure the cross-sectional area of undamaged pieces of the frond, then you can calculate the tensile strength (breaking mass per unit cross-sectional area) for that species. Can you relate this to the habitat of the particular species?

■ Osmoregulation in marine non-vertebrates

Many seashore and all estuarine animals and plants experience changes in the solute potential of their aquatic medium that could be harmful if they become too extreme. For example, the effect of rain on the seashore at low tide could be potentially damaging to the seashore flora and fauna. In the case of estuaries the changes are regular and the fauna and flora are adapted to them; they are 'osmoregulators' (*Advanced Biology*, p. 383). Most marine species are 'osmoconformers'; they have limited powers of osmoregulation.

Investigate the ability of one or more of the following animals and plants to osmoregulate, by keeping them in various concentrations of seawater for up to 24 hours and weighing them at regular intervals. Some of the species listed are unable to osmoregulate (they are osmoconformers); some can osmoregulate, but only over a limited range of seawater concentrations.

Figure 3.18 Osmoregulation in seashore animals

Five specimens of each species were placed in turn in 10 dilutions of seawater for two hours and the percentage mass change was calculated.

Concentration of seawater	*Carcinus* Mass change/%	*Nereis* Mass change/%	*Arenicola* Mass change/%
100	100.0	100.0	100.0
90	98.8	103.8	101.9
80	104.0	114.4	109.8
70	99.2	122.3	116.0
60	100.0	130.2	125.6
50	100.0	225.5	130.3
40	101.7	240.2	156.6
30	104.3	250.4	145.4
20	105.2	255.1	141.1
10	108.6	251.0	146.0

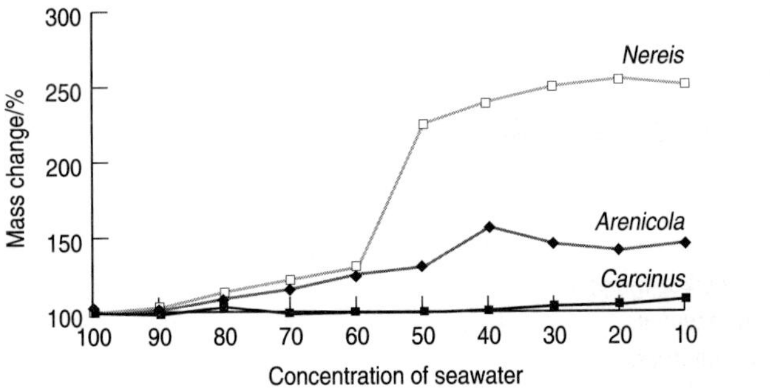

Display the data as a graph of percentage mass change over time, and relate changes to the environment of the species (Figure 3.18). Useful species to study include *Arenicola marina* (lugworm), *Nereis diversicolor* (ragworm), crustaceans found in rockpools, such as prawns (best weighed in a container since they are very active), *Carcinus maenas* (shore crab), and *Mytilus edulis* (mussel). You can also apply the technique to species of algae, selecting a few which are also found in estuarine areas.

■ Sand dune succession

Sand dunes are formed at the edge of the sea by the wind blowing sand which has been deposited by the sea and dried out at the upper tidal limits. Pioneer plants may grow on this new habitat. In time they will stabilise the sand and a classic pattern of succession will develop, provided that the habitat is undisturbed. Then newer dunes will develop on the seaward side of the stabilised dunes. The result is a series of dunes, roughly parallel with the sea, with the youngest nearest the sea. Sand dune succession begins with unstable sand and ends (climax) with woodland. Sand dune systems are very fragile, however, particularly during the early stages of development, and they can be easily destroyed by humans or cattle trampling on them.

To investigate the community structure of a sand dune system use a belt transect (p. 45) running from the new dunes to the older dunes, so that you are studying the various stages in succession. Record the height above your starting point, species present and percentage cover (Table 3.6). You also need to record abiotic factors (soil moisture, soil pH, soil depth and the proportion of humus, p. 22).

Present your data in a table, and then display the data in the form of graphs or kite histograms (p. 39), to show the signifi-

Table 3.6 Species list for a sand dune transect

Name	Stations									
	1	2	3	4	5	6	7	8	9	10
Rise (+) or fall (−) cm										

pioneer/colonisers of sand:
sea rocket
prickly saltwort
sand couch grass
sheep's bit

yellow dune/marram community:
marram grass
sea holly
red fescue
sand sedge
cat's ear
sea pink/thrift

grey dune/stable dune alkaline:
elder
gorse
buckthorn

grey dune/stable dune acid:
ling/heather
mosses
lichens

dune slack/alkaline:
creeping willow
bird's foot trefoil
daisy

flooded dune slack/acid:
grey willow
alder
sphagnum moss
ferns
yellow iris
water horsetail

climax community:
birch
oak
ash

cant changes along the transect line, and to furnish a picture of the sand dune habitat.

Can you piece together a food web for the sand dunes as a whole?

What evidence did you see for human actions that were destroying the stability of dunes?

■ Saltmarshes and mudflats

Saltmarshes are found in the quieter parts of estuaries where there is protection from wave action, often by a shingle or sand bar, and where the low-lying mud is regularly covered by the sea. The build-up of mud produces new habitat land which is then colonised by pioneer species. A primary succession develops as the mud is stabilised by the plants and builds up above tide level.

The pressure on mudflats is very great, however. All the main cities in the world and their associated industries are sited on estuaries, and so the pollution load on estuaries can be very high. Sea walls are often built and marshes drained, and the land used for agriculture, industry and housing.

Alternatively, they may be converted to tide-free harbours for leisure-boat uses.

Design a survey using a belt transect (p. 25) from bare mud to the well-stabilised edge of the saltmarsh. Changes of level are small but very important, as they are closely linked to the change of plant species and the stage in succession development. Draw conclusions about the relationship between shore profile and the vegetation, and the direction of the succession on the shore that you have studied.

What are the major threats to the saltmarshes you visited?

Birds feeding on mudflats are of special interest.

■ Data presentation, conclusion and evaluation

Present your data concisely, together with a summary of the problem you have investigated. Draw whatever conclusions you can, and suggest ways in which the study might now be tackled, in the light of your experience.

Make your presentation in the form of a poster statement, which may be either displayed or used as a visual aid for a talk to your group.

3.4 Data handling

(Skills and techniques)

■ Planning data collection

Experimental observations are referred to as **data**, and a single observation is a **datum**. The data you record may be **qualitative** (for example, 'more minibeasts were found in oak leaf litter than in pine litter') or **quantitative** (as 'pH of a particular oak litter sample was 6.9, whereas pine litter was pH 5.8'). Quantitative data may be **continuous** (for example, the values of pH recorded for soil samples may be any numerical value within a given range) or they may be **discrete** (the number of shrubs in a 27 m length of hedgerow will be some whole number but not a fraction of a shrub). At this stage it is important to remember that any data based on accurate observation are of potential value, and that any one type of data is not intrinsically superior to another.

When you are planning an investigation you need to think very clearly about the sort of data you anticipate. Make full use of the experience of your tutor or teacher, and be ready to take advice along the following lines:

1 Are they the right data? Avoid spending time measuring a factor which is going to be unimportant, and then find that you have also missed the important measurements.
2 Will you collect enough data? Data collection is often a compromise between what is theoretically desirable and what is actually possible in the time available. If there is no chance of returning to the site, however, make sure you account for every sensible variable.
3 Will you collect too many data? If time is limited, then reduce the number of readings so that you complete the task. A full picture with less detail is often more important than an unfinished task with an enormous amount of detailed data.
4 Are your data precisely related to the phenomenon you are investigating? In a transect through the shallow slope of a sandy beach, sampling stations need not be closer than 5 m apart, whereas on a steep rocky shore, where changes in fauna and flora are rapid, then stations need to be perhaps m apart at most. Similarly, if the temperature is changing rapidly then more frequent measurements are needed than if it was fairly constant.
5 Is your sampling procedure adequate? If the community, population or habitat is too large to observe and study overall, then you must work on a sample. There are several ways of sampling:
  • random, i.e. selected without a view or opinion of which portion is representative;
  • stratified, i.e. the subject (such as a wood or heath of different areas) is divided into subsets (sub-areas), and random samples are drawn from each subset;
  • quota, a fixed number (say 1 in 10 of the population) is studied.

■ Recording data

Record your data as and when you obtain them, using a recording sheet with space for all the information you require. Setting up the recording sheet is an important part of planning. The design of the sheet must be user-friendly, in the sense that you should be able to check the completeness of your record at a glance. The tables you design will indicate how often you must record. Allow space to record routine observations, and a facility to note abnormalities and unexpected circumstances, too.

Use 'data capture' technology if it is available (i.e. data loggers, p. 24, that collect data from sensors). Check the recorder to make sure that the calibration is accurate, and that the start time is correctly recorded. With this approach it is usually easy to measure more than one variable at a time, and so is ideal for correlations and relationships such as air and water temperatures. If you enter the data directly into a spreadsheet, you can print out neat tables which are easy to read, and use the data directly to produce graphs or charts.

■ Presenting data

Firstly, select from the data all that are important. Look critically at your results to identify any measurements that are clearly insignificant. Perhaps values of one of the 'variables', such as temperature, remained constant throughout the period you studied. Such a variable may be discounted, since it had no critical effect.

Secondly, as a result of your critical appraisal, clarify your table of data so that they can be more easily understood. It may be appropriate to 'round up' numbers to fewer figures. For example, rounding up is desirable to avoid appearing to give to data a greater level of accuracy than the measurements warrant. Often it is helpful to insert rows into your table that summarise data; for example, you could include a column that converts the results to percentages, or which presents the mean (the average), the mode (the most commonly occurring measurement or event) and the median (the middle event). Another clarification of data, the standard deviation, which gives an indication of the spread of the data either side of the mean, may be useful. We will return to this in the statistics section below. All these changes can be most quickly and accurately done on a spreadsheet.

Thirdly, display the important data, using a visual summary. Your intention is to make the ecological meaning and importance clear; trends and correlations show up much better when the data are displayed. Each of the different ways of displaying data has its own value. Choose one that meets your needs (Figure 3.19).

Graphs show relationships or trends between two variables, such as light intensity and oxygen production in plants (see, for example, Figure 3.19). In planning a graph, it helps if you keep in mind the question you want to answer, such as 'how do air and water temperature change over 24 hours?'

It is conventional to plot the dependent variable (variable being accurately measured) on the vertical (y) axis, and the independent variable (the variable altered by the experimenter) on the horizontal (x) axis. Label both axes and indicate the units. Plot the points with a sharp pencil using a cross or a circle and point. Join the points by a smooth curve only if you are confident that it indicates the likely points of intermediate readings; otherwise connect the points with straight lines. If you plot more than one line, then the points and lines must be different and be clearly labelled. If the two plots have different vertical axes, then the scales of the axes should be placed on either side of the graph.

Bar charts are used with discrete data to show relative proportions, such as the numbers of trees of different species in a wood. There should be small gaps between the bars, and the bars should be presented in order of magnitude; see, for example, Figure 3.19(a).

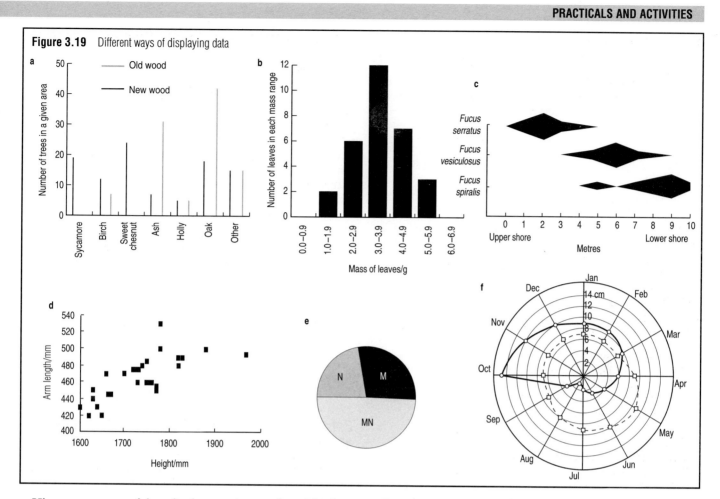

Figure 3.19 Different ways of displaying data

Histograms are useful to display continuous data. The bars touch, and the height and area of each bar must match the proportion of the data. The result is a frequency distribution histogram; see, for example, Figure 3.19(b). This way of displaying the frequency of data will reveal a lot if the spread of the data bars is carefully chosen; for example, if it is a reasonable assumption that limpets grow in length by 5 mm a year, then 5 mm bars (i.e. 0–4, 5–9 and so forth) will reveal the size of the year classes.

Kite histograms are used for displaying transect data. The horizontal length of the kite represents the range of the species over the transect, whereas the vertical height (amplitude) of the kite indicates the abundance of the animals or plants; see, for example, Figure 3.19(c).

Scatter graphs show relationships between two independent variables, such as the length and breadth of leaves. Where one of the variables is determined by the other it is customary to put the independent variable on the horizontal axis and the dependent variable on the vertical axis. From the scatter graph, the strength of the relationship (correlation) can be assessed; see, for example, Figure 3.19(d).

Pie charts are best used for showing relative proportions; see, for example, Figure 3.19(e).

Rose graphs (a cyclical graph or bar chart) has bars which indicate both the scale and direction of the data. Wind direction and force may be displayed in this way, for example Figure 3.19(f).

Pyramids are the way we graphically represent the biomass or energy content of different trophic levels in a food chain. The data are represented by the area of each layer; see, for example, Figure 4.3, p. 60.

■ Exploring data

Next, scan your data very carefully, asking yourself what seems to be implied by the results. You should seek to resolve the data into essential elements to aid comprehension. Look for patterns (such as organisms in clumps, rather than randomly dispersed), or look for relationships, positive or negative (such as woodlice mostly falling into pitfall traps on warm nights). Before you test the significance of the data using statistical methods, examine the magnitude of the effects that stand out. Write down this critical interpretation of your data, as a summary at this stage.

■ Statistical checks on data

Statistical tests should certainly be used when you are not sure about a numerical relationship you have sought to establish experimentally. For example, we may display the variability (standard error) of results obtained, and so judge the significance of any differences that appear. The outline guide below may help select the technique you need. Remember that many calculators include some statistical techniques. Microcomputers will run spreadsheet programs into which statistical tests are easily programmed, and dedicated statistical software is available to run these and other tests.

- You can test the difference between two means by their **standard deviation** (p. 47).
- You can then use standard deviations to calculate the significance of the difference between two means by the *t*-test (p. 48).
- You can test whether observed numerical results differ from the expected numerical result by means of a **chi-squared test** (p. 346).

- You can find out if a correlation exists between two variables by means of the **Spearman rank correlation coefficient** (p. 233).
- You can decide whether two sampled groups of organisms are from the same or from different populations by means of the **Mann–Whitney U test** (p. 50).

References

There are many books on statistical methods, and some seek to relate statistics to experimental fieldwork in biology. An example of these is:

N Chalmers and P Parker (2nd edn 1989) *The OU Project Guide, Fieldwork and Statistics for Ecological Projects*. Field Studies Council

A practical introduction to ecology at Advanced level that also has a chapter on statistical analysis within a final section on the processing of information is:

G Williams (1987) *Techniques and Fieldwork in Ecology*. Bell and Hyman

I Graham (1987) 'The applications of spreadsheets to data analysis in biology', *J. Biol. Ed.* 21(1), pp. 51–6

A Dreyfus, B Peinstein and Y Mazouz (1993) 'Keyboard instructions as concepts of the language of quantitative biology in spreadsheet-assisted activities', *J. Biol. Ed.* 27(1), pp. 39–45

A Cadogan and R Sulton (1994) *Maths for Advanced Biology*. Nelson

3.5 Using educational software

'Ecology Pack' from Kings College, includes the following programs:

1 **Biomass** The program explains the production of 'biomass' by a secondary consumer using a model of a managed reservoir which can be stocked with trout from the larval stage (fry) to adults. The fish population can be monitored over many years, and the program can demonstrate how human actions may affect the yield and maximise the return from a given resource.
2 **Pond Ecology** The program models the effects of fishing and pollution on numbers of phytoplankton, herbivores and fish in a freshwater community. By this means the balance within an ecosystem is demonstrated.
3 **Predator–Prey Relationships** The program demonstrates the interactions that may occur between a predator and its prey.
4 **Statistics for Biologists** The data-handling programs included are for calculations of mean, standard deviation, t and correlation r, and the chi-squared test.

'Ecology Disk' from Garland includes:

1 **Littoral Zonation** This program is a simulation of a seashore study, and provides data for the practice of presenting observations. Included are distribution maps that illustrate the patterns of distribution that may develop from extremes of exposure.
2 **Gore Point** This program is similar to the first, but it offers data on a larger number of species, and it permits investigations of the potential effects of desiccation from prolonged exposure and salinity changes.

The programs on both packs are available for Acorn RISC OS/Nimbus/BBC B and Master. Both are supplied by AVP of Chepstow.

3.6 Membership of the Field Studies Council (FSC)

An individual or an organisation (such as the science department of a school or college) can join the Field Studies Council as a member. Members receive the annual programmes of FSC Centres before they are available on general release, and can make bookings at a discount rate. They also receive the FSC magazine (published twice a year). Members can subscribe to the journal *Field Studies*, which is published once a year. Details are available from:

Field Studies Council Publications, Preston Montford, Shrewsbury SY4 1HW

or:

Scottish Field Studies Association, c/o Kindrogan Field Centre, Enochdhu, Blairgowrie, Perthshire PH10 7PG.

Projects

3.1 Comparing habitats: fast- and slow-flowing streams

Both structural and behavioural adaptations to maintaining a position in an aquatic environment may be detected by comparisons of flora and fauna in still and in slow- and fast-moving water.

References

D P Bennett and D A Humphries (1965) *Introduction to Field Biology*, p. 162. Edward Arnold

G Williams (1987) *Techniques and Fieldwork in Ecology*, p. 136. Bell and Hyman

3.2 The microhabitat of a fresh cowpat

The succession of eukaryotic organisms that cause the decomposition of animal waste, particularly that of herbaceous animals, can be investigated under controlled conditions.

References

R J Putman (1983) *Carrion and Dung*. Arnold Studies in Biology no 156. Edward Arnold

C T Ingold (1978) *The Biology of* Mucor *and its Allies*. Arnold Studies in Biology no 88. Edward Arnold

3.3 Indicator species and geology

The flora and fauna of habitats typical of chalk downland and a sandy hillside can be investigated for species that are restricted to these environments. But what is the physiological basis of any such restriction?

References

J Sankey (1970) *Chalkland Ecology*. Heinemann

A Leadley Brown (1978) *Ecology of Soil Organisms*. Heinemann

3.4 Slugs or snails of a garden or wood

Slugs and snails have an important role in the food chain. They are animals that can be investigated quantitatively with relative ease. Little is really known about their contribution to the ecosystem.

References
M P Kerney and R A D Cameron (1979) *A Field Guide to the Land Snails of Britain and North West Europe*. Collins
M Chinery (1977) *The Natural History of the Garden*, p. 78. Fontana/Collins

3.5 Mercurialis perennis *in woodland*

Dog's mercury is a woodland plant, flowering in spring time. Is vegetative growth more prolific in clearings or in the more shaded parts of woodlands? Is there any significant difference between the distributions of the male and female plants?

References
G Williams (1987) *Techniques and Fieldwork in Ecology*, p. 129. Bell and Hyman
C T Prime (1970) *Investigations in Woodland Ecology*, p. 23. Heinemann

3.6 The reproductive capacity of plants

How does the productivity of weed species compare with other robust species adapted to specialised habitats? Collecting and counting the seeds produced by individual plants can also form the basis of germination and seed viability studies.

Reference
T A Hill (1977) *The Biology of Weeds*. Arnold Studies in Biology no 79. Edward Arnold

3.7 Competition between bracken and associated species

The dead fronds of bracken are a source of natural inhibitors of the growth of competitor species. The effects on potential competitor plants of the presence or absence of decaying bracken fronds (or perhaps of extracts taken from them) can be investigated. **Hazard warning:** Special care is needed with bracken extracts, since carcinogenic substances may be present.

Reference
C T Prime (1970) *Investigations in Woodland Ecology*, p. 28. Heinemann

3.8 The effects of chemical substances on germination

Plants themselves are frequently the source of chemicals that inhibit germination of seeds of surrounding plants.

Reference
'The biology of bracken'. *Bot. J. of the Linnean Society* 73, pp. 1–3. Academic Press

3.9 The distribution of non-vertebrates in relation to plant cover

Can the communities of non-vertebrates to be found in different zones of the field layer in a woodland, or in long and short grass, be correlated with the microhabitats and food chains?

Reference
G Williams (1987) *Techniques and Fieldwork in Ecology*, p. 129. Bell and Hyman

3.10 Gall wasp spangles of oak leaves

Mature oak leaves are often parasitised by distinctive spangle galls, caused by the larvae of four distinct species of gall wasp. The competition and distribution of the parasites can be investigated.

Reference
T Lewis and L R Taylor (1972) *Introduction to Experimental Ecology*, p. 231. Academic Press

3.11 Grassland communities and the effects of trampling and grazing

Grassland occurs on hills, in parks and playing fields, and in fields and meadows. As such, it forms one of the commoner habitats. How is the species composition of the turf influenced by the effects of human trampling, or by selective grazing by farm animals?

Reference
G Williams (1987) *Techniques and Fieldwork in Ecology*, p. 131. Bell and Hyman

3.12 Earthworms and seeds

Large earthworms consume quantities of seeds, some of which are deposited in surface casts in a viable state. Plants with seeds that are readily ingested are likely to be at an advantage over other species. Earthworms may influence the composition of plant communities.

Reference
T G Pierce, N Roggero and R Tipping (1994) 'Earthworms and seeds', *J. Biol. Ed.* 28(3), pp. 195–202

3.13 Leaf size

The leaves of a tree can be sampled to test the hypothesis that the area of a leaf is largely determined by the environment (such as light intensity) but the shape of a leaf is mostly determined by its genetic make-up. Select a tree which has a wide canopy that is easy to reach, and then select leaves from five different positions across the tree. For each leaf, measure the length and width, and then estimate the area by placing the leaf on graph paper, drawing around the outline of the leaf, and counting the squares.

Is leaf area related to light intensity? Is leaf shape genetically determined or is it affected by the environment? In what ways are the leaves responding to environmental selection pressures and demonstrating a degree of adaptability?

3.14 The effect of coppicing on woodland

Within a large coppiced woodland it is often possible to identify areas where coppicing was carried out at different times. The thickness of the tree stems (coppiced poles) could be used as a guide to the age of the coppiced trees if the actual dates are unknown. The age of the coppiced woodland may be significant in that the more recently coppiced areas will have less dense foliage and more light can penetrate to soil level. Look for correlations between the age of the coppiced wood and the presence or absence of species of plants and animals.

3.15 Feeding patterns of birds on mudflats

When you observe birds feeding on sand or mudflats, you will often see several species feeding in the same area. Does this break the competitive exclusion principle (*Advanced Biology*, p. 65)? A study of the birds concerned in a bird identification book will reveal the length and shape of the birds' beaks (and perhaps also their diet). Follow this up by sampling the sand or mud by digging out the layers and sieving (take the sieve to the water's edge and wash out the sand and mud, leaving behind the crustaceans, molluscs and annelids). Correlate the length of beak to the animals being eaten.

A useful source of further ecological project ideas (based on articles adapted from the *Journal of Biological Education*) is: D Harding (ed.) (1992) *Ecological Projects*. Institute of Biology

Problems and assignments

3.1 Feeding relationships and food webs

Table 3.7 shows some of the feeding relationships noted by a team of ecologists in a broad-leaved woodland over a period of several days.

1 Construct a food web for the woodland at this time from these observations.
2 Give an example of a woodland organism that is:
   • at one of each of the trophic levels 1, 2, 3 and 4;
   • at more than one trophic level;
   • a primary producer;
   • a primary consumer;
   • a secondary consumer;
   • a tertiary consumer;
   • a herbivore;
   • a carnivore;
   • an autotroph;
   • a detritivore.
3 What are the likely immediate effects, and the possible long-term effects, on the numbers of leaf-eating organisms in the woodland of the destruction of kestrels, badgers and stoats by humans?

3.2 The establishment of a thermocline in deep water

In shallow ponds and lakes the water temperature varies very little with depth. In deep waters of temperate regions, in summer, a thermocline forms. A thermocline is the middle layer where temperature changes rapidly with depth. The temperature stratification of a typical deep lake in summer is illustrated in Figure 3.20.

A team of ecologists made measurements of the temperature and oxygen concentration of the water of this temperate lake in winter (January) and summer (June). Typical results are given in Table 3.8.

1 Plot a graph of the water temperature and oxygen concentration against the depth of the lake. Your graph will have four curves. These should be distinct, and clearly labelled.
2 What is the depth range of the thermocline formed in summer?
3 What physical properties of warm water and cold water, respectively, contribute to the establishment of a thermocline?
4 What abiotic factors, apart from water temperature, are quite different in deep water compared with the surface water? What causes each of these factors to be different?
5 In a deep reservoir containing drinking water, organic matter such as deciduous leaves tended to collect. Towards the end of the summer, water drawn from the depth was found to be unfit for drinking. Explain what part a thermocline played in the spoiling of this drinking water.
6 Where the thermocline persists, the warm upper layers can support a very limited biomass only. Why?

3.3 The distribution of organisms on a rocky shore

The biology of the seashore is introduced in *Advanced Biology*, pp. 48–55. You may find it helpful to read parts of this account to interpret the data below and to answer the questions.

Table 3.7 Feeding relationships in a woodland habitat

Food source	Exploited/eaten by:
fruits and seeds of trees and herbaceous plants	mice, badgers and blackbirds
leaves of trees and herbs	caterpillars, aphids, earthworms, rabbits and slugs
flowers of trees and herbs	butterflies and bees
mice	kestrels and shrews
caterpillars	tits and shrews
aphids	ladybirds
earthworms	badgers and blackbirds
rabbits	badgers and stoats
slugs	badgers and shrews
butterflies	tits and spiders
bees	badgers (honey) and spiders
ladybirds	tits and spiders
blackbirds	stoats and kestrels
spiders	shrews
shrews	stoats and kestrels
tits	kestrels

Badgers, kestrels and stoats had no natural predators

Table 3.8 Seasonal changes in a temperate lake

Depth/m	Temperature/°C[a]		Oxygen/ppm[b]	
	Winter	Summer	Winter	Summer
0	0	25	12	15
1	2.5	24.5	12	15
2	3.5	23.5	12	15
3	4	23	12	14.5
5	4	22	12	13
7	4	15	12	9
9	4	8	11.5	3.5
11	4	5	11.5	0
13	4	5	11.5	0
15	4	5	11	0

[a] To nearest 0.5 °C
[b] To nearest 0.5 ppm

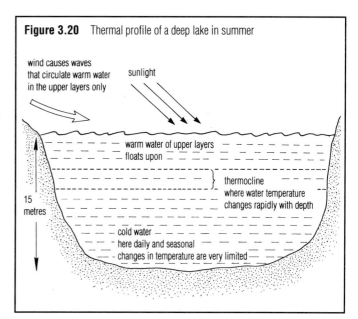

Figure 3.20 Thermal profile of a deep lake in summer

wind causes waves that circulate warm water in the upper layers only

sunlight

warm water of upper layers floats upon

thermocline where water temperature changes rapidly with depth

15 metres

cold water here daily and seasonal changes in temperature are very limited

Figure 3.21 Flora and fauna of a rocky shore

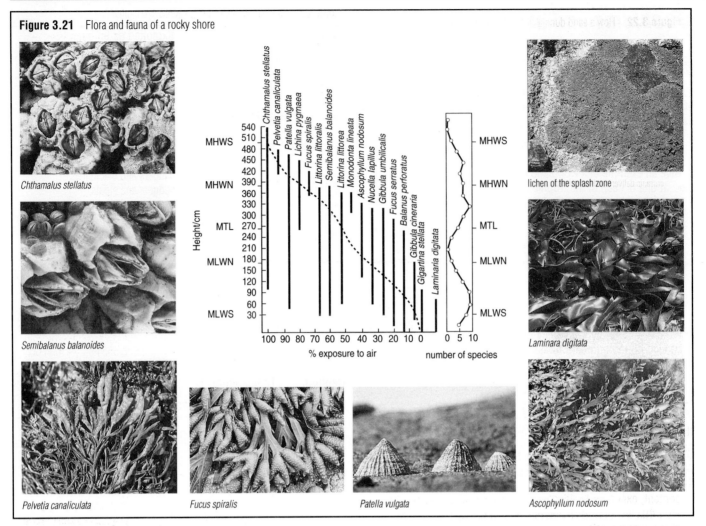

Chthamalus stellatus

Semibalanus balanoides

lichen of the splash zone

Laminara digitata

Pelvetia canaliculata

Fucus spiralis

Patella vulgata

Ascophyllum nodosum

In the bar chart in Figure 3.21, the distribution (range) of a selection of the organisms typically found on a rocky shore is shown in relation to the varying tide levels. In the graph alongside it, the total number of species that occur at each 30 cm vertically is shown.

By reference to the data in Figure 3.21, together with your general biological knowledge, answer the following questions.

1 a For the regions of the shore referred to as HWS and HWN, what do the letters S and N mean?

   b Approximately how often in a calendar month are there S and N tides? Why?

2 MHW and MLW stand for 'mean high water' and 'mean low water' respectively. What does MTL stand for?

3 The acorn barnacles *Chthamalus stellatus* and *Semibalanus balanoides* have different distribution patterns on the shore. Suggest possible explanations for this difference.

4 Water loss by exposed seaweed thalli can be investigated by measuring the change in mass of samples exposed to drying conditions for several hours. How would you expect drying in *Pelvetia canaliculata* to compare with that in *Fucus spiralis* and *Ascophyllum nodosum*?

5 *Lichnia pygmaea* is a lichen that grows among algae, but it occurs on the upper shore only, where seaweed growth is restricted. Suggest an explanation for this distribution pattern.

6 In what ways is the limpet *Patella vulgaris* adapted to survive periods of exposure?

7 Productivity of a rocky shore is said to be low. What does this mean?

8 The total number of species found in different zones of the shore varies. What biotic and abiotic factors typically restrict the presence of littoral species on:

   a the lowest parts;

   b the higher parts;

   of a rocky shore?

9 Research and draw up a food web for the organisms listed in Figure 3.21.

10 What features of the brown seaweed *Laminaria* can be interpreted as adaptations to life as an autotroph of the lower shore/sublittoral zone?

3.4 Succession in sand dune formation

Dunes may form where sand is being carried inshore by currents and deposited on the beach by high tides. Water drains away from the piled up sand. Dune formation is brought about by prevailing winds that are persistently 'on-shore'. Wind moves the sand, which then may be deposited on the leeward side of the pile, leading to the build-up of small hillocks. Plants that can survive under the harsh conditions in this dry, wind-blown and moving terrain tend to have rhizomes that grow through the sand just below the surface. The rhizomes and roots bind together the grains of sand, while aerial shoots sprout above the surface. Then sand piles up behind and on top of the shoots, leading to further growth by the plants and to the steady enlargement and stabilisation of the dune. Less 'pioneering' plants follow, and the heaped sand becomes even more stable, and

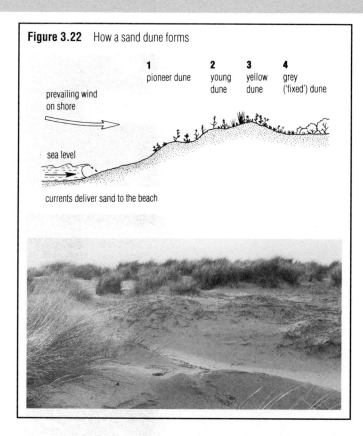

Figure 3.22 How a sand dune forms

the community more diverse in composition. The steps in the succession in sand dune formation are summarised in Figure 3.22. Table 3.9 gives a short species list of typical sand dune plants.

1 What are the likely physical conditions (e.g. sand stability, salt content, exposure to tides/sea spray, drainage, exposure to wind, etc.) that will influence the colonisation of the dunes at each stage of the succession?
2 List the features of the plants found at each of the four zones, and then explain how each feature may aid survival in the specific conditions there.
3 The ecologists studying the succession have concentrated on the early plant colonisers and have ignored the animal life, initially. Why is this appropriate?
4 Many established sand dune systems have been carefully fenced in to exclude cattle and to restrict access by people. Why has this been found necessary?

3.5 Diversity in polluted and unpolluted water

The occasional contamination of lakes and streams by raw sewage changes the physical environment and alters the composition of the aquatic community. In a river, these changes occur for some distance downstream. The situation is self-correcting, however, provided the contamination is not maintained indefinitely.

Data on the changes to running freshwater following sewage pollution are illustrated in Figure 3.23. Examine the data carefully, and then answer the questions.

1 a A major component of sewage is organic matter present as suspended solids. What changes are likely to occur to the organic matter as it moves downstream, and how are these changes brought about?
  b Explain the links between these changes and other developments in the abiotic environment shown.

Table 3.9 Typical species list of dune plants

Species	Found[a]	Special features of structure, growth or habit
dandelion (*Taraxacum officinale*)	(4)	perennial plant with persistent tap root
cat's ear (*Hypochaeris radicata*)	(3)	rosette plant, with long water-storing roots
gorse (*Ulex* spp.)	(4)	shrubby perennial plant, usually on acidic soils
prickly saltwort (*Salsola kali*)	(1)	prostrate, fast-growing halophyte
lichens	(4)	cover the soil surface, retaining water
ling (*Calluna vulgaris*)	(4)	sturdy perennial of dry (acidic) soils
Lyme grass (*Elymus arenarius*)	(1)	can withstand occasional immersion by spring tides
marram grass (*Ammophila arenaria*)	(3)	xerophyte that grows from vigorous rhizome branching through dry sand (cannot withstand damp soil)
mouse-ear chickweed (*Cerastium* sp.)	(4)	common 'weed'
ragwort (*Senecio jacobea*)	(4)	rosette habit, with poisonous leaves that few organisms can eat
red fescue (*Festuca rubra*)	(3)	succeeds on nutrient-poor soils; with a creeping stolon growing just below sand surface
sand couch grass (*Agropyron junceiforme*)	(2)	branching, fast-growing rhizome that can withstand immersion by spring tides
sand sedge (*Carex arenaria*)	(3)	has creeping stolon growing just below sand surface
sea convolvulus (*Calystegia soldanella*)	(3)	halophyte with succulent leaves and creeping rhizome
sea holly (*Eryngium maritimum*)	(3)	low-growing halophyte with a root system up to 2 m deep; insect-pollinated flowers, but sea-dispersed seeds
sea spurge (*Euphorbia paralias*)	(3)	very deep-rooting perennial plant
sea stock (*Matthiola incana*)	(3)	rosette habit with long tap root
sea rocket (*Cakile maritima*)	(1)	halophyte with fruits dispersed by the tide, obtaining nutrient from decayed organic matter of tide mark, but with deep tap root

[a] Shore zones as in Figure 3.22

Figure 3.23 Aspects of the pollution of a river by raw sewage: **a** and **b** physical and chemical changes to river water below a sewage outfall; **c** changes to microorganisms, protoctista and fungi; **d** changes to animals

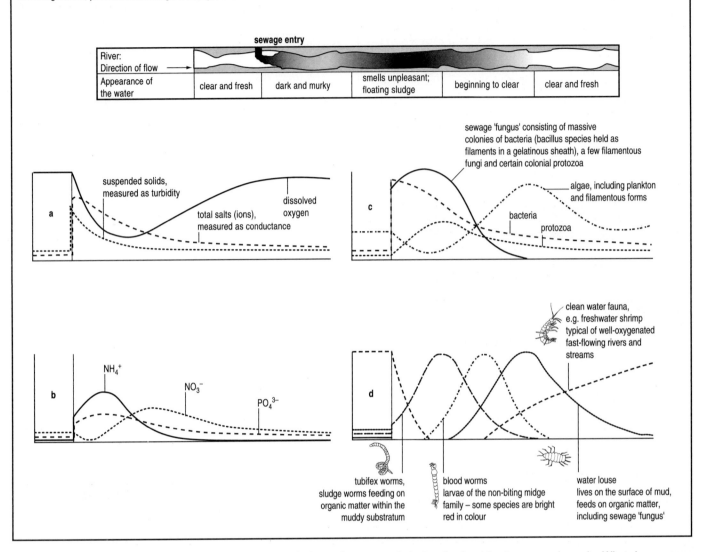

2 Anaerobic decay of organic matter containing combined nitrogen results in the production of ammonia.
  a What effects may this ammonia have upon many aquatic animal species?
  b Ammonium ions may be converted into nitrates. What evidence is there that this has occurred here? What is the value of nitrates to green plants of the river community?
3 Describe the way bacteria are involved in the conversion of ammonium salts to nitrates. What is their energy source for these conversions? (You can read about the issues involved in *Advanced Biology*, pp. 271 and 336–9.)
4 **a** What is the likely source of the soluble phosphates recorded in the river water below the point of contamination?
  b What use are these ions in the cells of green plants that occur in the river?
5 How would you account for the changes in the protozoan population in river water below the sewage inlet?
6 **a** Tubifex worms, bloodworms and water lice are not restricted to heavily polluted waters; they occur naturally in the muddy substrata of eutrophic streams and ponds. What do we mean by 'eutrophic'?
  b What features of structure or habit appear to adapt these species to organically polluted waters?
7 'Floating sludge' is a collection of organisms present after suspended solids had begun to decline. What may this sludge consist of?
8 Write out a food chain for the organisms close to the sewage inlet, and another food chain for the parts of the river where the clean water fauna is being re-established.
9 **a** When major rivers are temporarily polluted with sewage within an urban area, what can humans do to speed up the self-cleansing processes?
  b What specific problems manifested by such a polluted river are most likely to cause them to invest such effort and expense?
10 Another pollutant that is sometimes added into rivers is *hot* water. Outline the changes that might occur at a sewage-polluted site at which hot water effluent was also discharged.

3.6 Prey–predator relations

Competition between individuals of different species for precious resources (interspecific competition) may result in oscillations in population size, whether their relationship is one of prey and predator or parasite and host. Such relationships of population size are commonly illustrated in laboratory investigations where prey (or host) and predator (or parasite) populations are studied in a precisely controlled situation. The same relationships are believed to occur in nature, but here species exist in a multispecies context. For example, from food web studies we know that most prey are predated by more than one type of predator, and that many predators are also prey themselves.

The data in Table 3.10 were obtained by counting the numbers of a host species, a species of bean weevil (*Callosobruchus chinensis*), and the numbers of its parasite, the larva of the wasp *Heterospilus prosopidis*. These two populations were maintained under favourable, regulated conditions in Petri dish chambers, with an excess of *Phaseolus angularis* seeds, the weevil's food source.

The data in Table 3.11 were obtained by estimating the numbers of wood mice and bank voles and the number of pairs of tawny owls in Wickham Wood, Oxfordshire between 1947 and 1959.

1 Plot a graph of the data in Table 3.10 and a separate graph of the data in Table 3.11. Examine the curves carefully.
2 Comment on (by comparing and contrasting) the relationship between the numbers of bean weevils and their parasitic wasp larvae, and on the numbers of mice and voles and the predatory owl pairs.
3 What reasons may explain the lack of oscillations in the owl population in the wood?
4 What further studies could be undertaken to test the hypotheses within your explanation?

Table 3.10   Laboratory study of host and parasite populations

Generation	Host	Parasite
1	110	520
2	105	200
3	305	280
4	610	100
5	420	50
6	170	120
7	190	580
8	300	380
9	600	120
10	590	20
11	300	30
12	170	50
13	180	400
14	190	400
15	380	220
16	500	200
17	600	50
18	220	30
19	100	210
20	120	580
21	200	460
22	220	500
23	810	100
24	650	70
25	340	80
26	330	160
27	350	150

3.7 Statistical tests in ecology I

■ The 'middleness' and 'spreadoutness' of normally distributed data

Data obtained in biological experiments may show a **normal distribution**. By this we mean that when the frequency of particular classes of measurements (*y*-axis) is plotted against the classes of measurements arranged in ascending order (*x*-axis), a bell-shaped curve results (*Advanced Biology*, p. 614).

There are two aspects of normally distributed data that can be useful:
• how clustered are the readings (i.e. 'middleness'), and
• how spread-out they are (i.e. 'spreadoutness').
We can test the 'middleness' or central tendency of data, via mode, median and mean. The **mode** is the most frequent class of measurement; the **median** is the middle observation listed in order of magnitude; the **mean** is the arithmetic mean or average, that is the sum of all the values divided by the number of values (*Advanced Biology*, p. 613).

We can test the 'spreadoutness' or dispersion of data, via the standard deviation. The **standard deviation** (SD) is a measure of the spread of the measurements about their mean, and is defined as:

$$SD = \sqrt{\frac{\sum f(x - \bar{x})^2}{\sum f - 1}}$$

where *x* = individual measurements, $\bar{x}$ = the mean of the individual measurements, *f* = their frequency for grouped data, and $\sum$ means 'the sum of'.

Table 3.11   Field study of prey and predator populations

Year	Wood mice plus bank voles/acre		Tawny owl pairs
	Spring	Summer	
1947	–	–	19
1948	–	5	20
1949	16	6	20
1950	6	8	22
1951	5	7	24
1952	12	5	26
1953	3	5	25
1954	3	17	27
1955	3	12	29
1956	6	8	32
1957	15	10	30
1958	2	8	28
1959	12	21	30

The term $(x - \bar{x})$ is also referred to as *d*, as in the definition of SD given in *Advanced Biology*, p. 614.

Many calculators and spreadsheet programs are equipped to carry out statistical calculations like the following.

An ecologist investigated the reproductive capacity of two species of buttercup, *Ranunculus acris* (meadow buttercup) and *R. repens* (creeping buttercup). The latter species spreads vegetatively via strong and persistent growth of stolons (vegetative reproduction). Would this investment be reflected in a lowered production of fruit (product of sexual reproduction) compared with fruit production by the meadow buttercup, which reproduces sexually rather than vegetatively?

Using comparable sized plants growing under similar conditions in the same soil, the numbers of achenes (fruits) formed in 100 flowers of each of these two species were counted and recorded. The results are given in Table 3.12.

Using the data listed in Table 3.12, together with the pro forma given here, calculate for both species:

- the median and mode values;
- the mean and standard deviation.

	Ranunculus acris	Ranunculus repens
Mode:		
Median:		

Calculation of mean and standard deviation for a set of grouped data

Values obtained in ascending order (x)	Frequency (f)	fx	Deviation of x from the mean $(x - \bar{x})[=d]$	d^2	fd^2
	$\Sigma f =$	$\Sigma fx =$			$\Sigma fd^2 =$

Mean of data $= \dfrac{\Sigma fx}{\Sigma f} =$

$$SD = \sqrt{\dfrac{\Sigma fd^2}{\Sigma f - 1}} = \sqrt{\dfrac{\quad}{\quad}} = \sqrt{\quad} =$$

Thus the mean of the sample _____ = _____, and the SD = _____.

3.8 Statistical tests in ecology II

■ The *t*-test

The *t*-test was devised and published in 1908 by a brewing scientist who worked for Guinness. He had to assess the quality of malting barley samples with confidence, working on the limited data (i.e. very small samples) available each growing season. In this test, *t* is the difference between the means of two small samples (<30) showing normal distribution, divided by the standard deviation of the difference:

$$t = \frac{\text{difference between means } (\bar{X}_A - \bar{X}_B)}{\text{standard error of the difference between means}}$$

An ecologist was investigating woodland microhabitats, contrasting the communities in a shaded position with those in full light. One of the plants was ivy (*Hedera helix*), but relatively few occurred at the locations under investigation. The issue arose: were the leaves in the

Table 3.12 Achene production in *Ranunculus* species

Number of achenes	Frequency	
	R. repens	R. acris
15	1	0
16	1	0
17	1	0
18	2	1
19	4	1
20	4	1
21	8	1
22	7	1
23	9	3
24	10	4
25	16	4
26	9	5
27	10	5
28	4	6
29	5	8
30	3	14
31	1	12
32	1	10
33	2	7
34	1	3
35	1	2
36	0	3
37	0	2
38	0	3
39	0	2
40	0	2
41	0	0

shade actually larger than those in sunlight? Leaf widths were measured, but because the size of the leaves varied with the position on the plant, only the fourth leaf from each stem tip was measured. The results from the plants available were as follows:

Widths of sun leaves/mm	32, 24, 30, 33, 31, 26, 32, 37, 43, 31, 38, 26
Widths of shade leaves/mm	34, 26, 45, 41, 36, 33, 37, 42, 35, 35, 36, 36

Steps in the t-test

1 The **null hypothesis** (negative hypothesis) assumes the difference under investigation has arisen by chance; in this example the null hypothesis is 'There is no difference in size between sun and shade leaves'. The role of the statistical test is to determine whether to accept or reject the null hypothesis. If it is rejected here, we can have confidence that the difference in the leaf sizes of the two samples is statistically significant.

2 Next, check that the data are normally distributed. Arrange the data for sun leaves and for shade leaves into simple size- classes, as in Table 3.13 (and plot a histogram, if necessary).

3 List the observations (*X*) for sun leaves (X_A) and shade leaves (X_B) in two columns, using the pro forma layout. Then perform the following calculation to determine *t* for the data.

4 Now look up the values in the t-table in Appendix 2 on p. 436.

Look down the 'Degrees of freedom' column to the number matching your calculation. Then move across the table at this level until you reach the column headed $p = 0.05$ (significance level 5%). This is the level of probability normally used in biological work. Write down this value of t:

t for $(n_A - 1) + (n_B - 1)$ degrees of freedom at $p = 0.05$ is

t as calculated is

5 If the value of t that you calculated exceeds this value of t, the null hypothesis is rejected, and the difference between the two samples is significant.

Is the difference significant in this case?

Table 3.13 Sizes of sun and shade leaves of *Hedera helix*

Size-class /mm	Sun leaves (A)	Shade leaves (B)
20–24	24	
25–29	26, 26	26
30–34	30, 31, 31, 32, 32, 33	33, 34
35–40	37, 38	35, 35, 36, 36, 36, 37
40–44	43	41, 42
45–49		45

The t-test for unmatched samples

Sample 1 Observations (X_A)	Deviation of observation from mean $(X_A - \bar{X}_A)$	Square of deviation $(X_A - \bar{X}_A)^2$	Sample 2 Observations (X_B)	Deviation of observation from mean $(X_B - \bar{X}_B)$	Square of deviation $(X_B - \bar{X}_B)^2$
Sum of observations $\Sigma X_A =$		Sum of squares of deviations $\Sigma(X_A - \bar{X}_A)^2 =$	Sum of observations $\Sigma X_B =$		Sum of squares of deviations $\Sigma(X_B - \bar{X}_B)^2 =$
No of observations $n_A =$			No of observations $n_B =$		
Mean of the sample $\bar{X}_A = \dfrac{\Sigma X_A}{n_A} = \underline{\quad} =$			Mean of the sample $\bar{X}_B = \dfrac{\Sigma X_B}{n_B} = \underline{\quad} =$		
Variance $V_A = \dfrac{\Sigma(X - \bar{X})^2}{n_A - 1} = \underline{\quad} =$			Variance $V_B = \dfrac{\Sigma(X - \bar{X})^2}{n_B - 1} = \underline{\quad} =$		

Standard error of the difference between means of populations A and B

$$= \sqrt{\frac{V_A}{n_A} + \frac{V_B}{n_B}} \quad = \sqrt{\ldots + \ldots} = \sqrt{\underline{\quad\quad}}$$

$Given\ t = \dfrac{\text{difference between means}}{\text{standard error of the difference between the mean}} = \dfrac{\bar{X}_A - \bar{X}_B}{\sqrt{\dfrac{V_A}{n_A} + \dfrac{V_B}{n_B}}} = \dfrac{\underline{\quad}}{} =$

Degrees of freedom $= (n_A - 1) + (n_B - 1) =$

3.9 Statistical tests in ecology III

■ The Mann–Whitney *U* test

The Mann–Whitney *U* test is designed to compare the medians (*not* the means) of two unmatched samples. It can be used to decide whether two sampled groups of organisms are from the same or different populations. The test is suitable for data that are not normally distributed. The samples to be compared may be unequal, but neither must consist of fewer than five measurements, or of more than 25 individuals.

An ecologist was investigating the grasshopper population in a large area of permanent meadowland, and selected two sites for sampling. At these sites the local populations were sampled by making sweeps with an appropriate net. Seven sweeps were made in area A and six sweeps were made in area B.

The numbers of grasshoppers trapped on each occasion were as follows:

Site A	13	41	9	21	64	11	51
Site B	52	15	25	77	40	66	

At first glance the sizes of the local populations appear different. For example, the mean of site A samples is 30, whereas for site B it is 46. Can we assume from these data that there is a significantly larger population of grasshoppers at site B?

Steps in the Mann–Whitney **U** test

The null hypothesis (negative hypothesis) assumes the difference under investigation has arisen by chance; in this case, 'There is no difference in the sizes of two populations of grasshopper in areas A and B.' The role of this test is to determine whether to accept or reject the null hypothesis. If it is rejected here we can have confidence that the difference in the sizes of the two samples is statistically significant.

1 Rank the data of the two samples in increasing order of size.

Site A

_____

Site B

2 a For each measurement in sample B, count how many samples in group A are smaller (for measurements that are the same, score $\frac{1}{2}$). Tabulate as follows:

Sample B measurements	*Number of sample A measurements that are smaller*

The total of sample A measurements that are smaller $(U_A) =$ _____

b For each measurement in sample A, count how many samples in group B are smaller.

Sample A measurements	*Number of sample B measurements that are smaller*

The total of sample B measurements that are smaller $(U_B) =$ _____

3 Check your arithmetic is correct:

$$U_A + U_B = n_A \times n_B$$

where n_A is the number of measurements in sample A, and n_B is the number of measurements in sample B.

4 Choose the smaller value of *U* obtained. Look up the critical values of *U* at the 5% significance level in Table A2.3 on p. 437. This occurs at the intersection of the values for n_A and n_B.

If the smaller calculated value for *U* is less than or equal to the tabulated value, then the null hypothesis is rejected.

If it is greater, the null hypothesis is confirmed, i.e. there is no statistical significance in the differences between samples.

3.10 Features and characteristics of major biomes

The inhabited part of the Earth is known as the **biosphere**. A large part of the terrestrial biosphere is occupied by distinctive, stable zones called **biomes**, normally characterised by their dominant vegetation.

Biomes tend to be very large, possibly so large as to occupy major parts of continents. You may already be familiar with biomes such as tropical rain forest, temperate deciduous forest and grassland/savanna. The worldwide distribution of the major biomes is illustrated in *Advanced Biology*, p. 45.

Assignment

You can best become acquainted with the distinctive and characteristic features of selected biomes by researching and then contrasting the features of:

- tropical rain forest with temperate deciduous forest;
- grassland/savanna with desert.

Contrast the outcomes of your reading and research in tables you draw up for the purpose. Appropriate headings for the tables might include:

- where the biomes tend to occur (latitude and altitude range);
- average rainfall and mean temperature experienced;
- typical features of soil;
- dominant plant species;
- typical food chain observed in periods of active plant growth;
- characteristic dominant carnivore (tertiary or quaternary consumers);
- typical effects of human life.

References

Advanced Biology Chapters 3 and 4, including p. 45, Figure 3.2; p. 57, Figure 3.21

J L Chapman and M J Reiss (1992) *Ecology; Principles and Application*, Chapter 17, pp. 214–27. Cambridge University Press

3.11 Quick test

1 Distinguish between the following pairs:

   a biosphere and biome;
   b ecosystem and ecotone;
   c biotic factor and abiotic factor;
   d boreal forest and temperate forest;
   e food chain and food web;
   f primary producer and primary consumer;
   g topographic factor and edaphic factor;
   h clay soil and sandy soil;
   i commensalism and mutualism;
   j predation and grazing;
   k niche and habitat;
   l density-dependent factor and density-independent factor;
   m primary succession and secondary succession;
   n flow of energy and cycling of nutrients;
   o tide and wave.

2 What technique or equipment do you associate with the following:

   a estimating population sizes of small, mobile animals;
   b analysing a plant grassland community;
   c measuring soil pH;
   d a belt transect;
   e studying a soil profile?

3.12 Essay assignment

Select one of the following:

- You are required to investigate the differences in the common species to be found throughout a mature oak wood in general, and also in the area of a fallen oak tree. State what methods you would use and how they would be carried out. Suggest the main differences you would expect to find between these two areas within a wood.

or:

- Given a rocky seashore habitat, discuss examples of competition that occur between common organisms that may influence their distribution.

4 Humans and the environment

Summary

In the long history of the Earth there have been many profound, naturally occurring changes to the land masses, oceans, atmosphere and climate. Human activities have occurred only relatively recently, by comparison, but these too have been very influential. The growth rate of the human population in the past 200 years has been spectacular, and this issue remains problematical. Not all the impacts of humans on their environment are harmful, however; science and technology have achieved much that is relevant to the solving of ecological problems.

The harmful environmental effects of the human species arise because of the huge size of the human populations; no part of the Earth can escape human influence. The many harmful impacts of human actions include:

- the destruction of woods and forests (**deforestation**);
- **soil erosion** due to improper land use;
- a danger of the enhancement of the '**greenhouse effect**' due to change in the composition of the atmosphere;
- '**acid rain**' damage to habitats and organisms;
- the **destruction of the ozone layer**;
- excessive use of **pesticides**;
- the disposal of the constantly accumulating **waste materials**.

Conservation involves the application of ecological principles to the management of the environment so that a balance is maintained, despite human activities. Conservation measures are urgently required over virtually the entire Earth surface. They are necessary if we are to combat the **destruction of habitats** and the **extinction of species**, to exercise control over human population growth, and to facilitate the appropriate and **sustainable use of the Earth's resources**.

Practicals and activities

4.1 A contribution to conservation

(Data generating)

The objective of conservation groups is to protect and enhance local wildlife and habitats, both common and rare. Naturalists and conservationists often combine to create greater appreciation of the local wildlife and its environment, and much greater awareness of the effects of human activities. They usually work on the care and protection of representative habitats, and they seek to protect and maintain habitats that experience multiple use. The species that are protected include badgers, bats, snakes, lizards, toads, frogs and newts, wild birds and local plants.

Organisations seek the active participation of people of all ages, by providing opportunities for everyone to enjoy wildlife through the protection and maintenance of the remaining wild places. They usually enthusiastically accept the opportunity to address senior school, sixth-form college and further and higher education groups. They may supervise young persons' work at Duke of Edinburgh Award activities. They will certainly hope for commitment and action, and they should be able to identify tasks and studies leading to the protection of threatened local environments and endangered species. Young people of like mind might be expected to invest some time and energy as an intensive input over one weekend or week, or a more extensive commitment over part of one year, involving attendance for part of a day from time to time. Activities can take place at all times of the year.

■ Aim

To contribute to the conservation of a representative habitat in your locality, or contribute to the study of a particular species with a view to improving its chances of survival.

■ Risk assessment

- Working through local organisations with other volunteers, with an appropriately experienced officer with training at an agreed, supervised task, is sufficient to take account of hazards and avoid significant risks.
- Always discuss and obtain approval for all that is proposed with teachers, tutors or supervisors at your school or college, and leave a record of your proposed plans and activities with them, and with a parent, relative or guardian.

■ Method

The initial contact with an appropriate local group can usually be established by contacting either:

The British Trust for Conservation Volunteers (BTCV), 36 St Mary's Street, Wallingford, Oxfordshire OX10 0EV

or:

the Nature Conservation Group or Countryside Ranger Service at the Leisure Services Department of your local authority council offices

or:

the Secretary of your local (voluntary) wildlife group, such as the County or Regional Naturalist Trust, through your local library.

Work may involve attendance at planning and training sessions, and activities may include:

- wildlife observation and data collection;
- footpath clearance, fencing work and stile building;
- rough ground clearance;
- heathland maintenance;
- hedge laying and tree planting;
- pond, canal or lake maintenance;
- alien species clearance;
- dry-stone wall maintenance;
- ditch clearance and drainage improvements;
- coppicing or pollarding as appropriate.

■ Data presentation

Keep a diary of your initial meetings, training and preparatory visits, and of your contributions (with others) to the conservation of a habitat and the observations of a particular species. A photographic record of the work, together with follow-up studies, would be particularly useful.

■ Conclusions

- Make a critical assessment of the ways your work contributed to an active, planned piece of conservation in which wildlife habitats were created and future developments were anticipated, and was not simply an act of preservation.
- Make a careful record of data about the occurrence and behaviour of wildlife, and make this data available to local naturalists with a particular interest or responsibility for these organisms.

■ Evaluation

Can the adage 'Think globally, act locally' be made effective in your experience?

4.2 The colonisation of wasteland

(Investigation)

Waste land is surprisingly common in both urban and rural areas (Figure 4.1). The term includes abandoned agricultural or horticultural land (possibly awaiting 'development'), domestic rubbish tips, dump sites for abandoned machinery and vehicles, derelict industrial sites (some with soil contami-

nated with chemicals), housing clearance sites in city centres and suburbs, derelict railway sidings with chippings where the railway 'sleepers' lie, abandoned builders' rubbish, unused pathways and roads, and decaying concrete or tarmac surfaces around redundant buildings. There are so many different types of waste land that the methods adopted to investigate them may need to be quite variable. The 'history' of sites has to be taken into account, too.

■ Risk assessment

The risks identified for general ecological work (pp. 19 and 30) apply here. Identify any particular hazards associated with your chosen site (chemical pollutants, old machinery, etc.) and make an appropriate assessment of risk.

■ Aim

To investigate the succession of flora and fauna colonising a waste land on a selected site and (if time permits) to compare this pattern with that of a contrasting type of waste land (for example, abandoned horticultural land with an inner city housing clearance site).

Further, to suggest a management plan for one habitat as a nature reserve or haven for wildlife.

■ Method

In the planning and conduct of this study, you and your team must consult your teacher or tutor as to the feasibility, safety and advisability of your approach, giving your detailed plans for comment at frequent intervals.

1 Select your site(s) carefully; the criteria should include ease, convenience and safety of access, evidence that some recolonisation is taking place, good prospects that the site(s) will not be 'developed' during the study and the availability of permission to revisit the site(s) periodically.

2 The methods you choose need to be carefully adjusted to the needs of the site, but are likely to involve a preliminary analysis by means of a belt transect (p. 25) from barren areas into well-colonised areas, analysing the flora and fauna, and the pertinent abiotic factors (pp. 20–4). Remember, the origins of the flora on waste land can be

Figure 4.1 Town sites with potential for ecological investigation

very varied; they may include seeds in dumped vegetable matter, garden escapes, 'bird seed' escapes such as sunflower (*Helianthus annus*), canary grass (*Phalaris canariensis*) and the shoo-fly plant (*Nicandra physalodes*), as well as the wind-borne 'weeds'. Carry out an initial collection of the common plants, identifying them (and preparing a reference card of each species, with a photograph and/or a pressed leaf and flower, perhaps).

3 Investigate why the barren areas are bare, and also how quickly and by which pioneer organisms they are colonised. If you are investigating a waste site, make enquiries with local authorities or site-owners about the previous use of the land and the possibility of any known pollutants.

4 Set up records of the birds and any mammals known to visit the site periodically.

5 If you have long-term access to the site, set up a recording procedure to detect and quantify changes in the biota and abiotic conditions with time.

6 If permission is given and the sites are sufficiently extensive, investigate the effects of treatment with commercial chemical fertilisers and organic fertiliser on parts of the area you have marked out. Follow any effects on recolonisation of the enriched areas.

7 From your observations of wildlife in the area, and your developing knowledge of the local colonisation (succession) sequence, suggest what wildlife is likely to take advantage of this development. Make basic plans to suggest how this immigration of wildlife can be supported.

■ Data presentation

- Make a record in transects and tables of the data on abiotic and biotic features of the site; use an Ecology program (p. 40), if it is available. Add any general information you have discovered about the site from other authorities.
- Suggest a likely succession to stable climax if the site were to remain undisturbed.
- Write a concise statement of your conservation proposals for the area.

■ Conclusions

- What are the main deterrents to recolonisation of the site studied?
- What are the pioneer colonisers? Which plants are best able to survive, and why?
- What are the likely origins of the 'alien' (i.e. not indigenous) plants? What are the advantages and disadvantages of vigorous growth of 'alien' plants?
- To what extent do other areas of 'green' (parks or overlooked or abandoned land nearby) act as a 'reservoir' of species?
- Can a site be 'managed' for conservation merely by being left untouched? What are the practical issues in conservation of small sites like this?

■ Evaluation

If possible, follow up your work by visiting an urban site that has been turned into a green area (your local authority Planning Office or Parks Department will be able to advise you).

Investigate the methods local conservationists use to reduce competition, and to improve fertility.

How is the local community involved in the development, if at all?

4.3 The acidity of rain

(Data generating)

Rain, a dilute solution of carbonic acid, has a pH of 5.6. When the pH is lower than this we talk about 'acid rain'. This acidity is due largely to the presence in the atmosphere of sulphur dioxide from the burning of coal and oil, and nitrogen oxides (NO_x) from car exhausts. Acidity is deposited from the atmosphere as rain or snow ('wet' deposition), and as solid matter ('dry' deposition).

■ Aim

To measure the acidity of rain in the vicinity of your school or college.

■ Risk assessment

- A rain gauge should not be positioned where access may be dangerous.
- Otherwise, good laboratory practice is sufficient to take account of any hazards and avoid significant risks.

■ Method

It is essential to monitor rainfall and the pH of the rain over a period of several weeks at least, and possibly over a year or more. A safe place to position a rain gauge might be an enclosed quadrangle or fenced-off area at ground level. Use a rain gauge that can be securely anchored or attached; although glass rain gauges are preferable, plastic gauges are safe and satisfactory. The data in Table 4.1 were obtained from the precipitation collected in a plastic rain gauge. The gauge must be emptied once a week at least and the amount of rain and its pH measured. Make sure that it will be free of unintended interference over the period of the readings.

For comparison and corroboration purposes, data on rainfall (for the period of the study, for example) can be obtained from the National Weather Centre. Data on the atmospheric acidity detected locally may perhaps be obtained from the Council's Environmental Officer.

Table 4.1 The pH of rain collected in the grounds of a South London school over a two-year period

Month	Monthly median pH for 1993	Monthly median pH for 1994
January	4.8	4.1
February	4.8	4.35
March	4.55	4.1
April	4.75	4.0
May	4.55	4.4
June	4.4	4.4
July	4.6	4.5
August	–	–
September	4.3	4.1
October	4.25	4.25
November	4.1	4.45
December	4.2	4.45

Values were obtained by transferring the weekly precipitation to a laboratory and measuring the pH electrometrically

■ Data presentation

Tabulate your data (weekly readings). Avoid the pitfall of taking a monthly average of the data, since the pH scale is logarithmic (*Advanced Biology*, p. 122).

The data may be plotted as a line graph.

■ Conclusions

- Comment on the changing acidity of the rain, and the possible causes of the seasonal tendencies.
- Is the pH significantly low enough to be a concern? What is the overall trend?

■ Evaluation

To what extent do the amount and frequency of the rain showers affect day-to-day pH?

4.4 The effect of acidity on Gammarus

(Investigation)

The shrimp *Gammarus pulex* is a very active freshwater crustacean, living under stones and amongst water weeds at the side of the river. It is the food of several fish species. It is found in oxygenated water of chalk and other streams, but not in water of pH 5.8 or less. Persistent acid rain may affect the pH of a stream unless there is a significant amount of calcium hydrogencarbonate present. In fact, crustaceans like *Gammarus* are 'pollution indicators' by their absence (p. 34).

■ Aim

To investigate the effect of slightly increasing acidity on the behaviour of *Gammarus*.

■ Risk assessment

Good laboratory practice is sufficient to take account of any hazards and avoid significant risks.

■ Method

A few gammarids should be collected and kept in well-aerated cool stream water, together with a sample of stream water for your investigation. Measure the pH of the stream water on collection.

After the experiments have been completed the gammarids must be returned to the habitat from which they were collected.

1 Investigate by observation the behaviour of the animals, by placing about 10 gammarids into a shallow dish containing their natural stream water. Record your observations.
   - How do they move around – do they swim, walk, crawl?
   - Is their behaviour apparently affected by any variations in the laboratory environment, such as light intensity or direction?
2 Set up an experimental dish in which gammarid behaviour can be investigated. Divide the bottom of a white dish into three areas and place on the bottom in the separate areas dif-

Table 4.2 Scoring levels for gammarid behaviour

Time/min:	1	2	3	4	5
behaviour: swimming					
moving over stones					
moving between weeds					
not moving					

ferent types of substrate, such as small stones, sand and pond weed. Cover with paper and fill up the dish with stream water. Carefully remove the paper so that the different microhabitats are left undisturbed. Introduce about 10 gammarids, and leave them to 'acclimatise' to this environment.

3 Design and plan a scoring method so that you can keep a careful record of gammarid behaviour. One way is to count and record how many animals are carrying out different types of behaviour, perhaps at one-minute intervals (Table 4.2).

4 Using the behaviour scoring system that you have devised, determine which microhabitat the gammarids seem to prefer.

5 Now, set up a fresh dish with the preferred material on the bottom and carefully fill up with stream water. Measure the pH of a sample of the water, and then add 10 gammarids. Leave them to acclimatise for five minutes.

Observe and record the animals' behaviour over a five-minute period. Then remove the gammarids and add five drops of dilute sulphuric acid to the water (take care when handling this acid). Remeasure the pH.

Re-introduce the gammarids, and allow them to acclimatise again. Then observe and record behaviour over a further five-minute period.

Repeat this cycle of actions until your check shows that the pH has dropped to about 4.0. Terminate your experiment at this point, and return the gammarids to the original stream water. Do not work below pH 4.0, as a lower pH might harm them.

■ Data presentation

Present your results in explanatory tables.

If one particular type of behaviour clearly changes with changing pH of the water, then present that data as a bar chart.

■ Conclusions

• To what extent were the behavioural patterns of *Gammarus* apparently influenced by acidity?
• Would this change of behaviour contribute to survival problems in a stream? Why?

■ Evaluation

To what extent do you feel that your behaviour experiments depend on observations that are entirely subjective? Assess the objectivity of the data.

4.5 The effect of acid rain on soil

(Investigation)

Acid rain has little effect on chalky soils; the carbonates neutralise acidity quickly. But it may have an immediate effect on thin, acid upland soils where there is little natural buffering (no carbonates).

The effect of acid rain on clay soils is more complex. Clay mineral particles (silicate crystals) in soils naturally attract and absorb positively charged mineral cations. These mineral ions may be leached from the soil and lost if the rain water is very acid. If acid rain persists, poisonous ions such as those of aluminium eventually become soluble and may be leached out into groundwaters, and move into streams, rivers and lakes.

■ Aim

To investigate the effect of acid rain on soil.

■ Risk assessment

Good laboratory practice is sufficient to take account of any hazards and avoid significant risks.

■ Method

You are required to set up an investigation of the ions that will leach from different soil samples when exposed to distilled water, water at pH 5.6 and water at pH 4.0 ('acid rain').

1 Place equal amounts of the soil samples in separate plastic funnels, after partly closing the exit with a pebble. Do this with the several types of soil provided (loam, chalky soil, sandy soil, peat and wood ash), making sure that each is clearly identified with a label.
2 Irrigate each sample successively with 50 cm³ of:
   a distilled water;
   b tap water adjusted to pH 5.6;
   c tap water adjusted to pH 4.0.
   Collect the water that drains through the soils in separate, labelled beakers.
   You will be able to adjust the pH of water with the addition of a few drops of dilute sulphuric acid. Check pH values with pH papers.
3 Test the water draining through the soils, and also a sample of the tap water for the presence of the following ions: aluminium, iron, calcium, potassium and nitrate. Also test the pH of the water. Use test strip papers. Record the data.

■ Data presentation

Tabulate the data. As changes in mineral content are likely to be small, it is often helpful to convert the data to percentage changes and use them to produce a presentation of the data as bar charts.

NOTE TO TECHNICIAN

Each student group will require (or require access to):
• samples of chalk soil, loam, sandy soil, peat and wood ash, in quantities to part-fill the plastic funnels used;
• five plastic filter funnels;
• five stands and clamps or tripods;
• five 100 cm³ beakers;
• 100 cm³ measuring cylinder;
• 800 cm³ distilled water;
• dilute sulphuric acid 0.1 mol dm⁻³, labelled 'care – acid';
• plastic teat pipette;
• test strips for: pH, aluminium, iron, calcium, potassium and nitrate;
• small pebbles.

■ Conclusions

• Comment on the ability of the soil to 'buffer' acid rain (i.e. reduce the effect of the acidity).
• What was the effect of wood ash on 'acid rain'. Why?

■ Evaluation

This investigation is based on soil samples in an artificial environment. Is it possible to collect a topsoil sample from a habitat you are studying, using a corer, in order to repeat the experiment?

■ 'Science across Europe' initiative

One of the 'Science across Europe' projects is focused on acid rain. The aim is to investigate the causes of acid rain in your locality. Students fill in a questionnaire, and they exchange answers with students in other schools in Europe (by fax). The choice of language is decided by the schools involved.

Details of 'Science across Europe' can be obtained from:

The Association for Science Education, College Lane, Hatfield, Hertfordshire AL10 9AA, UK.

The project is being extended to parts of the world outside Europe.

4.6 The effect of sulphur dioxide on seedling growth

(Investigation)

Sulphur dioxide, one of the products of the combustion of fossil fuels, is a gas that contributes to 'acid rain'. Farmers therefore need to know what effect it may have on crop growth.

■ Aim

To design and conduct an investigation of the effect of sulphur dioxide on the growth of maize and barley seedlings.

■ Risk assessment

• Operations in which vapour from sodium disulphate(IV) may escape should be carried out in the fume cupboard.
• Otherwise, good laboratory practice is sufficient to take account of any hazards and avoid significant risks.

Figure 4.2 Seedlings suitable for Practical 4.6

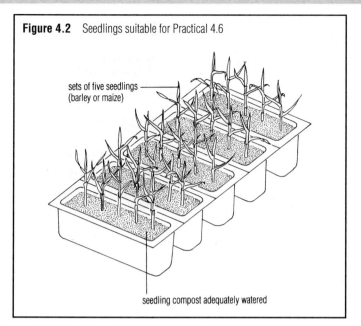

sets of five seedlings
(barley or maize)

seedling compost adequately watered

■ Method

You are provided with small trays of maize and barley seedlings (five of each per group), grown up to the stage of the first few leaves being 'open' (Figure 4.2).

A 10% (w/v) solution of sodium disulphate(IV) is also provided. Within an enclosed space, this solution will produce a higher concentration of sulphur dioxide than is normally present in environmental emissions.

Also provided is a supply of transparent plastic bags. Once sealed, these are relatively impermeable to sulphur dioxide (and water vapour, of course).

It is suggested that a typical experiment would last one week. Other materials available are distilled water, measuring cylinders and beakers.

Ask your teacher or tutor if you feel there is other equipment you would like access to, explaining your reasons.

NOTE TO TECHNICIAN

Each group will require:
- 10 small plastic seedling trays of the type divided into small subcompartments, five containing maize and five containing barley, five seedlings per tray, grown in seedling compost; at the start of the experiment period the first leaves of the seedlings should be emerging through the coleoptiles;
- 100 cm^3 of 10% (w/v) sodium disulphate(IV) (sodium metabisulphite);
- 100 cm^3 and 10 cm^3 measuring cylinders;
- beakers of various sizes;
- watch glasses or Petri dishes that will hold about 20 cm^3 liquid;
- 10 transparent plastic bags (approximately 20 × 30 cm^2) with secure tie-strips;
- access to a fume cupboard and to an undisturbed, illuminated position for plant growth;
- any further apparatus requested by the group and sanctioned by the teacher/tutor.

■ Data presentation

Present your data to show the outcomes, including differences between species, so they are easily comprehensible to the reader.

■ Conclusions

- Can you generalise on the signs and symptoms to look for in cereal crops exposed to harmful levels of sulphur dioxide?
- What are the comparative effects on maize and barley plants?
- To what extent are the outcomes of a trial like this likely to be repeated in commercial crops exposed to similar levels of acid rain?

■ Evaluation

Can you suggest how the investigation could have been made more relevant to conditions in the natural environment of crops?

4.7 The decomposition of plastic

(Investigation)

There is pressure on industry to manufacture products which either can be recycled or, if discarded, do not contribute to pollution. Biodegradable plastic is an example of the latter.

Much plastic is tough material, designed to resist degradation and breakdown by natural processes. You will, however, have noticed that certain plastic carrier bags carry a logo ('Biopol' is one example) that indicates the bag will readily decompose (biodegrade) due to the action of microorganisms, if kept damp and in contact with microorganisms and soil minibeasts.

■ Aim

To investigate how quickly biodegradable plastic breaks down, and the role of certain organisms in the process.

■ Risk assessment

Good laboratory practice is sufficient to take account of any hazards and avoid significant risks.

■ Method

The two types of biodegradable plastics are:
- plastic impregnated with readily biodegradable substances (usually cellulose, starch or even a protein) that will encourage the breakdown of the plastic; in the soil, the biodegradable part of the plastic attracts microorganisms and helps their numbers increase, so that they then break up the long-chain molecules of both the natural and the man-made polymers;
- plastics containing antioxidants to resist the oxidation of the polymer when exposed to sunlight, but also containing chemical activators which speed up the oxidation process under soil conditions.

You should use discs of several types of plastic (biodegradable and traditional) for your enquiry. Cut the discs using a sharp cork borer pushed through layers of the plastic, against a wooden block. Bury representatives of the complete range of samples in plastic containers of different soils; try to include soil from woodland areas.

The rate of breakdown should be monitored regularly (at least monthly). Do this by measuring the amount of plastic bag still left intact against a grid made by photocopying 5 or 10 mm^2 graph paper on to an OHP transparency, and counting the squares still covered by plastic. Alternatively, lay the discs on graph paper and draw round them. Then count the squares covered by plastic.

You might investigate the effects of excluding soil non-vertebrates (such as slugs) from attacking the bag and allow only bacteria and fungi to bring about decomposition. Do this by enclosing the disc samples in nylon mesh (made from 'tights', possibly of different meshes) before burying them.

NOTE TO TECHNICIAN

Each student group will require:
- a range of plastic bags (students ought to be required to supply these);
- no. 6 cork borer and wooden block to cut against;
- stout plastic containers (such as yoghurt cartons) with small perforations added to sides and base, into which samples (with soil added) can be buried;
- materials to make the decomposition-detecting grid (as described above).

■ Data presentation
Relate the rate of breakdown to the type of plastic and type of soil. Compare the rate of breakdown in the presence and absence of microfauna.

■ Conclusions
- Which biodegradable plastic is apparently most quickly degraded?
- Which types of soil are most endowed with the necessary microorganisms and minibeasts?

■ Evaluation
Which would be more environmentally friendly, recyclable plastic or biodegradable plastic?

Is there another possible way to avoid environmental harm from an excess of packaging materials?

4.8 Storing nuclear waste

(Investigation)

Radioactive isotopes are used in the generation of electricity, and in industry, medicine, research and in defence. One outcome of their use is the production of radioactive waste, some of which is reprocessed and used again and some of which is discharged into the atmosphere and the sea. Much, however, has to be stored, completely isolated from the environment, until the radiation it emits is sufficiently reduced to be safe to living things. The half-life of a radioactive isotope is the time taken for its radioactivity to drop to half of its initial value. The half-life of phosphorus-32 is 14.3 days, but that of carbon-14 is 5.7×10^3 years and uranium-238 is 4.5×10^9 years. Plutonium-239 remains lethally poisonous for 250 000 years. As a consequence, the selection, design and management of nuclear waste sites is a critically important issue.

The UK Government, responsible for the national strategy for the management of all radioactive waste, set up UK Nirex Ltd in 1982 to carry out the storage of low- and intermediate-level radioactive waste. Nirex has carried out its surveys and now plans for the deep storage of radioactive waste near Sellafield in Cumbria.

■ Aim
To explore the issues of the use of radioactive isotopes, and safe storage of radioactive waste.

■ Risk assessment
Good laboratory practice is sufficient to take account of any hazards and avoid significant risks.

■ Method
Investigate in outline:
1 the extent, and specific advantages, of the use of radioactive isotopes in industry, medicine and research, using an Advanced level chemistry textbook;
2 the case for safe storage, and the criteria for selection of sites of storage of radioactive waste, using the information pack and software program supplied by UK Nirex;
3 a concise shortlist of the potential disadvantages of using radioactive isotopes in terms of the safe disposal of the waste, using a selection of the resources available from:
- Greenpeace, for example 'Deep Crisis – Britain's Nuclear Waste: Who's Burying Who' (July 1991), 'The IAEA File: 1992 – Greenpeace International' (September 1992);
- Friends of the Earth, for example 'Nuclear Power' (November 1991) and 'Radioactive Waste' (August 1993)

NOTE TO TECHNICIAN

Each student group will require:
- access to a microcomputer (Acorn Archimedes, IBM clone, Apple Macintosh or RML Nimbus);
- software program 'Choosing a site' with information pack and a range of publications and videos, available from UK Nirex Ltd, Curie Avenue, Harwell, Didcot, Oxfordshire OX11 0RH (telephone 01235 833009);
- educational resources relating to nuclear waste available from Greenpeace, Canonbury Villas, London N1 2PN (telephone 0171 354 5100);
- educational resources relating to nuclear waste available from Friends of the Earth, 26–28 Underwood Street, London N1 7JQ (telephone 0171 490 1555).

■ Data presentation
Prepare a concise wall paper:
- identifying the natural sources of radioactivity and the typical levels of exposure;
- the advantages and disadvantages of the use of radioactive isotopes from the standpoint of their value to humans;
- the issues of safe disposal.

■ Conclusion
Prepare a brief statement of your opinion on this issue.

■ Evaluation
An issue like this generates strong feeling in many people. Listen to the opinions of those with whom you disagree, whatever stance you take. Remember, to know and understand the opinions and value judgements of those with whom you disagree gives your own case the greater strength.

4.9 Studying atmospheric dust

(Investigation)

Dust is a major atmospheric pollutant, and the particles in our atmosphere occur in a range of sizes. The largest, those defined as coarse particles (diameter about 100 µm), are visible to the naked eye, and dense enough to collect quickly on exposed surfaces. These are generally not dangerous to our health, for those that are inhaled become trapped in the mucus high up in the bronchi.

The finest particles have diameters of 10 µm or less. These tend to remain suspended in air, and they can penetrate deep into the lungs. These tiny smoke particles are known as PM10s. They may exceed 200–300 µg m^{-3} in the atmosphere of big industrial cities. PM10s are believed to be responsible for 10 000 deaths per year in Britain, due mainly to respiratory diseases like bronchitis and asthma, as well as to heart disease.

■ Aim

To investigate the particles in our atmosphere large enough to be seen by light microscopy.

■ Risk assessment

Good laboratory practice is sufficient to take account of any hazards and avoid significant risks.

■ Method

You can trap atmospheric dust on the surface of exposed microscope slides coated with a thin film of petroleum jelly. You will be supplied with slides that have been exposed for a fixed period, in contrasting situations.

You can assay the dust that has accumulated on an exposed surface by adhesion to small pieces of clingfilm pressed on to the surface. Plant leaves may be used for this. You can compare the solid pollutants on evergreen leaves aged one to three years (holly, *Ilex aquifolium*), one to five years (Douglas fir, *Pseudotsuga menziesii*), and one to seven years (Sitka spruce, *Picea sitchensis*). Once the clingfilm pieces have been exposed, mount them on microscope slides for examination.

When patches of dust particles are found, count the numbers occurring in a fixed area of the slide. You can identify a standardised 'area' of slide with the aid of an eyepiece micrometer.

NOTE TO TECHNICIAN

Each group will require (or require access to):
- a selection of appropriately exposed petroleum jelly-coated microscope slides;
- clingfilm;
- microscope slides, fine forceps, fine scissors;
- a microscope with high-power objective;
- eyepiece micrometer;
- leaves, as detailed above.

■ Data presentation

Make a table to compare your estimates of dust pollution you detect in different situations.

■ Conclusion

Correlate the incidence of dust pollution with the possible sources of the dust.

■ Evaluation

On what night in the UK year is the concentration of atmospheric dust likely to be highest? What are the viable alternatives to the periodic burning of garden rubbish?

Projects

4.1 Conservation of owls

There are five common species of owl in the UK, of which the tawny owl (*Strix aluco*), barn owl (*Tyto alba*) and the little owl (*Athene noctua*) occur in farmland, woods, coppice, and rough land in lowland Britain. All our owls are threatened by the intensity of human use of the environment, and by changing farming methods. The owl community can be studied in an area, although they may be nocturnal, crepuscular, or otherwise shy, quiet organisms. For example, owls usually swallow their prey whole but cannot digest hard materials like bones. These are 'coughed up' as pellets, which can be collected from the ground below roosts. The contents of owl pellets can be analysed to find out about owl diet. Refer to the 'Window on Owls' project pack, from WATCH, The Green, Witham Park, Lincoln LN5 7JR.

4.2 The human waste revolution

Of the waste produced by human communities, not all finds its way into a dustbin or disposal point in the first instance. The rubbish that is discarded by humans in wild or otherwise little-disturbed environments is a reflection of affluent lifestyles (and of a thoughtless or uncaring approach to such habitats). But the materials discarded are potentially significant for wild organisms. For instance, bottles and other containers may accidentally become 'pitfall traps', the plastic 'retainers' for packs of drinks cans may trap larger animals, and a wide range of discarded detritus may be eaten, decayed and decomposed by the organisms of the habitat, or by organisms that visit. The rubbish collected within a known area can be analysed for its influences on wildlife, and from the viewpoint of biodegradability, too. It may be of interest to compare human-derived rubbish in two contrasting habitats in relatively close proximity.

4.3 Tropical rain forest products, and their alternatives

A survey of the tropical rain forest products in common use in your locality may reveal the extent of our apparent dependence on the products of countries such as Brazil, Zaïre and Indonesia. What are the alternative materials or products, and why is it that they are often not selected? What 'education' initiatives in your locality would be most effective in making others aware of the worldwide tree crisis?

4.4 Hedge surveys

We are currently losing 6500 km of hedge every year. In rural districts it is possible to research the ages of hedges, using local and national records. The age and structure of a hedge boundary may be correlated with the types and diversity of the wildlife it supports. Plant Life, an organisation that campaigns to conserve all wild plants and appropriate habitats, organised a Great Hedge Survey in 1993, in connection with it long-term aim of maintaining ancient boundary hedges throughout the UK. The organisation can be contacted via the Natural History Museum, Cromwell Road, London SW7 5BD.

Problems and assignments

4.1 Human population growth

Life on Earth probably dates from 3200 million years ago (mya), but, in the development of life, humans are recent arrivals (less than 1 mya). Early human populations grew extremely slowly, and only very recently have the numbers of humans started to double within the span of a very few years (logarithmic growth rates). For example, world population was at about one billion in 1850, but it had doubled by 1930, and doubled again by 1970. The human population is projected to reach eight billion by about the year 2020.

In the case of humans, the birth and death rates are influenced by complex political, social and economic factors, in addition to the ecological factors in population change that may influence all species.

Table 4.3 Projected world population change, 1990–2025

Region	Population/millions		Population/% of total	
	in 1990	by 2025	in 1990	by 2025
developed countries	1205	1353	23	16
less-developed countries	4087	7151	77	84

The world's population is not distributed equally over the globe. Table 4.3 illustrates this, and gives an estimate of the changing pattern of population by the time it is anticipated to be at eight billion.

Factors in population growth can be discovered by examination of the population's age–sex structure histograms (known as **population pyramids**) of developed and less-developed countries (Figure 4.3). Examine these histograms and then answer the following questions about them.

Figure 4.3 Population pyramids compared

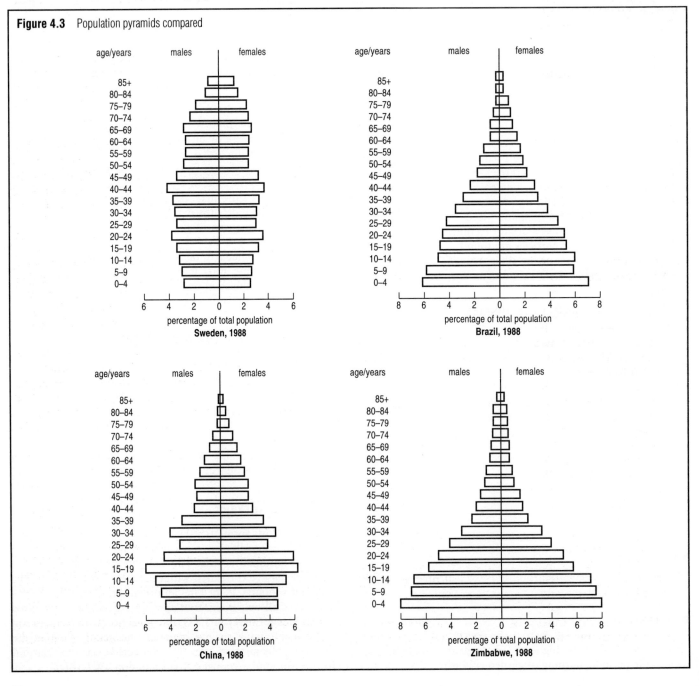

1 What shape of population pyramid results from a situation of high birth rate, high infant mortality and generally deprived nutritional status of the population?

2 Which country shown has the highest infant (under five years) mortality rate?

3 At what age does the gradual decline in the numbers of the population begin in:
   a Sweden;
   b Brazil;
   c Zimbabwe?

4 How may the 'pinch' at the base of the Chinese pyramid be best explained?

5 A serious famine racked one of these four countries between 1959 and 1961. Which country was it?

6 The population pyramid for the UK in 1850 was very similar to that for Zimbabwe in 1988. Make a careful list of the more significant changes within the UK between 1850 and 1950 that might account for the UK now having a population pyramid profile very similar to that of Sweden.

4.2 The 'Green Revolution'

Panel 4.1 The 'Green Revolution': advantages and disadvantages

Before the advent of modern agriculture, grains and vegetables existed in thousands of varieties. Now, only a few of these varieties are used (Table 4.4).

Table 4.4 Limited diversity in American agriculture

Crop	Varieties available	Major varieties in use
maize (corn)	197	6
wheat	269	10
soybean	62	6
rice	14	4
potatoes	82	4
peanuts	15	9
peas	50	2

Many experts believe that this loss of variety, or genetic diversity, could have a significant impact on world agriculture. So why is genetic diversity dwindling?

1 The newer varieties often have a higher yield on mechanised farms. Between 1903 and 1976, new varieties of wheat allowed American farmers to double their yield, and new varieties of maize (corn) allowed them to quadruple output. The newer varieties were better suited for mechanical harvesting, and they responded to irrigation and fertilisers. Seed companies benefited economically through concentration of marketing on a few varieties.

2 The extension of this success to worldwide agriculture came via the Green Revolution. It began in 1944, when the Rockefeller Foundation and the Mexican Government established a plant breeding station in NW Mexico. The programme was headed by Norman Borlaug, a plant geneticist from the University of Minnesota, who helped develop a high-yield wheat plant. Before this development, Mexico imported half the wheat it consumed each year, but by 1956 it was self-sufficient in wheat production. By 1964 it was exporting half a million tons. Borlaug was later awarded a Nobel prize for this work.

3 The success in Mexico led to the establishment of another plant breeding centre in the Philippines. High-yielding rice strains were developed there, and introduced into India in the mid-1960s. Again the results were spectacular. India more than doubled its wheat and rice production in less than a decade and has become self-sufficient in wheat production.

4 Impressive though it was, the Green Revolution contributed to the decrease in agricultural diversity. One of the most important concerns is the loss in genetic resistance to disease. Local varieties of plants are acclimatised to their environment; natural selection has ensured this. Newer varieties on the other hand may have little resistance to insects and disease. Moreover, the planting of expansive fields of one genetic strain (monocultures), facilitates the spread of disease. Simplifying ecosystems removes environmental resistance that normally keeps potential pest populations in check. The potato famine in Ireland in the 1840s is one of the famous examples of the effects of reducing diversity. Only a few varieties of potatoes were planted in Ireland. When *Phytophthora infestans* began to spread among the plants there was no back-up supply of resistant varieties. Within a few years two million Irish perished from hunger, and another two million emigrated.

5 In addition to their susceptibility to disease, high-yield varieties are also generally less resistant to drought and flood. In 1970 the southern corn blight wiped out nearly 25% of the US corn crop. The American peanut crop (consisting of two varieties) was almost entirely destroyed in 1980 by drought and disease.

6 Reduced genetic diversity, a trend commenced in the Neolithic Revolution, is being accelerated by a relatively new phenomenon: the destruction of tropical lands where many of the ancestors of our modern crops grow. Their fate is crucial to agriculture. Why? The future will require plants that can survive climatic changes, drought, disease and insects. These ancient ancestors could provide the genetic material needed to improve our crops. Thus reducing genetic diversity through deforestation and farming could have far-reaching effects on the future of agriculture.

From: DD Chiras (1991) Environmental Science: Action for a Sustainable Future, *3rd edn,* Benjamin Cummings

Answer the following questions, using your wider reading and general knowledge, and the information in Panel 4.1.

1 What have been the chief advantages of the Green Revolution since its early successes in the 1960s and 1970s for:
 a the less-developed countries of South America, Africa and Asia;
 b the developed countries of America and Europe?
2 What is meant by 'genetic diversity'?
3 The high-yielding wheat plant that Borlaug helped breed not only carried many more fruit to each inflorescence, but had a very short stem and a larger leaf area than varieties it replaced. How did these two features contribute to improved productivity?

4 List the range of characteristics that a geneticist is most likely to seek to change in crop plants such as wheat, rice or maize in order to improve productivity.
5 What characteristics of local populations of food plants may enable them to survive adverse conditions such as abnormal drought, floods and epidemics of parasites and predator species?
6 As a result of the 'Green Revolution', many countries with huge populations have vastly improved grain production. What features of the varieties used make them:
 a accessible to wealthy farmers and landowners with large land holdings and existing resources of mechanical aids to farming;
 b unavailable to the poorest farmers and tenants?

4.3 The world energy crisis

In Figure 4.4, the great disparities that exist between countries in primary energy use are highlighted, and this is followed by two scenarios (projections) for global primary energy use in the next millennium. In the second of these the 'consensus view' is the 'business as usual' approach, but the 'sustained world view' is built on a planned programme for radical improvements in efficient uses of energy by human communities.

Panel 4.2 Whose population problem?

At the Population Summit in New Delhi last October, attended by the bulk of science academies around the world, there was much talk of the developing nations and how they ought to apply their population policies with greater energy and urgency. There was all too little talk of the developed nations and how they ought to formulate population policies of their own. Not a single one has a worthwhile policy of any sort. Yet as developing nations pointed out at New Delhi – and will doubtless and justifiably do again at the International Conference on Population and Development in Cairo this September – most developed nations have a population problem insofar as their consumption patterns exert an exceptionally disruptive impact on the global ecosystem.

During the 1990s, the world will take on board another 95 million people each year. Of these, 90 million will be in developing nations and only 5 million in developed nations. However, because of the ultraprodigal lifestyles of the rich nations, their newcomers will cause more emissions of greenhouse gases than will the additional people in the developing nations.

Britain's extra 115 000 people per year will consume more fossil fuels than the 2.4 million new Bangladeshis. So which nation also needs a population policy? We have yet to start on a broad public debate on how many people are good for Britain, and how many Britons are good for the world. True, the average British family has only two children. But when we consider their consumption of raw materials and their production of pollutants, and compare them with the global average, we find the 'real world' size of a British family is over 10 children.

Before pointing a critical finger at developing nations, Britain might well ponder the virtue of planning to achieve zero population growth with all due despatch. We could attain that through the simple expedient of eliminating all unwanted births. It would help our economy too. Family planning services show a cost–benefit ratio of 1:5. A win–win situation if ever there was one.
*From: N Myers (1994) Biologist **41**(6), p. 138*

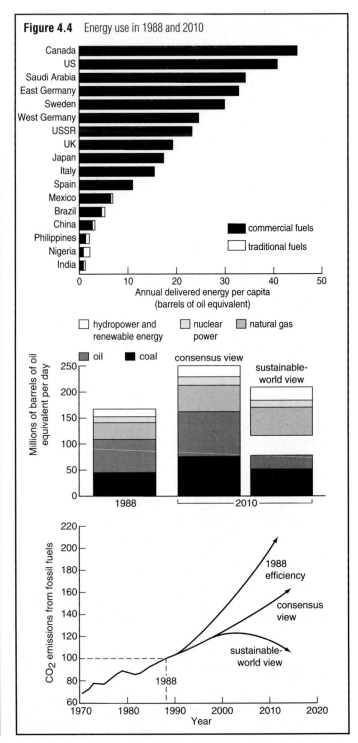

Figure 4.4 Energy use in 1988 and 2010

In Panel 4.2 a scientist, in a personal statement, argues for a change in the population policy of developed countries, such as the UK, in response to the disparity in consumption of resources between the populations of developed and less-developed countries.

Answer the questions below.

1 What are the environmental reasons why it is essential to tackle the disparity in energy consumption that exists between less-developed and developed countries? What, for example, are the most likely consequences of our continuing largely to ignore the issue?

2 In your opinion, what should be the programme of priorities in a country like the UK to tackle this issue? Make a list of your points, so that you can present a 'wall newspaper' item for peers, and make preparations to talk about it to your group, if asked.

3 How might we have to change our lifestyles in order to make fewer demands on the Earth's resources?

4.4 Saving the rain forests

> **Panel 4.3** Facts about forests
>
> Running like a girdle around the equator, tropical forests cover some 900 million hectares. They are divided between South America (58%), Africa (19%), Asia (10%) and Oceania (10%). Brazil contains almost 33% of the total, and Zaïre and Indonesia each has 10%. Thus Brazil, Zaïre and Indonesia jointly own more than half of the world's tropical forest.
>
> Undisturbed by humans, rain forests are very stable ecosystems and contain ancient and diverse forms of life. They are habitats for at least 50% of all the animal and plant species on Earth; they can be thought of as the 'gene pool' for animal and plant life. In the Amazon jungle, for instance, over 2500 species of trees are known, with up to 400 in a single hectare. Yet because most life exists in the forest canopy, which is still unexplored, no one in fact knows the true abundance of species. Meanwhile, the tropical forests are not unpopulated. These forests are homes and territory to an estimated 50 million tribespeople.
>
> In 1950, 30% of the Earth's land mass was covered with tropical forest, but by 1975 this was only 12%, and in 1988 only 6%. Satellite photographs reveal that Brazilian forest is being lost at four times the rate previously estimated. Nigeria and the Ivory Coast are expected to be completely logged out by the year 2000, and Costa Rica will by then have lost 80% of its forests. 80% of rain forest in Ghana has already disappeared, as has some third of Malaysia's unique Sarawak rain forest. At current rates of destruction the world's rain forests will be gone in 50 years.
>
> *From: Ecoropa Information Sheet 17, 1989*

Answer the following questions, using the information in Panel 4.3 and that in *Advanced Biology*, pp. 78–82, together with your wider reading and general knowledge.

1 Explain in concise notes *two* important ways in which deforestation may affect local climate.

2 How does deforestation lead to flooding on the plains below the forest area?

3 'A hectare of rain forest supports 800 000 kg of plants and animals for ever, or its underlying land will support 200 kg of beef a year – about 1600 hamburgers – *for a few years only*.'
  a How is tropical forest land that has been deforested and sown as grassland, for example, for the rearing of cattle, fertilised for productive growth?
  b Why is the productivity of this grassland so short-lived?

4 Rain forests have been very severely reduced during particular periods in geological history (for example, about 16–17 million years ago, *Advanced Biology*, p. 673), yet they recovered subsequently. What features of the current deliberate deforestation process may jeopardise natural regeneration of these forests now?

5 List the practical measures that an individual human who lives in the UK can take to help sustain the worldwide rain forests.

4.5 Organic farming

Organic farming involves maintaining soil fertility and crop and livestock productivity by the use of fertilisers obtained from legumes, green manure, animal manure and compost, and by the use of mineral-bearing rocks such as lime. Weeds are reduced by mechanical cultivation and crop rotation. Damage done by insects and other pests is minimised by crop rotation and possibly by biological pest control. Organic farmers avoid the use of chemical fertilisers, pesticides, growth regulators and livestock feed additives. In this approach they are striving to use a knowledge of ecology rather than of chemistry in the production of good food. The intention is also to maintain wildlife and natural habitats, thereby reducing environmental damage in the process of human food production.

Answer the following questions.

1 Explain the way in which particular legumes can be used to maintain soil fertility of meadowland soil.

2 What is meant by 'green manure'? How does it differ from 'compost'?

3 How might crop rotation contribute to the reduction of weeds? Give an example.

4 What might animal manure contribute to the soil that green manure grown in the field may not?

5 What is meant by biological pest control? Give an example.

6 What advantage has agriculture 'based on chemistry' contributed to the drive for human food production?

7 What are the potential dangers of using a broadly effective insecticide against aphid infection of a wheat crop?

8 There are aesthetic and moral reasons for protecting natural wildlife. What economic reasons can you suggest for the maintenance of a diverse flora and fauna?

9 In what ways does an insecticide like DDT, when used against insect pests in agriculture, actually pose a threat to humans?

10 What steps could be taken to prepare the consumer to accept organically grown crops instead of food products produced by 'agribusiness'?

4.6 Satellite imaging and the productivity of the oceans

Satellite observations of the Earth's surface have dramatically increased our understanding of the processes that control the primary productivity of our oceans, and, in particular, the part plankton plays in the global carbon cycle. This is because the colour of the sea is directly related to its biological productivity. Scanning instruments in space allow the productivity of the world's oceans to be estimated. This is because algal blooms are indicated in the printout of scanner images as intense orange areas; purple areas are where there is least plankton. Extensive algal blooms consistently develop in high latitudes in spring, around the continental coast lines. These follow on periods of winter storms when the ocean waters are stirred up.

The colours of a satellite image are shown in *Advanced Biology*, p. 83, Figure 4.14. Alternatively, see M R Lewis (1989) 'The variegated ocean: a view from space', *New Scientist*, 7 October 1989, pp. 37–40

From your wider reading and general biological knowledge, answer the following questions.

1 What abiotic conditions will most favour the growth of algae in marine conditions?
2 How do these conditions arise in the oceans at high latitude, around land masses in spring?
3 Why are algal blooms apparently not normally produced in the wide-open spaces of mid-oceans, particularly in the warm seas at or near the Equator?
4 Draw a diagram of the carbon cycle involving marine organisms, rather than terrestrial animals and plants.

5 If the fate of the bulk of the algal bloom, when its life cycle ends, is to sink to the ocean bottom and decay there over a long period, what is the likely effect of algal blooms in a 'greenhouse effect' world?
6 The most productive fishing grounds correspond to the regions of the sea where seasonal algal blooms are a feature. Why is this the case?

4.7 The carbon dioxide question

In 1982, a scientist wrote:

'That the atmospheric content of carbon dioxide is increasing now seems well established. As a result, some latitudes could become warmer and wetter, but the effects may not all be bad. In sum, the carbon dioxide question is obscured by many unknowns and uncertainties.'

This statement is still very largely true today. The reasons for this are broadly the following.

1 The primary cause of the current rise in CO_2 concentration is the combustion of fossil fuel. As the human population rises, and particularly if living standards in developed countries are maintained and those of less-developed countries improve significantly, then energy demand will increase substantially. Fossil fuel reserves are finite, however.
2 The forests and the oceans are the major 'sinks' for CO_2. Land vegetation and phytoplankton in the oceans fix similar amounts, but the most productive CO_2 sinks on land are the trees of the forests, and these are disappearing at an alarming rate. Figure 4.5 shows an estimate of the annual carbon fluxes, together with a list of the world's major carbon reserves.

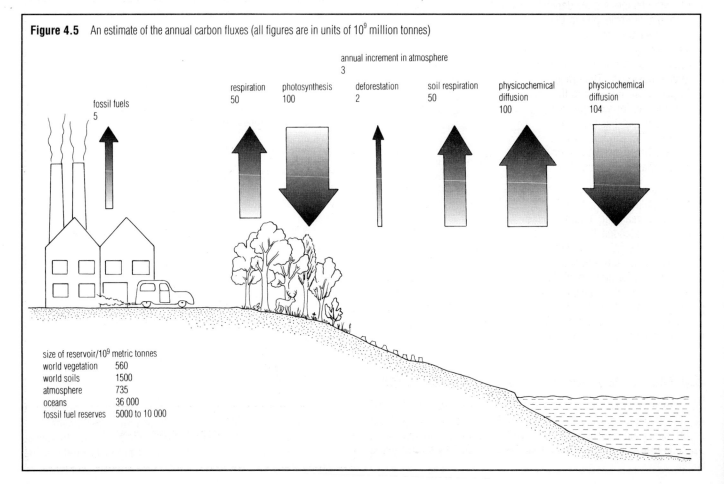

Figure 4.5 An estimate of the annual carbon fluxes (all figures are in units of 10^9 million tonnes)

annual increment in atmosphere
3

respiration 50 · photosynthesis 100 · deforestation 2 · soil respiration 50 · physicochemical diffusion 100 · physicochemical diffusion 104

fossil fuels 5

size of reservoir/10^9 metric tonnes
world vegetation 560
world soils 1500
atmosphere 735
oceans 36 000
fossil fuel reserves 5000 to 10 000

Figure 4.6 Projected effect of increased precipitation on tree growth

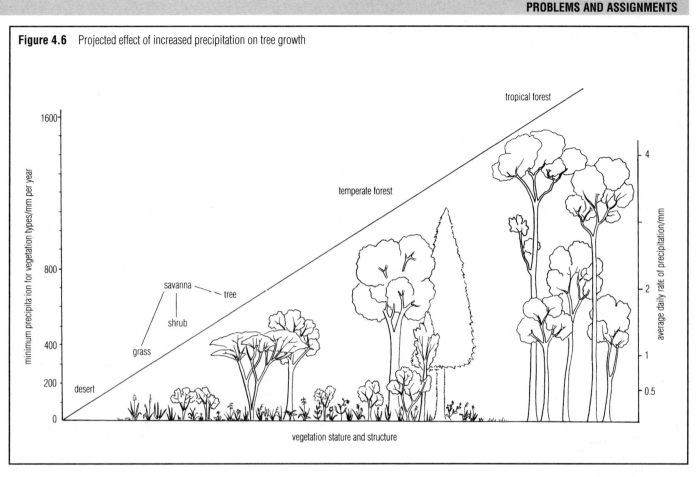

3 Climate change is considered the most likely effect of increasing amounts of atmospheric CO_2 (and of other gases in our atmosphere that trap terrestrial infrared radiation). If the temperature increases (referred to as a 'greenhouse effect'), the water vapour capacity of the atmosphere will rise. Water vapour is another 'greenhouse gas'. The precipitation pattern would change.

4 Of particular interest are the ways in which plants are likely to be affected by, for example, a doubling of atmospheric CO_2 concentration. It has been calculated that there may be an increase in crop yield of around 33%. How trees might respond appears not to have been investigated conclusively. Figure 4.6 shows the projected effect of increased precipitation on tree growth.

Consider the issue of global warming, referred to as the 'greenhouse effect', highlighted here, together with those aspects of the issue you have already read and thought about.

Open an extended table in which you can list, in note form, the important and significant consequences of the rising atmospheric CO_2 levels, using the subheadings 'Possible advantageous outcomes' and 'Possible harmful outcomes'. The ramifications of this issue are so diverse that you should expect to keep your list open for some time, as further consequences and possible outcomes become apparent.

For further information see *Advanced Biology*, pp. 82–4, and the Further Reading listed on p. 97.

4.8 The ozone layer: formation and destruction

The ozone layer is formed in the stratosphere (between 18 and 40+ km above the surface of Earth) from the reaction of oxygen from green plants initiated by ultraviolet (UV) radiation in sunlight. Most ozone is formed over the Equator, and is circulated by stratospheric winds.

Figure 4.7 Evidence for an 'ozone hole' in the stratosphere

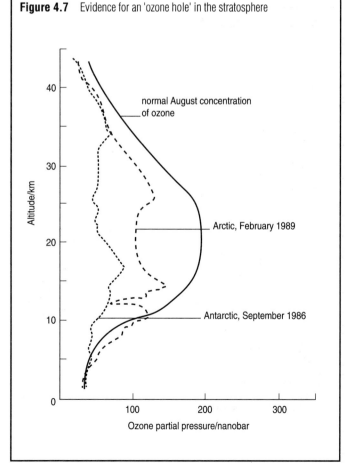

Destruction of this high-level ozone occurs in spring and summer above the poles, where icy particles act as reaction surfaces. Here ozone (O_3) is destroyed by short-lived radicals (R·) of chlorine and nitric oxide (N_2O) formed by UV radiation acting upon nitrogen dioxide (NO_2) and chlorofluorocarbons (CFCs).

'Normal' levels of stratospheric ozone, and evidence for a seasonal 'ozone hole', are shown in Figure 4.7.

The UV light-driven reactions of ozone formation and destruction are:

$$O_2 \rightarrow O· + O· \qquad O_3 + O· \rightarrow 2O_2$$
$$O· + O_2 \rightarrow O_3$$

The pollution-driven reactions of ozone destruction are:

$$R· + O_3 \rightarrow RO + O_2$$
$$RO + O \rightarrow R· + O_2$$

1 Why is most ozone formed in the stratosphere above the Equator?
2 Explain precisely how the naturally occurring reactions of ozone formation *and* breakdown combine to create a barrier limiting the penetration of our atmosphere by UV light.
3 In the lower atmosphere N_2O and CFCs occur as virtually inert gases which escape to the stratosphere only very slowly. What condition in the stratosphere causes them to react, yielding radicals?
4 If the further contamination of our atmosphere by oxides of nitrogen and by CFCs was terminated immediately, for what reasons would the depletion of the ozone layer be expected to continue for very many more years?
5 What are the chief sources of the atmospheric pollutants nitrogen dioxide and CFCs?

4.9 Quick test

1 Distinguish between the following pairs:

   a deforestation and desertification;
   b 'greenhouse gases' and 'acid rain';
   c infrared and ultraviolet radiation;
   d Neolithic and Industrial Revolutions;
   e biomass and fossil fuels;
   f dry deposition and wet deposition;
   g molecular oxygen and trioxygen (ozone);
   h radical and ion;
   i stratosphere and troposphere;
   j conservation and preservation in the countryside;
   k chlorofluorocarbons and oxides of nitrogen;
   l control by pesticide and biological control;
  m DDT and 2,4-D;
   n landfill and incineration;
   o representative ecosystems and the sustainable use of resources.

2 What do you understand by the following?

   a alternative sources of energy;
   b solar flux;
   c maintenance of the ozone layer;
   d toxicity of organochlorine insecticides;
   e the Red Data Books.

4.10 Essay assignment

Select one of the following:

- Discuss the possible biological significance of the 'greenhouse effect' to a community of terrestrial organisms living in a temperate climate.

or:

- Describe appropriate conservation management activities that may be applied to *either* a chalk downs grassland *or* an ancient water meadow. Explain the biological principles on which these measures are based.

5 Biology and industry

Summary

Biology underpins numerous important areas of **commercial and industrial activity**, too many to mention in detail, in fact. The approach to understanding biology's relationship to industry in this chapter is by selected case studies.

Current examples of the impact of biological systems in industry include the **water industry**, concerned with the **supply of clean water** and with the **treatment of sewage**. A supply of clean water is an essential requirement of a healthy human community. The treatment of sewage to produce clean water, largely achieved by microorganisms, renders the water fit for re-use, eventually as drinking water.

Agriculture and **fishing** are other major industries that are both traditionally and increasingly dependent upon biological principles. Similarly, the **preserving and storage of food** is an industrial and commercial activity that we can identify as an aspect of applied biology.

Biotechnology, the industrial application of biological processes, is as old as brewing, cheesemaking and baking, but it has important modern developments too. Modern biotechnology is largely based on new developments in **fermenter technology**. Closed fermenter systems exploit a particular species of bacterium or fungus cultured in otherwise sterile conditions, rather than several different microorganisms involved in one process in an 'open' fermenter. Typical products of commercial significance include 'single-cell' proteins, antibiotics and a human hormone, e.g. insulin. The production of the last-named by bacteria has also involved **genetic engineering** (p. 356). Products are often improved by the use of enzymes in industrial processes (**enzyme technology**).

Biological fuel generation will gain in importance as fossil fuel runs out. Currently, fuel for the internal-combustion engines of cars and trucks may be obtained by **fermentation of sugar** extracted from sugar cane to produce ethanol. In addition **methane** (fuel) is being produced worldwide from the anaerobic decay of organic matter, via many different low-impact processes.

Practicals and activities

5.1 Visits to a water treatment works

(Data generating)

Since the development of large towns in the Industrial Revolution, the disposal of sewage in urban communities has raised health issues. The first confirmed cholera victims in the UK, in this period, died in Sunderland in 1831. There followed numerous outbreaks of cholera in the UK until 1866, all part of a worldwide outbreak (pandemic). Cholera and other water-borne diseases (*Advanced Biology*, pp. 101 and 535) are transmitted via drinking water contaminated by sewage. This causal link was established in the UK in 1858, in the Carnaby Street/Soho Square residential district of London. This issue, together with the infection of people who fell into the River Thames, and an increasingly offensive smell from the river in hot weather (very evident to the Members of Parliament at

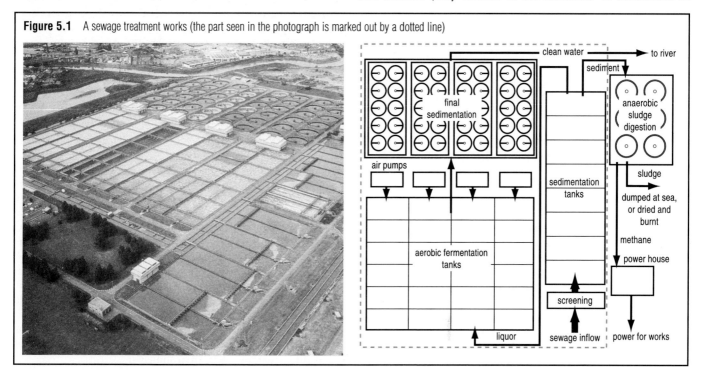

Figure 5.1 A sewage treatment works (the part seen in the photograph is marked out by a dotted line)

Westminster), eventually led to the construction of purpose-built sewers across London, and an improved drinking-water supply. Not until very recent times, however, were modern sewage works constructed (Figure 5.1).

■ Aim
To understand the modern treatment of water.

■ Risk assessment

- At a water treatment works, visitors are obliged to obey the rules and regulations laid down by the Water Authority. These are issued to the visit organiser beforehand, and are normally read to participants.
- Sewage tends to generate offensive smells at early stages in the process, when the flow rate is slowed. Most of the smell is due to thiols, products of the bacterial breakdown of sulphur compounds.
- There are potentially dangerous pathogens in untreated sewage. Avoid contact with exposed surfaces, and avoid any contact with mouth, eyes, etc. until you have washed your hands at the end of the visit. Appropriate facilities are provided for visitors.

■ Method 1: A sewage works
Sewage treatment is an ancient biotechnology that has been updated to make allowance for an increasing human population and changing patterns of industrial and commercial activity. By manipulation of aeration, flow and temperature, a range of microorganisms destroys organic matter to leave clean water. An excess of nitrate ions can be bacteriologically reduced during the treatment. Effluent is discharged into a river without harmful effects; most of our tap water has passed through a sewage works on its way to our drinking supply.

During your tour of a works, make concise notes on each step in the process, noting both the treatment applied and the underlying biological reasons.

1 The origin of the effluent
Effluent originates from homes (domestic sewage), and from workplace sites (trade waste). Both types of sewage are frequently treated together, but some trade waste may have to be pretreated. Pretreatment is normally to reduce the concentration of substances poisonous to microorganisms at the works. Identify any local examples of this. Has the works ever received a batch of poisonous substances in the sewage that temporarily killed the sewage microorganisms, so interrupting the treatment process?

2 Primary treatments
Primary treatment involves the removal of grit and the screening out of any large solid objects that have got into the drains. In the primary settlement tanks the flow of sewage is temporarily terminated to allow suspended solids to sink. This is the critical step to primary treatment. Why? How long does this phase last? This is where you may see visiting wildlife feeding on the sewage. In what way might this pose a health risk?

Subsequently, the liquid part (the bulk) of the sewage is piped on to an aerobic fermentation tank. Once the liquid has gone from the tank, the settled solids are scraped up and piped as a slurry to anaerobic digestion tanks.

3 Aerobic fermentation of sewage liquors
In this phase, aerobic bacteria convert dissolved organic chemicals into CO_2, H_2O and various ions, and into the substance of bacterial cells themselves. Bacteria settle out later. There are different ways of aerating sewage liquor.

Trickle beds The sewage liquor is sprayed over 'beds' filled with blast furnace clinker, or with shingle and sand. A layer of bacteria and protozoans develops in a jelly biolayer attached to the substrate, and these consume the dissolved organic matter as the liquor trickles over them. These beds will work undisturbed for decades. How long does this phase take? How often is the liquor recirculated to purify it successfully?

Activated sludge The sewage liquor flows slowly through huge tanks whilst a large quantity of air is pumped through it. The active ingredient is known as 'activated sludge'. What will this consist of? How long does this phase take? At the end of your tour you may be allowed to take a sample with you for microscope examination at your laboratory. Why should it be a fresh sample?

Stirred, with pure oxygen treatment Sewage may be stored in a covered tank and continuously stirred whilst oxygen gas is pumped in. This expensive process is effective where space is at a premium.

Where a quantity of raw sewage has escaped into a river in a city centre region, a specialised boat may ply up and down pumping compressed air into the surface waters, particularly if the weather is warm and the river flow is slow. Why is this necessary? What are the likely consequences if this is not done?

4 Reducing the nitrates
The concentration of dissolved nitrates in sewage liquor can be reduced by action of denitrifying bacteria. This requires the temporary introduction of an anaerobic phase, which is arranged by using a lower flow rate and a reduction of aeration to a rate just sufficient to stir the liquor. As a result, nitrates are converted to nitrogen gas. Why are high levels of nitrates in public drinking water a problem? In waterlogged soils the same bacteria may be active. Why are they considered a problem in this situation?

5 Final settlement
The activated sludge is allowed to settle out. Then the water flows over weirs at the edge of the tank into the nearest river. Why is a waterfall of value at this point?

6 Sludge
Meanwhile, the sludge (settled solids) is transferred to anaerobic digestion tanks. Here it is kept warm, and bacteria digest it, producing methane gas and carbon dioxide. The gas output is usually mixed with diesel oil, and burnt to supply power to electricity generators in a pump house. The electricity produced is often sufficient to supply much of the needs of the works (including the air compressors, for example). The digested sludge is disposed of, sometimes as a fertiliser of sorts. In future, more of this product will be incinerated. It will no longer be possible to dump it at sea. Is there a problem with heavy metals in the sludge? What are the problems of dumping at sea? What are the concerns about the future burning of sludge within urban environments?

Alternative methods of dealing with sewage and farm waste

One possibility is the use of reed beds, since these have the ability to thrive in waterlogged environments which are rich in organic waste. The plants being used are the reed *Phragmites* spp., the bulrush *Typha latifolia* and the yellow iris *Iris pseudacorus*. The final treatment is an aerated pond. Solids must first be trapped and composted at high temperature to render them safe to handle.

In another method, farm waste (slurry) from stock yards and silage-clamp effluent is made to trickle through bales of straw. The straw slows down the effluent and allows bacteria to break down the organic acids before the waste reaches any watercourse, and there reduces the BOD.

Laboratory examination of activated sludge

A sample of activated sludge can be examined by microscopy (low and high power) to observe the organisms involved in aerobic sewage treatment, provided the sample has been kept cool and well aerated, and is examined quickly. The sample may need to be diluted with tap water. The protozoans are best viewed live, and may be seen feeding on the bacteria.

NOTE TO TECHNICIAN

The activated sludge brought from the works should be kept cool and aerated. Use a tall beaker, an aquarium pump/air block, and cover with plastic clingfilm to reduce aerosols.

Each student group may require:
- microscope slides and coverslips;
- bacterial stains;
- teat pipettes;
- autoclave or disinfectant for disposal of used equipment/materials.

■ Method 2: A drinking-water plant

The treatment of drinking water is related to the origin of the supply. Water from a borehole normally requires only chlorination, whereas water abstracted from a river and that taken from a large uncovered reservoir will vary in quality from day to day. This water will need a full water treatment cycle before it is safe to drink.

At the works you visit, the following steps may occur. Enquire into each step, and the time it takes for water to be treated at each step.

1 A flocculation process may be needed to remove the really fine clay particles. What agent is used to precipitate the clay? How does it work?
2 Aeration will rid water of hydrogen sulphide gas and aromatic compounds such as benzene. Where might these pollutants have come from?
3 Sand filtration stages are commonly used. The sand builds up a biolayer of microorganisms which naturally clean the water. What will these microorganisms remove?
4 Chlorination is normally carried out in large tanks with numerous baffles to guarantee good mixing. Water is exposed to a high level of chlorine (0.5 ppm) for at least 30 minutes, to make sure that the disinfection is complete. How does chlorine kill microorganisms? The excess chlorine is removed with sulphur dioxide, and water leaves the treatment works with about 0.2 ppm chlorine present.
5 If there is a particular problem, UV light may be used as an additional safeguard. What will UV light do?

6 Is anything else added to water? At what stage, if at all, is fluoride added to help prevent tooth decay?

The treated water is stored in a covered reservoir, close to the consumer.

■ Data presentation
Write a report of your visits, as directed above.

■ Conclusions
- Comment on how dangerous pathogens are removed from sewage without the intervention of chemical treatments or special antibacterial methods.
- Why does drinking water from most sources still require antibacterial treatment during treatment for the consumer?

■ Evaluation
How might the water quality of a river close to water treatment plants be evaluated?

5.2 Estimating numbers of microorganisms by the dilution plate method
(Skills and techniques)

A sample of pond or river water, or a soil sample, may contain vast numbers of microorganisms, far too small and numerous to be counted even with the high power of the microscope. By means of the serial dilution technique, samples are plated out so that each colony that grows represents a single cell or spore in the original sample. In this way, the numbers of microorganisms in the water can be estimated accurately. Bacteria can be cultured on nutrient agar (NA) plates, and fungi on dextrose peptone agar (DPA) plates. The principle of serial dilution is shown in *Advanced Biology*, p. 99 and in Figure 5.2.

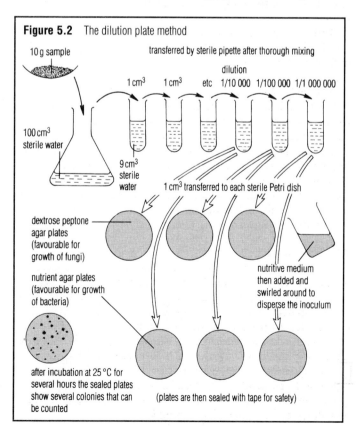

Figure 5.2 The dilution plate method

10 g sample

transferred by sterile pipette after thorough mixing

dilution

1 cm³ 1 cm³ etc 1/10 000 1/100 000 1/1 000 000

100 cm³ sterile water

9 cm³ sterile water

1 cm³ transferred to each sterile Petri dish

dextrose peptone agar plates (favourable for growth of fungi)

nutrient agar plates (favourable for growth of bacteria)

nutritive medium then added and swirled around to disperse the inoculum

after incubation at 25 °C for several hours the sealed plates show several colonies that can be counted

(plates are then sealed with tape for safety)

■ Aim

To make an estimate of the numbers of microorganisms (bacteria and fungi) in a water sample.

■ Risk assessment

The following are essential precautions to take in all microbiological work:

- wash your hands with soap and water before and after all practical work;
- do not put your fingers near your face (mouth, nose or eyes) during the experimental work;
- mark out your work area with a sheet of lining paper, and keep all apparatus within this zone;
- keep Petri dishes and plugged flasks, etc. closed or stoppered, except when opening them for transfer or inoculation;
- tape Petri dish lids to the dish base immediately after they are inoculated (but not completely, all the way around, since this might exclude air and encourage growth of any anaerobic bacteria present) – do not open these Petri dishes until they have been sterilised;
- plates that have been exposed must finally be sterilised (pressure cooker/autoclave) before the contents are disposed of and the dishes washed;
- at the end of the experiment, dispose of the lining paper, and swab down the bench with disinfectant.

■ Method

You are provided with a sample of pond or river water, collected in a sterile flask.

1 Carry out serial dilutions of this water sample to provide for dilutions between 1:10 000 and 1:1 000 000. To do so, number seven test tubes consecutively, 1 to 7. Using a sterile safety pipette (or sterile plastic syringe), place 9 cm^3 of distilled water into tubes 2 to 7 inclusive, and 10 cm^3 of the given water sample into test tube 1. Then, using the safety pipette, transfer 1 cm^3 of water sample from tube 1 to tube 2, seal tube 2 with a sterile bung, and shake the tube to mix the contents thoroughly. Using the safety pipette again, transfer 1 cm^3 of the diluted sample from tube 2 to tube 3. Seal this tube with a bung and shake the contents of this tube to mix. Repeat this progressive dilution procedure from tube 3 → 4, 4 → 5, 5 → 6 and 6 → 7. The final three tubes contain the water sample at the dilutions you require (1:10 000, 1:100 000, 1:1 000 000).

2 You are provided with six sterile Petri dishes, for culturing microorganisms. Label three 'NA' (for culturing and counting bacteria), and then label one of these 'dilution 5' (1:10 000), one 'dilution 6' (1:100 000) and the third 'dilution 7' (1:1 000 000). Label the other three 'DPA' (for culturing and counting fungi), and then label them similarly.

3 Now prepare and inoculate the 'NA' Petri dishes. In a water bath at about 45 °C is a stock flask of (molten) nutrient agar (labelled NA). Pour NA into each Petri dish in turn to a depth of about 5 mm, raising each Petri dish lid at a slight angle only, to do so. Whilst the nutrient agar is still liquid, use a sterile pipette to transfer 1 cm^3 of the appropriate diluted water sample to each plate, again raising the Petri dish lid the minimum needed to do so. Replace the lid and mix the contents by gentle swirling motions. When the contents have set solid, seal each dish with Sellotape.

4 Using the stock flask of (molten) dextrose peptone agar (labelled DPA) also held in the waterbath, prepare and inoculate the 'DPA' Petri dishes exactly as described for 'NA' dishes. When the contents have set solid, seal each dish with sellotape.

5 Invert the plates (to prevent any condensation from reaching the agar surfaces), and leave them in an incubator set at 25 °C. Without opening any inoculated Petri dish, examine the plates at intervals of several days, marking with a chinagraph pencil the presence of each colony as it appears. Count the number of colonies formed in each dish. If the sample was adequately diluted, each colony will have arisen from a single bacterium or spore.

6 Finally, multiply the number of colonies formed in each dish by the dilution factor to get an estimate of the number of bacteria (from NA dishes) and fungi (from DPA dishes).

NOTE TO TECHNICIAN

Each student group requires:

- access to a sample of fresh pond or river water, held in a sterile flask;
- four sterile safety pipettes (1 cm^3) or sterile plastic syringes;
- 14 sterile test tubes, with sterile rubber bungs, held in a test tube rack;
- chinagraph (or glass-marking pen);
- 100 cm^3 of distilled water;
- six sterile Petri dishes;
- Sellotape;
- water bath at 45 °C, containing 100 cm^3 of sterile NA in a plugged, labelled flask, and 100 cm^3 of sterile DPA in a plugged, labelled flask (NA and DPA can be obtained, ready prepared, from biological suppliers (p. 431));
- access to an incubator at 25 °C.

■ Data presentation

Present your results in a table.

■ Conclusion

What is the approximate size of the bacterial and fungal community of your sample?

■ Evaluation

If you were to test whether any of the bacterial community came from sewage, the 'NA' plates would be incubated at 37 °C. Why?

What would be the problems in estimating the size of the fungal population in a soil sample from the number of colonies counted in a dilution plate?

5.3 A visit to a fish farm

(Data generating)

Fish farming has a long history in human communities all over the world. Farming of fish is profitable because fish have low body temperatures and low basal metabolic rates (because their bodies are supported by their aquatic medium). Consequently, they show high protein conversion rates (i.e. the amount of 'feed' that becomes body protein). Fish also have high fecundity; thousands or even millions of eggs are laid each season, depending on the species. Many eggs are fertilised, too, but survival rates in nature are very low.

Figure 5.3 (left) A fish farm. (right) Trout farming is now a significant industry

Europeans have had a greater interest in marine fish (*Advanced Biology*, p. 102) than in freshwater fish, although the farming of fish like the freshwater trout is now a significant industry (Figure 5.3). In the UK, the farming of salmon, of crustaceans such as lobsters, and of molluscs such as mussels and oysters has also been commercially successful. Farms use natural or constructed inland ponds or floating cages in sheltered marine bays or lochs.

■ Aim
To understand the current practice and problems of fish farming.

■ Risk assessment

- At an industrial or commercial plant, such as a fish farm, visitors are obliged to obey the rules and regulations laid down by owners, as communicated by the local manager or staff.
- The exposed nature of the sites may generate special risks. Additional care will be necessary in extremes of weather, when working near the water's edge, and when walking along unprotected gangways, for example.

■ Method
During a tour of a fish farm, find out all you can about the breeding and rearing processes and the harvesting steps. Try to answer the following questions, and identify the underlying biological reasons for the answers.

1 How productive is the process in terms of the 'crop' and the time taken to grow it?
2 Compounded feed is normally delivered in pelleted form, often automatically. What is the content of the pellets? What are the sources of protein and other ingredients used? How is the correct feeding level determined?
3 Are dyes put into pellets to enhance natural colour in the fish muscle? If so, is this because the fish will not get enough in their artificial food?
4 When food pellets are fed to caged fish, some pellets drop to the sea/lake floor and there decompose. What sort of pollution might this cause? What effect might it have?

5 Fish parasites, such as sea lice, may spread quickly in dense populations of fish. Are parasites such as lice treated with pesticides, or can they be biologically controlled (many species of large fish depend on smaller fish to remove parasites from their skin)? What preventive methods are used?
6 Fish normally have a restricted breeding season. How is the breeding season effectively extended, so that a fish farm can produce populations of fish that breed at (say) three or more times during a year? Do the measures involve the application of hormones, the variation of environmental signals (light or temperature regimes), or perhaps the import of eggs from other parts of the world?

■ Data presentation
Write a concise report, establishing the essential details of the processes used to achieve a regular supply of quality fish for sale.

■ Conclusion
Draw conclusions about the environmental effects of the methods used.

■ Evaluation
All animal farming techniques are open to criticism. Comment on the ecological consequences of fish farming as a means of production of protein for human consumption, and on how humane it is compared with other forms of animal protein production.

5.4 Biological oxygen demand

(Skills and techniques)

Very little oxygen dissolves in water, and its solubility actually decreases with increasing temperature. If water becomes polluted with organic waste (such as raw sewage, farm slurry or silage effluent) its oxygen content is very seriously depleted, a condition known as **eutrophication**. This occurs when the bacteria present in water oxidise the organic matter.

In warm weather, all the oxygen dissolved in the river or stream at a point of heavy pollution may be used up, causing the death of all aerobic aquatic organisms, including the fish, for some distance downstream. The Biological Oxygen Demand (BOD) is the amount of oxygen (mg dm^{-3}) consumed in the sample held in the dark for five days at 20 °C.

BOD is calculated from two matched water samples taken from a particular site simultaneously. The dissolved oxygen content in sample A is determined immediately (using a chemical method known as the Winkler method, or by means of an electronic instrument called an oxygen electrode). Sample B is incubated in the dark for five days at 20 °C, during which time bacteria break down the organic matter. Then the remaining oxygen in sample B is determined. BOD is the difference in oxygen concentration of the two samples. BOD measurements are less accurate where:

- pollutants (such as heavy metals) that inhibit bacterial metabolism are also present;
- the organic pollutant resists decay (cellulose, for example, is biodegraded more slowly than sugars or organic acids).

Determining BOD is a time-consuming process at an introductory level. Instead, it is possible to compare the BOD of two water samples using methylene blue dye, which remains blue only as long as there is oxygen present (Figure 5.4).

■ Aim

To compare the BOD of two water samples (for example, water from a polluted river, and water taken from the same river at a point where the effects of that pollution are not experienced).

■ Risk assessment

- Special care is necessary when working near waterways (rivers or canals) or deep standing water (lakes or flooded sand pits). Work in a group with supervision when collecting samples.
- Otherwise, good laboratory practice is sufficient to take account of any hazards and avoid significant risks.

■ Method

1 Take two samples (A and B) in 250 cm^3 bottles with ground-glass stoppers. In sampling, avoid agitation of the water.
2 Add 1 cm^3 of 0.1% methylene blue solution to each sample, using a pipette that reaches to the bottom of the bottles. Replace the stoppers without trapping any air.
3 Incubate the bottles in the dark at a temperature of 20 °C. Examine them daily.
4 Note the time taken for the contents of each bottle to go colourless. The greater the degree of eutrophication of a water sample containing methylene blue, the quicker it will become colourless.

NOTE TO TECHNICIAN

Each group requires:
- two 250 cm^3 glass bottles with ground-glass stoppers, suitable for collecting air-free samples;
- one 1 cm^3 pipette, access to a solution of 0.1% methylene blue, access to an incubator at 20 °C.

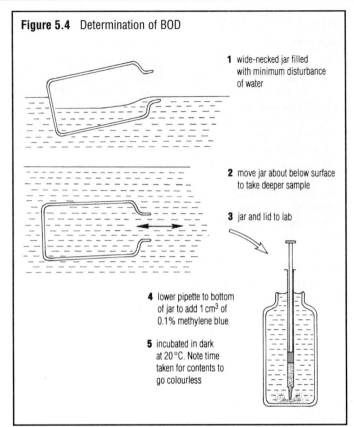

Figure 5.4 Determination of BOD

1 wide-necked jar filled with minimum disturbance of water

2 move jar about below surface to take deeper sample

3 jar and lid to lab

4 lower pipette to bottom of jar to add 1 cm^3 of 0.1% methylene blue

5 incubated in dark at 20 °C. Note time taken for contents to go colourless

■ Data presentation

You can record the time for complete decolorisation by drawing a bar graph, noting the particular environments from which samples A and B were obtained.

■ Conclusion

Is it possible to speculate on the major source of the pollution in your samples?

■ Evaluation

How is the comparative pollution level affected by heavy rain?

5.5 Industrial uses of enzymes: fruit juice production

(Investigation)

There is a growing market for fruit juices. Juice can be extracted from pulped fruit at raised temperature (about 60 °C) and under pressure, but this is an expensive process and the amount of juice extracted is significantly less than expected. The enzyme pectinase catalyses the breakdown of cell wall polysaccharides to sugars (*Advanced Biology*, pp. 130 and 163). Pectinase is used to clear wine and fruit juices. More recently, this enzyme, and sometimes also cellulase (which catalyses the breakdown of cellulose to glucose), have been employed in fruit juice extraction to improve productivity. How much more juice will result when one or both of these enzymes are used?

■ Aim

To design and conduct an investigation of the effectiveness of enzymes in the extraction of apple juice.

■ Risk assessment

- It is an absolute rule that nothing introduced into or produced in the laboratory may be eaten or drunk.
- Apples must be cut up with care on a board to protect your hands and the bench surface.
- When the blender is used, do not open it until the machine is switched off and the blades have stopped turning.
- Take care not to inhale enzyme powders; wear a face mask if there is a danger of this.
- Handle Clinitest tablets with forceps. Wear eye protection.

■ Method

Design and conduct an experiment to compare the yield in volume of juice obtained from apple pulp by:
- hcat trcatment and pressure;
- incubation with pectinase;
- incubation with pectinase and cellulase;
- incubation with water (a control).

Discuss your experimental design with your teacher or tutor before you begin the experiment.

Preparation of apple pulp

Peel and chop the apples and pulp in the blender. Allow the pulp to stand at room temperature (25 °C) for 30 minutes, using a beaker covered by clingfilm. During this time natural enzyme inhibitors in the pulp are inactivated by oxidation. Then divide the pulp (about 100 cm^3) into four equal samples.

Juice extraction by heat/pressure treatment

Heat one portion of apple pulp to 60 °C for 30 minutes in a beaker covered by clingfilm. Then, using multiple layers of muslin, squeeze out the juice from the cooled pulp, collecting it in a measuring cylinder. Keep the juice in a labelled flask in the refrigerator.

NOTE TO TECHNICIAN

Each student group will require:
- eight large apples;
- knife and chopping board;
- domestic blender;
- 250 cm^3 beaker, clingfilm to cover;
- 25 cm^3 measuring cylinder;
- 0–100 °C thermometer;
- waterbath at 60 °C;
- layers of butter muslin;
- three large filter funnels;
- three 50 cm^3 measuring cylinders;
- filter papers;
- four 50 cm^3 conical flasks, with bungs and labels;
- waterbath at 30 °C;
- three 10 cm^3 beakers;
- cellulase powder, pectinase powder;
- access to top-pan balance;
- 10 cm^3 plastic syringe;
- two 50 cm^3 beakers and labels;
- distilled water;
- access to refrigerator;
- Clinitest tablets and colour card;
- four test tubes, test-tube rack.

Juice extraction by enzyme action

Incubate the other portions of apple pulp at 30 °C, for one hour, one with pectinase, one with pectinase and cellulase, and one (control) with distilled water. Use 2 cm^3 of 2% (w/v) enzyme solutions. Measure the juice released by filtering the treated pulp through filter paper, and collect it in measuring cylinders. Keep the juice in labelled flasks in the refrigerator.

An optional extension of the study

Compare the reducing sugar concentrations in the juice samples. Wearing eye protection, and using a fresh Clinitest tablet in a test tube for each sample, add 1 cm^3 of juice extract. After the reaction is complete, read off the approximate sugar concentration from the Clinitest colour chart.

Another optional extension

Contrast different varieties of apple, at different stages of ripeness.

■ Data presentation

Tabulate your data, and display the results to emphasise the differences. Use bar charts if you feel these would help.

■ Conclusions

- Write a concise summary of the differences in the treatments, and why they may have caused differences in juice recovered.
- If you carried out the optional extension work, what differences did you find in the reducing sugar content of your samples, and between types of apple?

■ Evaluation

What are the sources of error in this investigation? Which of these could have been avoided?

5.6 The production of yoghurt

(Investigation)

Yoghurt is produced by the action of the bacteria *Lactobacillus bulgaricus* and *L. thermophilus* on milk held at about 40 °C for up to five hours. In the conversion of liquid milk, some of the proteins present are broken down to peptides and used, and some of the sugar is respired by the bacteria. Organic acids, including lactic acid, accumulate and the pH falls. This causes the remaining protein to coagulate, so the yoghurt sets. Ethanal and other products of bacterial metabolism give the yoghurt a characteristic flavour.

The time taken for the pH to fall to the point at which the yoghurt sets influences the quality of yoghurt. Yoghurt sets more quickly if the bacteria are able to respire glucose in quantity from the outset. Also, the type and quality of the milk used is critical. If milk contains antibiotics the lactobacilli may be harmed. Manufacturers add skimmed-milk powder to some brands, which helps to thicken the yoghurt, among other effects. However, this increases the lactose content. Lactose is a disaccharide found in mammalian milk. Some people are allergic to lactose, so for other yoghurts the milk is pretreated with the enzyme β-galactosidase (lactase) to hydrolyse lactose to glucose and galactose.

■ Aim

To investigate yoghurt production.

■ Risk assessment
- It is a rule that nothing introduced into or produced in the laboratory may be eaten or drunk.
- Good laboratory practice is sufficient to take account of any hazards and avoid significant risks.

■ Method
Investigate the yoghurt-making process using different types of milk to which yoghurt starter culture is added.

1 Prepare the starter culture by warming 100 cm^3 UHT milk to 40 °C in a 250 cm^3 conical flask, and then adding 10 cm^3 of freshly purchased natural yoghurt. Cover immediately with clingfilm, and incubate at 40 °C for 12–15 hours (**'day-before' task**).

2 Purchase lactose-reduced milk ('Lactolite') from a chemist's shop; alternatively, prepare a sample of lactose-free milk by incubating UHT milk with the enzyme lactase (NCBE Lactozym) in the proportion of 0.5 cm^3 enzyme to 500 cm^3 of milk, held in the fridge for 24 hours (**'day-before' task**).

3 Prepare at least two concentrations of enriched milk by adding suitable quantities of skimmed-milk powder to two portions of UHT milk.

4 Obtain samples of different milks, such as fresh unpasteurised (if available), pasteurised, UHT, semi-skimmed and skimmed milk.

5 Set up two yoghurt-production tubes (boiling tubes sealed with clingfilm) for each of the milk samples you have selected to work with. Use 10 cm^3 samples; add 1 cm^3 of yoghurt starter culture to each tube, and stir before resealing the tube with clingfilm. Incubate tubes in a waterbath at 40 °C for five hours.

6 Observe at 30-minute intervals, and record how quickly the milk mixtures begin to 'set' and become firm.

7 Using the milk mixture in one of the tubes, assess and record the change in number of bacteria present by the resazurin test (0.005% resazurin solution) after two hours' and four hours' incubation. Resazurin (a redox dye) is grey/purple in the absence of bacteria, and progressively changes from purple to violet to blue to pink to white with increasing bacterial activity. For the resazurin test, stir in 0.5 cm^3 of the dye to 5 cm^3 of a milk sample in a test tube and incubate at 40 °C for 10 minutes, then note the colour.

8 Using the second tube, measure and record the pH of the culture at intervals. Use either a pH meter and probe, or pH papers.

9 At the end of the experiment, check the glucose level in each tube with Diastix test strips.

NOTE TO TECHNICIAN

Each student group will require (or require access to):
- natural yoghurt;
- packet of skimmed milk powder (e.g. 'Marvel');
- lactase enzyme (e.g. Novo Lactozym available from NCBE);
- a variety of milk samples;
- conical flasks, clingfilm to seal;
- graduated pipettes or plastic syringes;
- boiling tubes and stands;
- stopclock;
- water bath at 40 °C;
- pH meter and probe, or pH papers (acid range);
- resazurin (0.005% solution);
- Diastix test strips for glucose.

■ Data presentation
Set out a table of data, with each milk type having columns recording time of setting, resazurin colour, pH and final glucose content.

■ Conclusions
- What is the critical pH necessary to obtain a yoghurt set?
- With which milk did you obtain an early set?
- Is pretreatment with lactose enzyme effective? How do the glucose concentrations compare?

■ Evaluation
What insights have you acquired into the issues involved in science-based food manufacture?

5.7 Building and testing a fermenter
(Investigation)

In biotechnological industries microorganisms are often grown in liquid cultures, using a fermenter vessel. An industrial fermenter is a large vessel where the conditions (e.g. pH, oxygen, temperature, concentration of substrate) are monitored, and where automatic valves regulate input of fresh medium, and the sampling or harvesting of products. Realistic 'model' fermenter systems are marketed for schools and colleges, but these are expensive. A fermenter made from a clear plastic fizzy-drink bottle (labels removed), in which the mixture is stirred by an aeration system, as used for a fish tank, is easy to make and use. The simple apparatus may include a means of monitoring growth of the culture (and possibly one or more of the physical conditions within the fermenter). A simple fermenter provides ideal conditions in which yeast can be grown, for ex-ample, and so it is possible to mimic a biotechnological industrial process. Yeast is one of the microorganisms (sometimes in a genetically modified form) that is often used in industry in order to produce a valuable organic chemical.

■ Aim
To investigate the changes in yeast population and substrate concentration in a plastic bottle fermenter.

■ Risk assessment

- 1% sodium chlorate(I) is irritant. Wear eye protection.
- Sterilise equipment and materials at the end, prior to disposal.
- Take care when using a hot cork borer to cut holes in a plastic bottle. A heatproof mat is needed on the bench. The hot cork borer should be insulated from your hand by a cloth to prevent burning. Hold the borer with the hot end uppermost in the Bunsen flame.

■ Method

Designing and constructing a simple fermenter
Figure 5.4 shows a suitable arrangement of the apparatus. Wash the plastic bottle and sterilise it with 1% sodium chlorate(I) solution or 10 minutes, then rinse with sterile water. Cut holes (into which rubber bungs must fit) in the bottle with a hot cork borer. These will allow the air-input and sampling ports to be assembled.

The plastic bottle should be no more than two-thirds filled with the culture medium. Use an aquarium diffuser to create

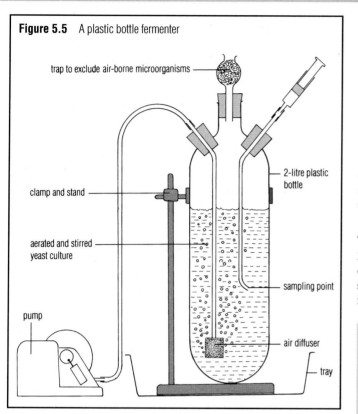

Figure 5.5 A plastic bottle fermenter

trap to exclude air-borne microorganisms

clamp and stand

aerated and stirred yeast culture

pump

2-litre plastic bottle

sampling point

air diffuser

tray

aerobic conditions. Clip the air flow so that it is not too fast, which creates a high froth. The air bubbles will also stir the medium (an alternative is to use a magnetic stirrer and follower). A cotton wool bung should be placed in the top of the bottle. Putting your hand over the air outlet will allow air pressure to force a sample up into the barrel of the syringe. Keep the sample tube closed when it is not in use (or it will function as a siphon).

A useful refinement is to stand the plastic bottle in a temperature-controlled water bath (an aquarium heater and thermostat are suitable for this).

Setting up a yeast culture
All glassware used in microbiological culture work must be clean and sterilised.

Prepare the culture medium by dissolving the following substances in a litre of sterilised (boiled and cooled) distilled water in a large vessel:

Glucose	20.0 g
NH_4Cl	2.7 g
KH_2PO_4	0.7 g
KCl	0.7 g
$MgSO_4$	1.2 g
Yeast extract ('Marmite')	2.0 g

Add 5 g of dried baker's yeast together with a magnetic follower. Cover the culture with clingfilm and allow it to mix, using a magnetic stirrer, for about an hour.

Checking that yeast cells are viable
You can detect dead cells in the culture by placing two drops of it on a microscope slide with a tiny drop of methylene blue, covering with a coverslip and observing under high-power magnification. The active yeast cells will decolorise the stain, but dead cells will be stained blue. Carry out repeated counts of groups of 20 cells, recording the proportion that are alive, to provide an accurate picture of the state of the culture.

Monitoring yeast growth
You can monitor the growth of the yeast population by colorimeter measurements of the change in optical absorbance of the suspension, or by direct counting of cells in a haemocytometer. To take these measurements, remove a sample of the yeast suspension (thoroughly mixed) at regular, timed intervals.

Using different substrates
Glucose is just one of the possible sugars to use as the substrate. With it, fermentation is fast. What happens to the rate of fermentation if sucrose or maltose is provided as the main substrate? An 'induction' step may take quite some time. Some species of yeast cannot ferment lactose at all.

Collecting data
The experiment may run for up to five days, when maintained at 25 °C. Collect samples twice daily, allowing data to be recorded on changing sugar concentration (using Clinistix or Diastrix strips), yeast cell growth (colorimeter or haemocytometer readings), viable cells (methylene blue count), and possibly pH.

NOTE TO TECHNICIAN

The student will need access to the following items:
- plastic bottle (two litre);
- 1% sodium chlorate(I) (hypochlorite) solution;
- sterile water (distilled water, boiled and cooled);
- cork borer and bungs;
- short lengths of glass tubing;
- aquarium aerator and diffuser;
- cotton wool;
- chemicals to make up medium, plus access to other carbohydrate sources;
- dried baker's yeast;
- microscope slide, coverslip and microscope;
- 0.1% methylene blue (redox indicator);
- colorimeter or haemocytometer;
- Clinistix or Diastix strips.

■ Data presentation
A table of data is required, showing the times of sampling and the data collected. Manipulate the data to aid interpretation (for example, work out the ratio of viable to non-viable cells as a percentage of the maximum count).

■ Conclusion
Comment on the length of any lag phase, and the lengths of other phases in the growth of the culture. Can the percentage viability of the yeast cells and the uptake of the sugar (disappearance of the substrate) be correlated?

■ Evaluation
Comment on the sources of error or inaccuracy that you can think of.

Can you relate this exercise to the issues that may arise in the management of an industrial biotechnological plant?

How could the apparatus be refined?

Reference
R Truman and R Gullis (1988) 'A software controlled fermenter incorporating a cheap immersible turbidity sensor', *School Science Review* **69**(248), pp. 514–18

5.8 An introduction to immobilised enzymes
(Investigation)

Enzymes are expensive to produce. In industrial production, immobilised enzymes (trapped on the surface of beads) can be used in a continuous reaction process. Thus, separation of end-products from the enzyme catalyst occurs largely automatically. The use of immobilised enzymes in an industrial application is therefore more efficient and economical than when 'free' enzymes are used in a batch process.

■ Aim
To produce and test an immobilised enzyme.

■ Risk assessment

Good laboratory practice is sufficient to take account of any hazards and avoid significant risks.

■ Method
First, make the immobilised enzyme pellets. There are three steps to this process.

1 Prepare a solution of sodium alginate by stirring 2 g of sodium alginate into 100 cm^3 of distilled water in a beaker held in a waterbath at 40 °C. The alginate becomes dispersed within about 10 minutes.
2 Next, produce an enzyme–alginate solution, by cooling the alginate solution to 35 °C and stirring 2 cm^3 of invertase solution 'concentrate' into 40 cm^3 of the alginate solution.
3 Now produce pellets by filling a syringe with the alginate/invertase solution and then allowing this liquid to drip into a beaker of calcium chloride solution (100 cm^3 of CaCl$_2$, 0.1 mol dm^{-3}). Jelly-like globules are formed, which can be harvested with a nylon/plastic sieve. Wash the beads with distilled water, whilst held in the sieve.

Test the pellets by suspending about 30 pellets in a nylon mesh bag in a sucrose solution (50 cm^3 of 5% sucrose w/v) in a conical flask, held in a waterbath at 40 °C, stirring the solution meanwhile. Test the solution for reducing sugar using Diastix, first on addition of the enzyme pellets and then at five-minute intervals until the result is constant. Record how long it took for complete hydrolysis of sucrose.

The pellets may be harvested, washed with distilled water, and tested on fresh sucrose solution. How many times can the alginate/invertase pellets be used in this way, effectively?

■ Data presentation
Record the times for the colour change of Diastix to the end-point by means of a table. Can you devise a way of presenting your results as a graph that emphasises the outcome of your experiment?

■ Conclusions
• How effective was the immobilised enzyme? How many times can it be used?
• Was there any way of recovering the enzyme and re-using it if it were not in pellet form?

■ Evaluation
A source of error in this experiment is lack of sensitivity and range of Diastix. Suggest ways of improving the assessment of the reducing sugar.

NOTE TO TECHNICIAN

The student group will require:
• 2 g sodium alginate;
• water baths at 35 and 40 °C;
• 2 cm^3 of invertase concentrate;
• plastic syringe;
• measuring cylinder;
• 100 cm^3 calcium chloride solution, 0.1 mol dm^{-3};
• nylon/plastic tea strainer;
• 300 cm^3 of a 5% sucrose solution;
• nylon mesh;
• stopclock;
• Diastix;
• beakers and stirring thermometer.

5.9 Commercially available rennins compared
(Investigation)

Rennin, an enzyme secreted in the stomachs of many very young mammals, catalyses the conversion of a soluble milk protein, caseinogen (also referred to as sodium caseinate), into casein, which is then precipitated in the presence of calcium ions as calcium caseinate (called curds). The result is that the milk solidifies, leaving a thin watery liquid (whey). In the stomach, this reaction is a prelude to protein digestion in animals where the bulk of the diet is milk.

Today, rennins are used in large quantities in the dairy industry, principally in cheese manufacture. Different forms of the enzyme are readily available, at relatively low cost. For example, rennin is available in a form of extract from calves' stomachs, sold as liquid 'rennet' or junket tablets in many grocery stores. It is also available as Maxiren, a calf rennin from genetically engineered yeast, and as Reninlase, a naturally occurring fungal protease. The latter two are available from NCBE (p. 434).

■ Aim
To investigate the activity of commercial rennins.

■ Risk assessment

• It is a rule that nothing introduced into or produced in the laboratory may be eaten or drunk.
• Wear eye protection and protective clothing if strong acid is used.
• Otherwise, good laboratory practice is sufficient to take account of any hazards and avoid significant risks.

■ Method
Assume you are a food technologist in the employ of a manufacturing firm. The issue on which your advice is sought is: 'Which rennet preparation is most effective, and under what conditions does it work best?'

Design and conduct experiments on which to base a critical comparison of the activity of rennin enzymes, so that you can respond factually.

As with all research scientists, you may seek some advice from the literature, as part of your planning process. A useful reference for you is J Gill and T Saunders (1987) 'Rennin – a neglected enzyme', *J. Biol. Ed.* **21**(4), pp. 248–50.

The practical effect of rennin on fresh milk is to change its viscosity. Some observers feel they can detect the moment it starts to set; others choose the point when it has set solid (and the curd does not fall from an inverted test tube).

Design experiments to compare setting times of milks (fresh milk or UHT?), treated by different rennins, possibly at different pH. What sort of acid (or alkalis?) could be introduced into milk for this purpose?

NOTE TO TECHNICIAN

Student groups might require (or require access to):
- two or three types of rennin, as listed above;
- 10 test tubes in a rack and a 10 cm^3 syringe for each type of rennin being used;
- access to pasteurised and UHT milk samples;
- 100 cm^3 fresh milk in a beaker for each type of rennin;
- water baths set at 25 and 35 °C;
- stopclocks;
- laboratory reference copy of Gill and Saunders (1987) (see above).

■ Data presentation
Draw up a table of data.

■ Conclusion
Write a succinct report, summarising your experimental approach, in order to justify your recommended source of rennin and setting conditions.

■ Evaluation
A possible source of error in this enquiry may be that you cannot be sure that the concentrations of enzyme being used are comparable. Is there anything that can be done about this (supposing you had a larger laboratory and appropriate technical assistance)?

5.10 Designing and testing a urease biosensor
(Investigation)

Urea [$CO(NH_2)_2$], an excretory product of many animals, is hydrolysed by the enzyme urease to carbon dioxide and ammonia. The release of ammonia from the reaction tends to raise the pH.

$$CO(NH_2)_2 + H_2O \xrightarrow{urease} CO_2 + 2NH_3$$

Urease is used in renal dialysis machines to eliminate urea from the dialysate. Immobilised urease is used, and the ammonium ions produced are removed by an activated carbon filter. A urease detector (exploiting the change of pH) can confirm the activity of the enzyme preparation. As a consequence of this biotechnological development, the design of these machines has been improved. Today, a dialysis machine can be both smaller and more mobile.

■ Aim
To make a biosensor sensitive to the activity level of a solution of urease.

■ Risk assessment

- Combining the use of a microcomputer in interfacing with an (electrical) pH meter requires that all 'wet operations' are kept entirely separate from the computer and its electrical power connections.
- Otherwise, good laboratory practice is sufficient to take account of any hazards and avoid significant risks.

■ Method
Work through the following steps.

1 A pH meter will require careful calibration checks before it is adapted as a component in a sensitive detector. Use a buffer solution of known pH to do this. Repeat the calibration step each time the apparatus is set up.

2 Construct your urease biosensor by wrapping a single layer of filter paper around the bulb of a pH probe (avoid contact between the bulb and fingers!). This will need retaining in situ by a plastic collar of sorts, made from flexible plastic tubing or plastic sheet/film, wound in place and secured lightly but firmly in position.

3 Clamp the probe, with the filter paper attached, so that the tip dips into a solution of urease (10% w/v). Leave it in this position for five minutes.

4 Then clamp the probe, lightly drained of the urease solution, in a urea solution of known concentration. As the urease reacts with the urea, ammonia is released, and the pH will rise. Follow the change in pH by the pH meter. After a fixed time (say 10–15 minutes), read and record the pH. Repeat the process with two other urea solutions of different, known concentrations. Between readings, wash the probe in distilled water. If there is time, recalibrate the probe for each urea concentration.

5 Then clamp the detector into a urea solution of unknown concentration. Once again, carry out the bioassay, and record the pH change.

6 If you have a pH probe that is interfaced with a computer, then carry out the experiment as described, but you will be capturing the data, and you will print out your results in the form of a graph.

NOTE TO TECHNICIAN

Student groups will require (or require access to):
- pH meter with probe;
- material to make a plastic collar that fits loosely over the pH probe bulb;
- filter paper;
- scissors;
- solutions (50 cm^3 each) of:
    10% w/v urease solution,
    urea solutions, 0.1, 0.5, 1.0 and 2.0 mol dm^{-3}
    a urea solution between 0.1 and 2.0 mol dm^{-3}, labelled 'X';
- computer monitoring equipment + data-handling software, if pH probe can be interfaced.

■ Data presentation
Tabulate your data. Plot a graph of pH change against urea concentration, and use the graph to calculate the concentration of the unknown urea solution.

■ **Conclusion**

Check the accuracy of your estimation of the concentration of the urea solution marked 'X'. If data capture has been employed, and the pH changes with time can be plotted, compare the speed of the reaction and the critical times for the readings at different urea concentrations.

■ **Evaluation**

What are the advantages in using a biosensor for measurements of urea for renal dialysis patients?

How could your biosensor be improved?

Projects

5.1 Effects of weed competition on crop plant growth

The case for herbicides (or for mechanical weeding) assumes that vigorously growing weeds compete successfully for essential resources for plant growth, and that the productivity of crop plants is thereby reduced. How productive is a seed tray of 'rapid cycling' *Brassica campestris*, and by how much is productivity reduced when the trays are seeded with one or more weed species? Are some weeds more harmful than others? A selection of 'wild' weed seeds will be required.

References

'Growing instructions for rapid-cycling *Brassica campestris* (fast plants)'. Teachers' Guide. SAPS (Science and Plants for Schools), Homerton College, Cambridge CB2 2PH

R J Chancellor (1966) *The Identification of Weed Seedlings of Farm and Garden*. Blackwell

5.2 Milk deterioration under different storage conditions

Milk deteriorates with age, even after pasteurisation, as a result of bacteria which are already present or which subsequently invade. Deterioration can be delayed by lowering temperature, and by heat treatment (as in UHT milk). Resazurin dye is a pH indicator and a redox dye (changing colour as it is reduced) that is used to indicate the level of bacterial contamination. Investigate the freshness of milk from various sources, subjected to different storage conditions and degrees of exposure to air.

5.3 Size of the bacterial community in soils

Bacteria that inhabit soil can be estimated by the dilution plate method (p. 69). How do the numbers of bacteria vary in different soils, and in different positions in a soil? Is there a distinctly well-populated zone in the soil around plant roots? What are the likely causes of uneven distribution of soil microorganisms?

5.4 Antibacterial and antifungal agents in natural plant species

Plant species can be tested for the ability to inhibit the growth of microorganisms on agar plates. Aqueous extracts of leaves can be placed in 'wells' cut in nutrient agar plates. The agar in the plate may be seeded with yeast or with a harmless saprotrophic bacterial culture and closed with tape. The growth of the microorganism colony on agar may be observed, and any inhibition of growth in the vicinity of natural plant products detected.

5.5 Cellulase activities of different soils

Certain microorganisms in soil have the ability to digest cellulose to sugars, using an enzyme (cellulase). The ability to produce cellulases is of great ecological (and potentially economic) significance. Agar plates containing the soluble form of cellulose (CMC agar) can be used to assay soil extracts for cellulase activity, and 'wells' cut in the agar can house different extracts. Zones around 'wells', shown up with Congo red dye, indicate the extent of cellulose breakdown. What soils are the best source of cellulase-producing organisms?

Reference

'Cellulase production', in *Practical Biotechnology – a Guide for Schools and Colleges*, p. 34–5. National Centre for Biotechnology Education, University of Reading, Whiteknights, Reading RG6 2AJ

Problems and assignments

5.1 Designing a desalination plant

Water covers three-quarters of the surface of the globe, but 99% of the world's water resources are in the oceans or locked in the polar ice caps. Our demand for fresh water is so great that we soon may need to reclaim water from the sea on a regular basis. Any form of distillation using fuel as the energy source is prohibitively expensive, but solar power can be tapped over areas of the Earth's surface at lower latitudes.

Design a still to obtain fresh-water from seawater, assuming you live in a climate which offers above-average exposure to sunlight. Explain your design by means of an annotated sketch.

What other product of the still would you be able to market, should your design be implemented and put into regular use?

5.2 Fertilisers in agriculture

The impressive increase in wheat grain yields in the UK since 1950 may be correlated with the application of synthetic chemical fertilisers in the same period. This point is made in the data in Table 5.1. Nevertheless, in recent years there has been a marked tendency for some farmers to switch to 'organic farming'. This is the name coined for a system that avoids or actually excludes the use of synthetic chemical compounds such as fertilisers, pesticides, growth regulators ('hormones') and livestock food additives. Instead there is a policy of relying on crop rotation, green manure, animal waste (farmyard manure), mechanical cultivation and, where possible, biological pest control. Organic farms are nearly as productive as conventional farms of comparable size. One study showed that organic farms require 60% less fossil fuel, and produce between 3 and 11% less than equivalent land farmed with fertilisers and pesticides. Not all organic farming performs as well as this, however.

1 Plot a graph showing the changing pattern of grain production and nitrogen fertiliser application within the UK between 1950 and 1979.
2 **a** In what chemical form is nitrogen most likely to be in nitrogen fertiliser?
   b What is the fate of the nitrogen in fertiliser, once it has been absorbed into plant roots?
   c Why does it apparently enhance plant growth so dramatically?
3 It is said that despite frequent applications of synthetic fertilisers, persistent cropping of fertilised land leads to a depletion of the soil's reserves of micronutrients and an increased tendency for loss of topsoil by erosion.
   a What is meant by micronutrients? Give three specific examples, and describe their roles in plant metabolism.
   b A crop rotation which includes green manure in the cycle can maintain and improve soil fertility. Suggest reasons for this.

4 The topsoil on farms that have been organically managed for many years is regularly found to have a higher enzyme content than equivalent soil of conventionally farmed land.
   a What is the most likely source of 'enzymes' in soils?
   b Give an example of a soil enzyme system of importance in the growth and development of flowering plant crops.
5 Organic crops are often cheaper to grow but have significantly lower yields than do crops grown with synthetic chemicals (fertilisers and pesticides). Suggest reasons for this.

5.3 Bovine somatotrophin

Cows secrete bovine somatotrophin hormone (BST) from the pituitary gland. This polypeptide hormone stimulates growth generally, and it specifically enhances milk production in lactating cows. It appears to work in this way by causing the diversion of feed nutrients to the mammary glands. A company involved in biotechnological developments, Monsanto, have via their Animal Sciences Division perfected a mechanism of genetically engineering the production of BST in microorganisms in a way that yields the hormone in quantities and in a form that can be effectively administered to cows. Experiments and trials indicate that supplementing the natural levels of BST by administering this hormone preparation as a subcutaneous or intramuscular injection on a regular basis results in the cows eating more and producing more milk. Moreover, the increase in production is proportionately more than the increase in food consumed. The efficiency of milk production is increased: the same amount of milk can be produced by fewer cows. Milk production rises within three days of the administration of the hormone, which is injected just after the peak of milk production occurs, and is maintained till the end of the lactation.

1 **a** What is involved in bringing a cow into 'lactation'? What does this term mean?
   b How is commercial milk production maintained during a lactation?
   c What is meant by 'genetic engineering'?
   d What are 'subcutaneous' and 'intramuscular' injections?
2 List the likely economic benefits to the farmer who opts to take part in a BST trial, and who has a large herd of milking cows and 'followers' (cows, heifers and calves kept as a separate herd, supporting the milking herd).
3 Make an annotated list of possible dangers for the cattle involved in such a trial.
4 What social and ethical issues are raised by this sort of development in agriculture? Make an annotated list of any advantages you can see, and the disadvantages you feel arise for our society, from this approach to animal husbandry and productivity.

5.4 Pesticides and pollution: a case study

The text in Panel 5.1 is an excerpt from a local newspaper published in North Yorkshire in 1994. Read the panel, and then answer the following questions.

Table 5.1 Wheat grain yields and application rates of nitrogen fertilisers in the UK, 1950–1979*

	1950–52	1953–55	1956–58	1959–61	1962–64	1965–67	1968–70	1971–73	1973–76	1977–79
grain/t ha^{-1}	2.7	3.1	3.2	3.6	4.2	4.1	3.9	4.3	4.4	5.3
fertiliser/kg N ha^{-1}	32	39	51	64	78	90	92	95	95	128

* The figures are three-year means.

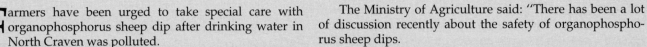

Panel 5.1 Water scare sparks safety plea over use of sheep dips

Farmers have been urged to take special care with organophosphorus sheep dip after drinking water in North Craven was polluted.

Residents in Selside reportedly became ill after their private borehole supply was contaminated with poisonous dip, which was more than 64 times over the legal limit.

One woman suffered nausea and vomiting and another began suffering from headaches.

The National Rivers Authority, Craven District Council's Environmental Health Department and the Health and Safety Executive investigated after a doctor alerted them to the danger.

Now the National Rivers Authority is deciding whether to take legal action against the farmer believed to be responsible for dumping the pesticide.

Sheep dip is used by farmers to kill parasites and scab and contains chemicals similar to nerve gas.

The controversial dips have been linked with illnesses such as paralysis, epilepsy, breathing problems, nausea, diarrhoea, dizziness and mental confusion.

Farmers must remember that after April 1 1995 everybody who buys OP sheep dip must have a certificate of competence or must satisfy the merchant selling the dip that they are the employer of, or acting on behalf of somebody who has a certificate.

The Ministry of Agriculture said: ''There has been a lot of discussion recently about the safety of organophosphorus sheep dips.

''Proper dipping plays an important part in the control of the disease. On the other hand some people think that OP dips should be banned altogether.

''But independent scientific advice is that their use can continue, as long as the people who buy them can show that they know what safety precautions to follow.

''So we are introducing a certificate of competence which will be the proof that you meet this requirement.

''This certificate will show that holders have passed a test of their knowledge of practical safety techniques.''

For more information write to MAFF, Government Buildings, Crosby Road, Northallerton, DL6 1AD.

Dr Mark Smith, Consultant in Public Health for North Yorkshire Health Authority said: ''Various sheep dip formulations are available and most contain OP pesticides. These may be absorbed into the body through the skin and lungs, as well as by drinking.

''Great care is needed in the handling and disposal of sheep dips as they can cause a range of ill effects in humans. In severe cases emergency hospital treatment is needed.'

From: **Craven Herald** *(18 November 1994)*

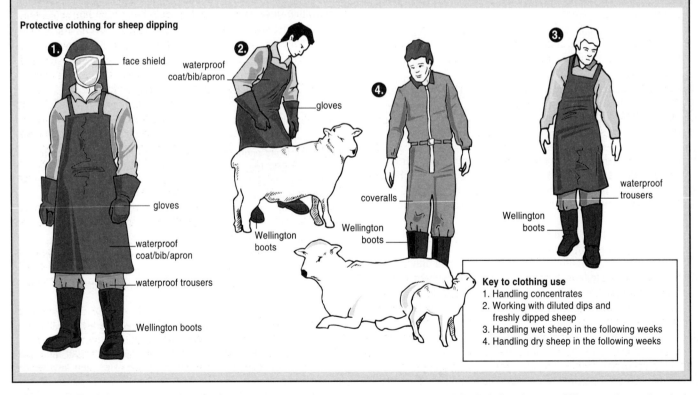

Protective clothing for sheep dipping

1.
- face shield
- gloves
- waterproof coat/bib/apron
- waterproof trousers
- Wellington boots

2.
- waterproof coat/bib/apron
- gloves
- Wellington boots

3.
- waterproof trousers
- Wellington boots

4.
- coveralls
- Wellington boots

Key to clothing use
1. Handling concentrates
2. Working with diluted dips and freshly dipped sheep
3. Handling wet sheep in the following weeks
4. Handling dry sheep in the following weeks

1 What is meant by groundwater? How does it accumulate, and in what way may it be tapped by human communities as a source of drinking water?

2 How might pesticide residues be dumped in such a way as to enter the groundwater?

3 Sheep dips contain organophosphorus compounds, which are known to block neurotransmitter metabolism (*Advanced Biology*, pp. 455–6) in the nervous system of a wide range of animals, and which are especially lethal to insects. Why are these chemicals used in sheep dips?

4 Why do human handlers of concentrated organophosphorus chemicals require so much protection for their safety?

5 How would a company manufacturing sheep dip have convinced itself and the MAFF authorities that harmful levels of pesticide residues do not persist at the time sheep are slaughtered for human consumption?

5.5 Biogas from waste: a design challenge

Biogas digesters are in service in both developed and less-developed countries. The anaerobic decay of organic matter such as paper and cardboard, waste food materials, straw and other farmyard waste and animal excreta, together with certain plastic and other organic rubbish from domestic and industrial waste bins, will ultimately yield copious 'biogas' consisting of methane (CH_4) and carbon dioxide. The organic matter must be kept moist and held at a temperature of 30–35 °C. Ubiquitous anaerobic saprotrophic bacteria convert the carbohydrates, lipids and proteins in waste to alcohols, organic and fatty acids, carbon dioxide and hydrogen gas. These products are converted to methane, carbon dioxide and water by specific methanogenic bacteria. So, rubbish deposited in underground tips, and waste placed in anaerobic digestion tanks, rapidly heats up and methane gas and carbon dioxide are produced. This mixture can be used as a domestic or commercial fuel.

Depending on the waste material used, another gaseous product is the poisonous and unpleasant-smelling gas hydrogen sulphide. This can be 'scrubbed out' if the gas produced from waste is bubbled through water (and the H_2S recovered as a by-product). Another safety issue that the biogas technologist has to face is that mixtures of 4–15% methane with air are explosive. Also, methane can escape through thin rubber tubing, but is contained by plastic vessels and plastic tubing, and by thick-walled rubber tube.

You are required to design a laboratory pilot plant to investigate the conversion of paper, cardboard, straw and leafy vegetable waste to 'biogas'. You should use as the fermenter a wide-necked plastic bottle or a two-litre plastic 'lemonade' bottle (with the waste finely cut up for feeding into the digester). The fermenter vessel will need to be held at about 30 °C. You could arrange for the temperature to be continuously checked, using a thermometer probe, and in this case you could investigate the correlation between temperature of waste and gas production. Methane is insoluble in water, so it can be collected by downward displacement of water in inverted containers. Use plastic tubing in your system, and design a 'scrubber' stage to remove hydrogen sulphide. Give special thought to the safety features you would build in, and the safety instructions you would have to issue to the team who would be testing your pilot plant.

Finally, find out from your local authority whether there is an old waste tip in your neighbourhood. Enquire about the steps taken to vent the 'biogas'.

5.6 Scale-up in biotechnology

A biologist may invent, or discover in the laboratory, a technology that has important industrial applications. In order to achieve an appropriate level of mass production and commercial success, the process will require 'scaling up'. Success in this is not automatic! Apart from unexpected economic changes, such as a change in the costs or supply of a raw material or energy, there may be practical and technical problems in taking the process from laboratory bench to bulk fermenter. The issues require forethought.

Imagine that you are working in the field of genetic engineering of yeast. You are seeking to produce a strain able to produce an expensive and short-lived biochemical substance of great value in drug manufacture. You are 'engineering' a yeast strain that, with an adequate supply of quite simple raw materials, can produce (and leach into the medium) the valuable biochemical in good quantities. From here, the extraction and isolation of the pure substance would be perfected.

There are three major steps to the establishment of this process as a biotechnological industry. These are:
- laboratory bench screening for a strain of yeast with the necessary activated gene(s);
- pilot plant investigation of the performance of the yeast strain under continuous culture or batch culture conditions;
- transfer of the process to full-sized plant and continuous production.

What will be the chief issues you would have to grapple with? List the problems and challenges you believe you will need to tackle in each of these three stages.

You can find some discussion of the process in the following sources:

A T Jackson (1985) 'Some problems in industrial scale-up', *J. Biol. Ed.* **19**(1), pp. 48–52

A Wiseman (ed.) (1983) *Principles of Biotechnology*. Surrey University Press

5.7 Testing for enzymes in 'biological' washing powder

Biological detergents are said to contain proteases and carbohydrases, but do they also contain lipases?

Enzymes are present because they are readily available to the soap powder manufacturer, and are efficient at removing certain forms of 'dirt' in clothes. There is demand for detergents that work at low temperatures (because of the fabrics and possibly the colours in use), and there is demand for low-phosphate detergents (for environmental reasons). For both of these reasons enzymes are commonly used. The enzymes chosen include some with optimum temperatures of only 10 °C or so, but other powders are frequently used at 60 °C.

Given a biological washing powder, plan a programme of tests that might establish the presence of enzymes. Plan investigations to determine the specific types of enzymes present, and their optimum temperatures. Use your knowledge of enzymes and of food tests.

The issues to settle at the outset are, firstly, what types of enzyme might be present and, secondly, how you could test for the presence of such an enzyme as one component in a washing powder.

Is it possible to test for the presence of a protein in dissolved powder or diluted liquid detergent? How could you determine the sensitivity of chemical tests for proteins?

If you suspect a protease is present, you might test for digestion of cubes of hard-boiled egg-white. What controls would you plan? If there is a protease present, how could you determine its optimum temperature?

If there is an amylase present, you might test for digestion of a starch suspension. What controls would you plan? If there is an amylase present, how would you determine its optimum temperature?

If there is a lipase present, you might test for the removal of a wax or solid fat stain (perhaps coloured with Sudan III dye) in a fabric sample.

Finally, how does the performance of the 'biological' washing powder, used at its optimum temperature, compare with the performance of a comparable 'non-biological' powder?

Present the outcome of your planning as a flow diagram of tests, showing the best sequence of experiments by which to come to definitive answers.

5.8 Quick test

1 Distinguish between the following pairs:

    a surface water and groundwater;
    b inoculation and sterilisation of a bacterial culture;
    c eutrophication and Biological Oxygen Demand (BOD);
    d activated sludge and anaerobic digestion;
    e pelagic and demersal fish;
    f cereal crops and root crops;
    g mechanisation and factory farming;
    h food preservation and food storage;
    i antioxidants and emulsifiers;
    j biotechnology and biochemistry;
    k open and closed fermentation systems;
    l lactic acid and casein;
    m *Penicillium* and penicillin;
    n mycoprotein and microorganisms;
    o extracellular and intracellular enzymes.

2 What do you understand by the following:

    a water cycle;
    b fish farming;
    c selective breeding;
    d preservation of food by chemicals;
    e immobilised enzyme?

5.9 Essay assignment

Select one of the following:

- Outline the role of microorganisms in the following industrial processes:
  a sewage treatment;
  b yoghurt manufacture;
  c antibiotic production;
  d single-cell protein formation.

or:

- Give an illustrated account of the industrial applications of enzymes. What is meant by an 'immobilised' enzyme?

Cell Biology

6 The chemistry of living things

Summary

Water makes up the bulk of all living things, and most of the other substances present in cells are compounds of carbon combined with hydrogen and oxygen. The results of chemical analysis of organisms reflect this, for the elements hydrogen and oxygen predominate. In fact, about 99% of the substance of cells is made of the four elements **hydrogen**, **oxygen**, **carbon** and **nitrogen**.

Water is a stable molecule; that is, it is relatively unreactive. It is also a **polar molecule** (it carries an unequal distribution of electrical charge), and so it forms **hydrogen bonds** with other water molecules, with many dissolved substances and with charged surfaces in contact with water. This confers some very unusual properties on water. Indeed, both the water molecule and the element carbon have unique properties that are vitally important to life. For example, the almost **unlimited diversity of carbon compounds** is largely due to **carbon's ability to bond with itself** to form a huge range of straight, branched and ring-shaped molecules. This diversity of carbon compounds is a key factor in accounting for the diversity of living things.

Many members of the **four major groups of carbon-containing compounds** that make up cells – the carbohydrates, lipids, proteins and nucleic acids – have **very large molecules**. They are known as macromolecules, being made of simpler molecules, repeating units (**monomers**), that combine together by removal of water to make giant molecules (**polymers**). Knowledge of the outline chemistry of these substances is essential to understanding the structure and functioning of all living things.

Carbohydrates are made of the elements carbon, hydrogen and oxygen, and have the general formula $C_x(H_2O)_y$. The building blocks of the larger carbohydrates are sugars known as monosaccharides.

Lipids also contain carbon, hydrogen and oxygen only, but here the proportion of oxygen is much lower than in carbohydrates. Lipids are a very diverse group of cell chemicals. They are not polymers.

Proteins always contain the element nitrogen, in addition to carbon, hydrogen and oxygen. Sulphur is sometimes present, too. The building blocks of proteins are amino acids, and the condensation reaction between amino acids to form peptides and proteins produces a peptide bond.

Other important chemicals of cells are the **nucleic acids** (DNA and RNA). The building blocks of these, the nucleotides, are also the molecules from which ATP is constructed (the cell's energy currency) and several important coenzymes essential to metabolism.

Practicals and activities

6.1 Testing for reducing sugars

(Skills and techniques)

There is no simple test that will detect the presence of all sugars, but many will reduce an alkaline solution of copper(II) sulphate to a brick-red precipitate of copper(I) oxide. When these sugars are heated for a few minutes at the temperature of boiling water with Benedict's solution, the precipitate gradually forms and a range of colours is produced. The colour changes can be used qualitatively to show that reducing sugars are present, and semi-quantitatively to indicate the concentration of a reducing sugar solution. Sugars that do not have this reducing property are called non-reducing sugars and cannot be directly detected with Benedict's solution.

■ Aim

To discover how reducing sugars can be detected using Benedict's solution, how this can be made semi-quantitative and how the test can be extended to register the presence of non-reducing sugars as well.

■ Risk assessment

- Eye protection is essential when heating water and solutions.

- Avoid contact of chemicals with the skin, and wear a laboratory coat.
- Take care with the Bunsen flame (use the blue flame when heating, and the yellow/orange flame at other times).
- Otherwise good laboratory practice is sufficient to take account of any hazards and avoid significant risks.

■ Method

Testing for reducing sugars

First, make yourself familiar with the colours obtained from the reaction with Benedict's solution and reducing sugar, by carrying out a test with glucose.

1 Heat a water bath (large beaker) of water to about 75°C. Since this takes some time, set it up before you begin preparing for testing.
2 Dissolve a small spatula-load of glucose (which is a reducing sugar) in approximately 2 cm³ water and add a roughly equal volume of Benedict's solution. Mix thoroughly; then put the test tube in the water bath and maintain it there for three to four minutes. More consistent results are obtained if the test tube is gently agitated during heating.
3 Carefully observe and make a note of the sequence of colour changes. The final colour in the sequence is brick-red.

Making the test semi-quantitative

The colour sequence could be obtained from sugar solutions of increasing concentration. It is therefore possible to use the test to give an approximate indication of the concentration of

Figure 6.1 Using the Benedict's test semi-quantitatively

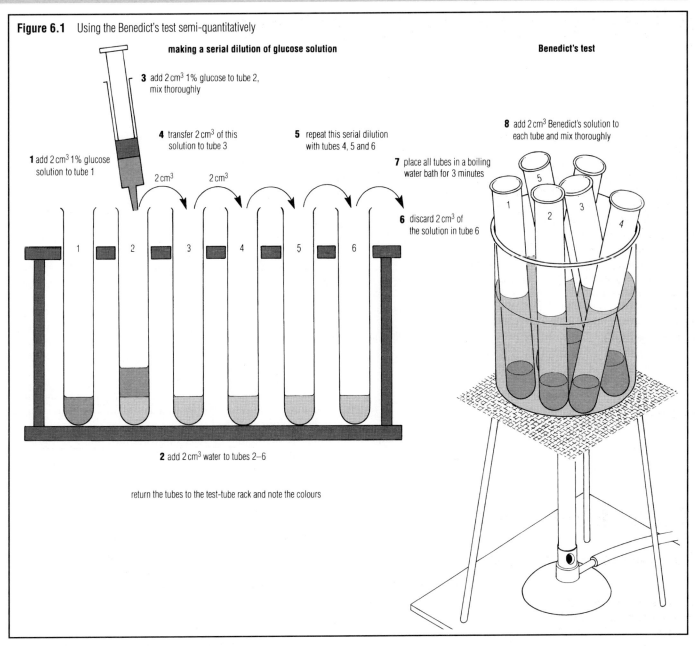

making a serial dilution of glucose solution

Benedict's test

3 add 2 cm³ 1% glucose to tube 2, mix thoroughly

4 transfer 2 cm³ of this solution to tube 3

5 repeat this serial dilution with tubes 4, 5 and 6

8 add 2 cm³ Benedict's solution to each tube and mix thoroughly

1 add 2 cm³ 1% glucose solution to tube 1

2 cm³   2 cm³

7 place all tubes in a boiling water bath for 3 minutes

6 discard 2 cm³ of the solution in tube 6

2 add 2 cm³ water to tubes 2–6

return the tubes to the test-tube rack and note the colours

---

a reducing sugar in solution (Figure 6.1). To discover the relationship between colour and concentration, accurate quantities need to be used.

1 Set up a serial dilution starting with a 1% glucose solution. To do this, label six test tubes, 1–6, with a marker pen, and place 2 cm³ 1% glucose solution in the first tube and 2 cm³ distilled water in each of the other five. Now add 2 cm³ 1% glucose solution to tube 2 and mix thoroughly before transferring 2 cm³ of this solution to tube 3. Work along the tubes, each time mixing the contents thoroughly before transferring 2 cm³ to the next tube, until you reach tube 6. Mix the contents of tube 6 and then discard 2 cm³. Add 2 cm³ Benedict's solution to each tube and again mix thoroughly.

2 Place all the tubes in a boiling water bath and leave them for a standard time (at least three minutes).

3 Remove and arrange the tubes in order, recording the colour against the concentration.

Testing for non-reducing sugars

Although all monosaccharides are reducing, some disaccharides are not (*Advanced Biology*, p. 128). When these non-reducing sugars are hydrolysed into their monosaccharide components, the aldehyde or ketone groups are exposed and will produce a precipitate with Benedict's solution. Hydrolysis can be achieved using either mineral acids or enzymes.

1 Dissolve a small spatula-load of sucrose in half a test tube of distilled water, and split the solution equally between two test tubes labelled A and B. To A add approximately 1 cm³ 0.1 mol dm⁻³ hydrochloric acid, but to B add the same volume of distilled water. Heat both tubes in the boiling water bath for one minute.

2 Remove both tubes and cool them under a tap to approximately room temperature. To tube A add a small amount of sodium hydrogencarbonate powder. (**Safety note:** the effervescence that follows can be vigorous if the tube is not thoroughly cooled or if too much hydrogencarbonate is added.) Keep adding small quantities of the powder until the addi-

tion of more does not result in effervescence. This indicates that the acid has been neutralised and the alkaline conditions necessary for the Benedict's test now prevail.

3 Add an equal quantity of Benedict's solution to each tube and heat for the standard time in the water bath. Remove the tubes and compare the final colours obtained.

NOTE TO TECHNICIAN

Each group requires:
- safety goggles;
- large beaker to act as a water bath (500 cm^3 or larger);
- six test tubes, test-tube rack and spatula;
- two syringes or graduated pipettes for measuring 2 cm^3;
- marker pen (permanent);
- 20 cm^3 Benedict's solution and distilled water;
- solid glucose;
- a few cm^3 1% (w/v) glucose solution;
- solid sucrose (this must be pure, if in doubt test with Benedict's to ensure that no glucose is present), 0.1 mol dm^{-3} HCl and solid NaHCO$_3$;
- test-tube holder, rubber bands (useful for holding tubes together in water bath).

■ Data presentation
- Set out precisely how Benedict's solution can be used to test for both reducing sugars and non-reducing sugars.
- Present the sequence of colour changes you might expect when this test reveals the presence of reducing sugars.
- Stipulate the conditions under which the test can be made semi-quantitative for glucose, including the significance of the colours obtained.

■ Conclusions
- You should be able to say how to detect whether a solution contains a sugar (either a reducing or a non-reducing sugar).
- You should be able to suggest the likely concentration that can be indicated by a particular colour from the reaction with Benedict's solution and, by calculation, indicate the molarity of a weak glucose solution that can just be detected by Benedict's solution, thus estimating the sensitivity of the test.

■ Evaluation
- Determination of a reducing sugar with Benedict's solution is considered at best semi-quantitative. Why does this test give only an approximate estimate of concentration?
- Why would it be unsafe to assume that you are in a position to state the concentration of reducing sugars other than glucose from this experiment?

■ Extension

1 Investigate the reducing properties of other sugars, using Benedict's solution. Test a range of sugars (perhaps fructose, lactose and maltose) to find out what reducing properties they have. What should be done to ensure a fair comparison of their reducing powers?

2 You are given samples of three solutions containing respectively a reducing sugar only, a non-reducing sugar only, and both a reducing and a non-reducing sugar, and a fourth liquid which is just water. Devise a method of identifying each liquid.

6.2 Detecting starch using I$_2$/KI
(Skills and techniques)

Although iodine is only sparingly soluble in water, it will dissolve readily in potassium iodide solution. The resulting solution (sometimes written I$_2$/KI for short) will react with starch to give a characteristic blue–black colour. It can be used to stain starch grains extracted from cells or starch grains within cells, enabling microscopic examination of the distribution of starch within plant tissues.

■ Aim
To investigate the nature of starch and the sensitivity of the starch test, and to compare starch grains from different plant extracts.

■ Risk assessment

Good laboratory practice is sufficient to take account of any hazards and avoid significant risks.

■ Method

The nature of starch

1 Place a little dry starch powder in a test tube and then add a drop of I$_2$/KI solution. Record the characteristic starch/iodine colour obtained.

2 Put a small amount of starch powder into half a test tube of water and mix well. Observe and record its solubility.

3 Divide the mixture into two portions and to one (A) add a few drops of I$_2$/KI solution. Allow it to stand in a test-tube rack for a few minutes and then observe the distribution of starch/iodine colour in the tube.

4 Transfer the contents of the other tube (B) into a boiling tube and heat it carefully in a Bunsen flame until it boils. Observe the change that takes place as the liquid nears boiling. Transfer it back to its original tube, cool it down and add I$_2$/KI solution. Make a note of any difference from tube A.

The sensitivity of the test for starch
Devise an experiment to test the sensitivity of the starch/iodine reaction. (See Practical 6.1 for an example.)

The microscopic appearance of starch grains
Many plants produce grains of starch as a storage product within their cells. Certain plants have been brought into cultivation because humans can make use of their starch food stores. Grains from different species often show different and recognisable characteristics.

1 Various examples of starch extracted from plants are available. Where samples are the plant material itself, extract the starch grains by scratching the surface of the food store with a scalpel and touching the scrapings on to a slide. Where powders are provided, place the smallest possible pinch directly on the slide. In either case, add a drop of water and carefully lower a coverslip into place.

2 Add a drop of I$_2$/KI solution at the edge of the coverslip, and draw it through using filter paper (Figure 6.2). This technique is called irrigation, and you may well have used it in your study of cells.

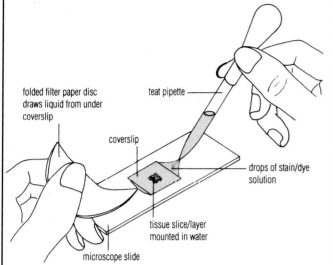

Figure 6.2 Irrigation technique in microscopy: stains or reagents are applied to the edge of the coverslip and a piece of filter paper used to draw liquid under the glass

folded filter paper disc draws liquid from under coverslip

teat pipette

coverslip

drops of stain/dye solution

tissue slice/layer mounted in water

microscope slide

3 If you apply the irrigation technique partially, so that the iodine does not penetrate completely across the coverslip, the grains of starch will show a range of staining, from black to unstained. The grains in the middle will look pale blue, and these are probably the best ones to study.

4 Make up a set of slides and examine them in turn. Observe and record the differences between starch grains of different origin. Your observations might include the relative sizes and shapes of the grains, which you can record by annotated drawings or tables of comparison. Other differences may also be apparent, such as whether the centre of growth is typically central (giving a symmetrical grain that looks circular) or off-centre, giving an elliptical grain. Cracks may radiate from the centre of the grain, and concentric growth rings may be visible.

NOTE TO TECHNICIAN

Each group requires:
- safety goggles;
- Bunsen burner;
- seven test tubes, test-tube rack and spatula;
- boiling tube, test-tube holder and marker pen (permanent);
- small beaker (100 cm^3) and source of distilled water;
- syringes or graduated pipettes (1 cm^3 and 10 cm^3);
- I$_2$/KI solution in dropping bottle;
- 1% (w/v) solution soluble starch (a few cm^3);
- microscope, slides, coverslips and filter paper;
- scalpel;
- samples of starch grains (for instance, wheat flour, cornflour, ground rice, semolina, tapioca or potato).

■ Data presentation
- What differences can you observe between (a) a mixture of starch powder in cold water, and (b) starch that has been heated in water to boiling point?
- Approximately what is the minimum concentration of starch (expressed in ppm) that can be detected using the standard I$_2$/KI solution?

- Your drawings of starch grains (which could be annotated) should show the ways in which starch grains from one source may be distinguished from those of another.

■ Conclusions
- Can I$_2$/KI solution be used to detect starch as a solid, a suspension or a solution?
- What changes take place in the solubility of starch as it is heated in water towards boiling point?

■ Evaluation
- What characteristics of a so-called 'starch solution' suggest that the starch has not formed a strictly true solution?
- Do you think it possible to identify a sample of starch from an unknown source?

■ Extension
What foods contain significant quantities of starch? If you were to test a range of common foods for the presence of starch, you would need to decide for each case the most appropriate way to test the material, bearing in mind whether it is a solid or liquid. What would you look for to enable you to decide if starch was present?

6.3 Testing for the presence of fat and oil
(Skills and techniques)

Lipids are characterised by their insolubility in water. To obtain even a dilute solution of a lipid, organic solvents must be used. Diluting the solution with water results in the formation of fine droplets of the lipid, which stay suspended as an **emulsion**, giving a cloudy appearance to the previously clear liquid. This is the basis of the emulsion test for fats and oils. Lipids exist as emulsions in butter and milk, but there is a fundamental difference between the emulsions in these two substances.

■ Aim
To observe the use of the emulsion test for fats and oils, and to explore the nature of the emulsions in butter and milk.

■ Risk assessment

- Wear eye protection. Avoid skin contact with chemicals, particularly dyes.
- Wear a laboratory coat to protect clothing.
- Take great care when using electrical equipment, like bench lamps and microscopes, when water is being used.
- Take care when using ethanol as it is highly flammable.
- Otherwise, good laboratory practice is sufficient to take account of any hazards and avoid significant risks.

■ Method
Testing for lipids in food substances

1 Label two test tubes A and B. To A add a small drop of olive oil and then about 5 cm^3 ethanol. Shake to dissolve as much oil as possible and leave to settle. Add about 5 cm^3 ethanol to tube B, which is the control. After a few minutes, decant off the top 2 cm^3 of the ethanol from both tubes into fresh test tubes containing 2 cm^3 cold water. Label these **a**

and **b**. Compare tube **a** with tube **b** by holding the two tubes side by side against a matt black background, and record the difference in opacity between the tubes. Keep the tubes as standards for comparison throughout the rest of the investigation.

2 Test the samples of food substances supplied for the presence of fats (or oils). Make a list of the substances and label a set of tubes with code letters to indicate the substance to be placed in each tube. Use only small quantities of food; grind up those that need it with a pestle and mortar, so as to ensure that each sample has a large surface area. Carry out the individual tests as above, allowing enough time for any undissolved matter to settle before you decant off the ethanol into cold water. Compare the results with the standards you have already created. Record the observations carefully, using a scale of opacity values 0, 1, 2, 3 or 4.

The emulsions present in milk and butter

Despite the hydrophobic character of lipids, in quite a few biological systems they exist together with water, often in the form of emulsions. In an emulsion, droplets of one liquid are suspended in another. The liquid supporting the droplets is called the **continuous phase**, while the liquid in droplet form is known as the **disperse phase**. Milk and butter are both complex emulsions, but they are very different in nature. Investigate what constitutes the continuous and disperse phases in these two emulsions.

1 Make a thin transparent smear of butter on a microscope slide using a mounted needle, and press a coverslip on top. Examine it under low power and then under high power. Prepare a slide of a drop of milk and examine it in the same way. Record your observations carefully.

2 Use the tip of a spatula to add tiny amounts of solid methylene blue dye to a little oil (1 cm³) in the bottom of a test tube. Add half a test tube of water and allow it to stand for five minutes. Repeat using Sudan III instead of methylene blue. Record the strength of colour in the two liquid layers and draw inferences on the preferential solubilities of both dyes in lipid and in water.

3 Use the information you have now gained about the dyes to learn more about the nature of the milk and butter emulsions. Mix small but equal quantities of the two solid dyes together. Then halve your mixture, adding one half to a

sample of milk and the other half to a little butter. Record the colours obtained and the appearance of the mixtures under the microscope. Account for the outcome by considering the nature of the water/lipid emulsions.

■ Data presentation and conclusions

• Tabulate the food substances tested, the observations made and the inferences that may be made about their content of fat or oil.
• Report the microscopic observations you were able to make on milk and butter.
• Describe and explain the distribution of dyes in the oil/water mixture.
• Decide which foods contain significant levels of fat or oil. (This may have been already presented in your table of food substances.)
• The microscopic appearance of milk and butter should enable you to deduce how they are composed.
• Decide the degree of solubility of both methylene blue and Sudan III in lipid and in water.
• Bearing in mind the overall colours of milk and butter mixed with a 50:50 dye mixture, make deductions about the continuous and disperse phase in each case.

■ Evaluation

Under certain circumstances it would be difficult to use this test, because the nature of the material being tested would interfere with the test itself. Suggest some of the problems that might be encountered in testing food substances.

■ Extension

Many seeds store fats and oils which, when respired, release a greater amount of energy per unit mass than carbohydrates do. Would you expect a correlation between the storage of lipid in a seed and its method of dispersal?

6.4 The biuret test

(Skills and techniques)

Copper salts in alkaline solution will form coloured complexes with adjacent pairs of —CONH— groups, which occur as the **peptide links** in proteins. This is known as the biuret test since the substance biuret, which also contains —CONH— groups, will give a colour with the test. Similar reactions also occur with —CSNH₂, —CNHNH₂— and —CH₂NH₂—, which may be part of compounds that are not proteins. Although a positive reaction does not show conclusively that a protein is present, in many circumstances this is the most probable explanation. The biuret test may be used as an indicator of the likely presence of a protein.

■ Aim

To test for protein by means of the biuret test.

■ Risk assessment

• The sodium hydroxide used is corrosive; it must be handled with care and caution. Eye protection must be worn.
• Otherwise, good laboratory practice is sufficient to take account of any hazards and avoid significant risks.

NOTE TO TECHNICIAN

Each group requires:
• six test tubes and rack;
• marker pen (permanent);
• microscope and bench lamp;
• four slides and coverslips;
• mounted needle and spatula;
• small quantities of methylene blue and Sudan III dyes;
• three watch glasses and dropping pipette;
• 5 cm³ milk and 2–3 g butter;
• olive oil and ethanol (50 cm³ of each);
• collection of food substances such as butter, margarine, biscuits, bread, nuts, cheese, egg-white;
• matt black paper (about 10 × 10 cm);
• access to hot water and detergent for washing test tubes during the practical.

■ Method

To save time, you need not measure the quantities referred to in this investigation accurately; judge them by eye as accurately as you can.

1 To each of five test tubes, labelled A–E, add about 2 cm³ of the solution to be tested. Then add about 2 cm³ of 10% sodium hydroxide to each sample and mix well by gentle agitation.

2 Add 0.5% copper(II) sulphate solution, drop by drop, shaking the tubes well between each addition. Continue until a definite colour can be seen.

　The colour will be the faint blue of copper(II) sulphate, if no soluble protein is present. The colour will be pink, lilac or pale violet if a protein is present.

■ Data presentation and conclusion

Present the data obtained as a table recording the colour produced and the inferences made.

NOTE TO TECHNICIAN

Each student group will require:
- test-tube rack with four test tubes;
- biuret reagents: (1) 10% sodium hydroxide solution, (2) 0.5% copper(II) sulphate solution, both supplied in dropping bottles with teat pipettes;
- access to the 'unknown' solutions, appropriately labelled, see p. 433.

■ Evaluation

What outcome would you anticipate if this test were applied to (a) fresh milk and (b) dilute apple juice?

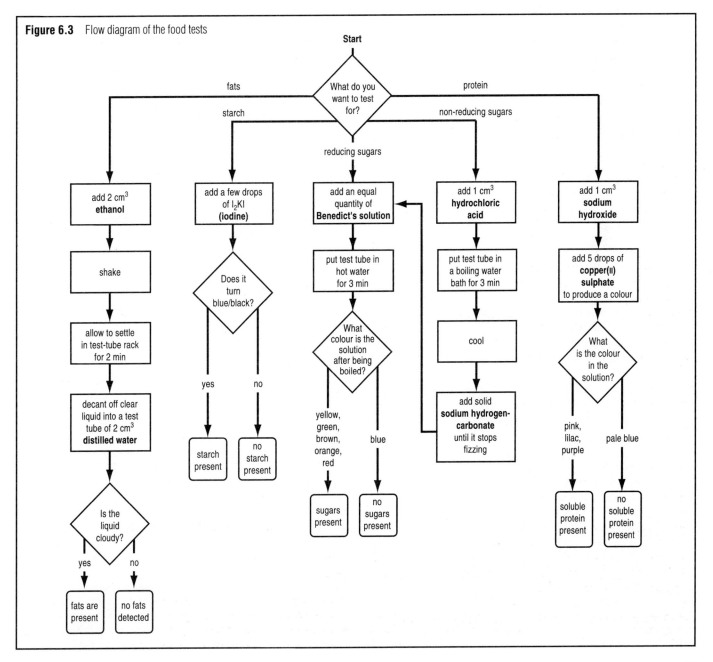

Figure 6.3　Flow diagram of the food tests

6.5 Water as a polar molecule

(Demonstration)

A molecule of water is formed when two hydrogen atoms combine with an oxygen atom. Its shape is triangular rather than linear. Overall the molecule is electrically neutral, but there is a small net negative charge on the oxygen atom and a net positive charge on both the hydrogen atoms. A molecule like water, which carries an unequal distribution of electrical charge, is called a **polar molecule**. This structural feature results in some unusual properties.

■ Aim

To demonstrate that water is a polar molecule.

■ Risk assessment

- If naphtha is used, the demonstration should be carried out in a fume cupboard by the teacher.
- Otherwise, good laboratory practice is sufficient to take account of any hazards and avoid significant risks.

■ Method

1 When a burette is filled with distilled water and the tap opened, a fine jet of water flows, and the water can be collected in a beaker. If a charged rod (static electricity) is held beside the jet, the water column is seen to be deflected. The effects of rods charged to varying extents can be demonstrated. (Remember, when a polythene rod is rubbed with a dry cloth the polythene attracts electrons and becomes negatively charged. In contrast, in similar circumstances Perspex becomes positively charged.)

2 Set up another burette containing a non-polar liquid of approximately the same viscosity (for example, paraffin heating oil), and attempt to repeat the demonstration.

NOTE TO TECHNICIAN

The demonstrator requires:
- two burettes (50 cm³ capacity);
- two 100 cm³ beakers (as reservoirs);
- polythene and Perspex rods and a dry cloth;
- access to tap water;
- 50 cm³ paraffin (heating oil), or naphtha.

■ Data presentation

A photograph or annotated sketch of the effects observed would be an appropriate record.

■ Conclusion

Can the observed phenomenon be explained in ways other than an attraction (or repulsion) between a polar molecule and an electrostatic field?

■ Evaluation

Can you list the important properties of water which can be attributed to its polar nature?

6.6 Properties of buffers

(Demonstration)

A buffer solution resists pH change when a small amount of acid or alkali is added. Biological systems depend upon buffer action to preserve a constant pH. For example, human blood maintains a pH of 7.35–7.45, even though the concentration of carbon dioxide (and therefore of carbonic acid) in blood varies greatly. Proteins form a very important component of the buffering capacity of the body. (The others are phosphate and hydrogencarbonate ions.) Proteins are buffers because the amino acid monomers from which they are formed contain ionisable groups that act as weak acids (—COOH) and weak bases (—NH$_2$). The amino acid is said to be amphoteric in this respect (*Advanced Biology*, p. 134).

■ Aim

To demonstrate the buffering capacity of an amino acid.

■ Risk assessment

- Take great care in working with strong alkalis and with strong acids (wear eye protection and protective clothing).
- Otherwise, good laboratory practice is sufficient to take account of any hazards and avoid significant risks.

■ Method

1 Using a sample of standard buffer at about pH 4, standardise the pH meter.

2 Dissolve about 0.10 g of alanine and make up to 100 cm³ with distilled water in a volumetric flask. Transfer to a beaker, and record the pH.

3 Add 10 cm³ of 0.1 mol dm^{-3} nitric acid, and record the pH again.

4 Titrate this solution against 0.1 mol dm^{-3} sodium hydroxide (strong base) with constant stirring (a magnetic flea and stirrer are useful), recording the burette readings and the pH at frequent intervals throughout the titration. It is suggested that you add 1 cm³ at a time until 8 cm³, 0.5 cm³ from 8 to 12 cm³, and 1 cm³ from 11 cm³ up to 28 cm³.

5 Plot a graph of pH against volume of base.

6 Then carry out a second titration. Add 10 cm³ of 0.1 mol dm^{-3} nitric acid to 100 cm³ distilled water in a beaker, and record the pH.

NOTE TO TECHNICIAN

Each group will require (or require access to):
- burette, 50 cm³ capacity, with burette stand;
- magnetic stirrer and flea;
- two 100 cm³ volumetric flasks;
- two 250 cm³ beakers,
- standard pH buffer solution at about pH 4.0;
- 0.1 g alanine, accurately weighed;
- 60 cm³ of 0.1 mol dm^{-3} sodium hydroxide solution;
- 25 cm³ of 0.1 mol dm^{-3} nitric acid;
- 10 cm³ bulb pipette and filler;
- pH meter with electrode probe.

---

7 Titrate this solution against 0.1 mol dm^{-3} sodium hydroxide (strong alkali) with constant stirring, recording the burette readings and the pH at frequent intervals throughout the titration up to 28 cm^3, as for the alanine/acid titration.

8 Plot your data on the same graph as the alanine titration, and note the extent to which the pH differs in the two titrations.

■ Data presentation

On your graph (pH on the y-axis, and volume of base added on the x-axis), make clear distinction between the curves for the alanine titration and for the nitric acid titration.

■ Conclusions

• Over what range does the amino acid solution show buffering capacity, and resist a pH change?
• What form is the amino acid in (a) at a low pH (pH 1–2), (b) at a high pH (pH 11)?
• At one point on your graph, the amino acid has no buffering capacity. What form is the amino acid in then?

■ Evaluation

Since carboxyl and amino groups of amino acids form peptide bonds in proteins, how is it that proteins are found to be efficient buffers?

Projects

6.1 Reducing and non-reducing sugars in ripening fruit

How do the quantities of reducing and non-reducing sugars change in the flesh of apple fruits as they ripen? The colour of apple pips is said to be an indicator of sweetness. Can you test this idea?

6.2 The distribution of a starch store in plants

The stems of bindweed (*Convolvulus* sp.) serve different functions above and below ground level. Investigate the distribution of starch in the stem of this plant. Suggest what advantages accrue to the plant from the location of its starch stores.

6.3 Seed dispersal and stored food

Many seeds, but not all, store fats and oils. One advantage of such lipid stores is that they release a greater amount of energy per unit mass, compared with carbohydrate stores. Where the mass of a seed may be a critical factor in dispersal, you might expect that the chief storage product would be lipid. Does such a correlation exist?

6.4 Change in amino acid content in plants and animal tissues

Individual amino acids may be isolated from extracts of plant or animal tissues by chromatographic techniques (pp. 113–14, 142–3 and 148). Amino acid spots on chromatograms can be identified by running known amino acids under identical conditions. The meristematic regions of plant stems are normally rich sources of amino acids. How do they change with time, or when the meristem is ready to switch from vegetative to reproductive development? How does the amino acid content of meat (muscle) from a butcher's shop vary between 'white' meats, such as chicken or pork, and 'red' meat such as beef?

Problems and assignments

6.1 Moles, in theory and practice

The mole is the scientific unit for the amount of a substance. It is introduced in *Advanced Biology*, p. 121. The following questions refer to the definitions given there, and to the ways we commonly use the term 'mole' in carbohydrate chemistry, as an example.

Testing for reducing sugars with Benedict's solution is illustrated in *Advanced Biology*, p. 128.

1 What do we mean when we refer to:
   a a mole of glucose;
   b a molar solution of glucose?
2 You are asked to prepare one litre of a $0.1 \, \text{mol} \, \text{dm}^{-3}$ glucose solution. Describe how you would do this, including stating exactly what you would have to measure accurately. (Relative atomic masses: $H = 1$, $C = 12$, $O = 16$.)
3 Describe how you would make $50 \, \text{cm}^3$ of a glucose solution of concentration $0.05 \, \text{mol} \, \text{dm}^{-3}$ from a glucose solution of $0.1 \, \text{mol} \, \text{dm}^{-3}$.
4 You have prepared one litre of a $0.1 \, \text{mol} \, \text{dm}^{-3}$ glucose solution. You are also provided with a supply of Benedict's solution.
   a Explain what Benedict's solution consists of, and how it can be used to detect sugar.
   b Using your $0.1 \, \text{mol} \, \text{dm}^{-3}$ glucose and the Benedict's solution, suggest a procedure by which you could estimate the amount of reducing sugar in an unknown solution X.

6.2 Water as a biologically important molecule

The structure and properties of water that particularly relate to life are discussed in *Advanced Biology* on pp. 119–20 and p. 125. The following questions can be answered with reference to this information.

1 Water molecules at room temperature are said to form a 'lattice', held together by hydrogen bonds. Construct a labelled diagram of three water molecules (as space-filling models) showing this lattice structure.
2 Substances with molecules of a similar mass to those of water (like CO_2, NH_3 and CH_4) are gases at room temperature. What features of water maintain it as a liquid at this temperature range?
3 Within the water molecule, atoms of hydrogen and oxygen are held together by covalent bonds. Explain what the term 'covalent bonds' means.
4 Typically, animal cells burst when frozen. What property of water, apparent only as it cools, is responsible for this effect in frozen tissue?
5 Water can be seen to function as a 'temperature buffer' for living things when exposed to higher than normal temperatures. What properties of water help to stabilise the cell and its environment in these conditions?
6 What is the advantage, to a freshwater community, of water's maximum density of $4 \, °C$?
7 Write a simple equation for the hydrolysis of sucrose.
8 What part does the ionisation of water play when an ionic substance, such as sodium chloride, dissolves?

6.3 The structure of proteins

Read the text below about the structure of proteins, and then answer the questions that follow. (In thinking about the issues raised here, you may need to refer to *Advanced Biology*, pp. 133–7, to check up on the structure of amino acids and the peptide bond, polypeptide structure and the structure of proteins.)

Panel 6.1 The proteins

The proteins are a major class of macromolecules found in all living organisms. An individual cell may contain several thousand different ones. Proteins are built up by linking together chemical units called amino acids. The linking reaction is a condensation and the bond formed is called a peptide bond. About 20 types of amino acids are typically found in living systems – the same 20 regardless of the cell type or organism. Just as linking together the 26 letters of our alphabet produces an enormous range of words, sentences and eventually books, linking together amino acids produces an extremely versatile class of macromolecules.

Proteins are typically unbranched chains consisting of several hundred amino acid units (a polypeptide chain). However, they may not occur naturally as long thin molecules. In solution, most of the soluble proteins tend to coil up into a helix (α-helix) or fold into pleated sheets (β-sheets) to form more or less globular structures, stabilised by weak hydrogen bonds. This structure is referred to as the secondary structure of the protein, distinguishing it from the amino acid sequence itself which is the primary structure of the protein.

In addition, in a typical soluble protein, sections of α-helix and β-sheets are linked by sections of polypeptide chain in which no particular structural arrangement is obvious. The result is a three-dimensional structure, known as the tertiary structure of protein. The links are typically of covalent crosslinks between two atoms of sulphur present in certain amino acids in different parts of the chain. To some extent such links impose the overall shape on the molecule, but probably most important are the weak forces between different amino acid residues and peptide bond atoms.

Some proteins are composed of a single polypeptide chain, but many have more than one polypeptide chain, stabilised by weak bonds. These folded polypeptide chains are called 'subunits'. Proteins which are built up from subunits are said to have quaternary structure. A well-known example is haemoglobin, made of four polypeptide chains which fit together tightly.

From: E J Wood and W R Pickering (1982). Introducing Biochemistry, *pp. 52–61. John Murray*

---

1 How would you define 'macromolecule'? What features of macro-molecules make them different from other organic molecules of the cell?
2 What structural features do amino acids have in common?
3 Write down the reaction between two amino acids to form a dipeptide, using structural formulae. Show why it is referred to as a condensation reaction.
4 What is the difference between a polypeptide and a protein?
5 Make a simple table, listing the differences between the primary, secondary, tertiary and quaternary structure of a protein.

6.4 The chemical composition of living organisms

The chemical make-up of living things is discussed in *Advanced Biology* on pp. 118 and 123. Table 6.1 there compares the chemical composition of the human body with seawater and the Earth's crust. The following questions can be answered by reference to this information.

1 The elements carbon, hydrogen, oxygen and nitrogen make up the bulk of all living things, whether animals, plants or fungi, for example. Why is this so?
2 What properties of the elements carbon, hydrogen, oxygen and nitrogen make them well adapted for the construction of biological molecules?
3 Apart from carbon, hydrogen, oxygen and nitrogen, certain other elements occur in living things, seawater and the Earth's crust at levels of 0.01% or above. What sorts of substances are these? State a significant role that these individual elements may have in the functions of particular living things.

6.5 Quick test

1 Distinguish between the following pairs:

a relative atomic mass and mole;
b polarity of water and the ionisation of water;
c ionic and covalent compounds;
d condensation and hydrolysis reactions;
e organic acid and alcohol;
f monosaccharide and disaccharide;
g reducing and non-reducing sugars;
h aldehyde and ketone;
i cellulose and starch;
j fats and oils;
k methyl and ethyl groups;
l saturated and unsaturated fatty acids;
m phospholipids and steroids;
n hydrophobic and hydrophilic;
o amino group and carboxyl group;
p polypeptides and proteins;
q primary and secondary structure of a protein;
r nucleotides and nucleosides;
s purines and pyrimidines;
t NAD and ATP.

2 Explain the importance of the following:

a hydrogen bonds and the properties of water;
b pH in biology;
c the ability of carbon to form covalent bonds with itself;
d optical isomerism and cell biochemistry;
e the amphoteric nature of amino acids.

6.6 Essay assignment

Select one of the following:

• Water is said to have unique properties. Explain what these are, and show in what ways these properties are so important to life.

or:

• Protein molecules take up elaborate three-dimensional shapes. Describe the form and structure of an α-helix protein. How do β-sheets of protein differ?

7 Cell structure

Summary

All organisms are made of cells and cell products. This concept is known as the **cell theory**, and embraces four ideas:
- the cell is the **building block** of living things;
- cells are derived from other cells by **division**;
- cells contain **information**;
- the cell is the site of **metabolism**.

Cells are extremely **small**; most are in the range 10–150 µm (1 µm = 10^{-6} m) in diameter. They must therefore be viewed by some form of **microscopy** for details of structure to be seen. As viewed by the light microscope, plant and animal cells are seen to consist of **cytoplasm surrounded by a plasma membrane, and to contain a nucleus**. Plant cells have a cellulose wall and permanent vacuoles, and sometimes contain chloroplasts. Most structures within cells are far too small to be resolved by light microscopy, however. Cells also exhibit a wide variety of shapes, largely associated with the performance of specialised functions.

Electron microscopy, together with the technique of disruption of cells (**cell fractionation**) to isolate the internal structures, have established the range of the organelles. Many of them are made of membrane built of lipid and protein. The understanding of the structure and functioning of the lipoprotein membranes of cells was central to the establishment of cell biology. The roles of the different organelles in the growth, behaviour and metabolism of cells are understood, at least in part.

The structure of the cells of **prokaryotes** (bacteria and cyanobacteria) is fundamentally different from that of **eukaryotes** (animals, fungi and plants). The former are **smaller**, without either the organised nucleus or the range of organelles seen in eukaryotic cells.

Viruses are another level of organisation, but they are non-cellular. They consist of nucleic acid and protein. Within a specific host cell they bring about their own replication and subsequent release, leading to the possibility of fresh invasions of other host cells.

Practicals and activities

7.1 Using the compound microscope
(Skills and techniques)

In the compound microscope the magnifying powers of two lenses are used to produce a greatly enlarged image of structures too small to be viewed by the naked eye. The lenses are positioned so that the eyepiece lens magnifies the enlarged image formed by the objective lens. In biology, the compound microscope is used mostly to investigate the internal structure of organisms by examination of thin sections, appropriately stained, and also preparations of unicellular organisms, unsectioned. Stains are used to increase the contrast between structures that would otherwise be indistinguishable in a transparent cell or tissue.

'**Magnification**' and '**resolution**' are important concepts in microscopy. Check up what these terms mean (see *Advanced Biology*, p. 147).

■ Aim
To practise the correct setting-up of a compound microscope for the examination of temporary and stained permanent mounts of thin sections of tissues or of suspensions of unicellular organisms.

■ Risk assessment

- When using slides, coverslips, laboratory tools (such as forceps or mounted needles), recommended stains and solvents, together with mounting materials, good laboratory practice is sufficient to take account of any hazards and avoid significant risks.
- The compound microscope is a precision instrument, handle it with care and protect it from dust by storing it under cover or in a box.
- When carrying the instrument always use two hands, holding it by the limb and under the 'feet' (base); put it down on the bench workstation without jarring. (Never carry any microscope by the microscope tube or stage.)
- Keep the lenses and working surface (the stage) clean and dry, uncontaminated by reagents, stains and fixatives. Take special care to avoid contact between the lenses and your fingers (and later, with any of the solvents, stains and mounting fluids in use).
- Lenses and the mirror should be wiped only with lens tissue. Do not use direct sunlight to illuminate the mirror or condenser lens of the microscope, since sunlight when focused on to the retina may damage the light-sensitive cells there.

■ Method

Use in low-power magnification

1 Examine the microscope for the position of the **coarse and fine adjustment**, the magnification of the **eyepiece lens** ($\times 10$ is more helpful than $\times 6$), and the types of the **objectives** – usually $\times 10$ (dark blue band – medium power) and $\times 40$ (green band – high power) (Figure 7.1). Examine also the movements of the **objective lenses** (they are mounted on a rotating turret called the **nosepiece**, and are clicked into position).

Below the stage, examine the movement (focusing) of the **condenser**, and the control lever of the **iris diaphragm**. (There is often a filter ring or tray at the base of the condenser, too, with its own handle.)

Focusing movements commonly move the microscope tube, and this is the situation described here. In some microscopes, however, it is the stage that is moved. The procedures are fundamentally the same for all makes and models of microscope.

Figure 7.1   The compound light microscope

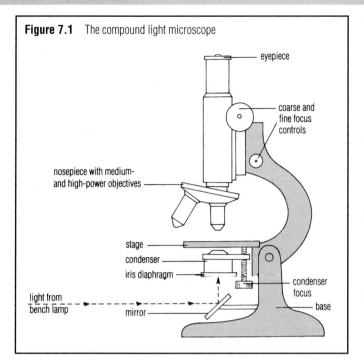

- eyepiece
- coarse and fine focus controls
- nosepiece with medium- and high-power objectives
- stage
- condenser
- iris diaphragm
- condenser focus
- light from bench lamp
- mirror
- base

2 Arrange the microscope so it is comfortably placed for you to use. Position the source of illumination as shown in Figure 7.1. The microscope can be used with the stage tilted (that is, at a comfortable viewing angle), provided wet mounts are not to be examined. Select the medium-power objective lens (×10 magnification with the dark blue colour code ring) by swinging round the objective nosepiece until the ×10 objective clicks into place.

3 Select a prepared slide with a specimen stained to show good colour contrast (such as a stained thin section of tissue, animal or plant). Place this slide on the stage, specimen uppermost, so the material to be examined is centred over the viewing hole. Clip the slide in position if the stage is tilted.

4 Now illuminate the specimen by using the lamp at about 20 cm from the substage mirror. Direct the light beam below the stage only, on to the plane (flat) surface of the mirror (the reverse side is concave, and is used in the absence of the condenser lens).

   Check that the iris diaphragm of the condenser lens (operated by the iris diaphragm lever below the condenser) is about half open.

5 Look at the microscope from the side. Rack down the coarse adjustment till the medium-power objective is about 5 mm from the slide. Then, looking through the microscope and using the coarse adjustment knob, rack up until the image is in sharp focus.

6 Next, the condenser must be focused. Rack the condenser up as far as it will go. Then using the lettering on the bulb surface (or a pencil mark made on the bulb), rack the condenser down slowly, until the lettering or mark is in focus. Since the lettering distracts, defocus very slightly (either up or down), until the lettering is no longer visible.

7 Adjust the iris diaphragm by temporarily removing the eyepiece, and looking down the tube. Fully close the iris diaphragm, and then open it slowly until its image fills three-quarters of the diameter of the back lens of the objective (Figure 7.2). Quickly replace the objective lens (if it is left out, it may be damaged, and the interior of the microscope will certainly become dusty).

Use in high-power magnification

1 For high-power work, first focus the microscope using the specimen to be examined as described above. Then carefully turn the objective nosepiece round till the high-power objective (×40, with the green colour code ring) is clicked into place (if the microscope was in focus at medium power, then the high-power objective lens will be close to the prepared slide but not touching it).

2 Look down the microscope and fine-focus the image by slowly racking up with the fine adjustment only.

Figure 7.2   Fine adjustment of the iris diaphragm

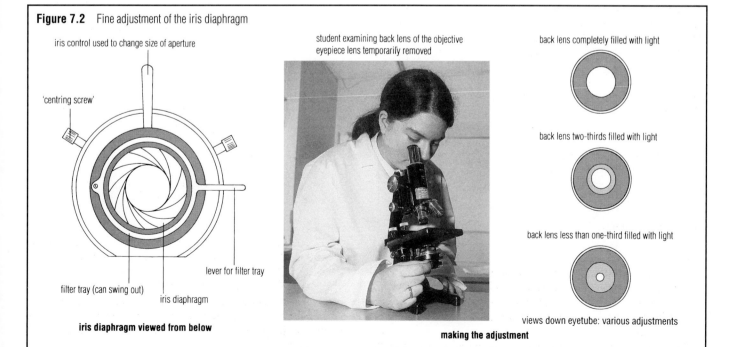

- iris control used to change size of aperture
- 'centring screw'
- filter tray (can swing out)
- iris diaphragm
- lever for filter tray

iris diaphragm viewed from below

student examining back lens of the objective eyepiece lens temporarily removed

making the adjustment

- back lens completely filled with light
- back lens two-thirds filled with light
- back lens less than one-third filled with light

views down eyetube: various adjustments

Carry out the observations of biological materials as suggested in Practical 1.1 on p. 2.

When you have finished your observations, re-set the microscope objectives to medium power, remove the prepared slide and store it in the correct slide tray, and see that the microscope is clean and dry before you put it away.

NOTE TO TECHNICIAN

Each student will require:
- compound microscope, preferably with ×10 eyepiece and ×10 and ×40 objective lenses, with lamp;
- access to lens tissue;
- suitable stained prepared slide.

■ Evaluation

Draw up a list of the typical points of error or faults that may arise in light microscopy. Check your list against the checklist given on p. 431.

■ Extension

Oil-immersion microscopy

Oil-immersion lenses are used when additional magnification and improved resolution are required: for example, when bacterial preparations are examined. **Oil-immersion lenses** have a magnifying power of ×90–×100. They have to be used with a drop of immersion oil, which has the same refractive index as the lens. (**Safety note:** avoid all contacts between immersion oil and the skin by the use of disposable plastic gloves.)

1 Screw an oil-immersion lens into the objective nosepiece of your microscope at a vacant port (Figure 7.3).
2 Set up your microscope so the slide is focused for high-power examination (×40 objective).

3 Swing away the ×40 objective, but do not engage the oil-immersion objective immediately.
4 Apply a drop of immersion oil from the dispenser to the slide, over the object being viewed.
5 Now click the oil-immersion lens into place. Focus using the fine-focus knob, first watching from the side of the lens. Lower the oil-immersion lens until it just touches the oil. Continue lowering the objective very slowly until the objective touches the coverslip. Now look down the microscope, and slowly raise the objective until the specimen comes into focus.
6 After completing your observations, wipe all immersion oil from the objective lens and the slide, using lens tissues.

Dark-ground illumination

This technique allows examination of live material without the need for staining. In dark-ground illumination, no direct rays from the light source reach the observer; only diffracted light from the object enters the objective lens, and the object on the slide appears as white outlines against a dark background (reversed contrast). For 'approximate' work at medium-power magnification you can adapt a standard 'bright-field microscopy' condenser by placing a circle of black paper so that only the marginal light rays reach the object. A special condenser is certainly required for high-power work, however.

Phase-contrast microscopy

Phase-contrast microscopy requires a special fitment (an **annulus**) to be added to the substage condenser, and the objective lenses must contain fitments known as '**phase plates**'. As a result, structures within living things become visible in high contrast, with excellent resolution of fine detail. In setting up this type of microscope the annulus and phase plates must be carefully aligned, a process that normally requires the use of a focusing telescope that fits to the eyepiece tube.

Special student phase-contrast microscopes come with full operating instructions.

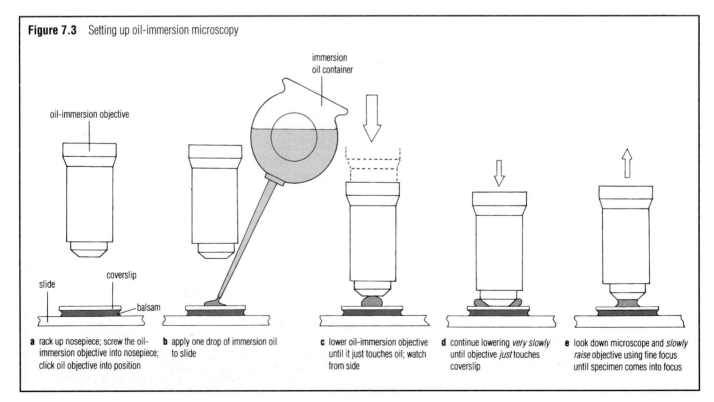

Figure 7.3 Setting up oil-immersion microscopy

immersion oil container

oil-immersion objective

slide   coverslip   balsam

a rack up nosepiece; screw the oil-immersion objective into nosepiece; click oil objective into position

b apply one drop of immersion oil to slide

c lower oil-immersion objective until it just touches oil; watch from side

d continue lowering *very slowly* until objective *just* touches coverslip

e look down microscope and *slowly raise* objective using fine focus until specimen comes into focus

7.2 Measuring microscopic objects
(Skills and techniques)

The size of an object observed down the microscope can be measured by observing it against a scale (eyepiece graticule), the scale itself being calibrated using a stage micrometer.

■ Aim
To measure the dimensions of microscopic biological objects.

■ Risk assessment
Good laboratory practice is sufficient to take account of any hazards and avoid significant risks.

■ Method
You are provided with an eyepiece graticule (eyepiece micrometer). This is a tiny printed grid, retained between two circular glass discs.

1 Clean it with lens tissue first, and avoid getting fingerprints on the glass as you install it.
2 Remove the eyepiece from the microscope and then unscrew the top lens.
3 Place the graticule correct side up on the 'shelf' halfway down (you will have to experiment with this).
4 Replace the upper eyepiece lens, and return the eyepiece to the microscope (Figure 7.4).

Carry out these steps quickly to avoid dust entering the microscope tube. The eyepiece graticule is held in the plane of the primary image and therefore is always in focus when the image is, whatever the magnification.

5 Measure objects by mounting slides on the microscope stage and focusing on the relevant part of the specimen. You may need to rotate the eyepiece so that the scale lies across the object.

6 Record the dimension of the object in arbitrary units (a graticule has numbered divisions). Suitable measurements to make and record to practise this technique include:
- the width of a lung capillary (from a slide with capillaries injected with coloured plastic prior to sectioning);
- the diameter of a parenchyma cell from the central pith of the stem;
- the diameter of a red blood cell;
  the diameter of a nucleus in a stained section of a flower bud;
- the length of a goblet cell in the epithelium of the small intestine;
- the thickness of a leaf;
- the length of an amoeba (stained preparation);
- the diameter of the stele (central conducting tissues) of a plant root;
- the width of a hair at the skin surface, as seen in a section of mammalian skin;
- the diameter of the largest xylem vessel observed in a monocotyledonous stem (TS).

7 To calibrate your eyepiece graticule, first hold up the stage micrometer slide in the light and observe the scale by means of a hand lens. Normally the scale has 10 × 1 mm divisions, with each division marked into 0.1 mm subdivisions. Since a millimetre = 1000 micrometres (microns, μm), how many microns are there in 0.1 mm? This will be the actual size of the smallest division on the stage micrometer.

8 Now examine the micrometer slide through the microscope. Focus on the calibration scale, and then rotate the eyepiece until the graticule scale lies superimposed (Figure 7.5). Observe how many eyepiece divisions are equivalent to how many slide divisions. Do this at both medium- and high-power magnification, for as the magnification is increased the eyepiece scale will cover a smaller area of the object, and each division measures a smaller length. Record the size of the divisions at each magnification.

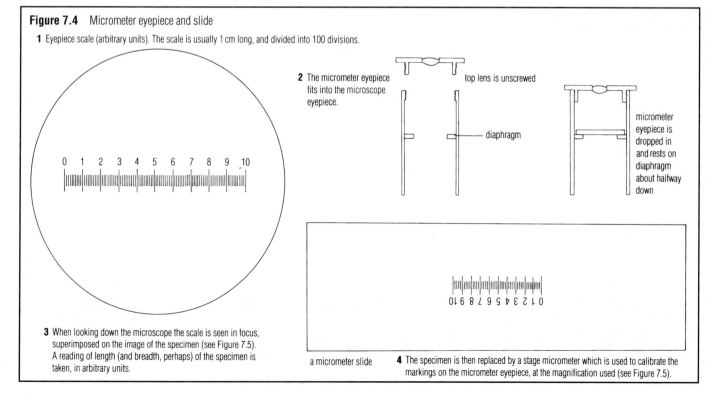

Figure 7.4 Micrometer eyepiece and slide

1 Eyepiece scale (arbitrary units). The scale is usually 1 cm long, and divided into 100 divisions.

0 1 2 3 4 5 6 7 8 9 10

2 The micrometer eyepiece fits into the microscope eyepiece.

top lens is unscrewed

diaphragm

micrometer eyepiece is dropped in and rests on diaphragm about halfway down

a micrometer slide

3 When looking down the microscope the scale is seen in focus, superimposed on the image of the specimen (see Figure 7.5). A reading of length (and breadth, perhaps) of the specimen is taken, in arbitrary units.

4 The specimen is then replaced by a stage micrometer which is used to calibrate the markings on the micrometer eyepiece, at the magnification used (see Figure 7.5).

Figure 7.5 Calibrating the eyepiece scale

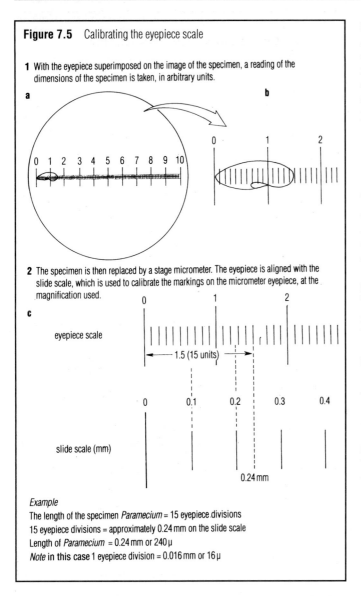

1 With the eyepiece superimposed on the image of the specimen, a reading of the dimensions of the specimen is taken, in arbitrary units.

a   b

2 The specimen is then replaced by a stage micrometer. The eyepiece is aligned with the slide scale, which is used to calibrate the markings on the micrometer eyepiece, at the magnification used.

c

eyepiece scale

← 1.5 (15 units) →

slide scale (mm)

0.24 mm

Example
The length of the specimen *Paramecium* = 15 eyepiece divisions
15 eyepiece divisions = approximately 0.24 mm on the slide scale
Length of *Paramecium* = 0.24 mm or 240 μ
Note in this case 1 eyepiece division = 0.016 mm or 16 μ

NOTE TO TECHNICIAN

Each student group requires (or requires access to):
- compound microscope with medium- and high-power objectives, with bench lamp (if necessary);
- lens tissue;
- hand lens;
- eyepiece graticule (eyepiece micrometer) and stage micrometer;
- a selection of 8–10 prepared slides of animal and plant tissues (see above).

■ Data presentation
List the eyepiece measurements (arbitrary units) of the objects you measured, recording whether at medium- or high-power magnification. Multiply these measurements by the length calculated for the divisions at the magnification used.

■ Conclusion
Comment on the range of sizes which were apparent in the structures measured, bearing in mind you have probably measured parts of whole organisms, a range of animal and plant cells and a cell organelle.

■ Evaluation
A step called 'fixing' attempts to minimise the shrinkage that occurs when biological material is sectioned, stained and permanently mounted for microscopic examination. In life, however, sizes may be different from those measured from microscope slides. How might a research microscopist overcome this problem?

7.3 Using the microscope to count cells
(Skills and techniques)

The total numbers in a population of non-motile, unicellular organisms may be estimated by counting the number of cells in representative samples, using a modified microscope slide counting chamber called a **haemocytometer**, together with a compound microscope (*Advanced Biology*, p. 404).

■ Aim
To use the microscope to obtain precise numerical data on the number of cells present in a sample of a culture of immobile, unicellular organisms.

■ Risk assessment

Good laboratory practice is sufficient to take account of any hazards and avoid significant risks.

■ Method
The haemocytometer (Figure 7.6) should be clean and dry at the outset.

1 By means of a pipette, place a drop of the cell suspension to fill the well over the grid at the centre of the slide. Then place the special (thickened) coverglass over, without trapping any air bubbles. Move the coverslip backwards and forwards with some pressure, until you can see coloured interference rings (Newton's rings) at the sides. At this point, the slide and coverglass are very close together, and the depth in the central chamber is uniform. Thus you can count a known volume of cell culture suspension.

2 Examine the grid microscopically, using a ×10 eyepiece with a ×10 objective lens for initial focus. The central squared area of the slide fills the field of view at this magnification. You will observe that the central squared area is subdivided into $5 \times 5 = 25$ smaller squares.

   Now switch the objective turret to the ×40 lens. You will observe that the 25 smaller squares are each subdivided into $4 \times 4 = 16$ of the smallest squares.

   Sharp focus onto the cells present in these smallest squares. Count the number of cells in several of the smallest squares. Include the cells that touch or are across the upper and right-hand boundary, but ignore those that cross the bottom and left-hand boundaries. (*Note:* for dilute suspensions count the larger squares, but for dense cultures count the smaller ones. If the culture is very dense you may need to make known dilutions of the culture before counting.)

3 Clean and dry the haemocytometer between counts of different samples, and when all counts are finished. Clean it by rinsing with a jet of distilled water, and dry by washing in propanone and allowing it to evaporate. Wipe the haemocytometer with lens tissue only.

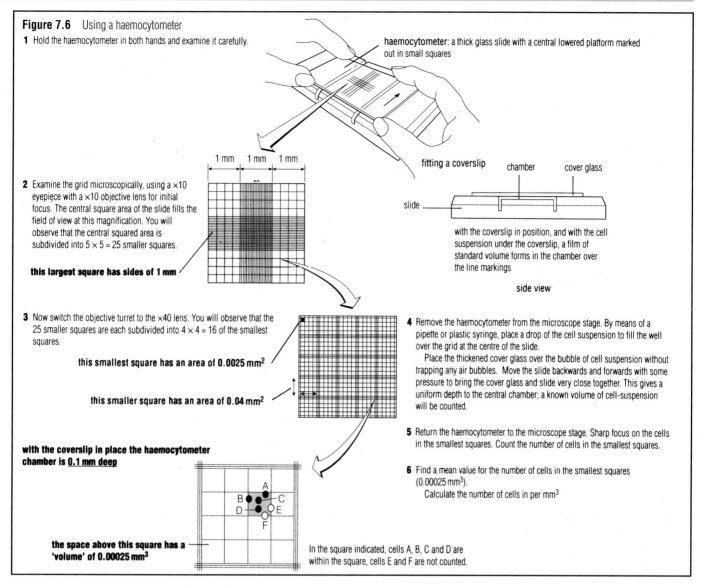

Figure 7.6 Using a haemocytometer

1 Hold the haemocytometer in both hands and examine it carefully.

haemocytometer: a thick glass slide with a central lowered platform marked out in small squares

2 Examine the grid microscopically, using a ×10 eyepiece with a ×10 objective lens for initial focus. The central square area of the slide fills the field of view at this magnification. You will observe that the central squared area is subdivided into 5 × 5 = 25 smaller squares.

this largest square has sides of 1 mm

1 mm 1 mm 1 mm

fitting a coverslip

chamber   cover glass

slide

with the coverslip in position, and with the cell suspension under the coverslip, a film of standard volume forms in the chamber over the line markings

side view

3 Now switch the objective turret to the ×40 lens. You will observe that the 25 smaller squares are each subdivided into 4 × 4 = 16 of the smallest squares.

this smallest square has an area of 0.0025 mm²

this smaller square has an area of 0.04 mm²

with the coverslip in place the haemocytometer chamber is 0.1 mm deep

4 Remove the haemocytometer from the microscope stage. By means of a pipette or plastic syringe, place a drop of the cell suspension to fill the well over the grid at the centre of the slide.
   Place the thickened cover glass over the bubble of cell suspension without trapping any air bubbles. Move the slide backwards and forwards with some pressure to bring the cover glass and slide very close together. This gives a uniform depth to the central chamber; a known volume of cell-suspension will be counted.

5 Return the haemocytometer to the microscope stage. Sharp focus on the cells in the smallest squares. Count the number of cells in the smallest squares.

6 Find a mean value for the number of cells in the smallest squares (0.00025 mm³).
   Calculate the number of cells in per mm³

the space above this square has a 'volume' of 0.00025 mm³

In the square indicated, cells A, B, C and D are within the square, cells E and F are not counted.

NOTE TO TECHNICIAN

Each group of students will require (or require access to):
- sample of culture solution of unicellular non-motile organisms, such as *Chlorella*;
- compound microscope and lamp;
- haemocytometer with coverglass;
- pipette (1 cm³);
- distilled water wash-bottle
- small bottle of propanone;
- lens tissue.

If the cell culture requires (serial) dilution, students will also require:
- boiling tubes in a stand;
- marker pens;
- 1 cm³ pipette;
- 10 cm³ graduated pipette;
- supply of distilled water.

■ Data presentation

The counting chamber is 0.1 mm deep. The central squared area is a 1 mm square divided into 25 main squares, each of which is subdivided into 16 smaller squares. The volume of suspension above the smallest squares is 0.00025 mm³. Thus the number of cells in the culture suspension given is:

$$\frac{D \times N}{S \times C}$$

where D = dilution of the original culture (if necessary)
   N = total number of cells counted
   S = number of squares counted and
   C = the volume of one 'square'.

■ Conclusion

You can calculate the total number of cells present. The manuals observe, however, that a very large number of cells need to be counted for the results to be significant. Why is this so?

■ Evaluation

The approach is time-consuming, and it is sometimes difficult to differentiate between single cells and a small clump, so careful observation is essential.

The count does not discriminate between living and dead cells. Living cells may be detected by the dilution plate technique (p. 287).

7.4 Observing the structure of cells
(Skills and techniques)

Individual cells are not only tiny but also largely transparent, and so they are difficult to observe. In light microscopy, it is common practice to add dyes or stains to introduce sufficient contrast, and so differentiate structure. Dyes and stains that are taken up by living cells are especially useful in this.

■ Aim

To observe the salient features of animal and plant cells, visible by light microscopy.

■ Risk assessment

- When working with dyes and stains, avoid contact with skin or clothing.
- Take care when using sharp dissection equipment, and when it is placed down on the bench beside you.
- Otherwise, good laboratory practice is sufficient to take account of any hazards and avoid significant risks.

■ Method

Observing the nucleus and cytoplasm in onion epidermis cells

A single layer of cells, known as the epidermis, covers the surface of a leaf. In the circular leaf bases that make up an onion bulb, the epidermis is relatively easily freed from the cells below, and can be lifted away from small pieces of a leaf.

1 Slice an onion bulb into 'rings' about 0.5 cm thick, and then cut one ring into pieces about 0.5 cm long. With fine forceps, peel off the epidermis from the inner, curved surface of one of these pieces. Place this film of tissue on a microscope slide in a drop of iodine (I_2/KI) solution and add a coverslip (p. 86).
2 Leave this temporary mount for one or two minutes, whilst the iodine penetrates the cell membrane. Then examine the cells by medium- and high-power magnification.

Iodine solution stains the living contents a light yellow, but the nucleus takes up the stain more strongly than the cytoplasm does; the bulk of these cells is filled by a vacuole which remains unstained. The leaf bases of the onion bulb are concerned with food storage, but the onion does not store carbohydrate as starch. This is fortunate for this investigation. Why?

Observing chloroplasts in moss leaf cells

The leaf of a moss plant is typically mostly one cell thick. Remove a single leaf from a moss plant, mount it on a microscope slide in a drop of glycerol, and add a coverslip. Then examine individual cells by medium- and high-power magnification. No stain or dye is employed in this investigation; what structures of these plant cells are visible?

Observing nucleus, cytoplasm and cell membrane in mammalian cells

Human cheek cells There is a widely held view that the Department for Education and Employment (DfEE) has banned experimental work in schools and colleges using human cheek cells. Following the Institute of Biology's advice, many teachers are able to allow students to observe human cheek cells, following rigorous safety precautions, as follows.

1 Sample 'smears' from the inside lining of a student's own cheek should be taken by the student with a fresh, unused cotton bud, removed from a pack for that purpose immediately beforehand.
2 After the smear material has been transferred to a single, clean microscope slide the used cotton bud must be submerged in sodium chlorate(I) (hypochlorite) disinfectant (1% solution, or absolute ethanol).
3 The microscope slide should be handled only by the student whose cells it carries.
4 After the microscope slide has been examined it should be immersed in 1% hypochlorite disinfectant solution, or absolute ethanol.

To observe the structure of human cheek cells, add a drop of methylene blue to the cell/saliva smear on the microscope slide and leave for one minute. Then remove the bulk of the methylene blue dye by withdrawing the solution into filter paper. Add a drop of glycerol, cover with a coverslip and examine some of the individual cells present by medium- and high-power magnification. How do these cells differ from the plant cells observed? Finally, place the used slide with coverslip intact into 1% sodium chlorate(I) solution, or absolute ethanol.

Reference

P Burrows (1993) 'That's banned, isn't it? Some safety myths in science', *School Science Review* (June 1993) 74(269), pp. 51–4

P Bunyan (1994) 'Biological myths and bans', *School Science Review* (Sept 1994) 76(274), pp. 79–80

Alternatives to cheek cells If the teachers' employers (the LEA or governors of non-LEA schools and colleges) prohibit human cheek cell sampling, then there are suitable alternatives.

The interior of the trachea of either a sheep or a pig may be scraped with a spatula. The cells and mucus collected are then placed on a microscope slide and stained and examined, as for cheek cells. Some observers find these cells easier to see than human cheek cells.

Alternatively, you may apply Sellotape across the skin of your wrist, after first carefully washing and drying it. Next,

---

NOTE TO TECHNICIAN

Each group will require:
- microscope and bench lamp, microscope slides and coverslips;
- white tile, sharp knife, strong scalpel;
- fine forceps;
- two mounted needles;
- access to dropping bottle of I_2/KI solution, 1% methylene blue and glycerol;
- onion bulb, moss plants and trachea of sheep or pig (from the butcher);
- spatula;
- Sellotape.

If human cheek cells are to be examined:
- box of cotton buds;
- jar of 1% sodium chlorate(I) (hypochlorite), or absolute ethanol, to drop used cotton buds, slides and coverslips into.

lay the strip of tape on to a microscope slide so that you can examine the skin cells which have attached to the tape, by medium- and high-power magnification. You can irrigate your temporary mount with 1% methylene blue, and observe the effects it has on individual cells the dye reaches.

■ Data presentation
Make large, clearly labelled drawings (p. 4) of the details of the cells you have observed.

■ Conclusion
Make a table of the cell structures observed, and record how each responded to the stains used.

■ Evaluation
What value, if any, is there in the concept of 'the generalised plant or animal cell'?

7.5 Staining bacterial smears

(Skills and techniques)

Bacteria are prokaryotes, and as such are extremely small cells (Figure 7.7); many bacteria are little larger than certain of the organelles in eukaryotic cells (cells of plants, animals and fungi). Bacteria require to be stained to make them visible for viewing by high-power/oil-immersion microscopy.

Bacteria can multiply by growth and cell division in a matter of minutes rather than hours, in favourable conditions, and some bacteria are dangerous pathogens. Great care must therefore be taken in all bacteriological work as a matter of essential routine.

■ Aim
To observe the sizes and shapes typical of bacterial cells, using bacteria present in yoghurt and tooth scrapings, by means of a (heat-fixed) smear and appropriate stains.

■ Risk assessment

Good laboratory practice is sufficient to take account of any hazards and avoid significant risks, since in this exercise bacteria are not cultured. If, however, your school or college prohibits any work with saliva (as a potentially infectious body fluid), then you must omit work with tooth scrapings as a precaution.

When working with microorganisms in a school or college laboratory, the following steps to 'good practice' are essential:

1 Wash your hands with soap and water before and after all practical work with bacteria.
2 Do not put your fingers near your face (mouth, nose or eyes) during the experimental work.
3 Have a working area marked out (with a sheet of lining paper, for example), and keep the apparatus you use within this zone.
4 Keep Petri dishes, bottles and plugged flasks closed or stoppered, except when you need to open them.
5 Inoculated Petri dishes must be immediately secured with Sellotape, and kept closed thereafter.
6 Agar plates that have been exposed must be sterilised in a pressure cooker or autoclave before the contents are disposed of and the dishes washed.

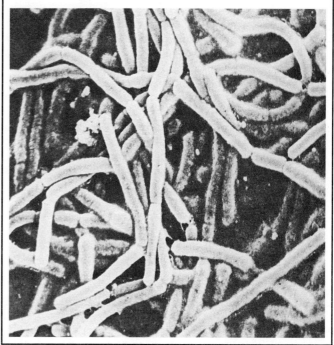

Figure 7.7 SEM of *Lactobacillus bulgaricus*, used as a 'starter' in the production of yoghurt from milk (×4155)

7 At the end of the experiment, dispose of the lining paper safely, and swab down the bench with disinfectant.
8 Submerge tools and equipment that have come into contact with bacterial preparations in sterilising fluid immediately after use (for slides, toothpicks and so forth); sterilise wire loops in a hot Bunsen flame.

■ Method
Bacteria in yoghurt

1 Select a clean microscope slide and pass it through a Bunsen flame twice (using tongs or forceps) to remove any traces of grease.
2 Sterilise an inoculating wire loop in the heat of the Bunsen flame, and use it to transfer a single drop of distilled water to the slide. Next transfer a little of the yoghurt (less than one drop) to the water and mix the two thoroughly. Smear the resultant suspension over the centre part of the slide to form a thin film, using the wire loop.
3 Allow the smear to dry in air. This can be accelerated by holding the slide high above a (blue) Bunsen flame, but take care that drying is slow enough to avoid shrinking and distortion of the bacterial cells.
4 Now 'fix' the air-dried film by passing the microscope slide through the hottest part of a blue flame, film side uppermost, without lingering. The slide should not become too hot for comfort when touched against the back of your hand.
5 Stain the bacteria with crystal violet stain for one minute by flooding the dried, fixed smear.
6 Pour off the crystal violet stain and wash clear with a gentle stream of distilled water. Blot the slide dry and then allow to air-dry.
7 Examine the stained smear directly (without a coverslip) first under high power, and then, after adding immersion oil, by oil immersion. Bacteria appear red–violet coloured.

Bacteria in tooth scrapings

1 Using a sterile toothpick, scrape the surfaces and crevices of your teeth and place the scrapings on a clean microscope slide.
2 Using a sterilised inoculating wire loop, add two to three loopfuls of distilled water to the scrapings and mix them together.
3 Transfer one loopful of the mixture to one end of a fresh clean microscope slide. Next add one loopful of nigrosin stain and mix the two together.
4 Create a film on the slide, using one end of another slide to touch the mixture and then slide it back across the whole length of the first slide, spreading the film (Figure 7.8). Place the second slide in the sterilising beaker as soon as it has been used.
5 Air-dry the film, without using heat.
6 When the stained film is dry examine it directly (without a coverslip) first under high power, and then by oil immersion, after adding immersion oil. With nigrosin the bacteria appear colourless, but surrounded by an intense blue–black zone (negative staining).

NOTE TO TECHNICIAN

Each student requires:
- sheet of lining paper approximately 50 × 60 cm at student work position;
- sterilising bath (250 cm³ beaker containing 1% hypochlorite solution, or 0.5% solution biocidal ampholytic surfactant);
- wire loop;
- Bunsen burner and heat-resistant pad;
- six microscope slides;
- sterile wooden toothpick;
- (commercial) natural yoghurt;
- coarse forceps or slide-holder;
- wash-bottle of distilled water;
- blotting paper or filter paper discs;
- bacterial stains (available in labelled dropping bottles): crystal violet stain (2% w/v crystal violet in 20% v/v ethanol/water), nigrosin (10% w/v in water);
- access to compound microscope with high-power and oil-immersion objectives, and immersion oil (with disposable plastic gloves and copious lens tissues to hand).

■ **Data presentation**

The range of bacterial shapes observed can be recorded by diagrams. The size range of bacteria present can be estimated by use of a micrometer eyepiece/stage micrometer (see p. 97).

■ **Conclusion**

The occurrence of bacteria on the surfaces of our bodies and on the food we eat can be guessed at.

■ **Evaluation**

What are the sources of danger from bacteria when you are working with materials such as yoghurt and tooth scrapings?

Project

Variations with cells of the same type

How variable are cells? To what extent do cells depart from a generalised structure by which they are characterised in typical line drawings?

Select one particular type of animal or plant cell and analyse how much variation in size or structure occurs in this cell type in a particular organ; e.g. involuntary muscle fibres in LS of an artery wall. Select the type of cell and the organ to investigate on the basis of the prepared slides that are available to you.

Alternatively, select one type of plant cell, such as epidermis or parenchyma in one organ (such as a stem or leaf) of a particular species. In this case you may choose to use either temporary mounts or prepared slides.

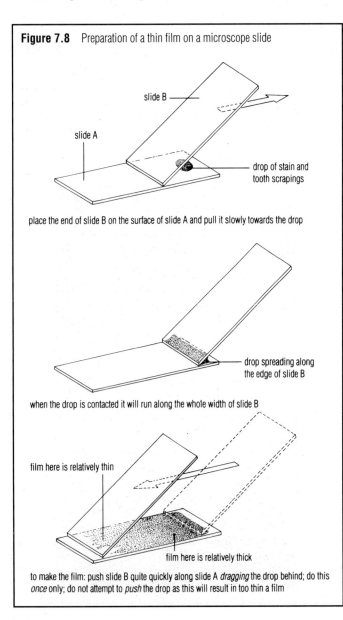

Figure 7.8   Preparation of a thin film on a microscope slide

slide B

slide A

drop of stain and tooth scrapings

place the end of slide B on the surface of slide A and pull it slowly towards the drop

drop spreading along the edge of slide B

when the drop is contacted it will run along the whole width of slide B

film here is relatively thin

film here is relatively thick

to make the film: push slide B quite quickly along slide A *dragging* the drop behind; do this *once* only; do not attempt to *push* the drop as this will result in too thin a film

Problems and assignments

7.1 Studying key figures in early microscopy

In *Advanced Biology* (p. 143) there is a listing of the key steps in the origins of cell biology. The contribution of Antoni van Leeuwenhoek (1632–1723), using a single-lens microscope, is outlined (p. 142).

Research the contributions of other microscopists whose work was also fundamental to microscopy and the study of cell biology: for example, Marcello Malpighi (1628–1694), Robert Hooke (1635–1707), Robert Brown (1773–1855) and Ernst Abbe (1840–1905).

Record your researches on one side of A4 paper in a matrix (as Table 7.1) under five subheadings, such as:
- where they lived and worked;
- how they earned their living;
- what education or training they had in science, and specifically in biology;
- whether their strength lay more in theoretical science or practical technology;
- their achievements that most influenced the development of biology.

Table 7.1

	Marcello Malpighi	Robert Hooke	Robert Brown	Ernst Abbe
Lived and worked:				
Earned a living as:				
Education/training in science: in biology:				
Theoretical scientist or practical technologist:				
Major achievements (influential in the development of biology):				

Sources

Encyclopaedias and dictionaries of biography available in public libraries, such as:

D Millar *et al.* (1989) *Concise Dictionary of Scientists*. Chalmers/Cambridge University Press

R Porter (ed.) (1994) *Dictionary of Scientific Biography*. Hutchinson

I Asimov (1975) *Biographical Encyclopedia of Science and Technology*. Pan

Discussion point

Is there a recognisable stereotype of the successful scientists? What sort of personal qualities appear essential for success in science?

7.2 Scanning electron microscopy and transmission electron microscopy compared

Scanning electron micrographs (SEMs) (Figures 7.7, 7.9) are rather different images from the transmission electron micrographs (TEMs) more traditionally seen in biology books. SEMs are shown as part of numerous illustrations in *Advanced Biology*, typically in Figures 9.5 (p. 190), 16.34 (p. 342), 18.2 (p. 378) and 27.22 (p. 603). Read the introduction to electron microscopy on p. 149 of *Advanced Biology*, together with the passage in Panel 7.1.

Panel 7.1 Scanning electron microscopy

In the scanning electron microscope a fine beam of electrons is moved back and forth across the surface of a prepared specimen. Depending on the topography and chemical composition of the surface, electrons striking the specimen are scattered, and some may cause secondary electrons to be displaced from the specimen. In the SE microscope some of these scattered and displaced electrons are collected in a nearby photomultiplier tube, and from them an image of the surface of the specimen is built up and displayed on a television screen (or is recorded as a photographic image). Scattered electrons vary in abundance and availability to the detector, according to the shape of the surface of the specimen. For example, crevices in the specimen produce far fewer detectable electrons than projections do. SEMs have a most impressive depth of field.

The resolution of this microscope is limited by the size of the electron beam, and is rarely better than 0.01 μm, which is much poorer than the transmission electron microscope, but greatly superior to that of the light microscope. Specimens are usually fixed or freeze-dried to preserve shape, and are then shadowed with a layer of heavy metal, prior to exposure in the SE microscope.

From: A V Grimstone (1979) The Electron Microscope in Biology. *Arnold Studies in Biology no 9. Edward Arnold*

Figure 7.9 (top) SEM of the head of an insect; (bottom) a photograph of a similar specimen

Light microscopy, TE microscopy and SE microscopy all have uses in the processes of biological investigation. Answer the questions below.

1 What are the particular uses of the light microscope, compared with electron microscopy?
2 What are the special features of SEM that are exploited in biological investigation?
3 What advantages does the TE microscope offer over other forms of microscopy?

7.3 Magnification and resolution, explaining the difference

Figure 7.10 shows some samples of grey 'tint'. Transfers made of this sort of material are frequently used to shade certain types of diagram. If you use a hand lens you may be able to see that these tints are all composed of small dots printed very close together. The dots are of different sizes, and clearly printed at differing distances apart.

Using your experience of examining these samples, explain the difference between 'magnification' and 'resolution', as used in microscopy.

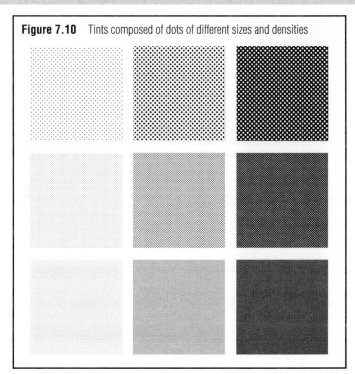

Figure 7.10 Tints composed of dots of different sizes and densities

7.4 Comparing eukaryotic and prokaryotic cells

First, examine the transmission electron micrographs (TEMs) shown in Figure 7.11. Note that the TEM of the bacterium has been enlarged much more than that of the plant cell. You can estimate the sizes of the cells and the labelled components from the scales given. Then answer the following questions.

1 The plant cell is described as a eukaryotic cell, the bacterium as a prokaryotic cell. What structures does the plant cell possess that distinguishes it from the bacterium?
2 Sketch an outline of the plant cell and its organelles in position. Annotate your drawing with the names and chief functions or roles of the structures and organelles visible.

3 Using the given scale, find the mean length of three of the mitochondria to be seen in the plant cell. How does this compare with the length of the bacterium?
4 The bacterium is clearly smaller than the plant cell. What other features of its structure would you list as characteristic of a prokaryotic cell?
5 a What organelle might be visible in a TEM of a pancreas cell that would not be seen in a plant cell?
 b What structures or organelles characteristic of plant cells would be certain to be absent from the pancreatic cell? (You can see a TEM of a pancreatic cell in *Advanced Biology*, p. 19.)

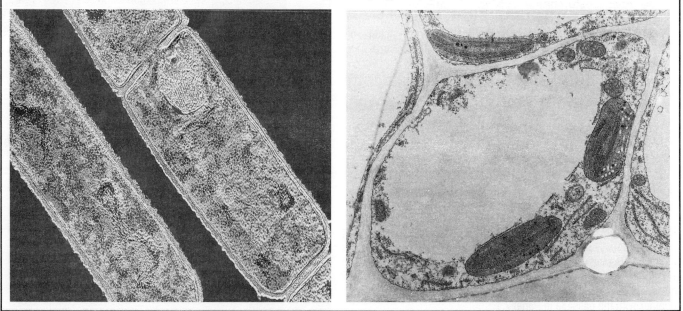

Figure 7.11 TEMs of a rod-shaped bacterium (*Bacillus subtilis*) (×10 730), and of a spongy mesophyll cell (×2500)

7.5 The fluid mosaic model of membrane structure

Read the text in Panel 7.2.

Panel 7.2 The structure of cell membranes

New lines of experiment have introduced a surprising and enlightening new feature into our picture of membrane organisation. This feature is the dynamic and fluid character of membranes, known as the fluid mosaic model, and it is rapidly becoming central to our thinking about how membranes function in cells.

As well as explaining a wealth of physical and structural studies, the fluid mosaic model opens up the possibility of explaining the functional properties of membranes and their dynamic roles in cells.

- At the general level it is consistent with our sense that the membrane-bound enzymes and transport systems must be flexible to carry out their tasks.
- We can begin to imagine an ion-transporting protein channelling and pushing a charged particle across a membrane by a kind of molecular peristalsis.
- The model makes it possible to imagine what happens when membranes fuse, as they do during secretion, when secretory vesicles fuse with cell membranes, and in the opposite process of endocytosis.
- It makes sense of the finding that the proteins of many membranes (including the plasma and organellar membrane) are made at ribosomes bound to endoplasmic reticulum (RER), and are initially inserted into the ER membrane on production.
- The fluidity of membranes allows these newly made components to be incorporated in the membranes of vesicles that bud from the ER and fuse with the Golgi, there to be directed to move to the cell surface or other destinations by further stages of vesicle budding and fusion.
- Membrane fluidity also explains membrane-bound receptor systems for hormones. These receptors are proteins that face 'outwards', and pick up circulating hormones. In response, an associated second membrane protein, facing 'inwards', acts on ATP in the cytosol and converts it into a 'second messenger'.

All in all, there is no doubt that the fluid mosaic model is a successful model that explains much that is known about membranes, and provides a framework to think about the unknown.

From: RB Freedman (1984), School Science Review *65(233), pp. 269–91*

Think about the ideas in the above passage in the context of:
- cell membrane structure (*Advanced Biology*, pp. 153–5);
- membrane transport (p. 224) and membrane 'pumps' (pp. 232–3);

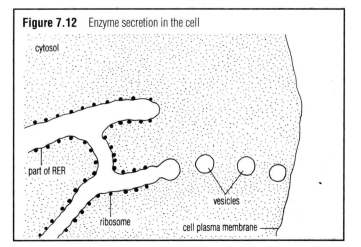

Figure 7.12   Enzyme secretion in the cell

cytosol

part of RER

ribosome

vesicles

cell plasma membrane

- ribosome function (p. 157);
- secretion via vesicles (Golgi apparatus, p. 158), neurotransmitters at the synapse (p. 161), and in cell wall formation (p. 162);
- and the mechanisms of hormone action (p. 479).

Then answer the questions that follow.

1. What is meant by the phrase 'dynamic and fluid' structure of membranes? What would an alternative arrangement be?
2. Make a labelled diagram of a small part of a fluid mosaic membrane, seen in cross-section, and annotate the structures to show why they take up their typical positions in the membrane bilayer.
3. The article talks about observations from 'physical and structural studies' that the fluid mosaic model explains. Give three specific pieces of evidence that support the fluid mosaic model.
4. Using an annotated diagram, explain what is meant by a flexible enzyme involved in pumping ions across membranes.
5. Make a copy of Figure 7.12, and then annotate it to explain the process by which protein enzymes may be formed, 'packaged' and then secreted from the cell.
6. Explain by means of a fully annotated sketch how a peptide hormone may trigger change within a 'target' cell.

7.6 The movement of cilia and flagella

Cilia and flagella are organelles that project from the surface of cells. The movements of flagella and cilia produce forces that may be used in various ways. The structure and functioning of cilia and flagella are illustrated in *Advanced Biology*, p. 161, and in Figure 7.13 below.

Figure 7.13   The structure of a cilium or flagellum

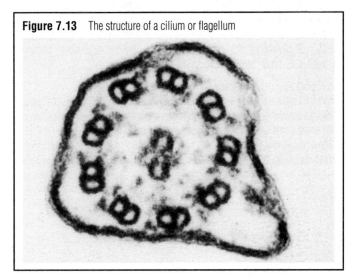

In cross-section, cilia and flagella can be seen to consist of an outer ring of nine pairs of microtubules, arranged around a central pair of microtubules. The whole is enclosed by an extension of the cell plasma membrane. The electron microscope has shown that the microtubule pairs within cilia and flagella are linked by side-arms. These 'arms' consist of protein enzymes that facilitate sliding movements of the microtubules, using energy from ATP. Apparently, in this way cilia and flagella bring about their characteristic beating movements.

In a paper titled 'A human syndrome caused by immotile cilia' the cytologist B A Afzelius reported that, in a group of male patients being examined because of sterility, sperms were found to be immotile. In fact, the tails (flagella) of the sperms of these people were unable to beat. This proved to be due to the total absence of side-arm protein between the microtubule pairs in the flagella. Most of these men were also found to suffer from chronic coughing and recurrent lung infection. These symptoms were linked to their inability to clear efficiently the mucus, with the inhaled dust particles it had trapped, from their lungs.

Answer the following questions, using your knowledge of cilia and flagella together with the above information.

1 Since cilia and flagella have the same internal structure and mechanism of movement, what features are used to tell them apart?
2 Name one unicellular organism that bears a flagellum, and one that bears cilia.
3 Where in the thorax of a mammal are cells bearing cilia found?
4 What has caused male sterility in common with lung infections in Afzelius's patients?
5 Microtubules are also found singly and in irregular groupings in the cytoplasm within many cells. Give an example of the ways these microtubules are associated with movement within cells.

7.7 Electron microscopy and artefacts

About 25 years ago quite a controversy raged as to whether the techniques of preparing biological samples for electron microscopy were so extreme (i.e. removed from life-like conditions) that the resulting electronmicrographs showed structures produced by these conditions, rather than present during the life of the cells. One example of this controversial position is illustrated by Harold Hilman and Peter Sartory in their paper 'A re-examination of the fine structure of the living cell and its implications for biological education', *School Science Review* (December 1980) **62**(219), pp. 241–52.

Read about the electron microscope and the ways in which specimens are prepared for electron microscopy in *Advanced Biology*, pp. 149–50. Then answer the following questions.

1 What do you understand by the term 'artefact'?
2 What features of the electron microscope, and the way in which living tissue is prepared for examination via TEMs, are most likely to cause artefacts to appear in the resulting images?
3 How may the technique of 'freeze etching' provide a mechanism for checking that the structures seen in a TEM are not artefacts?

7.8 Quick test

1 Distinguish between the following pairs:

  a nucleolus and nucleus;
  b magnification and resolution;
  c prokaryote and eukaryote;
  d animal cell and plant cell;
  e simple microscope and compound microscope;
  f electron microscopy and cell fractionation;
  g unit membrane and fluid mosaic model;
  h cilia and flagella;
  i tonoplast and plasma membrane;
  j phospholipid and protein;
  k smooth endoplasmic reticulum (SER) and rough endoplasmic reticulum (RER);
  l vacuole and vesicle;
  m cell wall and plasma membrane;
  n chromatin and chloroplast;
  o microtubule and mitochondrion;
  p primary cell wall and secondary cell wall;
  q plasmodesmata and pits;
  r bacillus and cyanobacterium;
  s transmission electron microscopy and scanning electron microscopy;
  t fixation and staining.

2 Which structure, membrane system or organelle do you associate with the following:

  a entry to and exit from a cell;
  b packaged lytic enzymes;
  c site of ATP synthesis and much of respiration;
  d control of the development and functioning of a cell;
  e site of protein synthesis;
  f secretion of proteins for export from the cell;
  g formation and secretion of lipids;
  h support and containment of a plant cell;
  i site of photosynthesis;
  j entry to and exit from the nucleus?

7.9 Essay assignment

Select one of the following:

- Illustrate the general structure of a eukaryotic animal cell as seen by electron microscopy. How does this cell carry out:
  a the packaging and export of proteins;
  b the destruction of defective organelles?

or:

- Describe the structure of the plasma membrane that surrounds and contains the cytoplasm of all cells. How does the structure of a bacterial cell differ from the structure of a typical eukaryotic cell?

8 Cell biochemistry

Summary

Metabolism, the sum of all the chemical reactions of life, includes both the build-up (**anabolism**) and breakdown (**catabolism**) of organic molecules. The molecules involved in the chemistry of life are referred to as **metabolites** or **intermediates**. Biochemists may investigate metabolism by detecting the presence in cells and tissues of the metabolic intermediates and the enzymes of the component reactions. Where pathways and reactions remain difficult to detect it may be necessary specifically to inhibit particular enzymes or to 'fix' intermediates by another chemical reaction, in order to establish what normally happens in the cells and tissues.

Energy for life comes from the **light energy of the Sun**, and is converted to **chemical energy** by green plants. Energy flows from organism to organism in the feeding processes that we summarise in food chains and food webs, but ultimately the energy of living things is lost to space as **heat energy**. Every molecule contains potential energy equal to the energy needed to form it. Metabolic reactions are coupled together, often involving **adenosine triphosphate (ATP)**, a reservoir of potential chemical energy. Reaction steps that require energy (**endergonic reactions**) are coupled with reactions that make available free energy (**exergonic reactions**).

Enzymes – biological catalysts made of protein – make possible all the reactions of metabolism. Enzymes control metabolism because each is **highly specific** in the reaction that it catalyses, because they are **very efficient**, and because their formation is indirectly **controlled by the cell nucleus**. The enzymes of cells are short-lived, and are constantly being re-formed. Enzymes work by forming a complex with the substrate molecule at a part of the enzyme surface called the **active site**. Various factors may alter the rate of enzyme-catalysed reactions, including the temperature, pH, the presence of co-factors and inhibitors, and allosteric effector substances. The effects on the rate of enzyme-catalysed reactions of factors such as these help us to understand how enzymes work as catalysts.

Practicals and activities

8.1 The effect of temperature on an enzyme-catalysed reaction

(Skills and techniques, Data generating)

The effect of temperature on the action of the enzyme lipase on milk lipids can be followed by measuring change in pH in a mixture of milk (substrate) and lipase (enzyme). The pH of the milk mixture is expected to fall as fatty acids accumulate:

$$\text{milk lipids (fat and oil)} \xrightarrow{\text{lipase}} \text{fatty acids} + \text{glycerol}$$

Lipase is a component of pancreatic juice, and in mammals is secreted into the duodenum during digestion. In the duodenum it works in the presence of bile, an alkaline fluid. The salts present in bile lower surface tension, causing fat globules to break up into tiny droplets.

In this laboratory experiment, the change in pH with time can be followed by taking readings with a pH meter.

Alternatively, pH change (for example) may be recorded by data logging, the process of experimental monitoring by electronic means. External apparatus, in this case a pH sensor, is linked to the computer. The output from the sensor must not exceed 1 V, or have a negative voltage. Monitoring equipment can be linked to any computer that has the necessary 'port' or socket by a Universal Interface (or the equivalent) and, if necessary, a connecting box, together with the appropriate linking leads and software. This permits fast, accurate monitoring of change and therefore improves the experimental process. The computer can also be used to analyse the data.

■ Aim

To measure the effect on the rate of enzyme action of increasing temperature, and to investigate the effect of the presence of bile salts on the action of lipase.

■ Risk assessment

- No pipetting by mouth is permitted; avoid contact with skin when handling enzyme solutions.
- Take special care when working with mains-voltage equipment (computer) near to water and aqueous solutions.
- Otherwise, good laboratory practice is sufficient to take account of any hazards and avoid significant risks.

■ Method

The experimental method

1 Set up the apparatus as shown in Figure 8.1, using the water bath at 20 °C.
2 Add 20 cm³ milk to the beaker, followed by 5 cm³ distilled water and 10 cm³ sodium carbonate solution.

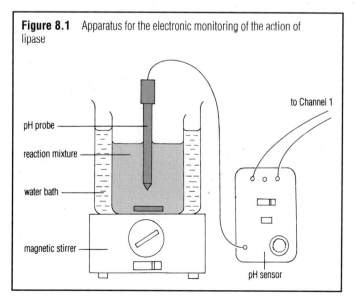

Figure 8.1 Apparatus for the electronic monitoring of the action of lipase

pH probe

reaction mixture

water bath

magnetic stirrer

to Channel 1

pH sensor

3 Place the beaker in the water bath and turn on the magnetic stirrer. Allow five minutes for temperature equilibration.

4 Start recording the pH (by pH meter or pH sensor linked to computer via analogue to digital converter), and immediately add 5 cm³ lipase solution. Record the pH change by hand or, if interfacing, by saving the data.

5 Repeat the process at 25, 30, 35, 40 and 50 °C, using fresh mixtures of milk, distilled water and sodium carbonate (as detailed for the experiment at 20 °C). To each, add enzyme as you start recording pH.

6 Finally, repeat the process at 35 °C with 5 cm³ bile salts solution in place of the distilled water.

Recording by interfacing

In interfacing, the sensor (a pH sensor, for example) produces an analogue signal, but the computer functions with digital signals. The analogue signal has to be converted to a digital one (a process known as A–D conversion). This is done by a BBC B microcomputer when the sensor and connecting box are connected via the analogue port on the computer. Other microcomputers (IBM-compatibles, Apple Macintosh and most others) require a connecting box or Universal Interface for A–D conversion, connected with leads appropriate to the computer, via the serial port which is standard on these computers.

1 Connect the interface (sensor and connecting box) to the computer (four-channel box to the A–D port of the BBC B, Universal Interface to the serial port of other micros).

2 Connect the probe to the pH sensor. Then, using appropriate leads, connect the sensor to the interface.

3 Switch on the computer, disc drive and monitor.

4 Load appropriate software (Philip Harris Datadisk Plus, for instance).

5 Then, following the screen menus, arrange for the pH sensor to be calibrated using a buffer solution of known pH, for the pH data to be recorded over a pH range of 2–12, and for a recording time of five minutes.

NOTE TO TECHNICIAN

Each student group will require (or require access to):
- water baths at 20, 25, 30, 35, 40 and 50 °C;
- 100 cm³ beaker (as reaction vessel);
- magnetic stirrer with flea;
- thermometer;
- 50 cm³ measuring cylinder;
- 10 cm³ plastic syringe;
- distilled water;
- 100 cm³ 0.1 mol dm⁻³ sodium carbonate solution;
- 150 cm³ whole fresh (pasteurised) milk;
- lipase solution, 5% (w/v);
- bile salts solution, 3% (w/v);
- electronic pH meter with probe, with buffer solution at pH 9 (for calibration), or pH sensor with connecting box and/or Universal Interface;
- microcomputer, disk drive and VDU, with printer attached.

■ Data presentation

A printer connected to the microcomputer will print out the pH change against time for each experiment. From the graph, determine the initial rates of reaction at each temperature, and plot these against temperature.

■ Conclusions

- Conclude how the rate of the reaction has been influenced by temperature. (The effects of temperature on reaction rates are discussed in *Advanced Biology*, p. 178.)
- What was the effect of the addition of bile salts? Why was it suggested that you used these at 35 °C?

■ Evaluation

If you attempted this experiment with a pH meter not connected (via interface) to a microcomputer, in what ways might your experimental results have been inferior?

8.2 The effect of enzyme concentration on the action of urease

(Investigation)

Urease is an enzyme which converts urea to ammonia and carbon dioxide:

$$NH_2 \diagdown \atop NH_2 \diagup C{=}O + H_2O \xrightarrow{\text{urease}} 2NH_3 + CO_2$$

It occurs in the final stage of excretory pathways in some marine invertebrates; in some legumes it converts stored nitrogenous compounds to ammonia prior to translocation.

In this investigation urease reacts with urea in an acidic environment (dilute ethanoic acid) and the changes in pH are observed as the urea is converted to ammonia.

■ Aim

To investigate the effect of increasing urease concentration on the rate of reaction.

■ Risk assessment

- Some enzymes cause allergic reactions in people handling them. Most enzymes prepared for detergent use are encapsulated (contained in granules formed by low-melting wax), but all enzymes and all enzyme solutions should be handled carefully. Avoid airborne dust from powdered enzymes, wear eye protection and mop up any spills immediately.
- Otherwise, good laboratory practice is sufficient to take account of any hazards and avoid significant risks.

■ Method

- Use 5 cm³ 1% urea solution acidified with 2 cm³ 0.1 mol dm⁻³ ethanoic acid in each test tube. Investigate the effect of the addition of 5 cm³ urease solution, working in

---

NOTE TO TECHNICIAN

Each group of students requires:
- test-tube rack and up to six test tubes;
- four labels or spirit marker;
- graduated pipette with filter or 5 cm³ syringe;
- 250 cm³ beaker (for rinsing pipette);
- 25 cm³ 1% urea solution;
- 10 cm³ ethanoic acid solution, 0.1 mol dm⁻³;
- 5 cm³ BDH Universal indicator (in dropping bottle);
- 30 cm³ 5% urease solution.

the range of 5% to 1% urease (1 cm³ urease solution + 4 cm³ distilled water).

- Measure the rate of reaction by timing the colour change of BDH Universal indicator (10 drops in each tube).

■ Data presentation

Present your results in a table.

■ Conclusion

Consider what has caused the change in pH and suggest why the speed of reaction varied in the tubes. (Study Figure 8.16 in *Advanced Biology* (p. 179) to see if it helps to support your explanation.)

■ Evaluation

- Do you think this experiment needs a control? If so, why? What would it be?
- What do you think would be the effect of continuing to increase the concentration of enzyme?
- In a living organism, what might be the advantage of an increase in rate of reaction with an increase in enzyme concentration?

8.3 The influence of substrate concentration on an enzyme-catalysed reaction

(Data generating)

Hydrogen peroxide is broken down by peroxidases in many organisms; its catalytic destruction results in the release of oxygen gas which can be collected and measured. A simple estimation of the oxygen release can be made by counting the bubbles through a standard nozzle:

$$2H_2O_2 \quad \rightarrow \quad 2H_2O \quad + \quad O_2\uparrow$$

hydrogen   the number of bubbles given
peroxide   off indicates enzyme activity

This experiment uses the peroxidase of yeast which is available without destruction of the yeast cells; a yeast suspension works as the enzyme solution itself.

The concentration of hydrogen peroxide solution is sometimes measured by the volume of oxygen that can be released from it. This convention has been used in this practical.

■ Aim

To investigate the effect of substrate concentration on the rate of an enzyme-catalysed reaction.

■ Risk assessment

- Eye protection must be worn when handling hydrogen peroxide.
- There should be no pipetting by mouth.
- Contact with the skin should be avoided, and clothing protected by a laboratory coat.
- Otherwise, good laboratory practice is sufficient to take account of any hazards and avoid significant risks.

■ Method

1 Assemble the apparatus as shown in Figure 8.2, without reactants, and adjust the temperature of the water bath to 20 °C. Support the side-arm test tube with a clamp, boss

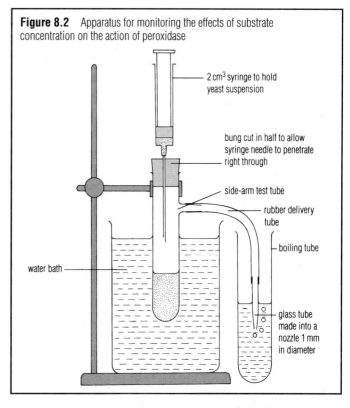

Figure 8.2 Apparatus for monitoring the effects of substrate concentration on the action of peroxidase

- 2 cm³ syringe to hold yeast suspension
- bung cut in half to allow syringe needle to penetrate right through
- side-arm test tube
- rubber delivery tube
- boiling tube
- water bath
- glass tube made into a nozzle 1 mm in diameter

and stand. Make sure the syringe needle is vertical so that fluid will be injected directly into the bottom of the test tube. Check that the bung fits the test tube without leaks and that the boiling tube is filled with water.

2 Measure out the first substrate concentration (4-volume hydrogen peroxide) into the test tube as shown in Table 8.1 and then 2 cm³ of pH 7.00 buffer.

Table 8.1 Solutions for Practical 8.3

Experiment number	1	2	3	4	5	6
distilled water/cm³	4.0	3.5	3.0	2.5	2.0	1.5
20-volume H₂O₂/cm³	1.0	1.5	2.0	2.5	3.0	3.5
concentration of H₂O₂	4 vol	6 vol	8 vol	10 vol	12 vol	14 vol

3 Make sure the yeast cells are evenly distributed through the suspension by stirring it up thoroughly. Then draw up 1 cm³ of the yeast suspension into the syringe. Have a stopclock ready and a table prepared for the results.

4 Fit the syringe into the apparatus and press the plunger in firmly so that the yeast suspension is squirted into the substrate and therefore thoroughly mixes from the outset. This is important for consistency of results. Disregard the initial rush of bubbles caused by the change in pressure as the yeast is injected. Start the stopclock at the moment this has passed. The depth of the bubble nozzle should be the same in each experiment, otherwise the pressure required to produce a bubble varies.

5 Count and record the cumulative number of bubbles released after each half-minute interval, up to at least six minutes.

6 Repeat at increasing concentrations of substrate, being very careful to clean out the side-arm test tube after each trial, and checking that the temperature remains constant throughout.

Each student group will require:
- a set of apparatus as shown in Figure 8.2, consisting of a side-arm test tube, a rubber bung (cut down), with a vertical syringe needle passing through it, and with a 2 cm³ syringe fitted to the needle;
- a short delivery tube fitted to the arm of the test tube, consisting of a glass tube with end drawn out, cut and flamed to produce a nozzle 1 mm at its outlet, with clamp, boss and stand to support;
- a 500 cm³ beaker as water bath, with a thermometer;
- a boiling tube and stopclock, and a calculator set ready to add one to the total each time the 'equal' key is pressed (for counting bubbles accurately when the delivery rate is fast);
- two 5 cm³ graduated pipettes;
- a supply of distilled water, 20 cm³ of 20-vol hydrogen peroxide solution, access to a stirrer (magnetic stirrer), and 1% (w/v) yeast suspension – each group will require about 10 cm³;
- 20 cm³ 0.2 mol dm⁻³ phosphate buffer solution at pH 7.0, p. 429.

■ Data presentation
- Present your results as a table showing the number of bubbles released after each half-minute for each concentration.
- For each concentration of hydrogen peroxide used, plot a graph of the number of bubbles released against time. These graphs will show an initial lag phase and then a fast reaction rate before slowing down as the substrate is used up in the reaction. To determine the initial rate, draw a line tangential to the steepest part of the curve (Figure 8.3). This slope can be read as the rate of reaction (bubbles per minute) for each substrate concentration.

■ Conclusion
Draw a graph of the initial rates of reaction against substrate concentration. You can now draw conclusions as to how the rate of reaction is affected by changing the concentration of the substrate in the reaction mixture.

■ Evaluation
These results can be used to determine the Michaelis constant (K_m), which can be determined by recognising the maximum velocity of enzyme activity under these conditions (V_{max}), finding half this value ($\frac{1}{2}V_{max}$), and locating from the graph the substrate concentration at this rate of reaction (*Advanced Biology*, p. 184).

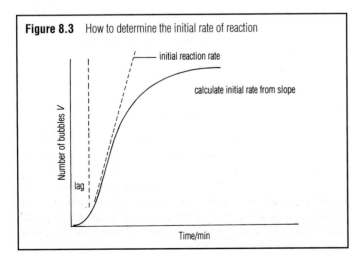

Figure 8.3 How to determine the initial rate of reaction

initial reaction rate

calculate initial rate from slope

Number of bubbles *V*

lag

Time/min

8.4 The effect of pH on the activity of an enzyme
(Investigation)

The shape of a protein is influenced by pH. Since the shape of a protein enzyme is also crucial to the functioning of the enzyme, changes in pH of the medium may affect the rate of an enzyme reaction. The optimum pH for an enzyme is the one at which the rate of the reaction catalysed is at a maximum. Optima of enzymes may vary according to the cellular (or extracellular) environment to which they are adapted.

Amylase is a very widely occurring hydrolytic enzyme, and it is available from various sources. This enzyme is of importance in the food and drink industry, and is used in biological washing powders, since it aids the removal of starchy and sticky dirt.

■ Aim
To investigate the effect of pH on the activity of amylase enzyme from different sources.

■ Risk assessment
- Some enzymes cause allergic reactions in people handling them. Most enzymes prepared for detergent use are encapsulated (containing granules formed by low-melting wax), but all enzymes and all enzyme solutions should be handled carefully. Avoid airborne dust from powdered enzymes, wear eye protection and mop up any spills immediately.
- Otherwise, good laboratory practice is sufficient to take account of any hazards and avoid significant risks.

■ Method
Compare the effect of pH of the medium on the action of 5% amylase solution obtained from the fungus *Aspergillus* spp., and 5% amylase solution prepared from a bacterial source for use in washing powders (such as NCBE, University of Reading, Termamyl).

1 You are provided with 1% starch solution, and citrate/phosphate buffer solutions in the pH range 2.0–8.0.
2 Conduct your investigations at a preselected temperature, say 30 °C, using the water bath provided.
3 The components of your reaction mixtures need to be pre-incubated at this temperature for about five minutes.
4 You can follow the progress of the 'digestion' of starch by transferring a drop of a reaction mixture to a drop of dilute I_2/KI solution on a spotting tile at regular intervals, and noting the colour. (Wash the glass rod before taking the next sample.)
5 Any results you obtain which appear to differ widely from other values obtained are best checked by repeating the experiment under the same conditions.

■ Data presentation
Present your results for both amylases on a single graph, which you will construct as you conduct the experiment.

■ Conclusions
- Identify the pH at which each particular amylase shows optimum activity.

- How may amylases with different optimum pH have arisen in the natural world?
- What is the advantage to a detergent manufacturer of an enzyme that operates effectively in a strongly alkaline environment (and at comparatively low temperatures)?

■ Evaluation
- What are the sources of error or inaccuracy in this investigation?
- What are the products of amylase action on starch? How could you have tested for the presence of these products?

8.5 The specificity of enzyme action

(Data generating)

A characteristic of enzymes as catalysts is their specificity; each enzyme catalyses one reaction, or at most a few closely related reactions. This is because only a few substrates have the appropriate molecular configuration to match the atomic arrangement of the enzyme's active site for binding and catalysis. We would therefore predict that only substances closely related to the enzyme's known substrate could possibly be alternative substrates for the same enzyme.

■ Aim
To investigate whether invertase will catalyse the hydrolysis of other disaccharide sugars closely allied to its substrate, sucrose.

■ Risk assessment
- Eye protection must be worn when handling these chemicals.
- There should be no pipetting by mouth.
- Contact of chemicals with skin should be avoided, and clothing protected by a laboratory coat.
- Otherwise good laboratory practice is sufficient to take account of any hazards and avoid significant risks.

■ Method
1 Set up the following solutions in numbered test tubes, as specified in Table 8.2. Add the invertase solution at the end, starting the stopclock as you do so. All volumes are in cm³, and all sugar solutions are made up using the ethanoate buffer solution at pH 4.7.

Table 8.2 Solutions for Practical 8.5

Tube number	1	2	3	4	5	6	7
5% sucrose	5.0			5.0			
5% lactose		5.0			5.0		
5% maltose			5.0			5.0	
pH 4.7 buffer (ethanoate)							5.0
distilled water				0.5	0.5	0.5	
invertase solution	0.5	0.5	0.5				

2 Sample the glucose content of each tube by using Clinistix strips at five-minute intervals, starting at time 0 (immediately after mixing the solutions) up to 20 minutes. Record the level of glucose after each test.

■ Data presentation
Tabulate the data on the appearance of glucose in the seven tubes with time.

■ Conclusion
Indicate the degree to which hydrolysis of the three sugars has been achieved by the invertase, and therefore draw conclusions on the specificity of invertase.

■ Evaluation
Find out, from reference sources, how different the alternative substrates are from the true substrate of the enzyme. From your results you should be able to say how small a change is necessary before a molecule becomes unacceptable as the substrate of an enzyme.

8.6 Enzymes and inhibitors

(Investigation)

A substance that reduces the activity of an enzyme is known as an **inhibitor**. An inhibitor may be a substance deliberately introduced into cells during biochemical investigation, but most inhibitors are substances occurring naturally in cells. Inhibitors may act directly or indirectly on an enzyme's active site. Types of enzyme inhibition are discussed in *Advanced Biology*, pp. 182–3.

You will investigate the effects of an irreversible, non-competitive inhibitor (a heavy metal ion) and a competitive inhibitor (a molecule with close structural resemblance to the natural substrate) upon the activity of the Krebs cycle enzyme, succinic dehydrogenase. Respiratory inhibitors like these are just as effective in animal tissues as in plant tissues, so they must be handled with extreme care.

Succinic dehydrogenase catalyses the oxidation of succinate to fumarate by the removal of hydrogen (as hydrogen ions and electrons). In experiments, this respiratory oxidation can be detected by the use of a dye, DCPIP (2,6-dichlorophenol-indophenol), which is blue when oxidised but colourless when reduced (Figure 8.4).

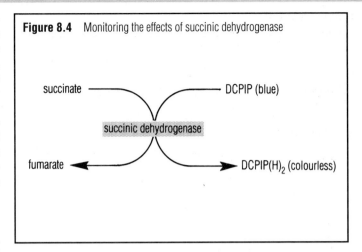

Figure 8.4   Monitoring the effects of succinic dehydrogenase

■ Aim

To investigate the effects of heavy metal ions (Ag^+) and malonic acid on the activity of succinic dehydrogenase obtained from plant tissue.

■ Risk assessment

- Enzyme inhibitors are metabolic poisons harmful to all forms of life. Handle them with great care. Students must not come in contact with the solids, but may work with small quantities of dilute solutions, held in labelled, stoppered bottles, if supervised. The hazards must be explained, as must correct handling procedures.
- The small volumes used should be measured out using a safety pipette (or syringe). Safety spectacles must be worn.
- Enzyme preparations containing added inhibitors should be in labelled tubes.
- When the experiment is completed, dispose of mixtures with excess water and rinse out the tubes before setting them aside for washing.
- Otherwise, good laboratory practice is sufficient to take account of any hazards and avoid significant risks.

■ Method

Making an enzyme preparation

A fresh preparation of 'enzyme' extract is prepared from three-day-old germinating French beans (*Phaseolus vulgaris*): use about 10 seeds. Remove the testas (seed coats), then chop and grind the seeds with $20\ cm^3$ of chilled sucrose solution ($0.4\ mol\ dm^{-3}$). Centrifuge the mixture for about 5 min in a bench centrifuge to remove cell debris. Store the supernatant liquid in a boiling tube, labelled 'succinic dehydrogenase extract', in an ice bath.

Investigating reaction rates

You are provided with:

- sodium succinate solution, $0.125\ mol\ dm^{-3}$ (substrate);
- DCPIP solution, 0.01% (dye);
- phosphate buffer, $0.15\ mol\ dm^{-3}$, pH 7.0;
- silver nitrate solution, $0.01\ mol\ dm^{-3}$ (**poison** – inhibitor);
- malonic acid solution, $0.1\ mol\ dm^{-3}$ (**poison** – inhibitor);
- distilled water;
- 'succinic dehydrogenase enzyme preparation'.

Using $5\ cm^3$ cuvette tubes, set up reaction mixtures to investigate the effects of the enzyme preparation and substrate solution on the dye solution in the presence and absence of the inhibitors. Follow each reaction in a colorimeter, using a red filter (600 nm). Record the change in percentage transmission over a 10-minute period.

You may have to experiment with the quantities of solutions used, since the activities of crude enzyme preparations are variable. It is likely that you will require $2.5\ cm^3$ buffer, $1.0\ cm^3$ of substrate and $0.1\ cm^3$ dye, with or without $0.5\ cm^3$ of an inhibitor. Keep the total volume of your mixtures the same by the addition of $0.5\ cm^3$ distilled water in inhibitor-free mixtures.

NOTE TO TECHNICIAN

Prepare the following solutions, and store in an ice bath prior to use:
- sucrose solution, $0.4\ mol\ dm^{-3}$ (for enzyme extraction);
- sodium succinate solution, $0.125\ mol\ dm^{-3}$ (substrate);
- 0.01% DCPIP (2,6-dichlorophenolindophenol, a hydrogen-accepting dye);
- phosphate buffer solution, $0.15\ mol\ dm^{-3}$, pH 7.0 (p. 429);
- silver nitrate solution, $0.01\ mol\ dm^{-3}$ (poison – inhibitor);
- malonic acid solution, $0.01\ mol\ dm^{-3}$ (poison – inhibitor).

Each student group will require:
- ice bath to hold enzyme preparation prior to experiment (small plastic bowl with ice cubes);
- stock solutions in labelled bottles in the following quantities (held in the ice bath):
  sucrose solution ($30\ cm^3$)
  substrate (succinate) solution ($10\ cm^3$)
  DCPIP solution ($10\ cm^3$)
  distilled water ($10\ cm^3$)
  phosphate buffer ($30\ cm^3$)
  and supervised access to:
  silver nitrate solution ($5\ cm^3$)
  malonic acid solution ($5\ cm^3$);
- boiling tube and label;
- six pipettes, $1\ cm^3$ graduated, with safety bulb;
- 10 *Phaseolus vulgaris* seeds, germinated for three days between layers of moist paper towelling;
- tile, strong scalpel;
- pestle and mortar;
- measuring cylinder, $20\ cm^3$;
- centrifuge and centrifuge tube;
- six $5\ cm^3$ cuvettes;
- access to a colorimeter with red filter (600 nm);
- stopclock.

■ **Data presentation**

Record on a graph the change in percentage transmission in the tubes over a 10-minute period.

■ **Conclusion**

Comment on which reaction mixtures change colour and which do not.

■ **Evaluation**

- Why is the volume of reaction mixture in all five tubes adjusted to be the same?
- Why are the ingredients kept at or about 0 °C prior to the experiment?
- Could the observed effects of silver ions and/or of malonic acid be reversed in any way?

Alternative investigation of enzyme inhibition

'Respiration in heart mitochondria – Teachers' Notes 4', Investigation 1 (Succinate as a respiratory substrate) and 2 (Inhibition of electron transfer from succinate), prepared for The Biochemical Society by A Myers as part of *Biochemistry Across the School Curriculum – Experiments for Use in the Classroom*.

8.7 The action of ATP on the contraction of muscle fibres

(Data generating)

Energy released from the hydrolysis of adenosine triphosphate is transduced by muscle fibres to the mechanical energy which causes muscular contraction. Even when muscle has been removed from the organism for some time, a sufficient part of its biochemical mechanism may remain operative for ATP to power muscular contraction.

■ **Aim**

To investigate whether addition of ATP to striated muscle can stimulate fibre contraction.

■ **Risk assessment**

⚠️

- Take care in the use of sharp instruments.
- Otherwise, good laboratory practice is sufficient to take account of any hazards and avoid significant risks.

■ **Method**

1 Take a clean microscope slide and arrange a strand of muscle on it so that it lies as straight as possible. Cut the strand, along its length, into as thin strips as possible. Use a rounded scalpel blade, with a pressing and rocking movement to avoid breaking the strips. Aim to get strips 20–40 mm long and 1 mm wide. Discard the remainder of the muscle tissue.

2 Use a marker pen to mark the underside of the slide to indicate the exact length of the muscle strip.

3 Add a few drops of distilled water to the strip, enough to wet the whole length. Leave it for a minute to see if this promotes any contraction and mark the new length if it does. Soak up the water with a filter paper, being careful not to disturb the muscle strip.

4 Repeat this operation to prepare a second slide with a comparable muscle strip.

5 Add a few drops of a dilute glucose solution to one strip and a few drops of ATP solution to the other. Mark the slides 'Gl' and 'ATP'. Mark any changes in length of the muscle strips.

6 Finally, discard the muscle and measure the marks to record any change in length of either strip.

NOTE TO TECHNICIAN

Each group will need:

- two clean microscope slides;
- marker pen (permanent);
- fine forceps, scalpel with rounded blade;
- dropping pipette;
- distilled water;
- 1% (w/v) glucose solution;
- ATP solution – this is available as ampoules containing 1 cm³ ATP solution, which can be drawn into a syringe: one ampoule will be sufficient for the whole class;
- strand of muscle – much depends on the quality of this strand. It is best taken from lean meat, such as pork, where the fibres of muscle are long and obvious. A thin strip is obtained by parting and peeling off the tissue with blunt forceps and a blunt seeker. The more fibres that run the length of the strand, the more effective is the result. Strips removed for the experiment can be kept in Ringer's solution or 50% glycerol if they are not to be used at once.

■ **Data presentation**

Express any change in length of the muscle strip as a percentage of the original length.

■ **Conclusion**

Bearing in mind that it is easy to disturb the fibre, which of the substances caused significant contraction? How does this fit in with your understanding of the action of ATP?

■ **Evaluation**

- Why was it experimentally important to add the substances separately?
- Why might you have expected the glucose solution to cause contraction?

8.8 Separation of amino acids by paper chromatography

(Skills and techniques/Investigation)

Chromatography is a very useful method for completely separating a tiny amount of a mixture of substances which are chemically related to each other. In practice it is a simple technique, although the theory of separation is complex.

■ **Aim**

To investigate the amino acids in fruit juices by paper chromatography.

■ Risk assessment

- The development of the chromatogram using ninhydrin solution (locating agent for amino acids) should be carried out in a fume cupboard, since ninhydrin is irritant.
- Eye protection must be worn.
- Otherwise, good laboratory practice is sufficient to take account of any hazards and avoid significant risks.

■ Method

1 From a roll of chromatography paper, cut off a length 5 cm longer than required to reach to the bottom of a large gas jar, which will serve as the chromatography tank. (Before handling chromatography paper, put on plastic gloves to avoid contamination of the paper with amino acids in the sweat on your skin surface.) Cut a wooden spill to fit across the mouth of the gas jar, and fold the top of the chromatography paper over it to allow the paper to hang down so that the lower edge is 0.5 cm above the base of the jar. Cut off spare paper from the top edge.

2 Remove the paper and, being careful not to splash the sides of the jar, pour in 60 cm³ of the solvent (butanol:glacial ethanoic acid:water). Cover the top of the jar with a thin polythene sheet and fix with an elastic band.

3 Rule a line 3 cm from the bottom edge of the paper in pencil. Along this line mark two origins, at least 1 cm in from the edge of the paper. Label these L for lemon and O for orange, or (if you are attempting to identify the amino acids) M for mixture. Identify your chromatogram with a mark at the top.

4 Load the origins on the chromatogram using extremely fine capillary tubes, formed from melting-point tubes, drawn out in a hot Bunsen flame and then left to cool. Dip one capillary into one fruit juice to take up some of the liquid. Then touch the capillary very briefly on the origin spot. Load only the smallest quantity possible in this way, and then allow the spot to dry. Repeat the loading process several times in order to build up the substances to be separated. Drying can be speeded up with a hair dryer, set on 'cool'. Spot out the other fruit juice or amino acid mixture in a similar way.

NOTE TO TECHNICIAN

Each student group will require (or require access to):
- a gas jar, preferably 30 cm tall;
- a plastic sheet and elastic band to act as lid;
- roll (or large sheet) of chromatography paper;
- scissors and disposable plastic gloves;
- wooden splint;
- 100 cm³ measuring cylinder;
- capillary tubes, formed from melting-point tubes;
- freshly extracted lemon juice and orange juice;
- aqueous solution of three amino acids (lysine, aspartic acid and leucine: 10 mg of each per 10 cm³ of water);
- 60 cm³ of chromatography solvent, of 4 parts butan-1-ol:1 part glacial ethanoic acid:1 part water (p. 429);
- hair dryer;
- access to oven at 100 °C, and ninhydrin spray.

---

5 With the tank in a safe place, lower the chromatogram into the tank, being careful not to let it touch the sides. Leave the chromatogram to run until the solvent front has travelled nearly to the top of the paper. With gas jars about 30 cm tall, the chromatogram will take about 18 hours (overnight), but small containers take less time.

6 Remove the chromatogram from the tank, and mark the level of the solvent front with a pencil. Allow the chromatogram to drain and dry. Then, using a fume cupboard, spray the chromatogram with ninhydrin solution. Dry the chromatogram in an oven at 100 °C. The amino acids will appear as coloured spots in 15–30 minutes. Circle each spot with a pencil, since some will tend to fade.

■ Data presentation

The chromatogram, suitably labelled, is the record of the experiment.

■ Conclusions

- It may be possible to identify the amino acids in the fruit juices by measurement of R_f values. The approximate R_f values in this solvent are: lysine, 0.14; aspartic acid, 0.24; and leucine, 0.73.
- If known amino acids were also used as markers, then their positions may also aid identification.

■ Evaluation

If possible, compare this separation with that obtained by paper electrophoresis (Practical 8.9).

Alternative method: thin layer chromatography

This chromatographic separation can be carried out on Polygram pre-coated thin layer chromatography plates. The method is extremely quick; the separation can be conducted during the practical class in which the chromatogram is loaded. The solvent in this case is propan-1-ol:water in the proportions 70:30; R_f values, of course, depend on the solvent used.

8.9 Separation by electrophoresis
(Demonstration by teacher/technician)

Many biological molecules carry an electrical charge, the charge depending upon the particular molecule and also on the properties of the medium in which it is suspended (such as its pH). In an electric field, charged molecules will migrate in solution to the electrode of opposite polarity. This is the principle of electrophoresis, and it is used to separate proteins and amino acids, for example. In laboratories where electrophoresis is routinely used, separations are normally carried out in polyacrylamide gel (PAG, *Advanced Biology*, p. 172). Paper electrophoresis is cheap, however, and can be used to demonstrate the principles of electrophoresis.

■ Aim

To demonstrate the separation and identification of the major amino acids found in orange juice (for comparison with a similar separation by paper chromatography described in Practical 8.8).

■ Risk assessment

- A potential electrical hazard arises from electrophoresis. The electrophoresis equipment must never be touched when the current is flowing. The demonstration should be set up with the electrical equipment disconnected from the power supply. When the demonstration is ready to start, the power pack is plugged in and the power switched on.
- At the end of the separation, the power must be switched off and the power pack disconnected before the electrophoretogram is retrieved for analysis.
- The development of the electrophoretogram using ninhydrin solution (locating agent for amino acids) should be carried out in a fume cupboard, since ninhydrin is irritant. Laboratory coat and eye protection must be worn.

■ Method

Kits for electrophoresis are available from several suppliers, complete with instructions. Entirely satisfactory results may be obtained with laboratory apparatus and equipment normally available, however.

1 The apparatus (Figure 8.5) consists of a glass tank with lid (or with clingfilm to cover), containing two crystallising dishes and a stand supporting a glass rod horizontally between and about 15 cm above the dishes. Place equal volumes of buffer solution in the dishes (necessarily the same volumes to avoid siphoning via the filter paper).

2 Place electrodes in the dishes so that a voltage current can be applied from an appropriate power pack, the positive electrode in the dish marked (+), and the negative electrode in the dish marked (−). Platinum electrodes, as used in the Hoffman voltameter, are suitable.

3 Take a strip of filter paper, 30 × 10 cm: in manipulating the filter paper strip, wear plastic gloves in order to avoid contaminating it with sweat (which you would find contains amino acids). Draw a faint pencil line across the strip, midway between the ends, and draw four pencil cross marks at 2 cm intervals along this line. Mark one end of the paper strip (+) and the other (−).

4 Apply the solutions to be analysed (see below) to the cross marks, drying the paper between spottings (use a hair dryer set on cool). The standard solutions (aspartic acid, lysine,

leucine) should be spotted about four times, whereas the orange juice needs to be spotted about six times.

5 Wet the filter strip from both ends in turn using buffer solution, but leave a dry strip in the centre (at the loading points). Blot the paper with dry filter paper discs to remove excess buffer solution. Then suspend the strip in position across the glass rod, so that the (+) end of the strip dips into the buffer solution in the (+) dish and the (−) end into the (−) dish. Use a fine capillary tube to moisten the centre of the filter paper with buffer between the loaded points, so that buffer diffuses quickly and evenly into the spots.

6 Cover the tank, connect the electrode to the power pack (DC supply, 120–350 V at 100 mA), and switch on the current. (The tank with lid safely isolates the apparatus when in use.) Run the experiment for 90 minutes at high voltage (350 V) or for 150 minutes at low voltage (120 V).

7 At the end of the experiment, switch off the current and disconnect the power. Then remove the paper from the tank and dry it in an oven at 100 °C. Spray the dried electrophoretogram with ninhydrin solution (in a fume cupboard), and re-heat the paper at 100 °C to develop the colour (Figure 8.6).

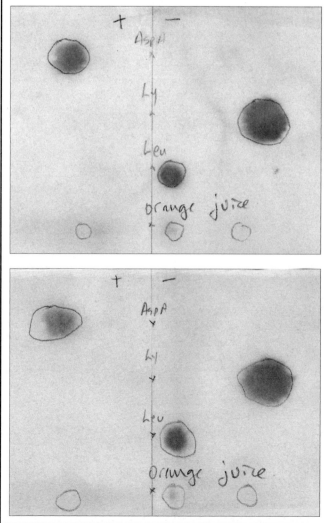

Figure 8.6 Paper electrophoretograms of orange juice, run on: **a** a Shandon kit (at high voltage); and **b** a laboratory-constructed apparatus (low voltage); the amino acids were disclosed with ninhydrin

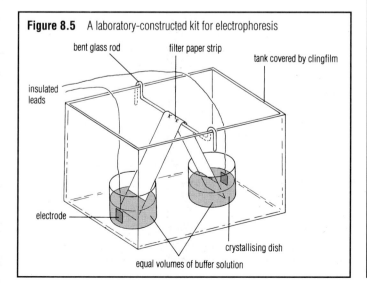

Figure 8.5 A laboratory-constructed kit for electrophoresis

NOTE TO TECHNICIAN

The teacher carrying out this demonstration will require the following equipment:

- apparatus and material for the electrophoresis equipment as described above, *or* a commercial electrophoresis kit from a laboratory supplier;
- one strip of chromatography paper (30×10 cm);
- pencil and ruler;
- fine capillary tubes;
- hair dryer;
- 'standard' amino acid solutions (10 mg cm^{-3}) of aspartic acid, lysine and leucine;
- fresh juice of an orange;
- 100 cm^3 of phosphate buffer solution, pH 6.0;
- ninhydrin solution;
- access to a fume cupboard and to a drying oven at 100 °C.

■ Data presentation
The dried electrophoretograms, suitably labelled up, using pencil, make a good record.

■ Conclusions
- The developed electrophoretogram demonstrates separation of amino acids. Comment on the positions of the individual amino acids at this pH. (Remember, amino acids with no net charge will stay in place in their initial positions, while positively charged molecules move towards the negative electrode, and negatively charged molecules towards the positive electrode.)
- From the separation involving fresh orange juice, identify the amino acids present in abundance.
- The process of paper electrophoresis can be compared with paper chromatography (Practical 8.8) as a method of separating and identifying the components.

■ Evaluation
What other properties of amino acids are due to zwitterion formation? (See *Advanced Biology*, p. 134.)

Projects

8.1 The properties of protein-digesting enzyme in fresh pineapple

Pineapple fruit (and stem tissue) contain bromelain, a protease enzyme. The action of bromelain on culinary gelatin can be used as an assay. The properties of the enzyme can be investigated, and the potential applications of an enzyme from plant material researched.

References
S R Dickson and G F Bickerstaff (1991) 'Pineapple bromelain and protein hydrolysis', *J. Biol. Ed.* **25**(3), pp. 164–6

G Bickerstaff (1988) 'Hidden powers of the pineapple', *New Scientist* (2 June 1988), pp. 46–8

8.2 The characteristics of one enzyme investigated

Taking one enzyme, for instance amylase from a fungal source (from a biological supplier), find the effects of temperature, pH, substrate and enzyme concentration on the rate of reaction. The enzyme plays a part in the baking industry in the 'improving' of bread, the process by which the consistency of dough is adjusted to make bread of desired qualities from modern bakery production lines.

Reference
P E Pritchard (1992) 'Studies on the bread-improving mechanism of fungal α-amylase', *J. Biol. Ed.* **26**(1), pp. 12–18

8.3 The free amino acids of citrus fruits

A range of fresh fruits is available. The amino acids occurring in the juice of these fruits can be investigated by chromatography (Practical 8.8) or electrophoresis (Practical 8.9).

Problems and assignments

8.1 Energy and metabolism: sources and fates

This assignment uses the concepts explained in 'Energy and metabolism' in *Advanced Biology*, pp. 168–9, and in 'ATP and metabolism', p. 173. It will help you to read and think about the ideas developed there before starting to apply them in the following exercise.

1 Choose a local habitat you are familiar with (a pond, wood, hedgerow or patch of waste land, perhaps). Give the name of an organism found there that is a typical example of each of the classes shown in the five boxes in Figure 8.7.
2 By what sequence of steps does the substances of a green leaf become incorporated into the muscles of a carnivore?
3 What is the ultimate fate of light energy that is incorporated into carbohydrate, lipids and protein in a green leaf?
4 Give three processes in metabolism in:
   a a green leaf;
   b a carnivore;
   in which heat energy is a significant waste product.
5 a In what form is the energy trapped in green plants passed to a herbivore?
   b Into what other forms may metabolic energy be transduced in a carnivore in the food chain?
6 What do you understand by the terms:
   a kinetic energy;
   b potential energy?
7 Give one example each of kinetic energy and potential energy:
   a in a green leaf;
   b in a leaf parasite.
8 Only about 10% of the substance of a sample of green leaf tissue, eaten by a herbivore, becomes incorporated into new herbivore tissues. List the sequence of processes by which significant quantities of the substance of leaf sample are 'lost' to the herbivore's body mass.

8.2 Manometry in biochemical investigation

Manometers are used to measure gaseous exchange by living things such as germinating peas or insect larvae. The Warburg manometer (*Advanced Biology*, p. 167) is often used in research laboratories. A simple manometer is illustrated in Figure 8.8. Examine the apparatus and then answer the following questions.

1 In a respirometer that is fully assembled and ready for use in an investigation:
   a why are both tubes immersed in water?
   b what is the purpose of the soda lime?
   c what is the purpose of the dead seeds?
2 Given the apparatus as shown:
   a why are the manometers constructed from capillary tubing rather than delivery tubing?
   b how could you use the syringes to measure the volume of oxygen absorbed in a given time?
   c explain how you would manipulate the three-way taps (and syringe) to replicate your measurement.
3 When the manometers are in use:
   a what is the significance of a rise in the level of liquid in either of the capillary tubes?

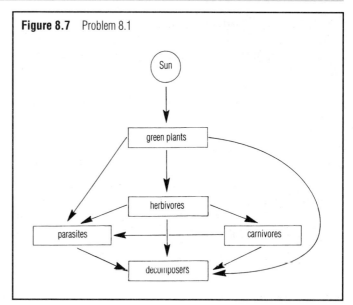

Figure 8.7   Problem 8.1

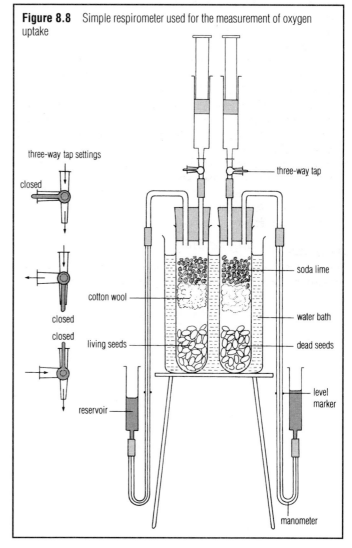

Figure 8.8   Simple respirometer used for the measurement of oxygen uptake

b why are you confident that change in gas volume in the test tubes is the result of a change in the volume of oxygen rather than in any other atmospheric gas?
c what would be the effect of a rise in temperature of the water bath?

8.3 Steps to glycolysis

The first part of glucose breakdown in tissue respiration may start with glucose as the substrate and end with the formation of pyruvic acid (pyruvate):

$$\text{glucose} \xrightarrow{\text{step I}} \text{fructose bisphosphate} \xrightarrow{\text{step II}} \text{triose phosphate} \xrightarrow{\text{step III}} \text{pyruvic acid}$$

$$C_6H_{12}O_6 \qquad C_6H_{10}O_6(P)_2$$

$$\begin{array}{cc}
CH_2O(P) & CH_3 \\
| & | \\
C{=}O & C{=}O \\
| & | \\
CH_2OH & COOH
\end{array}$$

where $(P) = PO_3^{2-}$.

1 Why is this part of tissue respiration logically referred to as 'glycolysis'?

2 Draw the structural formula for glucose in the form in which it reacts in cell respiration.

3 In step I, what is the significant and important change that occurs to glucose? Which ubiquitous coenzyme is involved?

4 For every molecule of fructose bisphosphate formed in glycolysis, how many molecules of triose phosphate are formed?

5 In step III, two molecules of ATP are formed from ADP for each molecule of triose phosphate metabolised. So what is the net production of ATP in glycolysis, for each glucose molecule metabolised?

6 The product of step III occurs in cells as pyruvate. Why is this so?

7 When glycolysis occurs in muscle actively involved in movement, there are two possible fates for the pyruvate formed. What are these?

8 One coenzyme involved in glycolysis is known as NAD.
  a What does NAD stand for?
  b What is the role of NAD in glycolysis?
  c In what form does this coenzyme occur as a result of the reactions of glycolysis?

8.4 Investigating catalase activity

The enzyme catalase is an oxidase, vigorously catalysing the decomposition of hydrogen peroxide (H_2O_2) to oxygen and water. Since hydrogen peroxide is a powerful oxidising agent that would denature proteins and interfere in metabolism if it accumulated, the widespread presence of catalase in tissues may be assumed to have a protective role. Dropping a piece of fresh liver tissue into hydrogen peroxide is a dramatic way of demonstrating the presence of catalase. The resulting effervescence can be exploited to measure the rate of enzyme reaction.

Read the account of a sixth-former's experiment in Panel 8.1, and then answer the following questions.

1 Plot a graph to show the effect of increasing substrate concentration upon the rate of enzyme activity.

Panel 8.1 Catalase activity

Ten graduated measuring cylinders (100 cm³ capacity) were labelled 1 to 10. A stock solution of '20-volume' hydrogen peroxide was diluted so that the cylinders all contained 10 cm³ of hydrogen peroxide solution, but of increasing strength. Cylinder 1 contained '1-volume H_2O_2', cylinder 2 contained '2-volume H_2O_2' and so on, up to cylinder 10 which contained '10-volume H_2O_2'. Ten samples of liver, each of approximately 1.1 g mass, were carefully weighed out, and the mass of each was noted. Mostly the correct mass of liver was cut in one piece, but for some samples an additional piece of liver was cut and added to make the exact mass sought.

One fresh sample of liver was added in turn to each cylinder, a stopclock started, and the maximum height of froth formed in two minutes was recorded. The results are given in Table 8.3.

Table 8.3

'Volume' of H_2O_2 in 10 cm³ of substrate	Mass of liver added/g	Volume of froth formed/cm³
1	1.16	14
2	1.16	17
3	1.14	26
4	1.15	28
5	1.17	35
6	1.14	38
7	1.14	39
8	1.17	41
9	1.15	42
10	1.16	42

2 How would you make the necessary dilutions of hydrogen peroxide substrate, as required for this experiment, given a stock of '20-volume' hydrogen peroxide solution, distilled water, and a 10 cm³ graduated safety pipette?

3 What safety precautions are necessary in conducting this experiment?

4 How could the student have modified the experiment to confirm that the effervescence was due to an enzyme present in the liver tissue?

5 What are the chief sources of potential inaccuracy in the way this experiment was conducted?

6 Show how the outcome of the experiment supports the idea that an enzyme has an active site where substrate molecules engage in turn. (You may choose to provide an annotated diagram for this.)

8.5 Quick test

1 Distinguish between the following pairs:

a anabolic reactions and catabolic reactions;
b kinetic energy and potential energy;
c endergonic reactions and exergonic reactions;
d intermediates and inhibitors;
e ADP and ATP;
f inorganic catalysts and biological catalysts;
g substrates and products;
h active site and activation energy;
i coenzyme and prosthetic group;
j 'lock and key' and 'induced fit' models;
k carboxyl group and amino group;
l competitive inhibitors and non-competitive inhibitors;
m allosteric activator and allosteric inhibitor;
n ethanal and ethanol;
o glucose and glycogen.

2 What technique or equipment do you associate with the following:

a the separation of charged particles (such as proteins or amino acids);
b the measurement of oxygen uptake by monitoring pressure change in a small flask;
c the measurement of light absorbed (or transmitted) by a solution;
d the isolation of a particular organelle fraction from a ground-up tissue sample;
e the separation of a mixture of substances by their distribution between a stationary phase (an absorbent) and the mobile phase (solvent)?

8.6 Essay assignment

Select one of the following:

• Describe the structure of the nucleotide DNA by means of a labelled diagram. Outline the distinctive roles of (i) ATP and (ii) enzymes in facilitating a cell process such as protein synthesis.

or:

• The discovery of the steps of metabolic pathways (such as the Krebs or Calvin cycles) has been a difficult and painstaking process. Why is this so? Outline the chief steps by which the biochemist, working in the laboratory, discovers a metabolic pathway.

9 The nucleus in division and interphase

Summary

In the **life cycle of a cell**, the period between cell divisions is known as **interphase**. At interphase the nucleus is not resting. Inside the nucleus are the **chromosomes**. Between cell divisions chromosomes direct and control the growth, development and functioning of cells by controlling protein synthesis. Most proteins are enzymes, and enzymes are essential for all chemical reactions related to cell structure and function.

When a cell does divide the nucleus divides first, followed by the cytoplasm. In the cycle of cell growth and division, the **chromosomes and the DNA they contain replicate** well before nuclear division commences.

Nuclear division, when it occurs, is by either mitosis or meiosis. In **mitosis** the daughter cells have an identical chromosome complement to the parent nucleus. Mitosis is associated with growth and with asexual reproduction. Mitosis is divided into four phases. The chromosomes appear already replicated as chromatids temporarily held together at the centromeres, as the nuclear membrane breaks down and a spindle forms. The fibres of the spindle pull the chromatids apart to form the basis of new nuclei at opposite ends of the cell. The cytoplasm then divides.

Meiosis consists of two divisions of the nucleus to form four nuclei, following only one replication of the chromosomes. In meiosis the chromosome number is halved. Each of these divisions is divided into phases with certain similarities to those of mitosis. The four nuclei formed are not identical. They contain an assortment of the maternal and paternal chromatids, and also recombinations of various parts of individual chromatids due to crossing over during meiosis. Meiosis is associated with sexual reproduction.

Chromosomes contain **genetic information** in a double strand of DNA. Information is in the form of the base sequence of this nucleic acid, and is referred to as the **genetic code**. A unit of information is three bases (hence the term 'triplet code'). The genetic code is faithfully **transcribed** into messenger RNA (mRNA) by a process known as transcription. mRNA passes to ribosomes in the cytoplasm where proteins are formed. Individual amino acids are identified by transfer RNA (tRNA) which carries a triplet code (anticodon) complementary to the code (codon) in the mRNA. At the ribosomes, amino acids – lined up in the correct sequence – are combined together by peptide bonds.

In the new technology of **genetic engineering**, genetic material is manipulated using naturally occurring enzymes that catalyse the breaking, joining and copying of DNA and RNA. Genes are transferred into prokaryotes with relative ease. These processes are revolutionising biotechnology, raising the possibility of improving commercial animal herds and plant crops by direct change in their genetic codes.

Practicals and activities

9.1 Mitosis in onion root-tip cells
(Skills and techniques/Data generating)

The apical meristem forms a small part of the root tip, and a proportion of the meristematic cells will be undergoing mitosis at any particular moment. To expose these, and to render chromosomes visible, the root-tip tissue is squashed and stained with aceto-orcein stain.

■ Aim
To see chromosomes and observe stages in mitosis in plant cells.

■ Risk assessment

- Avoid contact with aceto-orcein stain; wear eye protection and avoid inhalation of fumes during the heating phase.
- Otherwise, good laboratory practice is sufficient to take account of any hazards and avoid significant risks.

■ Method

1 Set up a 'steam bath' by heating about 200 cm³ of water in a 250 cm³ beaker.

2 Using fine forceps, remove an intact root from the rooting onion, and lay this on a microscope slide. Replace the onion with roots in water. Cut off and retain 0.5 cm of the extreme tip of the root, and transfer this tissue to a watch glass. Add 30 drops of aceto-orcein stain, and three drops of concentrated hydrochloric acid to help macerate the cells. As the steam bath approaches boiling, turn off the Bunsen, and sit the watch glass on top of the beaker. Leave it there for three minutes, taking care the stain does not evaporate away (top up with stain, if necessary). Turn the root tip to ensure even staining and complete maceration.

3 When three minutes is up, transfer the root tip to a microscope slide. Tease apart the cells of the root tip with a pair of mounted needles. Then add a drop of cold stain, and cover with a coverslip. Fold two or three filter discs into a pad. Apply this pad to the coverslip, and then press very firmly with the thumbs to squash the root-tip tissue.

4 Now examine your preparation. Ideally, you will see red-purple nuclei and almost colourless cytoplasm. If so, search for chromosomes and different stages of mitosis.

5 It is possible that you have overstained your section, giving cells that look evenly pink. Other errors that may occur include cells not separating sufficiently, or not squashing the tissues hard enough, or allowing the coverslip to slip sideways in squashing. In fact, it may be necessary to practise the technique a few times before producing a correctly stained preparation with stages of mitosis visible.

Student groups will require (or require access to):
- Bunsen burner, tripod, gauze, and bench pad;
- one beaker (250 cm³), with a watch glass that fits across the top;
- microscope slides, coverslips, filter paper discs;
- fine forceps, fine scissors, two mounted needles;
- dropping bottle of aceto-orcein stain;
- dropping bottle of concentrated hydrochloric acid (**Care:** corrosive!);
- compound microscope and bench lamp;
- an onion bulb standing on a small beaker containing water, with base of onion immersed (this requires setting up two to three weeks in advance, to allow prolific root growth);
- prepared slide of a thin section of an onion root tip taken through the apical meristem, stained to show chromosomes and nuclei.

■ Data presentation
Make fully labelled drawings of the stages of mitosis you are able to find.

■ Conclusions
- Work out the approximate proportion of cells undergoing mitosis within an apparently representative portion of the meristem.
- What proportions of these are at prophase, at metaphase, at anaphase, and at telophase?

■ Evaluation
If time permits, examine a prepared slide of a thin section of an onion root tip, stained to show chromosomes and nuclei. Compare the proportion of cells undergoing mitosis, and those at the different stages. Which stage of mitosis appears to you to take longest?

9.2 Preparation of anther squashes to observe stages in meiosis

(Skills and techniques/Demonstration)

In plants, the microspore mother cells in the anther divide meiotically and then become haploid pollen grains (microspores). By obtaining an anther at the right stage, very early in development, cells undergoing meiosis can be observed.

■ Aim
To observe stages of meiosis.

■ Risk assessment

- Avoid contact with aceto-orcein stain.
- Wear eye protection.
- Avoid inhalation of fumes during the heating phase.
- Take care when using a scalpel.
- Otherwise, good laboratory practice is sufficient to take account of any hazards and avoid significant risks.

■ Method

1 First, immature anthers have to be obtained. Select a young, growing flower cluster of *Tradescantia virginiana* and, without removing the flower cluster, cut away open flowers and any flower buds that have elongated stalks. Now select a flower bud that is only 2–3 mm long. Transfer this bud to a microscope slide placed on a white tile. Using mounted needles, tease out the anthers, without damaging them. Discard all other flower parts from the slide.

Alternatively, cut a bulb of hyacinth (*Hyacinthus orientalis*) vertically and a little to one side of centre. Dissect away the leaves from around the inflorescence. Remove one or two petals from around a lower flower, and remove two or three anthers using fine forceps. Place the anthers on a microscope slide.

2 Place the slide on a filter paper disc, and add two drops of aceto-orcein stain. Place a coverslip so that it rests on the intact anthers and, using the blunt end of a mounted needle, apply sufficient pressure to the coverslip to burst the anthers. Remove any excess stain from the slide at this point.

3 A little heat is necessary to bring about staining, but this must not be overdone. Have a blue Bunsen flame no taller than 2 cm high and, holding the slide at one end in a horizontal position, pass it just above the flame. It should just feel warm when held against the back of the hand. Pass it over the flame again a few more times, checking that the temperature of the glass continues to be bearable.

4 Next, examine the slide under medium-power magnification, looking for developing microspores with stained nuclei. Look for stages of meiosis. If you have overheated the tissue, the cells will be uniformly pink. If pollen grains are visible, then meiosis has already occurred, and the anthers selected were too mature. If the developing flower was too young, the cells appear uniformly round with large nuclei. (You may need to practise the technique a few times before you produce a preparation with cells stained correctly and with stages of meiosis visible.)

Each student group will require (or will require access to):
- a flowering plant of *Tradescantia virginiana* or a dormant bulb of *Hyacinthus*;
- white tile, filter paper discs, microscope slides and coverslips;
- two mounted needles, scalpel, fine scissors, Bunsen burner and bench pad;
- dropping bottle of aceto-orcein;
- compound microscope and bench lamp.

■ Data presentation
You will need to refer to photographs or drawings of stages of mitosis (for example, *Advanced Biology*, p. 188) to recognise the stages you find. Make annotated sketches of several stages, as time permits.

■ Conclusion
What stages of meiosis most frequently appear? Why do some steps appear to occur more frequently than others?

■ Evaluation
Why is it difficult to locate an anther showing stages in meiosis?

9.3 Building models of DNA

(Demonstration)

Understanding the DNA molecule and the way the information in the base sequence is 'tapped' for protein synthesis can be aided by the building of an appropriate model. Jim Watson and Francis Crick's original model was made of metal (Figure 9.1), but it was based on the known distances between chemical atoms and in hydrogen bonds. It was also the sort of model that facilitated predictions about the role of DNA, for example. The building of a much simpler model as part of your course is a practical exercise in which this otherwise largely theoretical topic may be explored to aid understanding.

■ Aim

To produce a simple (and preferably cheap) DNA model that would take no more than 30 minutes to build.

■ Risk assessment

Good laboratory practice is sufficient to take account of any hazards and avoid significant risks.

■ Method

Many starting points for models exist. You may choose to use one of the many pre-prepared ones, or you may prefer to design your own version.

1 Commercial kits are available from science education catalogues. Typically they cost between £50 and £100. For example, Philip Harris supply 'Nucleic acid biobits' and a 'Gene kit'. These come with detailed instructions. With careful use they can result in remarkably sophisticated structures.

2 'DNA, the marvellous molecule: its place in the story of life and evolution explained by means of cut out models'. This is a modestly priced 32-page booklet, printed on cardboard. It makes up into models of a short length of DNA double helix, a virus and two nucleotides.

Reference

B van Loon (1990) 'DNA, the marvellous molecule'. Tarquin Publications ISBN 0 906212 758

3 Children's construction toys have interlocking units, usually marketed in a range of colours. From these a simple model of DNA may be made. The types of construction toys available in toy shops change with fashions and prevailing technologies. An early example of the use of such a resource was the choice of Merit 'Criss Cross' units, as demonstrated by G H Duffett in the *School Science Review*. What do toyshops stock now, that might do an even better job?

Reference

G H Duffett (1974) 'Making models of DNA molecules is child's play', *School Science Review* (June 1974) 55(193), pp. 746–7

4 The dexterous and inventive manipulation of commonly available materials can result in extremely realistic models, often with good teaching and learning potential. An excellent example is the use of pipe cleaners, coloured plasticines and matchsticks, as demonstrated by Ann Copley in the *Journal of Biological Education*. Paper or cardboard models are designed and published from time to time, and offered as 'simple models' for us to try.

Figure 9.1 Jim Watson and Francis Crick with their demonstration model of the DNA double helix, taken at the Cavendish Laboratory, Cambridge, in 1953

References

A Copley (1990) 'A simple model to illustrate the essential structure of the DNA molecule', *J. Biol. Ed.* (Summer 1990) **24**(2), pp. 73–4

P Membiela *et al.* (1993) 'A model for demonstrating protein synthesis', *J. Biol. Ed.* (Summer 1993) **27**(2), pp. 92–5

NOTE TO TECHNICIAN

The sources of various models are detailed above.

■ Data presentation

The model is the presentation.

■ Conclusion and evaluation

Read Francis Crick's description of the role of various DNA models in the piecing together of the Watson and Crick hypothesis.

Reference

F Crick (1988) *What Mad Pursuit: A Personal View of Scientific Discovery*. Penguin

9.4 DNA extraction

(Investigation)

The discovery of the structure, properties and role of the DNA in cells, both prokaryotic and eukaryotic, is at the heart of the revolution we call cell biology. Despite this, there has been little experimentation with the laboratory procedures of extraction and analysis in school laboratories. This is because of the time needed for the procedures, the toxicity of some of the reagents used, and the lack of the necessary information. These reasons are no longer valid. There are currently available methods, kits and the necessary advice and help. The methods incorporate fundamental techniques used in current research in DNA.

■ Aim

To facilitate practical DNA investigations.

■ Risk assessment

The details of the necessary safety precautions are given in respective sources. The procedures carry no special hazard, other than those that can be avoided by good laboratory practice.

■ Method

Extraction and separation of DNA

DNA can be extracted from onion bulb. Finely chopped onion is briefly incubated at 60 °C, in a mixture of detergent and sodium chloride solution: the detergent causes cell membranes to rupture, and the sodium and chloride ions cause DNA molecules to coalesce. The mixture is then chilled to delay breakdown of the DNA itself. The tissue is blended briefly and the mixture is filtered, giving a filtrate containing soluble proteins and DNA. Finally, a protease enzyme is added to degrade the proteins associated with DNA, and a layer of ice-cold ethanol is floated on top of the extract. Precipitated DNA fibres form a web at the interface of the solutions, and can be drawn out on a rotated, fine glass rod.

References

National Centre for Biotechnology Education (1993) *Practical Biotechnology – a Guide for Schools and Colleges.* Department of Microbiology, University of Reading, Whiteknights, Reading RG6 2AJ

An alternative but similar approach is recommended by SAPS, using cress cotyledon tissue as the source. The necessary kit is available for purchase from SAPS once a training course for teachers has been attended.

Science and Plants for Schools (1993) 'Osmosis SAPS newsletter no. 5'. Homerton College, Cambridge pp. 2–3

Another method is to extract DNA from bacteria, such as *Escherichia coli*.

DNA Extraction Kit, Philip Harris Catalogue for Education.

DNA cleavage and fractionation

Restriction enzymes are used to cleave DNA strands, followed by electrophoresis to separate DNA fragments of different sizes. This advanced laboratory work is discussed in Chapter 29 (p. 351).

NOTE TO TECHNICIAN

The methods, equipment and chemicals are specified (and supplied in part or in whole) from the sources detailed above.

■ Data presentation

• The method should be recorded.

■ Conclusions

• Why is detergent effective in the disruption of membranes?
• Why must proteins be digested enzymically before pure DNA can be extracted?

■ Evaluation

• What are the advantages of familiarity with the practical steps of DNA extraction, whilst learning about the role of DNA in the intact cell?
• If DNA extraction is undertaken in association with DNA technology work (Chapter 29), then the DNA sample may be suitable for use with 'restriction enzymes' as part of an extended experimental procedure.

References

Progress in school- and college-level DNA technology is reviewed in:
M B Miller (1994) 'Practical DNA technology in school', *J. Biol. Ed.* **28**(3), pp. 203–11
G Peat and J Davy (1995) 'Accessible Sixth Form DNA Technology: SAPS and NCBE compared', *School Science Review* **76**(277), pp. 37–45

9.5 DNA and protein synthesis
(Videotape lecture/Demonstration)

The Biochemical Society publishes a series of videotape presentations. One, on DNA and protein synthesis, is introduced here. Two others are described in Chapter 12 (p. 140) and Chapter 29 (p. 351).

■ Aim

To illustrate the experimental methods used in research laboratories in the investigation of protein synthesis, and to review understanding of the mechanism of protein synthesis.

■ Risk assessment

No practical work is involved.

■ Method

There are three sections to the videotape, each lasting about 15–20 minutes. It will be helpful to see these sections on separate occasions, following up each part by discussion and further reading before viewing the next one.

Section 1: The Measurement of Protein Synthesis by Means of Radioactivity

Section 2: The Mechanism of Protein Synthesis

Section 3: Viruses, Bacteriophages and the Hershey and Chase Experiments.

NOTE TO TECHNICIAN

Access to a videotape player/TV monitor is required, together with a copy of the Biochemical Society's videotape *The Biochemical Basis of Biology – Videotape 2; DNA and Protein Synthesis*, produced by Dr E M Evans and Dr E J Wood, and a copy of the Teacher's notes supplied (available for use by the students).

■ Data presentation

Make notes on the key points as the videotape is played. Elaborate on these afterwards by group discussion, and by reference to the Teacher's notes and your textbook sources.

■ Conclusions

• What are the advantages of using radioactive isotopes in investigating complex cell processes like protein synthesis?
• In your view, what are the limitations of these techniques?

■ Evaluation

On this videotape you have been able to watch techniques that cannot be carried out in a general school or college laboratory. What else has the videotape achieved?

Projects

This chapter does not raise issues that lead directly to longer-term investigations. The behaviour of chromosomes in reproduction, and also the development of genetic engineering and DNA technology in particular, is discussed in later chapters (Chapters 26, 27, 28 and 29). Project suggestions are made in these chapters.

Problems and assignments

9.1 Mitosis

The four photomicrographs (Figure 9.2 A, B, C and D) show steps in mitosis in a plant cell, but they are arranged in the wrong order. Examine these photomicrographs carefully, and then answer the questions below.

1 Cells like those shown in Figure 9.2 occur in the apical meristem of a root tip. Starting with living tissue, what key steps must be carried out by a microscopist before photomicrographs like these can be taken?
2 List the letters A to D in the correct sequence, starting with the earliest stage and finishing with the latest.
3 a At which stage in mitosis is the DNA of the chromosomes replicated?
  b What is the condition of the chromosomes when they first appear in prophase of mitosis?
4 Figure 9.3 is a drawing of a cell at the stage of mitosis (metaphase) when chromosomes align at the equator of the spindle.
  a State whether this stage, as drawn, was observed in an animal or plant cell. How did you decide?
  b Identify the structures (i) to (v).
  c What is the function of structure (iv)?
  d Where does metaphase come in the rearranged sequence of stages A to D shown in Figure 9.2?
  e What is the number of chromosomes in the cell represented in Figure 9.3?
5 Four students each counted 100 cells observed at stages in mitosis in stained thin sections of a root-tip meristem of *Lilium* sp., recording the numbers at the various phases of mitosis. Their results are given in Table 9.1.

Table 9.1 Problem 9.1, question 5

Stage of mitosis	Student:			
	P	Q	R	S
prophase	64	75	68	73
metaphase	13	7	11	9
anaphase	5	2	8	5
telophase	18	16	13	13

  a What is the mean percentage of cells at each stage?
  b What do these results suggest to you about the process of mitosis in *Lilium*?

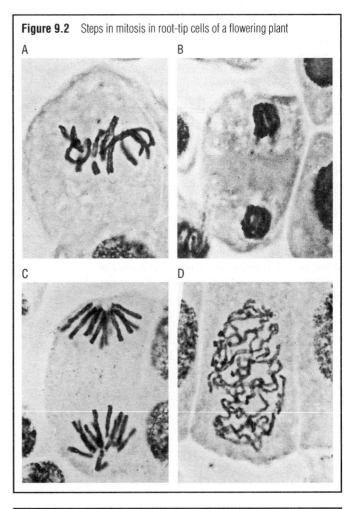

Figure 9.2   Steps in mitosis in root-tip cells of a flowering plant

A   B

C   D

Figure 9.3   Chromosomes at metaphase

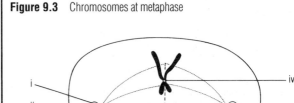

9.2 Mitosis and meiosis compared

The processes of the nuclear divisions, mitosis and meiosis, are illustrated in *Advanced Biology*, pp. 188–93, and the outcomes are contrasted on p. 186 and p. 193. Using this information and your general knowledge of biology, answer the following questions.

1 a When and where does mitosis normally occur in a flowering plant and in a mammal?
  b What are the products of the process of mitosis and cytokinesis of a cell?
  c How do the products of meiotic division differ from those of mitosis?

2 One important difference between mitosis and meiosis is the condition of the chromosomes as they become visible at the start of prophase. Make large, labelled drawings of a cell at the end of prophase in:
  a mitosis;
  b meiosis; showing prophase I.

3 In meiosis, bivalents are formed, but these structures are not formed in mitosis. What is a bivalent, and how does it arise?

4 By means of an annotated diagram, explain what we mean by 'crossing-over' between homologous chromosomes.

5 a What is meant by genetic variation?
  b Explain concisely the ways in which meiosis contributes to genetic variation.

9.3 DNA and protein synthesis; transcription and translation

According to the 'central dogma' of molecular biology, there is a one-way flow of coded information, from DNA in the chromosomes during protein synthesis in ribosomes of the cytoplasm. In Figure 9.4 this process is illustrated with reference to the formation of a tripeptide. Examine the diagram and then answer the following questions.

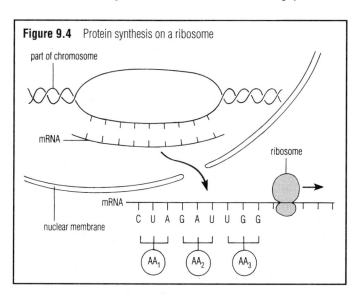

Figure 9.4 Protein synthesis on a ribosome

1 Information in DNA (and RNA), the 'genetic code', is a 'triplet code'. What does this mean?

2 Why do we believe the code is a triplet, rather than a singlet or doublet code?

3 The triplet code is said to be non-overlapping. What does 'non-overlapping' mean?

4 In Figure 9.4, what is the complementary base sequence of the coding strand for the length of mRNA shown?

5 Before amino acids are ready to participate in protein synthesis they require 'activation'. What does activation involve?

6 The following mRNA codons for three amino acids are as follows:

  leucine   = CUA, CUC, CUG and CUA;
  aspartate = GAC and GAU;
  tryptophan = UGG.

What are the corresponding tRNA anticodons for these amino acids?

7 What is the amino acid sequence in the tripeptide in the diagram?

8 The genetic code is described as a 'degenerate code'. What does this mean? Give an example.

9 The genetic code is said to be 'universal'. What does this mean?

10 What is the part played by the ribosomes in protein synthesis?

9.4 Quick test

1 Distinguish between the following pairs:

  a nuclear division and cell division;
  b mitosis and meiosis;
  c chromatid and chromosome;
  d nucleolus and nuclear membrane;
  e diploid and haploid;
  f centromere and centrosome;
  g crossing over and chiasma;
  h DNA and RNA;
  i purines and pyrimidines;
  j biotechnology and genetic engineering.

2 What do you understand by the following?

  a the cell cycle;
  b homologous chromosomes;
  c the chemical composition of the eukaryotic chromosome;
  d bacteriophage;
  e DNA double helix;
  f the central dogma of molecular biology;
  g semi-conservative replication;
  h the genetic code;
  i amino acid activation;
  j gene expression.

9.5 Essay assignment

Select one of the following:

• The genetic code is variously described as:
  a information;
  b a triplet code;
  c a degenerate code;
  d universal.
  Exactly what do these terms mean, and what is their significance?

or:

• Describe the parts played by enzymes in protein synthesis. What are the immediate and longer-term fates of the proteins commonly formed in cells?

10 Cell specialisation

Summary

After nuclear and cell division, most cells grow, develop and become specialised. **Growth**, leading to an increase in amount of cytoplasm, is a quantitative change. **Development**, the processes of specialisation (also known as differentiation), is a qualitative change. **Multicellular organisms** consist of many groups of specialised cells making up tissues and organs. (A **tissue** is a group of cells of similar structure that perform a particular function. An **organ** is a collection of tissues that perform one or more specialised functions.) The study of the structural and functional specialisation of cells to form tissues and organs is known as **histology**.

The **zygote** (fertilised egg cell) **of mammals** grows and divides repeatedly to form an **embryo** of three basic layers (**ectoderm**, **mesoderm** and **endoderm**). From the cells of these layers develop the body tissues of **epithelia**, **connective tissue**, **muscle** and **nerve**.

The **zygote of the flowering plant** forms an embryo within the seed. The embryonic stem (**plumule**), root (**radicle**) and leaf (**cotyledon**) consist of cells that develop to form the mature tissues **parenchyma**, **collenchyma**, **sclerenchyma**, **xylem** and **phloem**.

Practicals and activities

10.1 Exploring vertebrate tissues

(Data generating)

Four types of tissue are formed from embryonic cells: epithelia, connective tissue, nervous tissue and muscle tissue. The principle of vertebrate tissue specialisation is introduced here by reference to epithelia and certain connective tissues. The structure of muscle tissue is investigated in Chapter 22 (p. 260), that of nervous tissue in Chapter 21 (p. 246) and the composition of blood in Chapter 17 (p. 203).

■ Aim

To become familiar with the appearance, structure and occurrence of epithelia and connective tissues, as observed in mammalian organs, and to relate their structure to functions, where possible.

■ Risk assessment

Good laboratory practice is sufficient to take account of any hazards and avoid significant risks.

■ Method

Epithelia

The basic structures of four types of epithelium are illustrated in *Advanced Biology*, p. 208.

Using the medium- and high-power magnification of the microscope, examine the prepared slides listed below (or a similar selection). Look for the epithelia identified in the list, located as they are over the internal and external surfaces of the organs.

- Squamous or pavement epithelium: surface of Bowman's capsule, kidney; peritoneum lining the interior of the abdominal cavity.
- Columnar epithelium: interior of the gall bladder; interior of the rectum.
  - with goblet cells (mucus-secreting): interior of the duodenum.
  - with microvilli (or brush border): convoluted tubules of the kidney; villi of the small intestine.
  - ciliated: interior of the trachea; interior of the oviduct.
- Cubical epithelium: interior of the thyroid gland; collecting ducts of the kidney tubule.
- Stratified epithelium: interior of the vagina; outer surface of the skin.

Make a large, fully annotated drawing of one example of each of the epithelia listed above, drawing attention to the features which aid recognition, and to the role of the epithelium as far as this is clear.

Comparative study of cartilage and bone

The basic structures of cartilage and bone are illustrated in *Advanced Biology* on pp. 210–11.

Using the medium- and high-power magnification of the microscope, examine prepared slides of sections of hyaline cartilage of the cartilaginous rings of the trachea, and of the vertebrae of a mammalian fetus. Make a large, fully annotated drawing of one example of cartilage you have observed in section, drawing attention to the features which aid recognition.

Using the medium- and high-power magnification of the microscope, examine prepared slides of sections of bone, both compact and cancellous. Make a large, fully annotated drawing of a representative portion of the compact bone you have observed in section, drawing attention to the features which aid recognition.

Finally, draw up a table that contrasts the structure and function of bone and cartilage in the body.

Students will require the use of a microscope (medium- and high-power) with bench lamp if necessary, together with access to the following prepared, stained slides of mammalian organs:

- section of mammalian kidney;
- section of abdominal cavity wall;
- section of gall bladder;
- section of rectum, with body wall;
- section of intestines (duodenum and small intestine);
- section of trachea and thyroid gland;
- section of oviduct and vagina;
- section of external skin;
- section of young fetus, showing cartilaginous vertebrae;
- section of bone showing compact and spongy bone.

■ Data presentation

Record your observations as large, clearly labelled diagrams (p. 4).

■ Conclusion

Annotate the drawings you make with comments on structure in relation to function, or compare the tissues you observe by means of a table.

■ Evaluation

The microcomputer can increasingly be used as an aid to study of structure in biology. The program *Histology Without Tears* (for Acorn Archimedes – RISC OS 2 or 3, running from the hard disc, and requiring about 2.5 MB) is one example. Designed for undergraduates, it may be selectively adapted as a revision experience, p. 430.

10.2 Exploring flowering plant tissues
(Data generating/Skills and techniques)

Meristematic cells give rise to the primary cells and tissues of the flowering plant stem. The cells that make up these tissues can be examined in transverse and longitudinal sections (TS, LS respectively) in order to learn about their structure. These cells have important structural and functional roles in the stem.

■ Aim

To understand the structures of the cells that make up parenchyma, collenchyma, sclerenchyma (fibres), xylem and phloem, as seen in the dicotyledonous stem.

■ Risk assessment

- Take special care with razor blades (or razors) when sectioning plant tissues.
- Avoid contacts between your skin and any stains you use.
- Otherwise, good laboratory practice is sufficient to take account of any hazards and avoid significant risks.

■ Method

Hand-cut sections and temporary mounts

Cutting the sections Using part of a young plant stem at the internode region (no leaves attached here), cut thin transverse

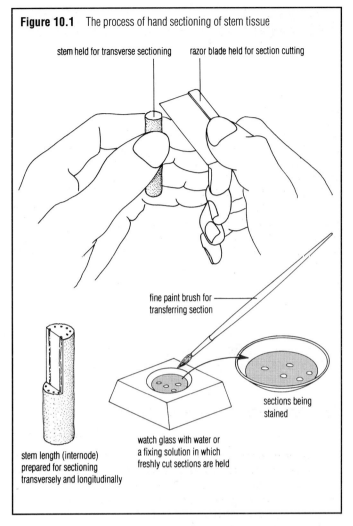

Figure 10.1 The process of hand sectioning of stem tissue

stem held for transverse sectioning

razor blade held for section cutting

fine paint brush for transferring section

sections being stained

watch glass with water or a fixing solution in which freshly cut sections are held

stem length (internode) prepared for sectioning transversely and longitudinally

sections using a one-sided razor blade, as shown in Figure 10.1. This technique yields good sections, but it may require practice. The following points are important:

- hold the stem between the thumb and the first joint of the index finger;
- hold the back of the razor blade between the thumb and index finger of the other hand;
- slide the blade towards you, using the pad of the finger behind your specimen as a guide for the blade;
- keep the thumb holding the stem low, to avoid being cut;
- wet the specimen and the blade to reduce friction – and keep them moist;
- cut sections as thin as you can get them;
- keep the blade at right angles to the stem, to avoid cutting any oblique sections;
- transfer the sections from blade to water in a watch glass, using a well-moistened paint brush.

Staining and mounting sections (temporary mounts)

1 Make a selection of your thinnest sections (they look the most transparent in water), and transfer them to microscope slides with the paint brush, about two per slide. Remember, incomplete sections ('wedges') often taper to one cell thick, so use these too.

2 Add a drop of toluidine blue to the sections on slides, leave for one minute for take-up of the stain to produce intense colouring, and then absorb the excess with filter paper. Add a little dilute glycerol as mounting fluid, and add a coverslip

(Figure 1.1, p. 3). Set up two or more microscope slides in this way; you cannot tell at this stage which sections will give you the best view of cells and tissues. Toluidine blue stains tissues as follows:

- parenchyma and collenchyma cell walls (largely cellulose, with pectins): pink/purple colour;
- sclerenchyma, xylem and tracheids (lignified walls): greenish blue/bright blue.

Examining the mounts Use both medium and high power of the microscope. Identify parenchyma, collenchyma and sclerenchyma (fibre) tissues for their positions and the appearance of the walls. The sclerenchyma cells are lignified, and normally have by far the thickest walls.

Draw two or three cells of each type, paying attention to size, wall thickness and the presence or absence of air spaces between cells

Sclerenchyma exists as fibres and occasionally as sclereids. Sclereids are studied in Chapter 18, p. 212.

Permanent mounts for phloem structure

1 Examine prepared slides of a TS and LS of a dicotyledonous plant stem. Look for the three types of cell you examined in temporary mounts (parenchyma, collenchyma and fibres), and check out how they differ in LS.

2 Now find the vascular bundles in both TS and LS. Locate the phloem tissue in the bundles. This occurs in the outer half of the vascular bundle, below the cap of fibres.

Examine the phloem tissue carefully. It may contain some parenchyma, but it consists mostly of sieve tubes and companion cells, in the ratio 1:1. Look for evidence of sieve plates in the ends of the sieve tube elements. If a TS has passed through the end wall of a sieve tube you will see the sieve plate in plan view. In LS the sieve plates may be seen in section, or obliquely, since the sieve plates often occur at a slight angle.

3 Make a record of the structure of phloem cells, drawing three or four cells (sieve tube elements and companion cells) as seen in TS and LS.

Macerated stem preparations

Chemicals can be used to break down the middle lamella between cells so that they no longer adhere, a technique called maceration. When macerated tissue is teased apart, individual cells can be observed. The techniques of maceration (e.g. Fraklin's method) are often potentially dangerous. They must be carried out by a technician, if they are attempted at all. Details of maceration technique can be found in appropriate advanced laboratory manuals. Canning rhubarb (leaf stalk) has a comparable effect, however, so that a piece of canned rhubarb is a useful, safe alternative to macerated stem.

1 Place a piece of canned rhubarb on a watch glass. Cut it into half and, from this smaller block of tissue, pick out one or more vascular bundles, using fine forceps. Place the lengths of vascular tissue on individual microscope slides. Using two mounted needles, tease the tissues apart. Cover with a drop of toluidine blue, and leave for one minute. Draw off the excess stain with filter paper, cover the tissue with dilute glycerol, and mount under a coverslip.

2 Examine your preparations under medium- and high-power magnifications. If the tissue is inadequately teased apart you may achieve better separation by placing your slide on the bench on filter paper, and then pressing down on the coverslip with your thumbs covered by a filter paper pad. (Allow no lateral movement of your coverslip, of course.) Afterwards, you may need to re-irrigate the tissue with glycerol. Place a drop on the slide beside the coverslip; it will enter by capillarity. Blot off excess glycerol and re-examine the slide.

3 Look for xylem vessels, fibres and tracheids among the separated cells. The xylem vessels and tracheids may exhibit different types of wall thickening, showing annular or spiral thickening or other more massively thickened lignifications.

Make drawings of a few xylem vessel elements, showing the junctions between vessel segments. Also look for tracheids. The end walls of these have not dissolved away, so you see complete, fibre-like water-conducting cells.

NOTE TO TECHNICIAN

Each student requires:

- compound microscope (medium- and high-power) and lamp;
- slides, coverslips and lens tissues;
- two mounted needles, fine forceps;
- a single-sided, stiff-backed razor blade;
- two watch glasses, paint brush, filter paper, and distilled water in wash-bottle;
- one dropping bottle of toluidine blue and one of 50% glycerol;
- short lengths (internodes) of the stem of a dicotyledonous plant, such as white deadnettle (*Lamium album*), cow parsley (*Antheriscus sylvestris*) or mint (*Mentha* sp.);
- prepared slides of TS and LS of a dicotyledonous stem, such as sunflower (*Helianthus annuus*), carefully selected to show phloem tissue clearly;
- pieces of tinned rhubarb petiole (*Rheum rhaponticum*).

■ Data presentation

Make careful, labelled drawings of two or three representative cells, drawn to scale. Since parenchyma cells are thin-walled you will need to use a single firm, clear pencil line. For most other types of cell (excluding phloem) the walls will need to be represented by two lines, the inner and the outer surface (or the middle lamella of adjoining cells).

■ Conclusion

Where you are able to do so, make an additional comment about the way the structure of a tissue appears to be related to function.

■ Evaluation

How variable are the cells of any one type within any one stem? How appropriate is it to talk about a representative group of two or three cells, in general?

Projects

This chapter does not raise issues that lead directly to longer-term investigations. The growth and development of animals and plants are discussed in later chapters (Chapters 19, 26 and 27). Project suggestions are made in these chapters.

Figure 10.2 Photomicrographs of three types of epithelium, seen in section plus an illustration of a section through a ciliated epithelium

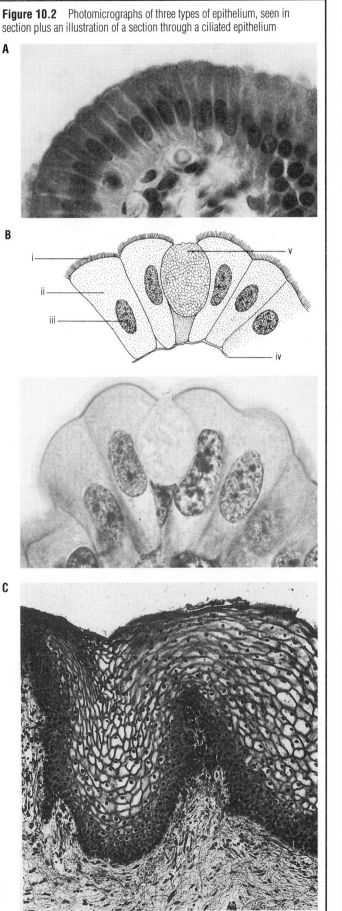

Problems and assignments

10.1 Epithelia

An epithelium is a tissue that lines an internal or external surface of an animal's body. The structure of the various types of epithelium is illustrated in *Advanced Biology*, pp. 208–9. Examine the photomicrographs of epithelia shown in Figure 10.2, and then answer the following questions.

1 Epithelia consist of relatively simple cells. What general role do they fulfil?
2 a What type of epithelium is represented by photomicrograph A?
   b Capillary blood vessels occur close to this type of epithelium in the body, and it often occurs in association with goblet cells. What part do the blood capillaries and goblet cells play in the function of this epithelium?
3 a What type of epithelium is represented by photomicrograph B?
   b Where in the body might such an epithelium be found, and how would it contribute to the function of the organs concerned?
   c Identify the features (i), (ii), (iii), (iv) and (v).
4 a The epithelium represented by photomicrograph C forms a tough, impervious barrier. How do the structure and growth of this type of epithelium make this possible?
   b Make a labelled drawing (tissue map) of a representative portion of the epithelium shown in C. Where in the body of the mammal might you expect to find this epithelium?
5 Epithelia are attached to the underlying tissues by means of a basement membrane. What does the basement membrane consist of?

10.2 Connective tissue

Blood and compact bone tissue are two important examples of connective tissues found in the mammalian body. Figure 10.3 shows the structures of these tissues. Examine this illustration and answer the questions below, using your existing knowledge or by reference to *Advanced Biology*, pp. 210–14.

Figure 10.3 Photomicrographs showing the structures (top) of blood and (bottom) of compact bone tissue

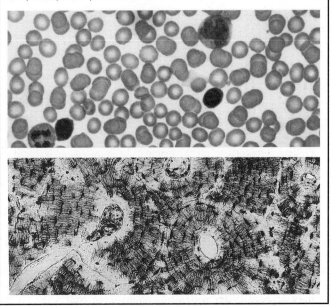

1 Connective tissues contain large amounts of intercellular material, called the matrix. In bone and blood the matrices are different in origin and composition. Draw up a concise table to contrast the matrices of blood and bone, their origins, compositions and functions.

2 **a** Where is compact bone typically located within the mammalian skeleton?

  b What is the role of the bone cells (osteocytes)? How are they supplied with nutrients?

  c Make an interpretative drawing of bone tissue as shown in Figure 10.3. Label the structures shown and state their functions.

3 Most of the cells in blood are erythrocytes (red cells).

  a Where are the red cells made, and what distinctive changes occur to them in production?

  b Make a large, labelled drawing of a red cell to show its mature structure.

4 The 'blood cell fraction' also consists of platelets and leucocytes (white cells).

  a What are platelets, and what is their role in the function of blood?

  b White cells, though of different types, have a broadly similar role in the functioning of blood. Outline the role of white cells.

  c In the photomicrograph (Figure 10.3, p. 129), what is the ratio of red to white cells? Is this ratio typical of human blood?

5 Blood has a key part in the survival of the mammal. List the processes of the body in which the contribution of the blood circulation is vital to survival of the organism.

10.3 Muscle

Figure 10.4 shows the structure of two different types of muscle found in the mammalian body. Examine this illustration, and then answer the questions below.

1 What are the essential features of muscle tissue that distinguish it from the other tissues of the body?

2 Muscle tissue of whatever type usually contains abundant mitochondria. What is the role of these organelles in the functioning of muscle tissue?

3 **a** Why is voluntary muscle so named?

  b Make large line drawings of the voluntary muscle and the cardiac muscle fibres shown in Figure 10.4, and label the structures you can identify.

  c The voluntary muscle fibre is referred to as a syncytium. What does this mean?

  d Make labelled sketches to show the relationship of the voluntary muscle fibre in the photograph, to the gross structure of a voluntary (skeletal) muscle.

4 There are three types of muscle tissue in the mammalian body. The type not illustrated here is referred to as involuntary muscle.

  a State three places in the mammalian body where involuntary muscle fibres occur.

  b Make a large labelled diagram to illustrate the structure of an involuntary muscle fibre.

  c What sort of contraction is involuntary muscle typically capable of?

5 **a** Write a concise sentence to describe the structure of cardiac muscle.

  b The impulses that stimulate contraction of cardiac muscle are described as 'myogenic'. What does this mean? How does it contrast with the situation in involuntary muscle?

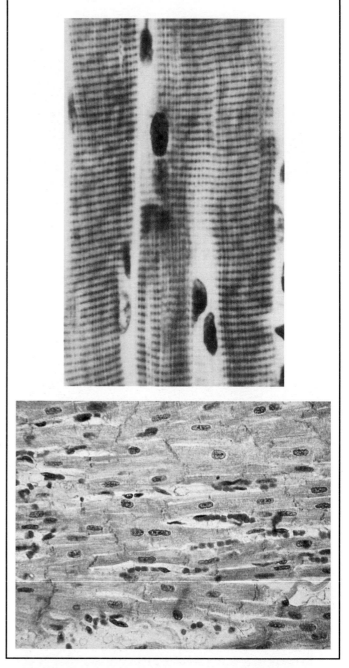

Figure 10.4 Photomicrographs of two types of mammalian muscle (magnification: top (×1100); bottom (×340))

10.4 Primary tissues of flowering plants

Figure 10.5 shows part of the stem of a flowering plant seen in TS. Examine the appearance of the cells of these tissues, and then answer the questions below.

1 Make a large, fully labelled tissue map of the vascular bundle to show the distribution of the tissues.

2 Which of the five tissues labelled are most likely to consist of or contain dead cells, empty of contents?

3 **a** The tissue labelled 'parenchyma' shows little structural specialisation. What roles or functions does parenchyma have in the life of the plant?

  b Make a large, labelled diagram to show the structure of a parenchyma cell, as seen in LS.

Figure 10.5 Photomicrograph of a stem of a flowering plant, seen in TS, with one vascular bundle much enlarged

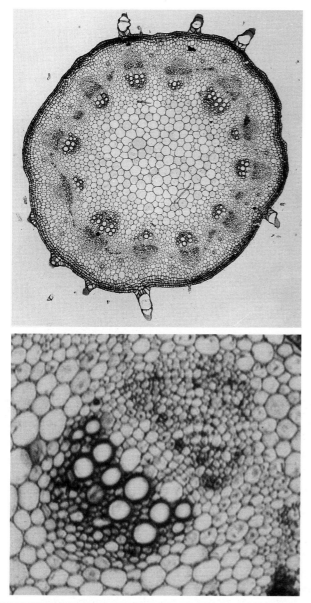

10.5 Quick test

1 Distinguish between the following pairs:

   a tissue and organ;
   b simple and compound epithelia;
   c compact and spongy bone;
   d erythrocytes and leucocytes;
   e voluntary and involuntary muscle;
   f sensory and motor neurones;
   g myelinated and unmyelinated fibres;
   h parenchyma and collenchyma;
   i fibres and sclereids;
   j xylem and phloem.

2 What do you understand by the following terms?

   a division of labour;
   b histology;
   c maceration;
   d connective tissue of mammals;
   e plasma;
   f syncytium or coenocytic arrangement;
   g nerves;
   h meristem;
   i tracheids;
   j primary tissues of plants.

10.6 Essay assignment

Select one of the following:

- By means of annotated diagrams, show the structure of a meristematic plant cell, and the changes undergone during differentiation of a parenchyma cell and a xylem vessel.

or:

- In what ways do the cells of:
   a the blood;
   b a neurone;
   c a voluntary muscle fibre
   differ from the general features shown by an unspecialised animal cell?

4 a The collenchyma occurs immediately below the epidermis. In what ways does the structure of the cells of this tissue reflect the functions of collenchyma in the living stem?

  b Make a large, labelled diagram to show the structure of a collenchyma cell, as seen in LS.

5 a What is the chief role of sclerenchyma (fibres) in the stem of the flowering plant?

  b At what stage of the growth and development of the flowering plant stem are fibres formed?

6 a By means of labelled diagrams, explain how a mature sieve tube cell with companion cell is formed from a procambial cell.

  b What is the chemical composition of the walls of phloem? In what ways does this differ from that of fibres?

7 a Xylem vessels are of different types, but this is apparent only when they are viewed in LS. Make an annotated diagram of four different xylem vessels, as seen in LS.

  b How does the shape of a typical fibre differ from a xylem vessel, when viewed in LS?

11 Movement in and out of cells

Summary

Substances enter and leave cells by **crossing the cell membrane** to and from an external aqueous environment, whether the cell is of an animal or plant, and in both terrestrial and aquatic organisms. Entry and exit of substances are involved in water uptake and loss, respiratory gas exchange, nutrition, secretion, growth, behaviour, response and coordination. The mechanisms of transport are **diffusion** and **osmosis**, **active uptake**, and **endocytosis** (phagocytosis or pinocytosis).

Diffusion is the movement of particles down a concentration gradient, from a region of high concentration to a region of low concentration. **Osmosis** is a special case of diffusion involving aqueous solutions separated by a partially permeable membrane. In aqueous solutions, because many of the water molecules are associated with the solute particles, they have a lower free energy, and are less likely to diffuse. Cell water relations are determined largely by the osmotic concentration of the cell sap (known as the solute potential) and the pressure potential of the cell (pressure due to the wall or the turgidity of the cell).

Active uptake by cells is a highly selective process. Energy is expended to maintain the membranes as leakproof barriers and in order to transport wanted substances across. Active transport occurs at special transport proteins in the membranes, known as primary and secondary pumps.

The **bulk transport** of substances across membranes also takes place. Solids and liquids may cross the membrane in small vacuoles or vesicles formed from cell membrane. The importing of substances by bulk transport is known as endocytosis. The reverse process results in the secretion of substances from the cell, and is known as exocytosis.

Practicals and activities

11.1 The thermal death point of cytoplasm
(Investigation)

The beetroot contains an intensely red, water-soluble pigment in the cell vacuoles. If the plasma membrane (a key component of the cytoplasm) is damaged, the pigment may escape in sufficient quantities to be detected in the aqueous medium around the tissue. One effect of heat on cell membranes is to denature the proteins in them irreversibly (*Advanced Biology*, p. 225).

■ Aim
To determine the temperature at which the beetroot plasma membrane is denatured by heat.

■ Risk assessment
Good laboratory practice is sufficient to take account of any hazards and avoid significant risks.

■ Method
Design and carry out an investigation to determine the approximate temperature at which membrane protein is denatured, using replicate cylinders of well-washed beetroot tissue.

1 Cylinders of tissue (cut to fit easily into the available test tubes) should be subjected to a fixed period in water at one of a range of temperatures between 25 and 65 °C.
2 This tissue sample should then be allowed to stand in distilled water for a fixed period (say 15 minutes) at room temperature, before being discarded. The water sample will contain any pigment that has escaped from the tissue.
3 The intensity of the colour of this solution can be measured with a colorimeter, using a filter that is complementary (for a red solution a blue filter is required). Set the scale zero using the solvent (distilled water) only.

NOTE TO TECHNICIAN

Each student group will require (or require access to):
- part of a fresh beetroot;
- tile, sharp knife, cork borer of appropriate diameter;
- 250 cm^3 beaker and access to sink, to wash cylinders in tap water;
- plastic forceps for manipulation of tissue cylinders between test tubes;
- water baths (tissue cylinders to be exposed to temperatures in the range 25–65 °C);
- thermometer and stopclock;
- colorimeter with blue filter;
- graph paper.

■ Data presentation
Plotting the colorimeter readings against the temperature will provide a curve from which the approximate temperature at which the escape of dye was accelerated can be read.

■ Conclusions
- Comment on the apparent thermal death point of beetroot cytoplasm, and its cause and effect.
- If the value is higher than you might expect (compared with the temperatures you may find denature typical plant enzymes, for example), comment on possible explanations by analysis of your experimental method. How quickly do the cells at the centre of your tissue cylinders experience the temperature of the water bath in which they are treated?

■ Evaluation
What improvements to your technique might enhance the accuracy of your method?

■ Extension
Is it possible to adapt your technique to investigate the effect of chemical substances (for example, strong solutions of ions, or organic solvents) on the permeability of membranes?

11.2 Cells and water potential

(Data generating)

The net direction of water movement in a cell depends on whether the water potential (ψ) of the cell solution is more negative or less negative than the water potential of the external solution. This is exploited in techniques for the measurement of water potential of plant tissues. Representative samples of tissue are bathed in solutions of a range of water potentials so that the solution which causes no net water movement can be found.

■ Aim

To measure the water potentials of a range of plant tissues.

■ Risk assessment

Good laboratory practice is sufficient to take account of any hazards and avoid significant risks.

■ Method

By microscopic examination and 50% plasmolysis

This technique is best applied to thin slices or single layers of cells of plant tissues having coloured vacuolar sap. Good examples include thin sections of beetroot tissue (*Beta vulgaris*), epidermal strips of rhubarb petiole (*Rheum rhaponticum*) or even staminal hairs of *Tradescantia virginiana*.

1 Place six to eight samples of the chosen tissue in distilled water in a Petri dish; the cells will become fully turgid. Tissue samples should be small enough to be transferred to a watch glass and be easily submerged in solution.
2 Place five watch glasses on white background paper (so that each can be identified), and fill each with sucrose solution of one of a range of concentrations: 0.2 mol dm^{-3}, 0.4 mol dm^{-3}, 0.6 mol dm^{-3}, 0.8 mol dm^{-3} and 1.0 mol dm^{-3}. Label the sucrose concentration in each watch glass.
3 Immerse a tissue sample in each sucrose solution, and note the time. Set up your compound microscope and lamp using a spare tissue sample from the distilled water.
4 Mount the sample on a slide under a coverslip in order to set up the illumination and magnification so that the field of view will contain at least 50 cells. Prepare a table in which to record percentage plasmolysis in the tissue samples at each of the five concentrations.
5 After 20 minutes have elapsed, examine the tissue samples immersed in sucrose solution in turn, mounting each in its own solution on a microscope slide under a coverslip. Count the number of cells in a group of 10 cells that are plasmolysed, whatever the degree of plasmolysis in the individual cell (Figure 11.1). Repeat this with four other groups of 10 cells for each concentration. Record your results, and then express the proportion of cells plasmolysed as a percentage.
6 Plot a graph of the percentage plasmolysis against the molarity of the sucrose solution. Read off the molarity of sucrose solution that causes 50% of the cells to be plasmolysed.

By measurement of change in length (or mass) of bulky tissues

1 This technique may be applied to plant tissue from which you can cut reproducible-sized cylinders that will fit into a test tube or boiling tube. The tissue sample should be fully turgid at the outset; soak it in water to ensure this. Examples of suitable tissues would include beetroot, potato tuber and carrot root. Cut the cylinders with a cork borer, wash them in tap water, and finally measure the lengths.

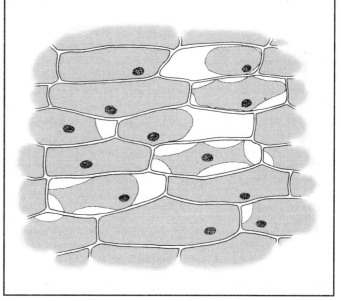

Figure 11.1 Photomicrograph of tissue strip showing about 50% plasmolysis

2 Immerse one cylinder in each of the range of five sucrose solutions provided (0.2 mol dm^{-3} to 1.0 mol dm^{-3}) in a tube, and leave them immersed for one day. Set up a table to record the length of a tissue cylinder from each of the five sucrose concentrations.
3 Finally, remeasure the length of each cylinder and record this. Calculate the change in length as a percentage of the original length.
4 Plot a graph of the percentage change in length against the molarity of the sucrose solution. Read off the molarity of sucrose solution that causes no change in length of the tissue strip.

Note: This method can be adapted to measure change in mass of tissue samples after immersion in sucrose solutions. In this case you should determine the mass accurately at the start, but the tissue samples need not be exactly the same size. After immersion, blot the tissue dry before weighing again.

NOTE TO TECHNICIAN

Each student group requires (or requires access to):
- one or more of the plant tissues as detailed under method;
- the five sucrose solutions in the range 0.2–1.0 mol dm^{-3}, 30 cm^3 of each;
- Petri dish and five watch glasses;
- tile, sharp knife, scalpel, cork borer, fine forceps, fine scissors, paint brush;
- compound microscope and lamp, with microscope slides and coverslips;
- test- or boiling-tube rack with five tubes, marker pen;
- small ruler.

If change in mass is to be measured:
- top-pan balance, box of filter papers.

■ Data presentation

Give your data as the original tables of results and calculations. Plot a graph, and record the molarity of the sucrose solution that appears to be comparable to that of the tissue.

■ Conclusion

Using the conversions in Table 11.1, quote the water potential of the tissues you have investigated.

Table 11.1 The water potential of sucrose solutions

Sucrose /mol dm^{-3}	Water potential /kPa
0.2	−540
0.4	−1120
0.6	−1800
0.8	−2580
1.0	−3510

■ Evaluation

- What are the significant causes of error or inaccuracy in these techniques?
- What improvements to the method can you suggest?

11.3 Cytoplasmic streaming in cells

(Demonstration)

The living cytoplasm of many cells is on the move, sweeping cell organelles about the cell. This natural process, referred to as cyclosis, may be of consequence in transport within an organism.

■ Aim

To observe cytoplasmic streaming.

■ Risk assessment

Good laboratory practice is sufficient to take account of any hazards and avoid significant risks.

■ Method

Using Tradescantia virginiana

Tradescantia (Moses in the bulrushes/Trinity flower) is a native plant of the eastern states of America, popular in Britain since the time of Charles I. It has rush-like leaves, and a succession of flowers with three petals, with conspicuous stamens. It is the purple hairs on the stamens that are used here.

1 Remove one stamen from the flower, grasping it near the base with fine forceps. Discard the anther.
2 Select a short length of the filament with intact hairs, and place in a drop of water on a microscope slide.
3 Lightly crush the filament with the flat part of the blade of a scalpel, and add a coverslip.
4 Examine the staminal hairs and the stem cells to which they are attached, under the medium and high power of the microscope. Does the cytoplasm lie only just beneath the cell wall here, or do strands of cytoplasm cross the vacuole? You may become aware of cytoplasmic streaming by the movements of cytoplasmic particles. Is there any particular direction to movement?

Using Elodea *(Canadian pondweed)*

1 Remove individual leaves from the stem of *Elodea* and mount each on a separate microscope slide, in a drop of water under a coverslip. Select a young leaf from close to the stem tip, and use also one or two more mature leaves, taken from further down the stem.
2 Look for evidence of cytoplasmic streaming, paying special attention to the elongated cells of the midrib region. Here, the chloroplasts may be seen circulating around the cell. Movements are frequently greatest in leaves that have been deprived of light prior to examination.

Using Amoeba proteus

1 Mount one or more amoebae in a drop of water from the culture provided. Cover with a coverslip, and locate the amoebae under medium-power magnification.
2 Observe the streaming movements in the cytoplasm by high-power magnification. Movements of the cytoplasm are associated with pseudopodium formation and with the feeding process. Once again, it is the movements of cytoplasmic inclusions that are observed.

NOTE TO TECHNICIAN

Each student group requires (or requires access to):
- compound microscope with bench lamp;
- microscope slides, coverslips, lens tissue;
- fine forceps, teat pipette, two mounted needles;
- *Tradescantia virginiana*, flowering;
- *Elodea* in pond water (maintained in low light prior to use);
- culture of *Amoeba proteus* (*Amoeba* cultures can be subcultured and maintained in heat-sterilised pond water to which a few boiled wheat grains have been added, as a substrate for bacteria on which amoebae feed).

■ Data presentation

Record your observations as one or more fully annotated sketches of the phenomenon of cytoplasmic streaming as you have been able to observe it.

■ Conclusion

What advantages of cytoplasmic streaming might arise for:
a plant cells;
b animal cells?

■ Evaluation

Is cytoplasmic streaming compatible with some TEM images of cells that appear to be packed with membraneous systems of ER (p. 105)?

■ Extension

A film sequence of cytoplasmic streaming, observed by phase contact microscopy, is shown in the teaching video *The Living Plant Cell: An Introduction to Plant Cell Biology*. The video may be purchased from Mylnefield Research Services Ltd, Scottish Crop Research Institute, Invergowrie, Dundee DD2 5DA.

Projects

11.1 Permeability of cell membranes to dyes of known molecular mass

A comparison of the penetration of dyes into the epidermal cells of onion bulb scale-leaves can be carried out. It is necessary to check that each dye has entered the cell and reached the vacuole, rather than merely having stained the walls around the cytoplasm. This can be confirmed by temporary plasmolysis of the cells.

Common laboratory dyes of known molecular mass include:

methyl red, 269;   neutral red, 289;
methylene blue, 320;   orange G, 452;
basic fuchsin, 571;   erythrosin, 990.

Is the penetration of dyes into cells related to their molecular mass?

Reference

J Roberts and D G Whitehouse (1976) *Practical Plant Physiology*, pp. 94–6. Longman

11.2 Active uptake by plant roots

Reference

S B Reynolds and M Inman (1987) 'A simplified method for investigating active anion uptake by higher plant roots', *School Science Review* 68(245) (June 1987), pp. 696–9

11.3 Determination of potassium and chloride uptake by plant storage tissue discs

An investigation of the concentrations of K^+ and Cl^- ions in samples of carrot root tissue discs (or other storage tissues), and the uptake of these ions by other samples of tissue discs under differing conditions (such as the presence or absence of air, or different temperatures), in the presence of $0.01 \ mol \ dm^{-3}$ potassium chloride solution.

Reference

J Roberts and D G Whitehouse (1976) *Practical Plant Physiology*, pp. 105–6. Longman

11.4 Factors affecting cyclosis

Cyclosis may be observed in a range of plant cells, and at variable rates. What external factors, including temperature, prior illumination and a range of dissolved substances in the external medium, appear to influence the process? How may observations of cyclosis be quantified?

Problems and assignments

11.1 Size, shape and diffusion

Students were provided with a block of gelatin containing an acid–base indicator, cresol red. This indicator is coloured red in alkali, but changes to yellow under acid conditions. A dilute solution of hydrochloric acid, test tubes and a rack were also provided. The experiment required the students to cut small, regular-shaped blocks of coloured gelatin of known dimensions, using a ruler, scalpel and tile, and then to immerse these blocks in acid solution. The time for the red colour to disappear completely from each block was recorded, using a stopclock. Table 11.2 summarises a set of results from one student's experiment.

Table 11.2 Results from diffusion experiment

Block size/mm			Surface area /mm^2	Volume /mm^3	Time for red colour to disappear/min
length	width	height			
10	10	10	600	1000	12
10	10	5	400	500	6.5
10	5	5	250	250	4.75
5	5	5	150	125	4.5
2.5	2.5	2.5	37.5	15.6	4.0

1 From the data given, calculate the surface area : volume ratio of each block used. Then plot a graph of this ratio against the time taken for the gelatin to lose its red colour.
2 What has caused the colour change within the gelatin blocks? Why has it occurred more quickly in some blocks than in others?
3 All movements of substances require energy. What is the source of energy for the movement of molecules in this experiment?
4 Apart from the distance over which diffusion occurs, state four other factors that affect the rate of diffusion.
5 What are the likely sources of inaccuracy in this experiment?

11.2 Water potential and the movement of water between cells

The water potential (ψ) of a cell is a measure of the tendency for water molecules to enter or leave the cell. Pure water has the highest water potential (zero), and the effect of dissolved substances is to lower the water potential. Solutions (at atmospheric pressure) have negative values of water potential. Water diffuses from regions of high water potential (less negative ψ) to regions of lower water potential (more negative ψ).

In the drawing of three adjacent plant stem cells shown in Figure 11.2, the solute potentials (ψ_s) and pressure potentials (ψ_p) are shown in kilopascals.

1 By means of an equation, state the relationship between water potential (ψ) and the solute potential (ψ_s) and pressure potential (ψ_p).
2 What are the water potentials of cells A, B and C?
3 What will be the direction of net water movements between these three cells (until equilibrium is reached)?
4 Two adjacent leaf cells of the same plant have initial solute potentials and pressure potentials (values in kilopascals) as shown in Figure 11.3.
   a At equilibrium, what will the water potential of the two cells be?
   b Why would you expect leaf cells in the light to have lower (more negative) values of ψ_s than those of the stem cells?

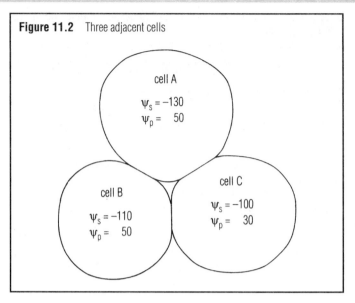

Figure 11.2 Three adjacent cells

cell A
$\psi_s = -130$
$\psi_p = 50$

cell B
$\psi_s = -110$
$\psi_p = 50$

cell C
$\psi_s = -100$
$\psi_p = 30$

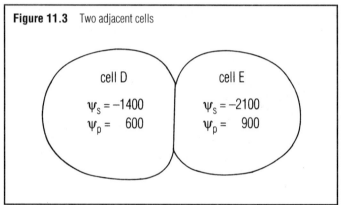

Figure 11.3 Two adjacent cells

cell D
$\psi_s = -1400$
$\psi_p = 600$

cell E
$\psi_s = -2100$
$\psi_p = 900$

5 Animal cells do not have a cell wall to protect them if the pressure potential rises. How is a raised pressure potential avoided in:
   a *Amoeba*;
   b a mammalian red blood cell?

11.3 The evidence for active uptake of ions by cells

The process of uptake of ions by tissues is often studied in plants using 'tissue discs'. These are thin slices of tissue, about 1 mm thick and typically between 0.5 and 1.0 cm in diameter, cut from cylinders of storage tissue such as carrot root, potato tuber or beetroot. After cutting, the discs are washed in running tap water for about three days, prior to use in experiments. During the period of washing the metabolic rate of the tissue increases markedly, and the tissue may develop a respiration rate comparable to that of immature, fast-growing tissues. Samples of about 500 discs may constitute a typical sample, although smaller quantities are used when the reaction vessel is small, such as a Warburg flask (*Advanced Biology*, p. 235).

1 What are the advantages to an experimental physiologist of the choice of thin discs of tissue, rather than larger blocks or longer cylinders of tissue?
2 What are the possible causes of the increase in metabolic rate of the cells of tissue discs over that of comparable cells in the intact storage organ?

3 Why are large samples consisting of hundreds of discs often preferred in experiments?

4 In one investigation, samples of storage tissue discs were incubated in a medium containing phosphate ions at 0.005 mol dm^{-3}, and aerated with air or nitrogen. After 24 hours it was found that the uptake of ions per gram of fresh mass was as follows:

	Uptake of phosphate/µmol
Tissue treated with air	33
Tissue treated with nitrogen	4

a What use are phosphate ions to actively metabolising cells?
b What is the likely effect on the metabolism of discs of bubbling nitrogen gas through the medium, rather than air?
c How might you explain the effect of the absence of oxygen on phosphate uptake by discs?

5 In another investigation, samples of storage tissue discs were incubated in a medium containing sodium chloride solution at 0.2 mol dm^{-3}, with some samples of discs held at 25 °C and others at 4 °C. After four days it was found that the uptake of ions was as follows:

	Uptake of ions/µmol per sample of five discs	
	sodium ions	chloride ions
Discs at 4 °C	82	46
Discs at 25 °C	180	144

a Examine the results carefully. What do they suggest about absorption of NaCl by the tissue discs? What do they suggest about the role of metabolism in ion uptake?
b When experiments of this type are repeated today, the physiologist often includes antibiotic in the medium. Why is this thought necessary? What effects might microorganisms have in these experiments?

11.4 The water potential of cells of an inflorescence stalk

In this investigation narrow strips of tissue, about 2 mm wide, were cut from a length of hollow stalk of a dandelion (*Taraxacum officinale*) inflorescence, about 2.5 cm long. Some of these short, slightly curved strips were then immersed in sucrose solutions of different concentrations, and one was immersed in distilled water. The changes in shape that occurred were observed, and the shapes of the strips after five minutes of immersion were recorded. The experimental procedure and some of the outcomes are recorded in Figure 11.4. Examine this illustration and then answer the questions below.

1 Care was taken to cut all the strips of stalk tissue from the same region of the flower stalk. What was the purpose of this precaution?
2 Exactly how much sucrose ($C_{12}H_{22}O_{11}$, $M_r = 342$) should be weighed out to produce one litre of a 0.5 mol dm^{-3} solution?
3 Given a 0.5 mol dm^{-3} sucrose solution, distilled water and a 20 cm^3 graduated pipette, how would you produce 20 cm^3 of a 0.1 mol dm^{-3} solution of sucrose?
4 What type of cells form the outer margin of the stalk, and how do they differ in structure from the cells of the outer cortex (the remaining cells of the tissue strips)?
5 What would be the shape of the tissue strip that was placed in distilled water, after about five minutes' immersion?
6 What changes have occurred in the cells of the tissue strip immersed in 0.5 mol dm^{-3} sucrose solution to cause the observed change in shape?
7 What is the approximate water potential (ψ) of the stalk cells? Explain your reasoning.
8 If the experiment were repeated with a stalk from a dandelion plant growing high up on an exposed wall after a period of low rainfall, what difference in the result would you anticipate?

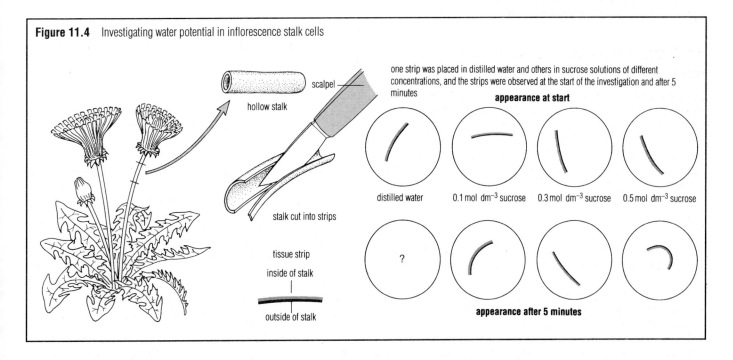

Figure 11.4   Investigating water potential in inflorescence stalk cells

11.5 Quick test

1 Distinguish between the following pairs:

a plasma membrane and cell wall;
b proteins and lipids in cell membranes;
c extracellular and intracellular liquids;
d partially permeable membrane and fully permeable wall;
e molecules and ions;
f passive diffusion and facilitated diffusion;
g free water molecules and water molecules of hydrated sucrose;
h solute potential and pressure potential;
i hypotonic and hypertonic solutions;
j turgid and flaccid cells;
k metabolic energy and kinetic energy;
l primary pump and secondary pump;
m endocytosis and exocytosis;
n vesicles and vacuoles;
o phagocytosis and pinocytosis.

2 Explain the importance of the following:

a concentration gradient in diffusion;
b water potential of a solution;
c contractile vacuoles in freshwater amoebae;
d ATP-linked changes in shape of carrier proteins;
e the concentration of metabolically useful ions in cells.

11.6 Essay assignment

Select one of the following:

• Describe the range of substances that are transported into and out of animal and plant cells. In what ways is the traffic across the plant membrane different from that entering and leaving a typical animal cell?

or:

• Explain what is meant by 'pumps' in the membranes of cells. What evidence do we have that such pumps are important in the movement of useful ions into plant and animal cells?

3

The Maintenance of the Organism

12 Autotrophic nutrition

Summary

Autotrophic organisms make their own organic nutrients from external supplies of relatively simple inorganic raw materials and energy. Photosynthesis is the manufacture of complex nutrient molecules, primarily **sugar**, using energy from **sunlight** and the simple raw materials **carbon dioxide** and **water**. This process occurs in cells containing **chloroplasts**, where light energy is trapped by the **chlorophylls**. **Oxygen** is the waste product. The green leaf of terrestrial plants is an organ specialised for photosynthesis.

Photosynthesis sustains the whole of a green plant's metabolism because the products of photosynthesis are also the **building blocks for all other metabolites**, using in addition **ions** absorbed from the soil. Furthermore, the **survival of all life depends upon photosynthesis** because all non-photosynthesising organisms get their nutrients from green plants, directly or indirectly. The **scale** of photosynthesis is such that virtually all carbon dioxide released each day (from respiration and combustion) is removed from the atmosphere in the light and refixed as combined carbon (**carbon cycle**). Photosynthesis also influences the proportion of oxygen in our atmosphere (currently 21%), all of which has been released from plants as a waste product (**oxygen cycle**).

The fact that photosynthesis consists of a **light step** and an **enzymic (or dark) step** was first discovered from physiological studies of the rate of photosynthesis under different conditions. The existence of these component steps was subsequently confirmed in biochemical studies. In the light reaction **water is split**, **oxygen is released** as a waste product, and reducing power (**NADPH$_2$**) and chemical energy (**ATP**) retained for use in the dark step. In the dark step **carbon dioxide is reduced to carbohydrate** after being added to an **acceptor molecule**, ribulose bisphosphate (**RuBP**). Glycerate 3-phosphate (**GP**) is a key intermediate. This is known as the **C$_3$ pathway**, because the first product is a three-carbon compound.

Several species of the green plants of arid regions (**CAM plants**) are able to fix carbon dioxide in the dark, forming a four-carbon acid as the product, and then release this carbon dioxide in the light, inside the cells, behind closed stomata. Here, photosynthesis can occur with reduced water loss from transpiration.

Carbon dioxide fixation using the same enzymes as in CAM also occurs alongside C$_3$ fixation in the light in some plants of the tropics and subtropical regions, known as **C$_4$ plants**. The four-carbon acid formed is then metabolised near the chloroplasts releasing additional carbon dioxide for photosynthesis. A higher concentration of carbon dioxide inhibits **photorespiration** in chloroplasts. In photorespiration, oxygen displaces carbon dioxide in the reaction with RuBP, releasing two-carbon products in place of GP.

Photosynthesis is of great **ecological, economic** and **environmental importance** to the whole living world, even though in nature only a tiny portion of the total energy of sunlight is fixed. Incidentally, not quite all autotrophic organisms use light energy. Certain autotrophic bacteria use chemical energy to generate sugars, a form of **chemosynthesis**.

Practicals and activities

12.1 The structure of the green leaf

(Investigation)

To understand the photosynthetic functioning of a leaf, you need to construct a mental image of the **three-dimensional arrangement of leaf cells**. This investigation uses different techniques to help you build up this concept.

■ Aim

To understand the three-dimensional structure of the living leaf from the examination of fresh tissue.

■ Risk assessment

- Wear eye protection and plastic gloves when handling 'super glue'.
- Take care with razor blades and scalpels.
- Otherwise, good laboratory practice will be sufficient to take account of any hazards and avoid significant risks.

■ Method

Comparison of stomatal distribution on the upper and lower epidermis

1 Avoiding the main veins, cut two adjacent squares (no bigger than 10×10 mm) from a laurel leaf blade (lamina).
2 Stick the two squares to separate microscope slides using a drop of 'super glue', different surfaces uppermost.
3 Label the slides, indicating which leaf surface was in contact with the glue (U = upper; L = lower).
4 Peel off the squares, and examine the glue surface for the impression left by the leaf cells.
5 Count the number of stomatal impressions visible under low magnification in one field of view for both slides.
6 Repeat the procedure for the upper and lower epidermis of a rhubarb leaf.

Examination of the leaf mesophyll cells

1 Stick a square of laurel lamina to a slide as before, with the upper epidermis in the glue. Slice it obliquely with a razor blade (Figure 12.1).
2 Examine the internal cells of the leaf across the cut surface, before they dry out. Do not add mounting fluid or a coverslip.

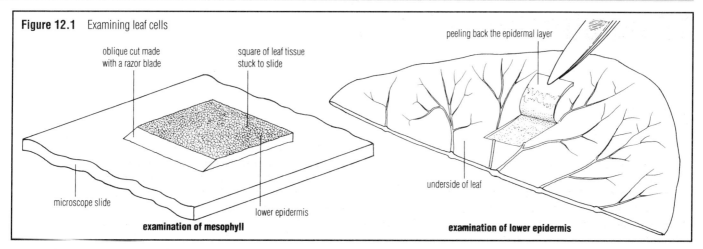

Figure 12.1 Examining leaf cells

oblique cut made with a razor blade

square of leaf tissue stuck to slide

peeling back the epidermal layer

microscope slide

lower epidermis

underside of leaf

examination of mesophyll

examination of lower epidermis

3 Record your observations of the leaf mesophyll structure by using annotated drawings.

Examination of the lower epidermal cells

1 Using a pointed scalpel or a razor blade, make three incisions in the underside of a rhubarb leaf to form an open square, with the open side towards the leaf margin. Use forceps to pick up this tab, and, folding it backwards, pull it towards the edge of the leaf (Figure 12.1).
2 Cut off the transparent epidermal peel from the tab and transfer it to a drop of water on a microscope slide.
3 Replace the water with toluidine blue to stain for one minute before remounting in water.
4 Draw a pair of guard cells and a few surrounding cells using high magnification.

NOTE TO TECHNICIAN

Each student requires (or requires access to):
- compound microscope (with medium- and high-power objectives) and lamp;
- slides, coverslips, lens tissues;
- fine forceps, pointed scalpel;
- marker pens (permanent);
- single-sided, stiff-backed razor blade, white tile to cut on;
- 'super glue' dispenser;
- leaves of laurel (*Prunus laurocerasus*) and rhubarb (*Rheum rhaponticum*);
- dropping bottle of toluidine blue stain.

■ Data presentation

Present a table of the comparative distribution of stomata in laurel and rhubarb.

Your annotated drawings of the mesophyll should indicate the position of cells relative to the air spaces round them, since this is important in understanding the pathway of gases. Indicate clearly the layer of mesophyll to which your drawings or comments refer.

Drawings of the epidermis should show cell shapes, sizes and organelles.

■ Discussion and conclusion

- Relate the differences in stomatal distribution to the function of leaves that stay on the plant all year round (laurel) and leaves that are produced in summer only (rhubarb).

- Relate the leaf construction you observed to the function of photosynthesis.

■ Evaluation

What advantages are there in looking at the arrangement of cells in a living leaf rather than in thin microtomed sections, dehydrated, stained and mounted?

Reference

H E Freeman (1984) 'Leaf histology – two modern methods', *J. Biol. Ed.* **18**(4), pp. 271–2

12.2 Photosynthetic pigments

(Skills and techniques/Data generating/Demonstration)

Chlorophyll pigments occur in green plant cells, in the **grana of the chloroplasts**. Unlike most pigments of plant flowers (anthocyanin pigments, p. 345), chlorophyll (in fact, a mixture of chlorophylls and carotenoids) is largely insoluble in water, but may be extracted with organic solvents. A chlorophyll solution like this absorbs light energy, but of course this energy cannot be used in photosynthesis. Instead, light energy absorbed by chlorophyll in solution is re-emitted as red fluorescence.

The photosynthetic pigments can be separated and identified by chromatography (*Advanced Biology*, p. 245). Care is needed, however, since chlorophylls are quite unstable away from the plant. For example, they will quickly bleach in direct sunlight, once removed from the structures of the chloroplasts.

■ Aim

To extract chlorophyll pigments, demonstrate their fluorescence, determine the absorption spectrum, and separate chlorophyll extract into its constituent pigments.

■ Risk assessment

- The organic solvents used are highly flammable and their vapours may be harmful. Do not use naked flames for water heating in the presence of these solvents. Avoid inhalation of vapour by ensuring good ventilation provision.
- Otherwise, good laboratory practice will be sufficient to take account of any hazards and avoid significant risks.

■ Method

Extraction of chlorophyll

Chlorophyll can be extracted from fresh leaves (spinach, nettle or grass leaves are most frequently used), or from dried, powdered leaves of green plants.

1 Dip fresh leaf material into boiling water first to kill the cells and make the cell membranes fully permeable to the solvent.

2 Finely cut about 10 g of leaf material (excluding the midrib and petiole) into a mortar and add a small quantity of washed and dried sand.

3 Grind up the leaf matter with 20 cm³ of propanone, using a pestle, to make a concentrated leaf extract.

4 Either filter the pigment solution or decant it (using a glass rod to hold back the debris), and place in a small glass centrifuge tube. Centrifuge the extract briefly, in order to clear all suspended organic matter.

5 Pour the supernatant solution into a small glass tube, seal with a bung, label it, and stand this chlorophyll extract in the dark, in an ice bath, until required.

Demonstration of fluorescence

6 Set up a powerful light source (such as a slide projector) in a darkened part of the laboratory. Position a clean glass tube containing the chlorophyll solution in the light beam, and observe the illuminated pigment solution against a dark background, at right angles to the light beam. Fluorescence appears as a ruby-red glow.

7 If a suspension of chloroplasts is also available (Experiment 12.4, p. 145), stand a similar tube containing a chloroplast suspension in a fully illuminated position beside the chlorophyll solution. Compare the performance of the two samples with respect to fluorescence.

Measurement of the absorption spectrum

This can be carried out with a colorimeter having a set of coloured filters.

8 Set the colorimeter to warm up for some 10 minutes before taking readings. Identical glass cuvettes are required, one containing the chlorophyll solution and the other the pure solvent (propanone).

9 Take the first colour filter, and set the colorimeter to zero absorbance using the cuvette containing pure solvent. Then measure the absorbance at that colour by the chlorophyll solution.

10 Repeat the procedure with each filter in turn, noting also the colour and code number of each filter. Using the chart provided with the colorimeter, note down the wavelength of peak transmission (nm) of each filter.

Separation of pigments by paper chromatography

1 Set up a simple chromatography tank by cutting a strip of filter paper to a size that can be retained in a slot in a bung that fits a large boiling tube, reaching down the tube to within 1 cm of the base, free of the tube sides.

2 Remove this strip (avoiding handling it other than at the edges), and place the solvent in the tube to a depth of about 1.5 cm. Close the tube with a replacement bung, stand the tube in a rack, and leave the tube to become saturated with solvent vapour (10 minutes).

3 Mark a pencil line across the filter strip at 2.5 cm from the base, and place a pencil cross in the centre of the line. This is the loading point. Lay the filter paper strip (a chromatogram) across two glass rods on the bench so the loading point is raised and air passes freely on both sides.

4 Load the chromatogram with the chlorophyll solution using an extremely fine capillary tube, formed from a melting-point tube, drawn out in a hot Bunsen flame and then left to cool (Figure 12.2). Dip the capillary into the chlorophyll solution to take up some of the liquid. Then touch the capillary very briefly on the cross you marked. Load only the smallest quantity possible in this way, and then allow the spot to dry.

5 Repeat the loading process many times in order to build up a tiny, dark green spot. You can speed up the drying with a hair dryer, set on 'cool'.

6 When it is ready, fit the chromatogram into the slotted bung. Replace the bung of the chromatography tank with this chromatogram and bung, lowering it fully but carefully so as to immerse the tip of the filter paper in solvent, but leaving the loaded spot clear of the solvent reservoir.

7 The solvent travels up the chromatogram quite quickly; within about 10–15 minutes, the solvent front will almost reach the bung. Withdraw the chromatogram at this stage, mark the position of the solvent front, and hang up the chromatogram to dry in a cool, dark place in the laboratory.

NOTE TO TECHNICIAN

Each student group will require (or require access to) the following.

For the extraction of chlorophyll:
- pestle and mortar, and a pair of sharp scissors;
- plant material (previously dipped in boiling water), or a supply of dried green leaf powder;
- small quantity of washed and dried sand;
- 50 cm³ measuring cylinder;
- supply of propanone (labelled 'highly flammable' and 'harmful');
- glass rod;
- bench centrifuge and glass centrifuge tubes;
- small glass tube with bung;
- ice bath.

For the demonstration of fluorescence:
- projector set up in a darkened corner of a laboratory (or darkroom).

For the measurement of the absorption spectrum:
- colorimeter with a set of filters, with manufacturer's filter chart;
- identical cuvettes to fit;
- teat pipette to charge the cuvettes with solvent/solution.

For the separation of pigments by paper chromatography:
- boiling tube with two bungs to fit (one slotted), in a rack;
- filter paper and scissors, to cut out an appropriate strip chromatogram;
- glass rods and hair dryer (if available);
- fine glass capillary tube;
- 30 cm³ of solvent, consisting of nine parts petroleum ether (bp 100–120 °C) to one part of 90% aqueous propanone (acetone) (p. 429).

Safety note: Solvents are highly flammable and harmful.

For the extension work (if required):
- a supply of washed and dried brown seaweeds and red seaweeds;
- 60 cm³ of 80% aqueous propanone.

Figure 12.2 (left) Loading a paper chromatogram, (right) the apparatus for a chromatographic separation

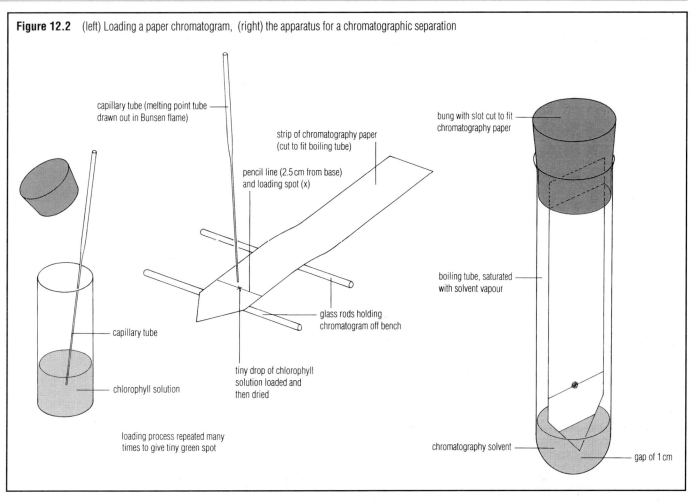

8 When the chromatogram has dried, mark the outlines of all the individual pigments you can make out (some will be much fainter than others). Store your chromatogram in the dark (between pages of your laboratory record book, for example) when not being examined.

■ Data presentation

Measurement of the absorption spectrum

The results will consist of a table of absorption at a range of wavelengths. Plot the values for absorbance (y-axis) against wavelength of transmitted light (x-axis).

Separation of pigments by paper chromatography

The pigment spots on the chromatogram may be identified by their colours and positions (R_f values, see Table 12.1), given the solvent used:

$$R_f = \frac{\text{distance moved by spot}}{\text{distance moved by solvent}}$$

Table 12.1 Paper chromatography of plant pigments

	R_f values for this solvent	Spot colour
Carotene	0.95	yellow
Phaeophytin	0.83	yellow–grey
Xanthophyll	0.71	yellow–brown
Chlorophyll a	0.65	blue–green
Chlorophyll b	0.45	green

■ Reference

L R G Valadon and D Bendall (1988) 'The separation of chlorophyll pigments by paper chromatography', *School Science Review* **69**(248) (March 1988), pp. 512–14.

■ Conclusions

- Why is it that the weak fluorescence visible in an illuminated chlorophyll solution is not visible in a chloroplast suspension?
- Compare the absorption spectrum you have obtained with a published spectrum (*Advanced Biology*, p. 247). Where across the spectrum of white light does maximum absorption by chlorophyll occur?
- How many individual pigments are typically present in chlorophyll solution? What can you discover about the chemistry of each group?

■ Evaluation

Why may the purity of the chlorophyll extract affect the fluorescence and the separation by chromatography?

■ Extension

If time permits, compare the composition of the pigment solution extracted from dried seaweeds (brown and red species) with those from green plants. Extract the pigments using 80% aqueous propanone, since the additional photosynthetic pigments in these plants are (unusually) slightly water-soluble.

12.3 The effect of light intensity on the rate of photosynthesis

(Data generating)

The rate of photosynthesis is influenced by external factors such as light intensity, carbon dioxide concentration and temperature. F F Blackman (1905) suggested that the rate of a process that is dependent on more than one factor is determined by the rate of the least available or lowest factor ('the **principle of limiting factors**'). You can test this hypothesis by investigating the influence of varying light intensity, using the volume of gas (oxygen-enriched air) produced by Canadian pondweed (*Elodea*) in a fixed time as a measure of the rate of photosynthesis.

■ Aim

To investigate the effect of varying light intensity on the rate of photosynthesis.

■ Risk assessment

Good laboratory practice will be sufficient to take account of any hazards and avoid significant risks.

■ Method

Setting up the apparatus

Figure 12.3 shows a simple microburette for measuring the output of gas (oxygen-enriched air) from a shoot of Canadian pondweed (*Elodea canadensis*). Bubbles of gas from the cut stem collect in the bulb of the apparatus and can be drawn into the capillary by carefully unscrewing the clip. The column of gas (perhaps 1 or 2 cm long) can then be measured.

1　At the start of the experiment, fill the apparatus with water by using the syringe. Mount the clip obliquely on the rubber tubing and screw it closed. (The oblique angle allows a greater length of tubing to be compressed.)

2　Collect a few shoots of *Elodea* and place them in a strongly illuminated beaker of water. Select a shoot that is producing bubbles and insert the stem into the microburette as shown. Add a little sodium hydrogencarbonate solution to the water to provide an adequate supply of carbon dioxide (about $10 \, \text{cm}^3$ of $1 \, \text{mol} \, \text{dm}^{-3}$ NaHCO$_3$ in $250 \, \text{cm}^3$ water will be enough).

Varying the light intensity

3　You can vary the light intensity by altering the distance between the lamp and the apparatus. Bear in mind that light intensity is inversely proportional to the square of the distance: that is, if the distance from the lamp is doubled, the light intensity at the plant diminishes to a quarter of what it was.

4　It may take a few minutes for a new rate of photosynthesis to become established after each change of light intensity. Consequently, you will need to take a series of readings until the rate becomes steady (until three consecutive readings are the same).

5　Suggested distances between the plant and the lamp are 135, 148, 165, 191, 233 and 330 cm. Each move from 330 cm will double the light intensity. When the distance is small, heat from the lamp may affect the temperature of the water, which in turn may affect the rate of photosynthesis. Keep a thermometer in the beaker to check on this. Alternatively you may be able to set up a heat trap, as in Figure 12.3 of *Advanced Biology*, p. 261.

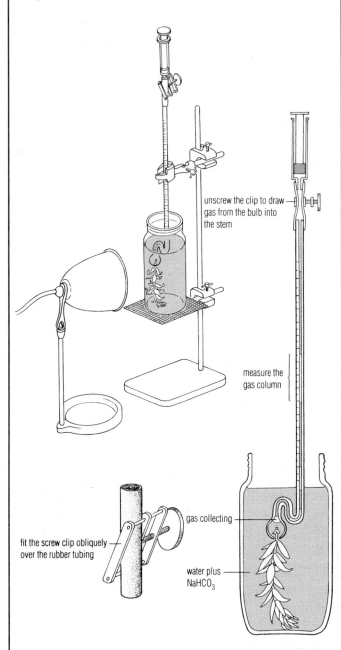

Figure 12.3　A simple microburette for measuring the output of gas from an aquatic shoot

unscrew the clip to draw gas from the bulb into the stem

measure the gas column

fit the screw clip obliquely over the rubber tubing

gas collecting

water plus NaHCO$_3$

NOTE TO TECHNICIAN

Each group of students requires:
- microburette* (wash with detergent and clean water before use to prevent bubbles sticking to the side of the bulb);
- 600 cm^3 tall beaker or tall coffee jar;
- clamp stand with clamp and boss-head;
- ring (or tripod) and gauze to support beaker;
- bench lamp (60 W);
- timer, or view of clock with a seconds hand;
- 10–20 cm^3 sodium hydrogencarbonate solution (84 g dm^{-3}).

* can be supplied by Philip Harris or made by following the instructions in D G Mackean (1983) *Experimental Work in Biology*, Teachers' Book, p. 106 (John Murray).

■ Data presentation

Record your results in a table, and plot a graph of measured volume of gas against light intensity.

■ Conclusion

Comment on the effect of changes in light intensity on the rate of photosynthesis. Was there a light intensity above which no increase in rate took place?

■ Evaluation

Comment on the experimental design, bearing in mind the following points:

• You did not measure the actual volume of gas produced.
• Is the volume of gas produced an accurate measure of the rate of photosynthesis?
• Apart from light intensity, what other variable might have changed in the course of the experiment?
• How can you be confident that the rate of photosynthesis had reached a maximum at each light intensity?

12.4 The Hill reaction

(Skills and techniques/Data generating)

Isolated chloroplasts, provided they are supplied with a hydrogen- or electron-acceptor (an oxidising agent), are able to evolve oxygen when illuminated. This reaction, named after the botanist who discovered it, is a **part of the light step of photosynthesis**, in which water is split and hydrogen is retained by a hydrogen acceptor. This hydrogen is subsequently used in the reduction of carbon dioxide to sugar (the **dark step**).

It seems that the natural hydrogen-acceptor of the cell is largely washed away in the chloroplast extraction process, and oxygen is evolved by the isolated chloroplasts only if a suitable oxidising agent is added. Here we shall use a dye known as DCPIP: this substance does not harm chloroplasts suspended in isotonic buffer, and when it takes up hydrogen (becomes reduced) it loses its blue colour. With a dilute solution of DCPIP present, the Hill reaction of isolated chloroplasts can be investigated.

■ Aim

To isolate active chloroplasts and investigate the Hill reaction.

■ Risk assessment

• Take special care when using a blender and the centrifuge.
• DCPIP is toxic and corrosive.
• Otherwise, good laboratory practice will be sufficient to take account of any hazards and avoid significant risks.

■ Method

Extraction of chloroplasts

This can be carried out as a group activity; the steps are shown in *Advanced Biology*, p. 256.

1 Switch on the colorimeter to warm up in readiness for the second part of the practical.
2 Remove the stalks and larger 'veins' from the fresh, chilled spinach leaves (approximately 50 g) provided, and cut the remaining leaf blade tissue into tiny pieces into a blender containing 120 cm^3 of ice-cold buffer solution.
3 Gently blend the tissue into the buffer over a 10–15-second period (all the leaf tissue should become submerged by this action), and then switch the blender to full speed for a further five seconds to form a green homogeneous 'soup'.
4 Filter the blended tissue (homogenate) through several layers of muslin (many layers of fine-mesh nylon 'tights' are an alternative), collecting the filtrate in a beaker standing in ice.
5 Pour equal quantities of the filtrate into two centrifuge tubes, and centrifuge at full speed for two minutes; discard the (supernatant) liquid in both centrifuge tubes.
6 Using a fine paint brush, re-suspend each of the green pellets at the base of the tubes in 15 cm^3 of ice-cold buffer. Combine these suspensions in one tube standing in the ice bath, and label it 'chloroplast suspension'.

Investigation of the Hill reaction

7 Set up four reaction mixtures as shown in Table 12.2, in colorimeter tubes (cuvettes), one at a time, adding the chloroplast suspension last (all volumes in cm^3) when you are ready to carry out the measurements.

Table 12.2 Reaction mixtures for investigation of the Hill reaction/cm^3

Tube	Buffer (0.1%)	DCPIP	water	Distilled suspension	Chloroplast
1	8.0	0.2		0	0.5
2	8.0	0.2		0	0.5
3	8.0	0.2		0.5	0
4	8.0	0		0.2	0.5

8 Carry out the following treatments to the tubes, in turn. (*Note:* Tubes 2, 3 and 4 are all control tubes.)

Tube 1 Place the tube in the colorimeter with the given filter in position, and adjust the scale to read approximately 0.7 on the 'absorbance scale'.

Remove the tube, expose it to bright light, and return it after 15 seconds to the colorimeter. Read and record the absorbance value.

Repeat this exposure/absorbance measurement cycle at 15-second intervals until no further change in the reading occurs (constant readings).

Tube 2 Place the tube in complete darkness (surrounded by aluminium foil in a darkened container) once the colorimeter absorbance has been adjusted to approximately 0.7.

Leave the tube in darkness for the same period of time that tube 1 took to show no further colour change. Then place tube 2 into the colorimeter and read and record the absorbance.

Tubes 3 and 4 Treat these tubes in turn in the same way as tube 1, maintaining the cycles of exposure and measurement (and recording) of absorbance maintained for the same period of time as it took for tube 1 to show no further colour change.

Note: It may be necessary to alter the volumes of dye so that the colorimeter will read on the scale, and depending upon the activity of the chloroplast suspension, so that the colour change in tube 1 takes no more than 5–10 minutes at most.

Each group will require (or require access to) the following.

For the extraction of chloroplasts:
- about 50 g spinach leaves;
- scissors;
- muslin (several layers), or many layers of nylon fine-mesh 'tights' material;
- 100 cm^3 beaker;
- blender (or pestle and mortar);
- bench centrifuge and centrifuge tubes;
- ice bath in a plastic bowl;
- test tube, labelled 'chloroplast suspension';
- 100 cm^3 of buffer solution, made by adding 6 g of glucose and 0.01 g potassium chloride to 100 cm^3 of phosphate buffer solution at pH 6.5 (p. 429) – ice-cold;
- stopclock.

For the Hill reaction investigation:
- the chloroplast suspension (in the ice bath);
- 50 cm^3 of glucose/KCl/phosphate buffer solution (above);
- 10 cm^3 of 0.1% DCPIP solution;
- 1 cm^3 and 10 cm^3 pipettes with safety bulb;
- photoflood lamp or 150 W lamp;
- colorimeter with colorimeter tubes (cuvettes) and a green filter;
- stopclock.

■ Data presentation

Draw a graph of change in absorbance (*y*-axis) against time (*x*-axis), and record the results obtained from all four tubes. Draw each curve distinctively (by using broken or dotted lines, for example), and label each with the tube number.

■ Conclusion

The reduction of the dye is represented by the equation:

$$2DCPIP + 2H_2O \rightarrow 2DCPIPH_2 + O_2$$

What conditions are necessary for DCPIP to be decolorised in this experiment?

■ Evaluation

- For this experiment, all laboratory glassware must be extremely clean and free from traces of other chemicals. Why?
- The various steps to the extraction were carried out at ice-bath temperature. Why?
- For the experiment itself (tubes in the light or the dark), the reaction mixtures were allowed to warm to room temperature. Why?
- Why is an isotonic pH buffer used to suspend chloroplasts, rather than distilled water?

Reference

J Roberts and D G Whitehouse (1976) *Practical Plant Physiology*. Longman

12.5 The enzymic synthesis of starch

(Investigation)

We use the presence of starch in leaves as evidence of photosynthesis, even though the immediate products of photosynthesis are sugars (with sugar phosphates, and several other metabolites). Sugars formed in photosynthesis are transported to all leaf cells and to other organs, and may be deposited as starch more or less anywhere in the plant. In this practical you will investigate the **machinery of starch formation** in plant cells.

■ Aim

To investigate the ability of plant tissues to form starch from sugar.

■ Risk assessment

- Special care is required when working with a blender (electric food mixer) and with a laboratory bench centrifuge (correct grade of centrifuge tubes).
- Otherwise, good laboratory practice will be sufficient to take account of any hazards and avoid significant risks.

■ Method

Step 1 The enzymic machinery for starch synthesis from sugar

1 A crude preparation of 'starch phosphorylase', the enzyme that catalyses the conversion of glucose to starch, can be made from a plant organ such as a potato. (In the intact potato this enzyme catalyses the breakdown of starch, too.)

   Peel a single good-sized potato, chop it into tiny pieces, and grind them to a pulp in a food blender (or by using a pestle and mortar). Obtain the juice from the pulp by squeezing the contents of the blender through several layers of muslin (or many layers of fine-mesh nylon 'tights' material), and remove the suspended starch grains by centrifugation. Test that all starch has been removed at this stage.

   Store the supernatant liquid in an ice bath, labelled 'starch phosphorylase'.

2 Set up small test tubes with reaction mixtures that will enable you to investigate the conditions necessary for starch synthesis. The mixtures summarised in Table 12.3 may be suitable; always add the enzyme preparation last, and only when you are ready to start the timing measurements. (All volumes are in cm^3.)

Table 12.3 Reaction mixtures for investigation of starch synthesis

Solutions (cm^3)	Tube			
	A	B	C	D
Glucose (3% w/v)	5	4		
KH_2PO_4 (0.2 mol dm^{-3})		1		
Glucose 1-phosphate (3% w/v)			5	
Distilled water				5
'Starch phosphorylase'	5	5	5	5

3 When the 'starch phosphorylase' preparation is added, mix the tube contents thoroughly, and stand each tube at room temperature. Immediately, and thereafter at three-minute intervals, withdraw a drop of the reaction mixture with a clean glass rod and test for the presence of starch using iodine in potassium iodide solution on a spotting tile. Continue testing for 15 minutes (or until starch is clearly present). Record the presence or absence of starch and the time taken for it to be formed.

Step 2 Starch formation in the green leaf

1 Completely destarch the green leaves of a healthy, leafy potted plant by maintaining it in total darkness for 48 hours; suitable plants might be geranium (*Pelargonium*) or busy lizzie (*Impatiens*), for example. Confirm the absence of starch by testing a leaf, and, if necessary, return the plant to the dark for a further 24 hours and then retest for starch. The test for starch is illustrated in *Advanced Biology*, p. 246.

2 Cut 40 discs of green leaf tissue from the destarched leaves, about 1.5 cm in diameter, using a cork borer pressing against a tile or wooden board. Sterilise the surface of the tissue discs by immersion in 1% sodium chlorate(I) solution (eye protection) in a beaker for three minutes.

3 Set up two 200 cm^3 beakers with 20 cm^3 of 3% glucose solution from which all dissolved air has been removed, and two more 200 cm^3 beakers with 20 cm^3 of distilled or deionised water from which all air has been removed. (Remove gases of the air by heating the liquids to boiling point, which also sterilises them, and allowing them to cool to room temperature in a stoppered flask, without any agitation. Run the solutions or water into the beakers down the side of the glass, very gently, without any shaking, so that air is not absorbed.)

4 Place 10 leaf discs, right side up, on the surface of the liquid in each of the four beakers, and cover each beaker with a watch glass that will allow access of air but exclude any dust or airborne spores of fungi or bacteria.

5 Place one beaker with glucose and one with water in the dark and the other two beakers under full illumination. Maintain the beakers at room temperature for 12 hours.

6 Finally, test the samples of leaf discs from each treatment, in turn, for the presence of starch. Record the conditions (whether light or darkness, with water or glucose solution) under which starch formed in leaf cells.

■ Data presentation
Record your method by means of an annotated flow diagram, and record your results in a labelled table.

■ Conclusions
• Under what conditions did starch formation occur?
• What are the advantages to the plant of storing excess sugar as starch?

■ Evaluation
• Were there adequate 'controls' in your procedures in Steps 1 and 2?
• What steps should be included to make certain that an enzyme is involved in Step 1?

NOTE TO TECHNICIAN

Each group will require (or require access to) the following.

For Step 1:
• good-sized potato, sharp knife and tile;
• food blender (or pestle and mortar);
• 250 cm^3 beaker and muslin (or fine-mesh nylon 'tights' material);
• centrifuge and centrifuge tubes;
• up to six test tubes, one with label, standing in simple ice bath;
• access to the following solutions, for each of which approximately 5 cm^3 will be required:
    3% glucose (w/v);
    KH_2PO_4, 0.2 mol dm^{-3};
    3% glucose 1-phosphate (w/v);
• distilled water;
• 5 cm^3 graduated pipettes.

For Step 2:
• healthy potted plant (*Pelargonium* and *Impatiens* are suitable);
• equipment for starch test (beaker, tripod, gauze, heat pad, Bunsen, forceps, test tube, ethanol, tile, I_2/KI solution (p. 434);
• cork borer to deliver discs of 1.5 cm diameter, with tile or wooden board;
• 25 cm^3 of 1% sodium chlorate(I) (hypochlorite) solution, labelled 'irritant';
• four 250 cm^3 beakers with watch glasses to cover, with labels;
• 50 cm^3 of 3% (w/v) glucose solution and 50 cm^3 of distilled or deionised water from which all air has been driven by boiling for 15 minutes, cooled in a plugged flask;
• strong light source maintained for 12 hours;
• access to a darkened container at room temperature.

12.6 The chromatographic separation of sugars
(Investigation)

Sugars, important products of photosynthesis, are also key **intermediates in cell metabolism**, in that they are converted into organic acids and other metabolites, and are built up into a wide range of substances essential in the growth and development of cells.

The potato tuber is a perennation organ: that is, it is a means by which the plant survives the unfavourable season. The dormant tuber contains a huge store of starch, held available for use on return of the growing season. The tuber also contains separate enzyme systems for synthesis and breakdown of starch. When the tuber is induced to sprout, starch is progressively turned to sugar and used in respiration and in the synthesis of metabolites for growth of roots and shoots.

■ Aim
To investigate the occurrence of sugars in plant tissues at different stages of development.

■ Risk assessment

• Take appropriate precautions when working with highly flammable solvents, and with concentrated acids and alkalis.
• Otherwise, good laboratory practice will be sufficient to take account of any hazards and avoid significant risks.

■ Method

Extracting sugars from potato tissue

1 Extract water-soluble metabolites by taking a weighed sample of tuber tissue (freed from the outermost 'skin'), cutting it into small cubes and grinding it with a little sand, together with the minimum quantity of distilled water ($5–10 \ cm^3$).

2 Squeeze the resulting pulp through several layers of butter muslin, and collect the juice and place it in a labelled and sealed specimen tube, for subsequent analysis.

3 Store in the freezer compartment of a refrigerator, if you are not planning to use it immediately for analysis.

Chromatographic separation of sugars in tissue extracts

4 Separate the sugars by thin layer chromatography using 'plates' made of inert polyester backing material that has been pre-coated with silica gel. Cut the plates with scissors to fit a simple chromatography tank (of enclosed test tube, beaker or larger container); after the experiment they can be punched for filing in a ring binder, if necessary.

5 'Load' the plates with tiny drops of the extracts, as illustrated on p. 143. The chromatography solvent is a solution of propan-2-ol : glacial acetic acid : water in the ratio 15 : 5 : 5. Running time depends on the size of the plates, but you should achieve an adequate separation in 60 minutes, when the solvent front may have moved about 5 cm.

6 Prepare standard solutions of sugars by dissolving 0.1 g of sugar in $5 \ cm^3$ of 10% aqueous propan-2-ol. Load and run these in exactly the same way as the extracts. Solutions should include glucose (a six-carbon sugar), and xylose (a five-carbon sugar).

7 The realising agent is 10% resorcinol in propanone, acidified with three drops of concentrated hydrochloric acid. Dip the dried plates in this solution and then bake them in an oven at 100 °C for 10 minutes. An alternative realising agent to experiment with is a mixture of ethanol (IMS) : water : 0.880 ammonia (**danger:** extreme care is required with this solution), in the ratio 40 : 5 : 5. This solution must be prepared only by a technician or a teacher.

The investigation

8 Make extracts from dormant tubers, tubers stored at low temperature (0 °C) and sprouting tubers, and compare the patterns of sugars extracted by thin layer chromatography.
  Alternatively a cereal may be investigated, comparing dormant (soaked) grains and 'seedlings' that have germinated for 5–10 days. Preparation of these tissues is described in D G Mackean (1983) *Experimental Work in Biology*, pp. 140–1 (John Murray).

■ Data presentation

Make a record of the sugar spots detected in the three samples, by reference to the positions of sugars from standard solutions. From the spot size and colour of the developed spots, make subjective judgements as to whether each sugar is present in low, medium or high concentration.

■ Conclusions

• How extensive are the changes in pattern of sugars in dormant, chilled and sprouting potato tuber tissue?

NOTE TO TECHNICIAN

Each student group will require (or require access to):
• samples of 50 g of potato tuber tissue which (a) is dormant, (b) has been stored at 0 °C for seven days, and (c) has been sprouting for about one to three weeks;
• tile, sharp knife, blender (or pestle and mortar);
• $10 \ cm^3$ graduated syringe/graduated pipette;
• butter muslin, test-tube rack, specimen tube, funnel;
• access to refrigerator with freezer compartment;
• glucose, xylose (and possibly other sugars) to make standard solutions;
• top-pan balance;
• $25 \ cm^3$ of 10% aqueous propan-2-ol;
• 'Polygram' pre-coated TLC plates (Philip Harris), scissors;
• simple chromatography tank (test tube, beaker, or similar), clingfilm to seal;
• melting-point tubes drawn out to make fine loading pipettes;
• hair dryer;
• $50 \ cm^3$ of chromatography solvent, as detailed above;
• $50 \ cm^3$ of both realising agents, as detailed above;
• access to drying oven set at 100 °C.

• Can the diversity in sugars be related to apparent levels of metabolic activity?

■ Evaluation

How could this separation be made quantitative, using thin layer chromatography?

12.7 Audio-visual aids relating to plant nutrition

CAL Plant Biology *disc from Garland*

This disc, which includes the program *Photosynthesis*, is available for BBC B, B+ and Master 128, and for Archimedes A3000 and A5000, and Nimbus 186. It is an interactive simulation of an experiment to determine the effect of light, carbon dioxide level and temperature on the rate of photosynthesis, using animated graphics of laboratory equipment assembled for a familiar experiment. The keyboard is used to input the variables, and the factors limiting the rate of photosynthesis are investigated. The program complements practical work or a demonstration of the experimental method, and quickly generates significant and reliable data for interpretation and discussion.

CAL Photosynthesis Parts 1 and 2 *in the Bio-Animate series*

This includes colour animation lessons with buttons to access visual learning tools or self-testing aids, including multiple-choice questions, problem-solving questions, and drag-a-label diagrams. A full index of topics and a glossary of terms are included. It is available for IBM PC and compatible computers (requires Windows 3.0).

The Biochemical Society videotape presentation The Biochemical Basis of Biology – Videotape 1; Cell Structure and Energy Production

The videotape is accompanied by teacher's notes. There are four sections to the tape, each lasting about 15 minutes. Three are relevant to this chapter (it may be helpful to see these sections on separate occasions, after the preceding part has been followed up by discussion and further reading):

- Section One: The Electron Microscope – explains how the microscope works, and why it is valuable in biology;
- Section Two: Subcellular Fractionation – explains how chloroplasts (and mitochondria) are extracted;
- Section Four: The Light Reaction of Photosynthesis – demonstrates some of the complexity of the light step.

The Scottish Crop Research Institute's video presentation The Living Plant Cell

This teaching video has been designed to accompany plant cell biology courses. It contains dynamic images of living plant cells and their organelles, and additional topics include chloroplasts and photosynthesis. All images are integrated into a comprehensive presentation on structure in relation to function. The video is accompanied by a teaching booklet, which includes useful suggestions for laboratory experiments. It is available from Scottish Research Institute, Ivergowerie, Dundee DD2 5DA.

Projects

12.1 Leaf mosaics

Looking down on leafy stems and branches in summer, we usually observe an almost continuous expanse of leaf surface in which individual leaves overlap each other only to a very slight extent. Investigate the leaf mosaics of a range of species of deciduous shrubs and trees in a local woodland habitat, contrasting the various mechanisms by which leaf overlaps are reduced or prevented (*Advanced Biology*, p. 265).

12.2 Sun and shade leaves

The anatomy of leaves may vary with the position on the plant, and some of the most important differences are those between leaves exposed to full sunlight on a daily basis (those at the top of the canopy, known as 'sun leaves') and leaves that are permanently shaded (those near the base of the plant, perhaps). Investigate just how variable the leaves are. Consider features such as area and thickness of leaf, the frequency of stomata, the number of palisade layers present, and the number of chloroplasts per palisade cell. Apply your analysis to two or more species present in the same habitat. What advantages might result from these differences in structure?

12.3 Compensation point

Compare the compensation points of samples of leaves taken from different plants, and held above a fixed volume of hydrogencarbonate indicator solution in a sealed test tube (*Advanced Biology*, p. 248). For example, working with identical masses of leaf samples from different plants, how quickly will yellow indicator change to purple, given a constant light

source positioned at a fixed distance from the tube? If possible, correlate your findings with the typical habitats in which the plants occur. What advantages for the plants arise from these differences in compensation point?

Reference

T J Ashton and G Robinson (1986) 'Teaching light compensation point: a new practical approach', *J. Biol. Ed.* **20**(3), pp. 189–94

12.4 Investigating photosynthesis with an oxygen electrode

An oxygen electrode (such as the Rank Oxygen Electrode, a reaction chamber where changes in dissolved oxygen are monitored), or an oxygen sensor and probe (Philip Harris equipment is suitable, in conjunction with the Universal Interface or DL plus), can be used to investigate oxygen liberation by water plants – by aquatic algae under different conditions of light intensity, for example. The output from these instruments can be monitored by a computer.

Reference

A J W Love and R M Spragg (1986) 'Assessing photosynthetic oxygen liberation using a BBC microcomputer', *J. Biol. Ed.* **20**(2), pp. 128–32

12.5 CAM plants and the changes in titratable acidity

The titratable acidity of tissue extracts of plants such as *Kalanchoë*, *Bryophyllum* or *Sedum* is said to increase during the hours of darkness but to decrease during daylight.

Investigate the change in titratable acidity in the leaves of one of these species. Is this a circadian rhythm, or do the plants respond to a dark period by increasing the acidity of the tissues, whatever the time in a 24-hour cycle? Use extracts of the tissue obtained by blending comparable leaf samples, and filtering them through muslin. Titrate extracts against 0.1 mol dm^{-3} sodium hydroxide using phenolphthalein indicator.

12.6 Nitrifying bacteria in the soil

Nitrifying bacteria occur naturally in many soils. They convert ammonium ions to nitrate, and do so as chemosynthetic organisms (*Advanced Biology*, p. 271). Their role in the nitrogen cycle is critically important. Collect soil samples, and 'wash' them well to remove soluble nitrates. Then add a solution of ammonium sulphate, and later test the soil samples again to see if nitrate has reappeared. Nitrate in water eluted from soils can be tested either with diphenylamine, as described in the reference below, or with one of the chemical test strips currently marketed (for example, the Merckoquant test strip for nitrate).

Reference

D G Mackean (1983) *Experimental Work in Biology*, pp. 90–1. John Murray

Problems and assignments

12.1 Carbon dioxide fixation by a green plant crop

Alfalfa (*Medicago sativa*) is a 'forage' crop. It is a leguminous plant that is grown widely in Europe (where it is known as 'lucerne'), in North and South America and in parts of Asia. It is planted on its own or with grasses, and ultimately the crop is grazed or mown for silage or dried as hay. No forage plant is a better source of protein. Consequently, the physiology and biochemistry of this plant have been much studied. In Figure 12.4, the net fixation of carbon dioxide (arbitrary units) by an alfalfa crop growing in the state of Iowa, USA, in late summer, is recorded for a 48-hour period. Examine this graph carefully. Then, using this data together with your general knowledge about plant nutrition and your wider reading, answer the questions that follow.

1 Parts of the curve of the graph show negative carbon dioxide fixation values. What does this mean, and what causes them?
2 At certain times during the experiment dense clouds occurred in an otherwise clear sky. Give two times during day 2 when clouds obscured the Sun for a significant period.
3 At what time in that day did the rate of photosynthesis reach a maximum? How do you know this?
4 What is the pathway by which carbon dioxide molecules from the air around the plant get fixed into carbohydrate in the alfalfa leaf cells? What is the other source of carbon dioxide that is used?
5 Water vapour is lost to the air from the alfalfa leaves, at least during the hours of daylight. Why and how does this water vapour movement occur?
6 Alfalfa is a crop plant that does not need to be treated with fertilisers containing nitrates, ammonium salts or any other form of 'combined nitrogen', and yet it is extremely rich in proteins. How does this crop plant obtain combined nitrogen for protein synthesis?

12.2 The effect of temperature on photosynthesis at high and low light intensities

The effect of temperature on the amount of gas given off by an illuminated plant stem was investigated, using the apparatus shown in Figure 12.5. Comparable *Elodea* stems were incubated in the light in 0.025 mol dm^{-3} sodium hydrogencarbonate solution at a range of temperatures from 5 to 25 °C for 30 minutes, so that the plant material was at the given temperature, and so that the solution was in equilibrium with the gas given off by the plant. After this time, gas production by each of the leafy shoots was then measured in the given apparatus by measuring the length of the gas bubble in the capillary tube over two-minute periods both at high light intensity and at low light intensity. The readings recorded are the values obtained when the rate of gas production had become constant, giving three identical readings (length of bubble in mm), and are summarised in Table 12.4.

1 By what procedure is the gas produced by the plant in a two-minute period measured in this apparatus?
2 What are the likely chief sources of error or inaccuracy in this investigational technique?
3 Why are the stems of *Elodea* held for 30 minutes in dilute sodium hydrogencarbonate solution at the different temperatures before being used in an experiment to measure gas production?
4 Given a white light source (a slide projector, for instance), how may it be arranged to deliver:
  a low light intensity; **b** high light intensity?

Table 12.4 Results of investigation into temperature effects in photosynthesis

Temperature/°C	High light	Low light
5	26	20
10	39	25
15	66	28
17.5	95	30
20	128	33
22.5	110	30
25	76	28

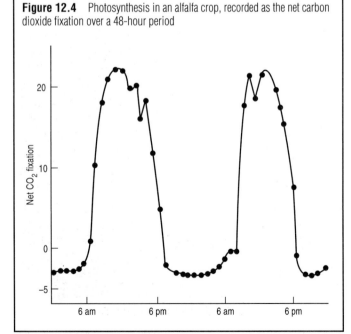

Figure 12.4 Photosynthesis in an alfalfa crop, recorded as the net carbon dioxide fixation over a 48-hour period

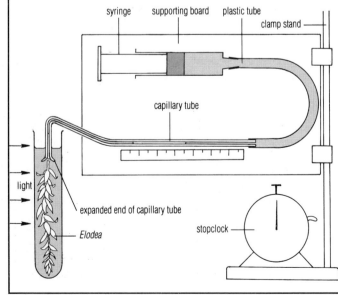

Figure 12.5 Apparatus for the measurement of the gas produced by illuminated *Elodea*

What special precautions need to be taken concerning the high light source?

5 Why is it necessary to use a white light source (and to avoid a domestic light bulb source, for example)?

6 Plot a graph of these results to show the effects of temperature on gas production.

7 Summarise concisely, in your own words, the effect of a rise in temperature between 10 and 20 °C on gas production by *Elodea* in high and low light intensities.

8 What sort of step or reaction potentially limits the rate of photosynthesis in a green plant with adequate carbon dioxide when held in:
   a low light;
   b high light?

9 The rate of reaction changes at the higher temperatures. What are the likely causes of the change?

10 Contrast the effects of temperature on a photochemical reaction (such as that which takes place when a photographic film is exposed) and other kinds of chemical reaction.

12.3 Summarising photosynthesis

Photosynthesis is a complex process consisting of two steps linked together.

1 Copy and complete Table 12.5 by summarising in your own words the aspects of the two steps indicated.

2 Construct and draw a flow diagram summarising the light and dark steps, showing the linkage between them, and giving as much detail of the processes as is practical to include in this type of diagram.

12.4 The leaf as a factory for photosynthesis

Aspects of leaf structure shown by a leaf of the plum tree (*Prunus domestica*) are illustrated in Figure 12.6. Examine this illustration, and using your wider observations and reading (for example, C J Clegg and Gene Cox (1988) *Anatomy and Activities of Plants*, John Murray), together with your knowledge of plant nutrition, and of photosynthesis in particular, answer the following questions.

Table 12.5 Comparing the steps in photosynthesis

	Light step	Dark step
Site in the chloroplast		
The type of reaction involved		
What is required in terms of substances (raw materials) and energy		
The biochemical or photochemical changes that occur, and the products formed		

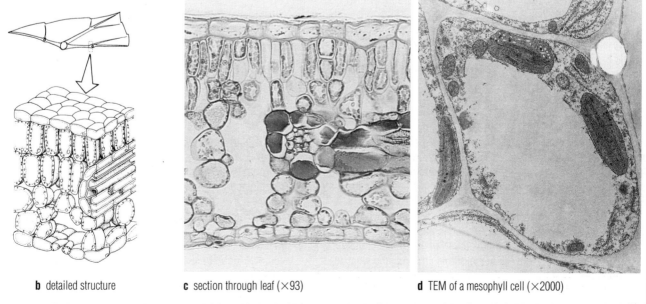

Figure 12.6   The structure of a plum leaf (*Prunus domestica*)

a leaf in section

b detailed structure   c section through leaf (×93)   d TEM of a mesophyll cell (×2000)

1 List the features of the gross structure of such a leaf that can be seen with the unaided eye and with a hand lens that appear to be adaptations to function, indicating what advantages each confers.

2 Some species of plant have tiny hairs growing out from the surface of the epidermis of their leaves, particularly from the lower epidermis. These give the leaf a white, downy appearance.

  a What advantage might these hairs confer on a green plant leaf?

  b Suggest three other special structural features found in some plants that might be expected to have similar effects.

3 The leaves of plants resist the actions of wind. What features of the anatomy of the leaf enable it to resist mechanical damage in this way?

4 How does water reach the chloroplasts in the mesophyll cells from the lumen of the xylem vessels?

5 The air spaces of the leaf are said to be continuous. What does this mean, and what is the importance of air spaces to the delivery of carbon dioxide to the chloroplasts?

6 The photograph shown in Figure 12.6(d) is a TEM of part of a green leaf.

  a What part of the leaf is it likely to be from?

  b Make a large, labelled drawing of one of the chloroplasts shown.

12.5 Photosynthetic productivity in natural and agricultural systems

Read Panel 12.1, and answer the questions below.

1 What do we mean by the term 'stored energy'?

2 Suggest some 'fibres' in common use, and show how they are obtained indirectly from the process of photosynthesis.

3 a Explain what is meant by 'renewable production of organic compounds'. Give some examples.

  b What non-renewable sources of organic compounds are currently used?

4 a The use of added fertilisers in agriculture enhances photosynthetic efficiency of the crop plants. How does this work?

  b Give two examples of elements made more available in fertilisers, and explain how their presence enhances productivity of the crops.

5 Suggest reasons why a desert is normally unproductive, in contrast to a reed swamp.

6 Suggest three ways by which we might exploit plant productivity more efficiently to meet some specific energy needs when fossil fuels grow scarcer.

Panel 12.1 The efficiency of photosynthesis

The products of photosynthesis represent stored energy. Each year, plant photosynthesis fixes about 10 times the world's annual energy consumption. The energy stored in biomass presently on the Earth's surface is equivalent to our proven fossil fuel reserves of oil, coal and gas. Solar energy conversion through biology, that is photosynthesis, supplies us with practically all our food, fuel and fibre – these products are derived from present-day photosynthesis, or indirectly from fossil fuels which themselves are products of past photosynthesis. Biological fixation of CO_2 into chemical products is the only known way of renewably producing organic compounds.

Of the spectrum of visible light, plants use radiation of wavelengths between 400 and 700 nm only, and this 'photosynthetically active radiation' comprises about 50% of the total radiation. Further losses due to reflection and transmission of energy by leaves mean that only 40% of the total available light energy reaches the chloroplast. In the chloroplast itself, the efficiency of the photosynthetic energy-conversion process, together with losses due to respiration, gives a final, maximum photosynthetic efficiency of approximately 5–7%. These values are obtained only under optimum field conditions during short-term growth periods. When values are averaged over the whole year they fall to between 1 and 3%, or less. The table below shows some practical photosynthetic efficiencies in terms of percentages of total radiation fixed.

Natural habitats (annual yields)/%		Crop yields from growing period/%	
reed swamp	1.6	rye grass	2.5
evergreen forest	0.8	wheat	1.5
deciduous forest	0.6	potatoes	2.3
desert	0.02	sugar cane	2.8

From: Biologist *1979* *26(1), pp. 16–22*

12.6 'High hopes for C₄ plants'

Read the excerpt from a report reproduced in Panel 12.2. To understand the terms used you may need to read an account of the C_4 pathway in photosynthesis, about photorespiration, and about crassulacean acid metabolism (CAM). For example, these issues are discussed in *Advanced Biology*, pp. 267–9

1 a Explain what we mean by C_3 fixation in photosynthesis.

  b Scientists refer to an enzyme involved in photosynthesis as 'Rubisco'. What is the full name of this enzyme, and what reaction does it catalyse?

2 Suggest why the C_4 photosynthetic mechanism confers an advantage to plants growing under conditions of:

  a high light intensity;

  b high temperature;

  c low water availability.

3 What reaction does phosphoenolpyruvate (PEP) carboxylase catalyse?

4 What features distinguish a CAM plant from other similar green plants?

5 What additional 'sink' of carbon dioxide may occur in aquatic sites, not found in surrounding dry land?

6 Make a drawing of a typical C_4 plant's leaf, in section around a leaf vein. Label the cells and structures to show the locations of C_3 and C_4 fixation.

Panel 12.2 High hopes for C₄ plants

The so-called C_4 photosynthetic mechanism equips plants with valuable competitive advantages under conditions of high light intensity, high temperature and low water availability. Their greater efficiency in trapping carbon dioxide means that they can exert a tighter control over water balance than most C_3 plants, but plants endued with the phosphoenolpyruvate (PEP) carboxylase initial carbon-fixing technique (which includes the crassulacean acid metabolism – CAM – plants) can also cope well with habitats in which CO_2 becomes scarce, as in the case of some aquatic environments in the middle of the day when planktonic photosynthesis is at its peak. It came as something of a surprise when CAM-type plants were first described from wet sites. But now another remarkable claim has been put forward by V S Rama Das and S K Vats of Palamur, India, who believe that C_4 plants may be at an advantage at high altitudes because of lower levels of ambient atmospheric CO_2.

C_4 plants operate a short-term mechanism for the fixation of CO_2 that involves the enzyme PEP carboxylase and results in the addition of the carbon from CO_2 on to a three-carbon receptor molecule, leading to a four-carbon product. This is then transported to specialised cells around the vascular bundles where the carbon is released once more and then permanently fixed by the conventional C_3 system using the enzyme Rubisco. One important advantage of the C_4 strategy is that PEP carboxylase has a higher affinity for CO_2 than Rubisco, so the C_4 plant is able to maintain photosynthesis at lower CO_2 concentrations (that is, it has a lower CO_2 compensation point).

It has long been evident that the C_4 photosynthetic mechanism is more commonly found at lower rather than higher latitudes. It occurs in a wide range of plant families, both dicotyledons and monocotyledons, but was first described in, and is perhaps most familiarly associated with, tropical grasses. As one moves polewards, the proportion of C_4 grasses among the species of this family gradually decreases, and only a very few grasses of the cooler temperate zone are C_4 in character. One such genus is the cord grasses (*Spartina*), which probably benefit from the water-relations advantages of the C_4 mechanism (all species of this genus inhabit salt-marshes, where salinity imposes physiological water stress).

From: Nature 1994 **367**, *pp. 322–3*

12.7 Designing an investigation

The apparatus illustrated in Figure 12.7 consists of a 20 cm³ plastic syringe with an extended length of capillary tube attached. The syringe contains water with healthy, active shoots of pondweed in an inverted position. Gas given off by the pondweed collects below the plunger of the syringe and displaces liquid down the capillary tube. The distance moved by the meniscus is a measure of the gas produced. The apparatus is supported in a well-illuminated position.

1 Design an experiment using this apparatus to investigate the effect of carbon dioxide concentration on the rate of photosynthesis. Describe the steps and procedures you would undertake in the correct order. Pondweed absorbs carbon dioxide from the medium, which should be a dilute solution of sodium hydrogencarbonate. You will require a range of solutions, starting perhaps with a 0.1 mol dm⁻³ solution of sodium hydrogencarbonate (NaHCO₃; Na = 23, H = 1, C = 12, O = 16). Show how to set up some stock solution, and how some of the stock solution can be diluted to give solutions of 0.05, 0.025 and 0.0125 mol dm⁻³ sodium hydrogencarbonate.

2 What are the likely sources of error in this experimental procedure?

Reference
P W Freeland (1985) *Problems in Practical Advanced Level Biology.* Hodder and Stoughton

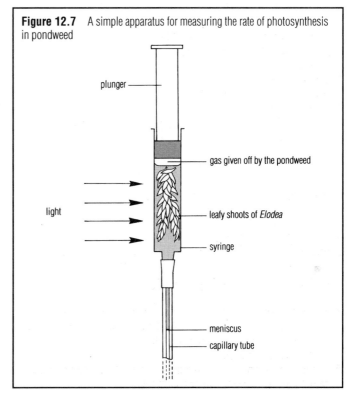

Figure 12.7 A simple apparatus for measuring the rate of photosynthesis in pondweed

plunger

gas given off by the pondweed

light

leafy shoots of *Elodea*

syringe

meniscus

capillary tube

12.8 Flow diagram summaries to complete

Figures 12.8 and 12.9 are flow diagrams summarising the processes of photosynthesis and the carbon cycle. Each includes a collection of terms you may use to complete the blanks. Not all the terms will be needed.

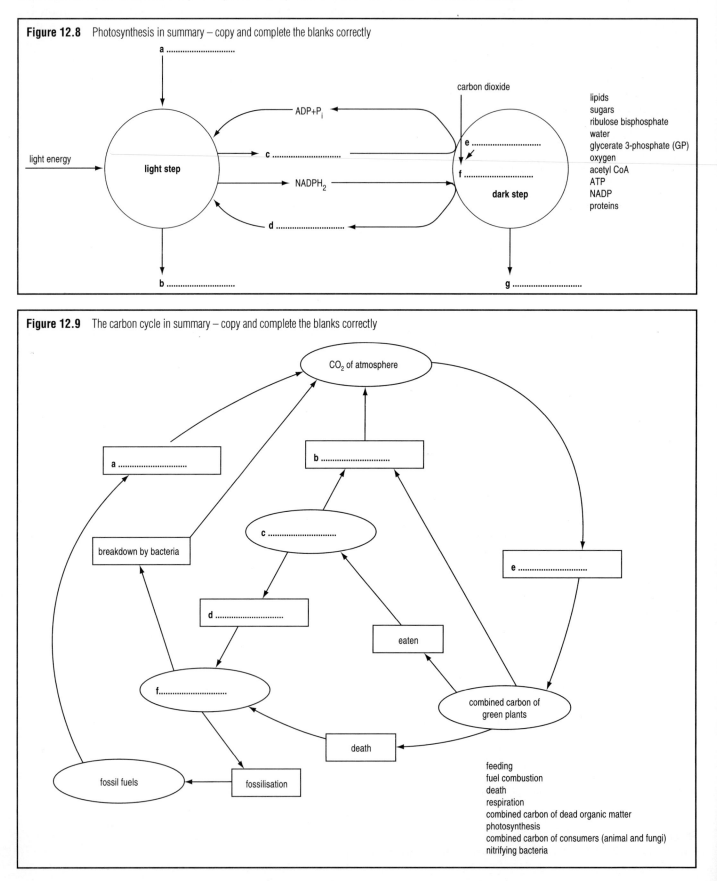

Figure 12.8 Photosynthesis in summary – copy and complete the blanks correctly

a ....

carbon dioxide

ADP+P$_i$

light energy

light step

c ....

NADPH$_2$

e ....

f ....

dark step

d ....

b ....

g ....

lipids
sugars
ribulose bisphosphate
water
glycerate 3-phosphate (GP)
oxygen
acetyl CoA
ATP
NADP
proteins

Figure 12.9 The carbon cycle in summary – copy and complete the blanks correctly

CO$_2$ of atmosphere

a ....

b ....

breakdown by bacteria

c ....

e ....

d ....

eaten

f ....

combined carbon of
green plants

death

fossilisation

fossil fuels

feeding
fuel combustion
death
respiration
combined carbon of dead organic matter
photosynthesis
combined carbon of consumers (animal and fungi)
nitrifying bacteria

12.9 Quick test

1 Distinguish between the following pairs:

   a photosynthesis and chemosynthesis;
   b chlorophyll and chloroplast;
   c grana and stroma;
   d absorption spectrum and action spectrum;
   e palisade and spongy mesophyll;
   f leaf veins and vascular bundles;
   g light step and dark step;
   h photolysis and photophosphorylation;
   i 'sun' and 'shade' leaves;
   j C_3 and C_4 pathways.

2 What equipment and/or technique do you associate with the following?

   a destarching a plant (leaves);
   b testing a leaf for starch;
   c extraction of chlorophyll from green leaves;
   d Sachs' half-leaf method of measuring the rate of photosynthesis;
   e detection of non-radioactive isotopes;
   f detecting the 'compensation point' of green leaves;
   g isolation of chloroplasts from green leaves;
   h two-dimensional paper chromatography;
   i preventing photorespiration in glasshouse crops;
   j 'energy farming'.

12.10 Essay assignment

Select one of the following:

- Explain precisely why the following equation is an unsatisfactory summary of photosynthesis:

$$6CO_2 + 6H_2O \xrightarrow{\text{light, chlorophyll}} C_6H_{12}O_6 + 6O_2$$

or:

- a Describe the broad steps by which light energy is converted to chemical energy in green plants.
  b Distinguish between the C_3 and the C_4 pathways of carbon dioxide fixation.

13 Holozoic nutrition of mammals

Summary

Heterotrophs use complex, **ready-made organic foods** as their source of nutrients. They **digest** these foods, and then **absorb** and **assimilate** the products of digestion. Essential nutrients are energy-rich molecules such as **sugars** and **fats**, combined nitrogen in the form of **amino acids** or proteins, and **water**, **minerals** and **vitamins**. The balance of essentials of a healthy diet for a mammal (such as a human) depends upon the age, sex and degree of physical activity of the individual. There are several variant forms of heterotrophic nutrition, but in holozoic nutrition (as in humans) food is taken into a digestive system for processing.

In human nutrition food is masticated by the actions of **teeth**, tongue and **saliva** in the mouth. Protein digestion commences in an **acidic environment in the stomach**, where the meal is temporarily stored. Most digestion occurs in the **small intestine**. Secretions from the gall bladder, pancreas and intestinal glands provide the environment rich in the necessary **digestive enzymes**. The **products of digestion** are absorbed by the **villi** in the wall of the small intestine, and reach the cells of the **liver** and the **rest of the body** via the **blood and lymphatic systems**. Absorption of **water** is completed in the **large intestine**.

There are distinctive adaptations of the guts of **carnivorous** and **herbivorous animals**, compared with those of **omnivores**. The particular challenge for the herbivorous mammal is its inability to secrete a cellulase enzyme in the gut. Plant cells, the bulk of the diet, need breaking down by the grinding action of the teeth, but digestion of the cellulose can be achieved only by the **action of bacteria** and other organisms that produce **cellulase**, whilst being housed in parts of the 'stomach' (of cattle and other ruminants) or the caecum (of animals like the rabbit).

Practicals and activities

13.1 Analyse your diet

(Data generating)

Ideally, the essential nutrients should be present in the foods we eat, in the amounts we need them. To find out the adequacy of your diet you must record what and how much you eat, and then analyse the **nutritional content** of the food and compare it with the amounts recommended for health, given your sex, age, height and activity level.

■ Aim

To make a critical assessment of the appropriateness of the diet of an individual.

■ Risk assessment

No practical work is involved.

■ Method

1 Record as a list all the foods and drinks you have taken in the immediate past over a period of 24 hours (minimum), or preferably three days, noting the quantities concerned. Take care to include in your list all snacks and drinks, as well as the contents of more formal meals.

2 Calculate the food value of the food and drink items, using published tables of food composition such as:
   - MAFF (1985) *Manual of Nutrition* (9th edn), pp. 105–15. HMSO
   - A E Bender and D A Bender (1986) *Food Tables*, pp. 20–3 and pp. 28–44. Oxford University Press

It is customary to focus on energy value (MJ), protein (g), vitamins A(μg), B_1, B_2 and B_3 (mg) and C (mg), and the minerals calcium and iron (mg).

3 Compare your average daily intake of each nutrient with that officially recommended by the Department of Health and Social Security, quoted in the MAFF *Manual*, the Benders' *Food Tables*, and in *Advanced Biology*, p. 273.

Alternatively, several **computer programs** exist to analyse your diet:

Analyse Your Diet by Garland. This set of computer programs (available for BBC B/Master, Archimedes A3000 and A5000, Nimbus 186 and IBM PC and compatibles) is based on the data in the MAFF *Manual of Nutrition* and enables students to analyse their diets without need to refer to the published documents detailed above. The program allows the entry of additional foods (from specialised or ethnic diets, for instance) using data from other sources.

Microdiet by Longman. This set of programs (available for BBC B/Master, and the Archimedes A3000 and 5000) is designed so that food intakes can be analysed:
   - to show the nutrients in individual items;
   - to estimate the cost of nutrients supplied by a given food;
   - to compare with recommended daily intakes; and
   - to find out the quantity of particular nutrients in any particular food.

Understanding Nutrient Requirements by DAB Computing. The program requires you to select a subject to study (sex, age height and body mass). You then create the 'activity diary' of this subject, entering the hours spent in various activities. You then investigate the effect of varying intake on body mass. There are additional useful features, and the program (available for BBC B/Master, Archimedes A3000 and 5000, and Nimbus 286) is accompanied by an explanatory booklet.

Two other programs, also available from DAB Computing – *Diet and Menus Planner* and *The Foods You Eat* – allow analyses of the nutritional value of meals.

Nutrition 2.0 by KimTec UK. This HyperCard stack (for use with Apple Macintosh) enables students to keep daily records of the nutritional value of their meals, and provides a nutritional analysis of each meal. The stack analyses nutrient value and their daily intake, in keeping with activity levels.

Food and Lifestyle by Nutrition and Education Department, Milk Marketing for England and Wales. This program can be used to analyse the nutrient, energy, saturated fatty acid, alcohol and fibre content of items in the diet. Typical diets can also be analysed, using five case studies stored in the program, and there are case study cards and shopping cards with which to structure students' learning. Available for BBC B/Master, Archimedes A3000 and 5000, Nimbus 186 and IBM PC and compatibles.

NOTE TO TECHNICIAN

Students will require access to the tables of food composition mentioned above, or to a microcomputer with printer, and one of the programs listed above.

■ Data presentation
Data should be tabulated.

■ Conclusion
The nutritional value of a diet depends upon the overall mixture of food eaten over a prolonged period. Consistently incorrect diet (rather than the occasional over-indulgent intake, for example) is highly significant. Nevertheless, good nutritional practice starts with individual meals. A balanced meal is one that provides adequate amounts of protein and energy, and of minerals and vitamins. It should also provide dietary fibre, and appropriately limited amounts of sugar, fat and salt. Comment on your diet in this light.

■ Evaluation
The wider issues of human diet and nutrition are introduced in:

A F Walker (1993) *Human Nutrition* (updated edition). Cambridge Social Biology Topics, Cambridge University Press

13.2 Studying the alimentary canal of a laboratory rat (mammal)
(Skills and techniques/Data generating)

The alimentary canal, or gut, is the digestive tract running from mouth to anus. Each region of the gut is specialised for a particular phase in the overall process of mechanical and chemical digestion of food, or for absorption of the products of digestion. **Gut structure and function** may be studied by dissection, especially where this is linked to studies of gut wall and gland structure, and to investigations of the action of digestive enzymes. It is not essential for dissection of a freshly killed animal to be carried out to become familiar with the issue in vertebrate structure and function, however. The use of models (if available), special video presentations, computer programs and CD-ROM resources can help in acquiring understanding of the layout, organisation and roles of the regions of the mammalian gut. Investigation of animal structure by dissection is an important skill of the biologist, with many useful applications, but it is not an obligatory component of your course.

■ Aim
To investigate the structure and organisation of the regions of the gut of a mammal in relation to function.

■ Risk assessment

In the conduct of dissection, special precautions for safety are essential.
* Protect your clothing by wearing a lab coat, fully buttoned.
* Because of the possibility of bacterial infections, disposable plastic gloves may be worn.
* When dissecting hard, tough tissues like bone and cartilage that may splinter, wear safety spectacles.
* If you cut yourself, treat the wound as if a serious cut.
* Dispose of all animal remains as directed by the technician or tutor.
* Wash your hands when you have finished work.
* Find out what hazards, if any, are presented by the preserving fluid. Take suitable precautions.

■ Method

External features
Examine the external features of a recently killed (or preserved) animal (see Figure 13.1, overleaf), carefully sketching and labelling the general body features that are typical of a mammal, and those that are specifically characteristic of the rat.

Dissection of the abdomen
Developing your dissection technique   The chief purpose of dissection in biology is to display the internal structures as part of an investigation of internal anatomy and function of an animal's body, but the skills of dissection are also applied in physiological and histological investigations, and in medical surgery. A rule of dissection is that an approved species of animal obtained from a biological supplier for dissection is humanely killed. Your obligation is to attend, appropriately prepared by prior study, and to make maximum use of the specimen for serious study. Animals that have to be killed should be used for as many investigations as possible. The safety rules listed above must be followed meticulously throughout the dissection.

When undertaking a dissection, follow these general points of procedure:
* Pin the animal to an appropriate surface (a dissecting board for a vertebrate, such as a rat, and the base of a dissecting dish for an invertebrate; see Practical 13.5, p. 164). Insert the awls and pins obliquely, so that there is minimal obstruction to the movements of your hands, and so that the body wall is stretched and tissues are under slight tension at all times.
* When opening the body cavity, and when cutting away structures, keep scissors pointing upwards and away from the structures to be exposed or freed.
* Use a seeker to remove connective tissue that holds tissues and organs together; in general, use scalpels and scissors sparingly, cutting away from structures you are seeking to free.
* Dissect along the line of blood vessels and nerves as far as possible, rather than across their path.
* Keep your dissection moist, but use a swab to remove body fluids that accumulate.

Figure 13.1   The rat: identify the features characteristic of mammals

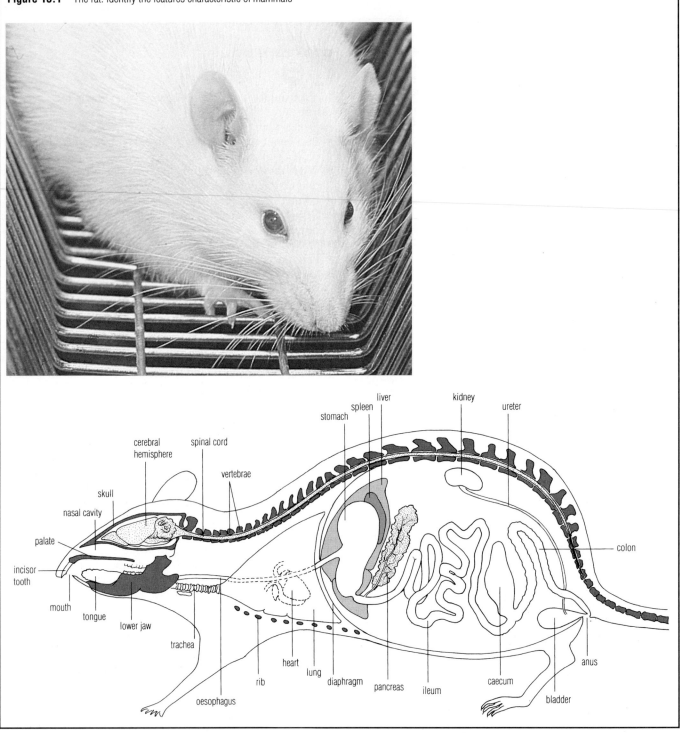

- Maintain your dissection equipment clean and dry, wiping each item with a slightly oily cloth before putting them away.

Steps to the dissection of the abdomen

1 With the rat secured ventral side uppermost, lift the skin in the mid-ventral line and make an incision through the skin only, leaving the inner body wall intact. Cut through the skin all along the mid-ventral line forwards to the mandible and backwards towards the anus, as indicated in Figure 13.2, avoiding the urinogenital openings as shown.

2 Pull away the skin from the body wall, using your hands and not any sharp instrument. Stretch the skin and pin it out as shown in Figure 13.2.

3 Lift the body wall with forceps. Using scissors, cut through the body wall along the mid-ventral line (Figure 13.3(a))to expose the contents of the abdomen. Cut the body wall away from around the base of the rib-cage, and pin it down. Carefully remove the fat obscuring the abdominal organs. Identify the structures *in situ* (see Figure 13.3(b) and (c)). Make a large labelled drawing of your dissection at this stage.

Figure 13.2 Rat dissection: the initial steps in the dissection of the abdomen

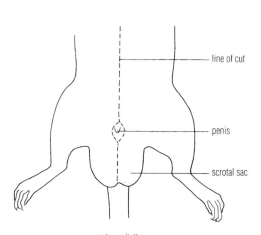

line of cut

penis

scrotal sac

male genitalia

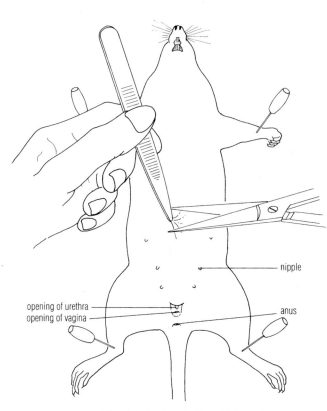

nipple

opening of urethra
opening of vagina

anus

1 the skin in the mid-ventral line is lifted and cut

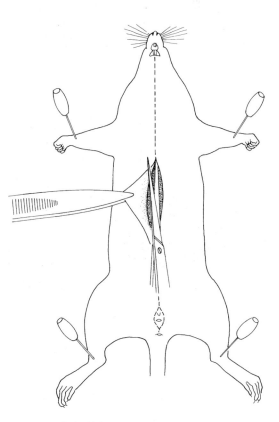

2 the skin is then cut with scissors along the mid-ventral line

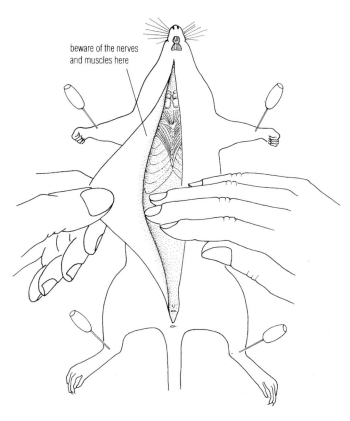

beware of the nerves
and muscles here

3 the skin is freed from the body wall by gloved fingers

Figure 13.3 Rat dissection: to reveal the alimentary canal

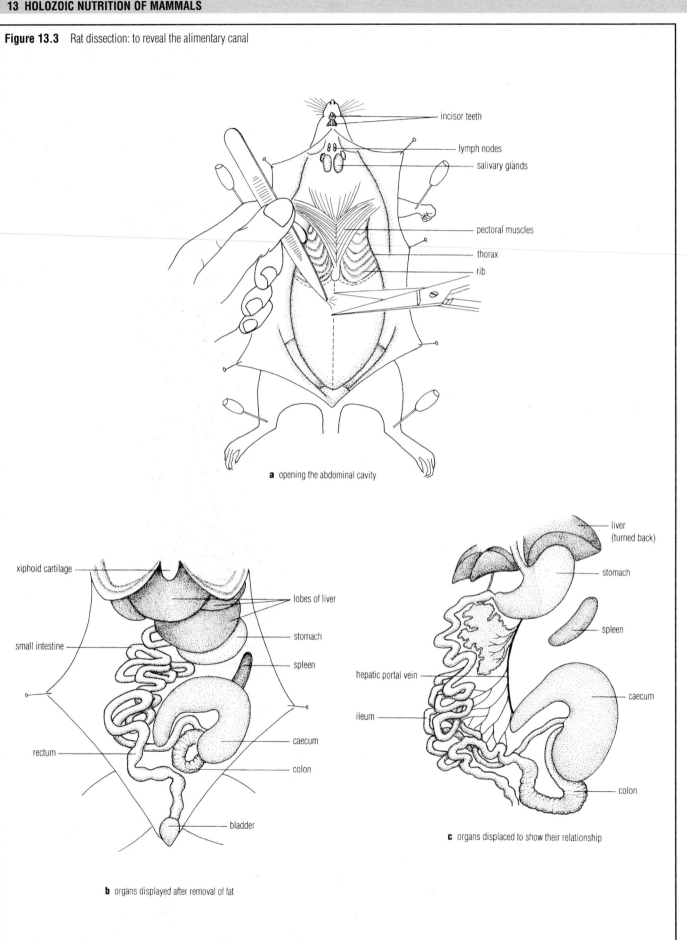

a opening the abdominal cavity

b organs displayed after removal of fat

c organs displaced to show their relationship

4 Now you can trace the path of the gut by hand, from the point where the oesophagus joins the upper part of the stomach, to the rectum at the other end of the abdominal cavity. Push the lobes of the liver forwards to assist your search. Move the structures obscuring your view gently, as you find and identify the oesophagus, stomach and spleen, the duodenum and pancreas, the hepatic portal vein held within the mesentery, the ileum, the caecum and appendix, and the colon and rectum.

5 Spread out the gut and associated glands to display the features illustrated in Figure 13.3(b). Take a photograph or make a drawing of the structures. Label your record.

6 Now trace the arterial supply to the intestines. Displace the stomach and the whole of the remainder of the gut to your left (the rat's right), and examine the stretched mesentery for the arteries that serve the intestines. The coeliac artery and the anterior mesenteric artery branch off from the dorsal aorta just anterior to the left renal artery. They may be par-

tially overlaid by fat and by lymph nodes, which you can peel away with fine forceps. Further down the body cavity, the posterior mesenteric artery arises where the dorsal aorta splits into the iliac arteries serving the hind limbs. The posterior mesenteric artery serves the rectum and colon. Make a drawing of the paths of these arteries as far as you can trace them.

7 Now remove the alimentary canal by careful dissection. Cut the oesophagus immediately above the stomach. Ligature the hepatic portal vein as close to the liver as you can. Cut through the rectum just behind the urinogenital system. Cautiously cut through the mesentery to free the gut, taking care not to cut the blood vessels (especially the dorsal aorta and vena cava) running along the body wall below the gut. Unravel and lay out the gut as in Figure 13.4. Finally part of the ileum may be retained in fixative/preservative solution (p. 162), ready for subsequent examination of the surface of the lumen of the ileum, using a hand lens or stereo microscope, as an extension exercise to Practical 13.3 (p. 162).

Figure 13.4 Rat dissection: the gut and associated glands unravelled and identified

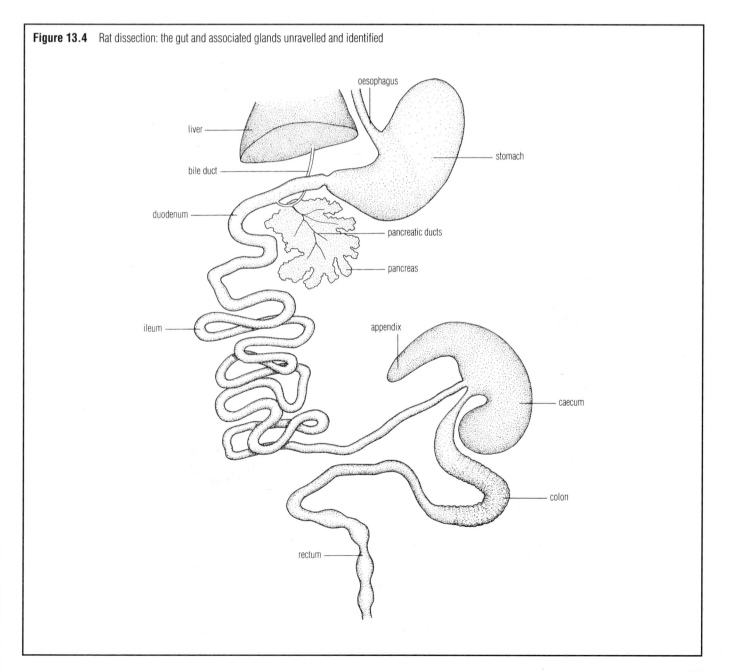

References

H G Q Rowett (1974) *The Rat as a Small Mammal*. John Murray

H G Q Rowett (1992) *Guide to Dissection*. John Murray

Virtual dissection

Computer software and CD-ROM, together with educational video, can be used to support or replace learning by dissection. The following resources may be used, singly or together, to learn about the alimentary canal of the mammal.

Video Rat Stack, from BioScience Programs, is an interactive package about the dissection and functional anatomy of the rat. It consists of the *Rat Anatomy Disk*, a videodisc which illustrates dissection of male and female rats and the associated laboratory dissection techniques (sequences of moving video and still video frames). This disc also holds images of histology sections and several line drawings. In addition a HyperCard stack (Apple Mac) organises the video images into an interactive learning program. Annotations and video images appear in response to the computer cursor.

Reference

M Quentin-Baxter and D Dewhurst (1995) 'An interactive laser video disc to teach the functional anatomy of the rat', *J. Biol. Ed.* 29(1), pp. 34–9

Vertebrate Dissection Guides – The Rat, by the TV Centre, the University of Portsmouth in association with the Institute of Biology. This videotape covers the functional anatomy of the rat. It is designed as a preparatory, practical and reference resource, which can either increase the success and enhance the experience of dissection, or act as an alternative. The external features and the digestive system (among other systems) are covered by photography, clear identification, use of graphic overlays, and three-dimensional computer animation. The video is accompanied by teacher's notes, including labelled and unlabelled diagrams.

NOTE TO TECHNICIAN

Students will require (or require access to):
- dissecting board;
- awls and pins;
- disposable plastic gloves;
- rat for dissection (embalmed rats, with or without injected blood vessels, are available);
- essential dissection equipment:
    two stainless steel dissecting needles, and one blunt, stainless steel seeker;
    fine forceps and blunt forceps (stainless steel);
    fine scissors and coarse scissors (stainless steel);
    fixed-blade, stainless steel scalpel, and two scalpel handles (Swann-Morton, sizes 3 and 4);
    packets of Swann-Morton scalpel blades, one of each of sizes 10, 11, 12, 15, 22 and 24;
    section lifter, teat pipette, fine paint brush;
    fixative/preservative solution (70% ethanol)
- camera with colour print film;
- video player and monitor (if Institute of Biology videotape mentioned above is available);
- Apple Macintosh microcomputer (4/40 MB or better), with Pal video disc player and separate high-quality television monitor (if *The Rat Stack* is available).

■ Data presentation

Record the dissection at key stages by line drawings or by photographs, both subsequently labelled.

■ Conclusion

In what instances were you able to infer functions of structures from your observations based upon dissection?

■ Evaluation

Is the dissection of an animal, whether freshly killed or preserved, an invaluable aid to learning about living systems in animals?

■ Discussion point

The ethics of the use of animals in medical/pharmaceutical research may arise in connection with dissection studies. Organisations that may provide materials and information of use to interested and concerned students include:
- Animals in Medicines Research Information Centre, 12 Whitehall, London SW1A 2DY
- Royal Society for the Prevention of Cruelty to Animals, Causeway, Horsham, West Sussex RH12 1HG
- British Union for the Abolition of Vivisection, 16A Crane Grove, London N7 8LB.

13.3 The histology of the ileum and pancreas
(Skills and techniques)

The gut (alimentary canal) is a **long, muscular tube** consisting of regions with a common structure, but with **local specialisations**. Glands are associated with the gut in various positions.

■ Aim

To learn to recognise the tissues and cell types that comprise the ileum and pancreas.

■ Risk assessment

Good laboratory practice will be sufficient to take account of any hazards and avoid significant risks.

■ Method

1 Examine the prepared microscope slide of the transverse section of the ileum (the longest part of the small intestine) under the medium-power objective lens. Working from the lumen outwards through the tissues, observe:
- the numerous villi projecting into the lumen;
- the glandular layer at the base of the villi surrounding the deep pits called the crypts of Lieberkühn;
- the thin muscularis mucosa beneath the glandular layer;
- the connective tissue and blood vessels of the submucosa;
- the layers of longitudinal and circular muscle;
- the outer coat called the serosa.

Map these features for a small section of the intestinal wall, indicating the thickness of the layers. (See *Advanced Biology*, Figures 13.6 and 13.32, pp. 279 and 288.)

2 On high magnification, study the unstratified columnar epithelial layer of the villus surface, noting the long, thin cells usually showing stained nuclei halfway along their length and with a heavily stained outer margin. This is the brush border consisting of microvilli, though their nature is not distinguishable at this magnification. Among these cells are the often empty-looking goblet cells which secrete

mucus. Make a drawing showing a few cells representative of this tissue.

3 You will not be able to see details of the capillary network inside the villus easily, unless the blood vessels have been coloured by latex injection before sectioning. If such a slide is available, examine and draw the pattern of capillaries within a villus.

4 Examine the prepared microscope slide of a section of the pancreas under low magnification. The gland is divided up into lobes joined by connective tissue which often pulls apart in the preparation of the material. Make careful observations to recognise:
- the exocrine pancreatic gland cells forming the bulk of the tissue, in groups (acini) which secrete into a central duct (which may not be visible);
- distinct patches of cells not showing this organised pattern, called islets of Langerhans, which secrete the hormones insulin and glucagon, and are therefore endocrine in function;
- arteries and veins, sometimes paired together, but cut at various angles as they pass through the section;
- the occasional ducts of the exocrine gland, lined with obvious epithelial cells;
- strands of connective tissue surrounding the acini, lobes and islets of Langerhans.

Map a representative area to show the relationship between these tissues, representing the blocks of acini in outline, but not any cellular detail.

5 Examine the acini using the high-power objective lens. Make a drawing of the cellular detail that can be seen in one acinus, and indicate the probable position of the central duct.

6 Also using the high-power objective, examine the cells of an islet of Langerhans. Make a drawing of these cells, giving as much detail as possible over a small area, but including the apparent spaces occupied by blood capillaries in the living tissue. (See *Advanced Biology*, Figure 23.5, p. 513.)

NOTE TO TECHNICIAN

Each student requires (or requires access to):
- compound microscope and lamp;
- prepared microscope slide of:
    mammalian ileum (TS, preferably human, or from the rat dissection (Practical 13.2))
    mammalian ileum (TS, injected)
    mammalian pancreas (TS or LS, preferably human).

■ Data presentation
Add clear titles and full labelling to all your drawings. You may add notes to record observations not apparent on the drawings.

■ Discussion and conclusion
- The ileum can be thought of as showing modifications of the basic structure of the intestine to suit the particular function it performs. Describe the particular features seen in this region that suit it for its function.
- The pancreas is an exocrine gland and an endocrine gland, and therefore shows features of both. List the observable microscopic characteristics of the tissue that you would expect to look for in other glands of an exocrine or an endocrine nature.

■ Evaluation
What other sources of evidence would enable you to understand the cellular arrangement of the ileum and pancreas more thoroughly?

13.4 Comparative study of skulls and dentition in mammals
(Investigation)

The skulls of mammals have important features in common, and also show significant differences that – at least in part – may be related to lifestyle, including **differences in diet.**

■ Aim
To investigate similarities and differences in the skulls of an omnivore, a carnivore and a herbivore.

■ Risk assessment
Good laboratory practice will be sufficient to take account of any hazards and avoid significant risks.

■ Method
Make careful comparative observations of the following features of the three skulls provided.

1 The human skull consists of 22 bones, most of which are held by immovable joints with interlocking edges (sutures).
- Are the sutures of the cranial bones of the three skulls you are examining of comparable structure?
- Approximately how many bones appear to make up the skull of the sheep (or another herbivore skull), and that of the dog (or another carnivore skull)?

2 The bones surrounding the cranial cavity and the bones of the jaws were well supplied in life with blood vessels and nerves, which entered the solid bone at special ports called foramina (*sing.* foramen).
- Compare the numbers and positions of the foramina in the skulls.
- What do you anticipate is the role of the blood supply passing to and from bones like these?

3 The eyes fit into special sockets, the orbits, which are pronounced features of skulls.
- Compare the contrasting positions on the cranium of the orbits in the three skulls.
- Can you estimate, very approximately, the total visual field in each of the three animals in life?
- To what extent do the fields of view of the two eyes overlap in each species?

4 The roof of the mouth consists in part of a shelf of bone, the bony palate.
- What is the consequence of a permanent division between the breathing apertures (nostrils) and the mouth as regards the role of the mouth in digestion?

5 The lower jaw bones (mandibles) articulate with the upper jaws at a hinge position.
- Compare the articulatory movements that are possible at this point in the three skeletons.
- What evidence can you find for the existence, in life, of a substantial musculature for movement of the jaws?

6 Dentition in most mammals consists of a variable number of incisors, canines, premolars and molar teeth. The adult human dentition is represented by the dental formula:

$$i\frac{2}{2}, c\frac{1}{1}, pm\frac{2}{2}, m\frac{3}{3}$$

where the numerator is the number of that type of teeth in one half (one side) of the upper jaw, and the denominator is the number of teeth in one half of the lower jaw.

- Examine the human (or pig) skull. Work out the numbers of teeth of each type that are present, using the dental formula given.
- Write the dental formula for each of the other two skulls provided.

7 Examine the incisor teeth of the three skulls in detail.
- Make a comparison of the shape and mode of operation of these teeth, in life.

8 Examine the three skulls for the presence and form of the canine teeth.
- Make a comparison of this part of the dentition in the three skulls.

9 Examine the premolar and molar teeth in the herbivore skull.
- Make a detailed analysis of the ways these show adaptation to a herbivorous diet.

10 Examine the premolar and molar teeth in the carnivore skull.
- Make a detailed analysis of the ways these show adaptations to a carnivorous diet.

NOTE TO TECHNICIAN

Each student group needs access to:
- skulls of an omnivore (such as human or pig); a carnivore (such as dog) and a herbivore (such as sheep);
- hand lens.

■ Data presentation
- Record your observations by means of fully annotated sketches.
- Summarise the most contrasting features by means of a table.

■ Conclusion
Apart from differences in dentition, what other aspects of skull structure may be related to differences in diet?

■ Evaluation
You have been unable to investigate differences between skulls from organisms of the same species. To what extent, if any, do you think the sorts of difference you have found might be attributable to differences between individuals, rather than to differences between species? Why is this a significant point to be answered?

■ Extension
Compare the relative positions of the foramen magnum in bipedal and quadripedal animals.

13.5 Amylase activity in the gut of cockroach
(Investigation)

The facility for digestion of the different classes of food in the diet is located in **particular parts of the gut** of mammals such as the human. Is this also the case in non-vertebrates such as the cockroach (*Periplaneta americana*)?

■ Aim
To investigate the distribution of amylase enzymes in the gut taken from a freshly killed cockroach.

■ Risk assessment
- The safety precautions for dissection (p. 157) apply here.
- Otherwise, good laboratory practice will be sufficient to take account of any hazards and avoid significant risks.

■ Method

Dissecting the gut of Periplaneta, *and obtaining gut tissue portions*

1 Secure the ventral surface of *Periplaneta* in wax in a dissecting dish, permitting dissection by removal of the dorsal body wall. Cut off the wing cases (elytra) and wings close to the points of attachment to the thorax.

2 Lift the tergum of the terminal abdominal segment with forceps, and make a cut up the right side of the body to just below the head.

3 Using the forceps peel aside the dorsal terga plates, cutting through the thoracic flight muscles and the connective tissue with a scalpel. Pin the whole dorsal surface of the body. Do not cover the dissection with water, because the purpose of this dissection is to remove the gut in lifelike condition, for physiological experiments.

4 The abdomen contains fat bodies, which need putting to one side. Free the gut from mesentery that holds it in place, by means of a blunt seeker inserted below and moved along the path of the gut. Pin out the gut as shown in Figure 13.5. Trim away the thoracic muscles, without damaging the salivary glands.

Testing for amylase activity

You are provided with a dark blue starch agar plate. Using a heat-sterilised cork borer (size 0.7 cm, perhaps) cut out eight, evenly spaced 'wells' in the agar plate, discarding the starch/agar disc cut out in each case.

Divide the alimentary canal and salivary glands, cut from the dissection, into portions. It is suggested that you should use portions of standardised length of gut, perhaps about 0.5 cm in length:
- salivary glands;
- anterior half of crop;
- posterior crop;
- gizzard and digestive caecae;
- mid-gut;
- ileum and Malpighian tubules;
- colon;
- rectum.

Place each portion in one of the starch agar wells and add distilled water to fill the compartment. Cover the plate with the lid, and secure it with tabs of clear adhesive tape. Incubate the plate at room temperature for up to six hours. Further change can be suspended by subsequent storage of the plate in a refrigerator.

References
P W Freeland (1974) 'Characterisation of digestive enzymes in freshly killed animals', *J. Biol. Ed.* 8(1), pp. 38–45

H V Wyatt (1974) 'Further experiments with digestive enzymes in freshly killed animals', *J. Biol. Ed.* 8(6), pp. 330–2

Figure 13.5 Dissection of *Periplaneta*: the digestive system showing the regions to be used in the experiment

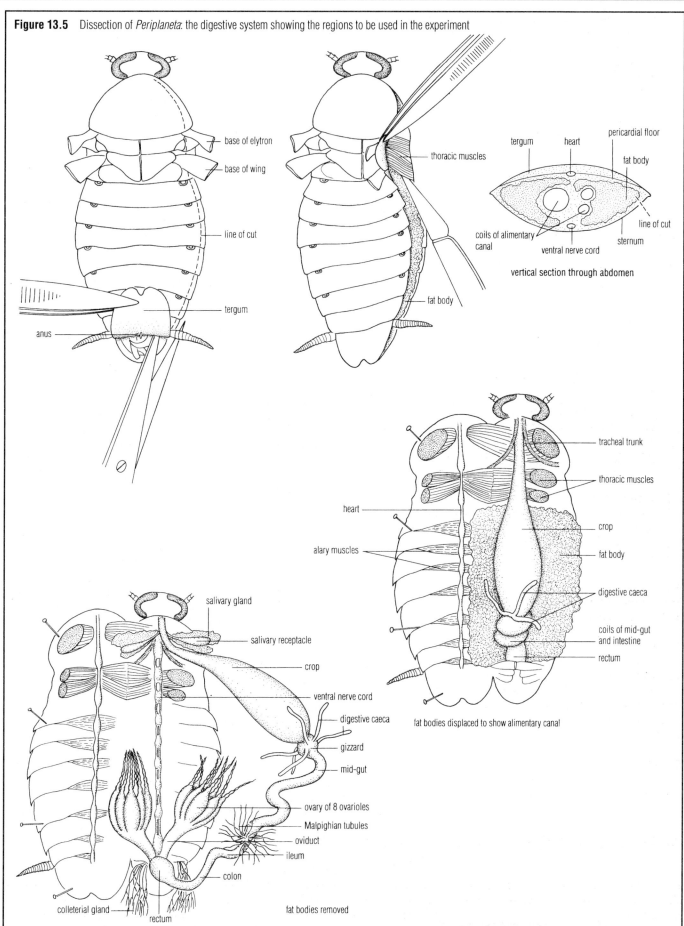

base of elytron

base of wing

line of cut

tergum

anus

thoracic muscles

fat body

tergum

heart

pericardial floor

fat body

line of cut

sternum

coils of alimentary canal

ventral nerve cord

vertical section through abdomen

tracheal trunk

thoracic muscles

crop

fat body

digestive caeca

coils of mid-gut and intestine

rectum

heart

alary muscles

fat bodies displaced to show alimentary canal

salivary gland

salivary receptacle

crop

ventral nerve cord

digestive caeca

gizzard

mid-gut

ovary of 8 ovarioles

Malpighian tubules

oviduct

ileum

colon

colleterial gland

rectum

fat bodies removed

G S Preece (1988) 'To demonstrate the distribution of invertase in the gut system of *Periplaneta americana*', *School Science Review* (June 1988) 68(249), pp. 744–5

H G Q Rowett (1982) *Guide to Dissection*. John Murray

NOTE TO TECHNICIAN

Each group of students will require:
- freshly killed *Periplaneta* (killed by placing in a screw-top jar in the ice box of the refrigerator overnight), mounted by embedding in wax as described in Rowett (1982) in a Petri dish;
- dissection equipment, as listed on p. 162;
- access to cork borer, 0.7 cm, with Bunsen and heat mat;
- starch/agar/iodine plate in a plastic Petri dish (p. 431).

■ Data presentation

- You can record your dissection of the gut of the cockroach by either colour print photography or drawings, or both. The record should be fully labelled.
- Digestion of starch in the agar by enzymes that diffuse out of the tissue creates transparent zones around the circumference of the wells. Measure and record the sizes of these zones.

■ Conclusions

- Which regions of the gut of *Periplaneta* are rich in amylase activity, and in which is this activity at a minimum?
- Non-vertebrates are opened via the dorsal surface to extract the gut, whereas a similar dissection of a vertebrate occurs via the ventral surface. What is the main reason for this different technique?

■ Evaluation

This technique can be extended to be a comparative study, using other non-vertebrates, including the earthworm, for example.

13.6 Proteases: the effect of pH on pepsin and trypsin

(Investigation)

Egg-white consists of a protein called albumen. If albumen is dissolved in water and boiled, a cloudy suspension of fine particles of denatured albumen is formed.

Proteases such as pepsin and trypsin can digest these solid particles to form **soluble peptides** and so produce a clear solution. Pepsin is present in gastric juice secreted by the stomach; trypsin is present in pancreatic juice secreted into the duodenum.

■ Aim

To compare the rates at which pepsin and trypsin digest an albumen suspension under different pH conditions.

■ Risk assessment

Good laboratory practice will be sufficient to take account of any hazards and avoid significant risks.

■ Method

Using buffer solutions to give a range of pH values, the rates at which the two enzymes turn egg-white suspension clear can be compared.

- You could try using 5 cm^3 of a 1% egg-white suspension plus 5 cm^3 of a range of buffers from pH 2 to pH 8, and adding 1 cm^3 pepsin or trypsin solution to each.
- Enzyme extracts and egg-white suspensions vary, so you might have to try different quantities and times.
- A water bath kept at about 40 °C will replicate body temperature approximately.

NOTE TO TECHNICIAN

Each group of students requires (or requires access to):
- 100 cm^3 citric acid/phosphate buffer solutions, pH 2, 3, 4, 5, 6, 8;
- 100 cm^3 albumen suspension (p. 432);
- 10 cm^3 1% pepsin solution;
- 10 cm^3 1% trypsin solution;
- test-tube racks and test tubes;
- graduated pipette or 5 cm^3 syringe;
- water bath at 40 °C;
- labels or spirit marker;
- stopclock.

■ Data presentation

Present your results as a table, showing the change in degree of clarity at each pH, with time.

■ Conclusion

Which of the pH values was most suitable for albumen digestion by pepsin and trypsin respectively?

■ Evaluation

- How did you estimate the degree of clearing in the test tubes?
- Could you have devised a more objective method?
- What do your results suggest about the likely pH of a mammal's stomach and duodenal contents?

Projects

13.1 The ascorbic acid (vitamin C) content of fruits and vegetables

The concentration of ascorbic acid can be estimated by titration of aqueous extracts made from fruits and vegetables against a set volume (perhaps 2 cm³) of 1% dichlorophenol-indophenol (DCPIP) solution. This solution is coloured, and ascorbic acid reduces DCPIP to a colourless substance. Your colour test can be standardised against a solution of ascorbic acid of known concentration. You might investigate the effects of length and conditions of storage, and the effects of various cooking methods, as well as comparing the concentrations of ascorbic acid in different fresh fruits and vegetables.

Reference
D G Mackean (1983) *Experimental Work in Biology: Food Tests*, pp. 30–1. John Murray

13.2 Comparing diets and 'calorie' intakes

Computer programs to analyse diet can be used to process data on the feeding habits of people in different circumstances. Such an investigation is bound to be limited to those who will take part voluntarily. Those who might participate include the elderly, the young, pregnant women, those in extremely physically demanding work and those with exceptionally sedentary employment and/or lifestyle. Data on diet over perhaps a seven-day period can be collected. Is there a tendency for people to select a balanced diet, appropriate to their needs? How overt, conscious and planned is this selection? Where have people obtained their attitudes and values towards food?

13.3 Investigating digestion using immobilised enzymes

Digestive enzyme solutions (amylase or sucrase, for example) solutions can be added to warm agar solutions and immobilised to line the inner tube of a Liebig condenser, thus simulating the gut. Substrate solutions (such as starch and sucrose) can be allowed to flow at a regulated rate, down the enzyme/agar mixtures at controlled temperatures (exploiting the water-filled jacket of the condenser), and the products of digestion detected. The effects of pH can also be investigated.

Reference
P Spencer (1988) 'Demonstration of digestion using immobilized enzymes', *School Science Review* 69(249), pp. 740–2

Problems and assignments

13.1 The Green Revolution re-examined

Read the passage in Panel 13.1 and then answer the questions below, using the information given together with your general knowledge and wider reading.

1 What sorts of evidence may support the observation that plant breeding by humans has gone on for ten thousand years?
2 People talk about the importance of 'genetic diversity'. How does this concept relate to the practice of plant breeding by farmers in developing countries, described here?
3 Suggest why the phrase 'useless weight in leaves' might be a questionable assumption, but the formation of heavier stalks is clearly a disadvantageous response by native plants to additional fertiliser.
4 What is meant by varieties that 'respond properly to fertilisers'?
5 For what reasons must extra cash be spent on insecticides when the new crops are grown?
6 Suggest some improvements in crop plants and in native agriculture that are likely to reduce hunger as opposed to only increasing food production, as the Green Revolution has mostly done.

13.2 Alcohol, diet and health

Ethanol can be consumed as spirits, fortified wine (sherry, for example), table wine or beer. Alcoholic drinks are a significant component of the national diet. The proportion of energy derived from alcohol is approximately half the energy we obtain as protein, on average. Alcohol is also a highly significant component of the diet because of its potentially adverse and harmful effects on the body. This is mainly due to the metabolic by-products into which ethanol is converted, chiefly ethanal. Ethanal is a very reactive compound which forms covalent bonds with functional groups such as —SH and —NH$_2$ on biologically active molecules. The shapes and properties of these molecules are changed as a result. Ethanal may react with certain neurotransmitters, too, interfering with their activity, and also reacts with lipid components of cells, such as phospholipids, interfering with their normal cell roles.

The ethanol content of different alcoholic drinks can be compared in terms of *units* of alcohol. The following each count as one unit:
- spirit (40% ethanol), one measure   = 10 g ethanol;
- fortified wine (20% ethanol), one measure   = 10 g ethanol;
- table wine (10% ethanol), one glass   = 12.5 g ethanol;
- beer (4% ethanol), half-pint   = 11.4 g ethanol.

As a result of a developing awareness of the harmful effects of alcohol, we are now encouraged to think of 'safe limits'. In January 1996 the government changed its safe limits for alcohol; it now recommends daily rather than the former weekly limits, as follows. For women: between 1 and 2 units per day may confer a health advantage; between 2 and 3 units per day confers no significant health risk; over 3 units per day is not advised. For men: between 1 and 2 units per day may confer a health advantage; between 2 and 4 units per day confers no significant health risk; over 4 units per day is not advised.

1 This question takes the form of a calculation concerning drinking, blood alcohol and 'recovery time'.

In the subject of this enquiry, a man of 80 kilograms (over 14 stones), body fluid made up 60% of the body mass. The ratio of body fluids found in cells and extracellularly is approximately 2 : 1. When alcoholic drinks are taken, ethanol enters the bloodstream quickly and is equilibrated between these intracellular and

---

Panel 13.1 One step forward: the Green Revolution

Plant breeding has been going on continuously for perhaps ten thousand years, ever since the first wild strains of wheat, rice and corn were domesticated. In the Third World it is still going on even among the poorest farmers, who are perpetually improving their seeds, picking out the healthiest and fattest plants as parents for next season's crops.

The native varieties this selection has produced are well adapted to the traditional conditions they have grown in. They are partly resistant to many local problems such as disease or periodic drought. But they are poorly suited for the most pressing problem in overpopulated lands: increasing the yield for a given area. When they are fertilised they tend to put on useless weight in leaves and stalks rather than into food grains.

Throughout the colonial period western scientific research almost totally neglected the food plants on which three-quarters of humankind depended for survival. Then, in 1943, the Rockefeller Foundation and the government of Mexico set up a programme that developed new tropical varieties of wheat that would respond properly to fertiliser. In 1960, to follow up the wheat success story, Rockefeller combined with the Ford Foundation to establish an international Rice Research Institute in the Philippines. Their first 'offspring', the famous high-yielding IR8, launched the Green Revolution.

The new seeds had an immediate and startling impact on food production. However, a farmer who wants to grow them needs extra cash for fertilisers, insecticides and the small irrigation improvements needed, and as wages for the additional labour taken on. The larger and richer farmers acquired the extra profits, while the landless and smallholders benefited little. Dryland farmers may have even suffered in competition, for in many places without sufficient water the new varieties performed worse than the old local varieties. The mechanisation that has often accompanied the Green Revolution may have wiped out as many jobs in farming as were initially created.

From: P Harrison (1979) Inside the Third World,
pp. 92–8. Penguin Books

---

extracellular compartments. Maximum blood ethanol levels develop in about one hour after consumption, but ethanol is steadily metabolised and removed from body fluids, at a rate of approximately 21 mg per 100 cm^3 per hour.

In the course of a convivial, accelerated bout of social drinking, our subject consumed two pints of beer and two measures of whisky, within an hour. He had to walk home!
a Calculate:
  i the grams of alcohol consumed;
  ii the theoretical maximum level of blood alcohol, assuming no loss from metabolism during the drinking period, giving your answer in mg per 100 cm^3. (Assume body fluid density is that of water.)

b In fact ethanol is metabolised. What would his blood alcohol levels be at:

  i three hours;

  ii six hours after the drinking occurred?

Compare these values with the 'legal limit' for blood alcohol for drivers.

2 a Ethanal, the chief oxidation product of ethanol, forms covalent bonds with certain functional groups. Name the major group of cell components which contain both —SH and —NH$_2$ groups. Where do these molecules commonly occur in cells?

b What adverse effects on the structure and functioning of cells are most likely to arise when ethanal forms covalent bonds with the —SH and —NH$_2$ groups of these mol-ecules?

3 Outline the sort of adverse effects you might anticipate when ethanal reacts with neurotransmitters in the body.

4 Ethanal also interferes with the structure and functioning of body lipids, including phospholipids.

a Describe where most lipid metabolism occurs in the body cells.

b What roles do lipids have in cell function?

5 Ethanol, at only a 4% solution, is sufficiently biocidal to start to kill yeast cells, and most if not all microorganisms (and other organisms, if present) in water. What has been the chief consequence for human life of this particular property of dilute ethanol?

13.3 The roles of cholesterol

Read the passage in Panel 13.2, and then answer the questions that follow, using your general biological knowledge and wider reading.

Panel 13.2 Cholesterol has many roles to play

Cholesterol is a natural substance that is an essential metabolite, but it is not an essential nutrient. The body can manufacture its own supply if none is present in the diet.

Without cholesterol, biological membranes would not function properly, and no closely related steroid can substitute for cholesterol in our bodies. Cholesterol is also converted into a variety of steroid hormones which have important regulatory functions. It is also converted into bile salts in the liver and these play a crucial part in the absorption of fat. But when less fat has to be transported around the body, less cholesterol is produced by the liver.

One reason why dietary cholesterol had a 'bad press' is that, when plaques build up on the inner walls of the arteries, cholesterol is one of the many substances contributing to the plaque. The cholesterol in plaques has been shown to originate from cholesterol carried in the blood in low-density lipoproteins. But contrary to popular belief, changing the amount of cholesterol in the diet has only a minor influence on blood cholesterol concentration.

From: M I Gurr (1979) Role of Fats in Food Production.
Elsevier

---

1 a What is the difference between a metabolite and a nutrient?

b Give two examples of essential metabolites and essential nutrients by reference to:

  i a green plant;

  ii humans.

2 Of what are biological membranes constructed? Where in the cell do membranes occur? What are the chief functions of cell membranes?

3 Give one example of a steroid hormone, and state a regulatory function for it.

4 How do we know that cholesterol is not an essential nutrient?

5 How are fats absorbed into the body? What part may cholesterol play in fat absorption?

6 a What do you understand by 'plaque' in reference to the arterial wall?

b Why are disruptions to the lining of arteries dangerous to health?

7 What are the component substances in lipoprotein?

8 Suggest why changing the amount of cholesterol in the diet may not be important to your health, but varying the amount of fat and lipid you take in is important.

13.4 Digestion in the stomach

Secretion of the digestive juices of the alimentary canal of a mammal is coordinated with the presence of food. For example, the secretion of gastric juice in the stomach is synchronised with the imminent arrival of food and is then maintained in the presence of food in the stomach. The various components of the control mechanism are summarised in Figure 13.6.

Evidence for the control mechanisms involved in gastric secretion comes from a range of experimental techniques:

- A gastric fistula (opening from stomach to exterior) allows the stomach contents to be sampled. Fistulas have been formed accidentally, as products of gunshot wounds, but normally they are surgically formed in an experimental animal.

- A stomach pouch (part of the stomach wall sealed off from the bulk of the stomach, and opening to the outside) allows the gastric secretion to be sampled. Gastric pouches can be formed with or without nervous connections with the rest of the stomach.

- A gastroscope (optical-fibre probe connected to a video camera) can be used to view the contents of the stomach directly.

- Stomach contents may be sampled. A fine plastic tube is 'swallowed' and passed down into the stomach. By this means samples of the liquid matter are withdrawn for analysis.

1 By means of a fully annotated sketch, show the structure of a gastric gland and the origin of the different components of gastric juice formed there.

2 What are the advantageous effects on digestion of the waves of muscular contraction that pass across the stomach wall when food is present?

3 Using one or more of the experimental techniques listed above, how could research workers have established:

a that the presence of food about to be eaten is the trigger for the secretion of gastric juice rich in pepsinogen?

b that for most of the time the food is in the stomach the flow of gastric juice is maintained by a mechanism other than nervous stimulation of the gastric glands?

c that a pH of about 1.5 is achieved in the stomach as the bolus of food reaches this part of the gut, and that one effect of this level of acidity is to kill bacteria in the liquidised food?

d the state of protein digestion as food leaves the stomach?

Figure 13.6   The control of gastric secretion

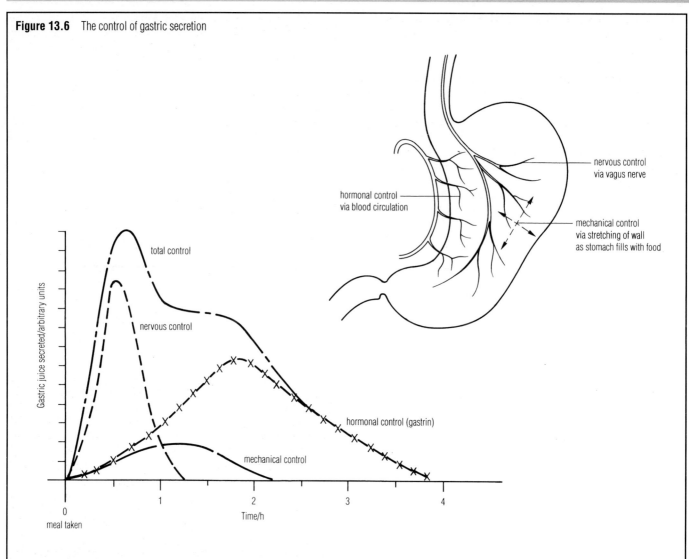

Gastric juice secreted/arbitrary units

total control

nervous control

hormonal control (gastrin)

mechanical control

0
meal taken

Time/h

nervous control
via vagus nerve

hormonal control
via blood circulation

mechanical control
via stretching of wall
as stomach fills with food

e that mechanical stretching of the stomach wall is a factor that induces the secretion of gastric juice?

f that the presence of partially digested protein in the stomach induces hormone-induced secretion of gastric juice?

4 How does the body prevent self-digestion of the stomach wall by the powerful protein-digesting enzymes present in the gastric juice?

5 Barium sulphate is insoluble and opaque to X-rays. How is this substance used to investigate abnormalities in stomach structure and function in humans?

13.5 Absorption in the villus

Figure 13.7 shows one columnar epithelial cell from a villus in the human small intestine (ileum) that is involved in the digestion of proteins and the absorption into the blood of the products of this digestion. Using the information gleaned from the diagram, together with your wider reading, answer the questions below.

1 The cell represented here would be found in the wall of the small intestine.

   a Draw and label a tissue map of the wall of the small intestine as seen in TS.

Figure 13.7   Protein digestion and absorption in the alimentary canal – a summary

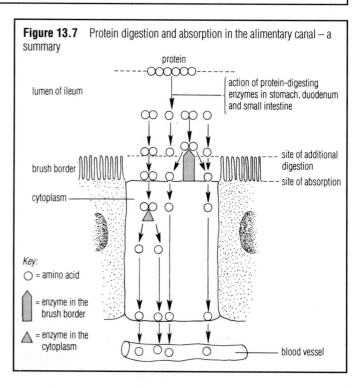

protein

lumen of ileum

action of protein-digesting enzymes in stomach, duodenum and small intestine

brush border

site of additional digestion

site of absorption

cytoplasm

Key:
○ = amino acid

= enzyme in the brush border

= enzyme in the cytoplasm

blood vessel

b Draw a separate diagram to show the detailed structure of a single villus, indicating where cells of the type shown in Figure 13.8 are found.

2 In Figure 13.7, the symbol for protein consists of a linear series of 'beads' condensed together. What substances are represented by the individual beads, and what type of linkage occurs between them?

3 Describe the digestion and absorption of proteins as shown by Figure 13.7.

4 In what form are the final products of protein digestion passed to the blood vessels of the intestine? How are they exported from the epithelial cells?

13.6 Quick test

1 Distinguish between the following pairs:

a heterotroph and autotroph;
b ingestion and egestion;
c trachea and oesophagus;
d mesentery and mucosa;
e dentine and enamel;
f herbivore and omnivore;
g molars and canines;
h vitamins and minerals;
i pepsin and trypsin;
j duodenum and ileum;
k villi and microvilli;
l bile and pancreatic juice;
m absorption and assimilation;
n ileum and colon;
o caecum and appendix.

2 What do you understand by the following terms?

a basal metabolism;
b anorexia nervosa;
c dental formula;
d peristalsis;
e gastric juice;
f hepatic portal vein;
g peptic ulcer;
h cholesterol;
i dietary fibre;
j lymphatic system.

13.7 Essay assignment

Select one of the following:

- What are the key differences in structure of the carbohydrates starch and cellulose? Describe the roles of these components of the diet in humans. Outline the processes by which cellulose digestion is achieved in the gut of a ruminant such as the cow.

or:

- In the ileum the products of digestion are absorbed into the body. Outline the structure of the wall of the ileum, and contrast the processes of absorption of the products of protein and lipid digestion.

14 Variety in heterotrophic nutrition

Summary

As we saw in Chapter 13, heterotrophs eat and digest complex, ready-made organic nutrients, and then absorb and assimilate the products of digestion. In **holozoic nutrition**, food is taken into a digestive system for processing. Mechanisms of holozoic nutrition are classified into three groups on the basis of size of the food eaten: small particles (**microphagous feeders** such as *Paramecium* and *Daphnia*), liquid (**fluid feeders** such as aphids and mosquitoes), and large particles (**macrophagous feeders** like *Hydra* and the earthworm).

    Saprotrophic nutrition involves the digestion of food on which the saprotroph lives and grows. It is of particular ecological significance because of the saprotroph's role in the recycling of matter.

Saprotrophs are of economic importance because of the part they play in decay and biodeterioration, and as active agents in fermenter systems. Saprotrophic nutrition is illustrated by a very wide range of bacteria and fungi, including yeasts.

    Parasitic nutrition involves living permanently on (ectoparasite) or in (endoparasite) another organism, and feeding at the expense of this host throughout the greater part of the life cycle. Parasites show pronounced modifications to structure, physiology and reproduction when compared with free-living relatives. These features include mechanisms for attachment, mechanisms aiding dispersal and the journey from host to host, and mechanisms for resisting the host's defence systems.

Practicals and activities

14.1 Food preference in non-vertebrates

(Investigation)

The feeding apparatus of an organism will determine what sort of food it can eat, but there is a wide variety of foods that can be tackled with the same apparatus.

■ Aim
To investigate food preferences in snails and locusts.

■ Risk assessment
Good laboratory practice will be sufficient to take account of any hazards and avoid significant risks.

■ Method
Note: These investigations need daily observations.

Food preference in a snail
A large *Helix aspersa* can be kept in an empty coffee jar with a loose-fitting or perforated lid.

- Place a few leaves of different plants in the jar overnight, and examine them the next morning to see which ones have been eaten (snails are nocturnal feeders). It is worth trying leaves of nasturtium, dock, pea, plantain, rhubarb, dandelion, lettuce and cabbage (or other brassicas). Offer a choice of only two or three different leaves each time. The leaves should not have already been attacked, and the outline should be easily recognisable or drawn on a piece of graph paper. Cut squares from very large leaves.
- Tip the leaves out each day and examine them for signs of feeding. It is best to replace them with fresh leaves each day, varying the choice to find a range of preferences.
- If one plant species is consistently avoided, try offering only that one species for a night's trial. Is it still totally rejected? Is it taste or smell or texture that the snail dislikes? If there are any signs of nibbling, it could be taste.

- To find the preferred food among plant species that are all accepted by the snail, you will need to make your observations more quantitative. You can do this by drawing the leaf outline on graph paper, and then measuring the missing area on the following day.
- Gardeners complain of the damage to their crops caused by snails. Do your results indicate whether this is due to a distinct preference by snails for cultivated brassicas, or is it that these are the only plants available in a snail's range?

Food preference in locusts (or grasshoppers)
You will need a suitable locust cage or similar accommodation for this investigation.

- Partly fill two small jars with water, label them with a marker pen, and place a bunch of leaves of two species of grass or cereals in each jar. Place the jars side by side in the cage so that they are equally available to the locust.
- Leave the locust in the cage for 24 hours, and examine the remains of the grasses next day. For quantitative results, choose pairs of grass or cereal species with leaves of a comparable width, cut them to a uniform length, say 150 mm, and measure the total length remaining after 24 hours.

NOTE TO TECHNICIAN

Each group will need:
- a suitable container, e.g. a large empty coffee jar, with a perforated lid;
- leaves of a range of plants (listed above);
- a large *Helix aspensa*;
- a supply of graph paper.

(If locusts are used):
- a locust cage;
- two small jars containing water, with different sources of green leaves (changed daily);
- locusts.

- Fragments of grass lying on the bottom of the cage may be difficult to assess. A piece of card between the two jars may help to keep the fragments separate.
- As with the snail, you will need to supply fresh material each day, varying the combination.
- Are soft grasses preferred to coarse grasses? Will locusts eat dicot leaves?

■ Data presentation
Present your data by means of tables and graphs.

■ Conclusion
What are the food preferences of these organisms?

■ Evaluation
Does 'captivity' influence the outcome of your investigation?

■ Extension
You will probably find that the snail used in the first part of this investigation has a regular pattern of feeding and resting. Where does it rest during the day? Can this pattern be changed by altering the dark/light regime?

Reference
R Barras (1996) 'Locusts for student-centred learning', *J. Biol. Ed.* **30**(1), pp. 22–6

Projects

14.1 Microphagous feeding in Daphnia

Daphnia, the crustacean water flea, swims by flicking its antennae; it uses its abdominal limbs to create a water current which draws water and suspended particles into the space between its carapace plates. Food particles are filtered out by bristles on the limbs and passed to the mouth to be ingested. The creation of the current and passage of food can be seen by placing *Daphnia* in a drop of water on a microscope slide, and observing under the lowest magnification. The gut can also be seen clearly, usually filled with microscopic green algae. *Daphnia* may be induced to feed on yeast cells. If the yeast cells are first stained with an acid–base indicator such as neutral red, then the ingested yeast cells can be observed by low-power microscope examination. Changes in pH can be detected by colour change in the ingested prey as it passes down the gut.

14.2 Aphids as feeders and prey

Aphid colonies can be found on the stems or leaves of plants (herbaceous and woody), in early summer. The growth of the colony can be assessed by counting numbers at regular intervals. Many species of aphids are 'tended' by ants. What is the effect of ants' tending on colony growth, compared with species where ants have been excluded? Horticulturalists' sticky fruit-tree bands applied below the experimental area will block the path of ants. The effects on a colony isolated in this way may be compared with observations of a colony of the same species living in a comparable branch, that is tended by ants. Do you need to prevent the arrival by air of ladybird species? What is the effect of ladybird predation on another, similar, aphid colony?

Reference
G J Skinner (1988) 'The use of ants in field work', *J. Biol. Ed.* **22**(2), pp. 99–106

14.3 Predation by spiders – the role of the web

All spiders are carnivorous, and most feed on living animals such as insects and other small arthropods. They feed by injecting poison and digestive juice, and sucking the liquidised contents of the prey from its body. The spiders also spin silk, and many build intricate webs by which the prey is trapped. Funnel-shaped webs are formed by some species, but the most attractive and easy to study are the circular webs that are built out across open spaces. The web-building and feeding behaviour of either the diadem spider (cross spider) or the garden spider is an ideal topic, since these arthropods have a catholic diet. Which animals are retained, and which are released if caught? How is a fresh web constructed? What is the response of the spider to accidental damage of the web at various stages in construction? How often does prey typically get trapped, and how does the spider respond to a glut of food? Trapped prey are detected by vibrations set up in the web. Using tuning forks, is it possible to find the frequencies to which the spider is sensitive?

Figure 14.1 The garden snail; habitat view

14.4 Feeding by slugs and snails

Slugs and snails rasp and scrape organic matter, using a spe-cial organ (the radula) working against a tough jaw plate. This apparatus is extended out of the mouth when in use. Land snails and slugs can be cultured in warm, humid conditions in captivity, and used to study food preferences (a variety of fruit and vegetables). The feeding mechanism may be observed first hand. The growth, development and life cycle may also be studied. The study may take the form of a comparison of the behaviour of two or more species of snail or slug.

References

J Gill and R Howell (1985) 'Food choice in the common snail (*Helix aspersa*)', *J. Biol. Ed.* **19**(1), pp. 6–7

J A Tranter (1993) 'The giant African land snail, *Achatina fulica*, and other species', *J. Biol. Ed.* **27**(2), pp. 108–11

D Pallant (1967) 'Slugs in school biology', *School Science Review* (June 1967) **48**(166), pp. 782–6

A Cook (1989) 'Exploited animals: slugs and snails', *Biologist* **36**(4), pp. 183–8

M Lazaridou-Dimitriadou (1990) 'Spotlight: snails', *Biol. Sci. Rev.* (November 1990) **3**(2), pp. 30–3

14.5 Feeding on leaves in the earthworm

Lumbricus terrestris (and certain other species) selectively pulls dead leaves into its burrow in hours of darkness. 'Plugs' of leaves protruding from burrow entrances may be a conspic-uous feature of the floor of woodland areas, particularly in autumn and winter, and provide a means of finding areas where worms are active. If the leaves are cleared from such a patch of ground, and equal numbers of dead leaves of differ-ent species are placed on the surface, then any selection of diet can be quantified. You will need to protect the leaves from any other source of movement, for example, by stretching a fine-mesh garden net over the plot. Alternatively you could work with worms in laboratory wormeries, with standardised leaf fragments from a range of species, and measure their rate of disappearance.

Reference

T G Piearce (1979) 'Illustrations of British earthworms', *School Science Review* (June 1979) **60**(213), pp. 701–7

14.6 Feeding on seeds in the earthworm

By collecting surface wormcasts and keeping them moist in the light for some weeks, it is easy to show that earthworms con-sume many 'seeds'. Large numbers of seeds survive gut transit, and the partial digestion of the testa may enhance germination which can be established experimentally for different plant species. You can plot the positions of wormcasts in grassland, and record the subsequent appearance of seedlings. Is it pos-sible to investigate whether the seeds of some species are pref-erentially selected?

Reference

T G Piearce, N Roggero and R Tipping (1994) 'Earthworms and seeds', *J. Biol. Ed.* **28**(3), pp. 195–202

14.7 Saprotrophic nutrition in Rhizopus

Rhizopus can be cultured on starch/agar plates (p. 431), and the extent of starch digestion measured by subsequently flooding the plates with iodine solution. What other nutritional requirements facilitate the growth of the fungus? In what form is combined nitrogen utilised (as nitrate or ammonium ions, or as specific amino acids)? The presence of other ions may facilitate growth. What temperature range is most effective?

14.8 Coprophilous fungi; succession on 'fresh' herbivorous dung

Fresh coprophilous dung (that of rabbits, sheep, cows, horses or other herbivores), incubated in a closed container in the warmth, almost instantly supports a surface growth of '*Mucor*-like' pin mould. This population is superseded rapidly by other fungi with larger fruiting bodies, and the succession normally ends with small 'mushroom' fruiting bodies of *Coprinus*, an ink-cap. Can you establish which spores are already present in the fresh dung? How does the succession of fungi vary with the species from which the dung was obtained? Can you discover whether any of the spores must have passed through the gut before they will 'germinate' in sterile dung? Spore dispersal in many of these fungi is light-sensitive, but which wavelengths are effective?

Reference
C J Clegg (1984) *Lower Plants*, p. 44. John Murray

14.9 Heat production in garden compost

When grass cuttings are composted in bulk in an insulated, ventilated container, a relatively high temperature develops. What conditions are essential for this process, and how high may the temperature go? In contrast, fresh grass cuttings, rolled to exclude air, may be made into silage. What are the significant differences in this case? Why has the silage got food value for a ruminant, but the compost has application only in soil improvement?

Reference
C J Clegg (1984) *Lower Plants*, p. 45. John Murray

14.10 Alcohol production in yeast

Brewers' yeast, added to a dilute solution of sucrose under otherwise sterile conditions, will quickly grow and ferment the sugar. The formation of alcohol (or rather the disappearance of the sugar) can be followed by measuring changes in relative density with a hydrometer. What factors influence the growth of yeast and the speed at which the alcohol will accumulate? What is the optimum initial sugar concentration? What influence does the presence of various inorganic ions, or of additional growth factors (from 'Marmite', for instance) have on yeast performance?

Reference
D R Berry (1982) *The Biology of Yeasts*. Arnold Studies in Biology no 140. Edward Arnold

14.11 Parasitic nutrition

Many wild plants of the hedgerow or woods are subject to parasitic infections. What is the incidence of mildews or rust infections, for example, on specific host plants? How are the physiology and growth of the host affected? How specific is a species of parasite, regarding other host species of the same genus? How does the parasite get dispersed, or 'over-winter', and inoculate fresh host plants? What conditions favour an epidemic, and what conditions enable the host to 'fight back'?

References
N D Paul and A J S Murray (1987) 'Simple investigations of the rust diseases of plants. I', *School Science Review* (March 1987) 68(244), pp. 492–8

A J S Murray and N D Paul (1987) 'Simple investigations of the rust diseases of plants. II', *School Science Review* (June 1987) 68(245), pp. 680–7

M C Edwards and P G Ayers (1979) 'Powdery mildew diseases of plants', *School Science Review* (March 1979) 60(212), pp. 475–88

D R Walters and P G Ayers (1983) 'Class experiments with powdery mildews', *School Science Review* (June 1983) 64(229), pp. 688–90

Problems and assignments

14.1 How do these organisms obtain nutrients?

The following organisms illustrate different ways of obtaining the nutrients for growth and development. For each, say whether its nutrition is:

  i heterotrophic or autotrophic;

  ii holozoic, saprotrophic, parasitic or none of these.

a *Lemna*, a tiny plant of one or two leaves and a minute rootlet, found floating on the surface of pond water;

b *Escherichia coli*, a bacterium living in the human alimentary canal, surrounded by the products of digestion and undigested fibre materials;

c *Monocystis*, a protozoan living for the whole of its life cycle in the seminal vesicles of the earthworm;

d *Culex*, a blood-sucking insect that visits various mammals irregularly;

e *Pilobolus*, a filamentous fungus growing in horse dung and also occurring as spores in the horse's gut;

f ivy (*Hedera helix*), a green plant climbing over tree trunks, for example, which becomes closely attached to its substratum;

g *Thiobacillus ferro-oxidans*, a bacterium of acidic ore dumps, living in the dark, converting iron(II) to iron(III) ions, and forming carbohydrates from carbon dioxide and water;

h *Paramecium*, a protozoan that forms food vacuoles in the cytoplasm from bacteria and diatoms in the surrounding pond water;

i small tortoiseshell butterfly (*Aglais urticae*), a garden butterfly laying eggs on nettle plants, and itself visiting the flowers of the michaelmas daisy.

j *Cuscuta*, a flowering plant with very tiny, colourless leaves, a thin climbing stem twined very closely around the stem of plants like the nettle, and having no roots when fully grown.

14.2 The life cycle of a plant parasite

Phytophthora infestans is a fungus-like member of the Protoctista. The life cycle of *Phytophthora* is illustrated in Figure 14.2. Examine this diagram carefully, and then, using this information and your wider reading, answer the following questions.

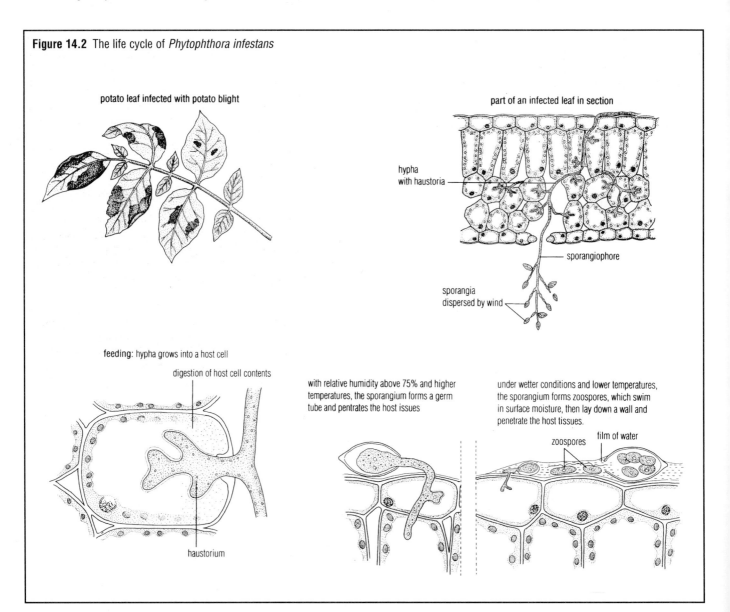

Figure 14.2 The life cycle of *Phytophthora infestans*

potato leaf infected with potato blight

part of an infected leaf in section

hypha with haustoria

sporangiophore

sporangia dispersed by wind

feeding: hypha grows into a host cell

digestion of host cell contents

haustorium

with relative humidity above 75% and higher temperatures, the sporangium forms a germ tube and pentrates the host issues

under wetter conditions and lower temperatures, the sporangium forms zoospores, which swim in surface moisture, then lay down a wall and penetrate the host tissues.

zoospores

film of water

1 What is meant by 'Protoctista'? What other organisms belong to this grouping?

2 State two features of structure shown by *Phytophthora* which can be described as 'fungus-like'.

3 Explain concisely two features that enable us to classify *Phytophthora* as a parasite.

4 Commercial potatoes grown in lowland Britain are cultivated from 'seed' potatoes, grown the previous year in Scotland. What are the biological reasons for this precaution?

5 To what features of this parasite could you point, in order to justify a belief that it is well adapted to its environment and lifestyle?

6 What feature might support the argument that *Phytophthora* is a relatively recently evolved parasite?

7 Some fungicides are described as 'systemic' and others as 'surface acting'. Explain the difference.

8 Bordeaux mixture, one of the original fungicides devised, provides a film of insoluble copper ions on the surface of potato leaves. These ions are poisonous only if they become dissolved in the cytoplasm of *Phytophthora*. How could this transition in solubility come about?

9 Healthy potato plants growing in the vicinity of a *Phytophthora*-infected plant are particularly vulnerable when the mean day temperature is 18–22 °C and the relative humidity is 91–100%. What is the most likely explanation of this?

10 Without knowledge of the life cycle of the fungus, human communities dependent upon potatoes as their staple food have at times been decimated, or worse. Suppose that a farming family has discovered signs of *Phytophthora* infection in their harvested potatoes; what first step would you advise them to take if the family is to survive and remain growers in succeeding years?

14.3 Quick test

1 Distinguish between the following pairs:

a holozoic nutrition and saprotrophic nutrition;
b microphagous and macrophagous feeders;
c food vacuoles and pseudopodia;
d cilia and setae;
e filter feeders and fluid feeders;
f sap and nectar;
g mandibles and maxillae;
h labium and labrum;
i *Hydra* and *Daphnia*;
j enteron and gut;
k protrusible tongue and extendable buccal mass;
l mycelium and fruiting body;
m *Mucor* and *Rhizopus*;
n malting and mashing of barley grains;
o ectoparasite and endoparasite.

2 What do you understand by the following?

a chemosynthesis;
b social insect;
c beneficial effects of earthworms;
d decomposers;
e cellulase;
f thermophilous fungi;
g extracellular digestion;
h platyhelminth;
i obligate parasite;
j adaptations to parasitism.

14.4 Essay assignment

Select one of the following:

- The female mosquito and *Plasmodium* live in close association for part of their life cycles. How do both of these organisms feed? What is meant by a 'vector'? List those features of the life cycle of the mosquito that can be exploited to reduce the dangers of malaria for humans.

or:

- By comparison with a free-living platyhelminth, illustrate the features of structure and life cycle of *Taenia* that can be considered as adaptations to parasitism. By what measures can the risk of human infection from tapeworms be reduced?

15 Respiration and gaseous exchange

Summary

Respiration occurs in every living cell and it results in the transfer of **energy** from food substances (mainly hexose sugar) to ATP, to facilitate the **work and activity of cells and organisms**. The cell-based breakdown of sugar, known as **cellular respiration**, leads to exchange of gases with the environment (**gaseous exchange**). In **aerobic respiration** sugar is oxidised to carbon dioxide and water and much energy is transferred. In **anaerobic respiration** sugar is only partially oxidised either to ethanol and carbon dioxide or to lactic acid, and much less energy is made available.

In Protoctista and other very small or very thin animals and plants, gaseous exchange occurs over the **whole surface** of the organism. In larger and more compact organisms, more **complex structures** and organisation are required to allow efficient diffusion of oxygen into every living cell. These structures range from stomata and lenticels, which serve the network of intercellular spaces in terrestrial flowering plants, to the tracheal system of insects by which air is 'piped' to every cell, and the elaborate lungs and gills with enormous surface areas that serve larger animals. The human lung system is ventilated by coordinated movements of rib-cage and diaphragm.

Cellular respiration involves the **glycolysis** of hexose sugar to form pyruvic acid (a three-carbon molecule). In aerobic respiration this is then completely oxidised to carbon dioxide via the **tricarboxylic acid cycle**, and to water via the **electron-transport pathway**. Most **ATP** is generated in this latter stage by **oxidative phosphorylation**. In anaerobic respiration (fermentation) pyruvic acid is reduced to **lactic acid** (for example, in human muscle during persisting rapid activity) or to **ethanol** and carbon dioxide (in plants and yeasts in the absence of air). A very little ATP is generated during glycolysis via substrate-level phosphorylation.

The rate of respiration can be measured by means of a respirometer. In humans a spirometer and kymograph are used to investigate breathing, and to measure gaseous exchange (O_2 uptake/CO_2 output). The **rate of respiration** reflects the organism's demand for energy.

Practicals and activities

15.1 Respiration rate and temperature

(Investigation)

In Assignment 8.2 (p. 177), the principles of manometry were introduced. The respirometer used in this investigation consists of a pair of matched **manometers** attached to boiling tubes, one of which contains living material; the other is a control.

■ Aim

To investigate the effect of increasing temperature on the rate of gaseous exchange and, by implication, the rate of respiration.

■ Risk assessment

Good laboratory practice will be sufficient to take account of any hazards and avoid significant risks.

■ Method

Setting up the respirometer

1 The design of the respirometer is shown in Figure 15.1. One boiling tube contains a known mass of living tissue, such as germinating wheat seeds. The other tube contains an equal mass of dead tissue, such as germinating wheat seeds that have been killed by boiling. The cotton wool plugs separate the living material from about 5 g self-indicating soda lime. The water bath maintains both tubes at a constant temperature.

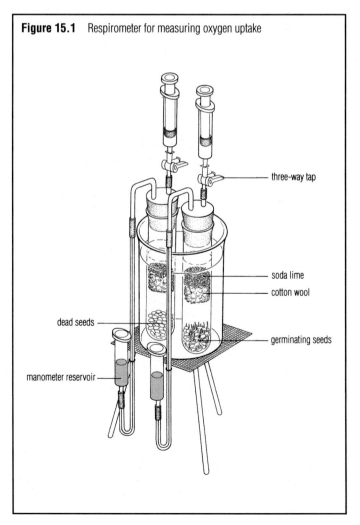

Figure 15.1 Respirometer for measuring oxygen uptake

- three-way tap
- soda lime
- cotton wool
- dead seeds
- germinating seeds
- manometer reservoir

2 Half-fill the manometer reservoir with water to which a dye has been added. Draw the liquid up into the capillary by putting the three-way tap in position (b) (Figure 15.1) and withdrawing the syringe plunger. If the level is seen to fall, there is a leak in the system.

3 Move the tap to position (c). This allows the levels to equilibrate and the marker can be moved to the starting level in the capillary.

4 To measure the rate of oxygen uptake, turn the tap first to position (a) and withdraw the syringe plunger to the $2\,cm^3$ mark. When you are ready to begin readings, turn the tap to position (b) and note the time. As the living material takes up oxygen, the liquid level in the capillary will rise. Depressing the syringe plunger returns the level to the mark, and the volume of gas taken up can be read from the distance moved by the plunger. Repeat this until an easily measurable volume of gas has been taken up.

5 Carry out all these operations with both tubes, and calculate the volume of gas taken up from any *difference* between the experiment and control. You will have to decide how many successive experiments to conduct in order to be confident that the rate of uptake is reasonably steady.

The effect of increasing temperature

For various reasons, including the time factor, it is best if each group is allocated a specific temperature at which to work. The temperature intervals will depend on the number of groups and the apparatus available, but it is a good idea to go up to 45 °C. Temperatures below room temperature can be achieved by adding ice to the water bath. If thermostatically controlled water baths are not available, the temperature can be raised by gentle and intermittent heating with a Bunsen burner, keeping an eye on a thermometer in the water bath.

Ensure that both tubes are in equilibrium with the temperature of the water bath before starting to take readings.

NOTE TO TECHNICIAN

Each student group will require (or require access to):
- top-pan balance;
- germinating seeds, e.g. 15 g (dry mass) wheat, soaked and allowed to germinate for three to five days, half of the seedlings to be killed by boiling;
- tripod, gauze;
- 500 cm³ beaker (or thermostatically controlled water bath);
- Bunsen burner (if no thermostatically controlled water baths);
- two boiling tubes, cotton wool plugs;
- 10 g self-indicating soda lime;
- 10 cm³ manometric liquid (water + culinary dye + a drop of detergent);
- dropping pipette;
- 2 cm³ syringe;
- two manometers (p. 429);
- two three-way taps.

Data presentation

Express your results as mm³ gas (oxygen) taken up per gram of living material per minute ($mm^3\,g^{-1}\,min^{-1}$). Collect results from the groups working at different temperatures, set them out as a table and then plot a graph of oxygen uptake against temperature.

■ Conclusion

What is the effect of an increase in temperature on the rate of respiration in your living material?

■ Evaluation

- Why can you assume that the volume change was due to oxygen uptake, rather than that of any other atmospheric gas?
- What was the point of including the control with dead seedlings?
- If the experiment is allowed to run for more than about two hours, the rate of oxygen uptake is seen to diminish. Why do you think this happens?
- What sources of experimental error might affect your results?

■ Extension

Instead of setting up a control, you could set up a similar experiment excluding the soda lime. In this way you could assess the respiratory quotient (or the onset of some anaerobic respiration).

15.2 Comparison of inspired and expired air using J-tube gas analysis

(Investigation)

If carbon dioxide and oxygen are absorbed in turn from a sample of air, the reduction in volume can be used as an estimate of the volume of these gases in the sample. This provides a way of assessing the changes in composition brought about by gaseous exchange.

■ Aim

To investigate how the composition of expired air differs from that of inspired air.

■ Risk assessment

- Any tube put to the mouth should be clean and sterilised.
- Eye protection is necessary when working with potassium hydroxide solution, which is a strong alkali and is corrosive. Pyrogallol is harmful.
- Otherwise, good laboratory practice will be sufficient to take account of any hazards and avoid significant risks.

■ Method

Collecting the sample

1 Set up an apparatus for collecting gas (as for downward displacement) by up-ending a gas jar full of water over a bee-hive shelf in a water-filled plastic bowl.

2 Inhale a breath, then exhale it again through a plastic delivery tube with the end under the surface of the water. Collect only the gas from the end of the exhalation into the gas jar.

Testing the sample

1 Fill the J-tube (Figure 15.2), drawing in water using the syringe, but being careful to hold only the syringe or plastic sleeve to avoid warming the tube itself with your hands.

Figure 15.2 The construction of a J-tube

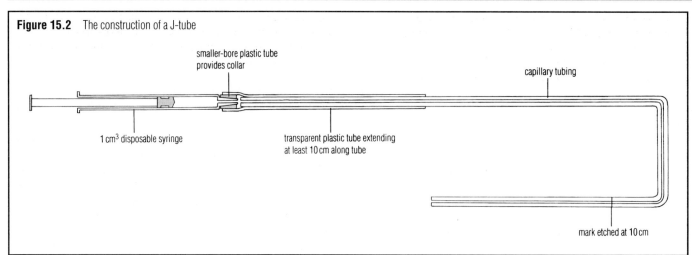

2 Insert the open end of the J-tube into the gas sample. Draw in a sample of the exhaled air, forming a bubble exactly 10 cm long (or measure its length to the nearest half mm), and seal it with a further centimetre of water.

3 Dip the end of the J-tube into potassium hydroxide solution and carefully move the bubble towards the open end to expel most of the water seal. Pick up approximately a 5 cm length of the potassium hydroxide solution. Rinse off any solution on the outside of the tube with water over a sink, and wipe dry with kitchen paper.

4 'Shunt' the bubble to and fro in the J-tube several times to absorb the carbon dioxide from the gas, then lay the J-tube on a ceramic tile to measure the bubble length (to the nearest half mm).

5 Moving the potassium hydroxide to the open end of the tube, mix into it an additional 5 cm of pyrogallol solution and shunt the bubble to and fro. The mixture turns brown as it absorbs oxygen. Remeasure the length of the bubble.

6 Empty the J-tube, and rinse it very thoroughly with dilute acid and clean water successively, before using it for another sample.

7 Repeat the procedure for a gas sample of air, collected by letting atmospheric air into a water-filled gas jar, then sampling from the gas as before. This ensures the method of obtaining a control sample is as similar as possible to the experimental sample.

NOTE TO TECHNICIAN

Each group will need (or need access to):
- J-tube constructed as shown in Figure 15.2 (alternative versions can be purchased from biological suppliers that have a greased screw inside a brass sleeve, which serves as the method of moving the bubble, but the type shown here can be made from apparatus usually available in the laboratory and is as easy to use as the more sophisticated construction);
- plastic washing-up bowl, beehive shelf and a gas jar (with lid), filled with water;
- sterile mouthpiece and plastic delivery tube (about 1 m);
- potassium hydroxide (2 mol dm^{-3}) and pyrogallol solution (2% w/v) made up immediately before use;
- weak hydrochloric acid (0.1 mol dm^{-3}) for washing out the J-tube between samples;
- kitchen paper for drying the outside of the tube.

■ Data presentation

- Present a table showing, for both samples, the original length of the bubble, its length after the absorption of carbon dioxide and its length after the absorption of oxygen.
- Assuming the bore of the tube is uniform, calculate the percentages of carbon dioxide and oxygen in the exhaled air and the atmospheric air.

■ Discussion and conclusion

Consider how the composition of inspired air has changed by the time it is expired, and account for these changes on the basis of your biological understanding.

■ Evaluation

Care should be taken to ensure that the temperature of the gas bubble stays constant through the experiment; what inaccuracies arise if it does not?

Reference

D F Robinson (1974) 'Gas analysis using capillary tube', *School Science Review*, 55(193), pp. 744

15.3 The structure and functioning of the insect's tracheal system

(Data generating)

The insect's exoskeleton is impervious to oxygen. Oxygen from the air reaches the tissues via a system of branching tubes called tracheae, opening to the exterior via controlled valves called spiracles. Many insects also have bellows-like air sacs in the tracheal system.

■ Aim

To observe the structure of an insect's tracheal system, and to investigate its functioning.

■ Risk assessment

- Special care is needed in the use of dissecting equipment (see p. 162).
- Staff regularly exposed to locusts (for example, where these insects are maintained in continuous culture) may develop an allergy due to contacts with airborne dust from the

exoskeleton and faeces. Adequate ventilation around the cage is essential. The wearing of a dust mask may help prevent, or minimise, the allergic reaction.

• Otherwise, good laboratory practice will be sufficient to take account of any hazards and avoid significant risks.

■ Method
Observing breathing movements
Respiratory movements may be observed in a range of insects, including stick insects, bees, beetles, moths and locusts.

1 The insect must be trapped in conditions that restrict flying and other fast movements. Use a small, clear-glass sample tube, flat-bottomed, with a polythene plug in which a few tiny ventilation holes are punched. Examine the animal using a stereomicroscope, once it has become calm.

2 Scan the sides of the thorax and abdomen for the tiny openings known as spiracles: one pair per segment is found in most terrestrial insects. If the spiracles are large enough (and the insect is inactive for long enough), try to see whether they are permanently open, or if they have valves that open and close.

3 The insects listed above have a system of air sacs as part of the tracheal system. The majority of the air sacs occur in the abdomen. Muscles of the body create pumping movements of the body wall, with an indirect effect on the air sacs. These movements are best observed in the abdomen. Movements may be increased under conditions of a slight rise in temperature, or slightly raised carbon dioxide concentration. Try the effect of exhaled air added to the sample tube by removing the stopper and breathing into the tube.

4 It may be possible to project the focused outline of the insect's body on to a screen using an overhead projector, or possibly by means of the beam of a slide projector. If so, the pumping movements of the body may be observed.

Free the insect (or return it to its cage), once the observations are completed.

Dissection of the tracheal system
Dissection of the dorsal surface of a freshly killed locust will expose the paired air sacs.

1 Before beginning the dissection, examine the spiracles now the animal is stationary, using a stereomicroscope. Adjust the lighting from above to be at an angle, to help you differentiate any small pits in the body wall from organised openings. Can you see detail in the spiracle valves?

2 Remove the insect's wings, then place the locust ventral side down in a small dissecting dish, and secure it with angled pins through head, tip of abdomen and limbs. With fine scissors, cut through the segments of the body, along the sides of the abdomen and thorax, keeping the scissor points up so that only the body wall is cut. Make the initial entries at the rear, between two segments, as shown in Figure 15.3. You will probably find the exoskeleton of the thorax extra tough. What advantage may this confer on movements in a live locust?

3 Remove the dorsal strip of exoskeleton you have cut, holding it with fine forceps, and freeing it from underlying connective tissue with a blunt seeker.

4 Submerge your dissection under water. Air-filled structures will now appear silvery; tracheae as very fine 'silver' threads. The air sacs should also become visible, although they may be partly obscured by fat and muscle tissue. Examine the tracheal and air sac system with a stereomicroscope.

Figure 15.3 Dissecting the tracheal system of a locust

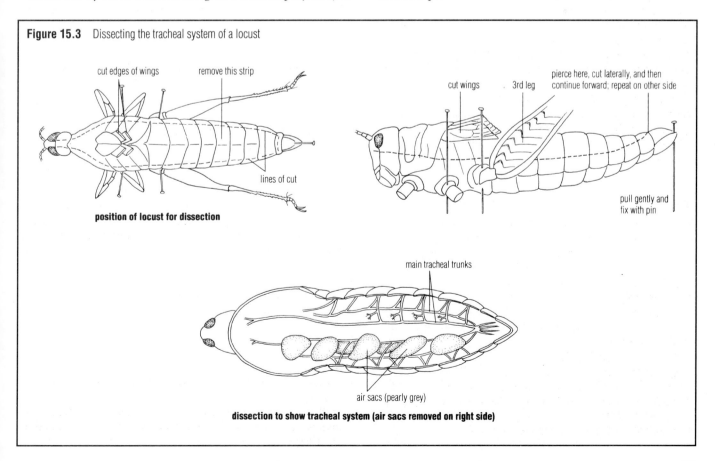

position of locust for dissection

cut edges of wings
remove this strip
lines of cut

cut wings · 3rd leg · pierce here, cut laterally, and then continue forward; repeat on other side

pull gently and fix with pin

main tracheal trunks

air sacs (pearly grey)

dissection to show tracheal system (air sacs removed on right side)

NOTE TO TECHNICIAN

Each student group will require (or require access to):
- appropriate insect(s) from the list above, held for transfer to a small observation tube;
- small, clear-glass sample tubes, appropriate for trapping an insect for observations;
- stereomicroscope;
- bench lamp;
- freshly killed locust;
- small dissection dish, dissecting instruments (pins, fine scissors, fine forceps, mounted needle, seeker).

■ **Data presentation**
- Make concise notes (or an annotated sketch) on the observations you have been able to make on spiracles, including their positions along the body wall.
- Make a table of data you have obtained on the rates of 'breathing' movements in the abdomen, possibly of different insects, under specific conditions.
- Make an annotated sketch of the position of the tracheal system and the air sacs, as seen in your dissection.

■ **Conclusion**
Is there evidence of a segmental plan to the layout of the ventilation system of the locust?

■ **Evaluation**
The cuticle of an insect is partially permeable to carbon dioxide gas. By what routes does this gas move from a respiring muscle cell to the exterior of the insect's body?

Reference
W M Clarke and M M Richards (1976) *The Locust as a Typical Insect*. John Murray

15.4 Investigating human breathing
(Skills and techniques/Investigation)

The pattern of change in lung volume during human breathing may be analysed with a **recording spirometer**. The spirometer chamber is filled with oxygen and any carbon dioxide given off is removed by a suitable absorbent. In this way, oxygen consumption can be measured. Results may be recorded by attaching the spirometer to a kymograph or, with the use of a position transducer, by a chart recorder or by interfacing with a computer and connecting box.

■ **Aim**
To become competent in the use of the spirometer to investigate human breathing, and to measure oxygen consumption under different conditions.

■ **Risk assessment**

- A teacher must be present at all times when students are using a spirometer.
- Investigations with rebreathed air require special vigilance.

Unless used for only a few breaths (measurement of vital capacity/reserve lung volume), the spirometer must be filled with oxygen.
- Oxygen forms explosive compounds with certain oils and greases, so such lubricants must not be put on the connections of oxygen cylinders (including the regulator), or on the tubing that connects to a spirometer (use water or soap).
- Wear eye protection when soda lime or 'Carbosorb' or 'Inicarb' (which changes colour when no more gas absorption can occur) is loaded into the carbon dioxide absorption compartment.
- The British Oxygen Company stipulate that medical oxygen should be used; the risks from using ordinary oxygen are insignificant, however.
- The experimental subject should be chosen from among genuine volunteers who are fit (they must not suffer from long-term complaints such as asthma, for example) and healthy (they must be free from short-term illness, such as the common cold). Conduct all data collection objectively; there must be no competition between individuals to prove 'superiority'.
- Exercise carried out as part of the investigations must not be excessive, and it must be an activity that can be carried out in total safety.
- The mouthpiece must be disinfected after each experimental subject has used it, by immersions in appropriately diluted Milton solution, freshly prepared, or in ethanol.

■ **Method**

1 First, check the following points on the spirometer provided.
  The lid of the spirometer (Figure 15.4(a)) is a Perspex box which forms a chamber of maximum capacity of about 7–8 dm^3, above a tank of water. The chamber may be connected to the mouth of an experimental subject by a removable rubber mouthpiece and flexible tube; a two-way valve allows the chamber to be closed off from or connected to the subject. Gas withdrawn from the chamber to the experimental subject passes through a carbon dioxide absorption chamber, which may be filled with a suitable absorbent. A nose clip is worn by the subject. Another inlet point on the spirometer allows the chamber to be filled with air (or gas from a cylinder).
  The lid of the spirometer is counter-balanced so that as gas passes into or leaves the chamber the lid rises and falls, and a scale attached to the lid allows changes in the volume of the chamber to be read off. Movements of the lid can be recorded by the movement of an extended arm attached either to a corner of the lid marking a slowly rotating drum of a kymograph, or to a position transducer that is linked to a chart recorder or to a computer via a connecting box.

2 Next, test the apparatus for air leaks. Fill the chamber with air by raising the lid with the gas inlet open, close off the valves, and place a weight of 200 g on the lid. There should be no movement of the lid in a five-minute test period. Finally, empty the air out of the chamber.

3 Now calibrate the spirometer/recording arrangement.
  - Arrange for the recording pen to be in contact with the lower part of the recording paper on the kymograph drum. (Alternatively, connect the position transducer to the arm of the chamber and to the chart recorder. Switch on the current to the chart recorder, and set the pen to the right-hand side.)

Figure 15.4 Using a spirometer

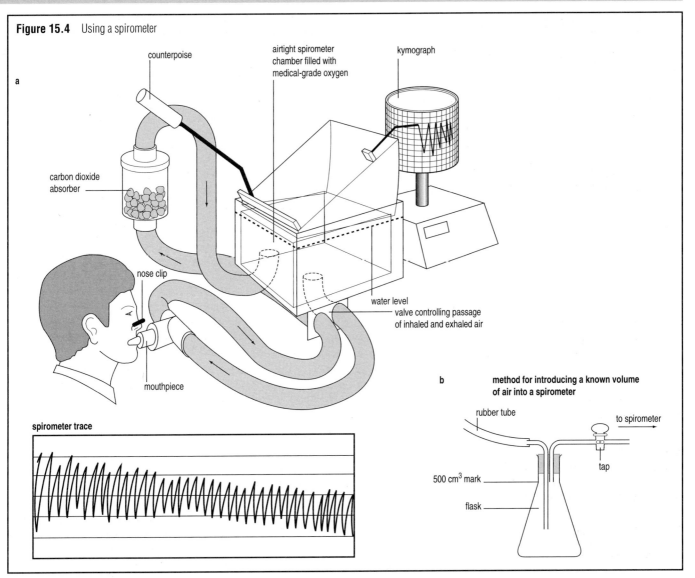

a

- counterpoise
- airtight spirometer chamber filled with medical-grade oxygen
- kymograph
- carbon dioxide absorber
- nose clip
- water level
- valve controlling passage of inhaled and exhaled air
- mouthpiece

spirometer trace

b method for introducing a known volume of air into a spirometer

- rubber tube
- to spirometer
- tap
- 500 cm³ mark
- flask

- Record the 'empty' position of the chamber as a kymograph mark on the paper (or set by ensuring the output from the position transducer is zero).
- Using a flask of known volume (approximately 500 cm³), displace this volume of air into the chamber by filling the flask with water as shown in Figure 15.4(b). Record this new volume on the kymograph drum or chart recorder. Repeat this calibration procedure until most or all the capacity of the chamber is calibrated.

4 Next you need to set up and practise with the spirometer.
- Check the apparatus is supplied with carbon dioxide absorbent.
- With the air released from the chamber and the two-way valve closed, fill the chamber with oxygen from a cylinder connected by rubber tube to the inlet valve.
- Arrange the recording pen so that a record of the movements of the chamber is made near the top of the paper.
- Fit a sterilised and rinsed mouthpiece into the breathing tube. Attach a nose clip and breathe through the tube. At first, have the two-way valve closed so that you are breathing atmospheric air. In this way you will become familiar with the sensation of breathing through the apparatus.
- When you are adjusted to this, open the two-way valve. You are now breathing the gas in the chamber. Breathe as

naturally as possible. Once an obvious rhythm is established, switch on the kymograph and record a few breaths. Then take one deep breath, filling your lungs to capacity, and exhale normally. After further normal regular breathing, exhale as much air as possible and then return briefly to normal breathing. When this record is made (Record 1), close the two-way valve and revert to breathing atmospheric air.

5 Now you can measure the oxygen consumption.
- With the chamber filled with oxygen, switch on the kymograph drum (1 mm s⁻¹) (or the chart recording paper at 2 mm s⁻¹), and set the two-way valve so that you are breathing oxygen from the chamber. Continue for a period of two to three minutes. The recorded trace (of a decreasing volume of the spirometer chamber) is a record of your oxygen consumption. Keep this recording trace, to which you will add a similar record of breathing after you have exercised.
- Now perform a set activity task (a fixed number of stool step-ups, perhaps), and take five minutes to recover normal breathing. Then repeat the recording of the oxygen consumption as described above. When this combined record of oxygen consumption is made (Record 2), the apparatus can be closed down.

Interfacing the spirometer to a computer

This can be done using a BBC B microcomputer via Philip Harris Data Disc with sensor and connecting box, connected via the analogue port on the computer.

1 Connect the position transducer to the connecting box, input 1 and ground. The connecting box connects to the analogue port. Switch on the position transducer.
2 Place Data Disc in drive 0. Insert a second formatted disc in drive 1 in order to store data.
3 Load the program, ⟨SHIFT BREAK⟩. The main menu will be displayed.
   Select CHANGE DRIVE FOR DATA ⟨RETURN⟩. Enter drive number 1.
4 From the main menu select CALIBRATE INPUT CHANNEL ⟨RETURN⟩.
   Select channel 1 ⟨RETURN⟩.
   Select GENERAL CALIBRATION ⟨RETURN⟩.
   State units: LITRES ⟨RETURN⟩.
   Raise spirometer to maximum required volume, say eight litres.
   Enter volume 8⟨LITRES⟩ ⟨RETURN⟩.
   Lower spirometer to zero volume.
   Enter volume 0⟨LITRES⟩ ⟨RETURN⟩.
5 Select from the main menu RECORD ANALOGUE DATA ⟨RETURN⟩.
   Select from recording options ONE CHANNEL AGAINST TIME ⟨RETURN⟩.
   Select from CHANNEL FOR RECORDING – CHANNEL 1 ⟨RETURN⟩.
   Enter the maximum estimated time for the recording, say 2 MIN ⟨RETURN⟩.
6 Fill the spirometer with oxygen, to perhaps six litres. Set the spirometer tap to 'outside atmosphere' and then connect the subject to the breathing tube. When the subject is breathing normally set the spirometer tap to 'spirometer'.
   As the subject is breathing in, press ⟨SPACE BAR⟩ to start recording, and carry out the sequence of measurements, as above.
7 When the recording is completed the screen will show PROCESSING DATA – RESULTS WILL BE DISPLAYED.
8 You now need to save data for further examination. From the options displayed at the bottom of the screen (right-hand corner), use the cursor key to select SAVE DATA ⟨RETURN⟩.
   Enter a short filename (e.g. your initials) ⟨RETURN⟩.
   Display menu now shown.
   From the menu, select UTILITIES ⟨RETURN⟩.
   To select PART OF DATA using two cursors: first use function keys f1 and f2 with CTRL to move the left-hand cursor to the part of the data you wish to examine, then move the right-hand cursor using function keys f3 and f4 similarly. Data is displayed at each end of the screen:
9 Using the UTILITIES option described above, determine:
   • respiratory rate (number of breaths per minute);
   • normal tidal volume;
   • inspiratory and expiratory reserve volume;
   • vital capacity.
10 When you have completed your experiment, press ⟨ESCAPE⟩ to return to the current menu; select MAIN MENU ⟨RETURN⟩.
11 Then remove both discs before switching off the computer.

NOTE TO TECHNICIAN

Before beginning this work, it is worth consulting the review of spirometers:

R Lock and C Wood-Robinson (1983) 'Equipment for recording human breathing', *J. Biol. Ed.* **17**(2), pp. 88–93

The investigation (group activity) will require the following:
- Philip Harris spirometer (or similar), with mouthpiece and nose clip;
- kymograph with recording paper (or position transducer attached to a chart recorder or interfaced with a computer with appropriate software, and connecting box);
- soda lime (or 'Carbosorb' or 'Inicarb'), inserted in the carbon dioxide absorbent compartment;
- oxygen cylinder with regulator and supply tube;
- disinfectant for mouthpiece – appropriately diluted Milton solution is suitable;
- stopclock;
- 200 g weights to test spirometer for leaks;
- 500 cm^3 flask attached to tap (water supply) and to spirometer chamber (via rubber tube) to deliver air of known volume, for calibration.

■ Data presentation

Label the print-outs from kymograph or chart recorder (Records 1 and 2) carefully, and state the specific conditions of the experiments. The axes (x-axis = time, y-axis = volume) must show scale/units.

■ Conclusions

- From Record 1 the tidal volume, the maximum expiratory volume, the inspiratory reserve volume, and thus the maximum inspiratory volume can be determined for the experimental subject (see *Advanced Biology*, p. 315).
- From Record 2, the change in volume of the chamber (volume of oxygen consumed) can be estimated, before and after physical activity.

■ Evaluation

- Calculate the approximate volume of air in the lungs of a typical experimental subject at rest, prior to normal inspiration of the tidal volume. Express the tidal volume as a percentage of this residue of air.
- What are the likely sources of error in your measurement of oxygen consumption in a subject attached to a spirometer?

15.5 Studying the thorax of the rat; dissection of the anterior blood circulation

(Data generating)

Lungs and heart are enclosed in an **air-tight compartment**, the thorax. If a freshly killed rat is used in carrying out a dissection of the alimentary canal (Practical 13.2, p. 157) part or all of a dissection of the thorax may be carried out at that time, before preservation of the cadaver for further studies. Once an animal has been preserved the diaphragm becomes hard and opaque, and the atmospheric tension within the thorax is lost.

■ Aim

To investigate the structure of the thorax and the layout of the blood circulation anteriorly.

■ Risk assessment

In the conduct of dissection, special precautions for safety are essential. These are listed on p. 157. Read them again now.

■ Method

Dissection of the thorax

The chief purpose of dissection in biology is to display the internal structures as part of an investigation of structure and function of an animal's body. Read about developing your dissection technique on p. 157, before you dissect the lungs, heart and thorax of a rat.

Features of the thorax

The thorax region should be examined in a freshly killed animal, immediately after dissection of the abdomen and removal of the gut (pp. 157–61).

A central ligament, the fusiform ligament, helps hold the liver in place below the diaphragm. Cut through this ligament with a scalpel to allow the liver lobes to fall back, exposing more of the diaphragm. Examine the diaphragm by raising the xiphoid cartilage, using blunt forceps. You can see part of the lungs and heart, and the posterior vena cava passing through the diaphragm.

Examine the rib-cage; the rat has 13 ribs, corresponding to the 13 thoracic vertebrae. How many ribs are attached to the sternum directly (true ribs), and how many are otherwise arranged? There is a distinct pattern to the distribution of muscles attached to the ribs; what structures are these muscles attached to?

Steps to the dissection of the thorax

1 With the partly dissected rat secured ventral side uppermost, hold the xiphoid cartilage with forceps, and pierce the rib-cage with the point of your scissors just beside the line of the attachment to the diaphragm. Repeat this on the other side of the rib-cage. As each side (pleural cavity) is pierced, air enters, and you will see the diaphragm come away from the contents of the thorax.

2 Cut all along this line of attachment of the posterior part of the rib-cage to the diaphragm, keeping the point of your scissors clear of the lung tissue below. The diaphragm will become free from the thorax wall. Secure a cotton thread to the xiphoid cartilage and tie off to the tail of the rat; the diaphragm is pulled back as shown in Figure 15.5(a). Continue to mop away any bleeding from minor arteries and veins that are cut as the rib-cage is cut away.

3 Now cut laterally, along the sides of the rib-cage from base to the apex, cutting both sides in turn. This is done to free the whole of the ventral part of the thorax wall, so that it can be lifted away, containing the sternum. Hold and lift the wall with forceps as it is cut free, so as to see below and thus avoid cutting the heart or lung tissues.

4 Remove the thymus gland using fine forceps to lift it off from over the heart, and the point of a sharp scalpel to cut it away at the apex of the rib-cage. Clear away the fat stored in connective tissue above the heart and major blood vessels. Take great care not to damage any blood vessels or

nerves (the latter are white in colour). Push the heart over to the animal's left side to observe the point where the anterior and posterior vena cavae join and enter the right atrium. Next, push the heart to the animal's right side and secure the heart here in order to be able to identify the blood vessels at this point (Figure 15.5(b)).

Carefully peel back the pectoralis muscles of both front limbs, freeing them from underlying structures with mounted seeker (a blunt needle) and scalpel, as necessary. Cut away the muscles close to their insertions. Very carefully cut away the clavicle (collar bone) on both sides to expose the anterior facial vein below it. Remove any fat and connective tissue that mask the external jugular vein. Similarly, remove the salivary glands and lymph nodes that mask the facial veins. Separate the nerves and blood vessels as you identify these (Figure 15.5(c)).

References and resources

The following resources can be used to support and enhance learning by dissection, or they may be used, singly or together, in place of dissection to learn about the thorax and blood circulation of the mammal:

- H G Q Rowett (1974) *The Rat as a Small Mammal*. John Murray
- H G Q Rowett (1962) *Guide to Dissection*. John Murray
- *Video Rat Stack* (Sheffield BioScience Programs); this interactive package about the dissection and functional anatomy of the rat is introduced on p. 162
- *Vertebrate Dissection Guides – The Rat* (the TV Centre, the University of Portsmouth in association with the Institute of Biology); this videotape is introduced on p. 162.

NOTE TO TECHNICIAN

Students will require (or require access to):
- dissecting board;
- awls and pins;
- disposable plastic gloves;
- rat for dissection (freshly killed or embalmed);
- essential dissection equipment (p. 162);
- camera with colour print film;
- video player and monitor (if the Institute of Biology videotape mentioned above is available);
- Apple Macintosh microcomputer (4/40 MB or better), with Pal video disc player and separate high-quality television monitor (if *The Rat Stack* is available).

■ Data presentation

- Make notes of your observations on the structure of the rib-cage and the arrangement of the muscles attached there.
- Make a large labelled sketch of your dissection at the stage at which the ventral wall of the rib-cage has been cut away.
- Make another sketch at the point of the final exposure of organs, blood vessels and nerves of the neck and thorax.

■ Conclusions

- Arteries and veins appear different in colour when dissected in a recently killed animal. What are the reasons for this?
- The trachea and bronchioles have horizontal rings of cartilage in their wall. What advantage do these confer?

Figure 15.5   Rat dissection: steps in the dissection of the thorax

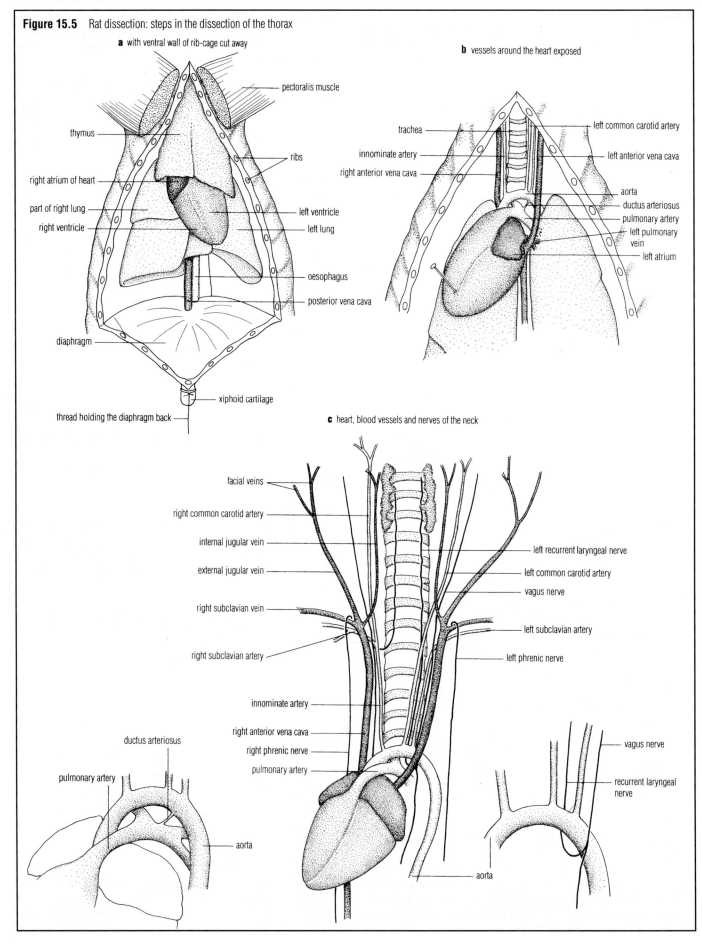

a with ventral wall of rib-cage cut away

pectoralis muscle

thymus

ribs

right atrium of heart

part of right lung

right ventricle

left ventricle

left lung

oesophagus

posterior vena cava

diaphragm

xiphoid cartilage

thread holding the diaphragm back

b vessels around the heart exposed

trachea

innominate artery

right anterior vena cava

left common carotid artery

left anterior vena cava

aorta

ductus arteriosus

pulmonary artery

left pulmonary vein

left atrium

c heart, blood vessels and nerves of the neck

facial veins

right common carotid artery

internal jugular vein

external jugular vein

right subclavian vein

right subclavian artery

left recurrent laryngeal nerve

left common carotid artery

vagus nerve

left subclavian artery

left phrenic nerve

innominate artery

right anterior vena cava

right phrenic nerve

pulmonary artery

ductus arteriosus

pulmonary artery

aorta

aorta

vagus nerve

recurrent laryngeal nerve

■ Evaluation

In a mammal's body the thorax is divided from the abdomen, and there is a distinct neck region. Comment on these features from the viewpoint of the efficiency of the animal's body.

15.6 Respiration in yeast, and the effect of temperature

(Investigation)

Respiration in yeast involves the production of carbon dioxide as a waste product. The rate of production of carbon dioxide is an indicator of the **rate of respiratory metabolism**.

■ Aim

To investigate the effect of temperature on the rate of respiration in a suspension of baker's yeast, *Saccharomyces cerevisiae*.

■ Risk assessment

Good laboratory practice will be sufficient to take account of any hazards and avoid significant risks.

■ Method

Pre-incubation of yeast

Dried yeast granules consist of dormant cells bound with an inert filler (normally starch). Yeast in this form requires a period of pre-incubation to induce full metabolic activity. To prepare a suspension of active yeast cells, weigh out 3 g of dried yeast, 3 g of glucose and 1 g of yeast extract (Marmite) and then dissolve and suspend them in 100 cm³ of distilled water in a conical flask. Plug the flask with cotton wool, and incubate the mixture in a water bath at 37 °C, for one hour.

Setting up the experiment

1 You are going to investigate the amount of carbon dioxide produced by identical samples of yeast suspension held at approximately 10, 20, 30, 40 and 50 °C. To do so, set up large expanded polystyrene beakers as water baths (held stable on the bench with Plasticine, if necessary) at these temperatures, mixing cold and hot water appropriately, and checking the exact temperature with a thermometer. Each water bath will contain one test tube, set up as described below. Label the water baths 1 to 5.

2 Label five test tubes 1 to 5, to reflect the temperature at which the contents will be held. Place 10 cm³ of the yeast suspension in each tube, and then place each tube in the corresponding water bath. Leave it there for five minutes, to allow the contents to reach the water-bath temperature.

3 From each tube in turn, withdraw about 7 cm³ of the yeast suspension by means of a teat pipette, and run this suspension into a small fermentation tube, so as to completely fill it. Invert the filled tube, and slide it, inverted, into the test tube from which the contents were withdrawn, whilst held close to the horizontal (Figure 15.6). If an air bubble appears in the tube, refill the fermentation tube and try again. Return any excess yeast suspension in the teat pipette to the test tube. As soon as the set-up is completed, return the test tube with the inverted, filled fermentation tube into its water bath. Note the time. Repeat this operation for each of the five temperatures selected.

4 At five-minute intervals, lift each test tube out of its water bath, and measure and record the length of the bubble of gas (carbon dioxide) that has collected in the inverted fermentation tube.

NOTE TO TECHNICIAN

Each student group will require (or require access to):
- balance;
- dried yeast, glucose, yeast extract, distilled water;
- 100 cm³ measuring cylinder;
- conical flask, cotton wool plug;
- water bath at 37 °C;
- five large expanded polystyrene beakers, Plasticine (to stabilise beaker);
- five thermometers (0–100 °C);
- hot and cold water supply;
- five test tubes, 5 cm³ graduated pipette, waterproof marker pen;
- teat pipette, five fermentation tubes;
- clock.

■ Data presentation

Draw a graph of the length of the gas bubble (*y*-axis) against time (*x*-axis) for each of the five temperatures.

■ Conclusions

- What effect has temperature had on the rate at which gas has accumulated?
- What is the effect of a temperature of 50 °C? What is the reason?
- Why is it necessary to plug the flask with cotton wool during pre-incubation?

■ Evaluation

Many yeasts are able to respire aerobically and anaerobically, depending on specific conditions. If a culture of yeast cells switches from anaerobic to aerobic respiration, what is the likely effect on the volume of carbon dioxide produced in unit time?

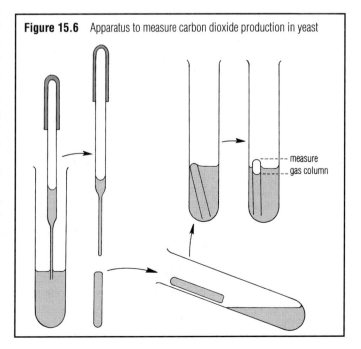

Figure 15.6 Apparatus to measure carbon dioxide production in yeast

measure
gas column

■ **Extension**

This practical can be adapted to investigate the types of substrate which yeast can use (monosaccharide and disaccharide sugars) and the time taken by a yeast suspension to adapt to exploit them (due to induction of new enzymes), the effect of substrate concentration, and the sources of combined nitrogen (inorganic and organic) which are used.

References

D R Berry (1982) *The Biology of Yeast*. Arnold Studies in Biology no. 140. Edward Arnold

P W Freeland (1973) 'Some practical aspects of sugar fermentation by baker's yeast (*Saccharomyces cerevisiae*)', *J. Biol. Ed.* 7(5), pp. 14–22

Projects

15.1 Studying fermentation via dough rising

Dough formed from a mixture of flour with added glucose, water and baker's yeast can be worked into a ball, dropped into a measuring cylinder, and the initial level recorded. The level of the dough rises and this can be noted at five-minute intervals. Exploiting this manifestation of anaerobic respiration, the effect of temperature, substrate (alternative sugars) and the presence/concentration of substances believed to inhibit specific stages in glycolysis or fermentation can be investigated. Special precautions are needed with respiratory inhibitors which are poisons – always handle these with a responsible adult present.

Reference

P W Freeland (1974) 'A variation on Bottle's experiment to measure the expansion of dough containing yeast and sugar', *School Science Review* (September 1974) 56(194), pp. 90–1

15.2 Biological oxidation through enzymic browning of apples

Mechanical damage to fruits often leads to browning. Browning is due to the action of enzymes (polyphenol oxidase, for example) catalysing the oxidation of phenolic substances naturally present in the fruit. The biochemical mechanism may be part of the electron-transport pathway in many plant species. What are the effects on enzyme action of temperature, pH, preservatives such as sulphur dioxide, and perhaps the absence of oxygen?

Reference

C L Liffen and H N Cleeve (1975) 'Some aspects of enzymic browning in apples', *J. Biol. Ed.* 9(3/4), pp. 127–33

15.3 Investigating lenticel distribution and function

Lenticels are specialised regions of the cork in which the cells are mostly unsuberised and consist of loosely packed parenchyma. They are often prominent features of young woody twigs. Does their distribution (number/surface area of cork) relate to the diameter of the stem, or is it specific to the species, or is it more or less standard for all woody twigs? For how many years do they remain visible, and what growth mechanism comes to hide them? Can air be driven through stem tissue to establish the continuity of air spaces throughout the plant? Can you establish that water vapour loss occurs through lenticels? Lenticels are a feature in the gaseous exchange mechanism of all woody twigs, but they are more prominent in some species, such as *Sambucus nigra* (elderberry).

15.4 Ventilation of the gills in bony fish

In bony fish living in an aquarium, such as the tropical guppy (*Poecilia reticulata*) or the native stickleback (*Gasterosteus aculeatus*), ventilation of the gills is observed in the movements of the operculum. The speed of ventilation in fish at rest can be estimated. What effect does vigorous swimming for periods of differing length have on the ventilation mechanism? Is the speed of ventilation at rest related to the size or age of the fish?

15.5 Exercise and breathing in humans

The frequency and depth of breathing can be measured by the spirometer (pp. 182–4). What effect does a standardised activity task have on the breathing process of subjects who were at rest immediately prior to this task? Is there a significant difference in the responses of a student who is fit and active in sport compared with one who is significantly more sedentary in lifestyle? (Follow all the safety precautions given in Practical 15.4, p. 182.)

Problems and assignments

15.1 A simple method of measuring respiration rate

A simple respirometer assembled in order to make measurements of the uptake of oxygen by maggots is shown in Figure 15.7. Examine the illustration carefully, think about how you would handle this apparatus, and then answer the questions below.

1 Whilst being assembled and during an experiment, the respirometer is held by a clamp and stand, rather than being hand-held. What advantages does this method of support confer?
2 If the apparatus is to give a reading of oxygen uptake, what type of substance must be placed in the perforated zinc cage above the maggots?
3 Why is it necessary to keep the maggots on a damp cotton wool base during the experiments?
4 Once the apparatus is ready, exactly what are the steps you must carry out to obtain some measurements, and then turn these into data on the uptake of oxygen by a unit mass of maggot tissue?
5 What is the major source of potential error in measurements of respiration made in a respirometer of this type? How could you overcome this problem?
6 Should you also be required to get some data on the output of carbon dioxide by the maggots, what modification to the apparatus would be required? How would you use the new measurements obtained to give you such data?

15.2 Measuring respiration by the Warburg manometer

In Warburg manometry a manometer is attached to a tiny flask containing a sample of the tissue under investigation (Figure 15.8, see overleaf). The flask is arranged so as to be submerged in a constant-temperature water bath. The manometer registers changes in the volume of gases in the flask. The changes in gas volume arise from respiration in the tissue in the flask. In fact, when taking readings, the volume of air in the flask is kept constant by lowering or raising the fluid in the closed limb of the manometer. This is done by adjusting the reservoir screw at the base. Changes in gas volume in the flask are then measured by reading the level of liquid in the open limb of the manometer. These readings are changed to gas volumes by multiplying by a flask/manometer constant.

1 You are required to use this apparatus to measure oxygen uptake per gram of fresh mass of potato tissue discs.
   a What would you need to know about the tissue discs before they are placed in the flask?
   b What substance would you have to add to the centre well of the flask?
   c After the experiment has proceeded for 15 minutes you need to take your first reading. Describe the steps in making a manometer reading.
   d What additional readings would you feel it necessary to take? What other experimental flasks would you set up as part of your investigation?

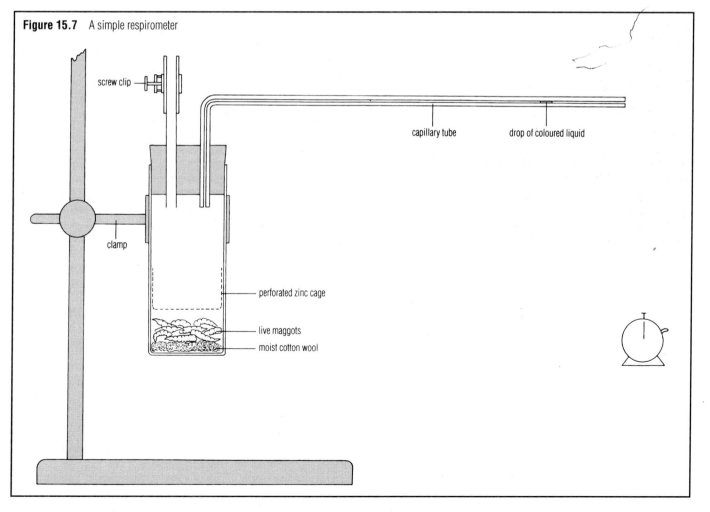

Figure 15.7 A simple respirometer

screw clip

capillary tube

drop of coloured liquid

clamp

perforated zinc cage

live maggots

moist cotton wool

Figure 15.8 A Warburg respirometer in use

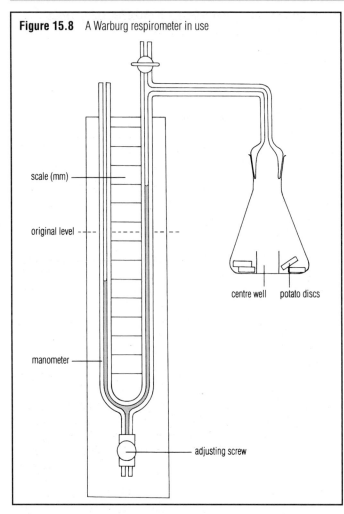

scale (mm)

original level

manometer

centre well   potato discs

adjusting screw

15.3 Measuring oxygen consumption with the spirometer

The spirometer is the standard instrument for measuring the capacity of human lungs, and consists of a chamber suspended above water. The lid of the chamber is arranged to rise and fall as the subject breathes. A permanent record is made of these movements. The chamber is filled with oxygen when the spirometer is used for the **measurement of oxygen consumption**. Between the mouthpiece and the spirometer chamber is a chamber with granules of a carbon dioxide absorber. Examine the labelled drawing of the spirometer in Figure 15.4 and the record of the breathing (of oxygen) of a subject after exercise shown in Figure 15.9. Answer the questions below.

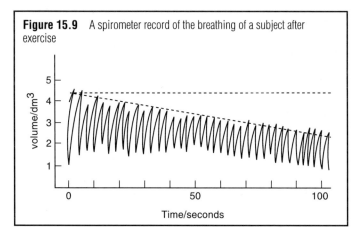

Figure 15.9 A spirometer record of the breathing of a subject after exercise

1 The chart in Figure 15.9 shows the volume of gas being taken in with each breath. This quantity is known as the tidal volume.
   a What causes variations in the tidal volume during normal body function?
   b How does tidal volume differ from vital capacity?
2 a During use of the spirometer, the subject is sitting so as not to see the chart print-out. Why is this necessary?
   b The subject wears a nose clip. Why is this necessary?
3 a When the spirometer is in use, does gas from the spirometer chamber pass through the carbon dioxide absorber compartment before or after reaching the lungs?
   b If there was no carbon dioxide absorbent present, what immediate effect would this have on the spirometer record of breathing?
4 a How can the depth and rate of breathing be assessed from the spirometer record?
   b What was the approximate depth and rate of breathing from the first 10 inspiration movements shown on the spirometer chart?
5 From the spirometer chart, calculate the consumption of oxygen per minute.
6 What safety precautions are essential in the conduct of experiments with the spirometer?

2 The apparatus shown in Figure 15.8 was used to measure oxygen consumption in a range of different tissues taken from one particular species of herbaceous plant during a period of steady vegetative growth. The results of the experiment are shown in Table 15.1.
   a What can you conclude in general about the regulation of the rate of respiration in a plant tissue?
   b Two tissues show the highest rates of respiration in the mature, growing plant. What cell processes in these tissues are likely to be linked to this respiration?
   c Phloem tissue respires more vigorously than xylem does. How do you account for this difference?
   d The stem cambium appears less active than the root apical meristem. What is the likely reason for this difference?

Table 15.1 Oxygen consumption in plant tissues

	Oxygen uptake/mm^3 per g fresh mass
Stem:	
xylem	3.1
cambium	24.5
phloem	14.6
Root:	
apical meristem	43.9
parenchyma of cortex	6.7
Leaf:	
mesophyll cells (in the dark)	41.5

15.4 The phases of tissue respiration

There are three major phases in tissue respiration: **glycolysis, Krebs cycle** and the **electron-transport pathway**. Table 15.2 lists 12 statements that may apply to one or more of these phases. Indicate which statement applies to which phases.

Table 15.2 The phases of tissue respiration

	Glycolysis	Krebs cycle	Electron-transport pathway
involves CO_2 release			
produces ATP			
occurs in the cytoplasm (cytosol)			
uses ATP			
occurs in the matrix of mitochondria			
is a series of redox reactions			
involves CO_2 fixation			
hexose molecules are the substrate			
involves CoA			
is a cyclic process			
occurs on the cristae of mitochondria			
yields intermediates for cell synthesis reactions			

15.5 Respiratory quotient of germinating seeds

Table 15.3 shows measurements of oxygen uptake and carbon dioxide output by a batch of germinating seeds, for a 50-hour period after soaking.

Table 15.3 Gaseous uptake/output by germinating seeds

Time/h	Rate of oxygen uptake /mm^3 h^{-1} per g fresh mass	Rate of carbon dioxide output /mm^3 h^{-1} per g fresh mass
0	0.0	0.0
10	19.1	13.4
20	25.7	18.0
30	53.2	41.9
40	78.8	64.9
50	112.5	113.0

1 Plot a graph of gaseous exchange against time for these seeds.
2 The respiratory quotient (RQ) is defined as the ratio of CO_2 evolved to O_2 consumed. Using data from your graph, calculate the RQ for these seeds at 15 hours, 35 hours and 45 hours.
3 What do the RQ values you have calculated suggest about respiration in these seeds at these times?
4 a In expressing gas exchange in terms of volume per g fresh mass, what possible error in the figures may arise?
  b What would be a more satisfactory method of expressing the amount of tissue involved?
  c To obtain this type of data, what changes to the experimental method would be required?

5 The rate of oxygen uptake changed markedly during the course of the experiment. Suggest an explanation for the rate of oxygen uptake in the periods:
  a 0–20 hours;
  b 30–50 hours.

15.6 Smoking and health

Panel 15.1 The unnecessary epidemic

Epidemics, we have been accustomed to think, are outbreaks of disease that spread rapidly from place to place, reach their peak within a matter of weeks or months and recede almost as quickly. That was certainly true of many epidemics of infectious disease that have occurred throughout history, but we now know that non-infectious diseases can behave in a similar way, save that the time taken for them to appear and disappear is measured in tens of years rather than weeks.

Tobacco has been smoked for centuries, at first in pipes or primitive cigars. With the development of machinery for the mass manufacture of cigarettes 140 years ago, cigarette smoking became increasingly popular. In all countries now, mortality in infancy, childhood and early adult life has been greatly reduced and, in many developed countries, reduced to such an extent that 98% of all live-born children can be expected to survive to 35 years of age against, for example, a figure of only 66% in England and Wales a century ago. Mortality at 35 to 69 years of age has, in contrast, been reduced very little and much of the reduction that could have occurred from the control of infection has been cancelled out by the increased mortality from tobacco. With modern standards of living, deaths under 70 years of age should be regarded as premature. Yet 32% of men who survive to 35 years in developed countries die before they are 70, and more than a third of these premature deaths may be attributed to tobacco. Women are beginning to smoke like men, but have collectively not smoked long enough, even in developed countries, to have much effect on their mortality.

The habit of smoking is spreading, and is being encouraged to spread, by salesmen, to the rest of the world. In many less developed countries the male prevalence of smoking now exceeds 50%. At present there are 2.3 billion children and teenagers in the world and, on current smoking patterns, about 30–40% will be smokers in early adult life. Up to half of them could be killed by smoking. It need not, however, happen.

Sir Richard Doll (personal communication)
Imperial Cancer Research Fund Clinical Trials Service Unit Radcliffe Infirmary, Oxford

After one of the early case-control studies of lung cancer, published in 1948, Richard Doll and colleagues began a study of the smoking habits of a very large number of people to see if those who smoked heavily had a significantly higher risk of developing disease. Doctors were chosen as the group studied, and over 40 000 (members of the British Medical Association) gave details of smoking habits and have been monitored subsequently. Some of the results of these studies are summarised in Table 15.4 (overleaf).

Table 15.4 Mortality among doctors

Cause of death	Annual death rate/million		
	Non-smokers	Continuing pipe smokers	Continuing cigarette smokers (25+ per day)
Heart disease	606	690	1184
Vascular system disease	282	325	583
Chronic bronchitis	9	42	209
Lung cancer	13	80	345
Other cancers	33	57	170

You are a science-trained citizen, living at a time when the nature of the smoking-related diseases epidemic is understood, but not yet overcome. It is put to us by Sir Richard Doll that, given the understanding of the consequences of cigarette smoking we now have, we are all conscience bound to try to help to overcome the epidemic as best we may. Using the information above, together with your wider reading:

- prepare a poster presenting factual material* about the links between cigarette smoking and disease, and suggesting some actions that those who read your poster could themselves take part in to counteract the epidemic;

or:

- prepare a short presentation*, no more than 10 minutes, which you could use at a formal gathering of people who are discussing issues of health and disease, effectively alerting them to the smoking epidemic issue;

or:

- prepare some informed and challenging questions you could put in turn to a group of parliamentary or local government candidates at a 'hustings' meeting, as a prelude to an election process. Your questions should require specific responses, and may need to include data which establish connections the candidates might not otherwise know (or choose to address). It is often good practice in political discussion to have supplementary questions to keep the responses to the point.

* In these cases, a histogram of the data on the annual death rates of doctors, given above, may be useful.

15.7 Quick test

1 Distinguish between the following pairs:

   a respiration and gaseous exchange;
   b aerobic and anaerobic respiration;
   c inspiration and expiration;
   d epiglottis and trachea;
   e bronchiole and alveolus;
   f tidal volume and vital capacity;
   g glycolysis and the Krebs cycle;
   h oxidising agents and reducing agents;
   i ATP and NAD;
   j lactic acid fermentation and alcoholic fermentation.

2 Explain the importance of the following:

   a surface area : volume ratio;
   b a ventilation mechanism;
   c an internal transport system;
   d tracheal system of insects;
   e countercurrent flow systems;
   f redox reactions;
   g cristae of mitochondria;
   h control of respiration rate;
   i a differential respirometer;
   j respiratory quotient.

15.8 Essay assignment

Select one of the following:

- Explain how the structure of the thorax facilitates gaseous exchange in humans. How does the habit of cigarette smoking impair gaseous exchange in the lungs?

or:

- Respiration (tissue respiration) plays an important part in making energy available for useful work, and in the supply of intermediates for cell syntheses. Explain how both are achieved in aerobic respiration.

16 Uptake and transport within plants

Summary

A living organism constantly transports materials to and from individual cells throughout its structure. In a plant, for example, **water** is drawn up from the soil and supplied to all cells. The bulk of water moves in the space known as the **apoplast**, which consists of the space within cellulose walls and the water-filled lumen of the xylem vessels – that is, it by-passes the cytoplasm. The bulk of water taken up the stem is lost from the aerial system as water vapour diffusing from the air spaces of the leaf, in a process called **transpiration**. Transpiration provides the driving force for water movement from roots to leaves. The **stomata** in the epidermis of leaves consist of guard cells surrounding a pore, and these permit gaseous exchange between the leaf and the environment. The closing of the stomata effectively reduces water loss by diffusion. Open stomata occupy a tiny area of the total surface area of the leaf, yet they present no significant barrier to the diffusion of carbon dioxide for photosynthesis.

Ion uptake, on the other hand, is a selective process in which energy from respiration is used. **Ions** occur in the soil solution, mostly at very low concentrations, and it is from here that plants accumulate them. The natural reserves of minerals are limited. The essential nutrients are involved in biogeochemical cycles, of which the water, carbon, nitrogen, sulphur and phosphorus cycles are important examples.

The element **nitrogen**, which makes up 80% of our atmosphere as dinitrogen gas, is only useful to plants in a **combined form** (for example, as nitrate or ammonium ions, NO_3^- or NH_4^+). For example, plants growing where nitrates are absent or at very low concentrations have evolved mechanisms which obtain combined nitrogen from specialised sources. These include the exploitation of nitrogen-fixing prokaryotes, housed in root nodules, and the digestion of animal protein by carnivorous plants.

Movements of **elaborated foods** in the plant occur in the phloem sieve tubes by a process known as translocation. It is mainly sugar (from the leaves) and amino acids (from the roots and the mature or ageing organs) that are translocated. The mechanism of phloem transport is unresolved; mass flow is an explanation that has been enthusiastically supported at times.

Practicals and activities

16.1 Measuring the rate of water uptake (and loss) in a shoot

(Investigation)

The potometer is designed to measure the rate of water uptake in a cut, leafy shoot. This will approximate quite closely to the **rate of water loss** from the leaves, and so the potometer can be used to measure and compare rates of transpiration in the shoot.

■ Aim
To investigate the effects of environmental change on the rate of transpiration.

■ Risk assessment
Good laboratory practice will be sufficient to take account of any hazards and avoid significant risks.

■ Method

Setting up and using the potometer

1 The construction of a simple potometer is shown in Figure 16.1. Lower the capillary tube until it dips into the beaker of water, and turn the three-way tap to position (a), withdraw the plunger from the syringe to draw water from the beaker to fill the capillary and syringe. Now turn the tap to position (c) and press in the plunger, forcing water into the rubber tubing until it wells over the top.

2 Push a suitable leafy shoot (smooth woody stems are best) firmly into the rubber tubing.

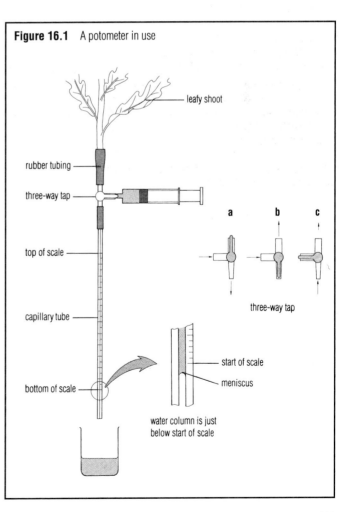

Figure 16.1 A potometer in use

leafy shoot

rubber tubing

three-way tap

top of scale

a   b   c

three-way tap

capillary tube

start of scale

meniscus

bottom of scale

water column is just
below start of scale

3 Now turn the tap to position (b), lift the potometer clear of the water and withdraw the syringe plunger just enough to bring the water column a few millimetres below the zero on the scale.

4 Transpiration from the shoot will cause water to be taken up and the water column will travel up the capillary. Note the distance travelled in a fixed time to give a measure of the rate of transpiration.

5 To obtain successive readings, return the water column to a level below the scale by turning the tap to position (a) and depressing the syringe. Return the tap to position (b), and take the next reading. Decide how many successive readings you need in order to obtain an accurate picture of the rate of transpiration.

6 If the apparatus is to be left unattended, put the capillary tube back in the beaker of water and expel all air from the apparatus. This will avoid air bubbles collecting beneath the cut stem.

Comparing rates of transpiration in different conditions

You can now investigate how the rate of transpiration changes when light intensity, temperature, humidity or air movement is altered.

You will need to take care to alter only one of these conditions at a time. If you simply took the apparatus out of doors, for example, you would change all four conditions at once.

Light intensity can be changed by moving the apparatus to a brighter position in the laboratory or placing a light source nearer the shoot (but beware of changing the temperature).

Humidity can be increased by enclosing the shoot in a plastic bag.

Air movement can be altered by using an electric fan, or simply by fanning with an exercise book.

NOTE TO TECHNICIAN

Each group of students will require:
• potometer (p. 429), beaker, clamp stand;
• suitable shoot (woody stem, 4–5 mm diameter) cut at least 30 minutes before the practical and kept in water in the laboratory;
• stopclock or seconds timer (or view of wall clock).

■ Data presentation

Set your results out in a table. If you varied three or more conditions, plot the average readings as a histogram.

■ Conclusion

What effect did the altered conditions have on the rates of transpiration?

■ Evaluation

• Why might the rate of uptake of water not be the same as the rate of transpiration?
• How many consecutive readings did you take after changing the conditions? What were your reasons for deciding on that number?
• How might your results be used to estimate the rate of transpiration of the whole plant from which the shoot was taken?
• Why might the rate of transpiration of a cut shoot not reflect the rate of transpiration of a similar shoot, in similar conditions but still on the plant?

16.2 Measuring stomatal aperture through water vapour loss

(Investigation)

Water vapour diffusing out of a leaf through the stomata can be detected by cobalt chloride paper (Figure 16.2), which will turn from blue to pink as it absorbs water. The time this takes to happen will indicate the **numbers of open stomata**.

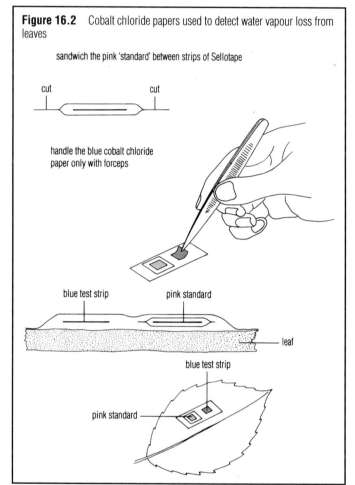

Figure 16.2 Cobalt chloride papers used to detect water vapour loss from leaves

■ Aim

To investigate the rate of water loss from the upper and lower epidermis of plants kept under different conditions.

■ Risk assessment

• When using 'super glue' you must wear eye protection and plastic gloves.
• Otherwise, good laboratory practice will be sufficient to take account of any hazards and avoid significant risks.

■ Method

1 You are supplied with two 10×10 mm squares of blue cobalt chloride paper, kept in a tube with silica gel to prevent the moisture of the air affecting their colour. Remove them only when necessary, using forceps to prevent them from coming into contact with the moisture of the skin.

2 Set up a colour standard by taking one square and gently turn it to an even pink, using the moisture of your breath, or by placing it in a humid atmosphere. Cut it into four equal-sized squares and seal each piece between two layers of sticky tape. Cut away all the spare tape, leaving a margin of just 2 mm round each square to maintain the seal.

3 Prepare to test the plants by taking the second square of blue paper from the container and cutting it into four pieces. Now make four mounts, each with an unsealed blue square beside a sealed colour standard on a larger piece of sticky tape.

4 Stick these, one to the upper and one to the lower surface of fully expanded leaves on the two plants supplied. One of the plants has been kept in the dark with low humidity and the other has been kept in the light with high humidity.

5 Now place both plants on the laboratory bench and record the time taken for each blue square to turn sufficiently pink just to match the colour standard next to it.

6 Compare the stomatal distribution on the upper and lower epidermis of the plant using the method described in Practical 12.1, p. 140.

NOTE TO TECHNICIAN

Each student will need:
- two pieces of blue cobalt chloride paper 10 × 10 mm, supplied in a sealed container (such as a small specimen tube) with a little silica gel;
- scissors, forceps;
- broad sticky tape (transparent book covering material is almost as flexible and easier to distribute to a class);
- two plants – shoots of privet (*Ligustrum* sp.) are suitable – kept in water. (Cover a specimen tube of water with clingfilm, strip the leaves off a portion of the plant stem and insert it through the film.) Keep one in a dark but dry place for at least an hour before use, and the other in a well-lit place enclosed in a transparent plastic bag to provide high humidity. They should be appropriately labelled for the class.

■ Data presentation
Present the recordings for upper and lower epidermis of both plants in the form of a table.

■ Discussion and conclusion
- Relate the time taken for the cobalt chloride paper to reach the standard pink colour to the stomatal density of the upper and lower epidermis.
- Explain what effect the pretreatment of the plant had on its rate of water loss.

■ Evaluation
Placing plants in different conditions prior to applying the cobalt chloride paper will affect the degree to which the stomata open. Because more than one variable has been changed, however, it is impossible to say which of the changes in conditions have brought about the effect.
- What conditions would it be worth investigating to find out what part they play in determining stomatal opening?
- What criticism would you make of a process like this one that measures water loss from a leaf by covering the leaf surface?

16.3 Mineral nutrient requirements in a green plant
(Data generating)

By growing plants (such as sunflower or barley seedlings) with their roots in aerated solution we can discover which **ions are essential for normal healthy plant growth** (*Advanced Biology*, p. 332). The technique, a form of hydroponics, can be adapted to use duckweed (*Lemna* sp.) floating in culture solution in a Petri dish.

■ Aim
To discover mineral nutrient requirements for healthy plant growth.

■ Risk assessment
Good laboratory practice will be sufficient to take account of any hazards and avoid significant risks.

■ Method

Collection of suitable Lemna *plants*
Lemna is a genus of simple aquatic plants consisting of one or more tiny pendulous roots and small green leaves. *Lemna* may grow quickly, forming a green carpet over the surface of stagnant water. Dipping into the surface layers of such a pond with a suitable net will yield a large number of these plants to bring back to the laboratory in pond water. This experiment should be carried out with *Lemna* plants that are all of the same species. Each student group will require about 50 plants. Figure 16.3 will help in identification.

Setting up the hydroponics experiment

1 Take nine Petri dishes and label them as follows:
   a complete culture solution;
   b minus nitrogen;
   c minus sulphur;
   d minus phosphorus;
   e minus potassium;
   f minus calcium;
   g minus magnesium;
   h minus iron;
   i distilled water.

   Into each dish measure out 15 cm^3 of the appropriate culture solution (or water) provided.

2 Count out five healthy *Lemna* plants of comparable size into each dish. If any plant has a small 'bud' developing, trim it away with fine scissors. Replace the lids of the dishes and incubate them all together, in a position that receives good even illumination.

3 Allow the experiment to proceed for several weeks. If there is a tendency for the medium to evaporate after some weeks, return the liquid level to the original, using distilled water.

4 Examine the plants about twice each week, using a hand lens. The plants can best be handled by means of a paint brush. For each dish record the following numerical information:
   - the number of live plants;
   - the number of green leaves;
   - the number of dead leaves (those turning yellow or white);
   - the length of the longest root, recorded once per week (or alternate weeks, depending on growth rate).

Figure 16.3   Species of *Lemna*

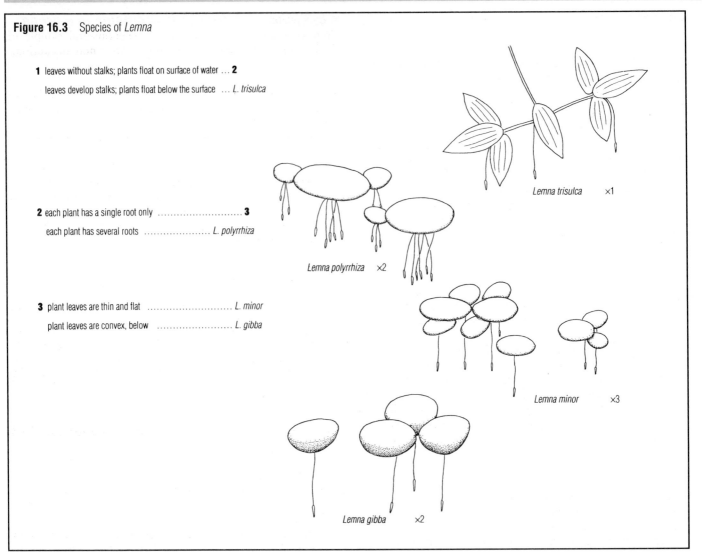

1   leaves without stalks; plants float on surface of water ... **2**

    leaves develop stalks; plants float below the surface   ... *L. trisulca*

2   each plant has a single root only **3**

    each plant has several roots .... *L. polyrrhiza*

3   plant leaves are thin and flat .... *L. minor*

    plant leaves are convex, below .... *L. gibba*

Lemna trisulca   ×1

Lemna polyrrhiza   ×2

Lemna minor   ×3

Lemna gibba   ×2

In addition, look for and record evidence of abnormal growth and development in the absence of any of the mineral nutrient ions.

NOTE TO TECHNICIAN

Each student group requires:
- a sample of pond water with an excess of *Lemna* plants, *or* a supply of 50 *Lemna* plants of the same species, in pond water;
- nine Petri dishes, 20 cm³ graduated pipette with safety bulb, supply of distilled water, waterproof marker pen, fine paint brush, hand lens;
- access to a bottle (100 cm³) of complete culture solution (p. 430);
- access to labelled bottles (100 cm³) of culture solutions with specific elements (potassium, calcium, iron, nitrogen, phosphorus and sulphur) missing, made from the complete culture solution formulation (p. 430).

■ Data presentation
- The bulk of the data generated is numerical, and can be summarised by means of a column graph.
- Make a listing of any growth abnormalities that appear to be associated with particular deficiencies.

■ Conclusion
As far as possible, relate the evidence obtained to the published accounts of the ions involved in plant growth, development and metabolism.

■ Evaluation
- What are the advantages and disadvantages of using *Lemna* as an experimental plant in place of a terrestrially growing flowering plant?
- Which of the two dishes, distilled water or complete culture solution, do you see as the 'control' dish?

16.4 Root nodules on leguminous plants
(Demonstration)

Bacteria of the genus *Rhizobium* occur as free-living soil organisms, but may also form **mutualistic associations** with the roots of flowering plant species of the pea family Leguminosae, forming characteristic nodules.

■ Aim
To demonstrate that the normal soil microflora is necessary and sufficient to allow root nodule formation in plants of the Leguminosae.

■ Risk assessment

Good laboratory practice will be sufficient to take account of any hazards and avoid significant risks.

■ Method

Sterilising seeds

Surface-sterilise six seeds of each of the following species (or similar) by immersing them in 70% aqueous ethanol for 10 minutes, and then rinsing them in three changes of distilled water.

leguminous plants:	red clover (*Trifolium pratense*);
	pea (*Pisum sativum*), or
	french bean (*Phaseolus vulgaris*);
non-leguminous plant:	barley (*Hordeum vulgare*).

Setting up the experimental pots

1 Fill one 10–12 cm diameter plant pot with ordinary garden soil. Plant in the soil (no more than 1 cm deep) three seeds of two species of leguminous plants and three seeds of barley. Label the pot 'Garden soil'.

2 Take the pot of sterilised soil. Plant in the soil (no more than 1 cm deep) three seeds of two species of leguminous plants and three seeds of barley. Label the pot 'Sterilised soil'.

3 Place the pots under identical conditions, favourable for the germination and growth of plants. Keep the soil in the pots moist by regular watering with distilled water. Leave until the plants have grown to a height in the range 15–25 cm.

Harvesting the plants

1 Harvest the plants by knocking them out of their pots and washing the root systems free from soil. Do this gently, to keep smaller roots intact.

2 Observe the roots carefully, noting whether the plant has a tap-root or a fibrous root system. Where are nodules, if present, found on roots?

NOTE TO TECHNICIAN

Each student group will require (or require access to):
- sterilised soil, sufficient to fill a plant pot of 10–12 cm diameter (this may be sterilised in an autoclave or large pressure cooker: cover the sterilised soil with aluminium foil to exclude airborne spores, and allow to cool to room temperature);
- small bucket half-filled with garden topsoil;
- two sterilised plant pots (diameter 10–12 cm);
- six seeds of red clover (*Trifolium pratense*), pea (*Pisum sativum*) or french bean (*Phaseolus vulgaris*), and of barley (*Hordeum vulgare*);
- three small beakers, with a bottle of 70% ethanol, labelled 'highly flammable';
- supply of distilled water;
- labels for plant pots;
- facilities for washing soil from plant roots;
- camera with appropriate film, to record results.

■ Data presentation

A good record can be made by photographing (or sketching) the plants and their root systems at harvest, washed free from soil. The results can be summarised in a table.

■ Conclusion

Your conclusions are based on an experimental sample of three plants, so you must present these with a note of caution.

■ Evaluation

- Find out about the attempts of genetic engineers to induce the facility of root nodule formation into species of cultivated grasses.
- Why would this development be of economic importance?

■ Extension

For details of an advanced investigation on nodule formation in clover plants, see *Research on the Nitrogen Cycle – a Sixth Form Study*, published by the National Centre for Biotechnological Education in association with the Agricultural and Food Research Council.

16.5 Translocation and fruit growth

(Investigation)

A fertilised ovary grows into a mature fruit at the expense of **elaborated food moved via the phloem** in the fruit stalk from the rest of the plant. Data on the growth of a fruit can be used to investigate phloem translocation, since the fruit is served by a relatively narrow stalk.

■ Aim

To estimate the rate of phloem transport of elaborated food materials.

■ Risk assessment

Good laboratory practice is sufficient to avoid a hazard.

■ Method

- First, weigh a fully grown fruit such as a cucumber, with part of the fruit stalk attached. The materials from which this organ has formed have travelled down the xylem and phloem of the stalk, subsequent to fertilisation of the ovules and the commencement of seed formation. In fact, about 90–95% of the mass of a plant is water, and in the case of a cucumber fruit it is advisable to assume the larger figure. So only about 5% of the mass of the fruit is 'dry' matter, delivered via the phloem.
- If you have access to an experimental crop of cucumbers grown in a greenhouse, you can study the rate of growth of the fruit. Otherwise assume that, typically, a large cucumber fruit forms from a fertilised ovule in about 15 days under normal growing conditions (*Advanced Biology*, p. 407).
- You will need to estimate the cross-sectional area of phloem tissue in the fruit stalk. Cut thin sections of the stalk, stain these to show phloem tissue (pp. 127–8) and then mount them for microscopic examination. Count the number of vascular bundles present. Estimate the mean cross-sectional area of phloem in a typical bundle. This requires the use of a micrometer eyepiece and stage micrometer (pp. 97–8). You will also need to examine the vascular bundles carefully, for this family of plant has 'bicollateral bundles', with phloem on both sides of the xylem – see C J Clegg and Gene Cox *Anatomy and Activities of Plants*, p. 14 (John Murray). Assume that about 50% of the total cross-sectional area of phloem is sieve tubes (the remainder being companion cells, parenchyma and fibres).

- You should now be in a position to estimate:
  a the total weight of dry matter that has passed down the phloem of the fruit stalk;
  b the time in days over which this has occurred;
  c the cross-sectional area of phloem sieve tubes through which this transport has occurred;
  d the estimated rate of flow of 'dry matter' in one hour along phloem sieve tubes occupying 1 cm^2.

NOTE TO TECHNICIAN

Each group of students will require (or require access to):
- top-pan balance;
- cucumber fruit;
- microscope and lamp;
- equipment to section and stain the fruit stalk tissues (p. 128);
- micrometer eyepiece and stage micrometer.

■ **Data presentation**
Data should be presented as a sequence of measurements, assumptions and calculations of dry mass transported (in g cm^{-2} h^{-1}).

■ **Conclusion**
Results are quoted in the literature for various species, and vary between 5.0 and 0.5 g dry mass cm^{-2} h^{-1}.

■ **Evaluation**
- List the sources of error in this calculation.
- What techniques could a laboratory plant physiologist undertake to produce a more accurate answer?

Projects

16.1 Rates of transpiration compared

Undertake a comparative study of transpiration from leafy shoots of different species, in which water loss is expressed per unit area of leaf. Comparative leaf areas can be estimated by drawing the outlines of all leaves of a shoot (after transpiration rates have been measured), cutting out the leaf shapes and weighing them. Can the different rates of transpiration be related to stomata numbers observed in the leaf epidermis?

16.2 Mineral deficiency symptoms in plants adapted to contrasting habitats

How do young plants grown from seed from contrasting habitats (such as saltmarsh, sand dune, acid soil, chalky soil) respond to hydroponic culture in complete culture solution, and when grown in culture solutions deficient in essential ions such as calcium, phosphate, magnesium, nitrate and iron? Do plants adapted to environments low in certain nutrients show a lessened sensitivity to deficiency of particular ions?

16.3 The behaviour of stomata in the field

Certain organic liquids differ in their ability to penetrate small openings, including the stomatal pores of leaves. By applying mixtures of two liquids, one liquid which penetrates easily and one that penetrates hardly at all (combined together in different proportions), it is possible to make an assessment of the relative degree of opening of stomata. A suitable range of solutions, held in labelled dropping bottles, is:

solution (Risk assessment needed):	1	2	3	4	5	6	7	8	9
parts 2-methylpropan-1-ol (isobutanol)	9	8	7	6	5	4	3	2	1
parts propane-1,2,3-triol (glycerol)	1	2	3	4	5	6	7	8	9

Ethanediol (ethylene glycol) can be used as an alternative to propane-1,2,3-triol.

A dark green colour appears in the leaf when liquid penetrates the substomatal cavities. By trial and error, find the highest number of the solution that penetrates the stomata. How do relative stomatal apertures vary through the day in different species (including C$_3$ and C$_4$ plants), or under wilt-inducing conditions?

Reference
T A Geyer (1963) 'Investigations into the behaviour of stomata in the field', *School Science Review* (March 1963) 34(153), pp. 390–4

16.4 Porometer studies

A porometer is a piece of equipment used to investigate mass flow of gas through a leaf. A simple porometer consists of a cup fitted to make an air-tight seal to the leaf surface using Vaseline or a gelatine washer. The cup is also connected via a T-piece to a glass tube dipping into coloured water. The other arm of the T-piece can be closed off with a clip, and when air is withdrawn from the apparatus, the liquid rises in the straight tube. The time taken for this liquid to fall a given distance is related to the number of open stomata in the leaf. How do porometer readings vary with the time of day, with weather conditions or with the species?

References
H Meidner and T A Mansfield (1968) *Physiology of Stomata*. McGraw-Hill

W M M Baron (1985) *Organisation in Plants*. Edward Arnold

16.5 Impressions of the leaf epidermis to investigate stomatal opening

Replicas of a leaf surface, made from fast-setting, non-toxic silicone rubber (Lastic, p. 433) used by dentists to prepare mouth impressions, can be used to examine details of cells of the epidermis, including the size of stomata apertures. The rubber is available as a white paste which will set quickly when mixed with catalyst.

This technique can be used to investigate how changes in stomatal aperture result from changes in external conditions, such as raised carbon dioxide levels, dry conditions and the distribution of stomata on 'sun' and 'shade' leaves. Alternative materials to experiment with include nail varnish or 'super glue' (p. 140; note the Risk assessment).

16.6 Diurnal changes in tree girth

The transport of water up a tree trunk by the force generated in the leaves due to transpiration means that water in the xylem is under tension. This tension develops in the hours of daylight when stomata are open and water loss may exceed water uptake. It is manifested in a shrinking in diameter of a tree trunk. This shrinking is reversed overnight (*Advanced Biology*, p. 329). Diurnal fluctuations in diameter are complicated in the growing season by an increase in girth due to secondary growth of the stem. Can these movements be detected and recorded for a tree close to your laboratory, using a metal strip placed around a trunk, and a strain gauge (a Philip Harris strain gauge is suitable) cemented to the strip and connected to a portable data logger such as EMU or a Philip Harris Universal Interface?

16.7 Nitrate reductase and nitrite reductase in plant tissues

Plants typically absorb combined nitrogen as nitrate and reduce it to the ammonium ion, which forms amino acids by reactions with specific organic acids. Amino acids are the building blocks of proteins. Enzymes in plant tissue are able to catalyse the reduction of nitrate to nitrite (nitrate reductase) and nitrite to ammonium ion (nitrite reductase). The concentration of nitrite and of ammonium ions can be measured in liquids, using Merckoquant nitrite-sensitive and ammonium-sensitive reagent strips. Plants from different habitats can be divided into stem, leaf and root tissues, and extracts of these assayed to find their ability to carry out these reductions.

Reference
P W Freeland (1985) *Problems in Practical Advanced Level Biology*, p. 42. Hodder and Stoughton

16.8 Trumpet hyphae in Laminaria stalk (stipe)

There are no problems over the supply of water in submerged seaweeds of any size, presumably, and this may explain the absence of water-conducting tissue in the larger algae. But how is elaborated food transported? The largest seaweeds in UK waters, the oarweeds, have a simple type of phloem cell (called trumpet hyphae) in the centre of the stalk and the blade. Investigate the distribution of these cells in seaweeds like *Laminaria digitata* in plants of different sizes, by cutting sections.

Reference
C J Clegg (1984) *Lower Plants*. John Murray

■ A resource that aids independent work in plant physiology
Investigating Plant Science is a CD-ROM designed for use by GCSE and A level students. It is available for Research Machines (Nimbus) and IBM and compatible multimedia PCs, but not for Acorn/Archimedes machines. The original concept was that of Richard Price (SAPS) and Angela McFarlane (Homerton College).

The contents are organised into eight sections and two tutorial options, centred on 11 featured topics of plant science: ecology, genetics, germination, growth, mineral nutrition, osmosis, photosynthesis, pollution, reproduction, transpiration and tropisms. The tutorials are 'Flora', a key to 150 wild plants found around many schools, and 'Plan', a step by step guide to planning an investigation. The other sections provide numerical data about plants, a glossary of technical words, images of plant structures, lists of plants suitable for investigations, references to published sources of particular use, stories about plants, studies based on pupils' investigations, and tips on a range of experimental techniques.

Problems and assignments

16.1 Stomatal numbers and the atmospheric concentration of carbon dioxide

Plant physiologists at the University of Cambridge observed that, when plants are grown at reduced partial pressure of atmospheric carbon dioxide around their leaves, they respond by developing a greater density of stomata per unit area of leaf epidermis. This discovery suggested two further investigations to them.

In Experiment 1, they examined the effect of growing batches of plants (of four different species) in air-tight enclosures under a range of partial pressures of CO_2, from 0.025 to 0.034%, on stomatal density in the leaves. The results confirmed that plants grown at higher partial pressures of CO_2 had a lower density of stomata in the epidermis.

In Experiment 2, they determined stomatal densities of herbarium-stored leaves of eight species of plants collected over a period from 1750 (when the partial pressure of atmospheric CO_2 was much lower) until recent times. The result confirmed the tendency for a higher density of stomata in the epidermis in plants grown at lower partial pressures of CO_2. Some of the plants used in Experiments 1 and 2 were of the same species.

1 What is the chief role of stomata in relation to photosynthesis in a green leaf?
2 a Why is it that CO_2 diffuses so readily into leaves through stomatal pores, when leaves are illuminated for any period of time?
   b What is the energy source for this movement?
3 What would you predict to be the likely effect on leaf stomata numbers of growing plants in an atmosphere of CO_2 above that in our present atmosphere?
4 What is the advantage to a plant in a raised-CO_2 environment, in terms of its water relations, in having fewer stomata?

5 What are the disadvantages to the plant of transpiration? Are there any advantages?
6 Studies of polar ice give evidence of lower atmospheric CO_2 levels in the period 1750–1850 than are present today. What major events caused a profound change in our atmosphere during the nineteenth century?
7 There is clear evidence that atmospheric CO_2 levels are continuing to rise. What are the causes of this?
8 When the Cambridge scientists counted stomata in herbarium specimens, they chose to count those in leaves on the main flowering stem, below the inflorescence. Suggest the reasons for this decision.
9 Comment on the value of plants of identical species being selected for the two experiments.
10 Are there any longer-term environmental effects of raised atmospheric CO_2 levels that may be considered harmful to plant life?

16.2 Deficiency symptoms in plants

Plants grown without soil but 'rooted' in inert, sterile chips will tend to grow well if supplied with a solution containing all the required macronutrients and micronutrients, together with sufficient oxygen. This discovery led to the system of cultivation known as hydroponics. The technique can be adapted to establish the importance of individual ions to the metabolism of the plant, and the consequences (deficiency symptoms) of the omission of particular ions. Figure 16.4 illustrates a healthy plant grown in this way, and plants grown in solutions deficient in certain essential ions.

Examine the drawings of these plants in Figure 16.4, and read the annotations concerning symptoms. Some essential ions are built up into compounds that are more or less constantly being broken down and re-formed into other similar substances. Deficiencies in these

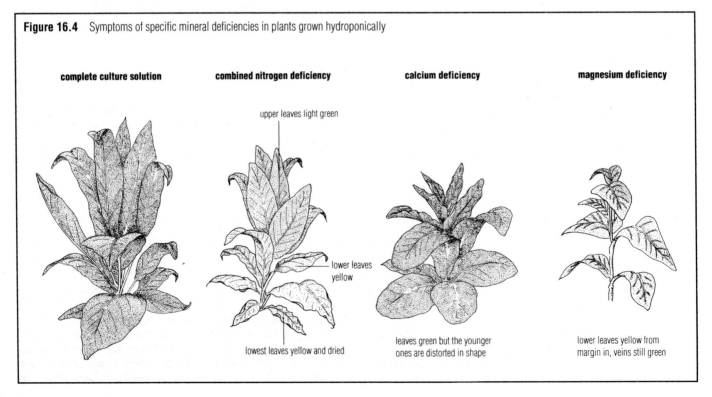

Figure 16.4   Symptoms of specific mineral deficiencies in plants grown hydroponically

complete culture solution   combined nitrogen deficiency   calcium deficiency   magnesium deficiency

upper leaves light green

lower leaves yellow

lowest leaves yellow and dried

leaves green but the younger ones are distorted in shape

lower leaves yellow from margin in, veins still green

substances show up in the older leaves. In plants, combined nitrogen (as nitrates, ammonium ions, amino acids and proteins) is a case in point. Other ions are built up into cell components that are only very slowly, if at all, broken down and then re-used. Deficiencies in these substances are shown at the growing points and in the youngest leaves. You can spot examples of these two types of substance in the illustrations here.

Now answer the questions below, using the information given, together with your biological knowledge and that gained from wider reading.

1 What are the advantages to the experimenter of growing plants supported in inert chips, rather than with their roots in soil?
2 Why is the aeration of the root environment such an important issue to flowering plant growth?
3 What do we mean by 'complete culture solution'?
4 How are essential substances like phosphates, nitrates and calcium ions taken into the plant? Does the mechanism differ from water absorption? If so, how?
5 How would you explain the observation that some leaves on plants deficient in combined nitrogen are pale yellow, rather than the normal dark green coloration?
6 What is the significance of the appearance of nitrogen deficiency symptoms only in the oldest leaves of the plant?
7 a Parts of plants deficient in calcium are structurally malformed. How does this observation tie in with a known role of calcium ions in plants?
  b Are the substances concerned metabolically stable, or are they frequently broken down and re-used?
8 Write a concise note on the role and metabolism of magnesium ions in green plant metabolism. Your note should account for the appearance and distribution of the deficiency symptoms.

16.3 Translocation and phloem structure

Examine the electronmicrograph of phloem tissue of the water lily (Figure 16.5). Then, using your knowledge of phloem structure and the way 'elaborated food' is believed to be translocated, answer the following questions.

1 a What are the major chemical components of the walls of the cells shown in this photomicrograph?
  b What stain might you use to confirm the chemical composition of phloem in sections cut for light microscopy?
2 In a TS of phloem, sieve tubes and companion cells occur in the ratio 1:1. Explain why you would anticipate this from the way phloem tissue forms.
3 a About five of the cells present in the TEM are sieve elements, and yet none show sieve plates. What is a sieve plate?
  b Why are sieve plates rarely visible in a TS of phloem tissue?
4 Make a large labelled drawing of a companion cell, and label the following features: nuclear membrane, mitochondria, position of cell plasma membrane.
5 By comparison with companion cells, sieve tubes show relatively little evidence of living contents. Why is this so?
6 a Translocation stops in a stem or leaf stalk in which a part has its cells experimentally killed (by heat treatment above 40 °C, for example). What does this observation suggest to you about the mechanism of transport in phloem?
  b How does phloem transport differ from transport of water in xylem vessels, in this respect?
7 From a mature leaf situated about mid-point in a flowering plant stem, sugars were found to be translocated to the stem growing

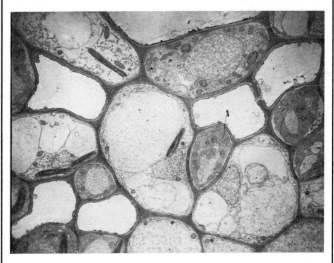

Figure 16.5 TEM of phloem tissue of the water lily *Nymphoides peltata*, showing parenchyma, sieve tubes and companion cells in TS

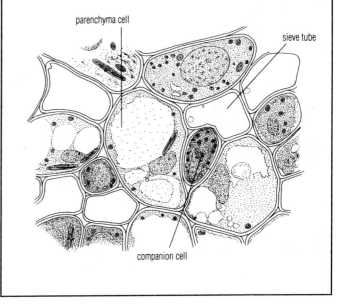

point early in the season, but the direction of flow was towards the roots later on. How could such information be discovered by plant physiologists?
8 By means of a concisely annotated sketch, explain fully one hypothesis for the mechanism of phloem transport.

16.4 Mycorrhizae and the growth of plants

The roots of very many plants are intimately associated, to mutual advantage, with species of naturally occurring fungi. A common type of association is described as ectotrophic. Here the fungus forms a mantle around the root, some hyphae penetrate between the cells of the cortex, and very many hyphae extend for great distances out into the surrounding soil. Foresters often inoculate the soil with mycorrhizal fungi around seedlings of forest trees before planting them on mountain hillsides where growing conditions are unfavourable. The results of an experiment on the effect on tree growth of inoculation of sterilised soil in which Sitka spruce seedlings were grown are

Figure 16.6 Effects of the presence of mycorrhizal fungus on root and shoot growth in Sitka spruce seedlings grown in sterilised soil

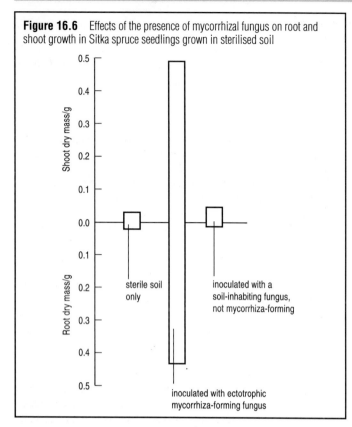

16.5 Quick test

1 Distinguish between the following pairs:

  a apoplast and symplast;
  b transpiration and translocation;
  c guard cell and subsidiary cell;
  d turgid and flaccid;
  e bayonet-shaped leaves and dorsi-ventrally flattened leaves;
  f potometer and porometer;
  g vascular bundle and stele;
  h pericycle and endodermis;
  i macronutrients and micronutrients;
  j cations and anions;
  k humus and mineral skeleton of a soil;
  l diffusion and active uptake;
  m nitrifying and denitrifying bacteria;
  n ectotrophic and endotrophic mycorrhizae;
  o sieve tubes and companion cells.

2 Explain the importance of the following:

  a cohesion of a water column;
  b diffusion gradient;
  c region of root hairs;
  d Casparian strip of endodermis;
  e water culture (hydroponics) of plants;
  f ion-deficiency symptoms of plants;
  g crop rotation;
  h *Rhizobium* in root nodules of leguminous plants;
  i aphid mouthparts as micropipettes;
  j the mechanism of phloem transport.

16.6 Essay assignment

Select one of the following:

• Give an illustrated account of the structure of a stoma, relating structure to function as you do so. What environmental factors are important in stomatal opening?

or:

• Describe the main steps in one biogeochemical cycle of importance to plant and animal life, making clear the roles of free-living and symbiotic microorganisms in the process.

summarised in Figure 16.6. You may need to read about this form of mutualism in *Advanced Biology*, pp. 339–40, before answering the questions below.

1 Mycorrhizal relationships are described as 'mutualistic'. How does this relationship differ from that of a parasite with its host?
2 What are the common conditions in the soil of mountain-side habitats that make a mycorrhizal relationship advantageous to coniferous trees planted as a crop?
3 In the experiment outlined in Figure 16.6:
  a why was it necessary to use sterilised soil in all pots?
  b why was it necessary to use no fungus with one batch of seedlings and a non-mycorrhizal fungus with another, in addition to the batch with the mycorrhizal fungus?
4 What has the mycorrhizal fungus obtained and supplied to the spruce seedlings that is not otherwise available to the seedlings, and that may account for improved growth performance?
5 What has the tree provided for the fungus? How has this trade-off been confirmed experimentally?

17 Transport within animals

Summary

There are many small animals in which the supply of oxygen to the cells is assumed to occur by diffusion alone, but most larger animals require an **internal transport system** that circulates a special fluid known as blood. The larger an animal and the more active its way of life, the more likely it is to have an internal transport system. Internal transport systems are of different types.

Blood circulatory systems are either **open systems**, with blood in haemocoels bathing the organs of the body (as seen in arthropods), or **closed systems** that deliver blood to tissues via capillary networks (as seen in vertebrates). The closed circulation system of fish is known as a **single circulation**, whereas the circulation of mammals is a **double circulation** in that blood goes twice through the heart each time it circulates through the body.

The mammalian heart has **four chambers**. The upper chambers, the **atria**, lead to the lower chambers, the **ventricles**. The chambers of the right and the left sides are separate. Blood in the chambers of the **right side** is received from the body and pumped to the lungs. Blood in the chambers of the **left side** is received from the lungs and pumped to the rest of the body. The sequence of contraction and relaxation of cardiac muscles of the heart walls, together with the resulting movement of the heart valves, is known as the **cardiac cycle**. The heartbeat originates in a structure in the wall of the right atrium, the **pacemaker**, but is regulated by the cardiovascular centre in the hindbrain, which also controls blood flow and blood pressure in the circulation system of the body.

The structures of the walls of the **arteries, capillaries** and **veins** relate to their functions; arteries carry blood under high pressure away from the heart, whereas veins carry blood under lower pressure back to the heart. At the capillary network, **tissue fluid** is formed and facilitates the exchange between the blood and the cells. Some of the tissue fluid returns via the lymph vessels of the **lymphatic system**.

The blood transports oxygen in combination with the **haemoglobin** in the red blood cells, as oxyhaemoglobin. Much of the carbon dioxide transported by blood is also carried in red cells, as hydrogencarbonate ions. At the same time, food, waste substances and hormones are all transported in the blood **plasma**, the straw-coloured fluid in which the blood cells are suspended.

The blood also has a key role in the complex **defence mechanism** of the body. These include the blood-clotting mechanism, and the immune system. White blood cells are concerned with phagocytosis of invading microorganisms, and in the antigen–antibody reaction. Human blood groups (ABO, rhesus) are also part of the immune system.

Practicals and activities

17.1 The structure of the mammalian circulation system

(Data generating)

Blood is circulated to the lungs and to the rest of the body by the actions of the heart, via arteries, capillaries and veins.

■ Aim

To become familiar with the appearance and structure of heart, arteries and veins, and where possible to relate their structure to functions.

■ Risk assessment

- In the conduct of dissection, special precautions for safety are essential. These are listed in Practical 13.2 (p. 157). Read them again now.
- Otherwise, good laboratory practice will be sufficient to take account of any hazards and avoid significant risks.

■ Method

Examining a mammalian heart

The heart you are provided with is from a sheep or pig, and most likely has been obtained by special arrangement with a butcher. (Most 'hearts' sold as food have the atria and much of the aorta/arteries cut off, leaving only the ventricles. If this is the only material available, there is rather little to gain from the exercise.) It is possible that a complete heart/lung set has also been obtained for general reference by the group. If so, make careful observations and frequent reference to it.

1 Identify the ventral (front) and dorsal (back) sides of the heart, the four chambers, and all the blood vessels entering and leaving the heart. The main veins enter the heart via the dorsal side. Note that the aorta is a thick-walled rubbery tube. The outer surface of the heart often shows an accumulation of fat, largely around the main blood vessels and over the upper part of the ventricles. Find the coronary arteries that supply the ventricle muscle. Make an annotated diagram of the external appearance of the heart.

2 Attach a rubber tube to a cold water tap. First, insert the other end into one of the vena cavae, turn on the tap gently, and see the uninterrupted flow of water through the right side of the heart. Then insert the end of the tube into a pulmonary vein, and see the flow through the left side. Turn off the tap.

3 Now insert the other end of the tube down the pulmonary artery into the right ventricle. Take care that the semilunar valves are not damaged in the process. Then, holding the pulmonary artery securely around the rubber tube, turn on the tap again carefully. Water pressure builds up within the heart, but little or no water leaves via the vena cavae. Why not? Why does the outward appearance of the heart change?

4 Using scissors, open the heart by cutting down the aorta whilst holding the dorsal side of the heart in the palm of

one hand (Figure 17.1(a)). Your incision should reach into the left ventricle and go down to the apex of the heart. Find the valves that occur at the base of the aorta at its junction with the ventricle wall. Observe the semilunar valves. You can see the valves that separate the ventricle (cut open) from the atrium (intact). Find out the role of the tendons ('heart strings') attached to them.

5 Find a pulmonary vein and, using this as an entrance, cut open the left atrium (Figure 17.1(b)). Note the difference in the thickness of the atrium and ventricle walls.

6 Make a final incision (again using scissors) down the pulmonary artery, into the right ventricle, reaching down to the apex of the ventricle (Figure 17.1(c)). Observe the semilunar valves and the tricuspid valve. Carefully compare the walls of the right and left ventricles.

7 If a plastic model of the mammalian heart is available (normally these are 'dissectible' into several parts), make a comparison of the chambers of the model and the heart you have dissected.

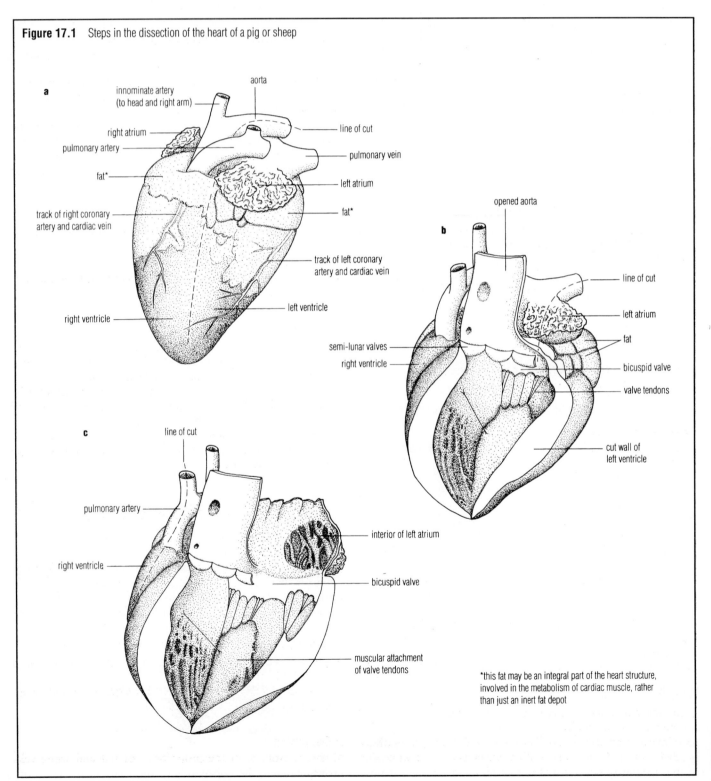

Figure 17.1   Steps in the dissection of the heart of a pig or sheep

a

innominate artery
(to head and right arm)

aorta

right atrium

pulmonary artery

fat*

track of right coronary
artery and cardiac vein

right ventricle

line of cut

pulmonary vein

left atrium

fat*

track of left coronary
artery and cardiac vein

left ventricle

b

opened aorta

semi-lunar valves

right ventricle

line of cut

left atrium

fat

bicuspid valve

valve tendons

cut wall of
left ventricle

c

line of cut

pulmonary artery

right ventricle

interior of left atrium

bicuspid valve

muscular attachment
of valve tendons

*this fat may be an integral part of the heart structure,
involved in the metabolism of cardiac muscle, rather
than just an inert fat depot

Heart sounds

By reference to *Advanced Biology*, p. 353, and working with a partner and a stethoscope, listen to heart sounds whilst the person breathes gently.

Heart muscle

Using a prepared slide of cardiac muscle, and by reference to *Advanced Biology*, p. 215, identify the structure of cardiac muscle.

Structure of arteries and veins

Blood is carried away from the heart under high pressure by arteries, and it is returned to the heart at much lower pressure in veins. As a consequence, there are marked structural differences to be observed in the walls of arteries and veins, when viewed in section. Using the illustrations and information in *Advanced Biology*, p. 355, observe a prepared microscope slide showing an artery and a vein in cross-section. Note the differences of thickness of the walls. Identify the distinct layers in their walls. Veins have small 'pocket' valves at intervals along their length, but your section is most unlikely to go through one.

NOTE TO TECHNICIAN

Each student group requires (or requires access to):
- dissection equipment (p. 162);
- a heart, obtained from a butcher, preferably with the atria, arteries and veins intact (sometimes it is also possible to obtain a complete heart/lung set, by arrangement);
- a rubber tube, attached to a cold-water tap;
- plastic model of a mammalian heart, if available;
- a stethoscope;
- microscope, with lamp;
- prepared slides of cardiac muscle;
- prepared slide showing mammalian artery and vein in section.

■ Data presentation
- Retain your labelled drawing of the external appearance of the heart.
- Using information in *Advanced Biology*, p. 351, draw a diagram to show the path of water and the action of valves between the ventricle and atrium, in the experiment in which tap water was run into the right ventricle via the pulmonary artery.
- Make a labelled drawing of your dissection and investigation of the aorta, left ventricle and left atrium, adding notes (annotation) on the roles of the valve flaps you draw, and on the relative thicknesses of the muscular walls of these two heart chambers.
- Make a fully annotated comparative sketch of the ventricles of the heart, drawing attention to the relative sizes of the internal chambers and to the thickness of the walls.
- Make notes on the heart sounds you heard via a stethoscope, and how you interpret these.
- Make a large labelled drawing of a branching cardiac muscle fibre, showing the striations, intercalated discs and the positions of nuclei.
- Make a clear tissue-map drawing of the outline of an artery and vein, and mark in the different layers of the walls in a representative portion. Label your diagram.

■ Conclusion

Given that the heart beats about 70 times a minute, 60 minutes an hour, 24 hours a day, 365 days a year, typically for 70 years or more, make a list of the essential and unique features that the heart muscle and valves must show.

■ Evaluation

How would a pocket valve have to be structured to prevent backflow of blood towards a capillary bed?

17.2 The composition of the blood

(Data generating)

There is a potential health risk in practical work using human blood, arising from the possibility of the presence in the blood of some individuals of viruses that cause hepatitis and/or AIDS. Consequently, you will probably investigate the **structure of blood by the examination of prepared slides**. Note that slides may be of human blood or blood of a different mammal. Prepared slides of the blood of other vertebrates are also frequently found in slide cabinets in schools and colleges.

■ Aim

To investigate the composition of the blood of a mammal.

■ Risk assessment

Good laboratory practice will be sufficient to take account of any hazards and avoid significant risks.

■ Method

1 Examine the mammalian blood smear preparation. Most of the cells you will see are red blood cells of distinctive shape and uniform size. The white cells have been stained to show the shape of their nuclei, and therefore show up clearly. Platelets, though they are tiny by comparison with red and white cells, are also made visible by staining.
2 If a prepared slide of amphibian or bird blood is also available, make a careful comparison of this blood with the mammalian sample.

NOTE TO TECHNICIAN

Each student group requires (or requires access to):
- microscope, and lamp;
- prepared slides of human and/or other mammalian blood, together with slides of the blood of other vertebrates (amphibian or bird, if possible), if available.

■ Data presentation
- Make a large, labelled drawing of the different cell types you can identify.
- If possible, state the differences between the blood of an amphibian (or bird) and a mammal.

■ Conclusion

Make an estimate of the proportions of red and white cells present.

■ **Evaluation**

• What important components of blood are *not* visible in a prepared slide?

• If a sample of blood was divided into two portions, and one portion was kept for several days in the refrigerator and the other portion was exposed to oxygen gas from a cylinder, what observation would you expect to make?

17.3 Exercise physiology

(Investigation)

General physical fitness of the human body can be measured in various ways, but a good indication can be obtained by measurement of pulse and blood pressure before standard exercise tasks, and then finding out how long it takes for these to return to resting values afterwards. A speedy return to the normal state implies an efficient and healthy cardiovascular system.

Contraction of the ventricles forces a **wave of blood through the arteries**. This can be felt as a pulse, particularly where the artery is near the skin surface and passes over a bone. The pulse informs us of the heart rate.

Blood pressure is a measure of the force exerted by the blood on the arteries. The highest pressure (systolic blood pressure) arises when ventricle contraction forces a large volume of blood into the arteries. This is followed by diastolic blood pressure, the lowest pressure during the cardiac cycle. Overall, blood pressure is a product of the cardiac output and regulation of the diameter of the arterioles supplying capillary networks all over the body.

■ **Aim**

To investigate cardiovascular fitness by monitoring human pulse rates and blood pressures.

■ **Risk assessment**

When working with a human organism as 'guinea pig' in pulse rate and blood-pressure experiments, make certain:

• that those involved are reasonably fit (they must not suffer from long-term complaints such as asthma), and healthy (they do not suffer from short-term illness, such as the common cold);

• that everyone understands and is confident about the nature of the experiment, the way the equipment works, and what they are required to do as experimenters and observers (there must be no competition between individuals to prove 'superiority', but rather a collection of data for consideration);

• that everyone knows the risk assessment that has been completed, and why the procedure as undertaken is entirely safe and permitted;

• that no one experiences prolonged involvement in any experimental situation in case the situation becomes unpleasant or threatening with time, bearing in mind not only physical stress (such as becoming faint or dizzy) but also emotional stress (students especially need to feel 'normal' in front of their peers, particularly regarding their own bodily attributes);

• that no medical or genetic 'diagnosis' is made as a result of experiments.

Otherwise, good laboratory practice will be sufficient to take account of any hazards and avoid significant risks.

■ **Method**

How to measure pulse and blood pressure

The pulse may be felt above the wrist (*Advanced Biology*, p. 356), taking a count over 15–30 seconds. Measurements of blood pressure have traditionally been made by use of a mercury sphygmomanometer (*Advanced Biology*, p. 359), which needed significant practice to use successfully. Now, a range of electronic instruments is available that simultaneously monitor blood pressure and pulse. Any limitations in accuracy in these are unimportant in a school or college context, because they are not being used in medical diagnosis, and they have the advantage of allowing investigations to continue during periods of physical activity. Their LCD display screens give visual prompts and error messages when steps are not carried out correctly. Omron instruments, for example, will, within about 20 seconds of installation, provide a digital display of systolic blood pressure, diastolic blood pressure and pulse rate; these are commercially available in pharmacists' shops as well as through biological suppliers.

Designing an investigation

Working in groups of two (or more), one person needs to be the experimental subject whose pulse and blood pressure are taken:

• after 5–20 minutes of quiet rest, sitting or lying completely still;

• after standing formally upright for five minutes;

• immediately after an agreed exercise task (stepping up on to and down from a stepping stool or bench for an agreed number of times each minute, for a fixed number of minutes), and at short intervals subsequently until the subject's pulse and blood pressure have returned to normal.

Quantifying cardiovascular efficiency

Various 'step test' routines have been designed. For example, in the 'three-minute step test':

stepping rate	$= 24$ steps min^{-1}
'step' height	$= 45$ cm
duration of exercise	$= 3$ minutes

Sit down immediately after completing the exercise. Count the pulse rate for 30 seconds after one minute of rest (the 'recovery pulse').

NOTE TO TECHNICIAN

An introduction to equipment for monitoring pulse and blood pressure is given in:

M Reiss (1989) 'Monitoring human blood pressure and pulse rate', *J. Biol. Ed.* **23**(2), pp. 80–2

Both N E S Arnold and Philip Harris publish catalogues that include pulse and blood-pressure monitors. The CLEAPSS organisation has evaluated these, and published its findings, made available to members.

Student groups will require use of an automatic, electronic pulse and blood-pressure detector, such as one of the Omron monitors.

If these are not available, a stopwatch and a mercury sphygmomanometer and stethoscope will be required. Considerable practical training may be needed for students to become familiar and skilled with this equipment. Alternatively, the blood-pressure reading may be taken by the teacher and recorded by the students.

Data presentation

The changes in blood pressure and in pulse rate from resting to strong exercise, and the profile of recovery to 'resting' state, can be presented as a table and in graph form.

If the 'three-minute step test' was undertaken, then:

$$\text{cardiovascular efficiency} = \frac{\text{duration of exercise (s)} \times 100}{\text{recovery pulse} \times 5.6}$$

where cardiovascular efficiency is assessed as:

0–27	= very poor;	49–59	= good;
28–38	= poor;	60–70	= very good;
39–48	= fair;	71–100	= excellent.

Conclusion

We vary widely in the time and energy we put into physical exercise such as working, cycling, swimming, training and taking part in sports and team games, on a regular basis. Can the results from members of your groups be correlated with the amount of 'training' undertaken?

Evaluation

- What part do conscious thoughts about heart rate (and thus pulse rate) have in influencing the observed rates?
- Does the answer vary with the individual?

References

CLEAPSS (1993) *Equipment and Materials for Human Physiology*. School Science Service, Brunel University, Uxbridge UB8 3PH

V H Heyward (1991) *Advanced Fitness Assessment and Exercise Prescription 2nd edn*, pp. 17–69. Human Kinetic Books

17.4 Audio-visual and microcomputing resources for learning

Studies of aspects of 'transport in animals' and the blood circulation in mammals may not lend themselves to 'hands-on' practical enquiry. They may be augmented by the use of video or computer-assisted learning. The resources available include the following:

The Immune Response and Immunization is a video presentation of the human immune system, showing how antibodies, T lymphocytes and B lymphocytes are produced, and how they defend against antigens. How certain diseases (including AIDS) elude the immune response is explained. The role of immunisation in the control and eradication of disease is illustrated, together with the operation of vaccines that confer passive or active immunity. The video, from Boulter-Hawker Films, is supplied with a teacher's pack.

ABO Blood Grouping is a CAL program available from AVP, using graphics and tabulated data to explain or simulate the process of taking blood samples, the use of antisera in blood tests, the principles of blood transfusions, an explanation of agglutinisation and the genetics of the ABO system. This software is available for BBC B and Master 128, Archimedes 3000 and 5000, and Nimbus 186 and 286.

Blood This program uses text, graphics and simulations to explain the immunological basis of ABO and rhesus blood groups. This software, produced by Sheffield Bioscience and available through Philip Harris, is suitable for BBC, Nimbus and IBM-compatible PCs.

17.5 The effect of temperature on the heart rate of Daphnia

As *Daphnia* is a small ectothermic animal, living in water, its metabolic rate is likely to relate very closely to the **water temperature**. The heartbeat of the animal may therefore be expected to increase with external water temperature.

Aim

To measure the heart rate of *Daphnia* at different temperatures.

Risk assessment

- Take special care when using electrical equipment (such as a microscope light) near to water.
- Take care when applying pressure to coverslips, as pressure may cause them to shatter into sharp shards.
- Otherwise, good laboratory practice will be sufficient to take account of any hazards and avoid significant risks.

Method

1 Cool some tap water by adding ice, to bring the temperature down to a suitable starting point (say 15 °C). Set up a microscope with a level stage. Half-fill a Petri dish base with the cooled water.
2 Transfer a large *Daphnia* from the culture to the special coverslip provided, using a paint brush. This coverslip has a tiny plastic ring attached, and the *Daphnia* is placed within this ring. Now place another coverslip on top of the 'cell' to retain the trapped animal, unharmed.
3 Gently turn this 'sandwich' over, holding it between your finger and thumb, and then place it under the surface of the water in the Petri dish. (At this point the lower coverslip may float away. This does not matter because a large *Daphnia* normally stays confined underneath the upper coverslip, as it sinks to the bottom of the Petri dish.)

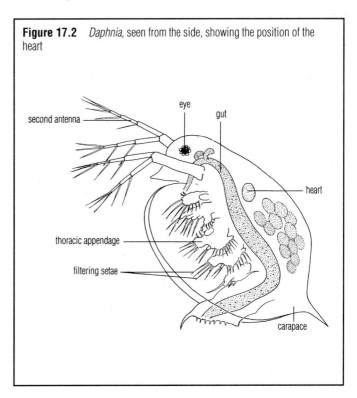

Figure 17.2 *Daphnia*, seen from the side, showing the position of the heart

4 Place the Petri dish on the stage of the microscope, and examine the *Daphnia* using the low-power objective, looking through the submerged coverslip. In the process of focusing, the objective lens will probably dip into the water; the lens will be unharmed, however, provided you dry it carefully at the end of the practical.

5 Locate the heart of the *Daphnia* (Figure 17.2), and practise counting heartbeats. To count easily, set up a basic calculator to add one digit repetitively (key in 1++, then press the = key in time with the heartbeat).

6 Once you have practised, measure the temperature of the water accurately, set up the calculator and count the heart rate for one minute.

7 Draw off some of the water and add warmer water to generate a higher temperature (by about 5 °C). If you take care, there is no need to take the animal out of the Petri dish. Once the water is mixed, the temperature can be accurately measured. Count the heart rate again.

8 Repeat the procedure, raising the temperature by about 5 °C each time, until you have at least five different recordings.

NOTE TO TECHNICIAN

The class will need a culture of *Daphnia* and each group will need:
- a compound microscope, light source, lens tissues;
- an animal cell (described above) and a spare coverslip;
- a Petri dish base;
- a paint brush;
- a small beaker for collecting water;
- a supply of ice and of warm water;
- a thermometer (or thermistor probe);
- a basic electronic calculator.

To prepare the small 'cells' for trapping *Daphnia*, take a piece of plastic tubing (3 mm internal diameter) and slice off a length of 1 mm. This might require a few tries before you obtain rings of even thickness. Place a minimal amount of 'super glue' on the ring and then press it firmly to a glass coverslip.

■ Data presentation
Present the data in a table and a graph to show the relationship between the rate of the heartbeat and the temperature of the water.

■ Discussion and conclusion
What relationship did you find between the heart rate and the temperature of the water?

■ Evaluation
What might be the advantage of an increase in the heart rate of *Daphnia* with increased ambient temperature?

Projects

17.1 Exercise and its effects on pulse rate
Measurements of pulse rate before and after standardised activity provide information on the 'recovery time' of the subject. Recovery time is a component of what is meant by fitness. How do recovery times vary in subjects who 'train' (that is, take regular physical activity) compared with those of more sedentary individuals of comparable age. Design the task with care, and trial it yourself and with a subject to be certain it is appropriate for the participants. Pulse rates may be measured in the subject's wrist by the experimenter, also holding a stopwatch.

Alternatively, analogue pulse meters with a scale visible to a larger group can be purchased.

17.2 Exercise and its effects on blood pressure
A study along the lines described above, based on the measurement of blood pressure rather than pulse. Digital blood-pressure meters are available.

Reference to both these projects
M Reiss (1989) 'Monitoring human blood pressure and pulse rate', *J. Biol. Ed.* **23**(2), pp. 80–2

Safety note: Remember, all exercise physiology work requires special vigilance on the part of the teacher and student. In all work with the human organism as 'guinea pig', bear in mind the precautions listed in Practical 17.3, Risk assessment, p. 206.

Problems and assignments

17.1 The structure and functioning of the heart

Examine the drawing of the heart and blood vessels (Figure 17.3(a)), and then answer the following questions.

1 In Figure 17.3(a), showing the heart in section, numbered arrows indicate direction of flow of the blood. Which of the following labels refers to which number?

aorta;	chordae tendinae;	inferior vena cava (blood from body/legs);
left atrium;	left ventricle;	left atrio-ventricular (bicuspid) valve;
pulmonary artery;	right atrium;	right atrio-ventricular (tricuspid) valve;
right ventricle;	semilunar valves;	superior vena cava (blood from arms/head).

Figure 17.3 a and **b** the human heart in section; **c** a graph showing pressure changes during the cardiac cycle

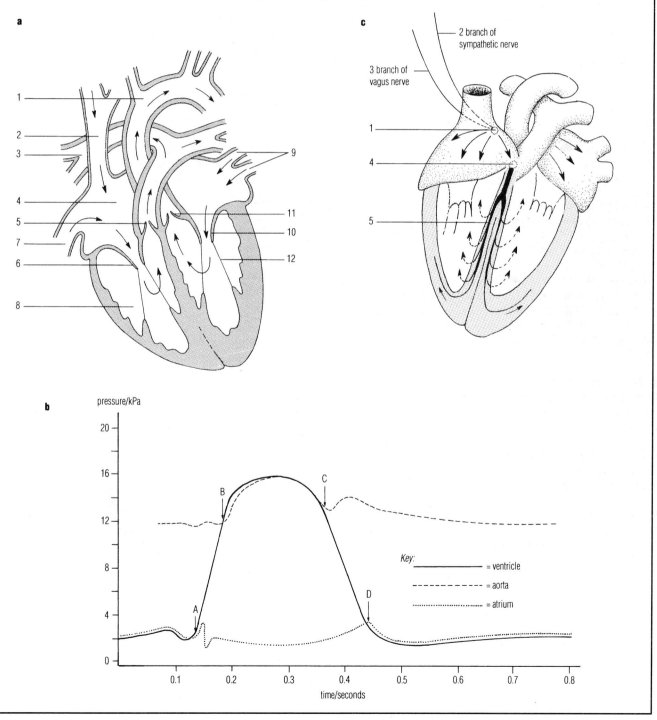

2 Where and what is the pericardium?

3 The right ventricle may be described as larger than the left. In fact, what is the difference in size of:

  a the muscular walls of the ventricles?

  b the blood-filled cavities of the left and right ventricles?

4 The cardiac cycle is the sequence of events of a heartbeat. In the cardiac cycle, state what is meant by the terms:

  a diastole;

  b systole?

5 In Figure 17.3(b), the pressure changes in the left side of the heart during a cardiac cycle are illustrated graphically. Select one or more letters on Figure 17.3(c), to indicate when:

  a the atrio-ventricular valve closes;

  b the semilunar valves close.

6 Calculate the pulse rate in beats per minute for this subject.

7 The heartbeat is myogenic in origin, but is regulated by the action of two nerves of the autonomic system.

  a What does 'myogenic' mean?

  b In what part of the brain do the autonomic nerves controlling heartbeat originate?

8 In Figure 17.3(c), which structure:

  a is known as the pacemaker (sino-atrial node)?

  b releases acetylcholine in the pacemaker?

  c is known as the sino-ventricular node?

  d is known as the bundle of His?

9 What other body system plays a direct part in regulation of the heartbeat, at least under certain conditions?

17.2 Arteries, veins and capillaries

Figure 17.4 shows the three types of blood vessel of the circulatory system. Examine these diagrams, and then answer the following questions using your wider reading and general knowledge.

1 Calculate:

  a the approximate diameter of the lumen;

  b the thickness of the wall;

of both the artery and the vein shown here, and state them in μm.

2 Explain how the structure of an artery can be related to its specific functions in the circulation of blood.

3 What structures (not shown here) occur attached to the interior walls of veins, and why are they needed for the successful operation of the circulation?

4 How would you define the term 'vein' (to differentiate it from an artery, for example)?

5 In the tissue around a particular capillary bed,

the hydrostatic pressure	= 1.2 kPa.
and the solute potential	= −1.4 kPa.

At the arteriole end of the capillary (entry point),

the hydrostatic pressure	= 4.4 kPa.
and the solute potential	= −3.3 kPa.

At the venule end of the capillary (exit point),

the hydrostatic pressure	= 1.7 kPa.
and the solute potential	= −3.4 kPa.

  a Is the net pressure at each point forcing water in or out?

  b Why is there a change in the hydrostatic pressure as blood flows through the capillary?

  c What causes the solute potential of the blood to be more negative than that of the tissue fluid?

  d What causes fluid to leave the capillary at the arteriole end?

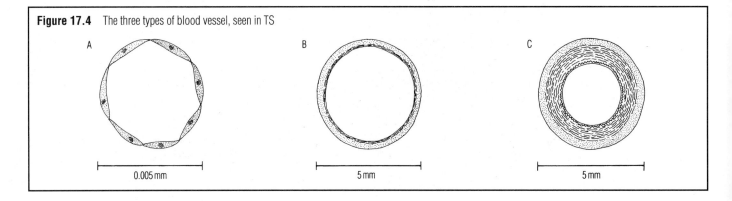

Figure 17.4   The three types of blood vessel, seen in TS

A   0.005 mm

B   5 mm

C   5 mm

17.3 Quick test

1 Distinguish between the following pairs:

   a haemocoel and coelom;
   b open and closed circulation systems;
   c single and double circulations;
   d atria and ventricles;
   e vena cava and aorta;
   f diastole and systole;
   g sino-atrial node and atrio-ventricular node;
   h arterioles and venules;
   i haemoglobin and myoglobin;
   j antigens and antibodies.

2 Explain the importance of the following:

   a respiratory pigments;
   b tissue fluid;
   c pericardium;
   d coronary arteries;
   e chordae tendinae;
   f heart sounds;
   g medulla oblongata;
   h pulse;
   i atherosclerosis;
   j lymphatic system;
   k carbonic anhydrase;
   l inflammation;
   m blood clotting;
   n phagocytosis;
   o blood transfusions.

17.4 Essay assignment

Select one of the following:

- Describe the major components of blood, and the parts they play in the function of transport.

or:

- Outline the events of the phases of the cardiac cycle. How is the heartbeat controlled to serve the body's needs?

18 Osmoregulation and excretion

Summary

Excretion is the removal from the organism of waste products of metabolism. Also excreted may be metabolites that are present in excess. What constitutes a waste product depends on the organism and its environment. The chief excretory product of green plants in the light is **oxygen**. The most important excretory products of animals are **nitrogenous waste** (ammonia, urea or uric acid) and carbon dioxide.

Osmoregulation, on the other hand, is the mechanism by which the balance of water and dissolved solutes is regulated in the organism. It results in the control of the **solute potential** of body fluids by regulation of the concentration of solutes (electrolytes and non-electrolytes). Plant cells with their cellulose walls are not vulnerable to excessive intake of water, but rather to water loss. In fact, plant tissues generally contain more water than animal tissues do. The availability of water influences the distribution of plants. Plants can be classified according to their ability to absorb the available water.

Animal cells, on the other hand, are not contained within a protective wall; they can be adversely affected by too much water as well as by too little. In animals the type of nitrogenous excretory product is linked to the **availability of water**; **ammonia** requires excess water for its safe disposal, and is excreted by many aquatic organisms. **Uric acid** can be excreted as a solid and is excreted by many animals adapted to a semi-arid environment. Animals have evolved a variety of excretory and osmoregulatory organs ranging from contractile vacuoles to kidney tubules.

The vertebrate **kidney** consists of millions of tubules (nephrons) that filter the blood in their Malpighian bodies. The volume and composition of the filtrate are modified as it flows along the tubule, both by **selective re-absorption** and by **secretion** of substances, resulting in the formation of a **concentrated urine**. Only birds and mammals have evolved a hairpin-shaped loop of Henle to the tubule. As a result of **countercurrent mechanisms** operating along this loop, extremely concentrated urine can be formed from the filtrate by the time it leaves the collecting ducts. The operation of the tubule and of the composition of the urine is finely controlled by the levels of specific **hormones** produced in the body in response to homeostatic **regulation of body fluids** by the brain.

Practicals and activities

18.1 Hydrophytes, halophytes and xerophytes; adaptations to the availability of water

(Investigation)

Grasses are all members of one family of flowering plants (Gramineae) and have an overall structural similarity that has become adapted to the differing degrees of water availability in their various habitats. A comparison of leaf structure in grasses from different habitats highlights some of the general differences that are seen in hydrophytes, halophytes and xerophytes.

■ Aim
To investigate the anatomical features shown in the leaves of grasses from habitats of different water availability.

■ Risk assessment
Good laboratory practice will be sufficient to take account of any hazards and avoid significant risks.

■ Method

1 Collect a specimen of a grass adapted to living in an aquatic habitat (a hydrophyte), choosing one that clearly grows with at least its roots normally under the surface of water (such as *Glyceria maxima*).
2 Cut sections of the stem, including the sheathing leaf base (the technique of cutting sections by hand is shown on p. 127). The leaf base will show much the same structure as the leaf lamina, but the stem provides a natural support enabling easy sectioning.
3 Transfer the thinnest sections of the leaf base to a microscope slide (discarding the stem sections), stain the leaf sections in a drop of toluidine blue for one minute, then mount them in dilute glycerol.
4 Prepare the leaf of a mesophytic grass in the same way; one which grows with a thick stem (such as *Dactylis glomerata*, wheat or barley) will be easier to section using the same technique.
5 Make a comparison of the leaves using these two slides with the prepared slide of marram grass (*Ammophila arenaria*). The latter grows on sand dunes and endures extremely dry conditions, and is therefore xerophytically adapted.
6 If specimens are available, then cord grass (*Spartina* sp.) can be investigated as a halophytic grass.
7 Comparisons should be concentrated on the following adaptive features:
   - the development of lignification within the tissues, such as the thickness of any lignified cell walls, and the development of sclerenchymatous or xylem tissue;
   - the presence of intercellular air spaces – for example, the presence of cavities within the tissue, or the development of large parenchyma cells with consequently large air spaces between the cells;
   - the extent to which anatomy suggests restrictions on the rate of evaporative water loss – examples could include the development of a thickened cuticle, reductions in stomatal numbers or their location in grooves or epidermal hairs;
   - special adaptative features, such as hinge cells that allow leaf rolling in conditions of water stress.

■ Data presentation

Tabulate the points of comparison, and make sketches of the tissue layout to illustrate the distribution of lignified tissues and intercellular spaces.

■ Discussion and conclusion

Discuss what trends are detectable in the anatomy of the grasses that live in waterlogged conditions compared with those that suffer considerable water shortage. If you have evidence from the examination of cord grass, add comments about its features, in relation to the main trends.

■ Evaluation

Although it may have been more appropriate to examine sections from living plants in all cases, comment on the difficulty that you might expect in sectioning marram grass.

18.2 Guttation and the soil solution

(Investigation)

Guttation is sometimes seen when plants are provided with warmth, high humidity and moist soil. It may occur because the solutes of the root cells generate a lower water potential in the root than exists in the soil water, resulting in an increased water uptake.

■ Aim

To design and conduct an investigation of the effect of the osmotic environment of the soil on the level of guttation in barley plants.

■ Risk assessment

Good laboratory practice will be sufficient to take account of any hazards and avoid significant risks.

■ Method

- You are provided with small trays of barley seedlings (maximum six per group) grown to a size where guttation from the leaf tips can occur, if suitable conditions are provided. Also provided is a 0.5 mol dm^{-3} sodium chloride solution, which can be diluted to provide a range of concentrations.
- You will need to design methods of providing suitable conditions for guttation to occur, not forgetting the need to make observations on the plants and methods of providing roots with differing osmotic environments. An experiment may last a few hours, at most overnight.

- Planning should include how you will obtain evidence of whether the plants are guttating or not. Ideally this would be quantitative.
- Ask your teacher or tutor if you feel there is other equipment you would like to have access to, explaining your reasons.

■ Data presentation

Present your data to show how the guttation of the plants has been affected by the osmotic environment of the soil.

■ Discussion and conclusion

On the evidence you have collected, decide whether the osmotic conditions of the soil play a part in determining the level of guttation. Explain your decision.

■ Evaluation

Provide a criticism of the technique you have used, and suggest ways in which you could collect data that was more reliable.

18.3 Structure and histology of the mammalian kidney

(Investigation)

The kidney is metabolically a very active organ. It consists of **two distinct regions**, which have different roles in the process of filtering the blood and regulating body fluid composition.

■ Aim

To investigate the gross and microscopic anatomy of the kidney.

■ Risk assessment

- Take care whenever you use scalpels.
- Wash your hands thoroughly after the dissection.
- Otherwise, good laboratory practice is sufficient to take account of any hazards and avoid significant risks.

■ **Method**

Dissection of a lamb's kidney

The gross structure of the lamb's kidney is similar to, but not the same as, the human kidney. It will help you understand the difference if you study the thick, transverse slices which have been prepared and also look at Figure 18.1.

1 Examine the external features of the kidney (Figure 18.1(a)), noting its general shape and the position of the renal artery and vein and the ureter (if the butcher has left these on).

2 Cut the kidney open by a longitudinal cut along the perimeter of the convex side (opposite to the hilum), but do not cut completely through the pelvis region (Figure 18.1(c)).

3 If you have managed to separate two more or less equal halves, you will see on each half a ridge of tissue partially obscuring the pelvic cavity. This is the renal crest, and corresponds to the pyramids you would expect to see in a human kidney. In effect, 12–16 pyramids have fused to form this single ridge. The transverse slices will confirm this.

4 Identify the opening of the ureter in the middle of the pelvis, and pass a blunt seeker through it to find the remains of the ureter.

5 In a fresh kidney, the cortex may look brown and the medulla a deep red, fading to white near the renal crest. Examine the cut surface with a hand lens. You may be able to see the glomeruli as red pin-pricks in the cortex, and the radial striations in the medulla showing the tracks of the collecting tubules and loops of Henle.

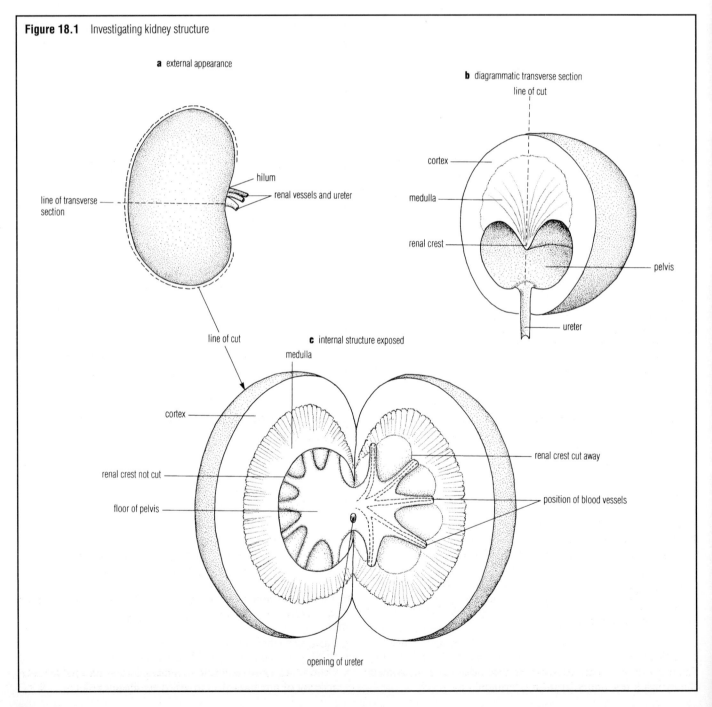

Figure 18.1 Investigating kidney structure

a external appearance

hilum
renal vessels and ureter
line of transverse section

b diagrammatic transverse section
line of cut
cortex
medulla
renal crest
pelvis
ureter

line of cut
c internal structure exposed
medulla
cortex
renal crest not cut
floor of pelvis
renal crest cut away
position of blood vessels
opening of ureter

6 Wearing eye protection, put a little hydrogen peroxide solution on the cut surface. There will be vigorous effervescence. After a few seconds, brush off the froth with a finger. The tracks of the renal tubules, collecting ducts and loops of Henle may be shown up by the strings of bubbles forming in them. The results will depend on the freshness of the kidney and how it has been cut.

7 Now cut away the renal crest on one half of the kidney. This will cut through the individual pyramids which contribute to the renal crest and reveal mounds of medulla, partially separated by the blood vessels (concealed under a layer of fat) running radially out to the cortex. Dissect away the lining of the pelvis, carefully removing some of the fat, to reveal the arteries and veins, which can be traced some way into the cortex. If the blood vessels have been injected, this will make the dissection easier.

Histology of the kidney

1 Examine the prepared slide under the low power of the microscope. Compare what you see with *Advanced Biology*, Figure 18.22, p. 393. Try to identify the glomeruli, the renal capsule (Bowman's capsule), the renal tubules, the collecting ducts and the loops of Henle (*Advanced Biology*, Figure 18.15, p. 387).

2 If the renal artery is injected with coloured latex (subsequently hardened by immersion in formalin), small pieces of the cortex can be dissected out and immersed in sodium hydroxide solution to dissolve away the tissues. The internal casts of the vessels, made by the latex, are left intact. It is not suggested that you should carry out this preparation but, if such casts are available, examine them (in a little water) under the microscope to see the form of the finer branches and the glomeruli.

NOTE TO TECHNICIAN

Each group will need (or will need access to):
- lamb's kidney (fresh or preserved);
- thick, transverse serial sections, cut from preserved kidney;
- dissecting board;
- large and small scalpels, scissors, forceps, blunt seeker;
- prepared slides of kidney sections;
- corrosion preparations of kidney vessels, if available, made as described on p. 430;
- a few cm^3 of 20-vol hydrogen peroxide solution, dropping pipette, hand lens (only if fresh kidneys supplied).

■ Data presentation

Record your investigation by means of annotated drawings of the gross and detailed anatomy of the kidney.

■ Conclusion

Summarise, in a list, those features of kidney structure which you can relate to function.

■ Evaluation

What is the principal difference between the gross structure of the lamb's kidney and that of the human kidney?

18.4 Water loss by woodlice

(Investigation)

Terrestrial animals are in potential danger of dehydration due to **evaporation of water vapour** from their bodies (and due to water loss in urination and defecation). Arthropods are the most numerically successful group of animals, distinguished by having a segmented body covered by a hard exoskeleton. Within this phylum are the crustaceans, most of which are aquatic: the woodlice (Figure 18.2) are, however, a group of terrestrial crustaceans. Traditionally, woodlice have been regarded as poorly adapted to life on land, but some species have physiological or behavioural mechanisms that control water loss. We assume the ability to survive in dry air is related to the degree of terrestrial adaptation of a species.

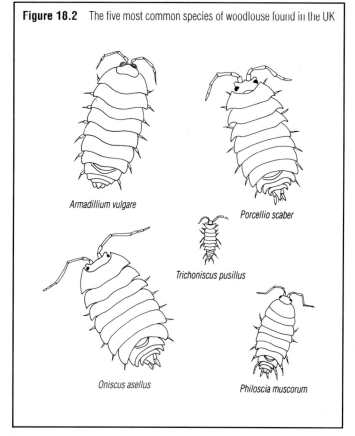

Figure 18.2 The five most common species of woodlouse found in the UK

Armadillium vulgare

Porcellio scaber

Trichoniscus pusillus

Oniscus asellus

Philoscia muscorum

■ Aim

To investigate the effect of relative humidity on the rate of evaporation from common species of woodlouse.

■ Risk assessment

- It is everyone's responsibility (both morally and legally) to ensure basic humane treatment of any living thing, in the laboratory or in the field.
- Good laboratory practice will be sufficient to take account of any hazards and avoid significant risks.

■ Method

1 Set up four experimental crystallising basins adapted for relative humidity studies of woodlice, as shown in Figure 18.3.

Figure 18.3 Apparatus to investigate the response of woodlice to different relative humidities

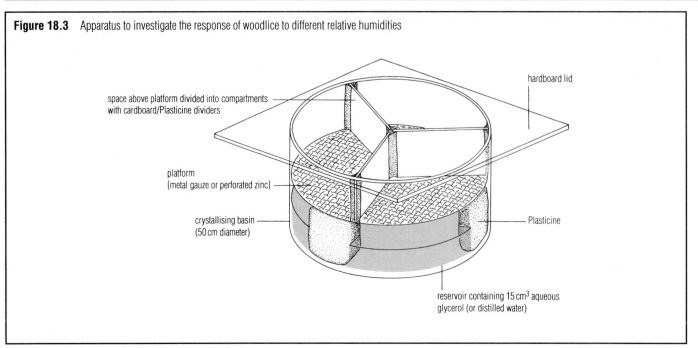

space above platform divided into compartments with cardboard/Plasticine dividers

hardboard lid

platform [metal gauze or perforated zinc]

crystallising basin (50 cm diameter)

Plasticine

reservoir containing 15 cm³ aqueous glycerol (or distilled water)

2 Into the reservoir of each chamber place 25 cm³ of one of the three aqueous solutions or distilled water given. The relative humidities, which should be added as labels to the respective basins, will be as follows:

aqueous glycerol at 85.50% = 40% relative humidity
aqueous glycerol at 70.35% = 60%
aqueous glycerol at 50.15% = 80%
distilled water   = 100%

3 Select samples of five woodlice of each of three species, weigh them in a Petri dish, and add them to a compartment in the crystallising basins so that at each relative humidity batches of woodlice from all three species are present. Keep the crystallising basins together on the laboratory bench (at about 25 °C) covered by a dark cloth.

4 At 20-minute intervals, uncover the basins, lift out the woodlice into a Petri dish, reweigh them, and return them to the same relative humidity environment. After 60 minutes (or after 20 or 40 minutes, if weight loss has been extreme), return the woodlice to their 'sandwich box' colony.

■ Data presentation

Record in a grid the data on initial and subsequent masses of each batch of woodlice of the three species under four different relative humidities. Plot a graph of the results for each species at the different humidities.

■ Conclusion

Is it apparent why one or more species lost less mass at the lower relative humidities than other species?

■ Evaluation

What are the most likely sources of error in an experiment of this type?

NOTE TO TECHNICIAN

Populations of woodlice of three of the five very common species are required, sufficient for each student group to work with samples of four times five (= 20) individuals of each of the species.

Woodlice occur in a wide range of habitats and can be found more or less anywhere there are microhabitats in which they can hide. Pitfall traps (p. 26) can be set overnight. Woodlice found can be identified from the key in:

S Hopkin (1991) *A Key to the Woodlice of Britain and Ireland* (Field Studies Council)

All British species are predominantly herbivorous, but they only rarely attack living plants. Instead they chew dead plant matter into tiny fragments, and also feed on fungi growing on leaves and faecal pellets. Each species can be kept in a clear plastic sandwich box into which a thin layer of soil has been placed. Add some pieces of bark and some leaf litter, and keep the culture moist (not wet) with a light spray of water once a week; add a few fresh carrot gratings at the same time. Kept in these conditions, woodlice will breed rapidly, and labelled cultures make an interesting addition to a laboratory display.

Each student requires (or requires access to):
- cultures of three species of woodlice (as above);
- plastic spoon for transferring woodlice safely;
- four 50 cm³ capacity crystallising basins;
- four pieces of hardboard for use as lids;
- four perforated zinc circular platforms, 50 mm diameter;
- Plasticine sufficient to support zinc platforms in crystallising basins at a height of 2 cm, and to support cardboard dividers on top of the platforms;
- 12 thin cardboard strips, 25 × 20 cm;
- piece of dark cloth to cover the four crystallising basins;
- 25 cm³ graduated measuring cylinder;
- stock solutions of aqueous glycerol at 85.5%, 70.35% and 50.15%, sufficient for each group to take 25 cm³ of each dilution;
- distilled water;
- stopclock;
- top-pan balance, to weigh to 1 mg.

18.5 Contractile vacuole function in Protozoa
(Investigation)

Freshwater Protozoa are hypertonic to their surroundings, and a **net inflow of water occurs**. One or more contractile vacuoles can be seen in the cytoplasm, actively removing water (with some ions, no doubt) from the cytoplasm. If their function is osmoregulatory, then change in the water potential of the environment should be reflected in altered rates of contractile vacuole functioning.

■ Aim

To investigate the activity of contractile vacuoles of protozoans in relation to water potential of the environment.

■ Risk assessment

Good laboratory practice will be sufficient to take account of any hazards and avoid significant risks.

NOTE TO TECHNICIAN

Each student group requires access to:
- cultures of living Protozoa such as *Paramecium*, *Discophyra*, *Vorticella* or *Carchesium*;
- teat pipettes and 1 cm³ graduated pipettes for transferring culture samples to slides;
- microscope slides, coverslips;
- microscope and lamp;
- 20 cm³ sucrose solution, 0.2 mol dm^{-3};
- distilled water;
- five watch glasses;
- 5 cm³ graduated syringe;
- stopclock.

■ Method
- You are supplied with cultures of one or more species of freshwater Protozoa having contractile vacuoles in the cytoplasm.
- Make temporary mounts of the species available, in the medium in which they are growing, and observe the activity of the contractile vacuoles. Can you measure the time taken for contractile vacuoles to form, fill up and empty?
- Set up a range of watch glasses with about 2.5 cm³ of dilute sucrose solutions at the following concentrations: 0.0, 0.05, 0.10, 0.15 and 0.2 mol dm^{-3}.

- To each watch glass add about 0.5 cm³ of the culture solution containing some of the Protozoa you are observing.
- After two to four minutes, make a temporary mount of some of the dilute sucrose/protozoan culture solution, and observe the contractile vacuoles in each case. Can you measure the time taken for contractile vacuoles to form, fill up and empty now?

■ Data presentation

Record your results as a table. If possible, plot a graph of speed of contractile vacuole operation against sucrose solution concentration.

■ Conclusion

Why do the rates of contractile vacuole operation vary with the external water potential?

■ Evaluation
- If ions, as well as water, are pumped out of the protozoan cytoplasm by the action of the contractile vacuoles, how are these replaced?
- If an inhibitor of respiratory metabolism was introduced, what might be the longer-term effect on these Protozoa?

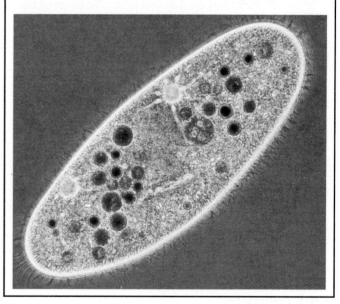

Figure 18.4 Light micrograph of *Paramecium* showing contractile vacuoles

Projects

18.1 Urea biosynthesis in liver slices

The use of liver tissue slices to investigate the synthesis of urea can be undertaken in a well-equipped laboratory situation, by students with an enthusiasm for biochemical issues.

Reference

A R Teal (1976) 'Urea biosynthesis using liver slices', *J. Biol. Ed.* **10**(4), pp. 185–95

18.2 Variation in leaf structure with habitat

The common features of the leaves of hydrophytes, halophytes and xerophytes can be investigated and compared with the features we meet in the leaves of typical mesophytes. This is a study of adaptation in response to particular environmental conditions.

18.3 Guttation and the effects of humidity and soil water potential

The phenomenon of guttation can be followed with soil solutions of decreasing water potential, and also in varying humidity. Can an 'advantage' of guttation for the plant be detected? What leaf structures are involved in the discharge of liquid water?

Problems and assignments

18.1 Osmoregulation and excretion crossword (Figure 18.5)

The clues

Across

1 The walls of the collecting duct and distal convoluted tubule, when ADH absent.
2 When the intake of water exceeds the body's normal requirements.
3 Surrounds the medulla.
4 Nephron with a long loop of Henle, extending deep into the medulla.
5 The convoluted tubule beyond the loop of Henle.
6 An immediately necessary treatment when acute kidney failure strikes.
7 A nitrogenous excretory product safe to dispose of only if excess water is available.
8 Primarily, the osmoregulation organelle in freshwater Protozoa.
9 The removal of the by-products of metabolism and substances present in excess.
10 The site of the countercurrent multiplier in the nephron.
11 This has walls fully permeable to water but only slightly so to sodium.
12 The capillaries associated with the loop of Henle.
13 A selective process, in the nephron, requiring energy from metabolism.
14 The first part of the nephron.
15 Adjacent streams, arranged to facilitate exchange between them.
16 From hydathodes, under high humidity.
17 Carries oxygenated blood to the kidney.
18 Molecular movement driven by the kinetic energy of the molecule.
19 High blood pressure, engineered in the glomerulus, causes this.
20 Composed principally of collecting ducts and the loops of Henle.
21 A variable property of the walls of the nephron.
22 A virtually insoluble form of nitrogenous excretory product.
23 By which the balance of water and solutes is regulated.
24 Hormone involved in the regulation of levels of sodium ions in the plasma.

Down

Make a fully annotated diagram to show the nature of re-absorption highlighted in the shaded area.

Figure 18.5   Osmoregulation and excretion crossword

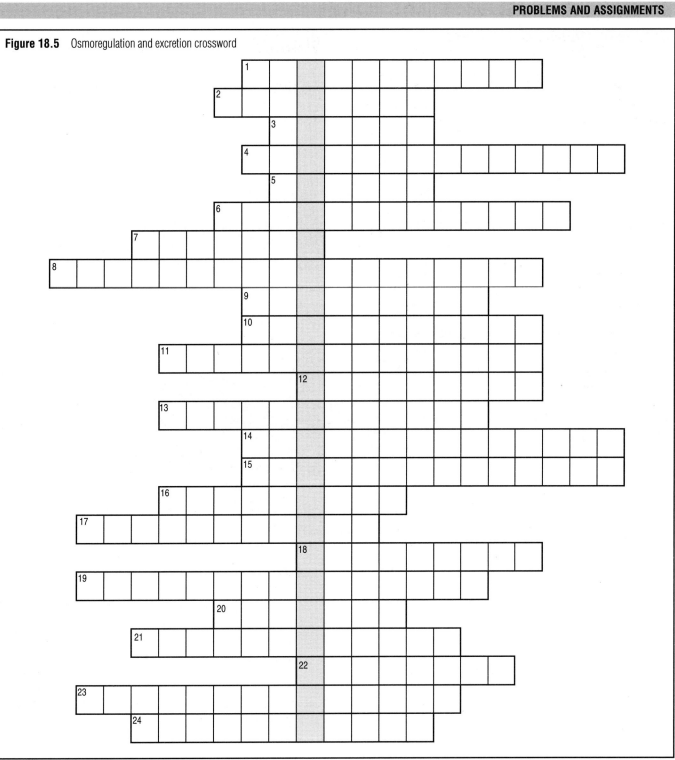

18.2 The functioning kidney tubule

The human kidney is about the size of a clenched fist and contains at least a million kidney tubules, each about 3 cm long. Figure 18.6 shows a mammalian kidney nephron, with the six distinct regions represented by letters A to F. Examine the diagram and then answer the following questions.

1 Name the regions of the kidney tubule, identified as A to F.
2 The ultrafiltration in the capsule is driven by the hydrostatic pressure of the blood plasma in the glomerulus (+9.6 kPa), less the water potential of the plasma solution (−2.5 kPa) and the hydrostatic pressure in the tubule (+2.4 kPa). Given these values, what is the net filtration pressure moving fluid out of the glomerulus?

3 Re-absorption of:
  a glucose;
  b water;
  c sodium ions;
occurs in the proximal convoluted tubule. By what process is each of these metabolites re-absorbed?
4 Mammals are capable of forming urine more concentrated than blood plasma. The loop of Henle, working with parallel blood capillaries (the vasa recta), is an important structure in this process. What are the roles of the descending and ascending limbs of the loop, in this process?
5 The permeabilities of the distal convoluted tubule and the collecting duct are variable. What happens to their permeability when the body's intake of water exceeds its normal requirements? What is the part played by ADH in this circumstance?

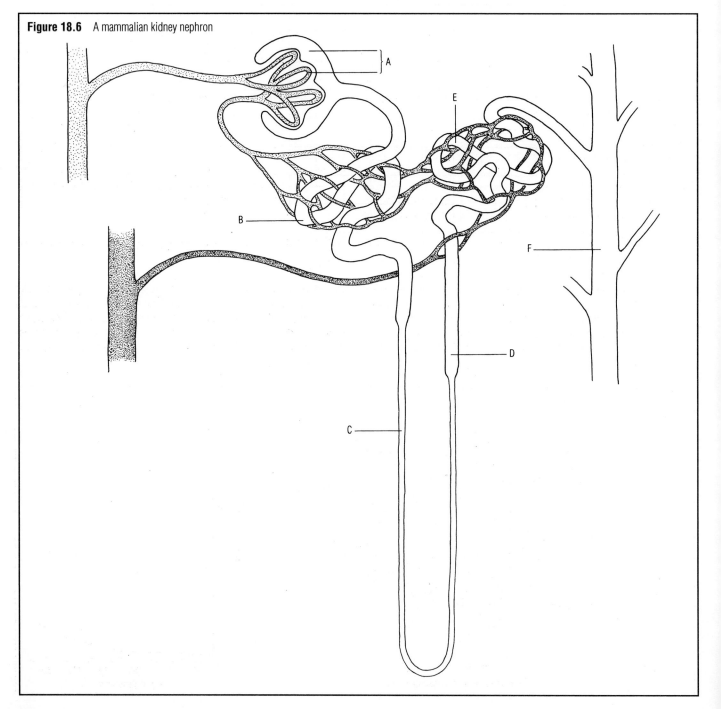

Figure 18.6 A mammalian kidney nephron

18.3 Halophytes: adaptations and survival

Halophytes are plants found in areas of high salinity such as estuaries and saltmarshes. Common examples are cordgrass (*Spartina* sp.) and glasswort (*Salicornia* sp.) (Figure 18.7). Data about germination of seeds of both plants are summarised in Table 18.1. Examine the illustration, and then answer the following questions, using knowledge obtained from your wider reading and general biological knowledge.

Table 18.1 The effect of salinity on percentage germination of saltmarsh plants

	Spartina townsendii	Salicornia europaea
Tap water	80	93
1% NaCl	21	45
2% NaCl	15	36
Seawater	3	38
5% NaCl	0	36
10% NaCl	0	12

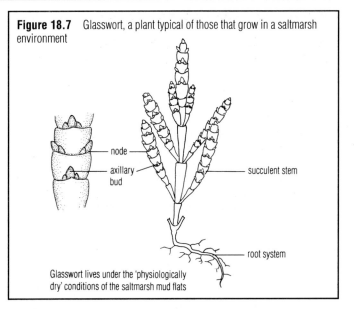

Figure 18.7   Glasswort, a plant typical of those that grow in a saltmarsh environment

node
axillary bud
succulent stem
root system

Glasswort lives under the 'physiologically dry' conditions of the saltmarsh mud flats

1 Saltmarshes are often part-flooded by seawater, and the salinity of these environments is noted for being extremely variable. What factors may contribute to this variability?

2 The external features of glasswort are shown in Figure 18.7. List the features that will favour survival in a saltmarsh environment, and say why each may confer some special advantage in these circumstances.

3 Table 18.1 illustrates the effects of tap water and saline solutions of a range of concentrations on germination in saltmarsh species.
   a How would you design an experiment to obtain reliable data on percentage germination in a similar group of plants?
   b Germination in both species is reduced by 10% sodium chloride solution. How do you think it has this effect?
   c Propagation in saltmarsh species like these sometimes occurs largely by seed but sometimes by vegetative growth (strong rhizome growth) as well. Which category do you imagine *Spartina* is most likely to fit?
   d How does vigorous growth of a rhizome achieve vegetative propagation (asexual reproduction), as well as healthy growth of the parent plant?

4 Adequate aeration to the root cells is important in all flowering plants, and this includes these species.
   a How does air reach the root cells in a common (mesophyte) weed such as dandelion?
   b In the anaerobic mud of a saltmarsh, how do root cells achieve aeration?

5 Saltmarshes are rich in many different ions, not just sodium and chloride (although these predominate). What are the sources of the ions in a typical saltmarsh?

18.4 The significance of xeromorphic features in a sand dune species

Xerophytes show features which may be expected to minimise water loss, in comparison with plants that flourish with an adequate water supply (mesophytes). Marram grass (*Ammophila arenaria*) colonises sand dunes around the coast. The structure of marram grass is illustrated in Figure 18.8. Examine this illustration, and then answer the questions below.

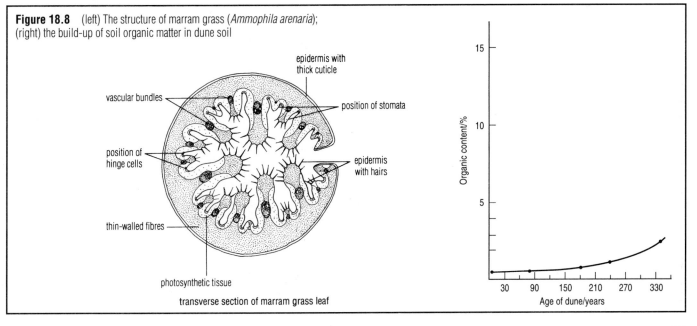

Figure 18.8   (left) The structure of marram grass (*Ammophila arenaria*); (right) the build-up of soil organic matter in dune soil

epidermis with thick cuticle
vascular bundles
position of stomata
position of hinge cells
epidermis with hairs
thin-walled fibres
photosynthetic tissue

transverse section of marram grass leaf

Organic content/%
Age of dune/years

1 Precisely what features of a sand dune habitat are likely to make it difficult for a mesophytic plant to survive there?

2 Marram grass, once established, exists as prominent tussocks of grass and, below the sand surface, a vigorously growing rhizome system.
   a What effects does this habit have on the dune system, and why?
   b How would you set up an experimental enquiry to investigate the relationship between marram grass growth and the changing structure of a dune system?

3 List the features of structure of the marram grass leaf that you consider xeromorphic features. Give your reasons.

4 The build-up of soil organic matter in dune soil is extremely slow.
   a What forms does soil organic matter normally take?
   b How is the percentage of organic matter in soil samples determined?
   c For the site that was the source of the data in Figure 18.8, approximately how many years did it take for the percentage of soil organic matter to double the value it had reached after 30 years?
   d Why is the accumulation of soil organic matter a highly protracted process in a dune system?

5 Some plants (not marram grass) fix carbon dioxide into organic acids in the dark, and then, with the stomata closed in daylight, release carbon dioxide from these acids for photosynthesis (these are known as CAM plants). How would this biochemical adaptation be advantageous to plants that grow under arid conditions?

18.5 Quick test

1 Distinguish between the following pairs:

   a excretion and secretion;
   b urea and uric acid;
   c hypotonic and hypertonic;
   d cortex and medulla of a kidney;
   e glomerulus and renal capsule;
   f ultrafiltration and selective re-absorption;
   g proximal and distal convoluted tubule;
   h loop of Henle and collecting duct;
   i cortical and juxtamedullary nephrons;
   j ureter and urethra.

2 Explain the importance of the following:

   a the wall of the plant cell in osmoregulation;
   b a contractile vacuole in freshwater Protozoa;
   c the waxy cuticle over the epidermis of a green plant's stem and leaves;
   d the excretion of solid uric acid by many insects;
   e the gills in osmoregulation in bony fish (marine and freshwater species);
   f width of the afferent and efferent arterioles of the Malpighian body;
   g re-absorption in the proximal convoluted tubule;
   h differential permeability in parts of a nephron;
   i a countercurrent system in the medulla;
   j effects of ADH on diuresis.

18.6 Essay assignment

Select one of the following:

- Osmoregulation and excretion are essential to survival in a freshwater protozoan and a terrestrial insect. Compare the mechanisms involved in both, relating these to the environment to which they are adapted.

or:

- By means of a labelled diagram, describe the gross structure of the mammalian kidney. Explain the roles of the processes of ultrafiltration, selective re-absorption, secretion and differential permeability in urine formation.

4 The Responding Organism

19 Growth and development

Summary

Growth results in an irreversible **increase in size**, in body mass and in amount of cytoplasm. **Development** is the change in the **degree of complexity** that accompanies growth. Growth and development are collectively known as morphogenesis, meaning 'origin of form'.

Growth is **measured** in terms of an increase in height, length, area or mass of the organism or part of it. Measurements of dry mass changes provide the most reliable data, but require the destruction of large batches of identical organisms. The results of growth studies can be expressed in ways which give different insights into the growth process. The usual plots are of growth, growth rate and relative growth rate against time.

A flowering plant grows from the embryo during **germination of the seed** at the expense of the stored food. The seedling undergoes primary growth to form the herbaceous (non-woody) green plant that is the primary plant structure. **Primary growth** is produced by meristematic cells at the tip of root and stem, the primary meristems. Woody plants, the trees and shrubs, undergo secondary thickening. The meristematic tissues responsible for **secondary growth** are the ring of vascular cambium in stem and root that forms secondary vascular tissues, and the cork cambium that forms the protective cork. Vascular cambium and cork cambium are lateral meristems.

Most non-vertebrates grow from fertilised egg to multicellular adult via several juvenile stages called **larvae**. When a larval form is different from the adult in structure and lifestyle the transition from larva to adult is abrupt, and is known as **metamorphosis**. The larval stage may be an important period of dispersal, growth and nutrition, and even of asexual reproduction.

Growth of vertebrates is mostly a more or less continuous process without abrupt transitions, but the frog does have a period of metamorphosis from aquatic to terrestrial form. Early development (**embryology**) involves **cleavage**, the division of a zygote into a mass of cells, **gastrulation**, the arrangement of cells into layers, and **organogenesis**, the formation of the organs of the body.

The **control of growth and development** is a complex process involving the DNA of the chromosomes, and the action of hormones and other chemical messengers. Growth is influenced by both **internal and external factors**, and is coordinated with environmental opportunities.

Practicals and activities

19.1 Differences between hypogeal and epigeal germination

(Data generating)

Dicotyledonous seeds are fundamentally similar in structure. The cotyledons are used by different plants in different ways, however, providing alternative strategies for the role played during germination.

■ Aim

To compare the structure of a sunflower (*Helianthus annuus*) fruit and a broad bean (*Vicia faba*) seed, and to characterise their different strategies of germination.

■ Risk assessment

- Use scalpels or razor blades carefully to avoid injury.
- Otherwise, good laboratory practice will be sufficient to take account of any hazards and avoid significant risks.

■ Method

1 Examine the external surface of the presoaked broad bean seed provided. The brown testa bears a black scar (the hilum), and the shape of the pointed radicle is visible through the testa at one end of the hilum. This is the location of a minute hole (the micropyle), which you can detect by drying the seed carefully with tissue and then squeezing it hard. A drop of water is exuded through the micropyle. Make a labelled drawing of the external features.

2 Remove the testa to reveal the two large cotyledons which, on the side of the embryo away from the radicle, can be prised apart, like opening a book. When you open them up you will find the plumule sandwiched between the cotyledons. Draw the embryo to show these structures.

3 Examine the fruit of a sunflower. This bears two scars: at the broad end, the pericarp bears a scar of the style, while at the pointed end is the scar of attachment to the inflorescence. Make a labelled drawing of these external features.

4 Since the sunflower fruit contains only one seed, as you peel off the pericarp the testa will come away along with it. The cotyledons of the embryo can be opened at the blunt end to reveal the plumule and radicle at the pointed end. Draw it in this condition.

5 Assemble a range of broad bean and sunflower seedlings at the various stages of germination, so that you can observe the sequence of development in each case. Tabulate the events that take place during the process of germination, giving the age of the seedling at each point. Note at each stage what structures of the embryo are growing, where the food for this process is coming from, and what part the cotyledons are playing in the development taking place. Particularly important is the fate of the cotyledons. In the bean these remain under the soil (**hypogeal germination**). In the sunflower, however, they are carried up to become the first photosynthetic surface of the seedling (**epigeal germination**) by the elongation of a region of the embryo called the hypocotyl. Make representative drawings of both seedlings to indicate the different fates of the cotyledons.

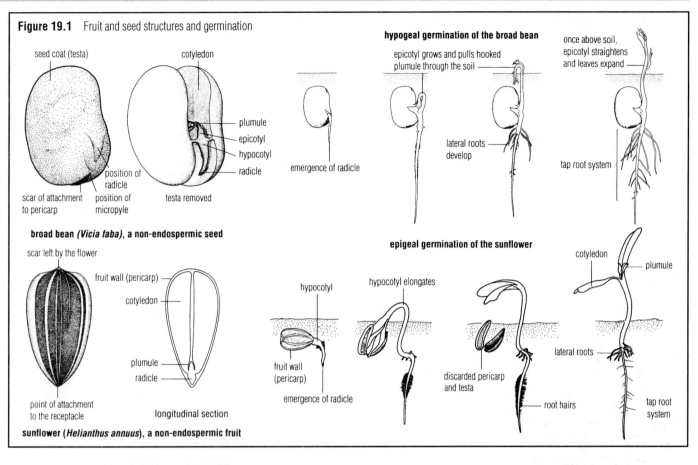

Figure 19.1 Fruit and seed structures and germination

hypogeal germination of the broad bean

epicotyl grows and pulls hooked plumule through the soil

once above soil, epicotyl straightens and leaves expand

lateral roots develop

tap root system

seed coat (testa)

cotyledon

plumule
epicotyl
hypocotyl
radicle

position of radicle
position of micropyle

scar of attachment to pericarp

emergence of radicle

testa removed

broad bean (Vicia faba), a non-endospermic seed

scar left by the flower

fruit wall (pericarp)

cotyledon

plumule
radicle

point of attachment to the receptacle

longitudinal section

sunflower (Helianthus annuus), a non-endospermic fruit

epigeal germination of the sunflower

cotyledon

plumule

hypocotyl

hypocotyl elongates

fruit wall (pericarp)

emergence of radicle

discarded pericarp and testa

lateral roots

root hairs

tap root system

NOTE TO TECHNICIAN

Each group will need:
- white tile, hand lens, scalpel or stiff-backed razor blade;
- a broad bean seed and a sunflower fruit that have been soaked overnight;
- seedlings of sunflower and broad bean at various stages of germination. The seedlings can be generated by sowing at intervals before the practical date (weekends need planning round). An appropriate sequence would be 14, 11, 8, 6, 5, 4, 3, 2 and 1 days before the practical. Allow one seed for every group plus a few spares sown in moist peat or vermiculite (which will wash off easily), in containers labelled with the date of planting.

■ Data presentation

Your labelled drawings will provide a comparison of the seed and fruit, and of the embryo shape. The germination sequence (including the timing of events) can be described in diary form or tabulated to contrast the events of epigeal and hypogeal germination. These are further brought out by the drawings of seedlings at an advanced stage of germination.

■ Discussion and conclusion

- Tabulate the differences between the epigeal and hypogeal germination shown by these seedlings.
- What are the possible advantages and disadvantages of each method of germination?

■ Evaluation

Explain why it is botanically accurate to speak of a sunflower 'fruit' and a broad bean 'seed'.

19.2 The role of the cotyledons in germination
(Investigation)

■ Aim

To investigate the influence of the cotyledons on seedling growth.

■ Risk assessment

- Care must be exercised in using scalpels.
- Otherwise, good laboratory practice will be sufficient to take account of any hazards and avoid significant risks.

■ Method

1 You are provided with some large dicotyledonous seeds which have been soaked in water for two days. Carefully peel off the testa of one, and prise the cotyledons apart. The embryo will remain attached to one cotyledon and the other one can be discarded. Prepare four cotyledons in this way.

2 Leave one half-seed intact; cut away three-quarters of the cotyledon from the second, and remove all but a fragment of cotyledon from the third. Finally use a fine (entomological) pin to prise off the embryo from the last seed (Figure 19.2). Measure the embryo and record its length.

3 Pin the four embryos and the attached cotyledons (or fragments) to the polystyrene block supplied, with the embryos almost touching the blotting paper and the radicles pointing downwards as shown in Figure 19.2. Moisten the blotting paper and then place the polystyrene block in the screw-top

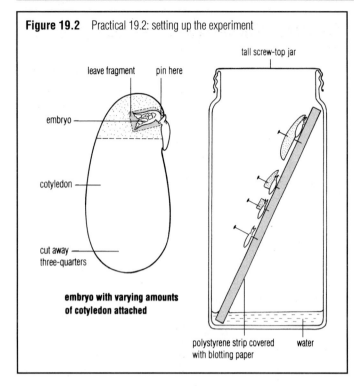

Figure 19.2   Practical 19.2: setting up the experiment

tall screw-top jar

leave fragment   pin here

embryo

cotyledon

cut away
three-quarters

**embryo with varying amounts
of cotyledon attached**

polystyrene strip covered   water
with blotting paper

jar containing about 10 mm water. Leave the jar in a shaded position for about one week.

4 After this period, make measurements on the seedlings to compare their growth.

NOTE TO TECHNICIAN

Each group will need:
- up to six seeds that have been soaked for two days; runner beans, French beans, broad beans or haricots are suitable (sterilisation is not necessary);
- large screw-top jar (a 200 g coffee jar is suitable);
- strip of polystyrene ceiling tile, cut to fit the jar, wrapped round with blotting paper or kitchen towel, which is then pinned in position (for full details see D G Mackean (1983) *Experimental Work in Biology, Teacher's Book*, p. 138, John Murray);
- scalpel or one-sided razor blade;
- four or five fine, rustless or entomological pins;
- tile or board for cutting seeds;
- ruler.

■ Data presentation
Make line drawings to show the appearance of each seedling, and construct a table to show the length of the radicle and epicotyl (or hypocotyl) and the number of lateral roots in each case.

■ Conclusion
What influence does the cotyledon appear to have on the growth of the seedling? What explanation can you offer? Has the isolated embryo grown at all?

■ Evaluation
Apart from providing food, what other substances might the cotyledon provide? How would you design an experiment to test the validity of your answer?

19.3 The region of plant cell growth at the stem apex

(Data generating)

The apical meristem at the tip of the stem cuts off cells that grow and enlarge, prior to differentiating into the mature cells of the primary stem.

■ Aim
To investigate the growth at the stem apex, examining the regions of cell division and of maximum cell enlargement.

■ Risk assessment
Good laboratory practice will be sufficient to take account of any hazards and avoid significant risks.

■ Method
1 Revise your understanding of the general structure of the stem apex, using C J Clegg and Gene Cox (1996) *Anatomy and Activities of Plants*, pp. 4–5, or *Advanced Biology*, p. 414.

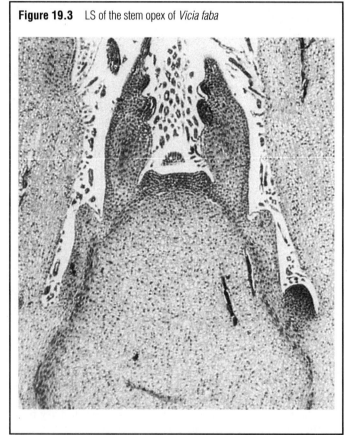

Figure 19.3   LS of the stem opex of *Vicia faba*

2 Examine a prepared slide of a LS of the growing tip of a very young stem, using medium- and high-power objectives. Identify the stem tip, stages in the formation of leaves, a site where a lateral bud is developing (in the axil of a leaf) and the region where cell differentiation is resulting in the formation of vascular tissue (much further down the stem).

3 By careful observation, identify the apical meristem region. Decide what features of the cells in this region you can use to differentiate it from the tissues immediately below. How many different stages in mitosis (*Advanced Biology*, p. 188) can you see, for example?

4 Make an approximate count of the number of cells that span the apical meristem, and also of those that make up the 'depth' of the meristem, from the tip of the stem to the base of the meristem, where cells are about to enlarge.

5 Using an eyepiece graticule in the high-power objective lens, make measurements in arbitrary units of:
- the diameter of a cell from the apical meristem;
- the length of a representative developing cortical cell of the stem and of its nucleus, selected from part of the stem where cell enlargement is clearly under way;
- the length of each of a line of 20–30 cells occurring down the centre of the stem, into the region of cell enlargement.

6 Using the stage micrometer provided, calibrate your 'arbitrary units' under high-power magnification (p. 98).

7 Assess the size of the interphase nucleus in meristematic cells and in cells which have enlarged and are ready for maturation.

8 Count the approximate number of cells that make the width of the stem at the point 20–30 cells down the stem.

NOTE TO TECHNICIAN

Each student group will require:
- compound microscope (with medium- and high-power objectives) and bench lamp;
- eyepiece micrometer (graticule) and access to a stage micrometer;
- prepared slide of a dicotyledonous stem (*Vicia* is suitable) in LS, stained to show nuclei and showing the regions of apical differentiation.

■ Data presentation
- Record numerical data in the form of a table.
- Draw to scale a tissue map of the stem tip in LS, from apex to region of differentiation. Label the map.
- Which cells below the growing point seem to retain meristematic activity? How do you know?
- Present a line graph of cell length from meristem cell to cortical cell (probably the region of maximum enlargement).
- Calculate the approximate number of lateral divisions (divisions that produce new rows of cells, down the stem) that occur between the meristem and the region of cell enlargement.
- Calculate the ratio of nucleus diameter to cell diameter, firstly for a meristematic cell, and secondly for an enlarging cell. What changes, if any, occur in the diameter of the nucleus after division, as cells enlarge?

■ Conclusions
- What processes occur between the meristem and the region of early differentiation, that is, in the region of cell enlargement?
- Does the process of cell enlargement start immediately cells are 'left behind' by the meristem, or is onset of cell enlargement delayed to some extent?
- What changes occur to the size of the nucleus as a stem cell differentiates?

■ Evaluation
What other growth and development processes occur at the perimeter of the developing stem?

19.4 Comparing the structures of young and old stems

(Investigation)

As plants grow taller they need increased support. In the youngest tissue, support is supplied by the turgor of the cells, but as the stem gets older cells develop which are more specialised in providing mechanical support.

■ Aim
A comparison of the extent of strengthening tissue in young and old stems.

■ Risk assessment
- When working with stains, avoid contacts with your skin.
- Take care when handling a razor for sectioning.
- Otherwise, good laboratory practice will be sufficient to take account of any hazards and avoid significant risks.

■ Method
1 Using the plant material provided, hand-cut transverse sections of both a young and an old stem (p. 127–8). Take care to keep the sections of the two tissues separate, and correctly labelled.

2 Stain representative sections, using toluidine blue or phloroglucinol with hydrochloric acid. This may be carried out on a slide or in a watch glass, depending on the numbers of sections to be stained (p. 127–8).

3 Make temporary mounts of both tissues, and cover them with coverslips. Examine your sections to identify all the tissues present. You may need to refer to *Advanced Biology*, pp. 218–23, or C J Clegg and Gene Cox (1994) *Anatomy and Activities of Plants*, pp. 6–9 (John Murray).

4 Make a careful comparison of the two stems seen in TS, noting the differences that have arisen with age. Some of your observations may be concerned with changes in the numbers and types of cells; in others you may need to look more closely at the thickness of the walls.

NOTE TO TECHNICIAN

Each student group will require:
- microscope (with medium- and high-power objectives), with bench lamp if necessary, with lens tissues;
- two microscope slides, coverslips and labels, watch glasses;
- paint brush, two mounted needles, razor blade or razor, filter paper;
- access to dropping bottles of toluidine blue or phloroglucinol and hydrochloric acid, and 30% glycerol solution;
- suitable plant material – for example, internodes of white dead nettle (*Lamium album*) or mint (*Mentha* sp.), although these may demonstrate some secondary thickening in the oldest part of the stem, or spider plant (*Chlorophytum*), although this is a monocotyledonous plant.

■ Data presentation
- Make tissue maps of representative portions of the young and old stems in TS.
- Tabulate the differences observed between young and old stems.

■ **Conclusion**

What are the significant differences in strengthening tissue that arise with ageing?

■ **Evaluation**

How does 'secondary thickening' differ from mere ageing of primary growth in a stem?

19.5 Studying insect life cycles

(Investigation)

In some species of insect, the larval stages (the juvenile form) are quite different from the adult form (**holometabolous life cycle**), and there is an abrupt change in development known as metamorphosis, prior to appearance of the adult. In other species, the larval forms are miniature adults, perhaps just lacking the wings of the adult (**hemimetabolous life cycle**). In both life cycles there is apparent 'intermittent' growth of the larva, caused by repeated moulting (ecdysis) of the external skeleton as the animal grows in size.

■ **Aim**

To investigate the contrasting life cycles of holometabolous and hemimetabolous insects.

■ **Risk assessment**

- Rearing the desert locust in captivity, in a confined space, can cause a health risk for some allergic individuals, and special precautions are required (pp. 180–1).
- Otherwise, good laboratory practice will be sufficient to take account of any hazards and avoid significant risks.

■ **Method**

Many insects can be reared in captivity for part or all of their life cycles. Suitable holometabolous species include:
- cabbage white butterflies, such as *Pieris rapae* (the small white) and *P. brassicae* (the large white);
- meadow brown butterfly, *Maniola jurtina*;
- oak leaf roller moth, *Tortrix viridiana*;
- green leaf beetle, *Gastrophysa viridula*.

Another insect with this type of life cycle, albeit with a rudimentary pupal stage, is the greenhouse whitefly, *Trialeurodes vaporariorum*, which can be cultured on 'busy lizzie' (*Impatiens* sp.).

Suitable hemimetabolous species include:
- the 'monster' stick insect, *Extatosoma tiaratum*;
- locusts, such as *Locusta migratoria* (the African migratory locust).

Most species selected for investigations can be maintained in a laboratory for all or most of their life cycle, with appropriate food sources (usually specific plant shoots cut and kept standing in water in a jar), in large glass (or transparent plastic) containers, the opening covered with muslin. Other types of cage can be constructed from aquarium tanks. Suppliers' catalogues list a wide range of insect cages. A home-made cage is shown in Figure 19.4.

■ **Data presentation**

Record in diary form information on the species, the source of eggs or larvae (or adults), the cage or container, the food source and its maintenance, together with observations on the

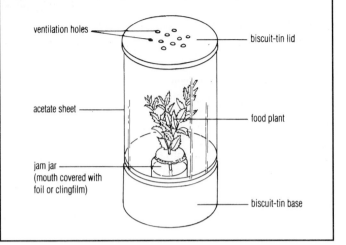

Figure 19.4   A simple cage for observing insect life cycles

ventilation holes
biscuit-tin lid
acetate sheet
food plant
jam jar
(mouth covered with
foil or clingfilm)
biscuit-tin base

growth, development, feeding, ecdysis and (where appropriate) pupation of the insects studied.

■ **Conclusion**

Present a comparison of the details of the life cycles of two contrasting species in the form of a summary table.

■ **Evaluation**

Is there value in studying animals in captivity when they may also be observed in the environment around the laboratory?

NOTE TO TECHNICIAN

It is necessary to select suitable holometabolous and hemimetabolous species. Both must be available as eggs or larvae, and a supply of the appropriate food source must be located. The following are sources of specific information, depending on the species, and on the space, time, and facilities that are available for this investigation:
- M Chinery (1993) *A Field Guide to the Insects of Britain and Northern Europe*. Collins
- W H Dowdeswell (1981) *The Life of the Meadow Brown*. Heinemann
- P W Freeland (1973) 'Ecology of the oak roller moth (*Tortrix viridiana*), a common woodland animal', *School Science Review* (March 1973) **54**(188), pp. 507–8
- J W Cox (1974) '*Gastrophysa viridula*, its life cycle and use in schools', *School Science Review* (December 1974) **56**(195), pp. 299–303
- W M Clarke (1976) *The Locust as a Typical Insect*. John Murray
- A Hitchon (1975) 'An initial study of the greenhouse whitefly *Trialeurodes vaporariorum* Westwood', *School Science Review* (September 1975) **57**(198), pp. 65–72
- J T Clark (1973) '*Extatosoma tiaratum* – a monster insect for schools', *School Science Review* (September 1973) **55**(190), pp. 56–61
- C F Stoneman, P W Freeland and A Whitney (1973) 'A locust cage and hatchery from plastic aquarium tanks', *School Science Review* (September 1973) **55**(190), pp. 86–8

A simple but effective cage can be constructed from a large biscuit tin (Figure 19.4). The sides must be extended with acetate sheet, and the lid fitted with ventilation holes. Inside the cage, a jam jar with water will support a shoot of the food plant.

19.6 Food use and growth in caterpillars
(Investigation)

Food is used to provide energy and to build and replace tissues. The percentage of food used in creating new tissues (growth) is a measure of the productivity of the organism.

■ Aim
To find out the proportion of food that contributes to growth in caterpillars.

■ Risk assessment
Good laboratory practice will be sufficient to take account of any hazards and avoid significant risks.

■ Method
The details of the method will depend on the number and age of the caterpillars, the variety of brassica plants used and the type of container. The method described here is just one possibility.

1 Line the bottom of a plastic bucket with a sheet of clean newspaper. Fill a jam jar with water and cover the top with aluminium foil, securing the foil with an elastic band. This reduces the chances of caterpillars or their droppings falling in the water.
2 Select three brassica leaves of suitable size and weigh them. If you are using leaves such as broccoli, the stalks can be pushed through the foil into the water. Cabbage leaves will have to be trimmed (before weighing) to create a stalk that reaches the water.
3 Place the jar with its brassica leaves in the bucket. Select 10–15 cabbage white caterpillars (half-grown caterpillars, about 20 mm long, are easy to handle) and weigh them. Place the caterpillars on the brassica leaves and cover the bucket with a cloth secured by an elastic band.
4 Examine the leaves after 24 hours. If they are nearly all consumed, complete the experiment as described below. If not, leave them for another 24 hours.
5 Use a paint brush to dislodge droppings from the leaves and the foil. Collect up the caterpillars and weigh them. Weigh the remains of the leaves, having dried the stalks. Finally, collect all the droppings and weigh them.

NOTE TO TECHNICIAN

Each group will need:
• a large container such as a plastic bucket or aquarium tank;
• jam jar, kitchen foil and elastic band;
• cloth to cover container and elastic band to secure;
• clean newspaper;
• two containers (plastic pots) to weigh caterpillars and their droppings;
• paint brush;
• a supply of brassica leaves (broccoli, brussels sprouts or cabbage, for example);
• access to a balance (10 mg).

■ Data presentation
Calculate the mass lost by the brassicas, the mass gained by the caterpillars and the mass of the droppings. Present your figures as a table, and calculate the percentage mass of the brassica leaves which has contributed to the growth of the caterpillars.

■ Conclusions
• What percentage of the caterpillars' food has been converted to new tissue?
• How can you account for the percentage that has not contributed to growth?

■ Evaluation
• What are the sources of error in this experiment? How could some of them be avoided?
• Apart from the outcome of feeding, what else could cause a change in mass of the brassica leaves and the caterpillars?

19.7 Early development in frog's eggs
(Skills and techniques/Data generating)

Frog's spawn becomes available in March and April. A small sample can be used to observe the early development in the frog. Steps in development of the amphibian egg are illustrated in Figure 19.6, p. 234 and overleaf (Figure 19.5) and the frog's life cycle in *Advanced Biology*, pp. 419–20 and 592–3.

■ Aim
To observe stages in early development in an amphibian.

■ Risk assessment
Good laboratory practice will be sufficient to take account of any hazards and avoid significant risks.

■ Method
1 You are provided with a small sample of frog's spawn in water. Using a binocular microscope (or dissecting lens with lamp), cut away the jelly from around one egg with the aid of fine scissors. Then pull away the toughest jelly from immediately around that egg, using two mounted needles.
2 Examine the embryo carefully. Depending on when the spawn was 'laid' and fertilised, and on the ambient temperature of the pond water, you should see a recognisable stage in development. This might include:
   • a fertilised egg early on in subsequent cleavage (Figure 19.6, stages 1–2);
   • later, with much larger cells at the vegetal pole (Figure 19.6, stages 3–4);
   • the blastopore and the slightly protruding yolk plug (Figure 19.6, stage 7);
   • the formation of the neural groove (Figure 19.6, stages 9–10).
3 The frog's embryo will survive without jelly around it for several days, provided you keep it covered with water. Turn off the lamp when you are not observing development. In this way you may continue to observe the development of the embryo for about three days.
4 In older 'eggs' and in tadpoles that have just emerged from the jelly (Figure 19.5), you may be able to observe some later stages:
   • embryo about to hatch, with 'sucker';
   • external gill stage, with 'cement' gland;
   • blood flow in the external gills (if a higher-power objective lens is fitted to your binocular microscope).
5 If frog's spawn is maintained in an aquarium tank in your laboratory, you may be able to observe the later stages of the development of the tadpole.
6 You must return the young tadpoles to the pond when the cycle of observations is completed.

Figure 19.5 The external development of the frog

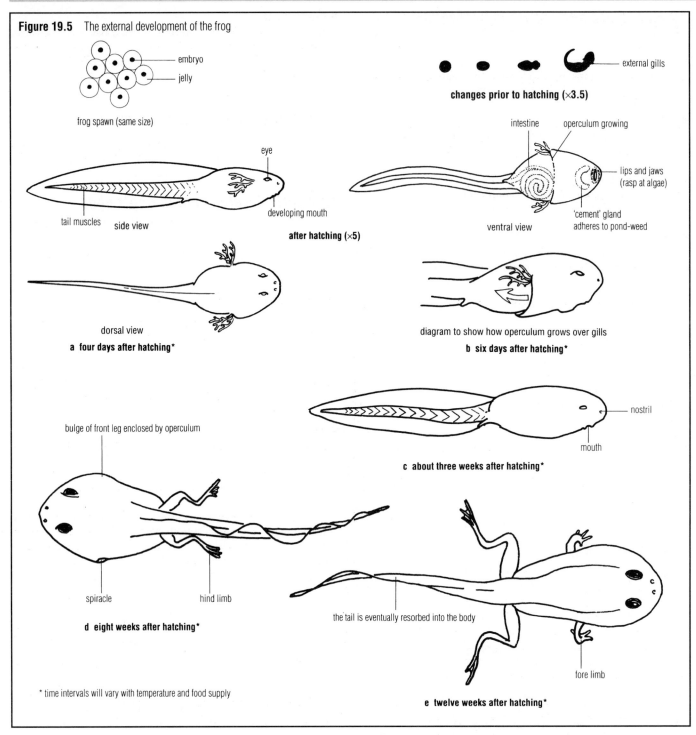

embryo
jelly
frog spawn (same size)

changes prior to hatching (×3.5)

external gills

eye
developing mouth
tail muscles   side view

after hatching (×5)

intestine   operculum growing
lips and jaws (rasp at algae)
'cement' gland adheres to pond-weed
ventral view

dorsal view
a four days after hatching*

diagram to show how operculum grows over gills
b six days after hatching*

bulge of front leg enclosed by operculum

nostril
mouth
c about three weeks after hatching*

spiracle   hind limb
d eight weeks after hatching*

the tail is eventually resorbed into the body
fore limb
e twelve weeks after hatching*

* time intervals will vary with temperature and food supply

■ **Data presentation**

Make fully annotated sketches of the steps in development you are able to observe.

■ **Conclusion**

If the development of the frog's spawn is followed over several weeks, using a laboratory aquarium, a diary of observations on developmental stages (with dates) can be maintained.

■ **Evaluation**

What environmental factors will influence the timing of development of frog's spawn?

Projects

19.1 The growth (productivity) of plants under artificial conditions

Measurement of plant growth is possible using batches of compact crops of 'fast' plants (*Brassica campestris*). Productivity may be determined in living plants by measuring increases in heights or leaf area index, and finally by measuring harvestable dry matter. This technique can be adapted to investigate the effects of, for example, a specific fertiliser regime.

Reference

Science and Plants for Schools *Growing Instructions for Rapid-cycling* Brassica campestris *(Fast Plants)*. Homerton College, Hills Road, Cambridge CB2 2PH

19.2 Percentage dormancy in seed stocks

All the seeds in any batch do not usually germinate immediately, or simultaneously. Collect seeds from two common weed plants (such as shepherd's purse, *Capsella bursa pastoris*, and dandelion, *Taraxacum officinale*), two common garden plants (such as edible pea, *Pisum sativum*, and sunflower, *Helianthus annuus*) and two very common hedgerow plants, all grown in the same locality. Using batches of 10 seeds, find the percentage that germinate under standardised conditions after harvesting, and after dry storage for an increasing period. What effect does cold treatment have on seeds that are slow to germinate? Do seeds need to have absorbed water before 'low-temperature' treatments are effective? Is water taken up more readily by seeds of species that germinate quickly?

19.3 Seed coat and germination

Seeds and fruits are contained within a 'coat', which appears to have a protective function. To what extent does this 'coat' inhibit germination? Compare germination rates in different species, batches of which are intact, or have one side of the coat 'sandpapered', or have the coat entirely removed. In the case of seeds that germinate more speedily with the coat removed, can you obtain evidence as to whether the entry of water or the escape of some endogenous inhibitor is responsible?

19.4 Enzyme production by embryo and endosperm halves of germinating seeds, and effects of GA

The mobilisation of the food store in seeds is triggered by hormones (gibberellic acid) released from the embryo as it takes up water and commences growth. The GA is believed to activate hydrolytic enzyme production elsewhere in the seed. This process can be investigated by culturing 'embryo' halves and 'stored food' halves of fruits like barley, cut immediately they have begun to take up water. The half-fruits are placed on starch/agar gel in Petri dishes. The halves which produce amylase will digest the starch. This is detected when the plates are flooded subsequently with iodine solution. What is the effect of having GA present in the starch/agar plates?

Reference

P W Freeland (1974) 'Determination of glucose production by embryo- and endosperm-halves of germinating barley', *School Science Review* (September 1974) 56(194), pp. 88–90

19.5 Growth of the sting of stinging nettles

How is the sting of the stinging nettle constructed? What cells are involved? How do discharged and undischarged stings differ in appearance? Does the appearance of stings differ with the age of the plant, or with position of the plant? If stings are discharged across an area of leaf, do other 'stings' regenerate? If so, how quickly?

Reference

A Fahn (1974) *Plant Anatomy*, Chapter 10. Pergamon Press

19.6 Structures of different papers

Investigate the differences in the composition of contrasting paper samples. Is starch used as a 'finisher' in all of them? Do the fibres in any of them still contain lignin? How different are the plant 'fibres' from which they are constructed (softwood tracheids or 'hardwood' vessels)? Do the majority of fibres run in any particular direction in some papers? How diverse in content is 'recycled' paper?

Reference

F W Jane (1970) *The Structure of Wood*. A and C Black

19.7 Investigating vertebrate embryology

Fertilised eggs of vertebrates undergo cell division and cleavage. Subsequently, the cells move about in a coordinated manner to make up the many-layered embryo. This process can be observed in the fertilised eggs of the hen or the frog.

References

W H Freeman and B Bracegirdle (1972) *An Atlas of Embryology*. Heinemann

M B V Roberts and T J King (1974) *Biology, A Functional Approach: Students' Manual*, pp. 258–60 (frog) and 261–2 (chick). Nelson

19.8 Inhibition of seed germination by the 'filtrate' from heather

Heather (*Calluna vulgaris*) is a slow-growing plant that nevertheless survives and dominates on heathland habitats. Does the plant produce any natural 'inhibitor' of germination in competing species, either when the heather is burnt (naturally occurring in heathland fires) or otherwise? Do other types of plant (for example, bracken, *Pteridium aquilinum*) produce substances that inhibit the germination and growth of seeds from other species?

References

P Lenz (1993) 'Inhibition of mustard seed germination by *Calluna* extract', *J. Biol. Ed.* 27(2), pp. 87–9

J Latto and H Wright (1995) 'Allelopathy in seeds', *J. Biol. Ed.* 29(2), pp. 123–8

19.9 Inhibition of germination whilst seeds are retained in the fruit

Seeds almost never germinate whilst they are retained within the fruit, even though conditions for germination are apparently present, and the seeds may be ripe and ready to germinate. Is an inhibitor present in the fruit wall? This hypothesis can be investigated in the tomato (*Lycopersicum esculentum*). The skins from tomato fruits of increasing age may be homogenised and extracted with ethanol, and the filtered extract absorbed on to filter paper. Cress (*Lepidium* sp.) or tomato seeds may be grown on these filter papers, with suitable controls, to find how many seeds will germinate in a given time.

Similarly, the germination of orange 'pips', freed from inhibitors present in orange juice, can be investigated.

Reference

J Gill and T Saunders (1985) 'A study of germination inhibitor levels in tomatoes during a period of post-harvest storage', *J. Biol. Ed.* **19**(2), pp. 112–13

19.10 Development in freshwater fish

A commercial fish hatchery/trout farm may supply fish 'eggs' for rearing in the laboratory. This requires a sink and running tap water, and it is worth attempting if the water supply is not overloaded with chlorine. To reach the 'fry' stage (when mouth feeding commences) normally takes about six weeks. Thereafter, how long the remaining fish can be kept depends on the food supply that can be organised.

Reference

E M Tuke (1974) *A Trout Hatchery in School.* School Natural Science Society

19.11 Growth in height in potted plants

A record of daily change in height of the stem of a growing plant can be made using a position transducer linked via a connecting box or Universal Interface to a computer, using appropriate software. With this system established, the effects of specific conditions on growth in height (light/dark, wavelength of light or the presence of a natural rhythm) can be investigated.

Problems and assignments

19.1 Growth of microorganisms

A liquid nutrient broth was made up from meat extract powder, glucose, potassium hydrogenphosphate and distilled water. Portions of this broth were transferred to conical flasks, which were then plugged with cotton wool and the plug covered by aluminium foil, prior to autoclaving. Three flasks were set up in this way.

The flasks were then inoculated with a bacterium, *Escherichia coli*, by the addition of 1 cm^3 of culture containing approximately 4000 bacteria per cm^3. The inoculated flasks were then incubated at 37 °C, and the numbers of bacteria counted in representative samples each hour.

It was found that the number of cells had risen to only 5000 per flask after the first two hours. Subsequently, the numbers of cells increased very quickly; in fact, they doubled every 30 minutes for the next three hours. Then subsequent growth became again very much slower, and by the time the cultures were six hours old the bacterial numbers had only increased by a further 10%. Finally, in the eight-hour-old cultures there was no further increase in numbers of bacteria at all.

1 The nutrient broth sustained rapid growth of the bacteria. Make a list of the essential nutrients required by such bacteria, and say which of the components of the broth provide each nutrient.
2 In what ways may the composition of the culture medium change, during the course of the experiment?
3 State the equipment involved and the steps by which a microbiologist estimates the numbers of bacteria per culture (at hourly intervals, for example).
4 Calculate the numbers of bacteria present as a result of the growth rate during the period between two and five hours of incubation, using the formula:

$$B_t = B_0 \times 2^n$$

where B_t = number of bacteria at the end of time t
B_0 = number of bacteria at the beginning of the time interval
t = time in minutes
n = number of generations.

5 a The final increase resulted in only 10% more bacteria. What is the final number of bacteria present?
 b Plot a graph of bacterial numbers against time, using the values at time 0, at 2 hours, 5 hours and 6 hours, and drawing the most likely curve.
6 What factors account for the rates of growth in bacterial numbers:
 a between 0 and 2 hours?
 b between 5 and 6 hours?
7 What safety precautions would need to be taken before, during and after this experiment by the microbiologist handling these cultures?
8 What was the reason for taking readings from three flasks, rather than just one?

19.2 Analysing growth data by means of the Spearman rank correlation coefficient

Sometimes in biological research we collect measurements in pairs for each individual of a sample. For example, in a study of growth of wild rabbits, the mass attained by individual rabbits feeding in different pastures was measured and so too was the quality of food available to each. Look at the data in Table 19.1.

Table 19.1 Rabbit body mass data

Rabbit	Body mass/kg	Pasture quality/g m^{-2}*
1	1.50	12.5
2	2.00	20.0
3	2.38	37.5
4	1.60	10.0
5	2.45	35.0
6	2.20	25.0
7	2.35	40.0
8	2.25	30.0
9	1.95	27.5
10	1.90	32.5

* Dry mass of vegetation produced in the growing season, to the nearest 0.5 g

Looking at Table 19.1, it seems as if the rabbits are heavier where the pasture quality is better. Does a significant correlation exist between the two variables? A way to answer this is to work out the Spearman rank correlation coefficient (r_s). The null hypothesis is that there is no correlation between body mass and pasture quality. (A statistical package or calculator may be programmed to work this out for you.)

Steps

1 Using graph paper, draw a scatter diagram of one set of measurements against the other, to see if a correlation appears to exist. The closer the dots come to lying on a straight line, the closer is the relationship. If the line slopes up from left to right the correlation is positive; if the line slopes down from left to right the correlation is negative. If the points are dotted around with no clear pattern, the two sets of measurement are independent. It is rare in biological research to find perfect correlations; the dots are usually quite scattered. Certainly, if the points are all squashed up together, or occur in some U-shaped curve, do not proceed. Otherwise, proceed to step 2.

Table 19.2 Rabbit body mass data: calculation

1 Rabbit	2 Body mass/kg	3	4 Pasture quality/ g m^{-2}	5	6 Difference in ranks (D)	7 D^2
1	1.50		12.5			
2	2.00		20.0			
3	2.38		37.5			
4	1.60		10.0			
5	2.45		35.0			
6	2.20		25.0			
7	2.35		40.0			
8	2.25		30.0			
9	1.95		27.5			
10	1.90		32.5			

$$\Sigma D^2 =$$

2 Enter the data from Table 19.1 into a new table, of the form shown in Table 19.2. Rank each set of measurements, recording the rank order (starting with the smallest value) in columns 3 and 5. (If any two measurements have the same value, then give them the average for their rank: for example, two readings at 1.6 in column 2 of Table 19.2 would share a ranking of 2.5, and the next highest value would be at ranking 4.)

233

Then work out the difference in the ranks by subtracting each rank in column 5 from the corresponding rank in column 3, and record these differences in column 6.

Add up the differences as a check on your accuracy (the total should be zero).

Next, square each of the differences, and record these values in column 7. Add up the squared differences. The total is ΣD^2.

3 The number of pairs of measurements in the sample is n. Work out:

$$n(n^2 - 1) =$$

4 The Spearman rank correlation coefficient r_s is given by:

$$r_s = 1 - \frac{6\Sigma D^2}{n(n^2 - 1)} =$$

5 A correlation coefficient close to $+1$ means there is a strong positive relationship between the variables (that is, an increase in one

variable is accompanied by an increase in the other). A correlation coefficient close to -1 means there is a strong negative relationship between the two variables (an increase in one variable is accompanied by a decrease in the other variable). A correlation coefficient close to 0 means a relationship is non-existent. Remember, correlation does not establish causation. The relationship could be a coincidence, or the phenomena may be independently dependent on another factor.

Compare your value of r_s with the critical values for the Spearman rank correlation coefficient in Table A2.4 (p. 437) for a test with a sample size of 10 pairs ($n = 10$). If the calculated value lies at or above the critical value at the 5% level of significance, then the null hypothesis is rejected.

In fact, the critical value of r_s (where $n = 10$) is
0.648 at the 5% significance level;
0.746 at the 2% significance level;
0.794 at the 1% significance level.

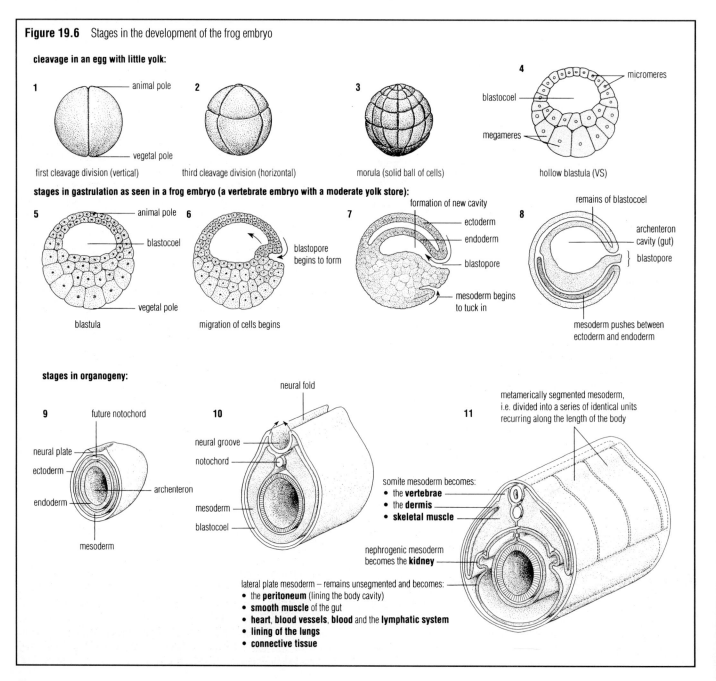

Figure 19.6   Stages in the development of the frog embryo

6 Is the null hypothesis rejected or confirmed? If rejected, can you think of further investigations that might be carried out to confirm that body mass in the rabbit is directly related to pasture productivity?

References

N Chalmers and P Parker (1989) *The OU Project Guide. Fieldwork and Statistics for Ecological Projects*, pp. 79–86. Field Studies Council

A Cadogan and R Sutton (1994) *Maths for Advanced Biology*, pp. 29–32. Nelson

19.3 Development of the vertebrate embryo

Details of amphibian development are not typical of the development of other groups of vertebrates, but all vertebrate embryos do go through similar stages. In Figure 19.6, steps in the development of an amphibian embryo are illustrated. The amphibian egg is one in which most stored food is found in the cytoplasm of one half of the cell (referred to as the vegetal pole of the cell). In the bird, the food store (yolk) is in a sac, external to the embryo.

1 What event triggers the first cell division of cleavage (the first stage in embryo development)?

2 What causes the unevenness of the divisions that form the cells of the blastula of an amphibian, with many smaller cells found in the end known as the animal pole and a few larger cells at the vegetal pole?

3 During cleavage many divisions produce a mass of cells. What happens to the size of the embryo at this stage?

4 After cleavage, the next step in embryo development is gastrulation. Here, coordinated movements of cells end in the formation of a three-layered embryo. It has been said that the cells of the vertebrate body acquire a 'sense of position' early in development. Early 'instructions' in the embryo to build particular regions of the body, and to move to the right place during gastrulation, are permanently retained.

  a What sorts of evidence might a research biologist use to support this statement?

  b In the frog, if the cells of an eight-cell blastula (Figure 19.6, step 2) are separated, each one can develop into a complete frog. However, at a later stage in an early embryo (Figure 19.6, step 10), if a piece of notochord is transplanted to a different position the ectoderm directly above it rolls up to form a tube. Suggest explanations to reconcile these apparently conflicting observations, and comment on the possible role of the notochord in amphibian development.

  c In human embryos at the six-cell stage, two cells can be removed to test for gender and for genetic defects. If the latter tests prove satisfactory, the remaining four cells may be returned to the mother's uterus. Why may this procedure be carried out at the six-cell stage but no later?

5 In an amphibian, the embryo becomes two-layered by the invagination (infolding) of sheets of cells, whereas in a bird embryo the cells migrate into position. What do you think is the principal cause of this difference in the process of gastrulation in an amphibian and a bird?

6 Cells of the gastrula continue to divide and move about, forming a triploblastic structure. What does 'triploblastic' mean?

7 List the major tissues formed by:

  a the ectoderm,

  b the mesoderm, and

  c the endoderm.

8 At the end of gastrulation the embryo is larger and now tubular. The next stage is called organogeny. What does this involve? Give an example.

9 During organogeny, the embryo develops metamerically segmented mesoderm (mesoderm divided into a series of identical units recurring along the length of the body). What features of adult vertebrates show evidence of this segmentation?

10 Two processes in development mask any underlying segmentation of the vertebrate body, particularly in amphibians, reptiles, birds and mammals. Which processes are these?

19.4 Quick test

1 Distinguish between the following pairs:

  a growth and development;

  b fresh mass and dry mass measurements of growth;

  c growth rate and relative growth rate;

  d lag phase and log phase in growth;

  e allometric and isometric growth;

  f limited and unlimited growth;

  g plumule and radicle;

  h epigeal and hypogeal germination;

  i apical and lateral meristems;

  j primary and secondary growth of plants;

  k endodermis and pericycle;

  l cleavage and gastrulation;

  m blastocoel and archenteron;

  n neural plate and neural tube;

  o holometabolous life cycles and hemimetabolous life cycles.

2 Explain the role of the following:

  a cell specialisation in multicellular organisms;

  b the haemocytometer in the measurement of growth of microorganisms;

  c the aleurone layer in the stored 'food' of the seed;

  d the procambial strand in vascular bundle formation;

  e medullary rays in secondary wood;

  f fertilisation in the initiation of cleavage;

  g yolk reserves in the fertilised vertebrate egg;

  h gastrulation in the formation of the embryo;

  i mesoderm in vertebrate embryology;

  j larval stages in the life cycle of non-vertebrates.

19.5 Essay assignment

Select one of the following:

• What are meristems and where are they found in plants? Describe the changes in a cell from a meristem as it differentiates into a xylem vessel element. How are the structures of xylem vessels and sieve tubes related to their functions?

or:

• What are the common features of juvenile or larval forms in the non-vertebrate animals, and what roles may they fill in the life cycle?

    Explain what is meant by metamorphosis. In what groups of animals does it occur?

20 Response and coordination in plants

Summary

Living things detect changes in their environment and respond. Plant responses are mostly slow **growth movements**. For example, young stems grow towards the light by growing faster on the darkened side. A response whose direction is related to the direction of the stimulus is called a **tropism**. The young stem is said to be positively phototropic. Stems and roots also respond to gravity (geotropism).

In **nastic responses** the response of a plant organ is not determined by the direction of the stimulus. One example is the closing up of a flower in the dark and its re-opening in the light (photonasty).

Early investigations of plant responses led to the discovery of **plant growth substances**. Subsequent investigations have added to the number of known active substances, which now include **auxins**, **gibberellins**, **cytokinins**, **abscisic acid** and **ethene**. Plant growth substances interact positively (synergism) or negatively (antagonism) in the control of growth and development.

The major **phases of plant growth and development**, such as germination, flowering, dormancy and leaf fall, occur at **environmentally favourable times**, and are mostly triggered by changes in day-length or in seasonal temperatures. Plant growth substances appear to be involved. A pigment, phytochrome, is involved in the light-triggered changes.

Many synthetic plant growth substances are used in industry, commerce and research. For example, a huge industry is centred on the production and use of herbicides.

Practicals and activities

20.1 Auxin and the growth of plant organs
(Data generating)

The leaf sheath (coleoptile) of an oat seedling contains cells which elongate when stimulated by naturally occurring plant growth substances called auxins. The chemical indolylethanoic acid (indoleacetic acid, IAA) is the most common auxin. IAA solutions can be used to investigate the relative effects of different externally applied concentrations of growth regulator.

■ Aim
To find the concentration of auxin that generates maximum growth response in oat coleoptiles.

■ Risk assessment
Good laboratory practice will be sufficient to take account of any hazards and avoid significant risks.

■ Method
1 Label the bases of six Petri dishes A to F. Place $18\,cm^3$ of 2% sucrose solution in each dish and cover with the lid. Add $2\,cm^3$ of IAA solution ($100\,mg\,dm^{-3}$) to dish A, and stir it thoroughly to mix.
2 Make a 10-fold dilution series. Start by transferring $2\,cm^3$ of the solution from dish A to dish B. Mix thoroughly. Then transfer $2\,cm^3$ of B to C and, again mixing before each transfer, $2\,cm^3$ from C to D, and $2\,cm^3$ from D to E. F is a control which contains no IAA.
3 Working in dim light, collect a pot of oat seedlings grown in the dark to the stage of having fully developed coleoptiles. Using a pair of scissors, select and cut 10 coleoptiles at their base, and return the pot to darkness. Do not use any coleoptile if the tip is broken by the first leaf growing up inside.
4 Line the coleoptiles up with their tips against the flat side of a ruler, as closely parallel as possible. Use a cutting device as shown in Figure 20.1 to remove an exact 10 mm of the coleoptile without the 3 mm of the tip. Using a paint brush, sweep them off the cutter into Petri dish A and place it in the dark. Repeat for all the other dishes, putting 10 coleoptiles in each dish.
5 Keep the dishes in a lightproof incubator at 27 °C for 24 hours, then remove and record the length of each coleoptile independently to the nearest 0.5 mm. For each concentration, calculate the mean length of the coleoptiles.

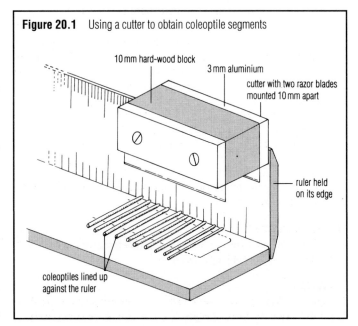

Figure 20.1   Using a cutter to obtain coleoptile segments

10 mm hard-wood block

3 mm aluminium

cutter with two razor blades mounted 10 mm apart

ruler held on its edge

coleoptiles lined up against the ruler

■ Data presentation

Subtract the mean length of the control coleoptiles from the mean of the other samples, since this represents the growth or osmotic extension that would have taken place in all samples during the incubation period. Plot the graph of the increase in coleoptile length against auxin concentration.

■ Discussion and conclusion

What concentration of auxin appears to produce maximal stimulation of coleoptile elongation?

■ Evaluation

Why is it unsafe to assume that the concentration of growth regulator in the external medium producing maximum stimulation is also the concentration producing maximum elongation when the auxin is produced within the cell?

20.2 Indoleacetic acid and leaf abscission

(Investigation)

Leaf fall results from the formation of an organised abscission layer at the base of the leaf stalk (petiole). It is a process characteristic of many woody plants in autumn, and is a component of the senescence process of ageing leaves. The ageing leaf no longer produces IAA, and this factor is important in initiating abscission. In fact, the ageing leaf also produces ethene, a gaseous plant growth regulator. Ethene from ageing leaves is believed to speed up leaf fall. Thus leaf fall, like other aspects of plant growth regulation, may be attributed to a change in the balance of two or more hormones, in the intact organism.

■ Aim

To investigate the effect of externally applied IAA on abscission, using potted plants.

■ Risk assessment

Good laboratory practice will be sufficient to take account of any hazards and avoid significant risks.

■ Method

Design an investigation of the effect of concentration of IAA on leaf fall in one or more species of appropriate, potted plants.

- Potted plants available in the laboratory that may be used include geranium (*Pelargonium* sp.), *Coleus blumei*, 'busy lizzie' (*Impatiens* sp.) and tomato (*Lycopersicum esculentum*). Plants selected should have 10 to 14 mature, healthy leaves (exclude the youngest two to four leaves, at the tip of the stem). You are provided with two concentrations of IAA in lanolin together with pure lanolin.
- For the plants you select, devise a mechanism of distributing the treatments of leaves so that leaves of different ages are used for all treatments.
- Leaves to be treated with lanolin paste should have the leaf blade (lamina) cut off at the point of attachment to the stalk. The exposed cut surface of the stalk may be treated by covering with IAA in lanolin, either 0.1% (treatment 1) or 1.0% (treatment 2), or with lanolin alone (treatment 3). About 25% of the leaves should be kept intact on each plant used. The treatments applied to cut leaf stalks may be recorded by hanging labelled paper ring reinforcements on the base of the stump.
- Keep careful records of the treatments applied and the positions of the leaves concerned. The plants should be maintained under favourable growing conditions (possibly a greenhouse, or the laboratory window area), making sure that they are appropriately watered, and that illumination is even.
- Examine the plants at weekly intervals, and make a record of the conditions of the leaf stalks at weeks three and six.

■ Data presentation

What percentage of the leaf stalks had undergone abscission at three weeks and at six weeks, for each of the treatments?

■ Conclusions

- What concentration of IAA was most effective at delaying abscission?
- What other factors may have contributed to the observed outcome (you may have been unable to control these)?

■ Evaluation

Is it possible to adapt your method of investigation to leaves attached to trees growing outdoors, near your laboratory? What would be the advantages of this approach?

■ Extension

1 A variation of this investigation, using excised stem segments that are cut in half and laid on moist filter paper in transparent plastic boxes, is given in *SAPS Newsletter no 6* (Spring 1993), as Student Sheet 6. If adopted, it might be wise to surface-sterilise the stem segments with 1% sodium

chlorate(I) (hypochlorite) (wear eye protection), since the material will necessarily have numerous damaged cells which bacteria and fungi may feed on. Microorganisms are also known to produce IAA in significant quantities under certain conditions.

2 You may chose to investigate the anatomical changes at the leaf base/stem junction in the plant(s) used by cutting sections (p. 127). Cells that have waxy walls (such as the suberised walls of the cork layer) may be stained with Sudan III stain. Lignified cell walls stain red with phloroglucinol and concentrated hydrochloric acid (**care!**). Alternatively, prepared slides of LS of the abscission layer may be used.

References
Science and Plants for Schools (1993) *Osmosis. SAPS Newsletter no 6.* Homerton College, Cambridge

H W Woolhouse (1972) *Ageing Processes in Higher Plants.* Carolina Biology Reader no 30

20.3 Investigating phototropism

(Data generating)

Although coleoptiles are short-lived structures, restricted to grass and cereal seedlings, they have been extensively used to investigate the mechanism of tropisms. The coleoptile is the tubular sheath which protects the first leaf as it pushes through the soil.

■ Aim
To identify the regions of the coleoptile which detect and respond to one-sided illumination.

■ Risk assessment

Good laboratory practice will be sufficient to take account of any hazards and avoid significant risks.

■ Method
1 You are provided with a Petri dish in which wheat seedlings are growing (Figure 20.2). Remove any seedlings which have fallen over, which have distorted coleoptiles or whose coleoptiles are shorter than 10 mm or longer than 50 mm.

> **Figure 20.2** Investigating phototropism
>
>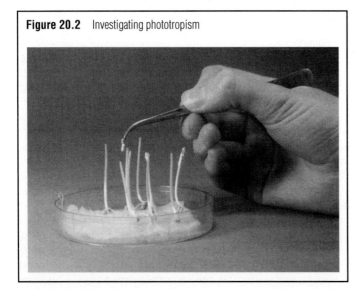

2 Treat the seedlings as follows:
- Use fine scissors to cut 5 mm from the tips of the coleoptiles of one-third of the seedlings.
- Use forceps to place aluminium foil caps over one-third of the seedlings.
- Leave the remainder intact.

3 Measure the coleoptile lengths in each group. Calculate and record the mean length for each group.

4 Moisten the cotton wool and place the dish 15–30 cm from a bench lamp, so that the bulb is level with the dish. Use a marker pen to mark the side of the dish nearest the lamp. If necessary, screen the dish from other sources of strong light.

5 Examine the seedlings after 3, 5 and 24 hours. Make drawings of a representative seedling from each group and, at the end of the experiment, measure the length of each coleoptile. (Do not include the leaf if it has emerged from the coleoptile.)

NOTE TO TECHNICIAN

Each group will need:
- dish containing wheat seedlings growing on moist cotton wool (see p. 433);
- four or five foil caps;
- fine scissors, forceps, both sterilised in 1% sodium chlorate(I) (hypochlorite) solution for one minute;
- bench lamp;
- clamp stand or box to raise seedlings level with lamp;
- marker pen, ruler.

■ Data presentation
- Make drawings of representative seedlings from each group after the different time intervals.
- Construct a table to show the average increase in length of the coleoptiles in each group.

■ Conclusions
- Did any of the treatments prevent or reduce growth in coleoptile length?
- Did any treatment prevent or reduce the response to one-sided illumination?
- What conclusion can you reach about the regions of the coleoptile which detect or respond to one-sided light?

■ Evaluation
- Could either of the treatments have damaged the coleoptiles sufficiently to make the results unreliable?
- Why was it advisable to sterilise the scissors and forceps?

20.4 The regions of detection and response to gravity in roots

(Investigation)

The root's apical meristem is just behind the root cap, and the zone of elongation is further behind this.

■ Aim
To investigate the regions of a growing root which detect and respond to one-sided gravity.

■ Risk assessment

- Care is needed when using scalpels or razor blades.
- Otherwise, good laboratory practice will be sufficient to take account of any hazards and avoid significant risks.

■ Method

You are provided with pea seedlings with straight radicles about 20 mm long, and three Petri dishes with strips of cotton wool.

1 Treat the radicles as follows:
- Lay a seedling on a ruler and carefully cut off 3 mm of the root tip. Do this with three of the seedlings.
- Use the same technique to cut 1 mm from the tips of three more seedlings.
- Leave three seedlings intact.
2 Label the Petri dishes A, B and C. Moisten the cotton wool strips and wedge the three seedlings from each group between the strips and the base and lid of a Petri dish (as shown in Figure 20.3). Keep the lids in place with adhesive tape or elastic bands.

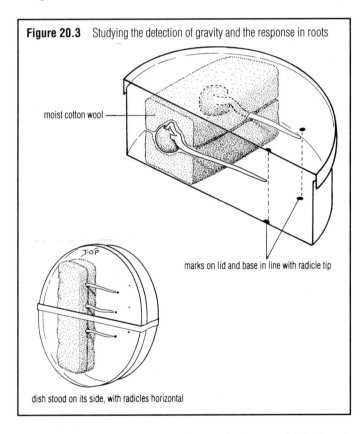

Figure 20.3 Studying the detection of gravity and the response in roots

moist cotton wool

marks on lid and base in line with radicle tip

TOP

dish stood on its side, with radicles horizontal

3 Use a marker pen to put marks on the base and lid of each dish exactly in line with the tip of each radicle. Leave the dishes in darkness for two days, on their sides with the radicles horizontal. Mark the upper edge of the Petri dish and add your initials.
4 After two days, note how the tips of the radicles have changed their position from your original marks (without removing the lids). Measure any increase in length.

The results from this practical may not always be clear-cut, so it is worth combining results from the whole class.

NOTE TO TECHNICIAN

Each group will need:
- nine pea seedlings with straight radicles (see p. 433);
- three Petri dishes with six cotton wool strips about 20 × 70 mm;
- marker pen, rule, scalpel;
- three elastic bands or access to adhesive tape;
- access to trays or boxes in which to leave the dishes.

■ Data presentation

Make drawings of a representative sample from each dish showing any increase in length or change in direction on the same drawing. Put the measurements on the drawings.

■ Conclusions

- Did either of the treatments impair or arrest growth of the radicles, or affect their normal positive geotropic response?
- How might your results help to determine which parts of the radicle detect or respond to one-sided gravity?

■ Evaluation

If the cut root tips could be replaced and held in position, what results would you expect?

20.5 Phototropism: the effective wavelength of light

(Investigation)

The responses of green plants to light are complex, and are mediated by light of different wavelengths. This investigation centres on the phototropic response of the young stem tip.

■ Aim

To investigate what wavelength of white light is responsible for the positive phototropic response of very young stems or coleoptiles, and to note other visible effects of light on development of the stem.

■ Risk assessment

Good laboratory practice will be sufficient to take account of any hazards and avoid significant risks.

■ Method

1 Small Petri dishes of seedlings, germinated and grown in the absence of light to a height of 1–3 cm, are provided. Seedlings are grown on moist filter paper or cotton wool (for example, cress, *Lepidium* sp., or wheat, *Triticum* sp.) or on seedling compost (for example, a 'fast plant' such as *Brassica campestris*). Select dishes with straight stems (or coleoptiles), and measure the height of the stems (or coleoptiles) at the start. Keep these in the dark until ready for use.
2 You are provided with 250 cm^3 glass beakers, and to the side of each is attached a rectangle of photographic filter, either red, blue or green. Using the black sugar paper and adhesive tape provided, make the remaining area of clear glass sides of each beaker lightproof. Each beaker has a close-fitting lid made from an inverted plastic Petri dish, rendered lightproof by a coat of black paint. Correctly assembled and placed on a window ledge, the apparatus will provide unilateral light of known wavelength to a Petri

dish of seedlings placed inside. Set up an additional beaker with totally opaque sides, and one beaker without any blackout or filter.

3 Mark the side of each Petri dish to indicate the direction of unilateral light, and then place it in a prepared beaker. Set up five beakers with each species of seedling used: one with each of the three coloured filters, one in total darkness and one that has unrestricted illumination.

4 Record the change in length of the stems or coleoptiles at the 2–4-hour stage, the 12–18-hour stage, and finally at the 24–30-hour stage, together with the degree of curvature typical of the stems (or coleoptiles), and the position of the curvature in relation to the total length of the stems.

NOTE TO TECHNICIAN

Each student group requires:
- a minimum of five Petri dishes (6 cm in diameter) of seedlings of the same species, as described above, grown in total darkness, to give stems (or coleoptiles) of height 1–3 cm;
- five 250 cm³ beakers, three with strips of photographic filter attached by adhesive tape, one red, one blue and one green;
- five plastic Petri dishes of size to make lids to beakers (when inverted), painted black;
- waterproof marker pen;
- sheet of black sugar paper, adhesive tape, scissors;
- access to an evenly illuminated window ledge (or greenhouse);
- forceps for handling seed trays (Petri dishes).

■ Data presentation
- Make annotated sketches to record the change in length of the stems or coleoptiles at the 2–4-hour stage, the 12–18-hour stage, and finally at the 24–30-hour stage. Add notes of the degree of curvature typical of the stems (or coleoptiles), and the position of the curvature in relation to the total length of the stems.
- Alternatively, record your results by means of photographs, taken by means of flash photography.

■ Conclusion
Make a table to summarise the effects of full illumination, total darkness, and unilateral blue, red and green light.

■ Evaluation
- Why may the total absence of light result in the greatest extension growth in the stem?
- Apart from filtering out all but one colour, what other effect will the filters have which might affect the plant's response?

20.6 Observing nastic movements

(Investigation)

The leaves of wood sorrel and many other cultivated species of *Oxalis* sp. fold up at night, as shown in Figure 20.4. This is considered to be a response to the lowering of light intensity as darkness falls (that is, a photonastic response). It could be a response to lower temperature associated with nightfall, however. It may be that it is not a response at all, but an endogenous rhythm (the leaves may be folding and opening on a daily basis independently of environmental stimuli), or influenced in

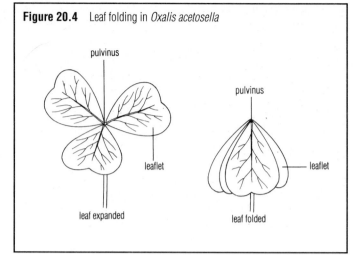

Figure 20.4 Leaf folding in *Oxalis acetosella*

part by some or all of these factors. Leaves also fold when they wilt, owing to loss of turgor in the cells of the pulvini.

■ Aim
To investigate the nastic movement exhibited by the leaves of *Oxalis* sp.

■ Risk assessment
Good laboratory practice will be sufficient to take account of any hazards and avoid significant risks.

■ Method
Design and carry out an experiment to investigate the nastic responses of *Oxalis* sp. To avoid problems of leaf closure through loss of leaf turgor, keep all experimental plants well watered. Good experimental design should involve objectivity and quantitative assessment, and the use of appropriate controls. Every attempt should be made to be objective; for example, can the degree of leaf folding be measured rather than judged?

Divide the investigation into subunits; attempt to answer simple questions first and then build up knowledge about those that are more complicated. Some suggestions for questions that might be attempted are given here.
- How long does it take for the leaflets to fold completely in darkness?
- How long does it take for the leaflets to open fully in the light?
- Is the response equally fast at different times of the day or night?
- Is this process affected by temperature?
- Is there evidence of an endogenous rhythm?
- What intensity of light is needed to cause folding (or opening) of the leaflets?
- What colour of light is most effective in causing opening? (Remember that a filter will not only alter the colour of light reaching the plant, but is also likely to change its intensity.)

■ Data presentation
Describe the details of the experimental set-up and the results obtained.

■ Discussion and conclusion
Explain your interpretation of the results, indicating what information has been obtained on the details of the nastic response.

NOTE TO TECHNICIAN

Each group will need:
- at least two plants of *Oxalis* sp. potted up and uniform in size and prior treatment, with leaves that are expanded fully with the leaflets horizontal (several varieties of *Oxalis* sp. are cultivated in gardens and sold in garden centres, so obtaining suitable plants should not present a difficulty);
- boxes to provide dark conditions and light conditions, and a range of coloured filters (with data on absorption and transmission characteristics supplied by the manufacturers);
- sources of light (bench lamps, or a powerful fluorescent light source);
- access to clocks/stopclocks;
- thermometers for measuring air temperature or probes connected to computers for continuous recording.

■ Evaluation

Make a critical appraisal of the experimental techniques you used, with suggestions for further experimentation or improvements in experimental technique that would provide results that were more dependable.

■ Extension

Many other nastic responses can be investigated in a similar manner:
- the flowers of crocus (*Crocus* sp.), tulip (*Tulipa* sp.) and winter aconite (*Eranthis haemalis*) are said to be thermonastic, opening when the temperature rises;
- the anther filaments of *Berberis* sp. and *Mahonia* sp. are thigmonastic and, if touched by the bristle from a paint brush, will fold rapidly inwards towards the centre of the flower (plants of both genera are commonly grown in parks and gardens, flowering from March onwards);
- daisy (*Bellis perennis*) and dandelion (*Taraxacum officinale*) are said to be photonastic because their flowers close at night.

Observation can show that several wild garden plants have leaf or flower movements which occur at dusk, and sometimes at other times during the day; for example, goat's-beard (*Tragopogon* sp.) has flowers which reputedly close at noon, and the flowers of evening primrose (*Oenothera* sp.) open at dusk since they are moth-pollinated.

Projects

20.1 Nutation in the stem tip

The phenomenon of the more or less continuous movements of plant stems can be observed by recording the helical path described by a stem tip as it grows (*Advanced Biology*, p. 425). Bindweed seedlings (*Convolvulus arvensis*) and many other climbing plants make exaggerated movements but other plants make quite distinct movements, too. At what point in the 24-hour cycle does most movement of this type occur? What external factors appear to affect the phenomenon? Is nutation restricted to young, vigorously growing plants?

Perhaps the common camcorder can be adapted to investigate this aspect of plant growth in a form of the technique of time-lapse photography?

20.2 Seed germination and light

In many species of seed, germination is stimulated by light (and inhibited by light in the seeds of a few other species, too). The ecological advantages of light-sensitive germination are less obvious than the well-documented sensitivity to temperature. The phenomenon of light sensitivity raises the issue of which wavelengths are effective, however, and what plant pigment system is involved. Different pigments are sensitive to different wavelengths, and the phytochrome system is triggered by both red and far-red wavelengths. Commercially available seeds with which it is practical to experiment include the 'Grand Rapids' variety of lettuce (*Lactuca sativa*) and the garden flower *Phacelia tanacetifolia*.

Reference

J W Hannay (1967) 'Light and seed germination – an experimental approach to photobiology', *J. Biol. Ed.* **1**(1), pp. 65–73

M J Wagner and A M Wagner (1995) 'A simple and effective filter system for experiments with light dependent processes in plants' *J. Biol. Ed.* **29**(3), pp. 170–2

20.3 Stem and root initiation and the control of extension growth in 'fast plants'

A mutant variety of the 'fast plant' *Brassica campestris* occurs as a rosette plant which, when treated with gibberellic acid (GA), shows normal growth. How must the GA be applied to be effective, and what concentration is most effective? This investigation, together with many other aspects of response and coordination, growth and development and flowering, can be undertaken with 'fast plants'; for example, these plants may be used to investigate the effects of plant growth regulators on shoot and root induction.

References

R Price (1991) 'Perfect plants for projects', *Biol. Sci. Rev.* (September 1991) **4**(1), pp. 32–6

M P Fuller and F M Fuller (1995) 'Plant tissue culture using *Brassica* seedlings', *J. Biol. Ed.* **29**(1), pp. 53–9

20.4 Hydrotropism or thigmotropism

Young plant roots respond not only to gravity but, some say, to water (hydrotropism). Other workers interpret the evidence as a response to touch (thigmotropism). The field lends itself to intensive enquiry. It is an area of study where there are many practical leads.

References

I A Dodds (1964) 'Hydrotropism', *School Science Review* (March 1964) 45(156), pp. 396–8

I A Dodds (1966) 'Hydrotropic response of roots', *School Science Review* (March 1966) 47(162), pp. 476–81

P W Freeland (1973) 'On hydrotropism', *J. Biol Ed.* 7(6), pp. 23–32

20.5 Apical dominance in stems; the roles of terminal and lateral buds

The fast-growing hedgerow shrub/small tree, elder (*Sambucus nigra*), can be used to investigate the effects of taking out the terminal bud and/or various lateral buds on subsequent extension growth. Growth of treated shoots can be compared with neighbouring untreated shoots.

20.6 Hormone rooting powder and the production of adventitious roots

Commercially available 'hormone' rooting powder can be applied to the cut ends of shoots of various species, and the effects on the subsequent development of adventitious roots quantified. What cultivation conditions (such as soil type, light regime, humidity) favour root formation? What size of aerial shoot is best able to support hormone-induced root growth? Which IAA substitute is marketed as the hormone in the product you are using? Can you compare this one with other 'artificial' auxins, available in your laboratory?

20.7 Bud break studies in woody shoots

Woody shoots form their next season's buds in high summer, but these buds then lie dormant until … when? Some species are naturally capable of breaking bud after exposure to a short cold snap, provided favourable conditions for growth follow. An example is forsythia (*Forsythia suspensa*). Investigate how soon after leaf fall in the autumn, a short period of cold treat-ment (applied to cut shoots) can lead to flowering. Does the length of cold treatment affect speed of flowering? What minimum temperature is critical?

20.8 Working with gibberellic acid and its effects on plant growth

This naturally occurring plant growth substance is expensive to purchase, but has dramatic effects when used at extremely low concentration. There are many useful leads in the available literature, suggesting valuable project work with plants available in dwarf and normally growing varieties, including several commercially available vegetables.

References

N Hession (1973) 'Simple experiments using giberellic acid', *School Science Review* (September 1973) 55(190), pp. 88–91

M A Allen (1974) 'Experimental work with giberellic acid', *School Science Review* (March 1974) 55(192), pp. 514–9

M A Allen (1975) 'Project work with giberellic acid', *School Science Review* (September 1975) 57 (198), pp. 87–92

20.9 Ethene triggers the ripening of fruit

Ethene, a gaseous growth regulator of great significance in plants, signals 'green' fruit to ripen (it has other important effects too). Ripened fruit itself releases ethene. Ethene is used commercially: green bananas, shipped from tropical regions, are treated with the gas two days before marketing them as the soft, sweet, yellow fruits familiar to us all. This same effect is exploited by parasitic and rot-inducing fungi as part of an attack on the host fruit tissue.

If a whole ripe tomato, or 'skin' from a ripe apple, is enclosed with green fruits it releases ethene which will ripen surrounding fruits. This response can be investigated. By how much is the ripening process speeded up in the presence of an ethene source? Are some species more sensitive than others? Can the presence of a gaseous 'hormone' that diffuses from ripe fruit be established experimentally? Does temperature influence the ripening process too?

20.10 Nastic movements of plants

Read Practical 20.6, 'Observing nastic movements' (p. 240). The extension work in this practical offers numerous ideas appropriate for study as longer-term projects.

Problems and assignments

20.1 The Avena curvature test

The concentrations of auxin in plant organs are normally assayed by a biological method, such as the *Avena* (oat) curvature test devised by the Dutch physiologist Went. The steps of this procedure are summarised in Figure 20.5. Examine this illustration and, using the information given and your general knowledge of plant growth regulation, answer the following questions.

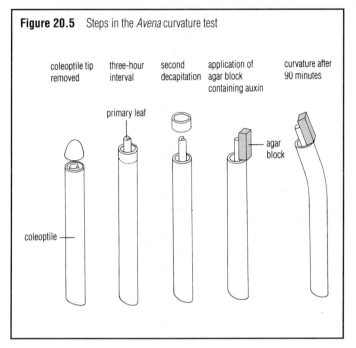

Figure 20.5 Steps in the *Avena* curvature test

coleoptile tip removed

three-hour interval

second decapitation

application of agar block containing auxin

curvature after 90 minutes

primary leaf

agar block

coleoptile

1 What is meant by the term 'coleoptile'? In what ways does this organ differ from a young stem (a plumule, for example)?
2 Coleoptiles are grown (and the *Avena* curvature test is conducted) in darkness. Why is this necessary?
3 Why is auxin assayed by a 'biological' method, rather than a chemical test?
4 a Why is it necessary to include precautions against contamination by bacteria?
  b What precautions can be carried out to minimise the chance of the presence of bacteria on the experimental coleoptiles?
5 As the second step in the process, the cut stump receives a further decapitation. Why?
6 When agar blocks are placed on cut stumps of plant organs, the atmosphere around the plant is adjusted to be at 100% humidity. Why?
7 Why is it possible to use the degree of curvature produced after 90 minutes as an indication of the amount of auxin in the agar block placed asymmetrically on the stump?
8 What controls would you plan to include if you were conducting this test to estimate the auxin present in a particular agar block?
9 The 'auxin' of Went's experiments is now assumed to be indoleacetic acid (IAA). What evidence exists to suggest that natural auxin is IAA?
10 Plant 'hormones' are now regarded as fundamentally different from animal hormones. Make a short table contrasting the important features of animal hormones and plant growth regulators.

20.2 Plant growth regulators interact

Batches of 10 short lengths of pea stems, cut from internodes of young peas, were floated on experimental solutions in Petri dishes and incubated. The solutions contained plant growth hormones: indoleacetic acid (IAA, $10 \, \mu g \, cm^{-3}$) in one, gibberellin (GA, $10 \, \mu g \, cm^{-3}$) in another, and both hormones combined (GA + IAA) in a third. The control dish contained no exogenous growth hormone. The extension growth of the stem segments was measured at intervals over a two-day period. The mean values of the gains in length that occurred are shown in Table 20.1.

Table 20.1 Gains in length of pea stems grown in presence of plant growth regulators/mm

| | Time/h | | | | | |
	6	12	18	24	30	48
Control	0.24	0.61	0.85	1.12	1.26	1.15
GA only	0.47	0.79	1.22	1.43	1.61	1.84
IAA only	1.23	1.92	2.54	3.19	3.51	3.66
GA + IAA	1.23	2.16	3.11	3.84	4.08	4.29

1 Plot a graph of the mean gain in length (mm) against time, making the individual curves distinct and identifiable.
2 The culture solutions contained a low concentration of a powerful antibiotic. Why was this considered necessary?
3 Batches of 10 stem lengths were used in each dish. Why was this considered necessary, since each length had to be individually measured on each occasion?
4 The stem lengths had been cut from 'internodes' of pea stems. What is an internode?
5 If you were to repeat this experiment, what precautions would you take in selecting the stem lengths for the four dishes?
6 Why is the tissue in the control dish referred to as being exposed to no *exogenous* growth regulators?
7 a Over what experimental period did the plant growth regulators have their maximum effect?
  b For what reasons may the effect of the exogenous growth regulators have decreased towards the later part of the experiment?
8 What evidence in the data suggests that GA and IAA interact to enhance their individual effects?
9 Give one other aspect of plant growth and development in which these two regulators positively interact.
10 IAA can be replaced by several other compounds, many of which are commercially available, and cheap. IAA and its alternatives also have a marked effect on stem extension when sprayed on intact plants. State one commercial application that has resulted from this.

20.3 Herbicides – is there any case for action?

Read the text extracts in the three panels on the next two pages, which are taken respectively from the newspaper the *Guardian*, the journal *Scientific American* and a textbook on farming and wildlife.

You are asked to explain to a group of your peers who do not study biological subjects:

a why herbicides are so widely used;
b what dangers they pose, if any, and why they pose them;
c what possible alternatives exist to the continued high usage of herbicides.

Using the text extracts as 'starter' points for your planning, prepare the points you would make in a 10-minute presentation, assuming that some of your audience are already likely to have contrasting attitudes to the issues.

Panel 20.1 Lettuce gets high pesticide rating

Dozens of samples of fruit and vegetables bought from shops in the past year were contaminated with pesticides above the legal limit, Ministry of Agriculture scientists disclosed yesterday.

Lettuces were among the worst examples, with 34 out of 77 samples containing above the maximum residue limit. One had 55 times the legal level.

Dr John Steadman, from the Department of Health, said it did not mean this was a 'killer lettuce', but officials accepted it was 10 times above the World Health Organisation's acceptable daily intake.

Dr Steadman, head of the toxicology and health department, said the lettuce was unlikely to cause acute toxic effects on its own. Lettuces with such an excess of pesticides were sporadic occurrences. It was highly unlikely that anyone would eat contaminated lettuces all the time.

Although there were many cases of illegal doses, the Ministry of Agriculture had not prosecuted anyone. One public analyst had taken legal action, but Peter Stanley, head of the working party on pesticide residues, who produced yesterday's report, said the ministry saw its role as preventing incidents recurring. The job of the working party was to test hundreds of samples and then examine why excesses had occurred. It advised farmers on the best agricultural practices to avoid excess contamination happening again. If abuses continued, action would be considered, he said.

Dr Stanley said the results were roughly in line with those of the United States. Advice given to manufacturers and farmers included changing instruction labels and timings of the treatments of vegetables to reduce the residue left when they reached the shops.

From: the Guardian *(28 September 1990)*

Panel 20.2 Herbicides

- Herbicides – weedkillers – are at present used by British farmers in far greater quantities than are all the other types of pesticides combined. In 1977 they used 17 000 tonnes of 'active ingredients' of all types of pesticides, and of this, 14 000 tonnes, more than 80%, was herbicide [Table 20.2].
- In 1942 an entirely different type of herbicide, the phenoxyacetic acids, or 'hormone weedkillers', started to be used. These herbicides soon became very widely used, and continue to be sprayed in greater quantities than any other group of chemicals.
- Herbicides, unlike some insecticides, do not become concentrated in living organisms, and are not transmitted in food chains, but their other effects can be devastating.
- In general it would appear that any ecological damage done by herbicides is not because of their toxicity, but because of their efficiency. Farmers have always tried to grow clean, weedfree crops, and have generally succeeded by labour-intensive, cultural methods. Chemical herbicides have done the job more efficiently and with less effort.
- There is even growing evidence that some farmers are using more herbicides than are necessary, and in fact that after a few years of clean cropping, higher yields may be obtained if their use is temporarily suspended.
- Some organic farmers state that they can keep their fields reasonably free from weeds without using chemical herbicides. This is generally true, though I am doubtful whether the results are obtained because

organic and not inorganic fertilisers are used, or because organic farmers generally eschew repeated plantings of the same crop on the same land, and use the type of rotation of different crops which was originally introduced largely to control weeds.

Table 20.2 Use of pesticides on crops in England and Wales (1977)

	Area treated/ha	Active ingredient used/t
Cereals:		
insecticides		
organochlorine compounds	1 000	6
organophosphorus compounds	294 000	107
other insecticides	272 000	43
seed treatments	3 358 000	48
fungicides	978 000	588
herbicides	4 408 000	8 026
other pesticides	188 000	263
Other arable crops:		
insecticides		
organochlorine compounds	40 000	35
organophosphorus compounds	274 000	99
other insecticides	180 000	416
seed treatments	430 000	2
fungicides	616 000	882
herbicides	918 000	6 131

From: K Mellanby 'Pests and pesticides', Farming and Wildlife, *pp. 108–15. Collins New Naturalist*

Panel 20.3 Sustainable agriculture

Traditional conservation-minded methods combined with modern technology can reduce farmers' dependence on possibly dangerous chemicals. The rewards are both environmental and financial.

A growing cross-section of American society is questioning the environmental, economic and social impacts of conventional agriculture. Consequently, many individuals are seeking alternative practices that would make agriculture more sustainable.

Sustainable agriculture embraces several variants of non-conventional agriculture that are often called organic, alternative, regenerative, ecological or low-input. Just because a farm is organic or alternative does not mean that it is sustainable, however. For a farm to be sustainable, it must produce adequate amounts of high-quality food, protect its resources and be both environmentally safe and profitable. Instead of depending on purchased materials such as fertilisers, a sustainable farm relies as much as possible on beneficial natural processes and renewable resources drawn from the farm itself.

Sustainable agriculture addresses many serious problems afflicting US and world food production: high energy costs, groundwater contamination, soil erosion, loss of productivity, depletion of fossil resources, low farm incomes and risks to human health and wildlife habitats. It is not so much a specific farming strategy as it is a system-level approach to understanding the complex interactions within agricultural ecologies.

From: Scientific American *(June 1990), pp. 72–8*

20.4 Quick test

1 Distinguish between the following:

a plant and animal responses;
b tropic and nastic responses;
c phototropism and geotropism;
d animal hormones and plant growth regulators;
e auxin and IAA;
f absorption spectrum and action spectrum;
g gibberellins and cytokinins;
h short-day plants and long-day plants;
i far-red light and red light;
j imposed dormancy and innate dormancy.

2 What do you understand by the following?

a nutation movements of plants;
b etiolation;
c bioassay;
d the statolith theory;
e growth inhibitors;
f interaction of growth regulators;
g phytochrome;
h dormancy;
i abscission;
j parthenocarpy.

20.5 Essay assignment

Select one of the following:

• 'The response of green plants to light is complex.' Explain what you understand by this statement, giving examples.

or:

• Give an illustrated account of the roles of plant growth regulators in the growth and functioning of the aerial systems of green plants.

21 Response and coordination in animals

Summary

Sensitivity in animals tends to involve **quick responses** and the adjustment of the animal's **behaviour**, in contrast with the slower growth responses of plants. Sensitivity in animals is based on **receptors** (the sense organs), **effectors** (the muscles and glands), **communication systems** (nerves and hormones), and possible co-ordination of responses by a **central control system** (the brain).

The nervous system is built of specialised cells (**neurones**). Electrical impulses are conducted along the nerve fibre extensions of neurones, and transmitted chemically from neurone to neurone across a **synapse**. Impulses are transmitted most quickly along giant nerve fibres and those with myelinated sheaths.

The **sense organs** consist of cells that convert light, pressure, sound and other stimuli into an impulse (electrochemical energy). Taste is detected in the mouth, smell is detected in the olfactory cells of the nose. The eyes are concerned with vision, and the ear with balance and body position as well as hearing. Receptors in the skin and the internal tissues detect other changes in the body's environment.

The nervous system of mammals is composed of the **central nervous system** (brain and spinal cord) and the **peripheral nerves**. Automatic responses of the body are controlled by reflex action, but sensory impulses also go to the **brain**. Some reflex actions can be overruled. The brain consists of fore-, mid- and hindbrain. In mammals the forebrain is enormously expanded as the cerebral hemispheres. The brain initiates activity, as well as monitoring and controlling reflex actions. The activity of the brain is a product of the electrical activity of the vast numbers of neurones.

The **endocrine system** consists of glands secreting **hormones** into the bloodstream, which carries them all over the body. Hormones play a key part in coordination of long-term growth and development changes and in shorter-term adjustment of tissue metabolism.

Practicals and activities

21.1 Histology of nervous tissue

(Data generating)

The nervous system is composed of nerve cells of two general types: highly specialised neurones, for the conduction of impulses (action potentials), together with surrounding unspecialised neuroglia, which support and nourish the neurones. In vertebrates, these cells are massed together to make the nervous system. This consists of the central nervous system of brain and spinal cord, and the peripheral nervous system. Individual neurones (or parts of them, such as the fine cytoplasmic fibres that conduct impulses and the myelin sheaths that may surround them) may be observed in stained sections of spinal cord and peripheral nerves.

■ Aim

To become familiar with the appearance and microscopic structure of spinal cord and the neurones from which the central nervous system is constructed, and to relate structure to function where possible.

■ Risk assessment

Good laboratory practice will be sufficient to take account of any hazards and avoid significant risks.

■ Method

The basic structure of neurones is illustrated in *Advanced Biology*, p. 216, and the arrangement of neurones in the spinal cord on p. 467.

Using the medium- and high-power magnification of the microscope, examine the prepared slides of spinal cord in TS, and of peripheral nerves in TS and LS (or a similar section).

Look for:

• individual neurones: cell bodies (containing a nucleus) and fibres (the beginnings of dendrons – or dendrites – and axons) of individual neurones which may be visible in stained preparations, while in some sections you may be able to observe the connections between the ends of nerve fibres and the cell body of another neurone (synapses);

• in the TS of a nerve, individual nerve fibres (axons) with their myelin sheaths, and the nucleus of a Schwann cell;

• in the LS of a nerve, myelin sheaths and nodes of Ranvier;

• in the TS of the spinal cord, 'white' and 'grey' matter, dorsal and ventral roots and dorsal ganglia.

NOTE TO TECHNICIAN

Each student will require:
• the use of a microscope (with medium- and high-power objectives), with bench lamp if necessary;
• access to prepared, stained slides of mammalian spinal cord in TS, with 'white' and 'grey' matter, with at least one section showing dorsal root and ganglion, and ventral root, and of peripheral nerves in TS and LS.

■ Data presentation

Make large, fully annotated drawings of:
• one or more neurones;
• part of a nerve in section, both TS and LS;
• the spinal cord in TS.

■ Conclusion

What features of neurones and their arrangement in the nervous system can be related to function?

■ Evaluation

Neuroglia are 10 times more abundant than neurones in the nervous system, yet only the Schwann cells have been observed in this practical. Why?

21.2 Resources for learning about nerve function

(Demonstration)

Practical study of generation of a resting potential and the propagation of an impulse (action potential) in mammals do not lend themselves to 'hands-on' practical enquiry. Study of this aspect may be augmented by the use of video and computer-assisted learning. The resources available include the following.

The Architecture of Cells: Special Structure, Special Function is a videotape available from Boulton-Hawker Films (p. 434). Part 3 (15 minutes) of this video is on 'Sensory and nerve cells'. It shows how the special structure of nerve cells enables them to communicate. A variety of receptors is introduced, and sensory organs are described (including various touch/pressure receptors, the eye and the ear).

Nerve is an interactive CAL program which aids understanding of resting and action potential, and simulates a frog sciatic nerve experiment, allowing measurement of conduction velocity, refractory period, and stimulus strength/response properties. This software is suitable for Acorn RISC OS, Nimbus 186 and 286, BBC B and Master, and is available from AVP (p. 433).

Nervous System: Part 1 of this double CAL package from CUP Microsoftware (p. 434) allows the student to follow the events of a nerve impulse by recreating the Hodgkin and Huxley giant axon experiments. This software is suitable for BBC B and Master.

Nerve Physiology, from Sheffield Bioscience Physiology Program/Philip Harris Ltd (p. 434), simulates experiments normally performed on the sciatic nerve of a frog, and illustrates the characteristics of an action potential. This software is suitable for BBC, Nimbus and IBM/PCs.

21.3 Brain structure in mammals

(Data generating)

The partly dissected, preserved rat used earlier (freshly killed or preserved specimen) for dissection of the abdomen (p. 157) and the thorax (p. 184), should be used for dissection of the brain. During preservation the brain tissue may have hardened slightly. By comparison with the bony cranium, however, brain tissue is extremely soft. It is easily damaged during dissection, unless special care is taken. Once the general structure of a rodent's brain has been observed and recorded, a general comparison with the brain of the human mammal can be made, using models and published diagrams.

■ Aim

To investigate the structure of the brain of the rat by dissection, and to make comparison of rat and human brain.

■ Risk assessment

- In the conduct of dissection, special precautions for safety are essential. These are listed in Practical 13.2 (p. 157). Read them again now.
- When cutting through bone or chipping bone away from soft tissue, wear eye protection.

■ Method

The chief purpose of dissection in biology is to display the internal structures as part of an investigation of structure and function of an animal's body. Read about developing your dissection technique on pp. 157–8, prior to dissecting the brain of a rat.

Steps to the dissection of the brain

1 Holding the rat dorsal side up, make a long slit through the skin on top of the head, running along the mid-line, from the tip of the snout to the rear of the head. Pull aside the skin covering the cranium. You will be able to see the brain (cerebral hemisphere) through the roof of the cranium (parietal bone). Using your scalpel, scrape away the muscles to expose the sides and posterior part of the skull, too (Figure 21.1).

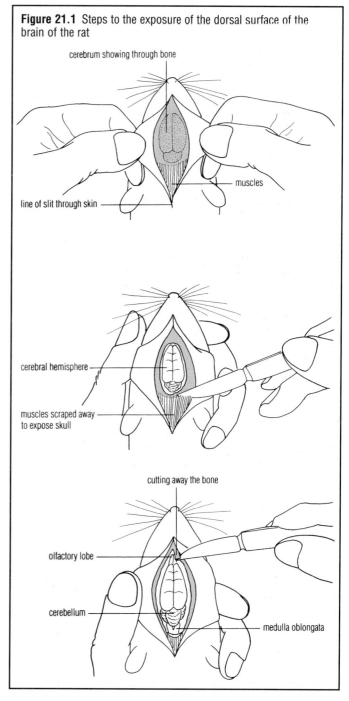

Figure 21.1 Steps to the exposure of the dorsal surface of the brain of the rat

cerebrum showing through bone

muscles

line of slit through skin

cerebral hemisphere

muscles scraped away to expose skull

cutting away the bone

olfactory lobe

cerebellum

medulla oblongata

2 Next, hold the side of the skull firmly between second finger and thumb, with the lower jaw resting on the first finger. Using the point of a sharp scalpel held horizontally, pierce the rear of the cranium so the scalpel passes under the parietal bone, lifting the bone above the brain surface. The parietal bone breaks up and must be removed. This exposes the cerebral hemispheres and, behind them, part of the cerebellum.

3 With great care, cut away the remaining bone covering the rest of the brain (olfactory lobes to the anterior, cerebellum and medulla oblongata to the posterior), using scalpel or scissors as necessary.

4 Make a drawing (or photographic record) at this stage.

5 Now remove the brain from what remains of the cranium by cutting through the cranial nerves and through the spinal cord. First, remove the anterior surface of the first two vertebrae (atlas and axis), so that the spinal cord can be cut through a little away from the base of the brain. Then cut under the olfactory lobes, and under the brain along both sides. Once all the connecting nerves are cut, lift the brain out and place it in a plastic Petri dish. View the brain with a binocular microscope, and use the drawings in Figure 21.2 to help you identify the structures.

6 Make drawings (or photographic records) at this stage.

Comparative study of brains

Examine a model of the human brain, and identify the structures visible by reference to an appropriate textbook, such as H G Q Rowett (1987) *Basic Anatomy and Physiology, 3rd edn*, pp. 62–5 (John Murray).

Compare the relative sizes of the major structures of the brain of rat and human, starting with the olfactory lobes, and including the cerebral hemispheres, cerebellum and medulla oblongata. Make a note of the chief functions of these distinct regions.

Additional references and resources

The following resources can be used to support and enhance learning by dissection, or they may be used singly or together in place of dissection to learn about the nervous system of the mammal:

- H G Q Rowett (1974) *The Rat as a Small Mammal*. John Murray;
- H G Q Rowett (1962) *Guide to Dissection*. John Murray;
- *Video Rat Stack*, by Megan Quentin-Baxter and David Dewhurst of Sheffield BioScience Programs (introduced on p. 162);
- *Vertebrate Dissection Guides – The Rat*, by the TV Centre, the University of Portsmouth in association with the Institute of Biology (see p. 162).

Figure 21.2 The exposed brain of the rat: dorsal, ventral and lateral views (for the nomenclature of the spinal nerves and details of the organs they innervate, see *Advanced Biology*, p. 470, Table 21.3)

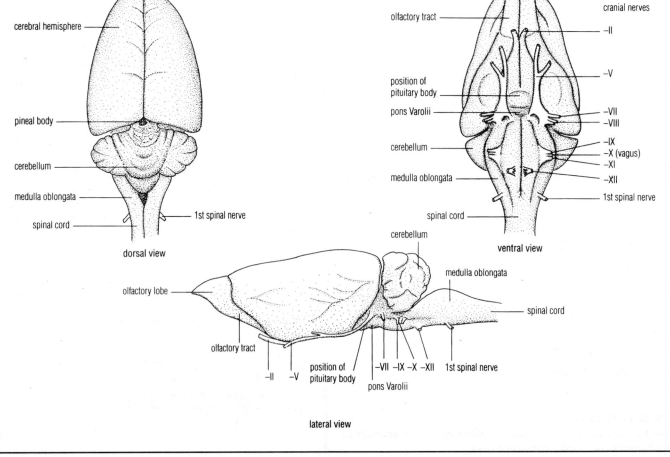

■ Data presentation

Make large labelled sketches of your dissection of the brain of the rat at the following stages:
- the dorsal surface of the brain exposed but *in situ*;
- the lateral view of the brain when removed from the cranium;
- the ventral surface of the brain.

Make a labelled sketch of the human brain in vertical section.

Construct a table to compare the relative sizes and shapes of the following parts of the brain of the rat and the human:
- in the forebrain – the olfactory lobes and the cerebral hemispheres;
- in the hindbrain – the cerebellum and the medulla oblongata.

■ Conclusion

On the basis of the main role/function of the various parts of the mammalian brain, summarise the differences in the brains of the rat and the human that may be related to differences in lifestyle or body structure.

■ Evaluation

Why do you think that cephalisation (the process of 'head' formation) has occurred at the anterior of the body of mobile animals?

21.4 Reaction times

(Investigation)

Even in simple reflex actions, there is a delay between the reception of the stimulus and the response of the effector. In voluntary actions this delay may be longer. There are several factors that might contribute to this delay.

■ Aim

To investigate the reaction time between visual and tactile stimuli and a muscular response.

■ Risk assessment

Good laboratory practice will be sufficient to take account of any hazards and avoid significant risks.

■ Method

1 It is necessary to work in pairs, a subject and an experimenter, though the roles can be switched for repeat experiments.

The subject marks a pencil line down the middle of the thumb nail and sits sideways at a bench with the forearm resting flat on the bench and the hand over the edge (Figure 21.3).

The experimenter holds a ruler vertically between the subject's first finger and thumb with the zero in line with the mark on the thumb nail, but not quite touching either the thumb or the fingers.

The subject concentrates on the zero and, as soon as the experimenter releases the ruler, grips it between thumb and finger to stop its fall. The distance on the ruler is recorded.

This is repeated four times and the mean distance calculated and converted to time by reference to the table in Figure 21.3.

2 The experiment is repeated (with the same subject) but this time with the subject's finger just touching the ruler and the eyes closed. As soon as the ruler is felt to start to fall, the subject grips it as before.

3 The approximate length of the nervous pathway from brain to muscle can now be measured using the ruler. This will be different for the two trials. (The muscles which move the fingers are in the forearm but the touch receptors are in the fingertips.)

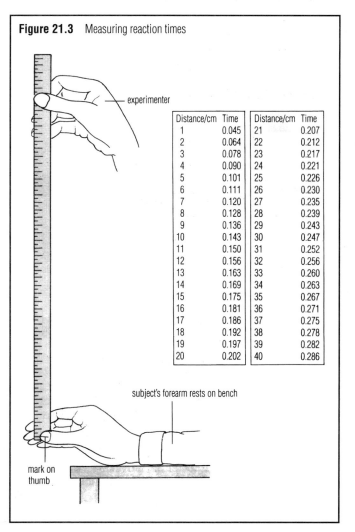

Figure 21.3 Measuring reaction times

Distance/cm	Time	Distance/cm	Time
1	0.045	21	0.207
2	0.064	22	0.212
3	0.078	23	0.217
4	0.090	24	0.221
5	0.101	25	0.226
6	0.111	26	0.230
7	0.120	27	0.235
8	0.128	28	0.239
9	0.136	29	0.243
10	0.143	30	0.247
11	0.150	31	0.252
12	0.156	32	0.256
13	0.163	33	0.260
14	0.169	34	0.263
15	0.175	35	0.267
16	0.181	36	0.271
17	0.186	37	0.275
18	0.192	38	0.278
19	0.197	39	0.282
20	0.202	40	0.286

experimenter

subject's forearm rests on bench

mark on thumb

NOTE TO TECHNICIAN

Each group will need a ruler (half-metre or similar).

■ Data presentation

- Make a table to show the reaction times and their means for both experiments. State your measurements for both nervous pathways. Present the data graphically.
- Assuming that the delay between stimulus and response is due to the time for the nerve impulses to travel between receptor and effector, calculate the speed of conduction.
- Discuss whether the differences between the length of the two nervous pathways made any significant difference to the reaction time.
- Nerve impulses can travel at up to 100 m s^{-1}. How does this compare with your calculations? What light does this value shed on the causes of reaction time?

■ Evaluation

The speed of conduction is only one of several factors which could contribute to the reaction time. What are the other likely factors?

21.5 Sensitivity of the skin

(Investigation)

The skin contains a great many sensory endings which respond to touch, heat, cold and pressure, and some which give rise to the sensation of pain when stimulated.

■ Aim

To investigate the distribution and density of touch receptors in the skin.

■ Risk assessment

Good laboratory practice will be sufficient to take account of any hazards and avoid significant risks.

■ Method

It is best to work in teams of three: a subject, an experimenter and a recorder. Each team is provided with a rubber stamp to mark out the test area and a blunt pin in a holder to provide the stimulus.

1 The subject inks the rubber stamp and marks test areas on the back of the hand, a fingertip and the inside of the forearm. The recorder prints three similar grids on a sheet of paper.

2 The experimenter now touches the blunt pin on to each of the dots in the marked skin areas in turn, working down the rows systematically. The following procedures must be observed:

- the subject must not be able to see what the experimenter is doing;
- the pin should be rested on the mark so that the head of the pin is just lifted clear of the holder and left for no more than half a second;
- the intervals between stimuli should last for at least half a second and should vary irregularly (so that the subject will not be able to anticipate the next stimulus);
- no part of the experimenter's hand or sleeve must touch the subject.

3 If the subject feels the stimulus he or she says 'yes', and the recorder ticks the corresponding mark on the paper grid. When all 25 marks have been tested, the percentage of positive responses can be calculated.

4 The experiment is now repeated for the other two skin areas.

NOTE TO TECHNICIAN

Each group will need:
- ink pad;
- rubber stamp with 25 'points';
- pin and holder.

The rubber stamp can be constructed by making saw cuts at 3 mm intervals in an eraser and cutting it into blocks with five rows of five 'points'. Alternatively, a no. 3 finger cone can be cut into four 1 cm squares, each of which is glued to a wooden holder (Figure 21.4).

To make pin holders, cut strips of fine-grained wood (thin dowel or beading), about $100 \times 5 \times 10$ mm, and drill 1 mm holes near one end. Heat the points of round-headed pins (plastic heads) to redness in a Bunsen flame, allow to cool slowly and cut off the points with pliers. Smooth the ends with a file or sharpening stone to give a flat cross-section. The pins should move freely in the wooden holder.

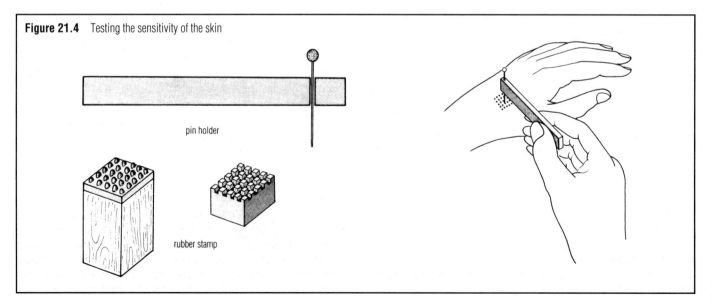

Figure 21.4   Testing the sensitivity of the skin

pin holder

rubber stamp

■ Data presentation

State the percentage 'sensitivity' of each area of skin tested.

■ Conclusions

• How did the different areas compare in their sensitivity?
• Is this what you would have expected from everyday experience?

■ Evaluation

• Would you expect the points which produced a positive response to correspond to single nerve endings?
• How would you expect the results to change if the experimenter used a heavier pin?

■ Extension

1 Try the same test on one of the skin areas you tested before but now:
  • cooled by holding an ice cube on it for 30 seconds;
  • dabbed (not rubbed) with a little alcohol for a minute;
  • rubbed vigorously for 30 seconds.
2 Also try increasing the weight of the pin (for example, by sticking an air rifle pellet to it with 'Blu-tack') and then testing an area of skin you tested previously.
3 Try checking the consistency of sensitivity by testing exactly the same area of skin at intervals of 30 minutes or even longer.
4 Design an experiment to determine the minimum distance apart for two simultaneous stimuli to be identified as distinct sensations. A suitable apparatus is a hairpin, bent and applied as shown in Figure 21.4. You will need to draw up a plan of single and double stimuli in advance so that you use both equally and 'at random'. The procedures listed above should be followed (where appropriate); the subject should be asked to say 'one' or 'two' in response to each stimulus. The distance between the points should be adjusted to find the minimum distance at which two separate stimuli can be recognised fairly consistently, and the test applied to different areas of the body. You will have to decide what percentage of correct responses counts as 'fairly consistent'.

  Suggest some possible reasons why different regions have different discriminatory powers.

21.6 Eye structure

(Data generating)

Because of the potential risks of the transmission of the infective agent for bovine spongiform encephalopathy (BSE), a disease of central nervous system tissues present in some cattle, the Department for Education and Employment has directed that bull's or cow's eyes cannot be dissected in schools and colleges. The structure of the mammalian eye may be studied by prepared slides and by the use of models, and by dissection of pigs' and sheeps' eyes.

■ Aim

To investigate the structure of the mammalian eye.

■ Risk assessment

Good laboratory practice will be sufficient to take account of any hazards and avoid significant risks.

■ Method

The basic structure of the mammalian eye is illustrated in *Advanced Biology*, pp. 462–4. If possible, examine an enlarged plastic model of the eye, dissectable into its component parts, to clarify your understanding of eye structure.

  Using the low-, medium- and high-power magnification of the microscope, examine the prepared slides (or a similar selection) listed below:
• slide of entire mammalian eye, in VS, *or* slides showing VS posterior part of eye in detail, and VS anterior part of eye in detail;
• slide of retina in VS (silver stain).

NOTE TO TECHNICIAN

Students will require (or require access to):
• enlarged plastic model of the eye, dissectable into the major component parts;
• microscope (with low-, medium- and high-power objectives), with bench lamp if necessary;
• prepared, stained slides as listed above.

For the extension work:
• stained prepared slides of VS of developing vertebrate embryo (chick or amphibian), through the developing eyes.

■ Data presentation

• Make a large labelled drawing of a thin section through a preserved, stained eye to show the positions of optic nerve, sclera, choroid and retina, cornea, conjunctiva, iris, ciliary body and lens.
• Make a tissue map of the parts of the retina, as seen in VS.

■ Conclusion

The eye is a delicate organ, built of distinct layers or structures, held together by connective tissues. In the preparation of thin, stained sections of a preserved eye, numerous changes occur. List the ways in which the eye structure shown in your tissue map is significantly different from the living condition.

■ Evaluation

• The eye appears as a complex sense organ quite distinct from the brain (apart from the optic nerve). What is the biological justification for the Government's directive that a fresh eye might be a source of the infective agent for BSE?
• BSE is said to be a disease caused by 'an infective agent'. Why do biologists speak and write about the disease-causing agent in this way?

References

R M Barlow (1991) 'Bovine spongiform encephalopathy', *Biologist* (April 1991) 38(2), pp. 60–2
S B Prusiner (1995) 'The prion diseases', *Scientific American* (January 1995), pp. 30–7

■ Extension

Using the prepared slides of thin sections of the head region of developing vertebrate embryos, draw labelled sketches to show the relationship between parts of the developing eye and the brain. What eye structures clearly originate from the outermost layer of the embryo (the ectoderm), rather than the neural tube tissue that forms the primary brain vesicles?

21.7 Judgement of distance

(Investigation)

It is generally assumed that having eyes set in the front of the head confers binocular vision and contributes to accuracy in judging distances.

■ Aim

To test whether the use of two eyes increases accuracy of distance judgement.

■ Risk assessment

Good laboratory practice will be sufficient to take account of any hazards and avoid significant risks.

■ Method

You will need to work in pairs, an experimenter and a subject, but the roles can be reversed when the experiment is repeated.

1 The experimenter, without allowing the subject to watch, sticks coloured pins upright into the marked block, placing each pin at an intersection of the lines so that no two pins are on the same line when viewed from the side or the front (Figure 21.5). It is best not to make a regular pattern.

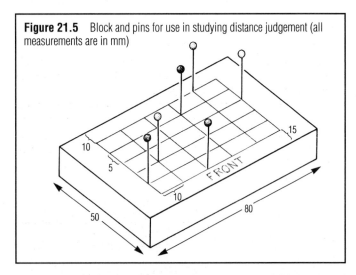

Figure 21.5 Block and pins for use in studying distance judgement (all measurements are in mm)

2 The subject closes one eye and the experimenter then passes the block to the subject, tilting it away from the subject so that the grid lines cannot be seen. The subject holds the block about 30 cm away so that he or she can see the front of the block, but not the sides or top.

3 The subject now calls out the order of the pins from front to back, and the experimenter records this.

4 Still holding the block in the same position, the subject opens both eyes and again calls out the order of the pins. This is recorded.

5 The experimenter changes the order of the pins and the experiment is repeated.

NOTE TO TECHNICIAN

Each student group requires:
- six glass-headed pins of different colours (from a haberdashers);
- block of expanded polystyrene 50 × 80 mm with rectangular grid forming five rows of five rectangles measuring 10 × 5 mm and with the 'front' labelled (see Figure 21.5).

■ Data presentation

Make a table to show the results of the three trials, when using one or both eyes. The results can be expressed as scores out of six, or as percentage success rates.

■ Conclusion

Do your results support the contention that binocular vision enhances distance judgement?

■ Evaluation

- If the block had been rotated slightly from side to side, how might this have improved your score when using only one eye?
- What sensory information from binocular vision could lead to an estimate of distance? This sense is thought to be effective only up to about 15 metres. How are we able to judge distances for objects further away than this?

21.8 Functions of the eye

(Investigation)

The cornea and lens produce an inverted, diminished, coloured image on the retina. This stimulates a pattern of nerve impulses in the optic nerve. This pattern is interpreted as 'vision' by the brain.

■ Aim

To investigate and explain some of the properties and functions of the eyes. The experiments are in themselves quick and simple to carry out. If you have not done them before, some of the results may surprise you. The challenge, however, is to explain why they happen in terms of the structure and physiology of the eye.

■ Risk assessment

Good laboratory practice will be sufficient to take account of any hazards and avoid significant risks.

■ Method

You are provided with various simple items of apparatus to be used as described below.

Inversion of the image

1 Shut one eye and hold the apparatus provided close to the other eye with the card touching your face. Point it towards a brightly lit area or window and look at the pinhead through the pinhole.

2 Again hold the apparatus close to your face, but this time with the pin nearer to you than the card. Hold the wooden base against your cheek-bone and move the apparatus about slightly while looking through the pinhole until you can see the pinhead as a silhouette against the pinhole.

3 In each case describe what you saw and try to explain the effects by means of ray diagrams.

The blind spot

You are provided with two cards, one with a dot and a cross, the other with a cross and an incomplete line.

1 Close your left eye and hold the first card about 60 cm from your face. Concentrate on the cross with your right eye and slowly bring the card closer to your face, still concentrating on the cross.

2 Repeat the experiment with the card held sideways so that the dot is above the cross.

3 Repeat the experiment with the card upside down, with the dot on the left side of the cross.

4 Repeat the experiment, but this time use the card with the cross and the line.

5 Describe what you observed in each case; explain the first effect with the aid of a line diagram and discuss the difference when you held the card sideways and upside down.

Why do we fail to notice the gap in the visual image caused by the blind spot? The second experiment gives you a clue.

Retinal capillaries

You are provided with a card with a pinhole in the centre.

1 Shut one eye, and hold the card close to the other eye. Look through the pinhole at a brightly lit sheet of paper about 30–40 cm away. Move the card about slightly with a circular motion so that you can see through the pinhole all the time.

2 Allow your eye to relax and a net-like pattern of capillaries will appear against the background after a few seconds, provided you keep the card moving.

3 There are no capillaries over the fovea. Can you pick out this area in the image you are forming?

4 If an image is held stationary on the retina, it seems to fade. Since the eyes are constantly making tiny, imperceptible movements, it is difficult to achieve a stationary image. It can be done by mounting a tiny projector on a contact lens. The projector moves with the eye and the projected image is stationary on the retina. In normal conditions the image does not fade because the eye movements cause the image to keep stimulating different areas of the retina.

5 In view of this information, why are we not normally aware of the capillary network in front of the retina? Why should the conditions of this experiment render the capillaries visible?

Broca's pupillometer

You are given a card with six pinholes in a regular pattern:

1 Shut one eye and hold the card very close to the other, actually touching your face, and look through the pinholes at a brightly lit sheet of plain white paper.

2 The pinholes will appear as a pattern of unfocused light discs. Some of the discs will appear to overlap, others will appear to be separate. Concentrate on a pair which are nearly touching but not overlapping.

3 Still concentrating on this pair of discs, open the other eye. Describe what you see.

4 In the eye and the camera, closing the iris diaphragm sharpens the image by using the centre of the lens. In view of this, explain the effects you have just experienced.

Eye dominance

1 Keeping both eyes open, hold a pencil upright at arm's length and line it up with a distant object such as a window frame. Close and open each eye in turn.

2 Notice any apparent change in position of the pencil and whether this was associated with closure of the left or right eye.

3 Which eye must you have used in lining up the pencil? This is your dominant eye. What are the relative numbers of left- and right-eye dominance in your class? Does it correspond to left- and right-handedness?

Binocular vision

1 Draw a small square (about 30 mm side) on a sheet of paper.

2 Keeping both eyes open, concentrate on this square.

3 Rest a finger lightly against the upper eyelid at the outer corner of your less dominant eye and press very lightly. Describe and explain what you see.

Recognition of colour

You are provided with a large cardboard 'protractor' and you will need four coloured crayons (red, green, blue, yellow) of the same size and thickness. Work in pairs as experimenter and subject.

1 The experimenter holds the protractor under the subject's arm, which is fully extended over the 90° line, and places a coloured pencil upright in the subject's hand. The subject must not see the colour.

2 Looking straight ahead (along the zero line of the protractor) and keeping the head still, the subject slowly moves the extended arm forward over the protractor.

3 The subject names the colour of the crayon as soon as he or she can identify it, and the experimenter notes the angle.

4 The experiment is repeated with the other colours, preferably more than once to see if the responses are consistent.

What was the approximate maximum angle at which colours could be recognised with confidence? What does this tell you about the colour sensitivity of the retina? How does this conform to your knowledge of the microstructure of the retina?

Colour vision

You are provided with a card with a bicoloured square.

1 Stare hard at the square for 10 seconds and then quickly transfer your gaze to the cross on the right of the square for five seconds. Describe what you see.

2 It is assumed that there are different receptor cells in the retina, each kind having its maximum sensitivity to a specific wavelength (corresponding to red, blue and green light).

3 Explain your observations, assuming that individual cells become 'fatigued' and cease to transmit nerve impulses after prolonged stimulation.

NOTE TO TECHNICIAN

Each student or group will need the following apparatus:

For studying inversion of the image:
- the device shown in Figure 21.6(a). Make sure that the pinhead can be seen through the pinhole from either side.

For studying the blind spot:
- photocopy the two images shown in Figure 21.6(b) and glue them to separate white cards.

To visualise retinal capillaries:
- cut discs about 6 cm in diameter from thin card and make a pinhole in the centre of each. The hole made by the spike on a pair of compasses or dividers is about the right size.

Broca's pupillometer:
- in the centre of a piece of thin card about 5 cm square make a pattern of fine pinholes as shown in Figure 21.6(c), and trim off the corners.

For the experiment on colour recognition:
- make the protractor from a 50 cm square of card cut from the side of a large cardboard box. Mark the lines with a felt-tipped pen.

For studying colour vision:
- photocopy or draw the diagram shown in Figure 21.6(e). Colour the centre of the square bright yellow and the border bright blue. Crayons or water-colours are suitable.

Figure 21.6 Apparatus needed for Practical 21.8 (see text)

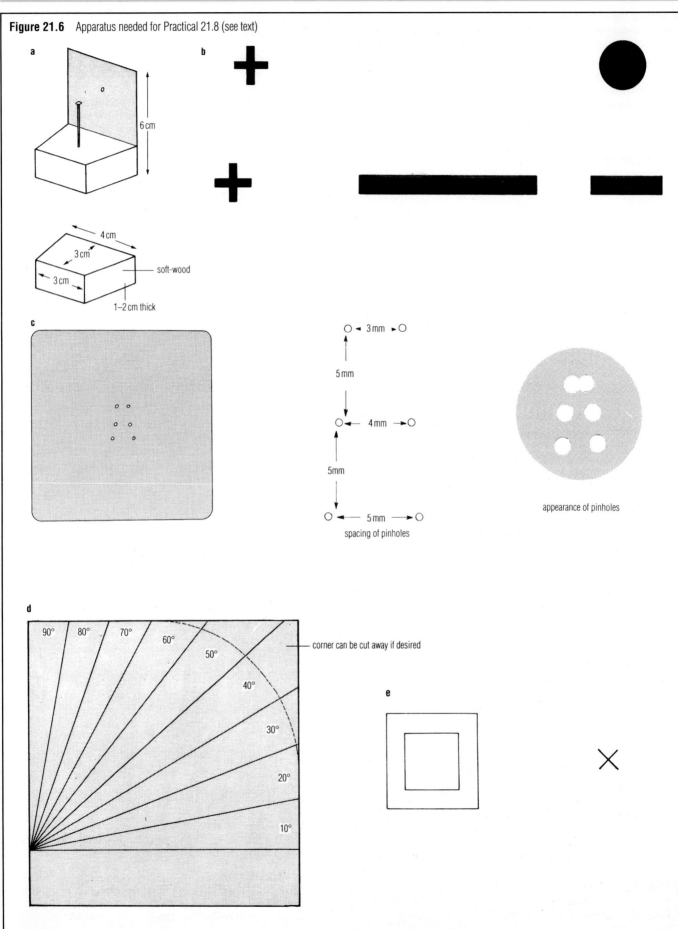

■ Data presentation and conclusion

Record your results concisely and also your explanations in terms of the physiology of the eye, preferably after general discussion with other students and your tutor.

■ Evaluation

We 'see' in our brain rather than in our eyes – and this is a fact that is not appreciated widely enough. Discuss.

21.9 Eye/hand coordination

(Investigation)

The brain has to integrate sensory information from many sources, and to initiate and coordinate actions appropriate to this information. Learning a new skill involves such coordination between sensory and motor systems.

■ Aim

To measure improvements in a learning skill and investigate the effect of previously acquired skills on the learning process.

■ Risk assessment

Good laboratory practice will be sufficient to take account of any hazards and avoid significant risks.

■ Method

The team consists of a subject and a recorder. You are provided with a printed star shape, pencil, mirror and cardboard screen.

1 Use masking tape to stick the star shape to the bench, with the 'mirror line' away from you and not less than 30 cm from the front of the bench. Prop up the mirror vertically on the 'mirror line', using a clamp stand or other support. Clamp the card in a clamp stand and arrange it between yourself and the mirror so that when you place a pencil point on the 'start' dot, you can see the star and your hand reflected in the mirror but not by direct vision (Figure 21.7).
2 Using your right hand if right-handed (left hand if left-handed), place the pencil point on the 'start'. When the recorder starts the stopclock, trace round the outline of the star looking only at the mirror image. Your line, no matter how erratic, must pass through every point. The recorder notes the time it takes you to complete the drawing.
3 Rub out the pencil line and repeat the experiment using the other hand and moving in the opposite direction.
4 Repeat this procedure at least twice more for each hand (that is, two or more consecutive trials with one hand followed by the same number of trials for the other).

NOTE TO TECHNICIAN

Each group will need:
- two or more printed star shapes: the bottom star shape in Figure 21.7 may be photocopied on to a master (two drawings will fit on an A4 sheet), and class copies made from this;
- plane mirror (a 10 cm mirror wall-tile from a DIY outlet is suitable);
- support for mirror;
- card 20 × 15 cm;
- clamp stand and clamp;
- stopclock or other means of timing.

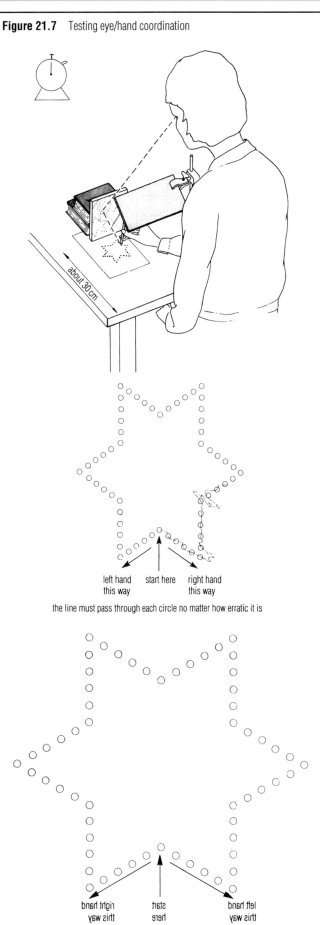

Figure 21.7 Testing eye/hand coordination

left hand   start here   right hand
this way   this way

the line must pass through each circle no matter how erratic it is

■ **Data presentation**

Make a table of your times and plot a graph of time (vertical axis) against the number of trials for each hand. Plot both curves on the same graph paper.

■ **Conclusions**

• In the first two trials, was there a significant difference between using right and left hands? Suggest why any difference might be expected.

• What evidence is there that learning has taken place?

• Was there a difference in the learning curves for the left and right hands? How might you explain such a difference?

■ **Evaluation**

What insight does this experiment give you into the problem of learning to write?

21.10 Histology of the pituitary and adrenal glands

(Data generating)

Hormones are chemical messengers secreted by exocytosis directly into body fluids and the bloodstream from the cells of the (ductless) endocrine glands. Hormones have their effects in the body over many minutes, hours or longer, and mostly on particular 'target' organs, although they circulate all over the body. The pituitary gland, attached at the base of the brain and working in association with the part of the brain known as the hypothalamus, is a key part of the overall long-term control and regulation mechanisms of the body. The thyroid gland, situated in the neck, close to the larynx, secretes two thyroid hormones that influence tissue metabolism in all cells. The adrenal glands, situated immediately above the kidneys, have two distinct regions, and many important roles in regulating body function. Adrenaline production and the 'flight or fight' response is only one, commonly known, function.

■ **Aim**

To become familiar with the appearance and structure of selected endocrine glands, and to relate their structure to functions, where possible.

■ **Risk assessment**

Good laboratory practice will be sufficient to take account of any hazards and avoid significant risks.

■ **Method**

The organisation of the endocrine system in mammals is described in *Advanced Biology*, pp. 478–82, and the system is summarised in Figure 21.46 on p. 479. The histology of the pituitary, thyroid and adrenal glands is illustrated in W H Freeman and B Bracegirdle (1967) *An Atlas of Histology*, pp. 118–22 (Heinemann).

Using the medium- and high-power magnification of the microscope, examine the prepared slides (or a similar selection) listed below:

• pituitary gland, sagittal section of whole gland;

• thyroid gland, section;

• adrenal gland, section of cortex and medulla.

1 In the preparation of the pituitary gland, look for the near-by hypothalamus and its connections with the posterior lobe of the pituitary. The tissue that makes up the anterior lobe is distinct from that of the posterior. These two lobes have a different origin in development, as well as different roles in metabolism.

2 In the thyroid gland, cells that secrete hormones take the form of a simple cubical epithelium.

3 The adrenal gland is contained within a capsule, and the contents are arranged as a cortex and medulla.

NOTE TO TECHNICIAN

Students will require (or require access to):

• microscope (with medium- and high-power objectives), with bench lamp if necessary;

• the prepared, stained slides listed in the text;

• (if available) a copy of Freeman and Bracegirdle (1967) (for details see text).

■ **Data presentation**

Draw labelled tissue maps of the pituitary gland and of the adrenal gland, highlighting the distinct regions. For the thyroid gland, make a labelled drawing of a representative portion of the hormone-secreting cells.

■ **Conclusions**

• What are the likely requirements of an endocrine gland cell?

• How are these met in the functioning body?

■ **Evaluation**

How does an exocrine gland, such as a salivary gland, differ from an endocrine gland?

Projects

21.1 Reaction time; individual differences

Reaction times are not difficult to measure. Is there evidence that an individual's reaction time varies significantly with time of day? Do those people who are gifted at activities (hobbies and sports) requiring exceptional physical coordination have superior reaction times? Ways of measuring reaction time are reviewed in the reference below.

Reference

CLEAPSS (1993) *Equipment and Materials for Human Physiology.* Available from the School Science Service, Brunel University, Uxbridge (p. 434).

21.2 Human range of hearing

Using a signal generator, can you obtain reliable (reproducible) information about the frequency range which individuals hear?

21.3 Location of direction of sound

A sound from your right will arrive in your right ear sooner and with greater intensity than in your left ear. Sound equidistant from both ears will stimulate them equally. Thus it should be more difficult to locate the source of a sound made in any part of a vertical plane passing through the head from front to back than that of any sound in the horizontal plane.

Design an experiment to put this to the test. A 'clicker' can be clicked at different positions, equidistant from each ear, in a vertical arc round the head and the blindfolded subject asked to point to the apparent source. This can then be compared with identification of sounds in the horizontal plane.

You will need to design a method of presenting the 'clicks' at consistent distances and known angles from the head, and then judge the level of accuracy achieved by the subject.

21.4 Studies in 'perception'

'Optical illusion' pictures are widely available. Use a selection of these to investigate the hypothesis that once one image has been 'seen' it delays or inhibits our ability to 'see' (construct) the alternative image. (A set of laminated cards showing simple illusions is available from the laboratory suppliers Philip Harris, Irwin-Desman and NES Arnold.)

21.5 Behaviour studies in Drosophila

The food preferences of *Drosophila* can be investigated in a simple T-maze. Arrange for some *Drosophila* to be placed in an empty specimen tube fitted with a bung and T-tube. To the other arms of the T-tube are fitted identical specimen tubes. To one of the additional tubes add a possible food source; to the other add nothing. After a period in darkness, observe and record the number of *Drosophila* in each tube. Different food sources can be investigated, including fruit in varying stages of decomposition. Is there a preference for the 'real thing' over a synthetic flavouring substance? Other suitably sized insects can also be used.

Other behaviour studies are suggested in the following reference.

Reference
E E Zuill (1975) 'Behavioural studies in *Drosophila*', *School Science Review* (September 1975) 57(198), pp. 73–7

21.6 Sensitivity in caterpillars

The sensitivity of caterpillars of the large white butterfly (*Pieris brassicae*) can be tested whilst they are feeding or resting on a cabbage leaf. A fine bristle (from a paint brush) can be glued to one end of a wooden handle and a coarse bristle (from a tooth brush) glued to the other end. The responses of the caterpillars to a light touch and a stronger touch can be observed and recorded. Different regions of the body or different sensory hairs can be stimulated and the reaction noted.

In addition, a piece of glass tubing may be pulled into a fine capillary, and used to draw up very small quantities of liquid by capillarity. The reactions to the vapour of aromatic liquids can be explored by placing the capillary close to the caterpillar.

Do successive stimuli of any kind result in 'habituation', (that is, diminution and finally disappearance of a response)?

Problems and assignments

21.1 Sequencing activity in a nerve fibre

Draw up a matrix as shown in Table 21.1 and complete it, indicating which actions occur in the functioning nerve fibre, and when they occur.

Table 21.1 Activities in a nerve fibre

	Resting potential	Early in action potential	Late in action potential	Absolute refractory period	Relative refractory period
Active transport of K^+ and Na^+ (linked)					
Facilitated diffusion of K^+					
Facilitated diffusion of Na^+					
Influx of Na^+ via open channels					
Outflux of K^+ via open channels					
ATP used to maintain resting potential					

21.2 The synapse

The structure of the synapse is shown in Figure 21.8. Examine this diagram and answer the questions below, using your general knowledge of impulse transmission.

1. Make a list of the labels for the structures A to G.
2. Is the impulse transmitted from G to A, or from A to G?
3. What is the role of the structures labelled B at this point in the functioning nerve cell?
4. Name two of the chemical substances commonly found in the tiny structures labelled C (though not necessarily in the same neurone).
5. List the sequence of events at D when an action potential arrives by which a fresh action potential is generated in G.
6. What happens to the transmitter substance after it has been active at F?
7. What is the general name given to drugs that relieve pain?
8. Some drugs are known to interfere with transmission of an impulse at the synapse. In general, what different types of effect can such drugs have here?
9. A 'chemical' synapse is illustrated here. What other type of synapse is found in the body?
10. How big is the gap at E?
    a 20 mm;
    b 20 μm;
    c 20 nm;
    d 20 pm.

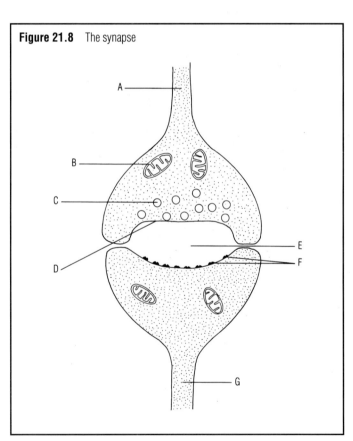

Figure 21.8 The synapse

21.3 The retina: structure and function

Figure 21.9 (opposite) represents part of the human retina in section. Examine this drawing and answer the following questions.

1. What type of neurones occur at A and make up the optic nerve?
2. What part of the brain do the neurones A make connection with?
3. The layer G in the wall of the eye is supplied with blood vessels. What is this layer known as?
4. A region of the retina known as the fovea consists of D-type cells only. Explain why the fovea is the region of most accurate vision.
5. Which labelled structures present are known as bipolar neurones? Why?
6. What is the role of the pigment cells F in the functioning eye?
7. What is the likely sequence of events when light rays fall on to the cell body of a E-type cell?
8. In what ways are the visual pigments in E- and D-type cells different?
9. What is the role of the structure at C?
10. Why is this type of retina described as 'inverted'?

Figure 21.9 The human retina in section

A

B

C

D

E

F

G

21.4 Quick test

1 Distinguish between the following pairs:

   a receptors and effectors;
   b reflex arc and reflex action;
   c action potential and resting potential;
   d active ion transport and facilitated diffusion;
   e neurones and neuroglial cells;
   f presynaptic neurone and postsynaptic neurone;
   g noradrenaline and adrenaline;
   h middle ear and inner ear;
   i pupil and iris;
   j suspensory ligament and ciliary body;
   k grey matter and white matter;
   l motor neurone and sensory neurone;
   m cerebral hemispheres and cerebellum;
   n nerve net and nerve cord;
   o hormone and pheromone.

2 What do you understand by the following?

   a giant nerve fibres;
   b cathode ray oscilloscope (CRO);
   c threshold of stimulation;
   d refractory period;
   e myelin sheath;
   f chemical transmission;
   g mechanoreceptors;
   h organ of Corti;
   i autonomic nervous system;
   j blood/brain barrier.

21.5 Essay assignment

Select one of the following:

- Describe the structure of a synapse and its method of operation. Since a synapse can be seen as an interruption in the transmission of the impulse, what roles may the synapse fulfil in the functioning organism?

or:

- By reference to two named hormones, outline the characteristic features of hormonal coordination in the mammal. To what extent are hormonal and nervous coordination of body function coordinated? Give examples.

22 Support and locomotion

Summary

Living things **support** themselves in positions to carry out the essential processes of life. The mechanical force (**stress**) an organism experiences comes from supporting the mass of the body tissues, from resisting the environmental forces (such as those due to wind) experienced by the body, and from movements of the organism.

Movement is a characteristic of all living things, and occurs within cells (as in cytoplasmic streaming) and by the cells and tissues of an organ (as in the pumping action of the heart). The movement of whole organisms is a different phenomenon, known as **locomotion**.

Most plants are stationary organisms, but many animals support themselves in a way that permits movements in the search for food and the avoidance of predators, and for reproduction, for example. In many multicellular animals the necessary support is provided by a **skeleton**. The roles of skeletons are to support the body, to act as a system of levers facilitating locomotion and to protect delicate organs. Animal skeletons are of three types: hydrostatic skeletons, endoskeletons and exoskeletons.

A **hydrostatic skeleton** consists of fluid contained in a limited space, enclosed by muscles. The fluid-filled compartments of the coelom of segmented worms, like those of *Lumbricus*, are examples. The body wall contains longitudinal and circular muscles that act antagonistically, powering the locomotion of the worm.

An **exoskeleton** protects and supports the body from an external position. The jointed exoskeleton of the arthropods, typical of insects, for example, facilitates walking (and jumping, sometimes) and flight, whilst containing the body and providing some protection, particularly from desiccation. The exoskeleton works efficiently in small animals.

An **endoskeleton** is a rigid internal framework of many component bones. In mammals the skeleton consists of the **axial skeleton** (skull and vertebral column) and the **appendicular skeleton** (limb girdles and limbs). Bones provide numerous points of attachment for the voluntary, skeletal muscles, and locomotion is made possible by the contraction of **muscles acting in antagonistic pairs** across **joints** between movable bones. Skeletal muscle consists of bundles of striped muscle fibres made up of a mass of parallel fibrous myofibrils. The alternate light and dark bands of the myofibrils are due to a system of interlocking protein fibres, which appear to slide past each other as muscles contract.

Locomotion in mammals is achieved by **movements of the limbs** which push down and backwards against the surroundings. Locomotion in water by fish and through the air by birds is facilitated by the **streamlined shape of the body**. Alternative methods of locomotion in the **Animal Kingdom** are **amoeboid movement**, as seen in some unicellular organisms such as *Amoeba* and certain white blood cells, and movement by **cilia and flagella**, which are whip-like organelles.

Support in flowering plants comes from the **turgidity of living cells**, the contents of which press against the inelastic cellulose cell wall. In woody plants the presence of dead fibres and xylem vessels, all with **lignified walls**, adds additional support.

Practicals and activities

22.1 Vertebrate skeletons compared

(Data generating)

The skeletons of vertebrates have common features, but also show significant differences that are exploited in classification (within the subphylum Vertebrata), and which may be seen as adaptations to particular lifestyles.

■ Aim

To investigate similarities and differences in the skeletons of a selection of vertebrates, and to relate these to lifestyle, as appropriate.

■ Risk assessment

Good laboratory practice will be sufficient to take account of any hazards and avoid significant risks.

■ Method

You are provided with a selection of three or four articulated skeletons of a selection of vertebrates, for example an amphibian, a bird and one or two mammals.

1 Examine each skeleton to identify the main features: skull, vertebral column, ribs, limb girdles and limbs.
2 Make a 'stick person' diagram of each skeleton, using an A4 sheet of paper for each, representing the sizes of the main features in correct relative proportions. An example of this sort of diagram is given in Figure 22.1, showing the rabbit skeleton in outline.

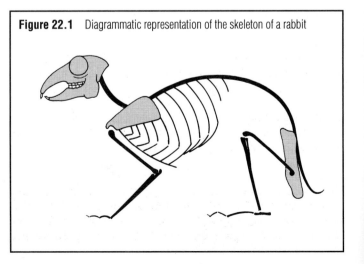

Figure 22.1 Diagrammatic representation of the skeleton of a rabbit

3 Annotate each diagram with the main features of the skeleton, bearing in mind the roles of the skeleton – support and muscle attachment (often there are noticeable flanges or reinforced areas where major muscle attachment occurs), movement across joints (the types of joints permitting walking/crawling, leaping, swinging/climbing or flying) and containment/protection of vital organs. Look carefully at areas of the skeleton for special features, including the following:

- the cranium and its articulation with the vertebral column;
- the vertebral column, the length (number of bones) in the different regions, and features for muscle attachment;
- the thorax, and the presence or absence of a rib-cage;
- the limb girdles, their size, muscle attachment facilities, and whether they articulate with or are fused to the rest of the skeleton;
- the fore- and hindlimbs, the differences between them, and the extent to which they depart from a generalised pentadactyl limb (see *Advanced Biology*, p. 492).

NOTE TO TECHNICIAN

Each student group will require access to a selection of articulated skeletons of different vertebrates such as:
- a frog, or other amphibian;
- a pigeon, or other bird;
- a rabbit and a human, or other mammals.

■ Data presentation
Record your observations by annotated diagrams, as described.

■ Conclusion
Tabulate the most prominent features of each skeleton that can be directly related to lifestyle and mode of locomotion.

■ Evaluation
Fragments of bone are often all that remain of extinct animals, and the analysis of such fragments often provides vital evidence of early life forms and lifestyles. Can you find any examples of this?

22.2 Histology of skeletal and muscle tissues
(Data generating)

Skeletal and muscle tissues are highly specialised.

■ Aim
To become familiar with the appearance and microscopic structure of skeletal and muscle tissues, and to relate structure to function where possible.

■ Risk assessment
Good laboratory practice will be sufficient to take account of any hazards and avoid significant risks.

■ Method
The basic structure of skeletal tissue is illustrated in *Advanced Biology*, pp. 210–12, and that of muscle on pp. 214–15. The histology of skeletal and muscle tissues is illustrated in W H Freeman and B Bracegirdle (1967) *An Atlas of Histology*, pp. 24–31 and 34–8 (Heinemann).

Skeletal tissue
Using the medium- and high-power magnification of the microscope, examine a prepared slide of a thin section of compact (hard) bone. Look for osteocytes and matrix arranged in Haversian systems (that is, in cylinders of bone surrounding central canals).

Optional extension Examine a prepared slide of a thin section of hyaline cartilage. Contrast the degree of organisation in compact bone tissue with the irregular arrangement of chondrocytes in the matrix of hyaline cartilage.

Muscle tissue
Using the medium- and high-power magnification of the microscope, examine the prepared slides listed below:
- voluntary (striated) muscle;
- effector nerve endings on voluntary muscle fibres;
- involuntary (smooth) muscle;
- cardiac muscle.

Look for:
- striated muscle fibres with peripheral nuclei and motor end plates;
- smooth muscle fibres with stained nuclei, one per fibre;
- cardiac muscle with branchings, nuclei, striations and intercalated discs.

NOTE TO TECHNICIAN

Each student will require the use of a microscope (with medium- and high-power objectives), with bench lamp if necessary, and access to the following prepared, stained slides of mammalian tissues:
- compact hard bone (thin section), showing lacunae and canaliculi of Haversian systems;
- voluntary (striated) muscle, stained for striations and nuclei;
- effector nerve endings on voluntary muscle fibres, showing motor end plates;
- involuntary (smooth) muscle, stained for myofibrils and nuclei;
- cardiac muscle, stained for striations and intercalated discs; and (if available) access to a copy of Freeman and Bracegirdle (for details see text).

For the extension work (if required):
- hyaline cartilage (thin section).

■ Data presentation
Make large, fully annotated drawings of representative portions of compact bone (with a note contrasting this structure with that of cartilage if the extension work is carried out), voluntary muscle, involuntary muscle and cardiac muscle.

■ Conclusions
- What features of hard bone structure can be related to its function?
- Contrast our knowledge of the structure of voluntary muscle myofibrils obtained by electron microscopy with the maximum detail of striped muscle fibre structure obtained by light microscopy.

■ Evaluation
Which of the structures you have studied in this practical do not show cellular organisation, and how can this be detected?

22.3 Composition of bone

(Investigation)

Bone consists of living cells in a matrix of collagen and calcium salts.

■ Aim
To investigate the effects of acid and heat on bone.

■ Risk assessment

- Care must be taken in using dilute hydrochloric acid and in heating the bone: wear eye protection.
- Otherwise, good laboratory practice will be sufficient to take account of any hazards and avoid significant risks.

■ Method
You are provided with two small bones from a chicken skeleton.

1 Place one of them in a test tube, cover with dilute hydrochloric acid and leave for 24 hours.
2 After this time, pour away the acid and wash the bone thoroughly with water. Try to bend or crush the bone.
3 Hold one end of the second bone in a hot Bunsen flame, heating it strongly for two minutes so that it chars at first and then glows red.
4 Allow the bone to cool on a heat-resistant mat and then try bending the bone or crushing the heated part with the end of a pencil.

NOTE TO TECHNICIAN

Each group will need:
- two chicken bones (preferably both the same);
- test tube and rack;
- dilute hydrochloric acid;
- a Bunsen burner, heat-resistant mat.

■ Data presentation
Describe any change in the shape, brittleness or flexibility of the bone which resulted from each treatment.

■ Conclusion
Explain the effect of each treatment on the composition of the bone and say how it affected the bone's properties.

■ Evaluation
What is the significance of the presence of living cells in bone, in addition to the non-living matrix?

22.4 Locomotion in non-vertebrates I: earthworm and locust

(Data generating)

In most animals, locomotion is a result of interactions of nervous, muscular and skeletal systems, causing the body to act on the environment, exerting forces that cause movement.

Apart from the rigid internal skeleton typical of all vertebrates, other types of skeleton are known, namely hydrostatic skeletons such as those of earthworms, and the hard exoskeletons of insects and other arthropods.

■ Aim
To demonstrate the distinctive nature of locomotion in organisms with contrasting skeletons.

■ Risk assessment

Good laboratory practice will be sufficient to take account of any hazards and avoid significant risks.

■ Method

Studying movement in the earthworm
Movement in the earthworm is described in *Advanced Biology*, pp. 486–7.

1 Place one of the large earthworms provided on moist blotting paper or filter paper, and observe the organised sequence of movements of the body.

   Watch the sequence of extension and then shortening (and widening) of each region of the body in turn. It may help to use a long-arm stereomicroscope to aid your observations of the changes to the body wall.

   Return the earthworm to the moist soil in the container, long before there is evidence that exposure of the animal is causing any dehydration. Use a fresh earthworm if necessary.

2 Place a fresh earthworm on a smooth, shiny piece of paper (or Perspex), and repeat the sequence of observations made above. This time the worm will make little progress, and you may well be able to hear a sound of 'slipping' chaetae. Use a stereomicroscope to observe the body wall and the (futile) movement of chaetae. Return the animal quickly to the soil in the container from which it came.

3 Using the medium- and high-power magnification of the microscope, examine prepared slides of the earthworm, in both LS and TS.

   Study the musculature of the body wall, and note how the circular and longitudinal muscles are arranged. What will be the effect on the body of alternate contraction of transverse and longitudinal muscles in the region of the section?

   TSs often pass through one or more of the chaetae, and it may be possible to see the arrangement of muscles that cause the chaetae to be extended or withdrawn, alternately, during locomotion.

Studying movement in the locust
Movement in insects is described in *Advanced Biology*, pp. 488–90. Remember that the locust is an insect that may fly, walk and hop, and that these methods of locomotion involve distinctly different processes. The forelegs are also used to hold food, at times.

1 If living locusts are available, housed in a glass-fronted cage, observe their feeding, walking and hopping movements. (Flight is uncommon in caged locusts.)
2 Using a preserved locust, examine the external appearance of the ventral surface of the thorax and the attachments of the legs. Is it possible to detect the planes in which the legs naturally move?

Measure and record the length of the femur and tibia of one of each of the pairs of legs, starting with the front pair.

Examine the joint between fibula and tibia sections of one of the legs. How would you describe this type of joint, and how does it work?

Examine the tip of the leg for evidence of a claw ending. Use a stereomicroscope to examine the legs. Is it possible to observe the arrangement of muscles through the intact wall (exoskeleton) of the femur?

3 Examine the wings of a preserved locust from the dorsal body surface. Move the individual wings to find out how flexible are the joints with the insect's body. How freely can the wings be moved?

Pin the animal to a cork or wax surface and then 'unpack' and pin out one of the upper wings. What is the likely role of this wing in the living insect?

Next do the same to the lower wing on that side. How does it unfold, as you spread it out?

The front and hind wings have distinctly different surface areas. Can you think of a way of comparing surface areas of the two wings fairly accurately?

Optional extension It is possible to study movement in a living locust, if one or more are available, and if you are prepared to attach (or have attached) the necessary harness to have control over the animal and be able to lift it off the ground. Once the legs are out of contact with a surface, the animal will commence flight, but stop when the legs are 'touched down' (the flight reflex).

One method of fitting a harness involves the tying of cotton thread (a running noose) around the thorax between first and second pair of legs. This manipulation is carried out on a locust that has been briefly cooled down in a refrigerator to render it inactive.

Reference
W M Clark and M M Richards (1976) *The Locust as a Typical Insect*, pp. 18–21. John Murray

Alternatively, using 'super glue', an attachment spar may be welded to the thorax. Once this is set up, it is found not to inconvenience the animal, which may be expected to have normal life expectancy subsequently, despite the experience. (Wear gloves to avoid skin contact with 'super glue'.)

Reference
D F Robinson (1978) 'Superglue and the locust', *School Science Review* (December 1978) 60(211), pp. 277–8

■ Data presentation
- Make fully labelled, annotated sketches to record your observations of movement in both the earthworm and the locust.
- Tabulate any numerical data, and then offer an explanation of its significance.

■ Conclusions
- What apparent advantages and what limitations to locomotion, if any, are imposed by the skeletons of these two animals?
- Are there comparably sized animals that have an endoskeleton with which to compare locomotion?
- Is their locomotion better related to their special environments than to their distinctive skeletons?

NOTE TO TECHNICIAN

Each student group will require (or require access to):
- a small plastic pot containing moist soil and two or three large healthy earthworms (see p. 27);
- sheet of blotting paper or rough filter paper;
- long-arm stereomicroscope, if available;
- sheet of glazed, shiny paper (or Perspex sheet);
- microscope (with medium- and high-power objectives), with bench lamp if necessary;
- prepared slides of TS and LS of earthworm;
- access to a cage of living locusts, if available;
- one or two specimens of preserved locust, on cork or wax dissecting surface;
- six stainless steel pins;
- sheet of graph paper and scissors (for measuring wing area, if required);

For the extension activity:
- locust harnessed for investigation of flight reflex, as described in the references mentioned in the text.

■ Evaluation
Is the size of an animal an important factor in influencing the type of locomotion that 'works' for that organism?

22.5 Locomotion in non-vertebrates II: Paramecium *and* Amoeba
(Demonstration)

Apart from locomotion by muscle action, other mechanisms for locomotion are found in the living world. These include amoeboid locomotion involving pseudopodia, and ciliary locomotion with cilia or pseudopodia.

■ Aim
To observe amoeboid and ciliary motion.

■ Risk assessment
Good laboratory practice will be sufficient to take account of any hazards and avoid significant risks.

■ Method
1 You are provided with cultures of *Paramecium* and *Amoeba*. Set up separate temporary preparations (p. 3) of these organisms, mounting them in their culture solution. In fast-swimming organisms like *Paramecium* it may help to add cotton wool threads, teased out on the microscope slide, to trap the organisms.

Keep your temporary mounts in a cool place (away from the microscope lamp beam) when they are not being examined.

2 Observe the 'swimming' action of *Paramecium* and the 'gliding' action of *Amoeba*. In both these organisms the observed movements may be associated with feeding, which in both involves the formation of food vacuoles in the cytoplasm.

3 Most detail in tiny organisms can be seen using phase-contrast microscopy, which is not normally available at this level. But with reduced intensity of illumination (using the iris diaphragm in the condenser), more details of the cell surface and cytoplasm can be resolved. Movement of the cilia covering the surface of *Paramecium* becomes visible and flowing movements in the cytoplasm of *Amoeba*, likewise.

NOTE TO TECHNICIAN

Each student will require:
- microscope (with medium- and high-power objectives), with bench lamp if necessary;
- microscope slides, coverslips, teat pipette, cotton wool;
- access to cultures of living *Paramecium* and *Amoeba*.

■ **Data presentation**

Make fully annotated drawings to record your observations of movement in these two organisms.

■ **Conclusion**

Construct a concise table to contrast the features of movement in these two organisms.

■ **Evaluation**

All locomotion of living things is dependent on metabolic energy. Do you think it likely that there are any fundamental differences in the ways cells make energy available for cellular activities, such as locomotion, whether for muscular, amoeboid or ciliary movements?

References

C R Curds (1991) *Protozoa and the Water Industry*. Cambridge University Press

R McNeill Alexander (1992) *Exploring Biomechanics: Animals in Motion*. Scientific American Library/W H Freeman

Projects

22.1 *Walking in insects*

Because of their small size and generally rapid movements, making observations on any aspect of insect locomotion can be difficult. Using stick insects, it is possible to observe the sequence of movement of the legs in walking. When a stick insect loses a leg (which it may do naturally) it grows a replacement. In the mean time, how does the absence of a leg influence the use in locomotion of the remaining five?

Reference

P Bragg (1992) 'The use of stick insects in schools', *School Science Review* (March 1992) 73(264), pp. 49–58

22.2 *Locomotion in snails*

The movement of land snails (or slugs) can be observed from below and above, using a sheet of Perspex or glass as the platform (or the sides of a glass aquarium used as the 'home' base). What is the role of the slime trail? How humid must the atmosphere be in general, for the animals to move? With artificial illumination, can you induce movements most common after dark to occur during our daytime?

Reference

R McNeill Alexander (1992) *Exploring Biomechanics: Animals in Motion*, pp. 57–85. Scientific American Library/W H Freeman

22.3 *Tracks and footprints*

Investigate the marks left behind by otherwise shy or nocturnal vertebrates. Footprints of birds and mammals made in soft, moist earth or mud can be captured as plaster casts. The marks left by amphibians and reptiles (which may include an impression left by the body, too) can similarly be made permanent. How easy is it to identify wading birds, for example, by their footmarks?

Reference

P Bang and P Dahlstrom (1972) *Animal Tracks and Signs*. Collins

Problems and assignments

22.1 Muscle: structure and function

Figure 22.2 Part of the structure of a myofibril, as seen by electron microscopy

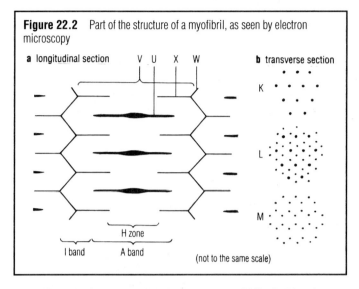

a longitudinal section

b transverse section

H zone

I band   A band

(not to the same scale)

1 **a** Where in the mammalian body do we typically find involuntary muscle? Where do we find voluntary muscle?
  b In what features of its structure does cardiac muscle resemble involuntary muscle and voluntary muscle respectively?
2 In voluntary muscle, bundles of fibres are bound together. Where do the myofibrils occur?
3 Figure 22.2(a) shows myofibril structure as seen in LS. Which structure labelled with a letter is:
  a the Z-line?
  b a sarcomere?
  c made of myosin?
  d made of actin?
4 **a** What event initiates contraction in a voluntary muscle fibre?
  b In the first step in contraction, the myofibrils become flooded with calcium ions (Ca^{2+}). Where are these released from?
5 During contraction there are changes in the apparent size of some of the bands and zones in a myofibril. Draw a grid as shown in Table 22.1, and complete it to show where these changes occur.

Table 22.1 Changes in a contracting myofibril

	No change	Shorter	Longer
H-zone			
A-band			
I-band			

6 Figure 22.2(b) shows three cross-sections (K, L and M) through part of a myofibril. Describe where in the LS drawing the plane of each of these three cross-sections will lie.
7 After calcium ions cause the removal of blocking molecules at the binding sites, cross-bridges form and the power stroke brings the thin filaments towards the centre of the sarcomeres.
   Draw labelled diagrams to show thin and thick filaments, the formation of a cross-bridge, and the mechanism of shortening.
8 ATP is essential for muscle contraction to occur. What mechanism supplies ATP to the heads of the cross-bridges during continuing muscle contraction?

22.2 Flight

1 'Flapping' flight as a distinctive means of locomotion has evolved in the Animal Kingdom more than once. Which major groups use, or have probably used, flapping flight?
2 The mechanisms of flight shown in insects and birds are described in *Advanced Biology*, pp. 488–90 and 504–6. Using this information, and your general knowledge of birds and insects, draw up a table identifying the fundamental differences between the structures and mechanisms for flight in insects and birds. Consider points about the skeletons, muscle arrangements, aerofoil (wing) structure, body shape and supply of oxygen.

22.3 Quick test

1 Distinguish between the following pairs:
  a compression and tension;
  b endoskeleton and exoskeleton;
  c circular and longitudinal muscles;
  d direct and indirect flight muscles;
  e axial and appendicular skeleton;
  f centrum and neural canal;
  g hinge joint and ball and socket joint;
  h sarcomere and myofibril;
  i actin and myosin;
  j haemoglobin and myoglobin;
  k lift and drag;
  l gliding and soaring;
  m cilia and flagella;
  n sol cytoplasm and gel cytoplasm;
  o radial and bilateral symmetry.

2 What do you understand by the following?
  a hydrostatic skeleton;
  b giant nerve fibres;
  c cuticle of insect's body;
  d 'slipped disc';
  e pentadactyl limb;
  f motor end plate;
  g sarcoplasmic reticulum;
  h cross-bridging myosin molecules;
  i creatine phosphate;
  j muscle spindle;
  k pitch, yaw and roll;
  l aerofoil;
  m pseudopodium;
  n turgidity of parenchyma cells;
  o reaction wood.

22.4 Essay assignment

Select one of the following:

• Give a concise summary of the sequence of events that occurs when resting voluntary muscle is stimulated and contracts. What mechanisms ensure a reserve supply of oxygen and ATP to contracting muscle?

or:

• The demands of flight in air and swimming in water are reflected in specialised features of structure. Contrast the specialisations to be seen in birds and fish that may be seen as adaptations to movement in these media.

23 Homeostasis and behaviour

Summary

In many animals internal conditions remain more or less constant, despite changes in the external environment. **Homeostasis** is the name given to the maintenance of a steady physiological state within the body, the outcome of which is a stable internal environment. Birds and mammals are particularly able to **self-regulate their internal environment**, including holding variables such as body temperature, blood composition (pH, blood sugar) and blood pressure within narrow limits. Self-regulation was discovered by **Claude Bernard in 1859**, from measurements of **blood sugar level in mammals** that had either consumed a large meal or had been deprived of food; blood sugar stayed relatively constant in both groups of experimental animals.

Self-regulation systems, also known as 'feedback' systems, involve sensitive **receptors** detecting bodily conditions, effectors to counteract change, **a control centre** where values are set and where incoming values are compared with the 'set' value, and **communication systems** linking these. In **negative feedback systems** the tendency to deviate from the set value is minimised, and this is the type of control common in living organisms.

In humans **blood glucose levels** are normally 90 mg 100 cm^{-3} (threshold value). Glucose is the usual 'fuel' molecule of most cells. It is the only fuel for brain neurones, which cannot store glucose at all: if blood sugar falls, brain function is quickly impaired. In the regulation of blood sugar level in the mammal, excess glucose is converted first to glycogen and subsequently to lipids in the liver, for storage there and around the body. If glucose supply is deficient then glycogen (and also amino acids and lipids) is converted to glucose, which is added to the blood. Muscles, however, do not contribute to blood sugar. Special endocrine cells in the pancreas respond to changes in blood sugar and release hormones that maintain the glucose at the threshold value.

The **liver** is a key homeostatic organ, being involved in the breakdown of defunct red cells, the formation of bile, the metabolism of carbohydrates and lipids, the deamination of excess amino acids, the formation of urea and the storage of fat-soluble vitamins and iron. Although the liver is metabolically active it is not normally a net heat-exporting organ of the body. Temperature regulation of homoiothermic animals such as mammals and birds is achieved by a complex regulatory mechanism in which the **thermoregulation centre in the hypothalamus** of the brain acts as the thermostat. Heat loss (and some heat gain) is mediated through the **skin, the largest organ in the body**.

Behaviour is defined as the way organisms respond to their environment and to other members of the same species. We sometimes talk of **innate** (or instinctive) behaviour and **learned** behaviour, but the distinction between the two is not clear-cut. Instead, animals display a range of different types of activities. Modern behaviour studies are based on the observation of animals in their environment, often aided by surveillance resources that permit behaviour to be studied with minimum interference by the observer. Very few animals lead totally solitary lives; most live in mutually tolerant pairings or **groupings** for most of their lives. Some species, such as ants, bees and other social insects, live in groups on a permanent and structured basis. Whether in solitary individuals or in groups, much animal behaviour shows a rhythmical pattern.

Practicals and activities

23.1 Studying the structure of the liver and pancreas

(Data generating)

The liver is composed of thousands of blocks of cells called lobules, formed from radiating rows (cords) of liver cells. The cords are separated by open channels (blood spaces) called sinusoids. The blood supply to the liver comes from the hepatic artery (oxygenated blood) and the hepatic portal vein (from the villi of the small intestine). This blood makes direct contact with the liver cells, and is drained from the liver by the hepatic vein. Also present in the lobules are bile canaliculi, which drain into bile ducts. The liver contributes directly to homeostasis, but its chief roles are bile production, the storage of fat-soluble vitamins, and the metabolism of carbohydrates, lipids and amino acids.

The pancreas is composed of enzyme-secreting cells arranged as a ducted gland (exocrine gland) that discharges pancreatic juice into the duodenum via the pancreatic duct, coordinated with the arrival of partly digested food from the stomach. But the pancreas also contains patches of cells, called islets of Langerhans, that secrete hormones into the bloodstream (endocrine glands). The pancreatic hormones (glucagon and insulin) regulate blood glucose levels.

■ Aim

To become familiar with the microscopic structure of the liver and the pancreas, and to relate structure to function where possible.

■ Risk assessment

Good laboratory practice will be sufficient to take account of any hazards and avoid significant risks.

■ Method

The basic structure and functions of the liver are illustrated in *Advanced Biology*, p. 514, and those of the pancreas on p. 513. The histology of liver and pancreas is illustrated in W H Freeman and B Bracegirdle (1967) *An Atlas of Histology* pp. 71–5 (Heinemann).

Using the medium- and high-power magnification of the microscope, examine the prepared slides provided of mammalian liver in VS, and pancreas in section, to contrast the structure of the two organs.

1 In the liver section look for:
  • the polygonal blocks of cells called lobules;
  • the position of branches of the hepatic vein, at the centres of the lobules;
  • branches of the hepatic artery, the hepatic portal vein and the bile ducts, between the lobules.

Under high-power magnification, differentiate the rows of liver cells from the blood sinusoids and the bile canaliculi (remember that in prepared slides they look very different from three-dimensional diagrams of working liver cells).

2 In the pancreas section look for:
  • the relatively large blocks or 'islands' of enzyme-secreting cells or 'acini' (singular, acinus), with blood vessels and pancreatic ducts, in section, in between;
  • the small patches of hormone-secreting cells (the islets of Langerhans) with tiny capillaries.

Optional extension

If electronmicrographs of liver and/or pancreatic cells are available, examine these as examples of cells that are metabolically very active. Look for the presence and relative numbers of organelles such as endoplasmic reticulum (both rough and smooth), mitochondria, the Golgi apparatus and (perhaps) the presence of batteries of pores in the nuclear membrane.

Refresh your memory of the roles of these organelles (*Advanced Biology*, pp. 155–9).

NOTE TO TECHNICIAN

Each student will require (or require access to):
  • microscope (with medium- and high-power objectives), with bench lamp if necessary;
  • prepared, stained slide of mammalian liver in VS (if pig liver sections are available these are preferable, since here the liver lobules are surrounded by connective tissue and are therefore visually more clearly defined; alternatively, sections of human liver or some other mammal may be held, in which the connective tissue tends only to surround the arteries, veins and ducts at the corners of the lobules);
  • prepared, stained slide of pancreas in section, showing islets of Langerhans, blocks (acini) of enzyme-secreting cells and branches of the pancreatic duct, with blood vessels, in section;
  • a copy of Freeman and Bracegirdle (1967) (for details see text), if available.

For the extension work:
  • transmission electronmicrographs of liver and pancreatic cells, available in cytology texts, or drug company publications on the ultrastructure of cells, or in teaching-aid packs commercially available.

■ Data presentation

Make large, labelled tissue maps of representative portions of the liver and the pancreas in section.

■ Conclusions

  • The roles of the liver are (broadly) to regulate the composition of the blood and to manufacture and secrete bile, which includes materials from defunct red cells.

  • The role of the pancreas is to secrete enzymes into a part of the gut, and hormones into the bloodstream.
  • In what ways are these structures well suited for their roles, bearing in mind their blood supply, and the arrangement of the cells?

■ Evaluation

What has the advent of electron microscopy added, in general, to the study of structure and function in specific organs such as the liver or pancreas?

■ Extension

From the organelles present in the cytoplasm, is there evidence for intense metabolic activity in liver and pancreatic cells?

23.2 Resources for learning about the role of insulin

(Demonstration)

Study of the role of hormones in blood sugar regulation does not lend itself to 'hands-on' practical enquiry. Instead, by the use of video or by computer-assisted learning, the issues of hormone regulation in homeostasis can be discussed.

The following resources are available:

Homeostasis: Maintaining the Body's Internal Environment is a 34-minute video, of which the final 16 minutes are concerned with water, oxygen and glucose homeostasis, including the general roles of regulatory hormones, and the feedback mechanisms of insulin, glucagon and appetite sensation in maintaining blood sugar levels. Produced by Human Relations Media Inc, USA and supplied by Boulton-Hawker Films Ltd (p. 434).

The *Animal Physiology Pack*, produced by Kings College, University of London. This CAL pack contains a program called 'Blood sugar', which models the relationship between the various factors affecting the level of glucose in the blood of a human. It illustrates the general principles of homeostasis in the process. Available for Acorn RISC OS (Archimedes), Nimbus 186 and 286 and BBC B+ Master microcomputers, and supplied by AVP (p. 433).

Insulin, produced by Brian Kahn for Cambridge University Press, is a CAL program that simulates the control mechanism for blood sugar level. The feedback mechanism involving insulin, glucagon and adrenaline is demonstrated as a pathway. Normal regulation is simulated, and the situation in insulin-deficient and glucagon-deficient people is used to show how sugar levels may change. The interactive presentation allows the effects of varying carbohydrate intake and hormone injections to be investigated. Available for BBC B+ Master microcomputers. Supplied by AVP or direct from Cambridge University Press (p. 434).

23.3 Investigating mammalian skin structure

(Data generating)

The skin is one of the largest organs in the human body; in the adult it covers an area of almost $20\,000\ cm^2$. In addition to containing and protecting the body contents (most importantly, normally preventing invasion by bacteria), the skin is involved in body temperature regulation, reception of stimuli, immunological functions and synthesis of vitamin D.

■ Aim

To become familiar with the structure of the skin, and to relate structure to function where possible.

■ Risk assessment

Good laboratory practice will be sufficient to take account of any hazards and avoid significant risks.

■ Method

The basic structure of the skin is illustrated in Figure 23.1 and the detailed structure of the epidermis (a stratified epithelium) is shown in Figure 10.6, a photomicrograph of the skin of the cervix, on pp. 208–9. The histology of the skin is illustrated in W H Freeman and B Bracegirdle (1967) *An Atlas of Histology*, pp. 94–7 (Heinemann).

1 Using medium- and high-power magnification, examine the prepared slide(s) provided of human skin in VS.
2 In the section(s) look for the divisions between the epidermis (normally darkly stained), the dermis and the subcutaneous layer (fat and connective tissue). In sections of skin from the scalp you will see numerous hair follicles in section. In sections of skin from highly cornified skin (such as the heel of the foot) the epidermis will be very much thicker than in skin from elsewhere in the body.
3 Under high-power magnification, differentiate the generative layer (Malpighian layer) at the base of the epidermis (stratified epithelium). The cells to the exterior progressively harden, flatten, die and fall off. The outer part of the dermis, where the cells are dead, is referred to as the cornified layer.

A hair follicle may be sectioned through a sebaceous gland. Within the dermis you may see (in part) sweat glands, sweat ducts or sweat pores. Also, within the dermis are different types of sense receptors but these have to be specially stained before they can normally be detected. The bulk of the dermis consists of elastic connective tissue.

NOTE TO TECHNICIAN

Each student will require (or require access to):
• microscope (with medium- and high-power objectives), with bench lamp if necessary;
• prepared, stained slides of human skin in VS (from different areas of the body, if possible).

■ Data presentation

Make a large, labelled tissue map of a representative portion of human skin in section, piecing together the general structure from various parts of the section where details can be seen.

■ Conclusion

The role of the skin is (broadly) to protect the body contents. In what ways are the observed structures well suited for this role?

■ Evaluation

The harmful effect of ultraviolet light on skin is much in the news. Why? What part of our skin is most at risk, do you imagine?

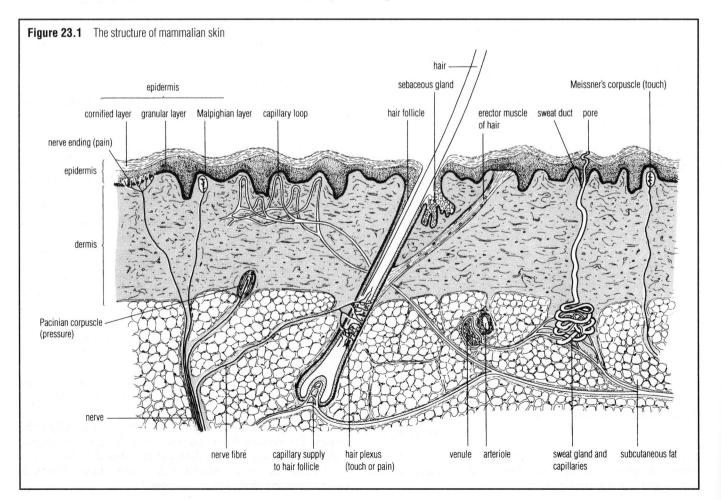

Figure 23.1 The structure of mammalian skin

23.4 Modelling heat loss

(Investigation)

Heat loss from a body is influenced by the amount of exposed surface area in relation to volume, by the difference between the internal and external temperature, by air movements and by the amount of insulation provided.

■ Aim

To model heat loss in animals, using laboratory apparatus, and with hot water as the 'interior' of the animal.

■ Risk assessment

- Take care when working with hot water.
- Otherwise, good laboratory practice will be sufficient to take account of any hazards and avoid significant risks.

■ Method

Design an investigation of heat loss from a range of containers (beakers, flasks and cylinders) that will provide different surface area:volume ratios, which you will need to calculate, into which identical volumes of hot water have been placed. Investigate also the effects of external temperature, moving air and degree of insulation, as best you are able.

Monitor temperature changes with a mercury thermometer, or with a digital thermometer with a long probe. Can you arrange for your data to be captured automatically, and printed out for you as a graph of heat change with time?

NOTE TO TECHNICIAN

Students may need a range of normal laboratory glassware, a supply of hot water and a thermometer (mercury or digital). Reasonable requests should be met. They may seek the use of a fan, a refrigerator and some forms of insulation. Dangerous or unsatisfactory proposals should be blocked by referring them to the teacher or tutor.

■ Data presentation

The results should be tabulated and graphed, as appropriate.

■ Conclusions

- Identify the factors that facilitate heat loss and heat retention.
- Use your data to explain why small mammals have a relatively high heat loss. Do your data add to your understanding of the causes of 'exposure' or 'wind chill'?
- What behavioural adaptations do animals use to help reduce heat loss?

■ Evaluation

To what extent do endothermic animals in general actually maintain a constant body temperature throughout life?

23.5 Woodlice and humidity

(Investigation)

The distribution of animals is influenced by a great variety of biotic and abiotic factors. The abiotic factors include temperature, light intensity and humidity.

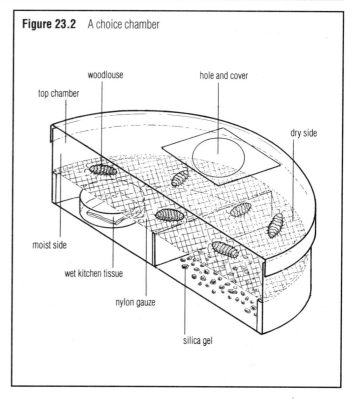

Figure 23.2 A choice chamber

labels: top chamber, woodlouse, hole and cover, dry side, moist side, wet kitchen tissue, nylon gauze, silica gel

Where the response consists of random movements in which the rate of movement is related to the intensity of the stimulus rather than to its direction, it is known as a kinesis.

■ Aim

To investigate the effect of a humidity gradient on the distribution of woodlice.

■ Risk assessment

Good laboratory practice will be sufficient to take account of any hazards and avoid significant risks.

■ Method

A choice chamber consists of a flat dish, such as a Petri dish. To establish a humidity gradient, divide the base by a partition; keep the animals above it by adding a nylon mesh or gauze (Figure 23.2). Place a piece of kitchen tissue, soaked in water, in the base on one side of the partition. On the other side place some silica gel (the crystals absorb water vapour). You will thus have set up a steep humidity gradient in the chamber.

Introduce 10 woodlice to the middle of the upper part of the chamber through a hole in the lid. Cover the hole and place the choice chamber under a box or cloth to exclude light. Examine the distribution of the woodlice every five minutes until no further change takes place.

Rotate the platform holding the woodlice through 180°, return the chamber to darkness and observe the animals as before.

You can make a qualitative comparison of humidities by placing squares of blue cobalt chloride (or thiocyanate) paper on each side of the platform.

How do the previous conditions of the woodlice affect the results? Try keeping them in a moist or a dry environment for a period before introducing them to the choice chamber.

Woodlice choose to inhabit dark, moist places. Which is more important, darkness or dampness?

Each group will need:
- choice chamber, 'home-made' from a Petri dish (see D G Mackean (1996) 'A cheap and cheerful choice chamber' *School Science Review* (June 1996) **77**(281), p. 70) or purchased from Griffin and George (p. 434);
- kitchen towel;
- silica gel crystals (about 8 g) preferably self-indicating;
- 10 woodlice (preferably kept in a dry dish for an hour before the experiment);
- paint brush for manipulating the woodlice.

If successive experiments are planned, students will need a fresh batch of woodlice for each experiment.

Figure 23.3   Polystyrene disc for studying clustering in woodlice

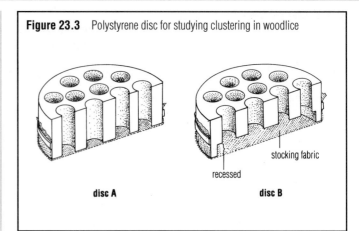

disc A   disc B

stocking fabric

recessed

■ Data presentation
- Make a table to show the number of woodlice on each side of the chamber at each observation.
- Use the chi-squared test to judge the significance of a 9 : 1 and an 8 : 1 distribution.

■ Conclusions
- Why, do you think, do woodlice prefer high humidity?
- Why was the choice chamber kept in darkness between observations?

■ Evaluation
- What do you think is the minimum number of woodlice needed in each experiment in order to get statistically significant results? (See *School Science Review* references: O N Bishop (1973) 'Choice, chance and the corkroaches' (June 1973) **54**(189), pp. 736–7; J Dunkerton (1979) 'Erroneous analysis of humidity preferences in Nuffield Advanced Biology' (September 1979) **61**(214), p. 164
- By observing the movements of the woodlice continuously throughout the experiment, can you see what aspect of their behaviour results in their final distribution?

■ Extension
Design experiments to find out the response of woodlice to:
- direction of light,
- intensity of light.

23.6 Clustering in woodlice

(Investigation)

One of the hazards of a terrestrial life is evaporation of water vapour from the body surface. Animals have developed different ways of reducing this loss. Insects, for example, have an impermeable cuticle. Other animals have behavioural or physiological adaptations which minimise water loss.

■ Aim
To find whether the behaviour of woodlice in 'clustering' does reduce evaporation.

■ Risk assessment
Good laboratory practice will be sufficient to take account of any hazards and avoid significant risks.

■ Method
- You are provided with two expanded polystyrene discs, each having 20 holes, and a base made from nylon stocking fabric. The base of one of the discs (B) is recessed to allow the woodlice to move freely (Figure 23.3). In the other (A), each woodlouse is kept separate from the others.
- You are also provided with two batches of 20 woodlice, matched approximately for size, which have been acclimatised to damp conditions for up to an hour.
- Working in a dissecting dish (to contain 'escapees'), place a woodlouse in each hole of disc A, covering each hole with a 1p or 5p coin to stop the woodlouse crawling out. A soft paint brush is useful to push the woodlice about, and a small polythene funnel with the stem cut short helps to deliver the woodlice.
- When all holes are occupied, pull the stocking firmly over the top, leaving one side partially open so that the coins can be tipped out together. Secure the stocking with an elastic band and pull it as taut as possible to stop the woodlice moving from one hole to another.
- Load disc B with 20 woodlice as well, but this time tip them all in at once through one of the holes. Secure the stocking over the top, as before.
- Weigh both discs and leave them exposed to air – on a tripod, for example – for at least 30 minutes (longer if possible).
- At the end of this period note the distribution of woodlice in each disc and weigh them again. Finally weigh both discs empty, together with the stocking fabric and elastic bands, so that you can calculate the mass of the woodlice.

Each group of students will need (or need access to):
- two polystyrene discs as described on p. 429;
- two tripods;
- balance accurate to 1 mg;
- two lots of 20 woodlice, matched approximately for size and kept in two Petri dishes with very moist kitchen towel for up to an hour before the experiment;
- paint brush for manipulating woodlice;
- small polythene funnel, with stem cut short enough to allow woodlice through;
- 20 coins, either 1p or 5p.

■ **Data presentation**
- Record the mass of each disc before and after the stated period of exposure and the mass of the apparatus without woodlice.
- Calculate the net mass loss and percentage mass loss in each case.
- Record your observations on the distribution of woodlice in each disc.

■ **Conclusion**

What effect does clustering behaviour appear to have on evaporation in woodlice?

■ **Evaluation**
- Could there be any other cause of mass loss, and how might it affect your results?
- If the woodlice in each sample were of markedly different sizes, would this significantly affect your results?
- Why, do you think, were the woodlice acclimatised to a very humid atmosphere before starting the experiment?

23.7 Phototaxis in blowfly larvae
(Skills and techniques/Data generating)

Blowflies (or 'bluebottles', *Calliphora* sp.) lay eggs in the carcasses of dead animals. When the larvae (maggots, known as 'gentles' to fishermen) hatch out they eat their way through the meat. When fully grown the maggots pupate on the surface of the meat and, in time, hatch as blowflies.

A taxis is a directional movement of the whole organism in response to a stimulus. Blowfly maggots can be negatively phototactic (helping maintain position within a carcass) or positively phototactic (at time of pupation).

■ **Aim**

To investigate the responses of blowfly larvae to light of varying direction, intensity and colour.

■ **Risk assessment**

- As you will be working in darkness or very low light, keep the working floor area free from obstructions.
- Wash your hands after handling blowfly larvae.
- When using colour filter sheets do not allow them to become overheated.
- Otherwise, good laboratory practice will be sufficient to take account of any hazards and avoid significant risks.

■ **Method**

The experiments have to be carried out in a room or laboratory blacked out or darkened by the use of curtains that exclude directional light. You are provided with 10 larvae (although more are available if required). You must account for all larvae at the end of the study. Carry out your experiments on a plastic tray to prevent maggot loss.

1 Place a sheet of graph paper on the tray and, using a pencil, outline a central square area of sides 2 cm. Place a bench lamp at one end of the tray, so that unidirectional white light falls across the graph paper. Otherwise, shield your tray surface from any other light source, if necessary.

2 Use one piece of graph paper for the 10 trials of the experiment. Mark on the graph paper the position and direction of the light source, and record the colour filter used.

For each trial, place one larva in the central square on the graph paper. Trace the direction of movement of the larva by drawing a line behind it as it moves across the graph paper (use a soft pencil). Make sure you do not cast a shadow over any part of the larva, nor touch it in any way. You might also record the time each larva takes to reach a point 10 cm from the centre of the start point (or to the edge of a square piece of paper). Use each larva only once in each experiment.

3 Carry out a control experiment, using very low, diffuse light (that is, without a direct light source).

NOTE TO TECHNICIAN

The laboratory or classroom needs to be blacked out or darkened by the use of effective curtains. Each student group will require:
- 10 living blowfly larvae in a container, supplied with a spare container;
- two bench lamps, metre rule;
- stopclock;
- black paper or cardboard and scissors, 'Blu-tack';
- plastic tray, not less than 50 × 40 cm;
- graph paper;
- a range of colour filter sheets (with details of transmission wavelength and percentage absorbance data).

■ **Data presentation**
- Each graph paper record of an experiment should have 10 tracks on it. These will give the directional response, if any. You may also have listed the times taken to reach a given distance.
- Devise a way of converting the tracks of the larvae into data that can be compared. For example, divide the paper into sectors radiating from the central point. Count the number of tracks in each sector. Present this data as a pie or rose chart (p. 39). Find the mean of the time taken.

■ **Conclusions**
- Were the movements of larvae in the dark (control) random? If not, are the rest of your experiments valid?
- Are the larvae phototactic? If so, are they positively or negatively phototactic? Are they colour blind to light of particular wavelengths?
- Add to your conclusion observations on how the larvae reacted to the light sources and the routes they tended to take.
- How does the behaviour of the larvae relate to their way of life?

■ **Evaluation**

Assess the validity of the colour filter experiments, in view of the fact that the filters provide light of different intensities.

■ **Extension**
- Repeat the original experiment detailed above, using a range of different coloured filter sheets fitted to the lamp.
- Repeat the original experiment, but vary the distance between the light source and the tray.
- Repeat the original experiment with a lamp at each end of the tray. This experiment can be repeated, varying the distance between the lamps.

23.8 Turning behaviour in woodlice or sea-slaters

(Investigation)

Woodlice, such as *Porcellio scaber*, and the much larger sea-slaters (*Ligia oceanica*) are similar isopods with limited visual powers, which use their antennae to navigate about the environment in the dark. The former are familiar terrestrial animals, while the latter live in crevices in piers and sea walls or at the top of the rocky shore. These animals show a similar level of activity and pattern of behaviour, and are suitable alternative organisms to investigate behaviour in a T-maze.

The T-maze offers a choice of a left or right turn at a T-junction, and the possibility of a range of experiences before the choice of turn has to be made.

■ Aim

To investigate whether an isopod's behaviour is influenced by its earlier behaviour. Or: is what the animal does next determined by what it did immediately before?

■ Risk assessment

- Take care of the woodlice or sea-slaters between 'runs' in the maze, returning them to dark, humid conditions between experiments.
- Otherwise, good laboratory practice will be sufficient to take account of any hazards and avoid significant risks.

■ Method

The experiments have to be carried out in a room or laboratory darkened by the use of curtains that exclude directional light. You are provided with a T-maze cut out of Perspex sheet, covered by a sheet of Perspex. Stand it on a clean sheet of paper or flat, washable surface. The channels of the maze are of a size that prevents the isopod you are working with from turning around in its tracks and reversing its direction. You also have five blocks by which the channels of the maze can be temporarily blocked off, if necessary.

1 You are provided with about 40 woodlice or sea-slaters in a dish covered by clingfilm, kept under a dark cloth. Using a plastic teaspoon and soft paint brush, you can introduce an animal to any point you choose in the maze by temporarily sliding the Perspex lid to one side and dropping a single animal at the required point.

2 Look at Figure 23.4, which represents the maze you are working with. Working with temporary blocks at G and F, and placing an isopod at D, find out which way the animal turns at B, following a forced right turn at E.

3 Next, place the temporary blocks at E and F, and placing the same isopod at H, find out which way the animal turns at B, following a forced left turn at G.

4 Record your results as S (same direction as previously) or O (opposite direction to previously). Devise a clear policy as to what constitutes a 'turn' (for example, either the initial movement of the head or the final direction taken by the isopod) and then stick to your ruling.

5 Return this animal to a second covered, darkened dish, to avoid re-using it immediately. Then investigate the responses of 35–40 isopods in these two situations.

6 Now find out whether you get the same pattern of results when the animal makes a 'journey' following the forced turn. This involves your using the full length of the maze, with side channels G and E and both J channels blocked. Require each isopod to first turn left or right at M, and, for both, record the direction of turn at B. Investigate the response of 35–40 isopods.

7 If the distance from M to B influences the outcome, then investigate whether a shorter distance (from J to B) has any influence on isopod decision making.

8 When the whole series of experiments is completed, return the isopods to their original habitat.

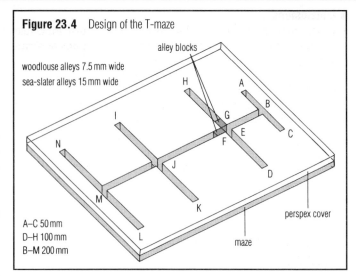

Figure 23.4 Design of the T-maze

alley blocks

woodlouse alleys 7.5 mm wide
sea-slater alleys 15 mm wide

A–C 50 mm
D–H 100 mm
B–M 200 mm

perspex cover

maze

NOTE TO TECHNICIAN

Each group of students requires:
- a container with about 40 isopods (woodlice or sea-slaters) in moist conditions, covered by clingfilm and a dark cloth, with a second, similar container for 'used' animals;
- plastic spoon and paint brush for handling isopods;
- a T-maze as shown in Figure 23.4 above.

■ Data presentation

- Tabulate your results as totals of 'sames' (S) or 'opposites' (O).
- If the numbers are roughly the same, then the choice is random.
- If the decisions are biased, the significance of the bias may need checking. The binomial statistical test is useful: see Table 23.1. (If the smaller total is equal to or less than the figure in the right-hand column of Table 23.1, then the results are significantly different at the 95% level.)

Table 23.1 Observing turning behaviour: binomial test

No. of isopods tested	Critical value of smaller total
40	13
39	12
38	12
37	12
36	11
35	11

■ Conclusions

- In the matter of turning, does the previous turn influence the next? If so, does it trigger the same or the opposite turn?
- Does a 'journey' influence memory?

■ Evaluation

Is there any chance that the isopod 'before' has laid or added to a trail that others respond to, positively or negatively?

Reference

P Openshaw (1983) 'What the isopod did next', *School Science Review* (March 1983) **64**(228), pp. 486–7

23.9 Resources for learning about animal behaviour

(Demonstration)

Experimental study of animal behaviour can be reinforced by the use of computer-assisted learning programs and video presentations designed for use at this level. The following resources are available:

Behaviour, produced by 'Nelcal' and supplied by AVP (p. 433) is a CAL package consisting of two programs. 'Maze' simulates 'trial and error' learning, in that the user has to find a way through a maze, drawn on the screen from the viewpoint of the occupant of the maze. The number of steps taken and the time taken are both logged. They can be graphically displayed as a 'learning curve'. The second, called 'Memory', tests the user's ability to recall information under different conditions. The package is available for BBC B and Master 128 microcomputers.

Stimulus/Response is a teaching video produced by the Association for the Study of Animal Behaviour, in association with the Universities of Bristol and Cambridge, and supplied by the Biology Department, Homerton College, Cambridge CB2 2PH.

In this video, animals are used to illustrate graphically the steps of behaviour phenomena, from 'stimulus' to 'response'. With pigs we see that stimuli are received from the very first moments of life, and the remarkable receptors of these animals are demonstrated. Hens are seen to run obstacle courses, and they are shown to have the mental capacities to learn from videos. Calves are used to show internal and external effectors, and we discover the surprising ways in which these animals are able to respond to the stimuli in their environment.

Projects

23.1 Mate guarding in brine shrimps

The brine shrimp (*Artemia salina*) can be purchased as dry eggs, and cultured in brine in a clean plastic bottle. A little sand is added, the bottle is laid on its side, and yeast is floated on to the surface every two or three days as food for the colony. Alternatively, algal primary producers can sustain the colony.

Culturing the colony must start several weeks before the observation period is planned. The colony is kept in a sunny location or under artificial light, at about 20–30 °C. The observer has to learn to recognise the sexes. The male uses moustache-like antennae to hold on to and guard the female, before fertilising the eggs. Some females throw off the male. Some males compete for females. A diary of observations should be kept.

Reference

M Dockery and S Tomkins (1995) 'Brine shrimps for behaviour studies', *Feedback, The ASAB Education Newsletter* no 3 (June 1995), pp. 12–15

23.2 Observing hedgehogs in summer

Surprisingly little is known about some of the most common of our native species. The extent to which this applies to the hedgehog can be gleaned from the reference sources cited below. At dusk in July and August you may perhaps be able to observe mating behaviour, for example. The issues of where the animals pass the hours of daylight, and when and how they commence their nightly foraging, are worthy of study. Do those near you normally return to the same 'nest'? Working under these conditions requires the observers to be in pairs, and to take steps to ensure their own safety, of course.

References

N Reeve (1994) *Hedgehogs*. T and A D Poyser
P Morris (1991) 'Spotlight: the hedgehog (*Erinaceus europaeus*)', *Biol. Sci. Rev.* 4(2), pp. 31–4

23.3 Mimicry studies

An organism is said to be a mimetic when it resembles a second organism, and benefits from the resemblance by deceiving a third organism. There are many examples of this. Dr Allen has experimented with artificial larvae made of pastry to investigate predation by wild birds. Further project ideas are suggested.

References

J A Allen and J M Cooper (1995) 'Mimicry', *J. Biol. Ed.* **29**(1), pp. 23–6
J A Allen (1994) 'Evolution in pastryland', *Biol. Sci. Rev.* 6(3), pp. 7–10

23.4 Human maze learning

Mazes run by humans using a pencil have certain advantages. An infinite number of mazes can be constructed, and there is an obvious fascination in investigations of ourselves, rather than (for example) minibeasts! In the reference below, the construction of a master maze is described, and its use in various trials is demonstrated.

Reference

R J O'Connell and C Snell (1973) 'Human maze learning', *School Science Review* (March 1973) 54(188), pp. 513–17

23.5 Studying human body temperature

Using a strip thermometer (not a fever strip) with the range of 20–40 °C, you can take your skin temperature in different parts of your body. Take readings over a 10-second period. Compare, for example, your skin temperature on limbs and forehead, and then compare these with your 'core' temperature, taken with a clinical thermometer held under your tongue for one minute. How do surface and core temperatures vary with exercise, and with drinking (hot and cold food), and at different times of the day? What is the range of temperature which should be considered 'normal' for you?

23.6 The human body clock and behaviour

Many aspects of body function vary in efficiency or effectiveness with time of day: they are said to demonstrate a circadian rhythm. Investigate how mental performance varies with time of day. Measure the core temperature of the body at the same time as doing the test, and see if there is any relationship between the two.

Reference

J Waterhouse and D Minors (1988) 'The human body clock. The ecology of time', *Biol Sci. Rev.* 1(2), pp. 14–19

23.7 The trails of ants

As ants move about, foraging for food, they leave a chemical trail of pheromones which allows other ants to join in. The trail must not last indefinitely, nor 'evaporate' too quickly. If lengths of the trail are obliterated, the trail walkers move about aimlessly until rejoining the former trail (with luck). By increasing the lengths that are obliterated, is it possible to find the time it takes for the original trail to disappear? Alternatively, in watching trail walkers, can you assess the amount of food supplies returning to the nest? Wood ants are generally large enough to make this latter task possible.

Problems and assignments

23.1 Regulation of blood glucose

Figure 23.5 shows the variations in blood sugar and insulin in a healthy person and a diabetic patient over a 48-hour period. Examine these data and, using them and your general knowledge of human physiology, answer the following questions.

1 a When glucose has entered the bloodstream, where in the body is it absorbed?

b Into what substance is glucose transformed for storage in body cells?

c What is the approximate threshold level of blood glucose (the level at which it is maintained) in the blood of the healthy person studied here?

2 In what ways is too high a glucose level potentially harmful to the body?

3 a Where in the body is insulin manufactured and released?

b What circumstances trigger a rise in blood insulin levels?

c About how often does this appear to happen in a 24-hour period in the healthy subject studied here? With what kind of event is this likely to be causally linked?

4 When insulin is caused to circulate in the bloodstream at raised levels, the concentration of blood glucose starts to fall. In which main tissues or organs is glucose uptake or metabolism altered by the presence of this insulin?

5 The diabetic person studied here received an insulin injection once daily, in the morning. What effect did this have on:

a blood insulin levels and

b blood glucose levels

during the ensuing 24 hours?

6 From the data in these graphs, suggest ways in which a research medical biochemist might be expected to be trying to improve the treatment for diabetes.

7 When blood sugar level falls below the threshold value in a healthy person, describe the sequence of events in the body which rectifies this situation.

8 If an abnormally low blood sugar level were to persist, what would be the most immediately life-threatening consequences for the individual?

9 If someone is persistently short of food (long-term starvation), what resources may the body draw upon in attempting to maintain blood sugar levels?

10 What forms of diabetes are known, and how do they arise?

23.2 Temperature regulation

A volunteer human subject was placed in a hot environment (a chamber at 45 °C) for an 80-minute period, without lasting ill effects. Meanwhile the body responded with an enhanced level of sweat secretion.

At 25-minute intervals the subject ingested ice, ostensibly to reduce discomfort. Actually, the ice was administered in order to investigate the mechanism by which body temperature is regulated.

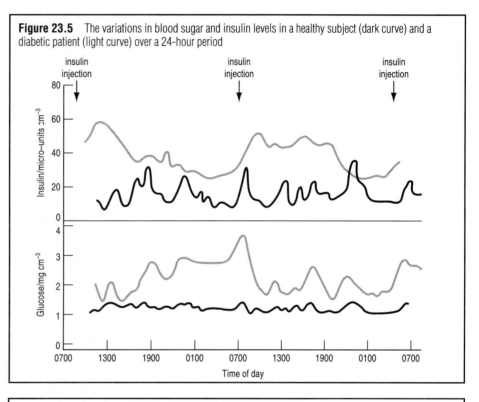

Figure 23.5 The variations in blood sugar and insulin levels in a healthy subject (dark curve) and a diabetic patient (light curve) over a 24-hour period

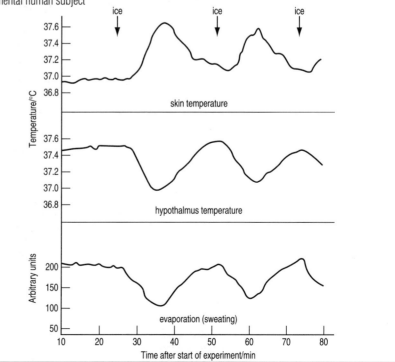

Figure 23.6 Relationship between skin temperature, hypothalamic temperature and sweating in an experimental human subject

Throughout the experimental period skin temperature, sweat production and the temperature of the hypothalamus were monitored continuously. The results are given in Figure 23.6. Examine this data and, using your knowledge of temperature regulation in an endothermic animal, answer the following questions.

1 The body of the experimental subject remained at a constant temperature for the first 20–30 minutes, despite an ambient temperature of 45 °C.

   a What would be the dangers to the body if its internal temperature was allowed to rise?

   b List the automatic (involuntary) responses of the body on detection of external raised temperature, as experienced here.

2 The experimental physiologists obtained their data on 'hypothalamic' temperature from a thermocouple placed beside the ear drum.

   a Explain why this measurement was obtained in this way.

   b Why was it necessary to have a record of temperature at this point in the body, as part of the investigation?

3 When ice was ingested, the level of sweat production quickly dropped.

   a Why did this occur?

   b List the sequence of events that occurred in the subject's body, from the arrival of solid ice in the stomach to the lowering of sweat production.

4 After examining the data, the scientists concluded that what they called the 'core' temperature of the body controlled sweat production, rather than heat receptors in the skin near to the sweat glands. Why is this conclusion justified?

5 If, alternatively, the subject had been placed in a very cold room:

   a By what mechanisms would the body have detected the low external temperature?

   b What would have been the body's automatic (involuntary) responses?

23.3 Quick test

1 Distinguish between the following pairs:

   a positive and negative feedback;
   b glucose and glycogen;
   c hyperglycaemia and hypoglycaemia;
   d hepatic artery and hepatic portal vein;
   e bile salts and bile pigments;
   f glycogenesis and glycogenolysis;
   g ectotherm and endotherm;
   h epidermis and dermis;
   i cornified layer and granular layer;
   j sebaceous gland and sweat gland;
   k hair papilla and hair follicle;
   l vasodilation and vasoconstriction;
   m innate and learned behaviour;
   n kineses and taxes;
   o habituation and imprinting.

2 What do you understand by the following?

   a homeostasis;
   b islets of Langerhans;
   c bile canaliculus;
   d liver lobules;
   e fat-soluble vitamins;
   f deamination of amino acids;
   g detoxification;
   h thermoregulation centre;
   i hypothermia;
   j melanocytes;
   k ethology;
   l reflex action;
   m conditioned reflex;
   n insight learning;
   o altruism.

23.4 Essay assignment

Select one of the following:

- Describe the roles played by the liver in the functioning of the body. Why is the liver described as a homeostatic organ?

or:

- Many animals show characteristic behaviour patterns in response to stimuli from the environment. Outline three examples of such patterns and explain the advantage each confers, choosing at least one in a vertebrate group of animals and at least one in a non-vertebrate group.

24 Health and disease

Summary

A species that causes a disease by infecting a host is described as **pathogenic**, and diseases that can be passed from one host organism to another as **infectious**. All the main groups of microorganisms include species that may cause diseases in other organisms, but relatively few microorganisms are harmful. Most animal diseases are caused by viruses (examples include influenza, rabies) or bacteria (typhoid, *Salmonella* food poisoning).

Antibiotics are naturally occurring biochemicals which at low concentration inhibit the growth of other organisms. They are natural products of microorganisms. The first antibiotic to be discovered, isolated and used in combating infection in humans was penicillin. Sexually transmitted diseases like gonorrhoea and syphilis are caused by bacterial species and lend themselves to both treatment and cure by antibiotics, if detected and treated early enough.

Very few animal diseases are caused by **fungi** (the exceptions include tinea and thrush). Similarly, the **protozoa** cause very few diseases, but those of humans may be devastating; they include sleeping sickness and malaria. The platyhelminth 'worms' include two classes that are all parasitic, and several members, such as the liver fluke and the tapeworms, parasitise humans.

Many **diseases of plants** are caused by viruses (such as the tobacco mosaic virus, and the virus causing leaf roll of potato). Others, such as damping off of seedlings and Dutch elm disease, are caused by fungi. **Fungicides** are important agents against disease in commercial crops.

Important **non-infectious diseases** include cancer, diabetes and the stress-related mental illnesses characterised by irrational behaviour. Preventive medicine is in fact more important in combating disease than the treatment of disease once it occurs. Preventive medicine, however, has often had to struggle for recognition of its importance and an appropriate share of resources.

Practicals and activities

24.1 'Flatworm' parasites of importance to humans
(Demonstration)

The flatworms or platyhelminths include two classes of animals whose members are all parasitic. This phylum is introduced in *Advanced Biology* on p. 35. Many of these parasitic flatworms infect humans or their stock animals and, if not treated, cause serious damage to the host species. The life cycle of the liver fluke (*Fasciola hepatica*) is illustrated in *Advanced Biology*, p. 422, and that of the beef tapeworm (*Taenia solium*) on p. 303.

■ Aim
To observe stages in the life cycle of a platyhelminth parasite.

■ Risk assessment
Good laboratory practice will be sufficient to take account of any hazards and avoid significant risks.

■ Method
You are provided with prepared slides of a liver fluke or tapeworm parasite. Examine these slides, and identify as many of the stages of the life cycle as you are able.

1 Draw a life cycle flow diagram using the names of the larval and adult stages rather than drawings. Mark on the diagram where and how the change of hosts occurs.
2 Now make clear and simple sketches of the stages in the life cycle that can be identified in the slides, labelling each with its name and that of its host.

Look out for review articles in science magazines such as *New Scientist* or *Biological Science Review* for accounts of the ways that species of flukes or tapeworms are currently of economic or 'health' importance to humans or their livestock. For example:

J Maurice (1994) 'Is something lurking in your liver?', *New Scientist* (19 March 1994), pp. 26–31

NOTE TO TECHNICIAN

Each student group will require (or require access to):
- a microscope (with medium- and high-power objectives), with bench lamp if necessary;
- prepared slides of stages in the life cycle of the liver fluke (*Fasciola hepatica*) or the beef tapeworm (*Taenia solium*), as required.

■ Data presentation
Make a record of the stages in a flatworm's life cycle, as outlined above.

■ Conclusion
Parasites often (but not always) have complex life cycles, with several larval stages. In addition to a main host, their life cycle may include a period of time in a secondary host, sometimes referred to as the vector.

Suggest reasons why this complexity of life cycle may be advantageous to the parasite.

■ Evaluation
In what ways may parasitic flatworms enter their vertebrate host?

24.2 Phytophthora infestans, *the cause of potato blight*

(Investigation)

Few diseases are so devastating they change the course of human history. One such is potato blight, the disease due to the fungal parasite of the potato plant, *Phytophthora infestans*, an organism that occupies a special place in the history of plant diseases. This fungus appears to have reached Europe in the 1830s. It ravages potato crops when conditions are warm and humid. It literally destroyed the potato crop in Ireland in 1845, subsequently causing the disastrous Irish Famine. Years later mycologists (Berkeley in the UK and de Bary in Germany) realised and then established that the tiny fungal threads of *Phytophthora*, among all the microorganisms in a rotting potato plant, had actually caused the disease. Subsequently it was discovered that the majority of plant diseases were caused by fungi. The concept of a 'fungicide' came in 1882 from the work of a French chemist (Millardet), who observed that vines that had been sprayed with a mixture of copper(II) sulphate and 'lime' (to discourage theft!) were free from fungal diseases, mainly mildews. This 'Bordeaux mixture' proved to be effective against potato blight, too. Meanwhile, vast numbers of the Irish, for whom potatoes were the staple diet, had died or emigrated.

■ Aim

To investigate the fungus that causes potato blight, and something of its scientific, economic and social consequences.

■ Risk assessment

Good laboratory practice will be sufficient to take account of any hazards and avoid significant risks.

■ Method

The biology of *Phytophthora infestans* is introduced in *Advanced Biology*, p. 304. The life cycle is described in P Lowrie and S Wells (1991) *Microorganisms, Biotechnology and Disease*, pp. 206–8 (Cambridge University Press).

1 Examine the prepared slides of an infected leaf of potato, showing the feeding mycelium stages in the fungus' life cycle.
2 Draw a life cycle flow diagram using the names of the stages, rather than drawings. Mark on the diagram where each stage occurs (for example, 'host plant leaf', or 'dormant tuber'), when the infection spreads, and the environmental conditions favourable to spread.
3 Now make clear and simple sketches of the stages in the life cycle that can be identified in the slide, labelling each with its name. This should include a haustorium (a feeding structure within leaf cells), and the sporangiophore protruding through a stoma in a position to release sporangia.
4 Search for review articles and textbooks that can answer the following questions:
   • 'Seed' potatoes used in the UK come from Scotland. Why is this necessary?
   • Spraying with fungicides against potato blight is recommended to potato growers when the crop experiences warm, wet (or humid) conditions, if these arise in July and August. Why?
   • Fungicides are either surface-acting or systemic. What is the difference between them? What are the potential drawbacks in their unrestricted use?

5 Find out the general rules which a microbiologist applies in order to confirm that a particular organism is the causative agent of disease. These are known as Koch's postulates. Why?
6 Research, by discussion with colleagues who study history, the extent of the social and economic consequences of the Irish Famine. How significantly is its influence rated in the history of these islands?

NOTE TO TECHNICIAN

Each student group will require (or require access to):
• microscope (with medium- and high-power objectives), with bench lamp if necessary;
• prepared slide of a stained section of a potato leaf infected with *Phytophthora infestans*, showing spore production.

■ Data presentation

A wall newspaper presentation is an effective way of presenting the outcome of your research. You can use this as a visual aid, if you talk to a group of your peers about the issues.

■ Conclusion

Should the study of science be more closely related to its social or other consequences for people?

■ Evaluation

Because several microorganisms have devastating effects as pathogens, is there a danger that people may view microorganisms in general as harmful?

24.3 *'Damping off' of seedlings*

(Investigation)

Pythium is a common fungus of normal soils, where it feeds saprotrophically on dead organic matter. However, if conditions become moist enough for fast, lank growth of seedlings, the mycelium of *Pythium* will survive at the soil surface among the seedlings, where it may parasitise the stems at soil level. The results are spectacular!

Pythium can be described as a 'facultative' parasite, because it switches to a parasitic mode if the chance arises, but is not obliged to be parasitic.

■ Aim

To investigate the conditions that favour 'damping off' disease of seedlings, and to observe the appearance of the fungus *Pythium* in host tissue.

■ Risk assessment

Good laboratory practice will be sufficient to take account of any hazards and avoid significant risks.

■ Method

The biology of *Pythium* is illustrated in *Advanced Biology*, p. 543. The life cycle is described in P Lowrie and S Wells (1991) *Microorganisms, Biotechnology and Disease*, pp. 208–9 (Cambridge University Press).

1 You are provided with six small trays of cress seedlings, grown in garden soil. You have access to water, so the seedlings can be maintained well watered. You are also

provided with plastic bags into which the trays will fit individually. If available, two small paper hygrometers of a size that would allow you to place one in a bag with a plant tray, are provided. Plastic bag ties are available, and you have access to laboratory stands and clamps. A maximum and minimum thermometer is available in your working area, for reference.

2 Design an investigation of the conditions that will induce 'damping off' disease in the cress seedlings. Set up a control group of seedlings under conditions that you are confident will prevent 'damping off' disease. Monitor conditions around the plants in as much detail as you are able. You can expect your experiment to run for a week to 10 days at most.

3 Finally, using any seedlings that become infected, investigate the appearance of plant tissue that is apparently being invaded by a fungal parasite. You should be able to squash tiny lengths of such 'stem' tissue in water on a microscope slide. Stain this tissue with a suitable fungal and plant tissue stain, and examine your temporary mounts under medium and high power (apply a coverslip first). Stains that may be available include methylene blue, toluidine blue and lactophenol.

NOTE TO TECHNICIAN

Each student group will require:
- six small trays of cress seedlings, grown in garden soil;
- plastic bags and ties;
- small paper hygrometers, if available;
- access to a maximum and minimum thermometer;
- other general laboratory equipment, as appropriate, if agreed by the teacher or tutor.

■ Data presentation
- Present a flow diagram of your experimental procedure and sketch the experimental and control set-ups you design. Set up a diary record of the physical parameters you decide to measure, and record your observations of plant growth in the same way.
- Make simple line drawings of the fungal parasite you observe among the tissue on which it feeds. Show any evidence of spore production in the same way.

■ Conclusions
- What conditions favour rapid 'damping off' infection? What conditions seem to lead to mild infection? What conditions appear to prevent infection?
- From your microscope work, could you identify stages in the *Pythium* life cycle?

■ Evaluation
Under what circumstances is 'damping off' likely to be a major problem to a commercial grower?

24.4 Antibiotics and bacterial growth

(Investigation)

Antibiotics are naturally occurring substances produced by some microorganisms, which have biocidal properties on other microorganisms. Antibiotics have been developed and exploited by humans in combating disease and in sustaining intensive rearing of livestock. The discovery of antibiotics is outlined in *Advanced Biology*, p. 535.

■ Aim
To investigate the effects of specific antibiotics on the growth of bacteria.

■ Risk assessment

- Microbiological work requires safety precautions. These are detailed in Practical 5.2 on p. 69.

■ Method
The effect of antibiotics on the growth of bacteria is an extension of a study of the culturing of microorganisms, given in Practical 25.1, pp. 284–7. Refer to that experiment for this practical.

Projects

24.1 Susceptibility to the common cold

Almost all of us succumb to certain common ailments from time to time. But some of us do so far more often than others. Is the tendency to 'catch a cold' a family trait, or can it be linked to our diet, or to some aspect of our environment, or even to attitudes? Or can our method of 'curing a cold' be linked to how often colds recur? In a social science research project like this there is a range of techniques you might adopt, but most likely you would design and use a questionnaire. There are rules and 'good practice' to apply in this field, which you may be unfamiliar with as a 'bench scientist'. Be prepared to investigate appropriate methods, including questionnaire design, before you start even a small-scale trial investigation.

Reference
J Bell (1993) *Doing your Research Project: a Guide to First-time Researchers*, pp. 58–69. Open University Press

24.2 Smoking and health

Smoking is on the decrease in most countries in the developed world (but we are exporting the habit to the less-developed world, which is serious). But here in Britain more young people are smoking, say the researchers. Why is this? What persuades people to get started? How do smokers and non-smokers respond to factual material on the detailed problems that smoking brings? What sort of approaches to smokers incline them to think critically about the habit? Again, this is a 'social science' research project. You will need to research the best methods to adopt. See the reference in Project 24.1.

24.3 A parasite of the earthworm's seminal vesicles

The seminal vesicles of the earthworm (*Lumbricus terrestris*) may be parasitised by *Monocystis agilus*, a protozoan that makes 'demands' that do not present a serious hazard for the host. How can the parasite reach this part of the host's body? How is it transferred to other hosts, from time to time? What stages in the life cycle of the parasite can you find in the contents of the seminal vesicles? You will need to research the breeding process of worms and the life cycle of the parasite, and make temporary stained mounts of the contents of seminal vesicles.

References

H G Q Rowett (1962) *Guide to Dissection.* John Murray
R Buchsbaum (1986) *Animals without Backbones.* University of Chicago Press

Problems and assignments

24.1 Food poisoning: the rising risks

You can extend your knowledge about this issue in the following useful sources:

J Maurice (1994) 'The rise and rise of food poisoning', *New Scientist* (17 December 1994), pp. 28–33
G Collee (1989) 'Food poisoning', *New Scientist* 'Inside Science' (21 October 1989)

1 Food poisoning due to bacteria, viruses and other organisms is rising in nearly all countries that keep records. The incidence of reported cases in the UK, in the period 1982–93, is summarised in Table 24.1.

Table 24.1 Incidence of food poisoning in the UK, 1982–93/cases per 100 000 of population

Year	Incidence
1982	30
1983	38
1984	42
1985	40
1986	48
1987	58
1988	78
1989	100
1990	108
1991	122
1992	130
1993	140

a Plot a graph of these figures.
b If the current trends are maintained, approximately how many cases per unit of population may be anticipated annually by the year 2000?

2 Imagine yourself as a scientific civil servant in a position to advise government on matters of public health. Respond to the following questions raised by your Minister, who clearly needs helpful advice to be able to formulate policy for future years, and to answer questions posed by political opponents.

a Suggested factors in the rise include 'better diagnosis' and 'an ageing population with an increasingly weakening immune system'. Can these have been factors in the rises, and why?

b I'm told that rivers are sometimes contaminated with raw sewage, and cattle and sheep drink from these rivers.
  i How may this contribute to food poisoning?
  ii What should I argue for in Cabinet, concerning the supervision of the water industry?

c Another source of contamination is 'sea foods' (shellfish and the like), I'm told.
  i How is it that shellfish manage to get contaminated with 'bugs' that can do harm inside humans?
  ii Can we actually do anything about the quality of waters around our coasts that may help?

d Your predecessor told me about new microorganisms that have appeared and started to make matters worse. One organism mentioned was called *Escherichia coli* 0157:H7, which can occur in some lightly cooked ('raw') hamburger meats, and which causes 'bloody diarrhoea' if eaten.

i Can 'new organisms' arise?

ii What should our advisers be telling the 'fast food' industry to do about this one?

iii What advice should we give the public in leaflets to be distributed?

e Another issue raised in an earlier advisory paper to me was about frozen meats (poultry, I think) that were not fully thawed before being cooked, or thawed but kept in the fridge with cooked meats, and then cut up for cooking alongside already-cooked food. They do go on, these bacteriologists! Can there be any problems from all this? Surely not! Tell me what is going on here.

Well, Minister, you reply . . .

24.2 Thyroid cancer in the Ukraine

Read Panel 24.1, which forms part of a letter to the journal *Nature* from eight scientists (seven working in the Ukraine and one from Oxford) published in June 1995. It concerns the incidence of one type of cancer around Chernobyl since the accident at a nuclear power station there on 26 April 1986. Then, using your general knowledge of human physiology and the information given, answer the following questions.

1 The thyroid gland overlies the trachea, near the larynx.
   a What sort of gland is it?
   b What role do its secretions perform?
   c Why is it that the iodine taken into the body becomes concentrated in the thyroid gland?

2 What are the characteristic symptoms of patients whose thyroid gland is:
   a overactive?
   b underactive?

3 By what routes did ^{131}I from the Chernobyl accident, having landed on the agricultural land around cities like Kiev, reach the bodies of people living in the cities, whether or not they were at home at the time of the accident?

4 Why did children receive doses on average higher than those received by adults?

5 Why exactly is ^{131}I likely to cause cancer in thyroid tissues?

6 The radioactivity to which the people of the Ukraine have been exposed since Chernobyl will steadily decrease as time passes. What factors are concerned in its fall?

7 Why do so many children, born *after* the accident, develop thyroid cancer?

8 Comment on the rate of diminution of the incidence of thyroid cancer with increasing distance from Chernobyl.

Panel 24.1 Thyroid cancer in the Ukraine

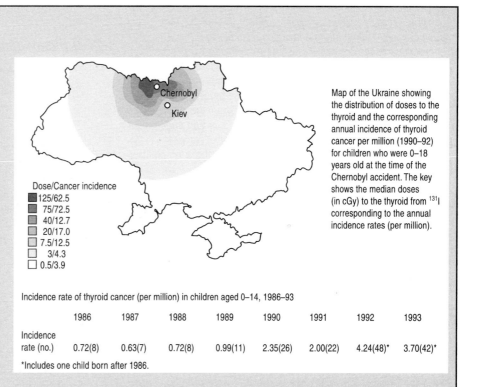

Sir—When a serious accident occurs in a nuclear power station, fallout from radioactive iodine (mainly ^{131}I) is often one of the main sources of human exposure to ionizing radiation. Radioactive iodine may be taken into the body by inhalation or in food, a major source being milk, and is concentrated in the thyroid gland. In May–June 1986, several weeks after the Chernobyl accident on 26 April 1986, measurements of thyroid content of ^{131}I were made for 150 000 people in the Ukraine, including 110 000 children aged 0–18 years at that time. Because the thyroid gland is small in children and they drink more milk than adults, children were estimated to have received doses that were on average three times higher than in adults.

The table shows the number of children aged 0–14 diagnosed with thyroid cancer in the Ukraine each year from 1986 to 1993 and the annual incidence rate per million. Incidence rates were fairly steady for the first 3 years, at around 0.7 per million per year, but have increased since 1989, the rate in 1993 being about five times higher than in 1986.

The increase in incidence of thyroid cancer in children in the whole of the Ukraine masks larger increases in the most heavily contaminated areas. The figure shows seven zones within the Ukraine divided according to estimated average thyroid dose in children. The legend gives the median dose to the thyroid and the annual incidence rate in children aged 0–18 at the time of the accident who were diagnosed with thyroid cancer in 1990–92.

From: Nature (*1 June 1995*), p. 365

Map of the Ukraine showing the distribution of doses to the thyroid and the corresponding annual incidence of thyroid cancer per million (1990–92) for children who were 0–18 years old at the time of the Chernobyl accident. The key shows the median doses (in cGy) to the thyroid from ^{131}I corresponding to the annual incidence rates (per million).

Dose/Cancer incidence
- 125/62.5
- 75/72.5
- 40/12.7
- 20/17.0
- 7.5/12.5
- 3/4.3
- 0.5/3.9

Incidence rate of thyroid cancer (per million) in children aged 0–14, 1986–93

	1986	1987	1988	1989	1990	1991	1992	1993
Incidence rate (no.)	0.72(8)	0.63(7)	0.72(8)	0.99(11)	2.35(26)	2.00(22)	4.24(48)*	3.70(42)*

*Includes one child born after 1986.

24.3 Whooping cough and vaccination

Whooping cough was the most lethal of the common illnesses of children in the nineteenth and early twentieth century. Today it is preventable by means of a vaccine, administered early in childhood. At present the disease makes 'comebacks' from time to time, largely because of the numbers of children not vaccinated (there have been fears about the safety of the vaccine). Deaths from the disease are extremely rare, however.

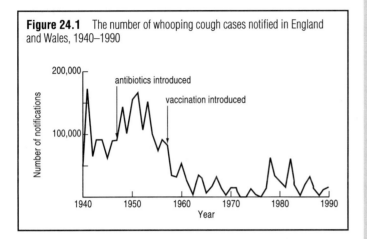

Figure 24.1 The number of whooping cough cases notified in England and Wales, 1940–1990

1 The causative agent of whooping cough is described as a tiny bacillus. What does the term 'bacillus' imply?
2 In what ways do bacteria that invade our bodies and feed there (as bacterial parasites), actually cause harm to the body?
3 What is a vaccine? How, in principle, is a vaccine produced?
4 Look at the graph in Figure 24.1. You will note that the incidence of whooping cough was tending to decrease before the introduction of a vaccine. The numbers of deaths from the disease had certainly declined since 1946. What reasons can you suggest for these improvements?
5 For what reasons, do you think, have the numbers of children being vaccinated fallen during recent years?
6 The effectiveness of most vaccines is constantly monitored. It is found that a new vaccine is frequently required to maintain the protection once offered by the former one. Why is this?

24.4 Quick test

1 Distinguish between the following pairs:

  a   antibiotics and vaccines;
  b   bacteria and viruses;
  c   exotoxins and endotoxins;
  d   gonorrhoea and syphilis;
  e   trypanosomiasis and malaria;
  f   flukes and tapeworms;
  g   necrotrophic and biotrophic fungi;
  h   benign and malignant tumours;
  i   infectious and non-infectious disease;
  j   circulatory and respiratory diseases.

2 What do you understand by the following?

  a   pathogen;
  b   health;
  c   Koch's postulates;
  d   germ theory of disease;
  e   'resistance' to antibiotics;
  f   food poisoning;
  g   viral transmission by aphids;
  h   fungicides;
  i   epidemiology;
  j   Dutch elm disease.

24.5 Essay assignment

Select one of the following:

- What features of a parasite distinguish it from an organism such as a female mosquito, which visits human skin for a blood meal? Outline the life cycle of a named parasitic organism of economic importance, highlighting the points where the infection may spread to fresh hosts.

or:

- What are antibiotics, and how were antibiotics discovered? How do antibiotic-resistant strains of pathogens arise? How do we attempt to control the spread of antibiotic-resistant bacteria?

The Continuity of Life

25 Viruses, prokaryotes, protoctista and fungi

Summary

Continuation of life from generation to generation is dependent upon **reproduction**, and involves the **copying** of the instructions (**nucleic acid** in the form of DNA, or RNA in certain viruses) that code for the structure and way of life of the organism. The instructions are then **shared** between the new individuals that originate from the parent organism and eventually replace it. In **asexual reproduction**, processes such as splitting, spore formation or budding give rise to new individuals: the progeny are genetically identical to the parent organism. **Sexual reproduction** involves the production of special sex cells (gametes), which fuse to form zygotes that grow into new individuals: the progeny are similar to the parent organisms, but not genetically identical.

Reproduction in the **viruses** is quite different from reproduction in living things. The virus nucleic acid, on entry to a host cell, takes over its enzymic machinery and switches it to the exclusive production of virus particles. Viruses are highly specific in their choice of host, some being **parasites** of a particular plant species, others of a particular animal species, and still others (known as **bacteriophages**) of a particular bacterial species.

Bacteria are unicellular, prokaryotic organisms that occur in vast numbers, virtually everywhere. Whilst some bacteria are parasitic and cause disease, most are saprotrophic. Bacterial cells reproduce asexually by dividing into two cells. Cell division is preceded by replication of the ring of DNA that occurs naked, in the cytoplasm of the cell. An unusual form of sexual reproduction is occasionally observed in certain species.

The **protoctista** exhibit an array of different life cycles, involving asexual or sexual reproduction, and sometimes both. The protoctista include the **algae**, which are photosynthetic organisms with cell structure and metabolism very similar to those of higher green plants. The algae include **unicellular** forms (like *Chlorella*), **simple multicellular filamentous forms** (like *Spirogyra*), and large, **multicellular plants showing division of labour within the plant body** (like *Fucus*).

The **protozoa** are the unicellular animal organisms of the protoctista. They mostly have heterotrophic nutrition (for example, *Amoeba* and *Paramecium*, with holozoic nutrition), and a few are actually parasitic and cause serious diseases in mammals (such as *Plasmodium*, which causes malaria). Reproduction of protozoa frequently involves **fission** of the cell after division of the nucleus.

The **fungi** too, have heterotrophic nutrition, many being saprotrophic organisms feeding on dead and decaying matter (*Mucor*, the pin mould, and *Agaricus*, a mushroom, are examples). The fungal body, a **mycelium**, often consists of fine, branching threads called **hyphae**. Fungi are eukaryotic organisms, although in many fungi the body is not divided into individual cells. At some stage in the life cycle spores are produced on a specialised part of the mycelium. The yeasts (*Saccharomyces*) are unicellular fungi of great economic importance.

Practicals and activities

25.1 Basics of bacteriology
(Skills and techniques/Investigation)

Although very many species of bacteria are perfectly harmless to humans (and life as we know it would not proceed without them!), bacteriologists handle all cultures as if they were pathogenic. Under suitable conditions bacteria grow at a great rate, and one potential danger arises from exposure to very large numbers. If an 'inoculum' of many hundreds of thousands of bacteria should happen to get into the body by accidental contamination, even if they belong to some harmless species, in these numbers they might have ill effects (allergic reaction or other illness). If they were of a pathogenic species, of course, the effects might be lethal, so we see to it that pathogens are not used in school or college work.

Consequently, bacteriologists employ **aseptic** (sterile) **techniques** to prevent bacteria from cultures contaminating the environment (including a human host) and, at the same time, to prevent bacterial cultures from being contaminated by microorganisms from the environment.

The essential guidelines for safe bacteriology in schools and colleges are laid down in *Microbiology: an HMI Guide for Schools and Further Education* (ISBN 0-11-270578-2), and in the DfEE publication (1996) *Safety in Science Education* (ISBN 0-11-270915-X), both obtainable from HMSO.

■ Aim
To acquire the skills and techniques of bacteriology, and to apply them in investigations of bacterial growth.

■ Risk assessment

The following are essential precautions to take in all microbiological work:
- Wash your hands with soap and water before and after all practical work.
- Do not put your fingers near your face (mouth, nose or eyes) during the experimental work.
- Never consume food or drink brought into, or used in, the laboratory.
- Mark out your work area with a sheet of lining paper, and keep all apparatus within this zone.
- Keep containers such as Petri dishes and plugged flasks closed or stoppered, except when opening them for transfer or inoculation.
- Sellotape Petri dish lids to the dish bases immediately after they are inoculated (but not completely, all the way around, since this might exclude air and encourage growth of anaerobic bacteria, if present). Do not open these Petri dishes unless they have been sterilised.

- Do not incubate cultures at temperatures approaching human body temperature (37 °C). 30 °C should be the upper limit for incubation.
- Plates that have been exposed must finally be sterilised (in a pressure cooker or autoclave) before the contents are disposed of and the dishes washed.
- At the end of the experiment, dispose of the lining paper, and swab down the bench with freshly prepared disinfectant.

■ Method

Setting up a sterile nutrient agar plate

A very common method of growing bacteria is on the surface of an agar plate in a Petri dish. Agar is a long-chain polysaccharide obtained commercially from certain seaweeds. An aqueous solution of agar will set to give a firm gel which remains solid below 97 °C (that is, in all incubation temperatures used). Agar is not normally digested by microorganisms. Appropriate nutrients for the growth of particular microorganisms must be added to the agar. Nutrient agar is a formulation containing peptone, meat extract (Bovril, for instance) and water, with agar. It is conveniently obtained in tablet form (agar and nutrients combined). To prepare the medium for use, two to three tablets are soaked in 15 cm³ of distilled water in a McCartney bottle (Figure 25.1), and then autoclaved (temperature of 121 °C for 15 minutes) or sterilised in a domestic pressure cooker (103 kPa for 20 minutes).

1 You are provided with a beaker of boiling water and a sterilised McCartney bottle containing 15 cm³ of nutrient agar. Place the McCartney bottle into the boiling water, to melt the agar. After a few minutes, temporarily remove the bottle (taking care to handle it with a cloth) and slightly unscrew the cap to allow the expanded air to escape from the McCartney bottle. When the agar is completely molten, remove the bottle and leave it to cool to a temperature just comfortable to handle (about 50 °C, but no cooler, for agar sets at 42 °C).

2 Now pour the agar into the sterilised Petri dish provided. Take up the bottle in one hand, and unscrew and hold the lid with the little finger of the other hand. Flame the mouth of the bottle for two to three seconds in the Bunsen, thus killing bacteria at the lid area. Next, lift the lid of the Petri dish sufficiently to allow the neck of the bottle to enter. Pour the molten agar into the dish. Replace the lid and swirl the dish gently, so that the agar is evenly distributed. Replace the McCartney bottle lid. Leave the agar plate to cool down and set solid.

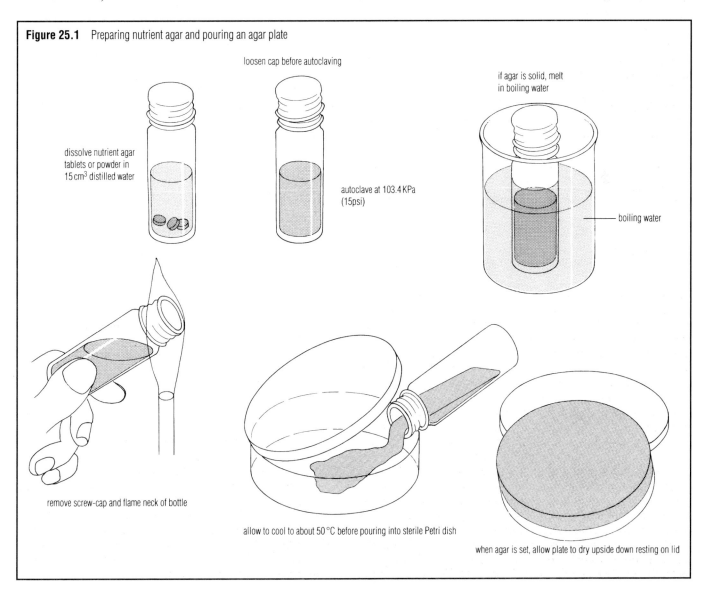

Figure 25.1 Preparing nutrient agar and pouring an agar plate

loosen cap before autoclaving

if agar is solid, melt in boiling water

dissolve nutrient agar tablets or powder in 15 cm³ distilled water

autoclave at 103.4 KPa (15psi)

boiling water

remove screw-cap and flame neck of bottle

allow to cool to about 50 °C before pouring into sterile Petri dish

when agar is set, allow plate to dry upside down resting on lid

3 Finally, dry off excess water by placing the plate, upside down and resting on its lid, in an incubator at 37 °C for about 30 minutes. Replace the lid (whilst the plate is still inverted), and then turn the dish over and store it on its base. The plate is now ready for use.

Inoculating and incubating plates

Inoculation of an agar plate is carried out with a sterile wire loop (Figure 25.2).

4 Sterilise a wire loop by flaming it in the hot part of the Bunsen flame, holding it pointing downwards almost vertically in the hottest, outer part of the flame to allow the whole length of the wire to redden. Allow it to cool for about 10 seconds, ensuring it does not touch an unsterilised surface. Once it has been used it must be resterilised before being put down.

5 The bacterial culture is provided on an agar slope in a McCartney bottle (screw cap) or test tube (cotton wool plug), or in a liquid culture (broth) in a tube (cotton wool plug). Using the sterilised innoculating loop in your right hand (if you are right-handed) and the culture container in the left, remove the screw top or cotton wool plug with the little finger of your right hand, and flame the neck of the culture container to sterilise the opening. Then scrape the surface of the culture on the agar with the sterilised, cooled innoculating loop (or insert into the broth), withdraw the innoculating loop, and replace the lid/plug, reflaming the neck of the stock culture container just before you do so. Then, raising the lid of the agar plate slightly using the left hand, apply bacteria to the agar with firm, gentle movements over the surface. Replace the Petri dish lid, and resterilise the innoculating loop before laying it down. (If you are left-handed, reverse the hands used in the above instructions.)

6 Secure the lid of the Petri dish to the base with adhesive tape, without excluding the entry of air (anaerobic conditions are avoided as anaerobic species are more likely to be dangerous). Invert the dish for the incubation phase, so that condensation does not collect on the culture. Place the dish in an incubator set at 25–30 °C, according to the species being cultured.

Examining a growing culture

Do not open your Petri dish at any time.

7 Examine your plate at least twice a day. Once colonies appear, a plate is best observed by illuminating from the

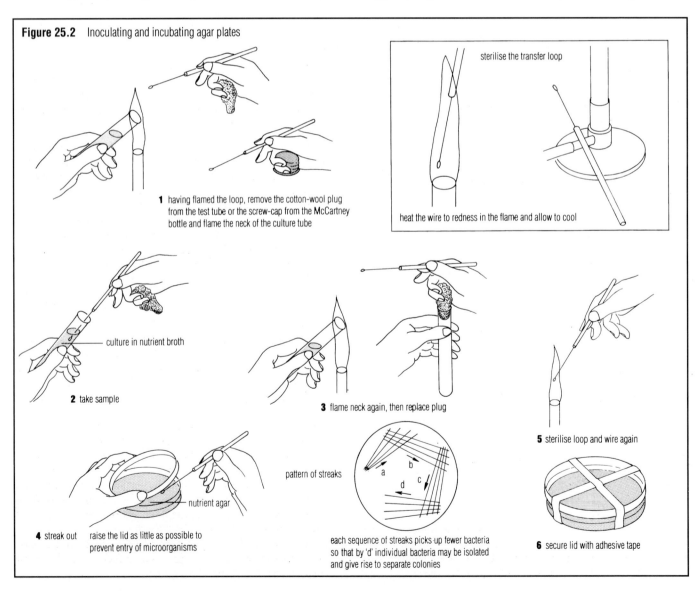

Figure 25.2 Inoculating and incubating agar plates

sterilise the transfer loop

heat the wire to redness in the flame and allow to cool

1 having flamed the loop, remove the cotton-wool plug from the test tube or the screw-cap from the McCartney bottle and flame the neck of the culture tube

culture in nutrient broth

2 take sample

3 flame neck again, then replace plug

5 sterilise loop and wire again

pattern of streaks

4 streak out raise the lid as little as possible to prevent entry of microorganisms

each sequence of streaks picks up fewer bacteria so that by 'd' individual bacteria may be isolated and give rise to separate colonies

6 secure lid with adhesive tape

back and then from the sides, to see details. Note and record, by means of annotated sketches:
- the timing of the growth of colonies,
- the colony characteristics, and
- any apparent interactions between particular colonies as they enlarge over the plate surface.

Colony characteristics of importance in the identification of bacteria include shape, size, colour, elevation (flat or raised), edge and surface texture (Figure 25.3).

Sterilisation and disposal of old plates/cultures

8 Place old cultures that are no longer required in their (unopened) Petri dishes, together in an autoclavable bag or other container, and put them into the autoclave or pressure cooker used to sterilise by heat and pressure. Plastic Petri dishes and other plastic equipment should be in one container, glass equipment (such as McCartney bottles or glass Petri dishes, which can be re-used when sterilised and clean) in another. When sterilisation is completed, dispose of the plastic equipment in the dustbin, and wash the glass equipment for re-use.

NOTE TO TECHNICIAN

Each student group will require:
- beaker, tripod, gauze, Bunsen burner, heat pad;
- supply of boiling water from a kettle;
- sterilised McCartney bottle containing 15 cm^3 of nutrient agar;
- sterile plastic dish (or glass Petri dish), with pen to label;
- inoculation wire loop;
- access to a culture of *Escherichia coli* or *Bacillus subtilis* or *Micrococcus luteus*;
- access to an incubator at 25–30 °C;
- access to the autoclave, and autoclavable bags (or pressure cooker with aluminium containers).

If a camera with colour film is available, use this to record the appearance of the plates.

■ Data presentation

Record your results by means of annotated drawings, and include a photographic record of the colonies, if possible.

■ Conclusion

How would the appearance of the colonies have differed if the plate had been flooded with a much-diluted soil solution (Practical 5.2, p. 69), rather than an inoculum of a pure culture streaked across the surface of the plate?

25.2 Bacterial contamination of stale milk
(Investigation)

■ Aim

To investigate the community of bacteria present in stale, pasteurised milk.

■ Risk assessment

- As for Practical 25.1 (p. 284); for all bacteriological work these safety precautions must be rigorously enforced.
- Otherwise, good laboratory practice is sufficient to take account of any hazards and avoid significant risks.

Figure 25.3 Agar plates with bacterial colonies growing

■ Method

You have access to a pint bottle of pasteurised milk, held in an ordinary refrigerator. Investigate how the numbers of bacteria change in the milk as it 'ages' from day to day, either with storage in a fridge, or at room temperature (or both, if time and resources permit).

1 Decide over how many days you can carry out this investigation. For example, it would be useful to have a count of bacteria in a sample taken 24 hours after purchasing the bottle and putting it in the fridge, followed by counting samples taken at two-day intervals, for a week.

2 Design your investigation with the following points in mind.
- The numbers of bacteria in milk are high. You will find that 1 cm^3 of fresh milk, spread out over the surface of a sterile nutrient agar plate, will grow so many colonies when incubated at 30 °C for 24 hours that you will not be able to count them all. You must employ serial dilution (pp. 69–70), and estimate the numbers of bacteria present in the original sample.
- It is suggested that you make three dilutions each time you sample the milk: one of 1/10, one of 1/100, and one of 1/1000. This involves transferring, with a pipette, 1 cm^3 of milk (or milk dilution) to 9 cm^3 of distilled water each time, and mixing thoroughly before sampling further.
- Transfer 1 cm^3 of each dilution over the surface of a sterile nutrient agar plate, using a clean pipette. Secure the lid to the base, label each dish with the age and dilution of the milk, and incubate at 30 °C for 24 hours.
- Count the number of individual colonies that appear, and then multiply this count by the dilution employed. This gives you an estimate of the numbers of bacteria in 1 cm^3 of the milk at this stage (age).

3 Draw up a list of the equipment you will need, and discuss the experiment and your requirements with your teacher/tutor before requesting items.

■ Data presentation

Record your estimates of the change in numbers of bacteria in 1 cm^3 of milk with time in a table. Plot a graph.

■ Conclusions

- Comment on the level of bacterial contamination in 'fresh' milk and on the effects of ageing.
- Speculate on the likely sources of the bacteria.

■ Evaluation

How could you attempt to satisfy yourself that the bacterial colonies observed have grown from the inoculum, and not from spores that entered (for example, from the air) during your manipulations of the equipment?

25.3 Bacterial growth in the presence of antibiotics

(Investigation)

■ Aim

To investigate the growth of a bacterial colony in the presence of various antibiotics.

■ Risk assessment

- As for Practical 25.1 (p. 284); for all bacteriological work these safety precautions must be rigorously enforced.
- Otherwise, good laboratory practice will be sufficient to take account of any hazards and avoid significant risks.

■ Method

1 You are provided with a beaker of boiling water, and a sterilised McCartney bottle containing 15 cm^3 of nutrient agar. Melt the agar and then leave it to cool to a temperature just comfortable to handle (about 50 °C), as described above.

2 Place the McCartney bottle in a water bath at 45 °C, and allow the nutrient agar to cool to this temperature (just above the 'setting temperature' of agar).

3 Using a culture of a saprotrophic (and therefore, non-pathogenic) bacterium such as *Escherichia coli*, *Bacillus subtilis* or *Micrococcus luteus*, inoculate the molten nutrient agar in the bottle (held at 45 °C), using a sterilised inoculation loop. Immediately plate out this nutrient agar in a sterile Petri dish that has been warmed in an oven at 45 °C (to prevent condensation). Allow the agar to cool and set (about 5–10 minutes at room temperature).

4 Using sterilised forceps, transfer a special filter disc of patches impregnated with a range of antibiotics to the surface of the inoculated nutrient agar. Make certain that all patches of antibiotic are in contact with the agar surface before closing and sealing the dish.

5 Incubate this plate at 30 °C for 24 hours. Finally, examine the culture without opening the dish.

■ Data presentation

Record which antibiotics are effective against the bacterium used. Where inhibition of bacterial growth has occurred, what is the appearance of the surface of the agar at this point?

■ Conclusions

- How have the antibiotics reached the cells of the bacteria?
- Antibiotics are extracted by the pharmaceutical industry from fungi, other bacteria and lichen cultures. What is the role of antibiotics in nature?

■ Evaluation

Why is it necessary to keep the plates sealed, even when antibiotics are present?

25.4 Disinfectants/antiseptics and bacterial growth

(Investigation)

Disinfectants and antiseptics are chemicals that kill or inactivate microorganisms, principally bacteria. Disinfectants are used to destroy bacteria in the environment (in sinks and drains, for instance) but are unsafe to use on the body.

■ Aim

To investigate the effects of disinfectants/antiseptics on bacterial growth.

■ Risk assessment

The essential precautions to take in all microbiological work are detailed for Practical 25.1. They must be applied here, too.

■ Method

1 You are provided with two sterilised nutrient agar plates and a liquid (broth) culture of *Escherichia coli*, *Bacillus subtilis* or *Micrococcus luteus*, or some other 'safe' saprotrophic bacterium. Use an L-shaped glass spreader to produce an even spread of bacteria over the agar surface. Sterilise the spreader by standing it in 75% ethanol and

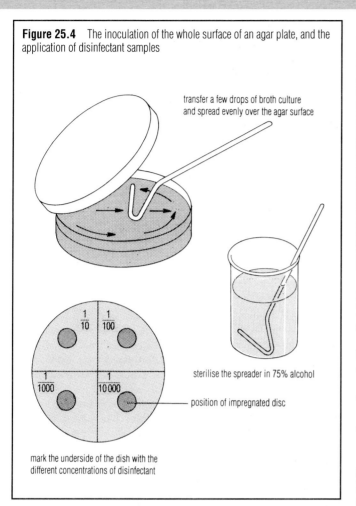

Figure 25.4 The inoculation of the whole surface of an agar plate, and the application of disinfectant samples

transfer a few drops of broth culture and spread evenly over the agar surface

sterilise the spreader in 75% alcohol

position of impregnated disc

mark the underside of the dish with the different concentrations of disinfectant

Each student group will require:
- beaker of alcohol, tripod, gauze, Bunsen burner, heat pad;
- two sterilised nutrient agar plates, waterproof marker pen to label;
- sterile plastic dish (or glass Petri dish);
- cork borer, L-shaped glass spreader, fine forceps, small pile of clean filter paper discs;
- access to a liquid culture of *Escherichia coli*, *Bacillus subtilis* or *Micrococcus luteus*;
- access to an incubator at 25–30 °C;
- two test tube racks, with four test tubes and a 10 cm^3 graduated pipette;
- access to two commercial disinfectants/antiseptics, such as Dettol and TCP.

If a camera colour film is available, use this to record the results.

■ Data presentation
Make a fully labelled sketch of the results observed in the nutrient agar plates.

■ Conclusions
- Relate the growth of the bacteria to the concentrations of disinfectant.
- Comment on the importance in household and commercial situations of using correct dilutions of disinfectants.
- Comment on the ability of bacteria to use apparently harmful chemicals as 'substrates' for growth.

■ Evaluation
How could you modify this procedure to be certain that the microorganisms that grew came only from the broth provided?

25.5 Resources for learning about bacteria
(Demonstration)

Experimental studies of microorganisms can be reinforced by the use of video presentations and CAL programs. The following resources are available:

Monera: Bacteria and Cyanobacteria is a video that is purpose-made for A-level courses in the UK. It is based on 'live' and time-lapse photography, animations and electromicrographs, which are used to outline the basic characteristics of bacteria and cyanobacteria. The presentation is divided into discrete sections about cell structure, size and shape, cell wall chemistry, reproduction and growth, transfer of genetic material, nutrition, respiration, and evolutionary perspective. Available from Boulton-Hawker Films Ltd (p. 434).

Antibiotics: The Mould, the Myth and the Microbes (a BBC *Horizon* production) is a video that reassesses (1986) the early history of penicillin, de-mythologising Fleming's role in its discovery and concentrating on the wartime research and development work of Florey, Chain and Heatley. Can be hired from Video Loans Club. Telephone: 0171 611 8246.

Bacterial Growth 2, produced by Mike Tait of Aberdeen University, is a CAL package written to support an undergraduate course on microbiology. Of special interest is the way computer simulations are used as an effective alternative to 'wet' practicals involving time-consuming and complex experiments that will not fit into normal laboratory sessions.

then quickly passing it through a Bunsen flame to ignite the alcohol. Allow it to cool for a few seconds before use. Using the sterilised L-shaped glass spreader, inoculate the surface of both agar plates, as shown in Figure 25.4. After use, stand it in alcohol in the beaker.

2 With the waterproof marker, divide the base of the two nutrient agar Petri dishes into quarters, and label them 1/10, 1/100, 1/1000 and 1/10 000. Turn the Petri dishes up the right way.

3 For both the commercial disinfectants provided, make serial dilutions to give solutions at 1/10, 1/100, 1/1000 and 1/10 000 of the original strength. Do this in the test tubes provided, transferring 1 cm^3 of disinfectant to 9 cm^3 of distilled water. Mix the solution well, and then transfer 1 cm^3 to a second tube, also containing 9 cm^3 of distilled water, and so on. Label all your dilutions to avoid confusion.

4 Label the base of each of the nutrient agar plates thus prepared with the name of one of the disinfectants/antiseptics.

5 Using a cork borer, cut out discs of filter paper from a small stack of clean filter papers. Handle these with forceps sterilised in a Bunsen flame. Immerse one disc in a dilution of one of the disinfectants/antiseptics, and place it on the surface of the agar at the centre point of the 'quarter' marked out on the underside with the respective dilution. Repeat this with all dilutions of both disinfectants/antiseptics. Set the plates to incubate at 25 °C for 2–3 days.

6 Examine each plate daily, and note the growth, if any, of the bacterial cultures on the nutrient agar around the treated filter discs.

Another aim is the development of the transferable skills of experimental design and data interpretation. Available for IBM PC/clones (386 or better) with Windows (3.1 or better) microcomputers, from Scotcal Software.

25.6 Ecology of the distribution of Pleurococcus
(Investigation)

Pleurococcus is an ubiquitous green alga growing on some surfaces of walls, posts and tree trunks.

■ Aim

To investigate the predominant factor(s) controlling the distribution of *Pleurococcus*.

■ Risk assessment

- Good laboratory practice will be sufficient to take account of any hazards and avoid significant risks.
- The rules of safe practice in fieldwork studies are given on p. 30.

■ Method

1 Identify a range of sites in the locality of your school or college laboratory (or your home) in which enough *Pleurococcus* is found growing to give a green colour to the surface (most noticeable after rain). If possible, select sites facing most points of the compass, or as many points as show *Pleurococcus* growth. These are likely to include tree-trunks, old stone or brick walls, gateposts, gravestones or wooden fence sections. Also identify comparable surfaces/ structures nearby, where no growth of *Pleurococcus* occurs.

2 Take a scraping of this surface growth and, on your return to the laboratory, examine it under the medium- and high-power magnification of a microscope.

3 Design an arbitrary scale of density of growth of *Pleurococcus*, ranging from:

'lowest score' = *Pleurococcus* absent,
to 'highest score' = surface completely covered with a dense covering of *Pleurococcus*.

The scale has to be one that you can apply consistently, to make comparisons of the density of *Pleurococcus* on different surfaces and of different points on the same surface.

4 Decide which abiotic factors (pp. 20–4) you wish to measure on the surfaces you will study. Some readings, such as those of light intensity, will be those to take whilst you assess the distribution of *Pleurococcus* where it grows, compared with nearby sites where algae are absent. For others, such as rainfall water run-off, you will need to set up monitoring devices to collect data over a longer period.

5 Carry out your investigation of distribution and of abiotic factors that may influence it.

NOTE TO TECHNICIAN

Student groups are likely to require:
- tape measure;
- 0.25-metre quadrat, marked out on a transparent plastic sheet;
- plotting compass;
- light meter;
- string, 'Blu-Tack', yoghurt pots or similar, to collect rain run-off from surface.

■ Data presentation

Present your data in tables, and by any other graphic methods that facilitate comparisons.

■ Conclusion

What environmental factors appear to determine the distribution of *Pleurococcus*?

■ Evaluation

To which environmental pollution is organisms like *Pleurococcus* vulnerable, do you think?

Reference

C J Clegg (1984) *Lower Plants*, p. 23. John Murray

25.7 Growth of Chlorella in 'eutrophic conditions'
(Investigation)

Chlorella is a unicellular alga that grows in pond water, particularly in the warmth of late spring and summer, provided the water is rich in nutrients. The water may turn bright green as a result. Such a 'bloom' of *Chlorella* occurs when fresh waters are polluted by a high concentration of nitrates and/or phosphates, such as occur in 'run-off' from over-fertilised land, or from sewage or silage effluent. Algal blooms are the early indicators of eutrophic conditions (*Advanced Biology*, pp. 100–1).

■ Aim

To investigate the relationship between nitrate and phosphate contamination and a *Chlorella* 'bloom'.

■ Risk assessment

Good laboratory practice will be sufficient to take account of any hazards and avoid significant risks.

■ Method

A stock *Chlorella* culture should be set up by inoculating $200 \, cm^3$ of complete culture solution (one providing all the nutrient ions needed by a green plant) in a $500 \, cm^3$ conical flask, with *Chlorella*. The formula for the culture solution is given on p. 291. The alga may be obtained as a pure culture from laboratory suppliers (such as Philip Harris), or from a sample of pond water already made bright green by the presence of algae: the latter will not necessarily be a monoculture of *Chlorella*, of course. Keep the stock culture in a warm, well-illuminated position in the laboratory, agitate it from time to time, and maintain the volume at $200 \, cm^3$ by making good any evaporation by the addition of tap water. Examine some of the *Chlorella* cells under the medium- and high-power magnification of a microscope.

Design and conduct an investigation into the growth rate of *Chlorella* in water contaminated with nutrients rich in nitrate and phosphate ions.

1 You can simulate contamination by the addition of various amounts of 'Tomorite' liquid tomato fertiliser (or Baby Bio liquid plant 'feed') to tap water. The manufacturer's recommended application of the fertiliser 'Tomorite' is approximately $1 \, cm^3$ to $500 \, cm^3$ of tap water, so the concentrations you use should span a range from more dilute to more concentrated than this.

2 Work with experimental culture solutions based on tap water in conical flasks of 200 cm^3 capacity. Inoculate each flask with a standardised quantity of the stock culture you have grown up for the purpose ('acclimatised' to your laboratory conditions) – say 10 cm^3 – and with varying quantities of 'Tomorite'. Of course, the final volume in each flask should be the same, say 50 cm^3. Set the flasks to incubate under standardised conditions of illumination and temperature, appropriate for the growth of the alga.

3 You should be able to see at a glance in which flasks the alga grows well. You will, however, need to quantify the growth rate of the algae. It is possible to do this by counting the cells in a haemocytometer (pp. 98–9), using a representative sample; this is extremely time-consuming, however, and there is probably no need for such precise counts. Alternatively, you can use a colorimeter or spectrophotometer to record the relative absorbance of samples of the cultures at regular intervals. The changes in absorbance are directly related to the number of cells in suspension.

NOTE TO TECHNICIAN

Each student group is required to design an experimental procedure here, but the following will certainly be required, the exact numbers depending upon circumstances:
- stock culture of *Chlorella*, set up in a 500 cm^3 flask, containing 200 cm^3 of complete culture solution (p. 430), to which is added a small quantity of *Chlorella* culture from a laboratory supplier or some pond water already rich in *Chlorella*; this will need to be incubated under good illumination, at a temperature of about 25 °C;
- 'Tomorite' (or similar liquid 'feed'), and pipette with safety bulb to make various dilutions;
- 200 cm^3 conical flasks to sub-culture the *Chlorella* in, with various dilutions of 'Tomorite';
- colorimeter or absorptiometer (with filter to give light at 410 nm);
- associated laboratory glassware and apparatus, to conduct the experiment;
- a position in the laboratory where the cultures can be grown in appropriate illumination and temperature.

■ Data presentation
- Record your results in a grid, showing the contents of each flask, and the change in absorbance due to algal growth. Plot a graph of the growth rates at different concentrations, making the individual curves distinct and clearly labelled.
- Make a labelled drawing to show the structure of *Chlorella* cells. Can you measure the size of typical cells (pp. 98–9)?

■ Conclusions
- What concentration of added 'Tomorite' was most favourable for growth of *Chlorella*?
- How do your results support the concept of limiting factors?
- Did you use a concentration high enough to actually inhibit growth of the alga?

■ Evaluation
For what reasons is a unicellular organism like *Chlorella* so popular with experimental scientists who investigate (for example) the biochemistry of photosynthesis?

Reference
C J Clegg (1984) *Lower Plants*, p. 22. John Murray

25.8 Observing filamentous algae
(Data generating)

Ponds and lakes are typical habitats in which to find filamentous algae. They grow profusely in spring and early summer, often forming a dense mat at the surface of ponds which contain water enriched with ions. Such growth is an example of an algal 'bloom'. *Spirogyra* is the filamentous alga which is often introduced as 'representative'. In fact, *Spirogyra* is only one of three or four unbranched filamentous algae that may form conspicuous floating masses. These organisms may be distinguished by the shape of the chloroplast in the cells.

■ Aim
To investigate the filamentous algae obtained from local ponds, and to observe key stages in the life cycle of *Spirogyra*.

■ Risk assessment
Good laboratory practice will be sufficient to take account of any hazards and avoid significant risks.

■ Method

1 You are provided with a sample of filamentous algae in pond water. Make temporary mounts of a few threads, teasing them out with mounted needles as best you can, before adding the coverslip. Observe the threads carefully, looking for different common species, as illustrated in Figure 25.5. Between March and June, look for signs of conjugation.

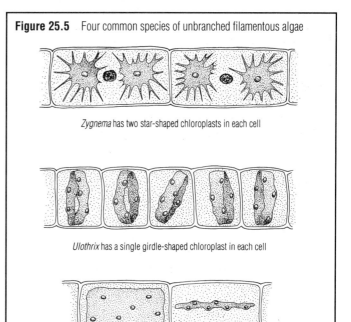

Figure 25.5 Four common species of unbranched filamentous algae

Zygnema has two star-shaped chloroplasts in each cell

Ulothrix has a single girdle-shaped chloroplast in each cell

Mougeotia cells each have a thin, flat, centrally placed chloroplast with numerous pyrenoids

Spirogyra has a ribbon-shaped chloroplast, spirally arranged in the cell

2 Using the prepared slides provided, observe the process of sexual reproduction by conjugation in *Spirogyra*. You can refresh your memory of the life cycle by reference to *Advanced Biology*, p. 558, or C J Clegg (1984) *Lower Plants*, p. 28 (John Murray).

The stage at which the contents of one cell migrate through the conjugation tube and fuse (fertilise) with the other cell (Figure 25.6) is often not 'caught' in prepared slides, but other stages are easily seen.

NOTE TO TECHNICIAN

Each student group will require:
- microscope (with medium- and high-power objectives), with bench lamp if necessary;
- beaker of pond water with strands of filamentous algae (if this practical cannot be conducted in the spring/summer terms, then pre-preserved material will be required);
- microscope slides, coverslips, mounted needles, pipette, blotting paper;
- prepared slides of sexual reproduction in *Spirogyra*.

■ Data presentation
- Make large labelled drawings of a representative portion of the different filamentous algae you find in the pond water, identifying each. If there are branched filamentous algae present as well you will need to refer to other reference sources.
- Make large, fully labelled drawings of the stages to sexual reproduction by conjugation that you observe in the prepared slides (or in living material).

Reference
A Leadley Brown (1970) *Key to Pond Organisms*. Nuffield Foundation/Penguin Books

■ Conclusion
Make a key (pp. 15–18) to differentiate the filamentous algae found in your sample.

■ Evaluation
Why are algal blooms viewed with such disfavour, considering they consist of tiny green aquatic plants that give off oxygen in the sunlight, and absorb excess nutrient ions in natural waters?

25.9 Observing fertilisation in the alga Fucus
(Data generating/Demonstration)

Wrack (*Fucus*) is a genus of cold-water marine algae, common around the coasts of Europe and elsewhere. There are several species that commonly grow anchored to rocks in the intertidal zone of the shore. The biology of *Fucus* is introduced in *Advanced Biology*, pp. 558–9, and in C J Clegg (1984) *Lower Plants*, pp. 30–1 (John Murray).

In season, gametes are released after low tides. During these periods of exposure, the thallus dries and shrinks slightly, forcing packages of gametes out of the fertile conceptacles. On the return of the tide these packages dissolve or burst and the individual gametes are released into the sea where fertilisation may occur. (This is a seasonal practical, to be carried out at a time when fertile conceptacles are available.)

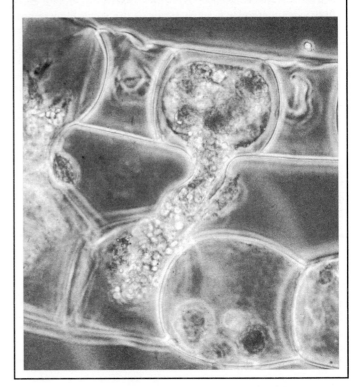

Figure 25.6 Phase-contrast photomicrograph of conjugation in *Spirogyra*

■ Aim
To learn about the biology of *Fucus*, and to observe fertilisation of the gametes in seawater.

■ Risk assessment
Good laboratory practice will be sufficient to take account of any hazards and avoid significant risks.

■ Method
1 You are provided with representative portions of the plant body (called a thallus) of one or more of the following species of *Fucus*, in which conspicuous fertile conceptacles can be seen at the tips of the thallus:
- serrated wrack (*F. serratus*), a hermaphrodite plant of the upper shore, normally fertile in summer and autumn;
- bladder wrack (*F. vesiculosus*), unisexual (male and female conceptacles on different plants), and normally fertile in spring and summer; this plant grows on the mid-shore, but forms 'hybrids' with other species of *Fucus*, some of which are very difficult to identify;
- flat wrack (*F. spiralis*), unisexual and normally fertile in spring and summer; this plant grows on the lower shore and is exposed at low tide only. The male conceptacles (and packages of antherozoids) are bright orange. The female conceptacles (and packages of ova) are olive green. This is by far the best material to study, if it can be obtained.
2 Make an annotated sketch to identify the features of the vegetative structures of *Fucus*, and note the differences between species, if possible.
3 If available, examine prepared slides of thin sections through fertile conceptacles of a species of *Fucus* to observe the groups of ova (eight) in each oogonium and antherozoids (sixty-four) in each antheridium.

4 Fertile thalli may be induced to release packages of gametes if they are left to dry in the air for between one and three hours (simulating low tide). Partially dried thallus material may be seen to exude mucilage coloured by the packages of gametes it contains (this effect is dramatic in *F. spiralis*). Collect the exudate from male and female conceptacles in a small beaker containing a little fresh seawater. Mix the contents, and make a temporary mount from the liquid suspension of gametes. Examine this by medium and then by high power, focusing on the ova. Look for the presence of antherozoids, and observe their behaviour.

NOTE TO TECHNICIAN

Each student group will require:
- portions of a living thallus of one or more of the following species of *Fucus*, having fertile conceptacles: serrated wrack (*F. serratus*); bladder wrack (*F. vesiculosus*), flat wrack (*F. spiralis*);
- hand lens;
- small beaker, small quantity of seawater;
- microscope (with medium- and high-power objectives), with bench lamp if necessary;
- microscope slides and coverslips, with filter paper;
- prepared slide(s) of thin sections through fertile conceptacles of *Fucus* (if available).

■ Data presentation
Make annotated sketches of:
- the differences in the structure of the seaweed samples provided;
- an oogonium and an antheridium, to show their relative sizes;
- the ova and antherozoids, if you have been able to observe them.

■ Conclusion
Is there evidence of chemical attraction of antherozoids to ova?

■ Evaluation
What advantage arises from a defined breeding season in *Fucus*?

25.10 *Observations on* Vorticella

(Investigation)

Vorticella is a genus of sedentary, stalked protozoa which can be found attached to pond plants such as *Lemna*. The genus is in the phylum Ciliophora (ciliates), whose members bear cilia. The cilia are used for locomotion or for creating feeding currents, or both (Figure 25.7).

■ Aim
To investigate some aspects of feeding and osmoregulation in *Vorticella*.

■ Risk assessment
Good laboratory practice will be sufficient to take account of any hazards and avoid significant risks.

■ Method

1 From a culture of *Vorticella*, remove a few fronds of duckweed and examine them in a drop of water on a slide under the low power of a microscope. If you can see *Vorticella* attached to the edges of the weed, add a coverslip but support the corners with small blobs of plasticine to avoid squashing the protozoa. The contractile stalks may jerk the protozoan out of the field of view from time to time but they will extend again after a second or two.
2 Study the 'bell' of the *Vorticella* to see as many structures as possible and to observe the distribution and activity of the cilia.
3 You can study the feeding current by drawing a suspension of carmine or drawing ink, or of yeast cells stained with Congo red, under the coverslip with filter paper ('irrigation' technique, pp. 86–7). You will need to experiment to find a suitable dilution of the particles. Make sketches to show the path of the feeding current and, if possible, the sites of ingestion and egestion.
4 After 15 minutes or so, flush the suspension away by 'irrigation' with pond water. You may be able to see particles in the food vacuoles. Do the food vacuoles follow a particular course through the unicell? How long do they spend in transit? Does egestion always take place at the same point in the cell membrane? If you have used yeast cells stained with Congo red, you may be able to observe changes of pH in the vacuoles.
5 Look for contractile vacuoles. How many are there? If there are more than one, is their filling and emptying synchronised or at random? What is the frequency of filling and emptying? (Practical 11.2, p. 133, can be adapted for *Vorticella* to find how the concentration of the external medium affects the vacuoles.)

References
P W Hawkins (1973) '*Vorticella*, a suitable protozoan for class practical work', *School Science Review* (December 1973) 55(191), pp. 308–13

P W Hawkins (1974) 'Contractile vacuole distribution in *Vorticella*, *Actinophrys* and *Arcella*', *School Science Review* (December 1974) 56(195), pp. 315–18

A R Jones (1980) 'Using the ciliate protozoan *Vorticella* in teaching', *J. Biol. Ed.* 14(2), pp. 119–26

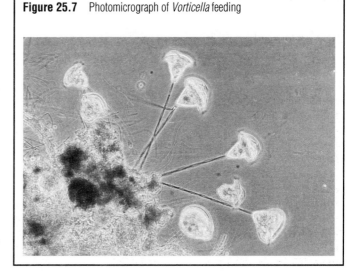

Figure 25.7 Photomicrograph of *Vorticella* feeding

NOTE TO TECHNICIAN

Each group will need:
- access to a culture of *Vorticella* (p. 431);
- microscope;
- slides, coverslips, small quantity of plasticine;
- drawing ink, or aqueous suspension of carmine or of yeast cells stained with Congo red;
- dropping pipette, filter paper.

■ Data presentation
- Make annotated drawings to show the distribution of cilia, the path of the feeding current and any pattern of movement (and change of pH) of the food vacuoles.
- On a separate drawing, indicate the position of the contractile vacuole(s) and make notes on the rate of contraction.

■ Conclusion
What is the method of feeding of *Vorticella*? How does it compare with that of *Paramecium*?

■ Evaluation
In what ways, do you think, do:
- the presence of a coverslip,
- the use of inorganic particles,

affect the reliability of your observations on feeding currents and the fate of the food vacuoles?

25.11 Mucor *as a coprophilous fungus*
(Demonstration/Investigation)

When samples of fresh dung from a herbivorous mammal are kept in a humid atmosphere in a laboratory, a succession of fungi develops. These organisms feed saprotrophically on substrates in dung, from simple metabolites like sugars, present in only tiny amounts, to the increasingly insoluble and resistant substances – including cellulose and, finally, lignin – that make up the bulk of the solid matter in dung. The fungi grow as a mycelium of hyphae forming over and in the dung. They become apparent when their 'fruiting bodies' form and discharge spores. A typical succession is illustrated in *Advanced Biology*, p. 301. The pin mould fungus *Mucor* is a typical early colonist (Figure 25.8).

Figure 25.8 Photomicrograph of pin mould (*Mucor* sp.)

■ Aim
To demonstrate *Mucor* as a member of a natural succession of coprophilous fungi in herbivorous dung, and to investigate spore production and the dispersal of spores in *Mucor*.

■ Risk assessment

- The essential precautions necessary in microbiological work with fungi are similar to those with bacteria (pp. 284–7).
- Wash your hands with soap and water before and after all practical work.
- Do not put your fingers near your face (mouth, nose or eyes) during the experimental work.
- Otherwise, good laboratory practice will be sufficient to take account of any hazards and avoid significant risks.

■ Method
1 You are provided with a sample of fresh horse dung in a beaker, covered by clingfilm. Incubate the sample at room temperature, keeping the filter paper at the base moist. Observe the fungal structures that appear in both (aerial hyphae, pin mould, larger fruiting bodies) over a period of a few days.
2 You are provided with two sterile malt agar plates (Petri dishes). As soon as you note the growth of fungal threads on the surface of the dung (within 24–48 hours), transfer some of this mycelium to the surface of one plate, using a sterile wire loop (p. 286). Incubate this plate at room temperature and observe the subsequent development of the fungus.
3 As soon as you observe pin mould (fungal threads with tiny dark pinhead sporangia) on the dung, transfer sporangia (spores) to the second sterile malt agar plate. Incubate this plate at room temperature and observe the subsequent development of the fungus.
4 When you note the development of sporangia (dark pinhead threads) on your agar plates, mount some of these structures in lactophenol blue on a microscope slide, and examine them under medium- and high-power magnification. Compare the structures you see with those on a prepared slide of *Mucor*, to confirm your identification.
5 Once you have confirmed the presence of *Mucor* on the second malt agar plate, incubate the plate without a lid, so that the culture begins to dry out. Using a binocular microscope, scan the surface of the plate regularly, searching for the presence of zygospores (products of sexual reproduction in *Mucor*).

■ Data presentation
- Record the sequence of fungi/fungal structures observed on the exposed and the covered dung over a period of several weeks (depending on temperature) in the form of a diary. Identify them as far as you are able.
- Make a drawing of the sporangium of *Mucor*, as observed and confirmed by comparison with a prepared slide.

■ Conclusions
- Is there evidence that *Mucor* was the first mould fungus to appear on the dung?
- Is there evidence that the *Mucor* came from spores in the air, or that it was present in the dung all along?
- What change in conditions appears to encourage *Mucor* to switch from asexual reproduction to sexual reproduction?

■ Evaluation

What is the general effect of the actions of coprophilous fungi in nature?

25.12 'Mushroom' fruiting bodies; structure and function

(Investigation)

There are thousands of species of 'mushrooms and toadstools' in the UK alone. They exist as feeding mycelia in the soil, or on dead or dying plant matter such as the trunks of dead trees. They are present all the year round, but we tend to become aware of them, usually in autumn, when the characteristic fruiting bodies appear and eventually discharge their spores. The fruiting bodies of most species are harmless and can be handled safely. A very few are very poisonous, however, and if these happen to be ingested the outcome can be fatal (see *Advanced Biology*, pp. 566–7). In this investigation, the common edible mushroom will be used, since safety problems are thus avoided. If you would like an introduction to 'mushrooms' in the field, you can attend the 'fungal forays' organised by local natural history societies on many weekends in the autumn, which are led by informed mycologists. The programmes are often advertised in local libraries.

■ Aim

To investigate the structure and function of the fruiting body of the common mushroom *Agaricus campestris*.

■ Risk assessment

Good laboratory practice will be sufficient to take account of any hazards and avoid significant risks.

■ Method

1 You are provided with mushrooms at different stages of development. Observe the structure of the largest mushroom. Compare this with the structure of the mushroom at the 'button' stage. Work out the broad sequence of developments by which a mushroom enclosed as a 'button' at the soil surface comes to discharge spores into the air.

2 Cut out a tiny portion of the dark 'gill' tissue on the underside of the largest mushroom. Mount this in lactophenol blue on a microscope slide, tease it apart with mounted needles and lightly crush it with the flat side of a strong scalpel, cover with a coverslip, and observe under the medium- and high-power magnification of the microscope.

3 Place the remainder of the open cap of the mature mushroom, gill surface down, on a piece of white (or light-coloured) sugar paper. Cover it with an inverted beaker or Petri dish, according to size. Leave it for a week before carefully removing and discarding the cap. The 'spore print' left on the surface of the sugar paper can be made permanent by spraying with artist's lacquer spray.

References

C J Clegg (1984) *Lower Plants*. John Murray
C T Ingold (1979) *The Nature of Toadstools*. Arnold Studies in Biology no 113. Edward Arnold
R Phillips (1981) *Mushrooms and other Fungi of Britain and Europe*. Pan Books
R E Thompson (1984) 'Growing mushrooms as a school project', *School Science Review* (March 1984) 65(232), pp. 498–9.

■ Data presentation

- Describe the sequence of changes from 'button' mushroom to fully 'open' mushroom at the stage of spore discharge, by means of annotated sketches.
- Record the arrangement of the spores of the mushroom at the surface of gill tissue, prior to the spore's being discharged.
- Attach your spore print to an A4 sheet of paper, and beside it draw a representative part of the arrangement of gills that will have discharged spores in this pattern. Do all gills hang from the perimeter of the fruiting body to the centre, where the cap is attached to the stalk? Details of the 'gill' arrangements are used by mycologists in the identification of species, as is mature spore colour.

■ Conclusions

- What part do fungi like the common mushroom play in the cycling of nutrients within the woodland ecosystem?
- What advantage arises from the existence of dark pigments in the walls of mushroom spores?
- What does the spore print tell you about the way the spores are discharged?

■ Evaluation

What is the difference between 'free-living' and mycorrhizal woodland mushrooms?

Projects

25.1 *Bacteria in the air*

Bacterial spores are present on surfaces and in the air, more or less everywhere. But are spores more commonly found where there are habitats in which they can flourish? The density of spores can be assayed by exposing sterile nutrient agar plates for a fixed period, sealing them, and incubating them to germinate spores and grow colonies where bacteria or bacterial spores have landed. The number of colonies counted indicates the degree of contamination of the air at the site of exposure. Investigate contrasting habitats (such as kitchens and public rooms (e.g. school hall)) and outdoor sites under various conditions (for example, before and after rainfall). Exposed plates must be sealed closed (Figure 25.2, p. 287) and not re-opened.

25.2 *Commercial antiseptics and the growth of bacteria*

Choosing a commercial antiseptic that you did *not* use in Practical 25.4, adapt the techniques introduced in that practical to determine the concentration ranges that inhibit bacterial growth and that do not affect growth, and the concentrations (if any) that enhance growth, using a common harmless saprotrophic bacterium.

25.3 *The growth of soil fungi on buried cellophane*

Place commercial cellophane in boiling water for 15 minutes to remove the chemicals this packaging material is treated with. Then cut 1 cm squares, apply each to the centre of a microscopic slide, and air-dry them on. Number the slides with a waterproof marker on the reverse side. Bury five or six of these slides upright in garden, lawn or agricultural field soil, at a depth of 3–5 cm (that is, in topsoil). At weekly intervals remove a slide, and gently rinse off the soil. Apply a drop of lactophenol blue to the cellophane, and cover with a coverslip. Examine the slide under medium- and high-power magnification of the microscope. Record the evidence of fungal growth, and any evidence of the activity of other organisms, by means of fully labelled sketches. Use this method to compare colonisation of cellophane in contrasting soils.

Reference
H T Tribe (1967) 'Practical studies on biological decomposition in soil: a simple technique for observation of soil organisms colonising buried cellulose film', *School Science Review* (November 1967) 49(167), pp. 95–122

25.4 *Antifungal substances in plants*

Make a selection of plant species that might present habitats favourable for the growth of yeast, and investigate the possibility that the plants produce substances that inhibit growth of the spores which are commonly found in the air. Using sterile malt agar plates (p. 430), inoculate their surfaces with a liquid culture of baker's yeast (*Saccharomyces cerevisiae*). Then, with a flame-sterilised cork borer, cut 'wells' in the agar and discard the plugs of agar removed. Taking species of plants of commercial importance that produce flowers or fruits that contain sugar, such as tomato (*Lycopersicum esculentum*), honeysuckle (*Lonicera periclymenum*), or raspberry (*Rubus idaeus*), make aquatic extracts from equivalent masses of flower, leaf, and seed/fruit tissues. Place equal volumes of the extracts in the wells in the agar plates. Incubate the plates and observe the growth of yeast.

25.5 Chlorella *growth and the effect of inorganic ions/pollutants*

The conditions under which *Chlorella* cultures grow and the cells divide are shown in Practical 25.7. Apart from nutrients in the environment, heavy-metal ions and various commercial pesticides may also reach pond water and affect growth of this alga. Investigate the effects on growth of *Chlorella* cultures under standardised conditions of one or more of these potential pollutants. Estimate growth rate by changes in the absorbance of the culture; you might also calibrate your readings by direct counts of cell numbers, using a haemocytometer and appropriate dilutions of a culture.

25.6 *Light sensitivity of* Euglena

A culture of *Euglena* can be used to investigate light-sensitivity in this organism. The culture is maintained in a small beaker or culture tube that is surrounded by lightproof black paper into which a small hole is cut. When a beam of light is shone on to the hole, the organisms can be seen to mass together at this point. By contrast, under even illumination or with the culture in total darkness, the organisms become randomly dispersed again. *Euglena* is clearly light-sensitive, but to what wavelengths of light does it respond? Using coloured filters which permit light of known wavelengths to pass, investigate which wavelengths of white light produce the greatest response.

25.7 *Digestion of acid/base indicator-stained yeast by* Paramecium

Cultures of *Paramecium* can be maintained, fed on yeast. Yeast cells may be dyed red with Congo red, but they have to be killed by heat for the successful uptake of this dye. What colour is Congo red at pH 3, and at pH 5? When samples of this dead, dyed yeast are taken up by *Paramecium*, they enter food vacuoles where digestive enzymes are secreted. What can be learnt about the processes of digestion in *Paramecium* by this technique? Remember, to observe fast-moving protozoa it is usually necessary to slow them down with a mesh of cotton wool fibres in the medium on the microscope slide.

25.8 *The effect of temperature on the growth rate of fungi*

A mature culture of fungi such as *Aspergillus* sp. or *Penicillium* sp. can be used to supply standard-sized plugs of agar with mycelium. Using sterile plates of potato–dextrose agar, place a tiny plug of fungal mycelium (cut with a sterilised cork-borer from the margin of the colony) in the centre of each dish. Incubate dishes at a range of temperatures, from 5 to 30 °C. Measure the size (diameter) of the colony that grows. How many replicate plates at each temperature should you use?

25.9 Investigating antibiotics in lichens

Only a tiny amount of a lichen thallus needs be removed to extract antibiotic, if present, and often it can be lichens on trunks and branches already earmarked for firewood that are used. Extractions are made on cavity microscope slides by immersing the sample placed in the cavity, in propanone (acetone) (highly flammable). The solvent evaporates easily, leaving the extract as a residue. Re-dissolved in water, this can be absorbed into filter paper, and placed on to a nutrient agar plate inoculated with a bacterial culture. The antibiotic substances themselves may be investigated by chromatography.

Reference

M St J Sugg (1979) 'A method for the extraction and assay of lichen-produced antibiotic', *School Science Review* (June 1979) **60**(213), pp. 689–92

25.10 Fungal parasites of wild plants of hedgerow or waste land

It is not necessary to restrict experimental work on fungal parasites to those of crop plants. All successful organisms, including weeds, are vulnerable to fungal parasites. Search for common weed species that are parasited, and investigate the extent of the infection and how it may be transmitted, for example. There are several references to successful work worth following up.

References

M C Edwards and P G Ayers (1979) 'Powdery mildews of plants', *School Science Review* (March 1979) **60**(212), pp. 475–88

D T Walters and P G Ayers (1983) 'Class experiments with powdery mildews', *School Science Review* (June 1983) **64**(229), pp. 688–90

A J S Murray and N D Paul (1987) 'Simple investigations of the rust diseases of plants I', *School Science Review* (March 1987) **68**(244), pp. 492–9

A J S Murray and N D Paul (1987) 'Simple investigations of the rust diseases of plants II', *School Science Review* (June 1987) **68**(245), pp. 680–7

Problems and assignments

25.1 Viruses

Read the text in Panel 25.1. Then, using your knowledge of microbiology and the information contained in the text, answer the questions that follow.

Panel 25.1 Viruses

Viruses are between 10 and 100 times smaller than bacteria, from 0.2 to 0.02 μm long. They differ fundamentally from prokaryotes and eukaryotes. In fact, viruses lie on the borderline of living things. They have, for example, no metabolism of their own: they do not respire, break down carbon compounds, fix CO_2 or do anything like that. When they infect a creature, they pervert its own metabolism, so that more of the virus is synthesised. This way of life is described as being 'obligatory intracellular parasites'.

Thus viruses are very important to us as the causative agents of disease. Many of these virus-caused diseases remain 'unconquered', in contrast with many bacterial diseases. Some viruses also attack bacteria, and some of them live harmlessly in their host until some stress causes them to develop.

From: J Postgate (1992) Microbes and Man, 3rd edn
Cambridge University Press

---

1 a What is a μm? How many μm are there in a metre?
b What is the typical size range of a bacterial cell, given in μm?
2 Draw up a table listing the key differences between prokaryotes and eukaryotes.
3 a How would you define 'metabolism'?
b What is meant by 'fix CO_2'?
c Name a major group of microorganisms that fix CO_2.
4 a Make a short list of the ways viruses can be said to 'lie on the borderline of living things'.
b Define the words 'obligatory', 'intracellular' and 'parasite'.
5 Give two examples each of:
a viral diseases of plants;
b viral diseases of animals;
c bacterial diseases of plants,
d bacterial diseases of animals.
6 Name one important way in which many bacterial diseases have been 'conquered' which is not effective against viruses.
7 a By what name are the viruses that attack bacteria known?
b Make a labelled sketch to show how viruses that attack bacteria actually introduce their nucleic acid into the host cell.
8 Many of the viruses that can live harmlessly in their host cell we now call 'retroviruses'. Explain what this name means, and where the virus survives in the host.

25.2 What science didn't know about disease

Read the text in Panel 25.2 and then, using your general knowledge from your wider reading, together with the ideas in this excerpt, answer the questions that follow.

Panel 25.2 A shock for the scientists

Until the later 1970s, it was believed in the developed world that infectious diseases were no longer much of a threat. Challenges to public health stemmed from non-infectious conditions such as cancer and heart disease. This view was quickly shattered in the early 1980s with the advent of AIDS. It was eventually established that AIDS was caused by a retrovirus. Retroviruses had been known from the beginning of the century, but by the mid-1970s none had been discovered to infect humans. The first AIDS cases were diagnosed in 1981 among young men in the USA. By 1988 a total of 66 500 cases had been reported in the USA, of which more than half had died.

From: R C Gallo and L Montagnier (1988)
Scientific American *259(4), pp. 25–32*

---

1 Suggest two important reasons why the developed world felt that infectious diseases were no longer a significant threat by 1975.
2 a AIDS is an abbreviation for Acquired Immune Deficiency Syndrome. What do we mean by 'syndrome'?
b What does the abbreviation HIV stand for?
c What is the connection between AIDS and HIV?
3 a Summarise, by means of a list, the human body's defence mechanisms against disease.
b Explain why it is difficult for the body's defence mechanisms to provide protection against HIV.
4 There are various ways by which HIV can enter the body. Outline three possible routes.
5 Describe how the medical profession can diagnose AIDS in a patient.
6 Special cells of our immune system, known as T4 cells, are 'targeted' by the HIV.
a What types of cell are the T4 cells?
b Where are they normally found in the body?
7 Retroviruses are so named because they are said to reverse the 'central dogma'. What is meant by the central dogma?
8 What sorts of measures can be used to control the spread of AIDS?
9 a What is the approximate size of the AIDS virus?
b Make a fully annotated sketch of the significant features of the structure of HIV.
10 Today, whilst the largest number of AIDS cases are found among males aged between 25 and 45 years, a small but increasing number of paediatric cases are occurring. What is meant by 'paediatric' cases, and how may these arise?

25.3 Neurospora: the metabolism of 'wild type' and mutants

The naturally occurring form of the fungus *Neurospora crassa* is known as 'wild type'. It can be grown in the laboratory on a medium containing glucose, mineral ions (including nitrates) and the vitamin biotin ('minimal medium'). From these, *Neurospora* 'wild type' is able to manufacture all the other metabolites it requires, including the 20 or so essential amino acids.

When *Neurospora* is exposed to doses of ultraviolet light, some mutant strains appear in the culture. Certain mutants are distinguished from the 'wild type' by an inability to produce enzymes catalysing the formation of particular amino acids. In one experiment, mutants M_1, M_2 and M_3 were found to be unable to produce one of the enzymes (e_1, e_2 or e_3) involved in the conversion of glutamic acid to ornithine to citrulline to arginine. Such mutants can be grown on media supplemented by addition of amino acids. This fact is exploited to discover which enzyme is no longer produced by a particular mutant. The outcome of one such experiment is shown in Figure 25.9.

In the conversion of glutamic acid to arginine by *Neurospora*, the following essential steps occur:

$$\text{glutamic acid} \xrightarrow{e_1} \text{ornithine} \xrightarrow{e_2} \text{citrulline} \xrightarrow{e_3} \text{arginine}$$

1 a Why do organisms require '20 or so' amino acids?
  b What essential cell components are manufactured from amino acids, and to what uses are the products put?
2 a From which components in the minimal medium are amino acids formed?
  b Broadly, what changes occur to these substances to produce an amino acid?
3 a What happens to a mutant strain inoculated on to an agar plate that does not contain an amino acid the mutant requires?
  b What happens to 'wild-type' *N. crassa* when inoculated on to an agar plate with supplementary amino acids?
4 What substance in the fungus is particularly damaged or, at least, may be chemically changed by exposure to ultraviolet light?
5 In this experiment, which of the enzymes e_1, e_2 or e_3 were no longer formed:
  a by mutant M_1;
  b by mutant M_2;
  c by mutant M_3?
6 An additional mutant (M_4) was later isolated, but failed to grow on any of the media used in this experiment.
  a What could the experimenter initially conclude about amino acid metabolism in M_4?
  b How could the experimenter further investigate amino acid metabolism in this mutant?

25.4 Zygomycete fungi

Figure 25.10 shows part of a zygomycete fungus, growing on the surface of soil. Examine the structure shown and, using your general knowledge about the fungi and of saprotrophic nutrition, answer the following questions.

1 Structure A in Figure 25.10 has grown across the surface of dead organic matter in the soil.
  a Describe how the component nutrients of proteins, lipids and polysaccharides in the organic matter are made available to the cytoplasm in A.
  b How are nutrients absorbed into A and transported within the fungus to points such as B?
2 Where, and by what processes, does the fungus obtain:
  a water,
  b essential ions,
  for growth and development?

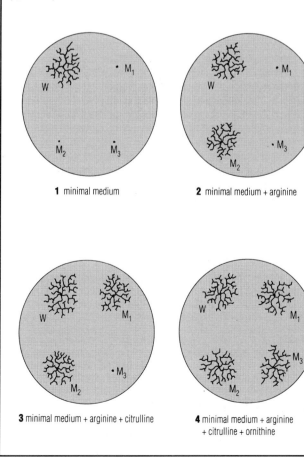

Figure 25.9 Culturing wild-type and mutant strains of *Neurospora crassa* on agar plates; the circles represent Petri dishes containing agar medium. All the plates were inoculated with wild-type *Neurospora crassa* (W) and various mutant strains (M1, M2 and M3). The plates held either 'minimal medium' (1) or minimal medium supplemented by the addition of one or more amino acids (2, 3 and 4)

1 minimal medium

2 minimal medium + arginine

3 minimal medium + arginine + citrulline

4 minimal medium + arginine + citrulline + ornithine

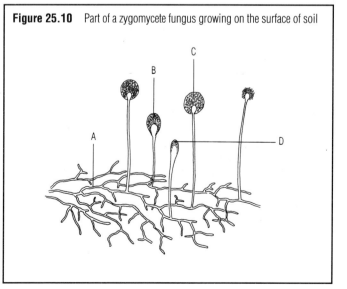

Figure 25.10 Part of a zygomycete fungus growing on the surface of soil

3 After a microhabitat rich in food has been colonised, when do structures such as B, C and D start to form?

4 How could you demonstrate that structure D is sensitive to light and positively phototropic?

5 a What living contents are to be found in D?

b What changes occur to the contents when structure D develops into B?

6 Structure C develops a darkly pigmented appearance. What changes to the contents are responsible for this pigmentation?

7 How may the contents of C escape? What may happen to them subsequently?

8 When the dead organic matter is used up, or if the soil dries up, how may this organism survive to colonise fresh, favourable microhabitats?

25.5 Quick test

1 Distinguish between the following pairs:

   a DNA and RNA;
   b asexual reproduction and sexual reproduction;
   c tobacco mosaic virus and a bacteriophage;
   d cocci and bacilli;
   e cell wall and mucilaginous capsule;
   f isogamy and oogamy;
   g unicellular and filamentous algae;
   h stipe and lamina;
   i antheridium and oogonium;
   j cilia and flagella;
   k heterotrophic nutrition and autotrophic nutrition;
   l mycology and bacteriology;
   m food vacuoles and contractile vacuoles;
   n sporangium and sporangiophore;
   o zygote and zygospore;
   p heterothallic and homothallic species;
   q *Mucor* and *Rhizopus*;
   r ascospores and basidiospores;
   s mushrooms and bracket fungi;
   t biodegradation and biodeterioration.

2 Explain the importance of the following:

   a lysis;
   b retroviruses;
   c the conditions necessary for bacterial growth;
   d endospores formed by Gram-positive bacteria;
   e the dilution plate technique;
   f *Chlorella* as an experimental organism;
   g mucilage of a seaweed thallus;
   h *Neurospora* as an experimental organism;
   i budding in yeast;
   j microorganisms in biotechnology.

25.6 Essay assignment

Select one of the following:

• By means of a fully labelled diagram describe the structure of a rod-shaped bacterium. Carefully describe the chemical composition and roles of the following parts of the bacterial cell:
   a the cell wall;
   b the ring of DNA;
   c the cell membrane.
   Outline how a bacterium reproduces itself asexually.

or:

• The protozoa are a diverse group of eukaryotic, unicellular organisms. By reference to three protozoa you are familiar with, contrast the ways these organisms achieve:
   a nutrition;
   b locomotion;
   c asexual increase in numbers.

26 Life cycles of green plants

Summary

Green plants reproduce **sexually**, and often asexually too. With sexual reproduction in the life cycle, **meiosis** (the reductive division) must occur, since each time cells fuse the number of chromosomes per cell is doubled. The sex cells (gametes) contain a single set of the chromosomes of the organism, known as the **haploid** set. The zygote (product of the fusion of gametes) contains a double set of chromosomes, known as the **diploid** set. Thus in life cycles involving sexual reproduction there is a diploid and a haploid phase.

The timing of meiosis varies in the life cycle of different species. In a **haploid life cycle** meiosis occurs immediately after fertilisation. In a **diploid life cycle** meiosis occurs in the formation of gametes. In **alternation of generations** there are significant periods of both haploid and diploid phases, alternating. All green plants show this type of life cycle, in various forms.

Mosses and liverworts (the **bryophytes**) show alternating gametophyte (haploid) and sporophyte (diploid) generations of quite different morphology (**heteromorphic alternation of generations**). The small **gametophyte plant** is the dominant phase in the life cycle, and bears sex organs. The fertilised egg cell remains in the gametophyte and develops into the **sporophyte plant**, which grows from the gametophyte and is dependent upon it. The sporophyte produces haploid spores which are dispersed and grow into gametophyte plants, completing the cycle.

In **ferns** such as *Dryopteris*, the sporophyte is the dominant plant. Haploid spores are produced by meiosis, normally on the underside of leaves. The spores are dispersed and germinate to form the gametophyte, a tiny independent plant. In **conifers** such as the Scots pine, too, the sporophyte is the dominant plant, but here the gametophyte generation is reduced to a number of cells retained within the spores (microspores – pollen grains – and megaspore cells within the pine cone).

In the flowering plant the **flower** develops from the tip of a shoot, so the flower parts may be regarded as modified leaves. Flowers are usually **hermaphrodite** (as in *Ranunculus*, for example). A group of flowers on a stem is known as an **inflorescence**. The outermost parts of the flower, the **sepals**, enclose and protect the flower in the bud. The **petals** are typically brightly coloured in flowers that attract insects. The male parts of the flower, the **stamens**, contain the **pollen grains**. The female parts are the **carpels**, and consist of stigma, style and ovary. The ovary contains one or more **ovules** in which, in the embryo sac, is found the **egg nucleus** and the endosperm nucleus.

Pollination is the process by which pollen is transferred to the stigma from the anthers of the same flower or flowers of the same plant (self-pollination), or from flowers on a different plant of the same species (cross-pollination). **Fertilisation** occurs when a pollen grain grows on the stigma, and sends a pollen tube into the ovule, and one of the two male nuclei it contains fuses with the egg nucleus in the embryo sac. The second nucleus fuses with the endosperm nucleus (**double fertilisation**).

The **seed** develops from the fertilised ovule and contains an embryo plant and a food store. The **fruit** develops from the ovary and contains the seed(s). The seed is a way in which the plant survives the unfavourable season. It is also one way plants may be dispersed, prior to **germination** and the growth of new plants. The life cycle of the flowering plant can be interpreted as a heteromorphic alternation of generations (pollen grain = microspore, embryo sac = megaspore). On this analysis the flower is a spore-forming structure of a plant with two types of spore (heterosporous).

The angiosperms form a highly successful group that divides naturally into the **dicotyledons** and **monocotyledons**. Both groups are also capable of reproducing vegetatively (asexually) when parts of the parent plant become separated from the parent, and grow independently.

Practicals and activities

26.1 Life cycle of a bryophyte

(Data generating)

Mosses and liverworts make up the bryophytes. In these, the plant body consists of a tiny, slender stem bearing leaves (as in a moss) or a green leaf-like thallus growing on the ground (as in a liverwort). This is the haploid **gametophyte**. Out of this, at a certain time of the year, grows the diploid **sporophyte**, visible as a slender stalk and capsule. The sporophyte remains dependent on the gametophyte for nourishment.

So these tiny plants show an **alternation of generations** in their life cycle, between the haploid gamete-producing stage, the site of sexual reproduction, and the diploid spore-producing stage (asexual reproduction). (This is a seasonal practical, best carried out in late winter.)

■ **Aim**

To study the gametophyte and sporophyte of a liverwort (*Pellia epiphylla*).

■ **Risk assessment**

Good laboratory practice will be sufficient to take account of any hazards and avoid significant risks.

■ **Method**

1 Using a hand lens, note the structural differences between a moss and liverwort plant, by examining those provided.
2 Now look more carefully at the entire liverwort thallus (Figure 26.1), using a hand lens. Search for:
   - the central midrib to an almost ribbon-shaped thallus;
   - the form of branching of the thallus (dichotomous);
   - unicellular rhizoids attaching the lower surface to the soil;
   - small lumps along the midrib, the site of antheridia (male sex organs);

Figure 26.1 *Pellia*: the gametophyte

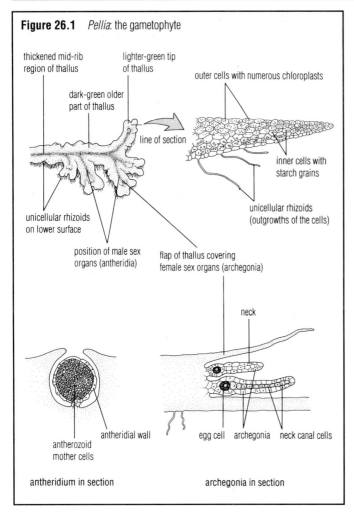

thickened mid-rib region of thallus

lighter-green tip of thallus

dark-green older part of thallus

line of section

outer cells with numerous chloroplasts

inner cells with starch grains

unicellular rhizoids on lower surface

unicellular rhizoids (outgrowths of the cells)

position of male sex organs (antheridia)

flap of thallus covering female sex organs (archegonia)

neck

antherozoid mother cells

antheridial wall

antheridium in section

egg cell   archegonia   neck canal cells

archegonia in section

Figure 26.2 *Pellia*: the sporophyte

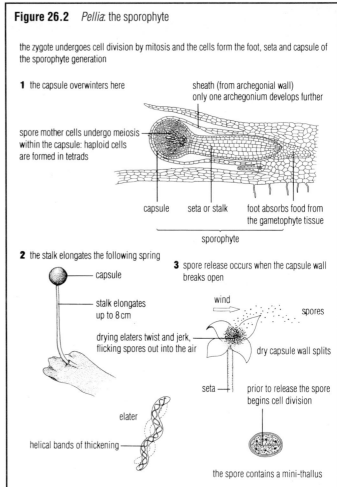

the zygote undergoes cell division by mitosis and the cells form the foot, seta and capsule of the sporophyte generation

1 the capsule overwinters here

sheath (from archegonial wall) only one archegonium develops further

spore mother cells undergo meiosis within the capsule: haploid cells are formed in tetrads

capsule   seta or stalk   foot absorbs food from the gametophyte tissue

sporophyte

2 the stalk elongates the following spring

capsule

stalk elongates up to 8 cm

drying elaters twist and jerk, flicking spores out into the air

elater

helical bands of thickening

3 spore release occurs when the capsule wall breaks open

wind

spores

dry capsule wall splits

seta

prior to release the spore begins cell division

the spore contains a mini-thallus

- a tiny flap of tissue near the growing tips of the thallus, known as an involucre;
- the sporophyte generation, formed from a fertilised archegonium (female sex organ), lying beneath the involucre.

3 Using fine forceps, peel back an involucre overlying a sporophyte (Figure 26.2). With a mounted needle, free the spherical capsule and short stalk (seta) from the green sheath (the calyptra). Transfer the capsule and stalk to a microscope slide. Now divide the capsule from stalk, and transfer the stalk to a different slide.

4 Cover the capsule with a drop of water, and the stalk with a drop of iodine. Cover both with coverslips. Apply gentle pressure with the needle tip, lightly crushing capsule and stalk tissues.

5 Examine the contents of the capsule under medium and then high power. There are two types of structure present, known as spores (which become multicellular) and elators. Note the differences.

6 Examine the stalk cells. These cells enlarge and elongate in spring, carrying the capsule up above the thallus. Note the presence of starch grains here.

7 Examine prepared slides of stained sections of *Pellia* thalli:
  - showing archegonia, and
  - showing a young sporophyte plant, with foot (buried in the gametophyte tissue), stalk and capsule, contained within a calyptra.

NOTE TO TECHNICIAN

Pellia is one of the commonest and most conspicuous liverworts of moist banks and ditches. Collect it in winter, plant it on damp soil in a pot, and keep it cool and moist, away from direct sunlight.

Similarly, a sample of moss, such as *Funaria*, common in woodland on recently burnt land, can be cultivated, ready for examination. Other common species show similar features.

Each group will require:
- microscope, slides, coverslips, two mounted needles, fine forceps, white tile, dropping bottle of iodine in potassium iodide solution, hand lens;
- Petri dish lid with a sample of the thallus of *Pellia*, and a few *Funaria* plants;
- prepared, stained slide of *Pellia epiphylla* showing archegonia, and also one showing a young sporophyte plant.

■ **Data presentation**
- Make an annotated sketch to record the features of structure of the gametophyte plant of *Pellia*.
- Make drawings of spores and elaters seen under the high power of the microscope, and also of representative cells of the stalk of the sporophyte generation of *Pellia*. Comment on the role or function of each.
- Construct a life-cycle diagram of *Pellia*, showing the two generations. When and where does meiosis, the reductive division, occur?

■ Conclusion
In bryophytes, alternation of generation is described as hetero-morphic. Why?

■ Evaluation
- How does 'dichotomous' branching differ from lateral branching?
- In the fossil record, bryophytes in general made a quite early appearance among land plants, but their numbers greatly increased after flowering plant trees evolved. Can you suggest an explanation?

26.2 Reproduction in the life cycle of the fern
(Data generating/Investigation)

Fern plants (sporophyte generation) are well-adapted terrestrial plants. They produce spores which are dispersed, and which may germinate to form tiny plants known as prothalli (gametophyte generation). Germination may be induced under laboratory conditions. If so, prothalli can be examined microscopically to see sex organs of the fern (archegonia and antheridia). The conditions necessary for germination may be investigated. (This is a seasonal practical, to be carried out in late summer.)

■ Aim
To observe the reproductive stages of the life cycle of the fern.

■ Risk assessment

Good laboratory practice will be sufficient to take account of any hazards and avoid significant risks.

■ Method

Spore release
1 Examine a frond of a fern which carries the sori (spore-producing structures) on its underside (Figure 26.3). Using a

hand lens or binocular microscope, observe an individual sorus, consisting of a cover (indusium) with sporangia protruding around the edges.

2 Scrape the underside of a leaf on to a dry slide to transfer fresh sporangia. Add a drop of 70% ethanol and a coverslip. Immediately examine the slide, using medium power, to see sporangium dehiscence and the release of spores.

   (*Note:* Since ethanol is more viscous than air, the movements of the sporangium wall are slowed down, and the spores are not actually dispersed, of course.)

3 Now, examine the intact fronds that have been left to dry overnight, sori side down, on clean white paper in a draught-free area. Pick up one frond carefully, and observe the distribution of the spores around the indusia, forming a spore print. (Spore prints may be preserved with artist's lacquer.)

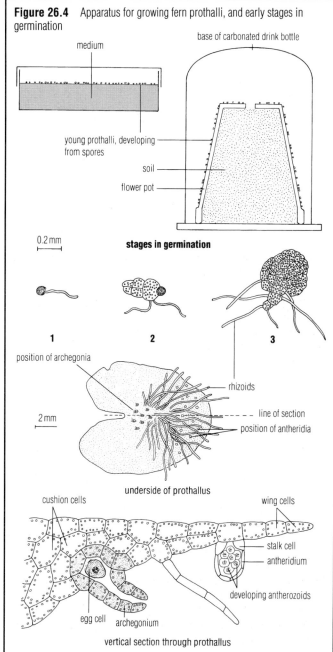

Figure 26.4 Apparatus for growing fern prothalli, and early stages in germination

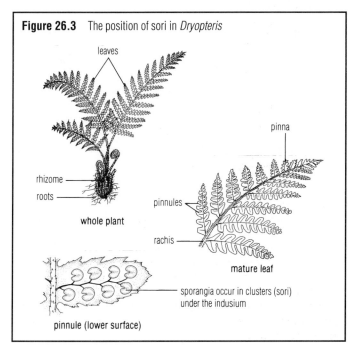

Figure 26.3 The position of sori in *Dryopteris*

303

4 Examine a prepared slide of a section through a fern leaf in the region of sori, paying attention to the leaf structure (mesophyll and vascular tissue), and the attachment of sporangia.

Spore germination

1 A very few spores may be set to germinate on the surface of a small quantity of complete nutrient solution, contained in a small glass dish such as a crystallising dish. The germination rate is normally high, and development very rapid, so prothalli quickly interfere with each other's growth and development if more than a very few spores are used.

2 Transfer sufficient spores on the tip of a wetted mounted needle, dipping it first into the spores, then in the solution. Repeat the transfer action once or twice.

3 Germination occurs in the light. Keep the dish covered with a Petri dish lid to prevent desiccation (Figure 26.4), and keep it away from direct sunlight. Provide illumination for at least 12 hours a day.

4 Spores normally germinate in three to four days, and within a week a green filament of a few cells, with one colourless rhizoid, can be observed. Specimens can be lifted out on a mounted needle, transferred to culture solution on a microscope slide, and observed under medium-power magnification. Continue to observe the development of the filament into a prothallus with many rhizoids in this way.

5 After four to eight weeks archegonia may arise on the underside of the prothallus, but antheridia are less common.

An alternative prothallus culture procedure

1 Fill an earthenware pot with soil, water with dilute nutrient solution, and stand it, inverted, on a Petri dish lid. Dust the sides of the pot with spores. During growth of the prothalli, the pot must be illuminated appropriately, but kept moist in a humid environment, under a transparent cover.

2 When individual mature prothalli are visible, scrape off a larger prothallus for examination. Mount it upside down on a microscope slide in a drop of water under a coverslip. Individually grown prothalli are most likely to show archegonia, whereas those that are smaller, and have grown clustered together, produce more antheridia. After immersion in water, it is common for the motile antherozoids to be released, and they may be seen.

3 After a further two weeks, examine fresh prothalli taken from the sides of the pot, using a binocular microscope. New sporophyte generation plants may be seen, visible as tiny leaves, emerging from where the archegonia were located.

References

For details of alternative methods of culture:
E Sheffield and J H Bastin (1978) 'Simple culture methods for fern prothalli', *School Science Review* (December 1978) **60**(211), pp. 286–9
J T Clark (1978) 'Demonstrating the early stages of ferns and mosses', *School Science Review* (December 1978) **60**(211), pp. 283–4
For the study of light quality on morphology:
M Campion (1980) 'Fern spore development', *School Science Review* (June 1980) **61**(217), pp. 695–7

■ Extension

Light is essential for spore germination and growth. What is the effect of germination in red light and far-red light, com-

---

For this exercise spores may be obtained from fertile fronds (available from July to September) of common ferns growing in the wild, such as bracken (*Pteridium aquilinum*) or male fern (*Dryopteris felix mas*), or from maidenhair fern (*Adiantum* sp.) grown as a house plant, which is fertile for a longer period of time.

Each student group will require (or require access to):
- a fertile fern sporophyll, kept in humid conditions for 12 hours before examination;
- hand lens or binocular microscope;
- microscope (with medium- and high-power objectives), with bench lamp if necessary;
- microscope slides, coverslips, 70% ethanol, fine forceps, two mounted needles;
- viable fern spores (obtain the spores from dried fern leaves, freeing them from dead leaf debris by 'filtering' through lens tissue or a nylon tea strainer. Spores will remain viable for many years, if stored in a fridge);
- intact fern fronds that have been left to dry overnight, sori side down, on clean white paper in a draught-free area;
- artist's lacquer (spray can);
- small crystallising bowl containing dilute culture solution to a depth of 1 cm, covered by Petri dish lid.

For the alternative method of culture, students will require:
- a small earthenware flowerpot containing soil, inverted on to a Petri dish lid, with transparent plastic cover, and watered with dilute culture solution (use complete culture solution (p. 430) diluted 50% or Baby Bio diluted to manufacturer's recommendation, then further diluted 50% with water).

For the extension, students will require access to:
- additional crystallising bowls with dilute culture solution, white and red light sources, and a mechanism for varying the period of illumination.

---

pared with germination and development in white light? Since light is essential, what is the minimum period of daily exposure to light that is required?

■ Data presentation

Make labelled drawings of:
- an individual sorus, viewed under the hand lens or binocular microscope;
- a sporangium that is discharging spores;
- a leaf in section, as seen from a prepared slide;
- stages in prothallus formation, noting the age of the prothallus at each stage;
- the archegonia and antheridia (if visible) on an inverted, older prothallus.

■ Conclusions

- How does the structure of a fern leaf compare with a liverwort prothallus? How does it compare with a flowering plant leaf?
- Make a flow-diagram summary of the life cycle of the fern, recording the approximate timing of major events.

■ Evaluation

What advantage may be gained if spores germinate only in the light, and only if the illumination is greater than 12 hours in a 24-hour period?

26.3 Flower structure I: regular and irregular flowers

(Data generating)

Flowers are reproductive structures. Pollen produced in anthers needs to reach the stigma of an ovule, either in a flower on the same plant (self-pollination) or on a different plant of the same species (cross-pollination).

Insects may be attracted to flowers for pollen and (sometimes) nectar, as food substances. In return, the pollen that adheres to their bodies may be carried to other flowers, possibly on other plants. Some plants have structural and/or physiological mechanisms that prevent self-pollination, but in many plants self-pollination (and self-fertilisation) is possible. (This is a seasonal practical, to be undertaken in springtime.)

■ Aim

To relate structure to function in flowers, and to compare regular and irregularly shaped flowers.

■ Risk assessment

- Take care with sharp scalpels or razor blades, both when in use and when placed down on the bench.
- Otherwise, good laboratory practice will be sufficient to take account of any hazards and avoid significant risks.

■ Method

The regular flowers of the buttercup

1 Using a hand lens, examine flowers of the inflorescence of buttercup (*Ranunculus acris*, Figure 26.5), including young flowers that have just opened, and older, wide-open flowers.
   - At the centre is the mass of individual tiny carpels, surrounded by stamens. Around these are the bright yellow petals forming an open cup. Below are smaller green sepals, covered by minute hairs. In unopened flowers the sepals clearly have a containing and protective role.
   - In the youngest open flowers, the stamens are curved inwards, concealing the carpels.
   - As the flowers age, the outer stamens stand erect, shed pollen towards the outside, and then come to lie against the petal. This development sequence is progressively repeated by the stamens nearer the carpels.
   - Eventually the carpels become fully exposed to insect visitors too.
   - By what various routes can insects reach the stamens and carpels in this flower?
   - In heavy rain, what protection of the stamens and carpels is possible?
2 Using a sharp, pointed scalpel (or razor blade) and fine forceps, take a mature flower apart, starting with the sepals. Lay the parts in order on a piece of paper.
   - Carefully examine the structural features of sepals, petals, stamens (of filament and anther) and carpels (of stigma, style and ovary), using a hand lens or stereomicroscope.
   - Are any of the component parts fused together, in addition to being attached to the stem tip (receptacle)?
   - Are the surface hairs, when present, large and dense enough to impede minibeast visitors?

- There is a nectary at the base of each petal. How large is it? Can nectar be seen in the flowers?
- The anthers of the stamens open (dehisce) in a particular way. In what direction within the flower is the pollen released?
- How many ovules are there in the ovary compartment of the carpel? Can you see 'inside' by holding a carpel up to the light?
- What happens to the stigma surface as it ages? Is it easy to tell stigma and style apart in this flower?

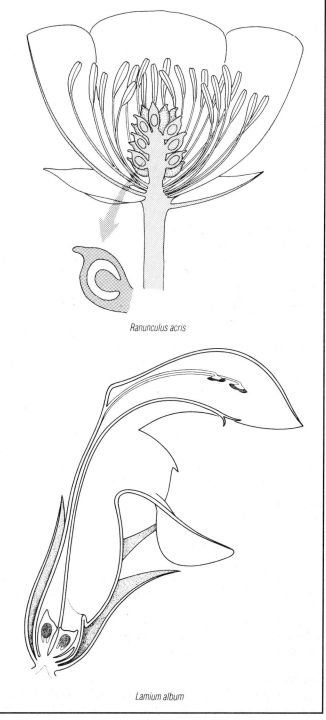

Figure 26.5 Flowers of the buttercup (*Ranunculus acris*) and white dead-nettle (*Lamium album*) in LS

Ranunculus acris

Lamium album

The irregular flowers of white dead-nettle

1 Using a hand lens, examine the inflorescence of the white dead-nettle (*Lamium album*, Figure 26.5). The flowers appear to be almost directly attached to the stem, in the axils of the leaves.

2 Using fine forceps, remove one or more flowers, so as to be able to examine them in detail.

- The sepals are fused into a tube (calyx tube) at their base. Can you deduce their number from the projecting, unfused parts? What is gained by a tubular construction?
- The petals are fused into a tube for much of their length (corolla tube). The tube is hooded. What is gained from this shape of corolla? Pull out and open up the corolla tube. What shape does the lower part of the tube take?
- Where are the stamens within this flower, and how many are present? Are the filaments of identical lengths? How are the anthers arranged?
- Investigate the stigma and style. Where is the stigma in relation to the anthers? When mature, what position and shape does the stigma take up? How long is the style in relation to the stamens?
- Cut open other flowers to see the fused ovaries. Is there evidence of nectar present? Can you locate tissue that appears to secrete nectar?
- By what route and mechanism can insects reach nectar at the base of this flower? What type of insects is likely to be excluded? What insects are best equipped to draw out the nectar? What parts of their bodies will carry out pollination?
- In heavy rain, what protection of the stamens and carpels is provided?

NOTE TO TECHNICIAN

Each student group will require:
- inflorescences, with several flowers, of *Ranunculus acris* and *Lamium album*, standing in water;
- a white tile, sharp pointed scalpel or razor blade, and fine forceps;
- bench lamp, hand lens, stereomicroscope (if available).

■ Data presentation

- Make annotated sketches of the component parts of the buttercup flower, commenting on roles that they perform.
- Construct a half-flower drawing of the buttercup flower, and label it.
- Construct a half-flower drawing of the white dead-nettle flower, and label it.
- Annotate both half-flower drawings to indicate what routes insect visitors may take, and what mechanisms exist to provide the pollen and carpels protection of any sort.

■ Conclusion

Draw up a table to compare the numbers, form and functions of the parts of the open, regular *Ranunculus* flower and the irregularly shaped *Lamium* flower. (Regular flowers are described as 'actinomorphic', irregular ones as 'zygomorphic'.)

■ Evaluation

- In what ways could you argue that the flower of the white dead-nettle is better adapted than that of the buttercup to the role of reproduction?
- In fact, both of these plants reproduce by means other than seed production. What are they?

26.4 Flower structure II: wind-pollinated flowers

(Investigation)

Plants adapted to pollination by wind (anemophilous plants) show a different set of adaptive features from those pollinated by insects (entomophilous plants). By examining one example, adaptive features common to other wind-pollinated species can be recognised.

■ Aim

To recognise the adaptive features of a wind-pollinated plant.

■ Risk assessment

- High levels of grass pollen in the air could result in hay fever or asthma attacks.
- Otherwise, good laboratory practice will be sufficient to take account of any hazards and avoid significant risks.

■ Method

1 Perennial rye-grass (*Lolium perenne*) has been collected and allowed to stand in an area where there is little air movement. Disturbing it as little as possible, examine the whole grass inflorescence as it stands. Notice the anthers attached to fine filaments hanging below the flowers. Gently blow them, to observe the effect that wind would have. Record your observations.

2 Pick off one anther and lay it on a slide. Use the magnifying tools available (hand lens, binocular microscope or monocular microscope) to examine its structure. Record your observations as a drawing to show the way the anther is attached to the filament and the way it splits open to release pollen.

3 Tap the anther on a microscope slide to release pollen grains and examine them dry under the monocular microscope. Note the shape of the pollen grain and the texture of its surface.

4 Using fine forceps, pick off a stigma protruding from the inflorescence. Examine it at different magnifications to work out how it is constructed. Mount it in a drop of water on a slide, add a coverslip and examine it under the microscope. Draw a small part of its appearance to typify the whole construction. Add notes to describe the structure of the complete stigma.

5 Remove one complete spikelet (a group of flowers lying to one side of the central axis, and alternating with the next spikelet). Then, starting from the base of the spikelet, remove the first green structure (a glume) and then a flower. Identify the perianth, which consists of a lemma and palea, both green and fitting closely to one another, unless the flower is open (in insect-pollinated flowers the perianth usually consists of the petals and sepals). Separate them to find the ovary (with two stigmas) and three stamens. In open flowers the lemma and palea are forced apart by the inflation of two small structures (called lodicules), situated at the point where the lemma and palea meet.

6 Make a labelled drawing of the structures you have successfully separated and identified. Record how many flowers there are in a spikelet and the approximate number in the inflorescence.

■ Data presentation

Your notes and drawings should provide a summary of the structure you have examined.

■ Discussion and conclusion

Describe the way in which the flower structure is adapted to pollination by wind. Consider:
- the number of flowers produced in one inflorescence;
- the construction of the stamen, including its size, the way it is attached to the filament and the nature of the filament itself;
- the features of the pollen grains;
- the perianth, including the number of parts and the function they perform (it is also worth considering the functions that they do *not* perform compared with the perianth of insect-pollinated plants);
- the stigmas, and how their construction provides a suitable adaptation to reception of wind-blown pollen;
- the part played by the lodicules (a unique feature of grasses).

■ Evaluation

Which of the adaptive features you have recognised in the grass flowers would be likely to occur in other plants adapted to pollination mainly by wind?

26.5 Microscopic structure of the anther and ovule

(Data generating)

The pollen grains in the anthers, and the embryo sacs within the ovules, develop in flowers long before they 'open', so it is tiny, immature flower buds that are sectioned and stained in order to observe these critical developments in the reproduction of angiosperms.

■ Aim

To observe the structure of a mature anther and embryo sac, and to relate structure to function.

■ Risk assessment

Good laboratory practice will be sufficient to take account of any hazards and avoid significant risks.

■ Method

1 You are provided with a prepared slide of a TS of a very young flower bud of *Lilium*. Examine this under medium-power magnification. Identify the structures present, relating them to their subsequent appearance in a mature flower (Figure 26.6).

2 Examine an anther in section under high-power magnification. Identify pollen grains, the pollen sacs in which they occur, and the remains of the tapetum, a layer which provides nutrients to pollen grains during development. Within the wall of the anther you should find the structures concerned with dehiscence of the pollen sacs (a thick fibrous wall around the pollen sacs, and the thin-walled stomium where the sacs later split open). The attachment of anther to filament may be seen, and there is a vascular bundle supplying the anther.

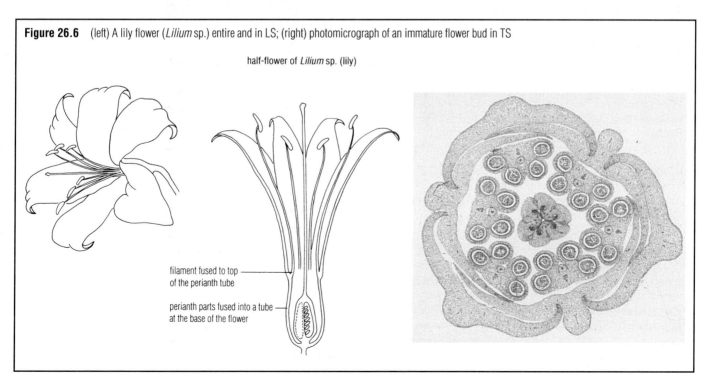

Figure 26.6   (left) A lily flower (*Lilium* sp.) entire and in LS; (right) photomicrograph of an immature flower bud in TS

half-flower of *Lilium* sp. (lily)

filament fused to top of the perianth tube

perianth parts fused into a tube at the base of the flower

3 Examine an ovule under high-power magnification. Identify the stalk region (the funiculus, attached to a region often called the 'placenta'), the parenchyma cells of the nucellus, and the embryo sac. Within one or more of the embryo sacs in your section you may be able to observe an egg cell, and the other cells and nuclei present in an embryo sac (polar nuclei, endosperm nucleus and synergid cells), although these may be difficult to make out.

NOTE TO TECHNICIAN

Each student group requires:
- microscope (with medium- and high-power objectives), with bench lamp if necessary;
- prepared slide of TS of young *Lilium* flower bud for general structure.

For the extension:
- flowers of *Lilium* that have opened (pollination stage);
- microscope slides, coverslips, squeezy bottle of distilled water, forceps, scalpel;
- micrometer eyepiece (graticule) and stage micrometer;
- prepared slides of TS of immature *Lilium* flower buds, showing stages in meiosis.

Reference
C J Clegg and Gene Cox (1992) *Anatomy and Activities of Plants*, John Murray. See pp. 58–9 for anther structure and development, and pp. 56–7 for structure and development of the embryo sac

■ Data presentation
Make fully labelled tissue map drawings of:
- a representative portion of the whole flower bud in section;
- an anther in section, recording the structure of the pollen grain in as much detail as is possible;
- an ovule in section, showing the embryo sac in as much detail as you can observe.

■ Conclusions
- What features of pollen grains are likely to be adaptations to function?
- What advantages arise from the positioning of the egg cell in an embryo sac, surrounded by other living cells (the ovule)?

■ Evaluation
Reproduction in an angiosperm involves more nuclei than one male gamete and one egg cell. What is the significance of this complexity?

■ Extension
- If *Lilium* flowers are available, mount some fresh pollen grains in water under a coverslip. Compare their size and appearance at pollination with those of developing pollen grains in an immature anther (prepared slide).
- If prepared slides of anthers showing early stages in pollen grain formation are available, look for stages in meiosis (*Advanced Biology*, pp. 190–3).

26.6 *Growing pollen grains*

(Investigation)

Pollen grains grow at the expense of nutrients (such as sucrose) on the stigma, and a pollen tube grows down through the style. Development of the pollen grain may be stimulated on agar on a microscope slide, and the growth of the pollen tube observed.

■ Aim
To observe the growing pollen tubes of *Tradescantia virginiana*.

■ Risk assessment

- Bottles of agar heated in a water bath to melt the agar can burst if their lids are not loosened off before placing them in the water.
- Wear eye protection when heating water to boiling over a Bunsen flame.
- Otherwise, good laboratory practice will be sufficient to take account of any hazards and avoid significant risks.

■ Method

1 Place a clean microscope slide in the base of a Petri dish. Molten agar (2%) containing 5% sucrose and a little boric acid is supplied in a warm water bath. Collect a bottle of agar and pour sufficient into the dish just to cover the slide with a thin layer of agar. Then allow it to cool and set.

2 Select a flower of *Tradescantia virginiana* and pick off one stamen with forceps. Gently tap the anther head along the agar, spreading pollen above the slide.

3 Incubate the dish with the lid on at 25 °C for one to three hours, then examine the agar surface under low-power magnification for the presence of pollen tubes. (If required the dish can be placed in the refrigerator at this stage until the next lesson.)

4 Cut the glass slide out of the agar, gently prising it up from one end and keeping the agar layer intact. Clean off any agar adhering to the underside of the glass and then examine it under low power on a level microscope stage without using a coverslip. Locate the pollen grains and examine them for the growth of pollen tubes.

5 Record observations on the proportion of grains germinating (i.e. the number of germinated grains compared with the number of ungerminated grains). Measure the rate of growth using a calibrated eyepiece scale, recording the increase in length at intervals over a 30-minute period; alternatively, estimate the length of pollen tube grown in a known period of time. It may be possible to see cytoplasmic streaming in the growing pollen tubes. Make a clear labelled drawing of a representative pollen grain and its pollen tube.

6 Apply a drop of methyl green pyronin directly on to the agar, leave it for 30 seconds then draw it up with filter paper. This will kill the cells but will stain some pollen tubes sufficiently to differentiate the greenish-looking nuclei in the tube from the pinkish-looking cytoplasm. Locate the position of the nuclei on your drawing.

■ Data presentation

Your drawing should represent the appearance of the pollen grain and the relative size and length of the pollen tube. Add comments to indicate the rate of growth and how it was estimated. State the proportion of pollen grains germinated.

■ Conclusions

- Calculate from your data how long it takes a pollen tube to grow down a style of 5 mm.
- Discuss the factors that may affect the number of grains germinating.
- Comment on the number and position of any nuclei found and any other observations that it was possible to make.

■ Evaluation

- If you have not seen the grain begin to grow, how realistic is a statement of rate of growth?
- How might the rate of pollen tube extension change during tube development?
- What mechanisms might operate to direct the growth of the pollen tube down the style?

■ Extension

The techniques used in this practical can be used to investigate the optimum concentration of sugar for pollen growth, or whether sucrose is the only effective sugar. Different flowers can be investigated for the conditions under which their pollen grains will germinate (0.3 mol dm^{-3} sucrose has been found effective for *Cheiranthus*, *Impatiens*, *Nicotiana* or *Fuchsia* and 0.5 mol dm^{-3} sucrose for *Lilium regale*), and the effect of borate ions can also be investigated.

26.7 Flower structure, pollination and its consequences in 'fast plants'

(Investigation)

The laboratory culture of 'fast plants' ('rapid-cycling brassicas' *Brassica rapa* syn. *campestris*) is described in Practical 28.3 (p. 337). Using these plants, it is possible to observe the steps to sexual reproduction in a flowering plant in its entirety, in a period of four or five weeks.

■ Aim

To investigate flower structure, carry out cross-pollination of flowers, observe pollen tube growth, measure fruit growth, collect seed, work out productivity per fruit/plant, and germinate and grow the progeny using the 'fast plant' *Brassica rapa*.

■ Risk assessment

Refer to the risk assessment for Practical 26.6.

■ Method

1 Using a hand lens, examine an individual flower of the 'fast plants' provided. You will get a clear idea of the flower in total if you systematically remove the outer structures present (sepals, petals, stamens) and lay them in sets on a sheet of paper. Look for the presence of nectaries (tissue that exudes a tiny quantity of sugar solution). Then construct a half-flower drawing of the flower (*Advanced Biology*, p. 584, shows the structure of a flower of the same family, which is very important commercially).

2 Pollination is possible as soon as the flowers are fully open, but there is a natural 'incompatibility' mechanism that ensures that pollen from the same plant does not normally fertilise its own flowers. If insects like the honey bee are excluded from the plants, then any pollination will need to be carried out by you. Use a cotton wool bud to simulate the action of an insect, transferring pollen between flowers of different plants. Pollination needs to be carried on for the greater part of a week. When they are completed, cut off and dispose of the remaining part of the inflorescence with unopened flower buds. The plant will then 'switch' to fruit and seed formation.

3 Pollen grains may be observed to 'germinate' and the pollen tubes grow in a mixture of the two solutions provided for this purpose, on a microscope slide. Place one drop of the 'pollen germination medium' and one drop of the 'sugar solution' on the slide. Add pollen grains. Within an hour you should be able to observe germination of the grains under medium-power magnification. Add a coverslip at this stage. Do not overheat the slide (by over-exposure to the microscope lamp), and do not let the liquid dry up.

4 Observe growth of the fruits. It is possible to measure growth in length as ovaries change into fruits. Note also the changes in the structure of the fruit wall, and the appearance of seeds within.

5 Seeds will be ready for dispersal in about two weeks from the end of pollination. Just before any dried fruit cases open, harvest the fruit individually. Work out the average numbers of seeds per fruit in each plant. Keep seeds from different plants separate.

6 Seeds of these plants have no dormancy period. They will germinate immediately if planted under suitable conditions (p. 337). Observe growth of the seedlings to the stage where normal vegetative leaves are formed (one week), and on to the appearance of the first flowers (about a further week).

■ Data presentation

Your diary or journal of results will include a record of some or all of the following:
- flower structure;
- a table of the cross-pollinations undertaken;

- a note of your observations of pollen 'germination' and pollen tube growth;
- a table of the change in length of fruit and notes on other aspects of growth of the fruit;
- data on seed productivity;
- a record of the growth rate of the progeny.

NOTE TO TECHNICIAN

You will need access to a commercial pyrethrum spray (such as an ICI 'Bug Gun'), in case of aphid infestation of the fast plants.

Each student group will require:

- batch of fast plants at about the two-week stage (full inflorescence formed, lower flowers just opened);
- hand lens, fine forceps, fine scissors;
- cotton wool buds for pollination, with glass tube with expanded polystyrene cap into which bud handles can be inserted between pollinations (the students may require one 'bud' per plant or more);
- microscope (with medium- and high-power magnification), with bench lamp if necessary;
- microscope slides, coverslips;
- 'pollen germination medium' and 'sugar solution medium' (see p. 431);
- fine dividers to measure ovary/fruit length;
- equipment for sowing and growing seeds of 'fast plants' (see p. 338).

■ Conclusion

What are the key steps to the processes you have observed that constitute sexual reproduction?

■ Evaluation

Is there a particular advantage of following a complex process through from start to finish, using a single species?

26.8 Embryo development in shepherd's purse
(Data generating)

After fertilisation the plant embryo develops within the embryo sac of the ovule, which itself matures to form the seed. The ovary, during the same period, is keeping pace with the developing ovules and is enlarging into the mature fruit. In the case of shepherd's purse (*Capsella bursa-pastoris*), the endosperm in the ovule remains fluid during a long period of the embryonic development and an embryo can be extracted from an ovule merely by squashing it. The ovule will burst and expel the green embryo almost undamaged.

■ Aim

To investigate the development of the growing embryo of a flowering plant.

■ Risk assessment

- Take care when working with sharp pointed scalpels and when the instruments are put down between use.
- Otherwise, good laboratory practice will be sufficient to take account of any hazards and avoid significant risks.

■ Method

1 You are provided with an inflorescence of shepherd's purse. Lay out five microscope slides and label them 1, 3, 5, 7 and 9. From the inflorescence pick the most mature green fruit and take this as fruit 1. It will be at or near the base of the inflorescence. Place fruit 1 on slide 1. Count upwards from this fruit removing those fruits that correspond to the numbered slides, and place each on its appropriate slide.

   Note: Keep the remaining fruits for additional readings if required. If the last fruit in the sequence is less than 4 mm, then you should use all the fruits rather than alternate ones.

2 Measure the size of each fruit (to the nearest mm) as shown in Figure 26.7.

3 Record the fruit size against its slide number.

4 Transfer slide 1 to a white tile and, holding one 'wing' of the fruit down, slit the opposite 'wing' with a sharp scalpel, in the same way that you might slit open a letter with a paper knife (Figure 26.8).

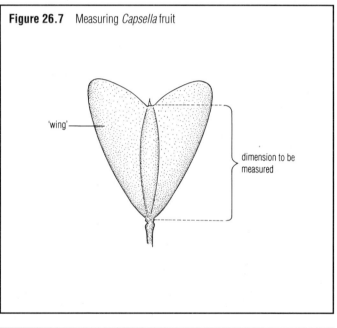

Figure 26.7   Measuring *Capsella* fruit

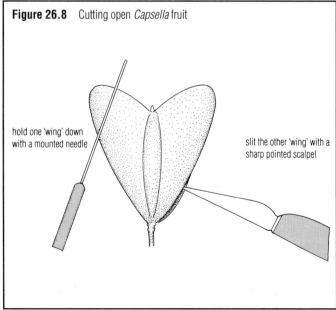

Figure 26.8   Cutting open *Capsella* fruit

5 Pick up the top flap of the fruit with forceps and peel it off to reveal the ovules (now developing seeds) close to the central septum that divides the two 'wings'. Remove four or five of these and arrange them in a drop of water on the same slide so that they are well separated. Discard the fruit and add a coverslip. Take a mounted needle, place the point exactly above an ovule and press gently until it pops. Repeat for all the other ovules on the slide.

6 Using a stage micrometer slide, measure the width of the field of view when the microscope is set up with the ×10 eyepiece lens and the medium-power (×10) objective. Knowing the actual diameter of the illuminated area you will be able to estimate the length of the embryos from the proportion of the distance they occupy.

7 Examine slide 1. You should now be able to find at least one ovule that has released its embryo intact. The embryo is dicotyledonous but the two cotyledons may be folded over in the most mature embryos. They may tear off when they are expelled from the ovule, so you may need mentally to 'reconstruct' the embryo in order to estimate its size. Judge the overall length of the embryo (assuming it were straightened out) compared with the diameter of the field of view. Record, by a quick sketch, the embryo shape and its estimated length.

8 Repeat the procedure for slides 3, 5, 7 and 9. Remember you are working towards fruits that are younger and have had less time to develop.

NOTE TO TECHNICIAN

Each group requires:
- inflorescence of shepherd's purse (*Capsella bursa-pastoris*);
- microscope with ×10 objective, bench lamp if necessary, five microscope slides, five coverslips, marker pen;
- mounted needle, scissors, forceps, scalpel with pointed blade (e.g. no. 11);
- stage micrometer slide;
- white tile, distilled water, dropper;
- graph paper;
- hand lens or access to a low-powered binocular microscope may be useful.

■ Data presentation

Tabulate the data about each fruit, giving its number, size, the shape of the embryo and your estimate of embryo length. Plot a graph of the size of the fruit against the slide number. It is easier to understand if you turn the scale of slide numbers round (9→1) so that it reads from young to old. On the same graph plot the estimated embryo length. You can then compare the growth of the embryo with the size of the fruit that contained it.

■ Conclusions
- From your sketches of embryos of different maturity, describe the changes that take place in the morphology of the embryo as it grows.
- From your graph, comment on the degree to which embryo growth keeps pace with fruit development.

■ Evaluation
- How could you estimate embryo size more accurately?
- Could the size of the fruit be used to estimate the stage of development of the embryo inside?

26.9 Fruit and seed dispersal

(Investigation)

Fruits and seeds can be hard to tell apart, although the biological differences between them are clear-cut.

For the success of the species, it is advantageous for at least some of the very many seeds and fruits formed to be dispersed widely before they settle into soil and germinate. There are many efficient adaptations that favour dispersal by animals (internally or externally), by the wind, by water or by some kind of explosive/propulsion mechanism on the part of the parent plant, for example. Consequently we often choose to classify seeds on their mechanism of dispersal. Many highly successful species show no apparent mechanism, however. Perhaps seeds of this type, along with other types of seed, are enthusiastically pounced upon by potential 'predators'. Indeed, the fate of very many fruits and seeds is to be eaten. Other fruits and seeds are carried off but dropped on the way, when the predator is distracted, or are stored in a private 'larder' at soil level, which is later overlooked or forgotten.

■ Aim
To investigate a range of seed dispersal mechanisms.

■ Risk assessment
Good laboratory practice will be sufficient to take account of any hazards and avoid significant risks.

■ Method
You are provided with a selection of fruits and seeds.

1 Examine the external appearance of these structures, and divide them into three groups: fruits; seeds; not known. What criteria will you use?

Remember, the seed forms from the ovule, and it has a single point of attachment, inside an ovary.

The fruit forms from the ovary. At this stage it is attached to the stem (or receptacle) of the parent plant, but has the stigma and style attached.

So theoretically, a seed has one scar and a fruit has two. The trouble in applying this simple rule is that later growth and development of seeds and fruits (associated with dispersal, for example) may mask the scars.

2 Now look at the group of fruits and seeds provided from the viewpoint of a possible dispersal mechanism. Classify them into one of six categories, more or less, on appearances:

wind-dispersed; dispersed by animals (internally); dispersed by animals (externally); dispersed by water; explosive propulsion; no special mechanism.

NOTE TO TECHNICIAN

Each student group requires:
- a hand lens;
- a selection of fruits and seeds, as diverse in type as possible. These can be collected as they become available, for many seeds and fruits (apart from succulent ones) can be stored and re-used. Some suitable examples are listed on p. 430.

■ Data presentation

* Make annotated sketches of two fruits and two seeds, showing the features by which they are identified.
* Make annotated sketches of examples of fruits and seeds according to their dispersal mechanism, giving two examples of each of the following categories:
  wind-dispersed; dispersed by animals (internally); dispersed by animals (externally); dispersed by water; explosive propulsion.

■ Conclusion

What are the special advantages to the angiosperms of seed production and dispersal, which are not found in other forms of plant reproduction?

■ Evaluation

Irrespective of the efficiency of the dispersal mechanism, subsequent germination and growth of a seed depend on where it eventually lands. Review the role of dispersal in this light.

■ Extension

Botanists also classify fruits as true fruits (made from the ovary alone) or 'false fruits' (containing stem tissues as well). True fruits are subdivided on the basis of their being 'dry' or 'succulent'. Dry fruits are divided according to whether they are dehiscent (break apart during dispersal) or indehiscent (remain intact). Then, all groups are subclassified as to whether one, two or more carpels are involved in each. There are specialised names for each type.

You can attempt this classification if there is time. The information is important to a taxonomist of flowering plants, but is less useful to the rest of us.

26.10 Vegetative propagation, natural and artificial

(Investigation)

Many plants have structural adaptations favourable for vegetative reproduction. By vegetative reproduction is meant the processes of increasing the numbers of organisms as a result of vegetative growth – that is, by an asexual process, rather than by sexual reproduction as a result of flowering. In addition, the buds, stems, leaves or roots of many plants have a distinct capacity for regeneration if broken off or damaged in some way, provided reasonable growing conditions are maintained. No doubt this fundamental capacity for vegetative propagation is just one of many reasons for the success of flowering plants.

■ Aim

To investigate aspects of the capacity of flowering plants for vegetative increase in numbers.

■ Risk assessment

* When working out in the field (on urban waste land, for example, or hedgerows or scrub land), make certain you remain in groups of two or three students, that your whereabouts are known to your teacher or tutor, and that your itinerary has been approved.

* Take special care when working with sharp dissection equipment, and when such instruments are placed down on the bench between use.
* Otherwise, good laboratory practice will be sufficient to take account of any hazards and avoid significant risks.

■ Method

Naturally occurring methods of vegetative propagation

Either search for particular examples of vegetative propagation in the locality of your home or, working in groups, observe a range of examples marked out in hedgerow, waste land or similar, near to your school or college. Make labelled sketches (or photographs) of the examples, and compile these into a collected wall newspaper presentation on the subject of natural propagation. The examples to be seen should cover the following range:

* *Creeping (or arching) stems and runners (above ground, more or less horizontal stems)*, which root at nodes along the length, and which eventually become isolated as separate plants.
  Examples: ground ivy   (*Glechoma hederacea*);
  yellow archangel   (*Lamiastrum galeobdolon*);
  cinquefoil   (*Potentilla reptans*);
  blackberry   (*Rubus fruticosus*).
* *Suckers (lateral stems) formed below ground as rhizomes or at the base of upright stems*, eventually becoming independent plants.
  Examples: yarrow   (*Achillea millefolium*);
  mint   (*Mentha* sp.);
  poplar   (*Populus canescens*);
  and aspen   (*Populus tremula*);
  plum   (*Prunus domestica*);
  sheep's sorrel (*Rumex acetosella*);
  creeping thistle (*Cirsium arvense*).
* *Underground stems growing horizontally (rhizomes)*, which branch and eventually die back to leave independent plants.
  Examples: iris   (*Iris pseudacorus*);
  couch grass   (*Agropyrom repens*);
  Yorkshire fog grass (*Holcus lanatus*);
  nettle   (*Urtica dioica*);
  dog's mercury   (*Mercuralis perennis*).
* *Bulbs (underground buds), corms (underground upright stems), swollen tap roots (with adventitious buds), root tubers (with adventitious buds) and stem tubers*: these are best observed in cultivated crop plants and garden plants. A selection is studied in the next section of this practical.

The vegetative structure of a bulb, stem tuber and rhizome

You can learn about the life cycle of bulbs, stem tubers and rhizomes in *Advanced Biology*, pp. 586–7. You are provided with examples of a bulb, a stem tuber and a rhizome.

1 Make fully annotated sketches to highlight the external features which you can relate to growth and development, and to the presence of a substantial food store by which new growth may be sustained.
2 Using the sharp knife, tile, scalpel and forceps provided, investigate the internal structure of the bulb, stem tuber and rhizome. Make annotated sketches to show how these are constructed, indicating the positions of stem, root, leaf and buds in each. Investigate the distribution of a food reserve such as starch.

3 Make concise notes about how the development of these plants leads to vegetative increase during a full season of growth.

The capacity for regeneration by root fragments and stem cuttings

Tap roots of dandelions (*Taraxacum officinale*) can be dug from a garden or waste land situation with the approval of the owners. The roots may be cut into standard lengths and kept moist (part-submerged in water) in small beakers or tubes, in a well-illuminated position. Normally leaves grow out from the callus that grows on the proximal surface and roots form on the distal surface, whether the segments are held upright, horizontal or inverted.

NOTE TO TECHNICIAN

Each student will require:

For the study of naturally occurring vegetative propagation mechanisms:
- access to a site where a range of vegetative propagation mechanisms can be observed; alternatively, individuals may bring back reports of examples seen elsewhere, and these may be assembled as a wall poster.

For the study of bulbs, stem tubers and rhizomes:
- daffodil bulb, potato stem tuber, iris rhizome;
- sharp knife, tile, scalpel, forceps, dropping bottle of iodine in potassium iodide solution.

For the study of root and stem cuttings:
- access to a supply of *Taraxacum* tap roots, or cuttings of privet (*Ligustrum vulgare*) or willow (*Salix* sp.).

A specific investigation, approved by the teacher or tutor, will require a range of standard laboratory apparatus which will be identified as part of the investigation proposal.

Design an investigation by which you can test these suggestions, and determine the minimum size of segment that will regenerate (but allow for the width of segment being significant, too).

Reference

P W Freeland (1974) 'Regeneration in root segments of dandelion; some suggestions for experimental work', *School Science Review* (June 1974) 55(193), pp. 725–9

Cuttings of plants are frequently used in horticulture in order to propagate species. The effects of 'hormone' rooting powders may be investigated (*Advanced Biology*, p. 446). Using species like privet (*Ligustrum vulgare*) or willow (*Salix* sp.), design an investigation of the ability of cuttings to form roots when maintained in tap water or moist rooting compost. What is the best depth to hold the submerged stem? How extensive should the aerial system be for quick rooting?

■ Data presentation

The outcomes of these investigations should be recorded on sheets of paper, which can be combined with the work of other groups in a related area to form a 'wall newspaper' presentation.

■ Conclusion

The results of studies will indicate the extent of adaptations for vegetative propagation, which may be summarised for emphasis as a conclusion.

■ Evaluation

To what extent is the facility for propagation linked to the accumulation of a food store within the parts that get cut off?

Projects

26.1 Bee preferences

Construct an artificial flower comprising a feeder made from a 35 mm film container with a length of melting-point tube just protruding through a tiny hole in the lid. Fill the container with 10% sucrose solution and put the lid on. Capillary action will cause the solution to rise up near the top of the melting-point tube. This feeding tube can be surrounded by the artificial 'flower', the container lid acting as a support. The feeder can be placed in the garden where bees are foraging and left set up so that it becomes a reliable food source which bees visit regularly.

Investigate the number of bee visits at feeders surrounded by different 'flowers'. For example, are petals more attractive than solid discs? Do lines indicating the food position change the feeding frequency or time taken to find the food? Does the area of colour make the feeder more noticeable to the insect? What colours are most easily seen? Do bees show preferences for particular colour patterns? (For example, there are many flowers that are blue with yellow centres, but few that are yellow with blue centres.)

26.2 Hoverflies as pollinators

Hoverflies (Syrphidae) are frequent visitors to flowers but are often rated as poor pollinators because they feed at a wide variety of flowers and have short mouthparts unable to penetrate into the flower. For some actinomorphic flowers hoverflies may be effective pollinators. Investigate this by:

- observing hoverflies feeding on particular plants and recording the frequency with which they transfer from one flower to another of the same species;
- trapping hoverflies, anaesthetising them and sweeping pollen from their bodies to find out how varied it is.

26.3 Are plants pollinated by both wind and insects?

Despite being catkin-bearing plants, which is a feature normally associated with pollination by wind, willows (*Salix* sp.) produce male flowers (pussy-willows) which are brightly coloured by their obvious anthers and are visited by bumble bees. Observe *Salix* plants in flower to find out if insects visit female flowers as well as male flowers, and if these insects are carrying pollen. Try to determine if the mechanism of pollination is by wind or insects or both.

26.4 Temperature in arum flowers

The arum lily (*Arum maculatum*) is known to have very unusual adaptations for pollination. Some reports suggest that an elevated temperature inside the spathe may encourage insects to enter the base. With thermistor probes and data recording devices it is possible to see if the plant does maintain a temperature within the base significantly higher than the surroundings. How long is this maintained? Does it fluctuate in a manner that would suggest it has an adaptive significance?

26.5 Hairs in foxglove flowers

The mouth of the foxglove corolla tube carries many long hairs, often interpreted as barriers preventing insects too small to bring about pollination from reaching the food sources. Devise simple experiments to decide if this barrier is effective in preventing small insects from crossing it.

26.6 Fruit and seed dispersal by various 'animals'

Humans can be effective dispersal agents for fruits and seeds. Set up a systematic investigation of the fruits and seeds to be found on clothing (more difficult) and in the mud of shoes (more straightforward) from samples of people making particular journeys. You may choose to assay the seed content of mud by allowing seeds present to germinate, and then identify the plants. (The problem in autumn is that seeds that have a dormancy period may escape your survey data.)

Another mechanism is to simulate the movements of a long-haired animal along a standardised length of hedgerow by dragging an old towel or woollen jumper through vegetation in a particular way, and counting the seeds that become attached. With a standardised 'animal', you can compare different habitats, and habitats at different times.

Reference

J Bebbington and A Bebbington (1993) ' "Merry's Ears" – dispersal of fruits and seeds', *J. Biol. Ed.* 27(3), pp. 166–9

26.7 Regeneration of root fragments and stem cuttings

Adapt the technique in Practical 26.10 to different species, or extend it to issues like the effects of specific nutrient ions, plant growth regulators, and light and dark.

26.8 Floral structure in a flowering plant family

You have learnt how to dissect a flower, examining the receptacle, sepals, petals, androecium and gynoecium. You know where to look for a nectary, and how the shape of a flower gives clues to the sorts of visitors it attracts. You appreciate the significance of stamens that mature and then wither before the stigma is ripe and accessible, or vice versa. You know how to record floral structure in half-flower, and plan drawings and annotated sketches. So now apply these skills to flowers of one family, such as the Leguminosae (cultivated and wild members), or the Cruciferae, or the Rosaceae. Taking the last-named family as an example, find flowers of the following genera (at least), and analyse and record what you discover:

Group 1: *Pyrus* (pear); *Malus* (apple); *Crataegus* (hawthorn).
Group 2: *Rubus* (blackberry); *Potentilla* (cinquefoil); *Geum* (wood avens); *Rosa* (rose).
Group 3: *Prunus* (peach, plum, cherry, apricot).

If you are going to select another family, get your teacher or tutor to help you select plants that bring out the diversity within the family, before you start.

Problems and assignments

26.1 The life cycle of a bryophyte

Figure 26.9 is a flow diagram of the life cycle of a bryophyte. So the moss or liverwort that you have studied (Practical 26.1) has this sort of life cycle. With that bryophyte in mind, answer the following questions.

1 a Make a simple, labelled drawing of the gametophyte plant you observed.
  b In what sort of habitat is it commonly found? At what time in the year does it grow like this?
  c Is the gametophyte described as diploid or haploid? What do these terms mean?
2 The female sex organ is referred to as an archegonium.
  a Make a labelled drawing to show the structure of the archegonium.
  b How are male sex cells able to locate and fertilise the egg cell in an archegonium?
3 The product of sexual reproduction is a zygote.
  a Where does the sporophyte generation of a bryophyte develop?
  b How does the sporophyte plant obtain the bulk of the nutrients it requires?
4 Cell divisions in sporophyte formation are by mitosis, but in spore production in the sporophyte, the nuclear divisions are by meiosis.
  a What is the essential difference in outcome of these two kinds of nuclear division?
  b Spores of the bryophyte are formed in 'tetrads'. What does this mean? Why are they formed so?
5 Show, by means of a labelled sketch, how spores were dispersed by your bryophyte.
6 Bryophytes are a distinct group of plants, quite different from algae or angiosperms of a comparable size. Draw up a simple table to give the significant differences of structure and life cycles in these three groups.

26.2 Spores in the life of a fern

The fern plant shown in Figure 26.10 grows on hedge banks, in woodlands or among rocks, and it survives well in direct sunlight or moderate shade. Examine the drawings and, using your knowledge of the biology of the fern and of the physiology of terrestrial green plants in general, answer the following questions.

1 What part do the tissues at A and at B respectively play in the nutrition of the fern?
2 a What function may structure C perform in the survival of the plant?
  b Where on the fern plant is a 'sorus' found? Make a fully labelled sketch of the appearance of a sorus as seen under a hand lens.
  c At what time in the year would you look for sori on the fern plant?
3 What key changes occur in the cells *within* a young, immature sporangium for them to become spores?
4 a For what general role are the cells at D and E adapted?
  b Describe by means of a labelled sketch how their roles are performed.
5 When spores of *Dryopteris* germinate on moist soil a fern 'prothallus' is produced.
  a What is a fern prothallus?
  b What part does it play in the life cycle?
6 Summarise in a concise list the unique features of a fern plant like *Dryopteris* that differentiate it from bryophytes and angiosperms (flowering plants).

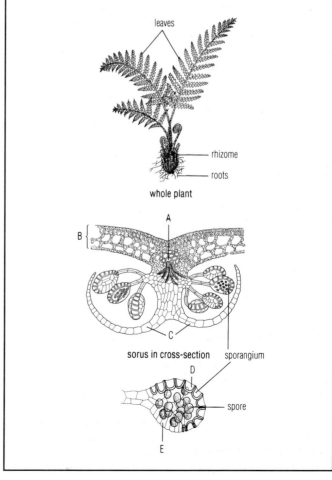

Figure 26.10 A plant of *Dryopteris*, the male fern, with an enlarged view of one of its spore-producing structures

leaves

rhizome

roots

whole plant

A

B

C

sorus in cross-section   sporangium

D

spore

E

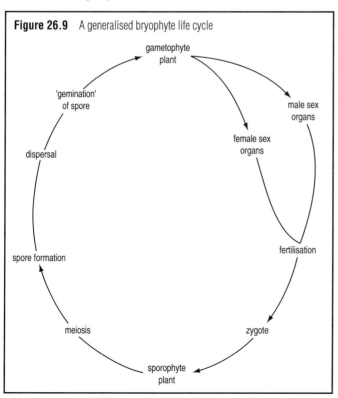

Figure 26.9 A generalised bryophyte life cycle

gametophyte plant

'gemination' of spore

male sex organs

female sex organs

dispersal

fertilisation

spore formation

meiosis

zygote

sporophyte plant

26.3 Conifers v. angiosperms: pointers to success!

Groups of organisms have appeared in the history of life on Earth at different times. Groups also differ widely in the numbers of species they comprise: some groups are more diverse than others. Conifers and flowering plants are a case in point. The fossil record shows the conifers appeared before angiosperms, but angiosperms have many more species and more diverse plant forms than conifers. Standing where we do in the history of life, angiosperms undoubtedly appear to us a more successful group. Think carefully about this point. You can read about the life cycles of both groups, and some of the implications, in *Advanced Biology*, pp. 575–85.

1 Make concise lists of the key reasons why conifers and angiosperms respectively can be held to be successful land plants. Number these points.

2 Point out the features in the angiosperm list which you feel may be most responsible for the pre-eminent success of these plants. These are the points you would concentrate on if you were asked to argue briefly about 'success' in the angiosperms with peers, or perhaps at an academic interview.

26.4 Pine trees and the environment

The data in Figure 26.11 relate to pine tree growing downwind of a major industrial city in the north of England, over a period of 31 years starting in 1950. Tree ring analysis of Scots pine (*Pinus sylvestris*) was carried out as a measure of annual growth rates. The annual figures are means of 16 trees.

Average rainfall was also monitored throughout the period, as an indicator of any effects of weather on growth rate. The rainfall was fairly constant throughout the period, with the exception of 1975 when rainfall was 76% of normal, and again in 1976, when there was a most severe national water shortage.

The period was one of intense lobbying by environmentalists to achieve the designation of urban areas as 'smokeless zones'. In a smokeless zone the amount of atmospheric pollution from most, if not all, sources is substantially reduced.

Examine the data in Figure 26.11 and, using the information given you together with your own wider reading, answer the following questions.

1 What features are responsible for the appearance of a growth ring as seen in a transverse section of the trunk.

2 a Calculate the approximate maximum effect of the period of drought in 1976 on the mean tree ring width.

   b Why is drought such a strong inhibitor of tree growth?

3 For the period 1965–75, calculate the approximate increase in:

   a the mean tree ring width;

   b the increase in the percentage of industrial areas covered by smoke control orders.

4 One of the atmospheric pollutants present in industrial smoke is dust particles of a wide range of sizes.

   a How could you demonstrate practically that dust reaches the pine needles of such trees, and that the quantity accumulated is greater on pine needles of greater age?

   b In what ways may dust have a harmful effect on the growth of a pine tree?

5 a Name one other airborne pollutant commonly present in the smoke from industrial chimneys.

   b In what ways is this substance potentially harmful to green plants?

6 What source of atmospheric pollution has generally not decreased over the period of this study, and subsequently?

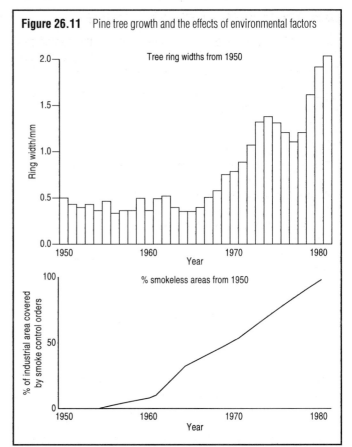

Figure 26.11 Pine tree growth and the effects of environmental factors

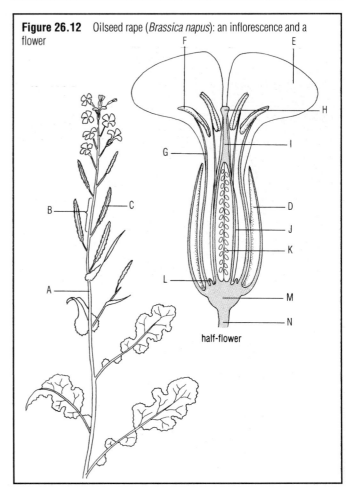

Figure 26.12 Oilseed rape (*Brassica napus*): an inflorescence and a flower

half-flower

26.5 The features of an inflorescence

Figure 26.12 is a drawing of the inflorescence of the oilseed rape plant, together with one of an individual flower, in longitudinal section. Examine these drawings, and then answer the questions below.

1 What distinguishes an inflorescence from the rest of the plant? What is an inflorescence?
2 Identify:
   a structure N;
   b structure A.
3 The youngest flowers are at the top of the plant. What sort of inflorescence does this make it?
4 What is the difference between a young flower and C?
5 The flower of rape has four petals (E) arranged in a cross. Of which family of flowering plants (to which rape belongs) is this typical?
6 Which structure is the receptacle? What parts of the flower are attached to it?
7 What are the roles in the developing flower of the green structures D?
8 Identify by name the structures B, F, H, I and K.

26.6 The development of the pollen tube

Figure 26.13 shows an SEM of a stigma after pollination, when the pollen tubes have started to grow, together with drawings of a pollen grain and a carpel in section, prior to pollination. Using your general knowledge of reproduction in flowering plants, together with the information in the enclosed pictures, answer the following questions.

1 What are the differences in structure and function of the wall layers A and B of the pollen grain?
2 **a** When the growing pollen tube eventually reaches an embryo sac, what is the fate of the nucleus C?
   b Which of the nuclei labelled E to H fuses with D to form a zygote? Which fuses with D to form the endosperm?
3 In this plant the diploid chromosome number is 16. What will be the number of chromosomes in nuclei of cells at J, F, D and G respectively?
4 When the embryo forms:
   a what will the ovary wall become?
   b what will the structure currently the 'ovule' be called?
5 Some pollen fails to grow on stigmas of the same plant, and the pollen is said to be incompatible. Since the pollen tube is dependent on the style tissue through which it grows, by what sorts of mechanism may incompatibility be caused?

26.7 Analysing a flower and designing a key

A botanist is studying the structure and pollination process in flowers of one family. A table of characteristics of three of the flowers has already been drawn up (see next page). The buttercup is another member of the family (Figure 26.14), but analysis of this flower is still to be carried out.

1 Look at Table 26.1 and the drawing of the flower. Using the information given, complete the table.
2 Using your completed table, construct a dichotomous key (see earlier example on p. 10) that would allow the four flowers to be identified

Figure 26.13 Pollination and fertilisation

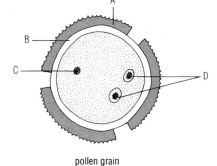

pollen grain

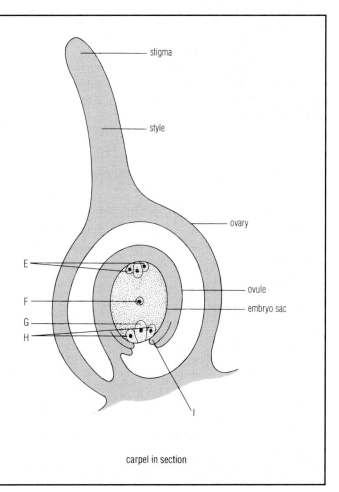

carpel in section

Figure 26.14   The buttercup flower

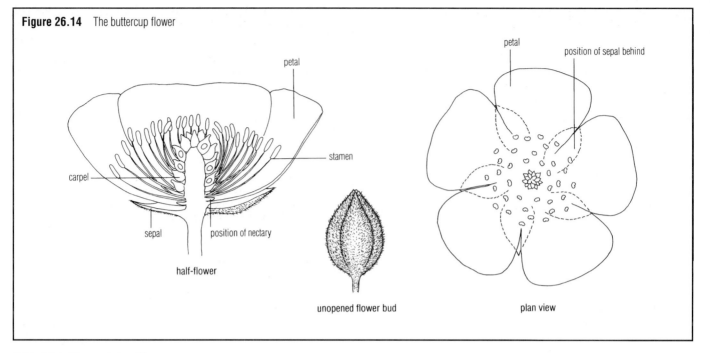

half-flower

unopened flower bud

plan view

Table 26.1 Characteristics of flowers

Characteristics	*Clematis vitalba* (traveller's joy)	*Caltha palustris* (kingcup)	*Aquilegia vulgaris* (wild columbine)	*Ranunculus acris* (buttercup)
Woody or herbaceous plants	woody	herb	herb	
Sepals, present or absent	4–5, petaloid	5, petaloid	5, green	
Petals, present or absent	absent	absent	present + spur	
Number of petals	0	0	5	
Stamens, few or many	many	many	many	
Carpels, few or many	many, 15–35	few, 5–15	few, 5	
Ovules per carpel, 1 or many	1	several	several	
Nectary, present or absent	present	present	present	
Position of nectary	filament of stamens	glandular hairs of carpels	at the end of petal spurs	

26.8 Wind pollination: the 'design' issues

Wind-pollinated plants include many of our commonest native trees, almost all the grasses, many seashore plants and some very successful families of herbaceous weeds. Wind pollination is a highly significant mechanism of pollination throughout the terrestrial world, and probably as numerically important as insect pollination.

Insect-pollinated plants attract insects to flowers (at a price), thereby increasing the likelihood of pollination. Wind pollination is entirely dependent on chance, with the pollen being dispersed more widely with increasing distances between stamens and stigmas (on different plants, preferably). What are the requirements for successful cross-pollination by wind? What arrangement will minimise effort and achieve greatest success?

Think systematically about the issues, step by step, from formation of the pollen till fertilisation is achieved.

Design a successful system, noting down the issues that arise at each step, and any problems that may result from your 'solution', too. Annotated sketches may be used to augment your notes, and illustrate the solutions you have in mind. The issues certainly include:

- not only the amount of pollen but also its shape and size;
- the type of structure from which pollen is ideally dispersed under most appropriate weather conditions;
- where large quantities of pollen are produced, how 'blanketing' of stigmas of the same plant is to be avoided;
- how to 'service' individuals that have achieved dispersal to new habits;
- how to minimise impediments to air movements (are leaves a problem?);
- the type of structure that is most efficient for trapping airborne pollen;
- whether the stigma/style design presents risks for pollen tube growth and successful fertilisation.

Reference

An interesting discussion of the issues in wind (and insect) pollination is found in:
M Proctor and P Yeo (1995) *The Pollination of Flowers.* Collins New Naturalist no 54

26.9 Quick test

1 Distinguish between the following pairs:

a haploid and diploid life cycles;
b mosses and liverworts;
c archegonium and antheridium;
d sorus and indusium;
e racemose inflorescence and cymose inflorescence;
f calyx and corolla;
g androecium and gynoecium;
h actinomorphic and zygomorphic;
i entomophily and anemophily;
j pollination and fertilisation;
k tapetum and stomium;
l intine and exine;
m ovule and ovary;
n integuments and micropyle;
o embryo sac and nucellus;
p endosperm nucleus and egg cell;
q endospermic and non-endospermic seeds;
r biennials and perennials;
s bulbs and rhizomes;
t budding and grafting.

2 What do you understand by the following?

a alternation of generations;
b gametophyte plant;
c sporophyte plant;
d epiphytes;
e fern frond;
f prothallus;
g double fertilisation;
h parthenocarpy;
i perennation;
j vegetative reproduction.

26.10 Essay assignment

Select one of the following:

- Give an illustrated account of the events in a flowering plant between:
  a pollination and fertilisation, by which a zygote is formed;
  b fertilisation and the formation of a non-endospermic seed.

or:

- By means of annotated flow diagrams, outline the life cycles of bryophytes and angiosperms. Assess the significance of the differences between these life cycles.

27 Life cycles of animals

Summary

Animals have **diploid life cycles**. An animal may produce one or many new individuals, although most organisms in the wild die before reproducing at all. New individuals may be produced by asexual or sexual reproduction. Asexual reproduction is far less common in animals than in plants.

Asexual reproduction by **budding** occurs in *Hydra*. In budding an offspring develops from part of a parent's body, becomes separated, and grows into an independent adult. **Parthenogenesis** is another form of asexual reproduction. It is a modified form of sexual reproduction in which the egg cell develops without fertilisation. Aphids, for example, produce very many generations of females parthenogenetically, starting from a fertilised egg that has 'over-wintered'. Male and female aphids are formed in late summer and mate, and fertilised eggs are laid.

In sexual reproduction gametes are produced in **sex organs**, which may be quite complex structures, and sexual reproduction may involve **elaborate behaviour patterns**. In sexual reproduction the male gametes are commonly very small and motile, whereas the female gametes are large and sedentary (**heterogamy**). Sex organs are commonly housed on separate male and female organisms, although they may occur on the same **hermaphrodite** individual, as in earthworms. Reproduction may be coordinated with a time of plentiful food supply (**breeding season**). **Fertilisation** may be **external** (for example, in the frog) or **internal**, when the sperms are deposited within the female. Internal fertilisation has evolved widely in the Animal Kingdom (for example, insects, vertebrates). Prolonged **internal development** of the fertilised eggs occurs in the mammals. Many species show some form of **parental care** of the young offspring; pronounced parental care is typical of the mammals and birds.

In sexual reproduction in mammals the **sperms** are produced in paired testes, the **egg cells** in paired ovaries. The testes and ovaries are the primary sexual organs or **gonads**. Associated with the gonads is a system of tubes and accessory glands that plays a key part in the transport, delivery, reception and storage of gametes. These are the **secondary sexual organs**. The role of the male reproductive system is to produce sperms, and to deliver sperms in a liquid medium (semen) to the vagina during copulation. The testes also produce the chief male hormone, **testosterone**. The role of the female reproductive system is to produce egg cells, to deliver them to the oviduct where fertilisation may occur, and to get the wall of the uterus into a condition favourable for implantation and development of an embryo. The ovaries also produce the chief female sex hormone, **oestrogen**.

The period of internal development, after fertilisation, is known as **gestation**. In humans, during this 40 weeks of pregnancy the growth rate of the new individual exceeds that at any other stage of life. The mother's body also undergoes profound physiological change, yet after the birth returns to the normal condition relatively quickly. Four separate hormones regulate the changes of pregnancy through to birth. The developing fetus grows at the expense of nutrients taken indirectly from the mother's blood, via the **placenta**. Throughout pregnancy, the **mammary glands** of the mother are prepared for milk production. Milk forms the only item of diet of the young mammal for a significant period of time after birth. The young mammals are dependent upon their parents, but in humans this period is longer than in any other species. It is a time when we inherit our culture.

Practicals and activities

27.1 Fertilisation in Pomatoceros

(Investigation)

Pomatoceros triqueter is a polychaete worm that is found on the lower shore, enclosed in a calcareous tube. The tubes occur attached to rocks, small stones and the shells of crabs, and are found all around the coast of the United Kingdom (Figure 27.1). The tube is 3–6 cm in length, off-white in colour, triangular in cross-section, and with a distinctive keel along the top. The worm has a fan-like crown of tentacles, which filter water for food, and absorb oxygen. The sexes are separate (dioecious species) and, outside of their tubes, are easily differentiated; they are purplish-brown dorsally, but the ventral surface of the females is red and that of the males is white. When male and female worms are freed from their shells at any time of the year they normally quickly release gametes into seawater, where fertilisation may be observed.

Figure 27.1 *Pomatoceros triqueter* tubes on stones on the lower shore

■ Aim

To observe fertilisation and the early divisions of cleavage in a marine, non-vertebrate worm.

■ Risk assessment

- Take care with sharp dissection instruments, both in use and when placed on the bench.
- Otherwise, good laboratory practice will be sufficient to take account of any hazards and avoid significant risks.

■ Method

1 You are provided with a sample of seawater, and a stone, shell or pebble recently obtained from a seashore with several off-white tubes encrusting on it.

 Using a pair of forceps, break off the narrow end of one of the tubes. Then, with strong dissecting scissors, cut through the flat keel for up to a quarter of the tube's length. Chip away the 'tube' material with forceps, and then push the worm free from the tube with a blunt seeker.

2 Examine the worm under seawater, and determine the sex from the body colour. Using this technique, place one male and one female worm into separate watch glasses and cover with a little cool seawater.

 Repeat this process as often as is necessary in order to obtain one male and one female worm. Retain worms of uncertain sex and duplicate worms in seawater in a small beaker.

3 Examine the contents of the dishes using the medium power of the microscope, looking for released gametes. Release normally occurs more or less immediately.

4 Once gametes are released, transfer eggs and sperms to a cavity slide. Add a coverslip, and examine the eggs with medium- and high-power magnification. The material is almost totally transparent, so you will need to reduce the lighting to a minimum, using the iris diaphragm of the condenser, in order to see cells at all (dark-ground illumination is best, if this is available). You may have to be patient to observe fertilisation (up to an hour).

 Soon after fertilisation occurs, the first division of cleavage will take place. If you keep the slide cool (laid in a Petri dish lid on damp filter paper), you should be able to observe further cell divisions over a 24-hour period.

NOTE TO TECHNICIAN

Each student group will require:
- microscope (with medium- and high-power objectives), with bench lamp if necessary;
- four watch glasses, cavity slides, coverslips, teat pipette;
- strong scissors, blunt forceps, blunt seeker;
- Petri dish, filter paper, small beaker;
- fresh seawater, held at about 10 °C;
- stone with numerous *Pomatoceros* tubes (occupied);
- access to a labelled jar containing 70% ethanol to kill and preserve worms used.

■ Data presentation

Make an annotated sketch of the worm, and record the appearance of an egg cell, and of one or two stages of cleavage.

■ Conclusion

Speculate on the advantages to *Pomatoceros* of the tendency to release gametes into seawater if it is dislodged from its tube.

■ Evaluation

The other polychaete worms you may be familiar with are *Nereis* (ragworm) and *Arenicola* (lugworm). In what way does the full-grown *Pomatoceros* appear to differ from either of these?

27.2 Breeding in fish, using the guppy

(Investigation)

Guppies (*Poecilia reticulata*) are small, freshwater tropical fish native to Venezuela, Barbados, northern Brazil and Guyana. They are easy to keep in tropical aquaria. Although they can survive in temperatures ranging from 10 to 30 °C, they will not breed below 20 °C.

Guppies are 'live-bearers', that is, the eggs are fertilised inside the female and undergo complete development before being born (ovoviviparity). One insemination is sufficient for several broods.

■ Aim

To observe the complete life cycle of a vertebrate.

■ Risk assessment

- Electrical equipment associated with a tropical aquarium must be correctly fused, earthed and maintained.
- Otherwise, good laboratory practice will be sufficient to take account of any hazards and avoid significant risks.

■ Method

If your school or college already has a tropical aquarium it can be used for this investigation, provided that the species already present will not eat the guppies and the temperature is maintained at about 25 °C. If you are setting up a tropical aquarium for the first time, you will need to consult a suitable guide book (see the 'Note to technician').

If experiments on temperature, feeding and so forth and observations on behaviour are to be carried out, it will be necessary for the guppies to have a tank to themselves.

Guppies can be obtained from pet shops or the aquarist departments of many garden centres. Dried food (which includes essential vegetable matter) and live food (*Tubifex*, *Daphnia*, brine shrimps) can be obtained from these sources. The amount of food required will depend on the number of fish but the feeds should be little and often, and just sufficient to be totally consumed within a few minutes. Uneaten food decomposes and makes the water foul.

The stock density should not exceed two fish per litre.

Try to observe and record the following:
- courtship and mating behaviour (the male inserts his modified anal fin into the female's cloaca to inseminate her);
- length of gestation period;
- birth of the young;
- numbers of young;
- number of broods;
- parental care given (if any);

- behaviour of the youngsters (for example, you may see them swim to the surface to fill their air bladders);
- rate of growth;
- time to reach sexual maturity (may be two or three months);
- changes at maturity;
- differences between the sexes;
- any signs of aggression between males;
- how big the fry have to be to avoid being eaten.

A pregnant female can be recognised by a dark patch (the crowded youngsters) on the underside of the abdomen. It is advisable to separate her from the others by placing her in a 500 cm³ beaker, two-thirds filled with water and floated in the aquarium tank. In this way, you will be able to see when the fry are born and to protect them from being eaten by other fish.

Experimental studies could include examination of:
- the response to different types of food;
- the effect of variations in temperature on the breeding cycle (very long-term);
- variations in growth rate of young with diet or temperature;
- the response (if any) of mature males to models of males in breeding colours (see *Advanced Biology*, p. 524).

Project 28.2, outlining some breeding experiments using guppies, is to be found on p. 344.

NOTE TO TECHNICIAN

Students will require (or require access to):
- aquarium with heater and aerator;
- male and female guppies;
- fish food;
- 500 cm³ beaker;
- small net for catching fish.

Details of how to set up and maintain tropical aquaria can be found in books such as D Mills (1986) *Guide to the Tropical Aquarium* (Salamander Books). Aquarist suppliers stock books of this kind.

■ Data presentation

Keep a diary of your observations, making sketches of the features of the fish at relevant stages in the life cycle.

■ Conclusion

Summarise your diary notes to give an account of the behaviour and life cycle of the guppy, including the results of any experiments you tried.

■ Evaluation

- What objection might be raised to conclusions drawn from observations on fish in an aquarium?
- What are the possible advantages of internal fertilisation and viviparity over external fertilisation and egg-laying?

27.3 Dissection of the urinogenital system of the rat

(Data generating)

The partly dissected, preserved rat used earlier (freshly killed or preserved/embalmed specimen) for dissection of the abdomen (pp. 157–62), the thorax (pp. 184–7) and the brain (pp. 247–9) should be used for dissection of the urinogenital systems.

■ Aim

To investigate the structure of the urinogenital system of the rat by dissection, and to make a comparison of rat and human urinogenital systems.

■ Risk assessment

- In the conduct of dissection, special precautions for safety are essential. These are listed in Practical 13.2 (p. 157). Read them again now.
- When cutting through bone, or when chipping bone away from soft tissue, wear eye protection.

■ Method

The chief purpose of dissection in biology is to display the internal structures as part of an investigation of structure and function of an animal's body. Read about developing your dissection technique on p. 157, before dissecting the urinogenital system of a rat.

Steps to the dissection of the urinogenital system

The urinary and reproductive systems are usually studied together, because they are anatomically closely associated. In your preserved rat, identify the external urinary and reproductive openings. These occur on the ventral surface, very much as in other mammals.

The *male system* (Figure 27.2) includes two testes and associated glands. The testes are retained in the body until the young rat is about 40 days old. The scrotal sac, into which the testes eventually descend, consists of a single fold of skin, but in the rat is internally separated into two compartments. The sacs are connected to the abdomen by wide passages, and the testes may be withdrawn in periods of sexual inactivity (rare). The reproductive ducts from the testes (the vasa deferentia) join the urethra, so there is a common urinogenital opening at the tip of the penis, itself contained within a substantial sheath of skin called the prepuce.

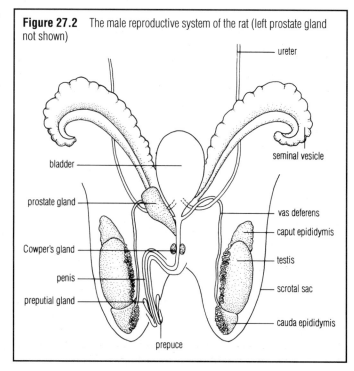

Figure 27.2 The male reproductive system of the rat (left prostate gland not shown)

ureter

seminal vesicle

bladder

prostate gland

vas deferens

caput epididymis

Cowper's gland

testis

penis

scrotal sac

preputial gland

cauda epididymis

prepuce

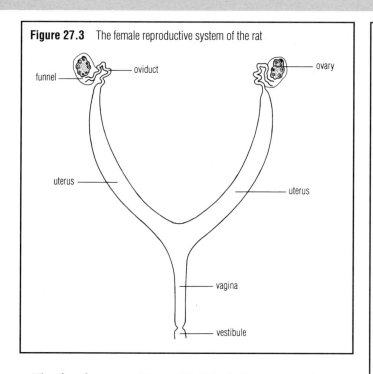

Figure 27.3 The female reproductive system of the rat

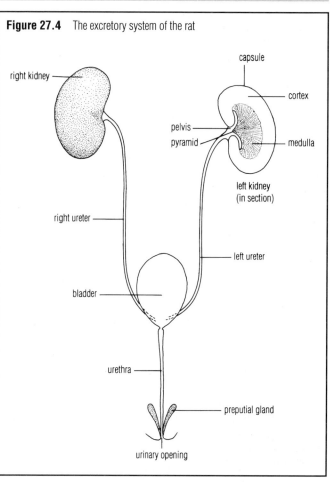

Figure 27.4 The excretory system of the rat

The *female system* (Figure 27.3) includes two ovaries, two oviducts and two uteri that open into the top of the vagina. The excretory system opens via a urethra, just anterior to the opening of the vagina; in the female the excretory duct (urethra) and the genital opening (vagina) have separate openings.

The female also has prominent nipples, associated with the mammary glands, along the ventral surface of the body, between the limbs.

In both male and female rats the right kidney is slightly anterior to the left (Figure 27.4), whereas in the human the right kidney lies slightly lower than the left kidney.

1 Begin the dissection by securing your rat to a dissection board, as in Practical 13.2 (p. 157). If the kidneys are still masked in the abdominal cavity, expose them by pinning back the liver.

2 Next, remove the muscle overlying the part of the pelvic girdle called the pubic symphysis.

3 Then, with the rat turned so that the head is pointing towards you and, using strong scissors, cut through the pubic symphysis bones in two places, as shown in Figure 27.5, taking special care not to cut any structure immediately below the bone. Remove the pubic bones. Hold the bladder to one side with a pin.

After this, the steps will depend on the sex of your rat.

Dissection of a female rat The narrow urethra overlies the broad vagina, and below them is the rectum. Carefully remove the connective tissue that obscures your view of the urethra, vagina and rectum.

4 Trace the ureters from the bladder back to the kidney, removing the fat that may obscure them.

5 Now find the small ovaries on the back wall of the abdominal cavity, and the artery and vein that supply and drain them. The oviducts are so fine that you may need a hand lens to see them. Alternatively, trace the broad part of each uterus, from the central vagina, to the ovary it serves.

(*Note:* If the rat was pregnant when killed for dissection, then the uterus and its blood supply will be more prominent, and you will see fetuses present (Figure 27.6).)

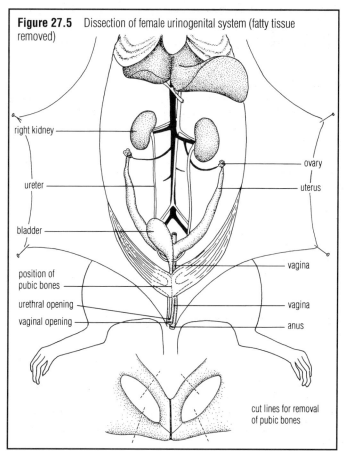

Figure 27.5 Dissection of female urinogenital system (fatty tissue removed)

Figure 27.6 Dissection of the urinogenital system of a pregnant female rat

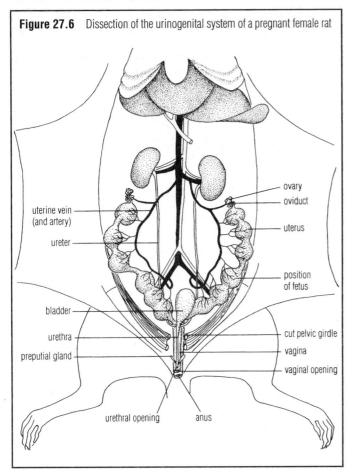

- ovary
- oviduct
- uterine vein (and artery)
- uterus
- ureter
- position of fetus
- bladder
- urethra
- cut pelvic girdle
- preputial gland
- vagina
- vaginal opening
- urethral opening
- anus

Figure 27.7 Dissection of the urinogenital system of a male rat

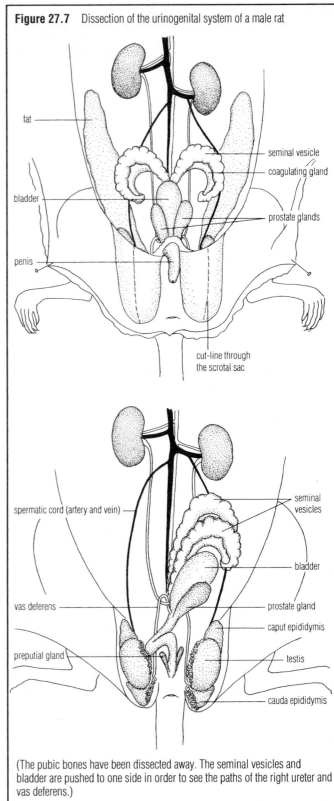

- fat
- seminal vesicle
- coagulating gland
- bladder
- prostate glands
- penis
- cut-line through the scrotal sac

- spermatic cord (artery and vein)
- seminal vesicles
- bladder
- vas deferens
- prostate gland
- caput epididymis
- preputial gland
- testis
- cauda epididymis

(The pubic bones have been dissected away. The seminal vesicles and bladder are pushed to one side in order to see the paths of the right ureter and vas deferens.)

Dissection of a male rat   Remove any connective tissue in the pelvic region if it obscures the vasa deferentia, urethra and rectum.

4 Cut through the wall of one of the scrotal sacs, as shown in Figure 27.7. Examine the testis, observing the epididymis and the vas deferens. Trace the vas deferens to the point of junction with the urethra.

5 Find the glands that are associated with the male reproductive system (as shown in Figure 27.7), including the seminal vesicle, coagulating gland, prostate gland and Cowper's gland.

6 The blood vessels to and from the testes (spermatic artery and vein) run together as part of the spermatic cord.

NOTE TO TECHNICIAN

Each student group will require (or require access to):
- dissecting board;
- disposable plastic gloves;
- rat for dissection (preserved/embalmed);
- essential dissection equipment (p. 162);
- (optional) camera with colour print film;
- video player and monitor (if the Institute of Biology video mentioned above is available);
- Apple Macintosh microcomputer (4/40 MB or better), with Pal videodisc player and separate high-quality television monitor (if *The Rat Stack* is available);
- copy of H G Q Rowett (1987) *Basic Anatomy and Physiology*, 3rd edn. John Murray.

Comparative study of urinogenital systems

Examine diagrams of the human urinogenital system, as shown in a textbook such as H G Q Rowett *Basic Anatomy and Physiology, 3rd edn*, pp. 125–31 (John Murray). Make a comparison of the male and female urinogenital systems, noting the features in which the systems in the two mammals are significantly different.

Additional references and resources

The following resources can be used to support and enhance learning by dissection; alternatively they may be used, singly or together, in place of dissection to learn about the urinogenital system of the mammal.

Two useful textbooks:

H G Q Rowett (1974) *The Rat as a Small Mammal*. John Murray

H G Q Rowett (1962) *Guide to Dissection*. John Murray

Video Rat Stack, by Megan Quentin-Baxter and David Dewhurst of Sheffield BioScience Programs. This interactive package about the dissection and functional anatomy of the rat is introduced in p. 162.

Vertebrate Dissection Guides – The Rat, by the TV Centre, the University of Portsmouth in association with the Institute of Biology. This videotape is introduced on p. 162.

■ Data presentation
- Make a large labelled sketch of the final stage of your dissection of the urinogenital system of the rat.
- Make a similar study and drawing of the system in the opposite sex, by reference to another student's dissection.

■ Conclusion

Construct a table to compare the male and female urinogenital systems, noting the features by which the systems in the rat and the human are significantly different.

■ Evaluation

To what other animals, apart from other mammals, are 'live young' born (viviparity)?

Reference

P J Hogarth (1976) *Viviparity*. Arnold Studies in Biology no 75

27.4 Mammalian gonads: oogenesis and spermatogenesis

(Data generating)

The mammalian gonads (ovaries and testes) produce gametes (secondary oocytes or sperms) and the chief sex hormones (oestrogen or testosterone). Secondary oocytes are formed by a process known as oogenesis, and sperms by spermatogenesis. The ovaries lie within the lower abdominal cavity, held in place by ligaments. The testes start off within the lower abdominal cavity, but in most male mammals they descend into an external sac (or sacs), known as the scrotum, either permanently or during periods of fertility.

■ Aim

To become familiar with the microscopic structure of a mammalian ovary and testis, and to identify steps in oogenesis and spermatogenesis.

■ Risk assessment

Good laboratory practice will be sufficient to take account of any hazards and avoid significant risks.

■ Method

The basic structure of the ovary and the process of oogenesis are illustrated in *Advanced Biology*, pp. 598–9, and the structure of the testis and the process of spermatogenesis are illustrated on pp. 595–7.

The histology of the ovary and testis is illustrated in W H Freeman and B Bracegirdle (1967) *An Atlas of Histology*, pp. 82–8 (Heinemann).

Using the medium- and high-power magnification of the microscope, examine the prepared slides (or a similar selection) listed below:

- Ovary, thin TS or LS: look at the general structure of the ovary, seen in section, with its germinal epithelium, cortex with scattered stages in the formation of ovarian follicles, and the medulla with blood vessels. Look also under high-power magnification at the cortex for steps in the development of primary follicles into ovarian follicles (once known as Graafian follicles).
- Ovary of pregnant mammal: look for the corpus luteum, which is an endocrine gland of pregnancy.
- Testis, TS and VS, both showing spermatogenesis: look for the numerous seminiferous tubules cut in various planes, with connective tissue, interstitial cells and capillaries between them. Look too under high-power magnification for the germinal epithelium, spermatogonia (sperm mother cells), primary spermatocytes and the nutritive (Sertoli) cells with developing sperms apparently embedded. The secondary spermatocytes are a short-lived phase; you will not be able to say for certain that there are any in your section.
- Human spermatozoa, smear: look for spermatozoa, with nucleus and acrosome, middle piece (containing mitochondria, which are too small to be seen in any detail by light microscopy) and the tails.

NOTE TO TECHNICIAN

Each student will require (or require access to):
- microscope (with medium- and high-power objectives), with bench lamp if necessary;
- the following prepared, stained slides of mammalian organs (or similar): ovary, thin TS or LS; ovary of pregnant mammal, showing corpus luteum; testis, TS showing spermatogenesis; seminiferous tubules, VS; human spermatozoa, smear.

■ Data presentation

Make large, fully annotated drawings as follows:
- a low-power tissue map showing the organisation of the ovary seen in section;
- high-power detail of the stages of developing ovarian follicles;
- high-power detail of a corpus luteum;
- a low-power tissue map showing seminiferous tubules cut in various planes, with connective tissue containing interstitial cells and capillaries between them;
- high-power detail of the germinal epithelium, spermatogonia (sperm mother cells), primary spermatocytes and the Sertoli cells with developing sperms embedded;
- high-power detail of spermatozoa, with nucleus and acrosome, middle piece and tail.

■ Conclusion

Draw up a flow chart comparing the processes of oogenesis and spermatogenesis, so as to illustrate the differences in outcome.

■ **Evaluation**

The hormones produced in the gonads regulate onset of sexual maturity and sexual activity. What triggers the gonads to function in these ways?

27.5 Resources for learning about human reproduction

(Demonstration)

The following resources are available to support learning about mammalian reproduction in general and reproduction in humans in particular.

Human Reproductive Cycle, produced by King's College/AVP and available from AVP (p. 433). This CAL program provides a model of the human reproductive cycle, showing the relationship between time of the month, the state of the ovaries and the thickness of the uterus lining. These events are related to fluctuating hormone levels, shown as a bar chart. The issues of changing body temperature, overall control of the menstrual cycle, and the effect of introducing spermatozoa can also be investigated. For BBC B and Master 128 microcomputers.

Female Reproductive Cycle, Fertilisation and Early Pregnancy, produced by Garland and available from AVP (p. 433), is a CAL program in two parts. Part One contains a diagrammatic illustration of the ovarian and uterine cycles, and shows the relationship between the cycles and the gonadotrophins and sex hormones. Part Two is a step-by-step illustration of the events occurring during fertilisation and implantation, and the hormonal changes occurring during early pregnancy. For BBC B and Master 128 microcomputers.

Menstruation and Pregnancy, produced by Netherhall Educational Software and supplied by Cambridge University Press (p. 434). This CAL program displays messages alongside a calendar to present events in the menstrual cycle, pregnancy and birth. It seeks to link biological processes to human consequences, as it follows the changes in a woman through pregnancy to birth. For BBC B and Master 128 microcomputers.

Sexual Reproduction in Animals, a BBC Enterprises teaching video supplied by Class Productions (p. 433), is a general review of external and internal fertilisation, eggs and their development, and the process of internal development.

Hormones and the Endocrine System, a teaching video produced by Human Relations Media Inc, USA, and supplied by Boulton-Hawker Films Ltd (p. 434), comes in three parts, of which Part 2 is concerned with hormones and human development. This part lasts 19 minutes of the total 53 minutes and provides an overview of the role of hormones in human growth and development and the changes from development in the uterus to adult life. The roles of hormones in the changes of puberty and in human reproduction are fully described. The hormonal events that control the menstrual cycle and the effects of hormones in pregnancy, birth and lactation are illustrated.

Projects

27.1 Environmental influences on reproduction

Hydra viridis is easily maintained in laboratory aquaria containing pond water at 20 °C, if well stocked with oxygenating green plants (such as *Elodea*), away from direct sunlight. An active culture can be subcultured in small 'ponds', created in beakers. Use these to test the hypotheses that an excess of nutrients leads to asexual reproduction by budding, and a fall of temperature to about 10 °C induces sexual reproduction and reduces *Hydra* to the contents of a protective capsule.

27.2 Life cycle in crustacean minibeasts

Fertilised eggs (and parthenogenetically produced ones) of crustaceans hatch out into nauplius larvae (*Advanced Biology*, p. 421). The development of eggs, through some or all of the six larval stages, may be observed over a period of three or four weeks, depending on the temperature and the species concerned. The minibeasts with their eggs can be obtained from pond water, and development can be observed in a sample maintained in a tiny 'pond' within a watch glass.

Cyclops If several female *Cyclops* with egg-sacs are kept in a small container (such as a 50 mm plastic Petri dish) of pond water, the eggs will hatch to nauplius larvae in a few days. These can be seen with a hand lens and transferred to a microscope slide with a dropping pipette. They are very tiny and hard to catch so it is best to transfer several drops of water to several slides on a black background. If the drops are examined with a hand lens, those containing nauplii can be selected for closer study under the low and medium power of the microscope. Some threads of cotton wool can be used to restrict their movement and a coverslip can be applied.

The nauplii undergo up to six moults before reaching the adult form in about three weeks. It may be possible to observe the different larval forms if samples are examined every two or three days.

Daphnia and *Simocephalus* These crustacea carry their eggs in a brood pouch in the dorsal part of their carapace. The larvae from the (unfertilised) 'summer eggs' develop to the adult form before they hatch and escape from the brood pouch, so the stages are not easy to see. The young may, however, be seen moving about in and escaping from the brood pouch. The 'winter eggs' are fertilised and remain in the brood pouch when it is moulted. They can remain dormant for months on the bottom of the pond.

Artemia salina (**the brine shrimp**) These are marine crustaceans, but the eggs can be bought from aquarist centres and hatched in seawater. They hatch as a late nauplius.

27.3 Pond snail development

Pond snails lay their eggs in a gelatinous mass attached, for example, to the underside of water lily leaves or to the glass sides of an aquarium. If the egg mass is removed as soon as possible after it has been laid, it can be kept in a Petri dish of pond water and the development of the embryos observed under the microscope over a period of a week or two. Centre your observations and recording on issues such as the increase in size, the first signs of movement and what appears to cause it, the appearance of eyes, the appearance of differentiation in the visceral hump and foot, the time when the heart can be observed beating, the appearance of air in the pulmonary cavity, and the emergence and subsequent activity of the young snails.

27.4 An aphid colony

Aphid infestations are common on many species of wild plants (including trees) in summer. The animals are visited by predators, they may be tended by ants, and the colony fluctuates in size. Observe a particular colony over a period of time, developing data on the growth in numbers of the aphids. What evidence is there of environmental factors affecting reproduction?

Reference
A F G Dixon (1973) *Biology of Aphids*. Arnold Studies in Biology no. 44. Edward Arnold

27.5 Autecology of a garden bird

Choose a species of garden bird that you are able to observe. Follow the behaviour of a breeding pair, from observations on courtship, nest building, size of clutch, influences of environmental factors and predators, to the eventual early fledging of the offspring.

Reference
D Lack (1943) *The Life of the Robin*. Witherby

27.6 Breeding behaviour in bird colonies

Some birds display distinctive and characteristic behaviour associated with courtship and breeding. This is especially the case in certain species that come together in dense colonies, after periods of solitary existence. And birds in colonies normally offer opportunities for observations of many individual pairs, more or less simultaneously. For example, we may observe coastal colonies of gannets (*Sula bassana*) in some parts of Britain, but other marine species (and some inland species) may be equally challenging, e.g. rooks (*Corvus frugilegus*).

Can you build up a diary of observations? Which parent does what (assuming you can recognise the male or female), or are both parents involved at all stages? Issues to consider are courtship activities, the collecting or materials and construction of the nest, proximity of the nests, incubation routine, time spent away from the nest by the parents (e.g. catching food), feeding of the occupants of the nest, typical numbers of eggs, young and fledglings, greeting or 'take over' ceremonies,

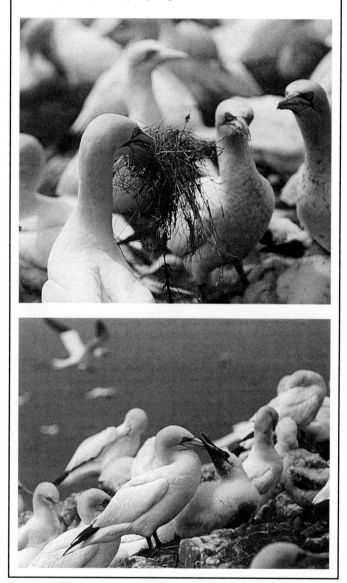

Figure 27.8   Breeding and rearing rituals in the gannet (*Sula bassana*). (These photographs, of colonies at Grassholm, were taken with a telephoto lens. It is important to avoid approaching nesting sites in any way that disturbs the birds or puts yourself in danger.) (top) The offering of nesting materials. (bottom) Feeding the young

the form and causes of aggressive behaviour, how long the chicks stay in and about the nest, evidence for obvious predators. Is it possible to record bird sounds, perhaps at a noisy part of the daily routines? Some, if not all, of these questions can be answered, perhaps.

327

Problems and assignments

27.1 *Gametes and fertilisation*

Figure 27.9 shows mature male and female gametes of a mammal at the time of fertilisation. These gametes are drawn to different scales. Examine the drawings and, using the information given together with your knowledge of sexual reproduction in mammals, answer the following questions.

1 **a** Approximately how many times greater is the diameter of the secondary oocyte than the length of the sperm head?
   b Name structures A, B, C and E.
2 **a** Where, within the reproductive organs of the female, does a sperm fuse with a secondary oocyte?
   b By what processes does a sperm reach a secondary oocyte, following ejaculation in the vagina?
   c What role do structures B perform to enable the sperm to carry out fertilisation?
3 **a** The female gamete is described as a secondary oocyte. Why?
   b At what stage of meiosis is D?
   c What are cells F? How have they arisen?
4 The zona pellucida is a glycoprotein barrier.
   a What is glycoprotein composed of? What type of enzymes is required to catalyse its 'digestion'?
   b How is the sperm able to cross this barrier?
5 **a** How does the sperm nucleus enter the cytoplasm of the oocyte?
   b What changes does the entry of the sperm nucleus trigger within the oocyte?
6 Male and female gametes contribute equally to the nucleus of the zygote, but the female gamete almost exclusively provides the cytoplasm of the zygote (= the cytoplasmic inheritance). Where in the cytoplasm of an animal cell are nucleic acids to be found, in addition to those in the nucleus?

27.2 *The cycle of change to follicles*

The data in Table 27.1 is a record of the mean diameter of follicles and corpora lutea in the ovary of a mammal over a period of 40 days:

1 Plot a graph to show the change in mean diameter of follicles (and corpora lutea) over the period of 40 days.
2 How do we know, from the data given, that fertilisation did not occur during these 40 days?
3 When was fertilisation most likely to happen, if insemination had occurred?
4 Draw a labelled diagram of the follicle at the time of fertilisation.
5 What is the role of the corpora lutea?
6 What hormones trigger the growth and development of follicles on days 0 and 20? Where are these hormones released from?

27.3 *The hormones of the menstrual cycle*

The menstrual cycle involves a synchronised, recurring sequence of changes in the lining of the uterus (uterine cycle), linked to a series of changes in the ovaries (ovarian cycle). You can read about these in *Advanced Biology*, pp. 600–1.

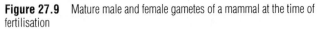

Figure 27.9 Mature male and female gametes of a mammal at the time of fertilisation

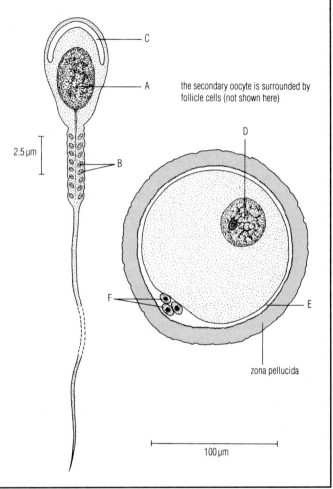

the secondary oocyte is surrounded by follicle cells (not shown here)

2.5 μm

100 μm

zona pellucida

Table 27.1 Changes in diameter of developing ovarian follicles and corpora lutea (all diameters in mm)

		Follicles	Corpora lutea	Next batch of follicles
Day	0	1.5		
	2	1.8		
	4	2.0		
	6	2.5		
	8	3.0		
	10	3.5		
	12	4.0		
	14	4.1		
	16	4.3		
	18	8.0		
	20	11.0		1.5
	22	6.0	6.0	
	24		8.0	2.0
	26		9.0	
	28		10.0	3.0
	30		9.5	
	32		9.0	4.0
	34		8.4	
	36		7.2	4.3
	38		6.4	
	40		5.0	11.0

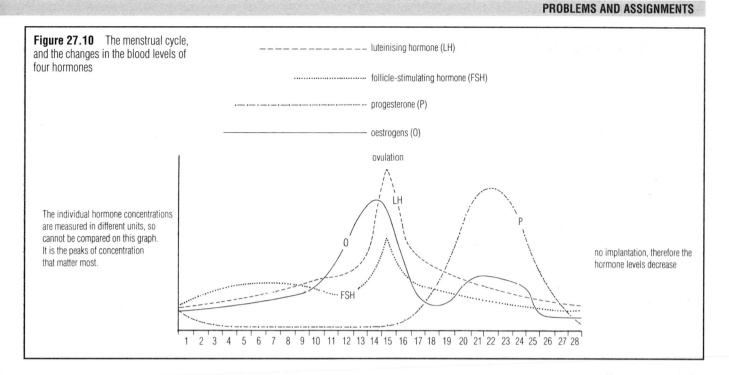

Figure 27.10 The menstrual cycle, and the changes in the blood levels of four hormones

— — — — — — — luteinising hormone (LH)

· · · · · · · · · · · · · follicle-stimulating hormone (FSH)

— · — · — · — · — progesterone (P)

————————— oestrogens (O)

The individual hormone concentrations are measured in different units, so cannot be compared on this graph. It is the peaks of concentration that matter most.

ovulation

no implantation, therefore the hormone levels decrease

The changes in the menstrual cycle are regulated by hormones (known as LH and FSH), released by the anterior pituitary and the wall of a developing ovarian follicle (oestrogens) and by the empty ovarian follicle (progesterone). The changes in the blood level of these four hormones over one cycle are illustrated in Figure 27.10.

Using this information, and your knowledge of sexual reproduction in humans, answer the following questions.

1 What are the distinguishing features of an endocrine (hormone-secreting) gland?
2 What sequence of changes occurs in the ovarian cycle over 28 days?
3 What sequence of changes occurs in the uterine cycle over 28 days?
4 a What hormonal change triggers ovulation?
  b What part do the walls (thecae) of the ovarian follicles themselves play in initiating ovulation?
5 After ovulation, the empty follicle heals over. What changes then occur to it?
6 What is the combined effect of higher levels of oestrogens and progesterone in the uterine cycle?
7 a What are the main consequences of the rising level of progesterone in the latter part of the cycle?
  b What are the main consequences of the subsequent fall in level of progesterone?
8 If the egg is fertilised an embryo starts to form immediately, before implantation in the uterus wall occurs. The outer layers of the embryo secrete a new hormone (HCG). What effect does HCG have on the ovarian cycle, and therefore on the menstrual cycle as a whole?

27.4 Oral contraception and hormone changes

One contraceptive method for women involves taking a daily 'pill', from the fifth day of menstruation for 21 days. The 'pill' contains small amounts of a synthetic oestrogen and larger amounts of a synthetic progesterone. The effect of taking the 'pill' in this way is to suppress ovulation. But a day or two after the 'pill' is discontinued, menstruation does occur.

Using your knowledge of the normal hormone changes of menstruation (for example, *Advanced Biology*, pp. 600–1, particularly Figure 27.20), answer the following questions.

1 What effect will the hormones of the 'pill' have on FSH and LH levels in the blood?
2 a What changes will be triggered in the ovarian cycle, as a result of taking the 'pill'?
  b What will happen in the uterine cycle at the same time?
3 Why must this type of 'pill' be taken daily from day 5 to day 25 of the cycle to be effective? (Rather than taking it only in the event of sexual intercourse, for example.)
4 The effects of the 'pill' have been described as an example of negative feedback.
  a What does 'negative feedback' mean?

Figure 27.11 One brand of the 'pill'

b Are the changes that result from taking the 'pill' an appropriate example? Explain your answer.

5 If the 'pill' is permanently discontinued from day 5 of a cycle, what sequence of sex hormone changes will occur as a result?

1 What is osteoporosis?

2 a What are the likely advantages of HRT for postmenopausal women?

  b What would you suggest as the order of importance of these advantages?

3 What are the actual and potential disadvantages of this treatment?

4 What alternatives are there for reducing the risk of osteoporosis?

5 What explanations can you suggest for the fact that supplementary calcium is not an effective measure against osteoporosis?

6 Why is progestogen included in the therapy?

27.5 The menopause and HRT

Read Panel 27.1, 'Hormones for healthy bones!', about some aspects of hormone replacement therapy. Then answer the questions that follow.

Panel 27.1 Hormones for healthy bones!

As a woman reaches the menopause, levels of the hormone oestrogen begin to decline in her body. When doctors first suggested replacing this hormone, people hailed the therapy as an elixir of youth. Oestrogens not only control the distressing, though transient, symptoms of the menopause, such as hot flushes; they also prevent atrophy of the vaginal tissues – and the associated feelings of loss of femininity that can follow such changes. A woman can enjoy sexual activity to an advanced age if she takes a pharmaceutical preparation of oestrogen to compensate for the decline in the production of this hormone that occurs in middle age.

Oestrogens also prevent the progressive reduction in the density of bone – osteoporosis – that places elderly women at high risk of fractures. (About half of all women can expect to have an 'osteoporotic fracture', either spontaneously or following a minor knock or fall, at some time in their lives.) Evidence is also accumulating that older women are less likely to develop coronary artery disease if they replace lost oestrogens.

Oestrogen replacement therapy is now known as hormone replacement therapy, because these days the preparation also contains another hormone, a progestogen.

The history of hormone replacement therapy, like that of the contraceptive pill, has not been without its troubles. By the early 1970s, studies in the US were showing that women who had taken oestrogens following the menopause had a higher risk of developing cancer of the lining of the uterus (endometrial cancer). This cancer is not particularly malignant and is usually detected early, when the chances of cure are high. However, doctors have eliminated the extra risk by adding a progestogen to the oestrogen. This combination of hormones prevents proliferation of the endometrium, so reducing the risk of malignant change.

Some women – and some doctors, too – have misgivings about hormone replacement therapy. Alan Fowler, an orthopaedic surgeon in Bridgend, has suggested that the postmenopausal woman who exercises, does not smoke, and who maintains her levels of vitamin D by eating oily fish or by moderate exposure to sunlight is unlikely to develop appreciable osteoporosis. Vitamin D enhances calcium absorption and bone mineralisation if these are defective – but neither poor absorption of calcium nor poor mineralisation of bone causes osteoporosis.

Will hormone replacement therapy to prevent osteoporosis become routine in Britain? That will ultimately depend, says Aitken, on whether women want it. He suggests that women who are now only in their 20s or 30s should be taught about the advantages of taking hormone replacement therapy when they reach the menopause. Many American women are obviously already convinced of the benefits. Even in the 1970s, 30 per cent of postmenopausal women in some parts of the United States were taking oestrogens.

From: New Scientist *(February 1987), pp. 32–5*

27.6 Changing male fertility?

Read Panel 27.2, 'Some of our sperms are missing!', about a handful of 'oestrogenic' chemicals suspected of disrupting male sexual development and performance. This is an excerpt from an article in the *New Scientist* of 26 August 1995, pp. 22–5. To weigh up the issues you need to check that you understand:

• the role of oestrogens in regulating female sexual function;

• what is meant by 'screening chemicals';

• the idea of hormone receptors in cell membranes with which particular hormones can react.

Now answer the questions that follow.

1 a List three forms of evidence in favour of the proposition that human male sexuality is threatened by chemicals in the environment acting like oestrogens.

  b List three forms of evidence that refute this possibility.

2 What are the difficulties that delay a resolution of this issue?

3 Prepare a brief talk that you could give to peers (or at an academic interview) explaining how you felt about this issue, and what you would recommend for the future.

Panel 27.2 Some of our sperms are missing!

'Everybody in the environmental movement is drawing their breath and saying my God, what if,' says Gwynne Lyons, pollutant consultant to the World Wide Fund for Nature. Her organisation, along with Friends of the Earth and Greenpeace, has recently campaigned against hormone-like pollutants – or 'endocrine disrupters' – in the environment. And she believes we need urgent action to reduce the exposure of humans and wildlife to these chemicals in water, food and air.

Yet last month, a report for the British government, by the Institute for Environment and Health at Leicester, found no direct evidence of a causal link between these environmental chemicals and reproductive problems in people. The report concluded that 'it is currently very difficult to assess' whether environmental oestrogens might be responsible for a fall in sperm counts or rising rates of testicular cancer. Lewis Smith, director of the institute, added that a ban on suspected chemicals would be premature.

Others are downright sceptical. 'I am absolutely not worried,' says Jack Cohen, a developmental biologist at the University of Warwick, who believes that the alleged fall in sperm counts is based on flawed statistics.

So who is right?

The strongest evidence that something is amiss comes from surveys of men's reproductive health, and in particular from semen samples analysed at sperm banks or fertility centres. According to studies in Denmark, Scotland and France over the past three years, the number of sperms generated by the average 'normal' man in an ejaculation has fallen substantially – by almost half – compared with samples taken 50 years ago. Over the same timescale, the rate of testicular cancer in adult men has doubled.

The study is flawed, says Cohen, because the World Health Organization 'changed the goalposts', raising the lower limits of a 'normal' sperm count, in the mid-1960s. 'The change in reference value accounts for almost all the decline, and what's left is probably just statistical noise,' comments Stewart.

If proving that sperm counts are falling is difficult, establishing a direct link with specific environmental chemicals – and ruling out the effects of changes in people's lifestyles and diets – is harder still. Certainly, the list of chemicals alleged to mimic or interfere with sex hormones is now vast. However, only a tiny number of these chemicals has actually been shown in lab tests to behave like a sex hormone. The research just hasn't been done, partly because there are no quick and easy ways to screen chemicals for oestrogenic effects. Nor is the degree of our exposure clear. What is known is more by accident than design.

For instance, in 1991 Ana Soto at Tufts University in Boston stumbled on the truth about one chemical, a common additive in plastics, when it leached from plastic tubing into the cells growing in the laboratory. She noticed that something was encouraging the growth of the human breast cancer cell line. The culprit, nonylphenol, turns out to act like an oestrogen hormone, and stimulates breast cells to divide. 'Industry uses about 300 000 tonnes of alkylphenol polyethoxylates (APEs) every year, 60% of which end up in water,' says Charles Tyler, a researcher studying oestrogens in the environment.

Some believe that oestrogen-like compounds in the environment may be contributing to the steady rise in the rate of breast cancer.

But epidemiologists in Britain are by and large sceptical of such claims. The increasing trend for women to have fewer children later in life is probably largely to blame, she suspects. Similarly, the steady rise in testicular cancer rates could also be linked to marked changes in lifestyle since the Second World War.

Attempts to blame human health problems on oestrogenic chemicals must also contend with the fact that fetuses are inevitably exposed to their mothers' bloodstream, which is awash with oestrogen during pregnancy. But Sharpe and his like-minded colleagues argue that while fetuses may be somehow protected against natural oestrogen, they are not safe from synthetic variants.

One sign that natural oestrogenic chemicals found in plants are benign is the longevity and good health of the Japanese. The Japanese diet is extraordinarily rich in oestrogen-mimics produced by plants such as soya beans. Yet there is no sign of increased infertility in Japan, and the nation's cancer rates are among the lowest in the world. Plant oestrogens may be something we've evolved to cope with, suggests Lyons at WWF. 'What is new is man-made chemicals mimicking hormones.'

The chemicals may also have additive effects, as researchers at Brunel have discovered ... the combined effects of a multitude of different chemicals could still be noticeable. 'We are particularly concerned that with the tens or hundreds of different substances acting on the same receptors,' says Lyons, 'even small amounts of pollutants in the environment could have quite startling effects.'

A report produced for the Danish government and published earlier this year called for urgent research, particularly into the exposure of women of childbearing age to oestrogenic pollutants. It also warned that existing methods of testing for toxicity may not pick up the harmful effects of oestrogenic pollutants.

From: New Scientist *(26 August 1995), pp. 22–5*

27.7 Early human development, and the issues of research on human embryos

If intercourse has occurred about the time of ovulation, then of the 250 million or so sperms ejaculated in the vagina, some 10 or so may be expected to reach the upper oviduct (once known as the Fallopian tube, in honour of the Italian physician who first described it) within about 24 hours. Here the process of fertilisation gets under way. The pre-implantation stage of human development begins with a secondary oocyte and a sperm, and ends with a tiny, early embryo, called a blastocyst, and takes place partly in the oviduct and partly in the uterus. The process of implantation in the uterus is not complete until about two weeks after fertilisation.

In experimental *in vitro* fertilisation (IVF) treatment of childless couples, 'eggs' (secondary oocytes) are withdrawn from an ovary using a hollow needle, under local or general anaesthetic. These are later mixed with sperms in a glass dish (hence the term 'in vitro'), and here fertilisation takes place. The resulting embryos are cultured outside the body for a few days, before up to three may be returned to the mother's uterus. Thus the early steps of pre-implantation development occur 'in a test tube', in IVF. The process normally leaves spare embryos; these may either be frozen for later implantation attempts should the first ones fail, or they may be used in research.

If, because of the genotypes of the parents, there is a possibility of a genetic disorder in the progeny, one of the cells of the eight-celled blastocyst can be removed without harming the remainder of the embryo. If genetic examination of this single cell indicates the absence of a disorder, then the embryo, now at a more advanced stage, may be selectively implanted.

This subject of human-assisted conception and the associated research possibilities using the 'spare' embryos generates widespread public interest and concern. In the UK, the Warnock Report in 1984 led to the Human Fertilisation and Embryology Act in 1990. Certain types of research on human embryos are legalised in the UK. The ethical issues raised by treatments for infertility remain for individuals to think about, however. Some of the issues include:

- the distress suffered by infertile parents;
- the importance of every offspring needing to be 'wanted', and the need for foster-homes for children;
- the ever-increasing world population;
- the WHO 'guestimate' that about 25% of babies are 'definitely unwanted';
- the need for information on causes of infertility, on causes of congenital disease, on causes of miscarriages, on better techniques of contraception and on methods of detecting gene and chromosome abnormalities;
- the fate of 'spare' embryos;
- the selective breeding of humans, in effect;
- the increase in situations where life or death decisions are taken by 'experts';
- the proportion of health service resources spent on experimental, intrusive work, compared with investments in prevention of ill-health;
- the pleasure the human race takes in solving fundamental problems of medicine, disease and health.

1 You should read an introduction to this subject, such as H J Leese (1994) 'Early human embryo development', *J. Biol. Ed.* **28**(3), pp. 175–80. This 'update' article gives more detail, and includes a reading list of accessible titles which will extend your understanding.

2 When you are ready, set up a debate on the issues of 'ethics' and the 'quality of life', ensuring that people of different persuasions are given the opportunities they need to explain their viewpoint.

3 Take notes of the valid points made in the discussion, so that you could speak either for or against the issue of human embryo research, if called upon to do so. To know both sides of a major issue is a very powerful position to be in.

27.8 Quick test

1 Distinguish between the following pairs:

   a   isogamy and oogamy;
   b   unisexual and hermaphrodite;
   c   external and internal fertilisation;
   d   ovoviviparity and viviparity;
   e   seminiferous tubules and epididymis;
   f   prostate gland and seminal vesicles;
   g   spermatogonia and spermatids;
   h   nutritive cells and interstitial cells;
   i   follicle-stimulating hormone (FSH) and luteinising hormone (LH);
   j   uterus and vagina;
   k   ovaries and oviducts;
   l   ovarian follicle and corpus luteum;
   m   uterine cycle and ovarian cycle;
   n   oestrogen and progesterone;
   o   morula and blastocyst;
   p   amnion and chorion;
   q   allantois and yolk sac;
   r   umbilical cord and placenta;
   s   amniocentesis and ultrasonography;
   t   pregnancy and lactation.

2 What do you understand by the following?

   a   diploid life cycle;
   b   budding in an animal;
   c   parthenogenesis;
   d   a clone;
   e   gonads;
   f   germinal epithelium;
   g   acrosome;
   h   endometrium;
   i   oestrus;
   j   human chorionic gonadotrophin.

27.9 Essay assignment

Select one of the following:

- Describe the role of hormones in maintaining the uterine and ovarian cycles. In the event of fertilisation, what change in the pattern of hormones occurs that maintains the embryo throughout pregnancy?

or:

- Contrast the processes of male and female gamete formation in the human mammal. How are sperms transferred from the site of production to the site of fertilisation at the time of ovulation?

28 Variation and inheritance; genetics

Summary

Genetics is the study of heredity, or the transmission of characteristics from one generation to another. Modern genetics began with the exceptionally thorough and painstaking work of Mendel, who created the discipline virtually single-handedly. Success was based upon an initial decision to follow the inheritance of only **one or two pairs of contrasting characters**, rather than the multitude of features an organism shows, as earlier students of inheritance had done. No one realised the significance of his work during his lifetime.

Mendel studied the inheritance of seven contrasting characteristics of the **garden pea**. He was fortunate, firstly in choosing a plant in which the visible characteristics studied were each controlled by a single 'factor' (we say, 'gene', today) and, secondly, in that when two pairs of contrasting characters were studied, he chose ones that were controlled by genes on separate chromosomes (no linkage occurred). Mendel showed that **'factors' did not blend** during breeding experiments, but **retained their identity**, and were inherited in **fixed mathematical ratios**.

Today we express Mendel's results in two concise laws. The **Law of Segregation** states that the characteristics of an organism are controlled by pairs of alleles which separate in equal numbers into different gametes as a result of meiosis. The **Law of Independent Assortment** states two or more pairs of alleles segregate independently of each other as a result of meiosis, provided the genes concerned are not linked by being on the same chromosome.

Since the rediscovery of Mendel's work, the bases of **modern genetics** (now the study of genes) have been secured by the establishment of seven additional principles:

- **Linkage:** there are many thousands of genes per nucleus, but often less than 50 chromosomes. Genes are linked together on chromosomes, and tend to be inherited together.
- **Crossing over:** there is a process of exchange between homologous chromosomes during meiosis. This gives rise to new combinations of characteristics.
- **Sex linkage:** sex may be controlled by sex chromosomes (in humans, the X and Y chromosomes). The characteristics controlled by genes on the sex chromosomes are linked to the sex of the individual.
- **Multiple alleles:** the gene for certain characteristics consists of more than two alleles, although only two of the alleles can occur in any one diploid individual at one time. The human ABO blood group, for example, is controlled by three alleles, I^A, I^B and I^O. A person can have identical alleles (homozygous), or two different alleles (heterozygous), and there are six possible genotypes.
- **Multiple gene action (polygenes):** many of an organism's characteristics are not controlled by a single gene, but by three, four or more genes often located on different chromosomes. The control of most characteristics is by polygenes.
- **Environmental effects:** variations in the phenotype (appearance) of an organism can arise through interaction of its genotype (genetic constitution) and the environment. An example is the honey bee community in which there are two genotypes present (male bees and female bees), but three types of individual (drones = males, and queen and workers = female. The difference between the females lies in the diet received in development.
- **Mutation:** an abrupt change in the structure or number of chromosomes, or in the structure of a gene.

Practicals and activities

28.1 Maize cobs and Mendel's First Law
(Data generating)

Without any knowledge of chromosomes and genes, and as a result of painstaking experiments conducted over many years, Gregor Mendel discovered that:
- within each organism are breeding 'factors' controlling characteristics like 'tall' and 'short';
- for each characteristic, there are two of these factors in each cell;
- one factor comes from each parent;
- the factors in a parent separate in the gametes, and either can enter an offspring;
- the factor for (say) 'tall' is an alternative form of the factor for 'short';
- the factor for 'tall' is dominant over the factor for 'short'.

Mendel realised all these fundamentals of modern genetics by interpreting the numerical results of experiments with the garden pea plant (*Pisum savitum*). He started out experimenting

Figure 28.1   Maize (*Zea mays*) in flower

Figure 28.2   Proforma I, for monohybrid crosses

Breeding experiment

parental (P)
phenotypes

genotypes

meiosis   meiosis

gametes

offspring (F$_1$)
genotypes

phenotypes

F$_2$ selfed
(or sibling cross)

meiosis   meiosis

gametes

offspring (F$_2$)
genotypes

genotypes ratio

phenotypes

phenotypes ratio

with the mouse (*Mus musculus*), but investigating breeding in animals upset his bishop! Mendel changed to plants so that he could continue his studies. We can rediscover what we call Mendel's First Law (he never stated his discoveries as 'laws', unfortunately) in the progeny of a maize plant.

■ Aim

To interpret the ratio of progeny of a maize cob (*Zea mays*) in terms of one of Mendel's two principles of inheritance, now known as his First Law.

■ Risk assessment

Good laboratory practice will be sufficient to take account of any hazards and avoid significant risks.

■ Method

1 You are provided with a maize cob. It consists of part of a former inflorescence that supported a very large number of individual flowers (Figure 28.1). Maize flowers are normally wind-pollinated. All that remains here are the fruits attached to the central stem. Estimate approximately how many fruits are present (number of rows × number of fruits in a typical row). This is the sample size you are working with.

2 Examine the lines of fruits carefully, for they are of different appearances. The cob you are examining has been selected to have fruits of two different appearances (phenotypes). Typical cobs that are available for use, and you are almost certain to have one of these alternatives to examine, include:
   - swollen fruits with a *smooth* outline and collapsed fruits with a *wrinkled* outline;
   - *dark-coloured* fruits (red/purple) coloured by anthocyanins in the aleurone tissue (see *Advanced Biology*, p. 411, Figure 19.13) and *yellowish* fruit (no additional pigment);
   - *non-shiny* (starchy) fruits and *waxy* fruits.

3 Count the fruits of each type, one row at a time, making certain you know which row you commenced with and which rows you have counted. Record the numbers of both types of fruit, row by row.

4 Is it necessary to count all the fruit present? Tally the numbers of each type in the rows. Work out the running totals of the dominant type, and express this as a percentage. When the addition of another row of data does not change the overall percentage, you have counted enough fruit.

5 Construct a hypothesis to explain the ratio of phenotypes present on the basis that the character you are studying is controlled by a single gene, the allele for the more numerous form being dominant to the allele for the less common form. Express your hypothesis as a genetic cross using the proforma I (monohybrid cross) shown in Figure 28.2. Note that this proforma incorporates the 'Punnett square' method of showing all the possible combinations of alleles.

NOTE TO TECHNICIAN

Each student group requires access to one (or more) of the following maize inflorescences bearing:
- *smooth* fruits and *wrinkled* fruits;
- *dark-coloured* fruits (red/purple) and *yellowish* fruits;
- *non-shiny* fruits and *waxy* fruits;
and a supply of the proforma I (monohybrid cross), shown here as Figure 28.2.

---

6 Test your hypothesis using the chi-squared test (p. 346, or *Advanced Biology*, p. 618).

■ Data presentation

Present your data, observations, counts, hypothesis and calculations as detailed above.

■ Conclusion

Mendel might have expressed his First Law as 'Each characteristic of an organism is determined by a pair of factors, of which only one can be present in a gamete.'

We state his First Law (the Law of Segregation) as 'The characteristics of an organism are controlled by pairs of alleles which separate in equal numbers into different gametes as a result of meiosis.'

Are your results in agreement with the First Law?

■ Evaluation

To produce the cob you have been studying, what steps will the experimental geneticist have had to take to ensure the parent plant grown from a pure-breeding smooth fruit (or dark-coloured fruit, or non-shiny fruit) was pollinated by pollen coming only from a fruit grown from a wrinkled fruit (or yellowish fruit, or waxy fruit)?

28.2 Maize cobs and Mendel's Second Law
(Data generating)

Mendel also studied the inheritance of contrasting characteristics (in the garden pea), and observed the way the characteristics came together in all possible combinations in the progeny. Had he stated his results as a law he might have said: 'Either one of a pair of factors might combine with either one of another pair.'

Today we state his Second Law (the Law of Independent Assortment) as 'Two or more pairs of alleles segregate independently of each other as a result of meiosis (provided the genes concerned are not linked by being on the same chromosome).'

■ Aim

To interpret the ratio of progeny of a maize cob in terms of one of Mendel's two principles of inheritance, now known as his Second Law.

■ Risk assessment

Good laboratory practice will be sufficient to take account of any hazards and avoid significant risks.

■ Method

1 You are provided with a maize cob. Estimate approximately how many fruits are present (number of rows × number of fruits in a typical row). This is the sample size you are working with.

2 Examine the lines of fruits carefully, for they are of different appearances. The cob you are examining has been selected to have fruits of four appearances (phenotypes). The following are typical cobs that are available for use, and you are almost certain to have one or both of them to examine:
   - fruits that are red and smooth, red and wrinkled, yellowish and smooth, and yellowish and wrinkled;
   - fruits that are yellow and smooth, yellow and wrinkled, white and smooth, and white and wrinkled.

Figure 28.3   Proforma II, for dihybrid crosses

Breeding experiment

parental (P)
phenotypes

genotypes

meiosis   meiosis

gametes

offspring (F₁)
genotypes

phenotypes

F₂ selfed
(or sibling cross)

meiosis   meiosis

gametes

offspring (F₂)
genotypes

genotypes ratio

phenotypes

phenotypes ratio

3 Count the fruit of each type, one row at a time, making certain you know which row you commenced with and which rows you have counted. Record the numbers of both types of fruit, row by row.

4 Is it necessary to count all the fruit present? Tally the numbers of each type in the rows. Work out the running totals of the commonest types, and express this as a percentage. When the addition of another row of data does not significantly change the overall percentage, you have certainly counted enough fruit.

5 Construct a hypothesis to explain the ratio of phenotypes present on the basis that the characteristics you are studying are controlled by single genes, the alleles for the most numerous forms being dominant to the alleles for the less common forms. Express your hypothesis as a genetic cross using the proforma II (dihybrid cross) shown in Figure 28.3. Note that this proforma incorporates the 'Punnett square' method of showing all the possible combinations of alleles.

6 Test your hypothesis using the chi-squared test (p. 39, or in *Advanced Biology*, p. 620).

NOTE TO TECHNICIAN

Each student group requires access to one (or more) of the following maize inflorescences:

- cob with fruits that are *red and smooth, red and wrinkled, yellowish and smooth*, and *yellowish and wrinkled;*
- cob with fruits that are *yellow and smooth, yellow and wrinkled, white and smooth*, and *white and wrinkled.*

and a supply of the proforma II (dihybrid cross), shown here as Figure 28.3.

■ **Data presentation**

Present your data, observations, counts, hypothesis and calculations as detailed above.

■ **Conclusion**

Do your results confirm the hypothesis put forward as the Second Law?

■ **Evaluation**

Why is it true to say that Mendel was extremely lucky at this point in his experimental work?

28.3 Mendelian crosses using 'fast plants'
(Investigation)

The rapid-cycling *Brassica rapa* syn. *campestris* ('fast plants') have been selectively bred to complete their life cycle very quickly, under continuous illumination from fluorescent lights, in a laboratory environment at 24 °C (Figure 28.4).

Seeds are best sown in a peat and vermiculite mix, and well-established seedlings appear within two or three days. The plant achieves a modest, manageable maximum height above soil level of up to 20 cm in four weeks. Flower buds are visible in about one week, and the complete inflorescence with open flowers is formed in two weeks from germination. Within the inflorescence there is uniform flower maturation, and the plant shows a high fertility. Given favourable conditions, the seeds germinate immediately upon harvesting. The plants may play host to several minibeast visitors and some pathogenic fungi, and steps may need to be taken to control these, particularly in genetics experiments. An aphid infestation will need immediate treatment.

'Fast plants' were bred at the University of Wisconsin, USA, by Professor Paul Williams. The use of this plant in the UK has been pioneered by the Science and Plants for Schools team (SAPS), based at Cambridge (see p. 434). The laboratory suppliers Philip Harris (p. 434) market a kit for growing 'fast plants', complete with all requirements except the light bank, about which detailed documentation is supplied.

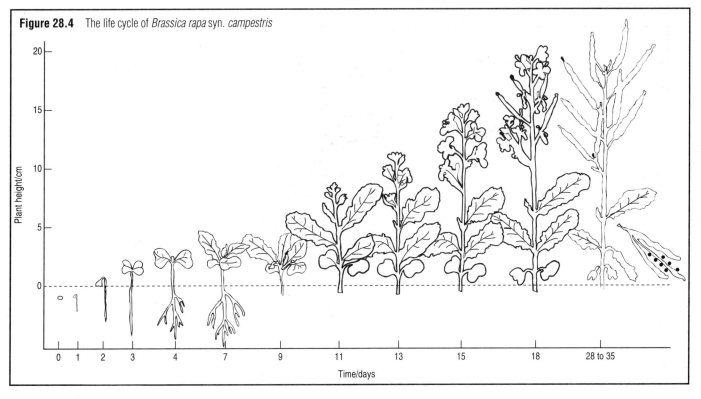

Figure 28.4 The life cycle of *Brassica rapa* syn. *campestris*

Plant height/cm

Time/days

References

R Price (1991) 'Perfect plants for projects', *Biol. Sci. Rev.* 4(1), pp. 32–6

S P Tomkins and P H Williams (1990) 'Fast plants for finer science – an introduction to the biology of rapid-cycling *Brassica campestris (rapa)* L', *J. Biol. Ed.* 24(4), pp. 239–50

■ Aim

To demonstrate Mendelian crosses with 'fast plants', and to test the progeny ratios obtained statistically.

■ Risk assessment

Good laboratory practice will be sufficient to take account of any hazards and avoid significant risks.

■ Method

You are provided with the following banks of 'fast plants' in flower:

- for Mendel's First Law: the 'normal' variety of rapid-cycling *Brassica*, with green leaves, together with a variety with yellow-green leaves;
- for Mendel's Second Law: two pure-breeding rapid-cycling mutants: yellow-green and rosette.

These plants are to be crossed to see if they breed plants that show whether the ratio of phenotypes in the F_2 generation match those that would be expected if Mendel's First and Second Law applied. Apply the chi-squared test to the results.

NOTE TO TECHNICIAN

The growing instructions for rapid-cycling *Brassica campestris* supplied by SAPS to members, or the instructions supplied by Philip Harris with the 'Rapid-cycling Brassica kit', should be consulted regarding the cultivation protocols.

For the demonstration of Mendelian ratios, the Philip Harris 'Simple genetic kit' and the 'Mendel's Second Law kit' are required.

Plants for crossing need to be grown up two weeks before they are required. Bees are the natural pollinators of this member of the Cruciferae, so careful steps must be taken to exclude insect visitors from the banks of plants, well before flower buds open, and until seeds are formed.

■ Data presentation

Present your hypothesis for the explanation of the crosses using the proformas I and II (Figures 28.2 and 28.3).

■ Conclusion

Do Mendel's Laws apply to the crosses you have carried out?

■ Evaluation

Studying the steps to reproduction using different hedgerow plants is also possible, and is interesting since many have attractive flowers with some fascinating pollination mechanisms. What are the specific advantages of using this single, artificially bred species instead?

■ Extension

Arabidopsis thaliana is an alternative 'fast plant' with many clear-cut mutant forms. Male sterile lines are available, making it easy to conduct crosses without having to emasculate the tiny flowers. The plants are reared in the same way as *Brassica rapa*, and complete their life cycle in six to eight weeks.

Reference

B Mulligan and M Anderson (1995) '*Arabidopsis thaliana*, a versatile plant for teaching and research topics', *J. Biol. Ed.* 29(4), pp. 259–69

28.4 *Drosophila melanogaster, for genetics investigations*

(Skills and techniques)

It was from original research on *Drosophila* (the 'vinegar fly') that the American geneticist, Thomas Hunt Morgan, established that Mendel's 'factors' are a linear series of genes on chromosomes (the chromosome theory of inheritance), in 1910. Since then vinegar flies have been of increasing importance in breeding experiments, mainly because:

- they have only four pairs of chromosomes ($2n = 8$);
- they have a generation time of 10–14 days at 25 °C, and produce hundreds of offspring: the adult females mature within 12 hours, and they can lay eggs within two days of emerging from pupation;
- they are relatively easily handled, and when lightly anaesthetised they remain immobile for about 10 minutes: in this time they can be sexed, the phenotypes counted or virgin females isolated, and new crosses set up;
- they have an XX/XY system of sex determination, and in addition to the normal form ('wild type') they exist in a whole series of fertile mutants.

In this introduction to working with *Drosophila*, the skills needed for setting up crosses and determining the results are practised.

Once you are familiar with the techniques of handling the vinegar fly, you can carry out crosses (Practicals 28.5 and 28.7) or simulate them by means of a microcomputer program (Practical 28.6), to generate results to interpret. Additionally, *Drosophila* may also be used for longer-term investigations.

■ Aim

To become familiar with the procedures for carrying out genetic crosses with *Drosophila*.

■ Risk assessment

- The anaesthetising of flies involves diethyl ether (ethoxyethane), which is highly flammable and poisonous. See that all naked flames are extinguished, and that the laboratory is especially well-ventilated. The ether should be dispensed from bulk in a fume cupboard, and only a small quantity dispensed there, into a labelled dropping bottle, for use in particular procedures. Replace the stoppers of your dropping bottle of ether and your etheriser immediately operations are complete. Put your ether bottle to one side in a safe spot when not required.
- Otherwise, good laboratory practice will be sufficient to take account of any hazards and avoid significant risks.

■ Method

Culturing medium and conditions

- Under laboratory conditions, the vinegar fly lives on a special preparation of nutrients with agar. The agar keeps the medium solid and 'in place' when the culture bottles are

Figure 28.5 Equipment used in handling *Drosophila*

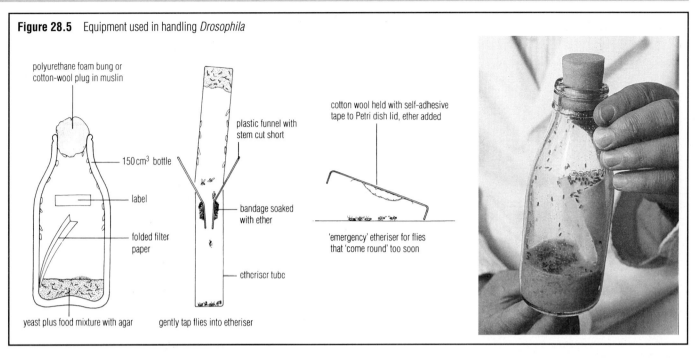

polyurethane foam bung or
cotton-wool plug in muslin

150 cm³ bottle

label

folded filter
paper

yeast plus food mixture with agar

plastic funnel with
stem cut short

bandage soaked
with ether

etheriser tube

gently tap flies into etheriser

cotton wool held with self-adhesive
tape to Petri dish lid, ether added

'emergency' etheriser for flies
that 'come round' too soon

---

up-ended to tap out the flies. Suitably prepared, sterilised medium (which contains 'nipagin' and propionic acid, to inhibit growth of fungi, bacteria and mites) will keep for several weeks if stored in a refrigerator at 2–4 °C. Culture medium can be purchased from biological suppliers in various forms, or prepared in the laboratory according to the simple formulation given in Jones and Rickards (1991) (see below).

- Flies may be cultured in small, flat-bottomed specimen tubes or in glass bottles of 150 cm³ capacity (shaped like a small milk bottle), plugged with cotton wool tied in muslin or a foam rubber bung (Figure 28.5). Cultures should be held at 25 °C. Temperatures lower than this cause the life cycle to be extended, and above 28 °C the males are sterile.

Handling flies

Vinegar flies are lightly anaesthetised with diethyl ether for examination or transfer to new cultures, using the equipment shown in Figure 28.5. The steps are as follows:

1 Moisten the cotton wool pad of your etheriser with a few drops of ether from the dropping bottle, and then wait for a few moments whilst the ether saturates the atmosphere of the tube.

2 Knock the culture bottle/tube sharply with the hand in order to dislodge the flies to the bottom, and then remove the bung. Immediately place the funnel of the etheriser over the opening of the bottle/tube, and then up-end both so that flies fall into the etheriser. Gently tap the sides so they all fall in. Now replace the stopper of the culture bottle/tube.

3 When all the flies have stopped moving, wait for a further 15 seconds and then shake them out on to a white tile. Here the flies can be examined, using a stereomicroscope (low-powered binocular microscope).

Do not let your examination of the flies run on beyond 5–10 minutes, if possible. Flies may start to become active again with time, however. Use an inverted glass Petri dish with filter paper soaked with a little ether to place over the flies momentarily, to return them to the totally anaesthetised

state. Keep this secondary etheriser ready, sitting on a spare white tile, beside where you are working. Try to avoid having to use it, though, for too much ether will kill the flies.

4 Move the unconscious flies gently, using a fine paint brush. In this condition you need to practise sexing them, creating groups of male and female flies (Figure 28.6), and perhaps tell normal (wild-type) and mutant strains apart, or isolate virgin females (see below).

5 Before the unconscious flies recover, return them to culture bottles, depending on the next stage of the investigation. A folded card is a satisfactory means of delivering unconscious flies to a culture medium bottle or tube. Have the bottle or tube on its side, and keep it so until all the flies have recovered (unconscious flies must not become stuck to the surface of the medium).

Dead flies, and flies to be disposed of, should be placed in the 'morgue' (see below).

Setting up a genetic cross

1 To set up a cross, transfer five to six males and five to six virgin females (see below) to an appropriately labelled bottle or tube of fresh culture medium.

2 Young adult females are virgin flies up to about 12 hours old. Then they will mate, and the female stores sperms for future fertilisations. Later mates will not necessarily be the parents of future progeny. A virgin female can be recognised by her ash-grey colour, and by the faecal pellet (black) visible through the lightly pigmented body wall of the abdomen.

3 To isolate virgin females, first remove all flies from an existing culture. Then, no more than 12 hours later, anaesthetise all the flies in the bottle, and separate the virgin females from the rest.

4 Where normal (wild type) is crossed with a mutant strain, then a reciprocal cross should be set up (that is, have one cross where the normals are males and the mutants are females, and a second one vice versa).

5 After seven days, dispose of the adults.

Figure 28.6 *Drosophila*: distinguishing wild-type males and females

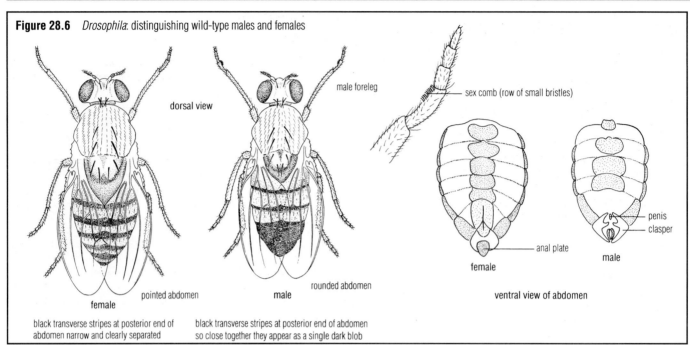

dorsal view

male foreleg

sex comb (row of small bristles)

penis
clasper

anal plate

female

male

female

pointed abdomen

male

rounded abdomen

ventral view of abdomen

black transverse stripes at posterior end of abdomen narrow and clearly separated

black transverse stripes at posterior end of abdomen so close together they appear as a single dark blob

Figure 28.7 The life cycle of *Drosophila* at 25 °C

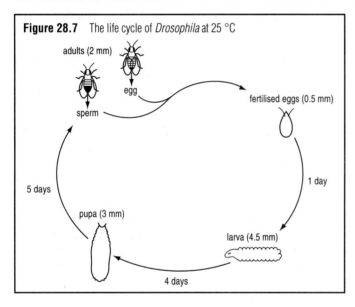

adults (2 mm)

egg

sperm

fertilised eggs (0.5 mm)

1 day

5 days

pupa (3 mm)

larva (4.5 mm)

4 days

Scoring the progeny

1 Adults normally emerge about nine days after eggs are laid, but many mutants take about 48 hours longer at this stage of the life cycle (Figure 28.7).

2 When adults are ready for scoring, anaesthetise the progeny and tap them out on to the white tile. Organise the different phenotypes into rows (two or four rows, according to whether a monohybrid or dihybrid cross has been conducted).

3 Separate each row into males and females, and count and record the numbers of flies of each type (Figure 28.8).

4 Return the progeny to the culture bottle/tube, or place in a new culture bottle, or dispose of the flies (see below).

Disposing of flies: the 'morgue'

It is essential that all flies are finally disposed of, and none be allowed to escape. Have a wide-mouthed specimen bottle containing 70% ethanol, labelled as a 'morgue'. Drop all dead flies, as well as anaesthetised ones no longer required, in the 'morgue'.

Figure 28.8 Some important mutant forms of *Drosophila*

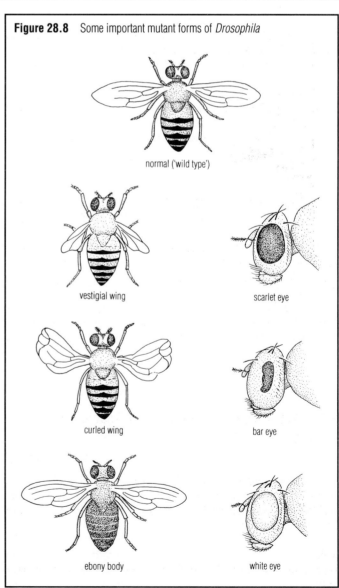

normal ('wild type')

vestigial wing

scarlet eye

curled wing

bar eye

ebony body

white eye

■ Data presentation
You need to keep careful records of dates, times, numbers and sources of flies, and media, and of the crosses undertaken, so that accurate conclusions can be drawn.

■ Conclusion
It is possible to investigate most aspects of Mendelian (monohybrid and dihybrid crosses) and post-Mendelian genetics (particularly linkage and crossing over), by means of *Drosophila* crosses.

■ Evaluation
What is meant when a *Drosophila* geneticist says that 'Crossing over at meiosis does not occur in the male *Drosophila*'? What is the significance of this statement? (See *Advanced Biology*, p. 625.)

Reference
R N Jones and G K Rickards (1991) *Practical Genetics*, Chapter 3 '*Drosophila* genetics', pp. 48–83. Open University Press

Note: This excellent reference source uses the *Drosophila* geneticists' notation for wild-type (normal) flies of '+'. The Association for Science Education and Institute of Biology, in *Biological Nomenclature* (1989), recommend that this notation be replaced in schools and colleges by upper-case (for dominant) and lower-case (for recessive) letters for the genes concerned in a cross, that is, the conventional symbols used in all other genetics notation.

28.5 *Mendelian crosses using* Drosophila *mutants*

(Data generating)

Monohybrid and dihybrid inheritance in *Drosophila* can be demonstrated by conducting experimental crosses, using normal ('wild-type') flies and flies carrying alleles for one or more mutant characteristics.

■ Aim
To obtain data to test Mendel's First and Second Laws statistically.

■ Risk assessment
The risk assessment for Practical 28.4 applies here. Pay particular attention to the precautions needed when using diethyl ether.

■ Method

A monohybrid cross
You are provided with a culture tube containing five to six homozygous normal ('wild-type') virgin females and a similar tube containing five to six homozygous vestigial-wing mutant males. (If time and resources permit, parent flies for a reciprocal cross will also be provided.)

1 Using the correct protocols for anaesthetising and handling flies (Practical 28.4, p. 338), combine male and virgin females in a fresh culture tube.
2 Once the flies have recovered, label your tube, identifying the parental types and adding the date, and incubate at 25 °C.
3 After seven days, you will see that the eggs laid have hatched into larvae, and some may have already pupated on the sides of the culture bottle. Remove the parent flies by the correct protocol, and dispose of them. Return the culture bottle to the incubator for a further seven days.
4 In the interval, work out what you *anticipate* the outcome of this cross will be. Do you expect 50% males and 50% females that are all 'normal' ('wild-type') in appearance, or may there be some that are male vestigial-wing and some female vestigial-wing?
5 After this time, anaesthetise all the adult progeny (F_1 generation) and count the numbers of flies, classifying them according to sex and wing shape.
6 Set up an F_2 sibling cross, using five to six male F_1 and five to six female F_1 flies, using a fresh culture tube. Incubate the culture at 25 °C. Dispose of the F_1 adults after one week.
7 After a further week, count and record the numbers of adult progeny, using the protocols described in Practical 28.4 and recording your results under the following headings: male normal; female normal; male vestigial-wing; female vestigial-wing.
8 Dispose of the progeny of the cross correctly.

A dihybrid cross
You are provided with a culture tube containing F_1 progeny (females and males) of a cross between male normal flies (with normal wing and normal body colour) and virgin female flies with vestigial wings and ebony bodies. (If time and resources permit, progeny from a reciprocal cross will also be provided.)

1 Work out what you *anticipate* the outcome of this cross will have been, before you examine the progeny. Do you expect 50% males and 50% females that are all 'normal wing' and 'normal body colour' ('wild type') in appearance, or may there be some that have vestigial wing and/or some with ebony body?
2 Using the correct protocols, anaesthetise all the adult progeny (F_1 generation), count the number of flies, and classify them according to sex, wing shape and body colour.
3 Using the correct protocols for handling flies (Practical 28.4, p. 337), combine male and female phenotypes with normal wings and normal body colour, in a fresh culture tube.

4 Once the flies have recovered, label your tube, identifying the parental types and adding the date, and incubate at 25 °C.

5 After seven days, you will see that the eggs laid will have hatched into larvae, and some may have pupated on the sides of the culture bottle. Remove the parent flies by the correct protocol, and dispose of them. Return the culture bottle to the incubator.

6 After a further week anaesthetise all the adult progeny (F_2 generation), and count and record the numbers of flies under the following headings:
- male normal (wing and body colour);
- female normal (wing and body colour);
- male normal wing and ebony body colour;
- female normal wing and ebony body colour;
- male vestigial wing and normal body colour;
- female vestigial wing and normal body colour;
- male vestigial wing and ebony body;
- female vestigial wing and ebony body;

7 Dispose of the progeny of the cross correctly.

NOTE TO TECHNICIAN

Each student group will require:
- the equipment and apparatus detailed for Practical 28.4.

*For a **monohybrid cross***:
- culture tube containing five to six homozygous normal ('wild-type') virgin females and a similar tube containing five to six homozygous vestigial-wing mutant males (if time and resources permit, parent flies for a reciprocal cross may also be provided).

*For a **dihybrid cross***:
- culture tube containing F_1 progeny (females and males) of a cross between male normal (with normal wings and normal body colour) and virgin female flies with vestigial wings and ebony bodies (if time and resources permit, progeny from a reciprocal cross may also be provided).

Note: segregated males and virgin females and ready-made crosses, as detailed here, are supplied by laboratory suppliers. They normally require about three weeks notice, however, and may specify a minimum quantity.

■ Data presentation
- Tabulate your data from the monohybrid cross, F_1 and F_2 generations.
- Tabulate your data from the dihybrid cross, F_1 and F_2 generations.

■ Conclusions
- Produce a hypothesis for your results from the monohybrid and dihybrid crosses by means of completed proformas I and II (pp. 334 and 336).
- Use the chi-squared test (p. 346, and *Advanced Biology*, pp. 614 and 618) to determine whether your results differ significantly from the predicted proportions.

■ Evaluation
- In the data obtained from a breeding experiment of this type, what are the likely sources of variation from the predicted proportions? Why do we not obtain results precisely as predicted?

28.6 Resources for learning about genetics
(Demonstration)

The following resources are available to support learning about Mendelian genetics.

Heredity Pack, produced by King's College/AVP and supplied by AVP (p. 433), includes a CAL program 'Inheritance', involving breeding investigations in *Drosophila melanogaster*, mice, humans and tomato plants, for an introduction to monohybrid and dihybrid inheritance. Available for Nimbus 186, Nimbus 286 and above, and BBC B and Master 128 microcomputers.

Genetics Disk, produced by Garland and supplied by AVP, is a CAL program in two parts. 'Inheritance, population genetics and chromosome mapping' is an introduction to Mendelian genetics. It includes, for example, 'Hybrid cross', an interactive simulation of the crossing of pea plants, and 'Dihybrid cross', which simulates an experiment with *Drosophila* with two pairs of contrasting characters. 'Population genetics' is a simulation based upon the Hardy–Weinberg Law. Available for Acorn RISC OS, BBC B and Master 128 microcomputers.

The CAL program *The Biology Explorer – Genetics*, supplied by Philip Harris Ltd (p. 434), simulates the crosses of diploid organisms. Students can investigate the inheritance of up to seven traits in several species. A picture of the offspring of crosses is generated, and their genotypes can be examined. The issues addressed are: monohybrid and dihybrid inheritance, meiosis, the concepts of genotype, phenotype, dominant and recessive alleles, homozygote and heterozygote, and Mendel's Laws. Also addressed are population genetics and the Hardy–Weinberg equilibrium, together with the elementary laws of probability. Student activities and lab work at different levels are generated. Teacher's notes are enclosed. Available for IBM PCs or clones (386 system with Windows 3.0 or better, colour monitor and 4 MB memory), or Macintosh (minimum 12-inch monitor, System 6.07 or better and 4 MB memory) microcomputers.

The teaching video *Meiosis: Key to Genetic Diversity*, is produced by Human Relations Media Inc, USA and supplied by Boulton-Hawker Films Ltd and Class Productions (p. 433). Part 1 shows how the process of meiosis reduces by half the normal diploid number of chromosomes in a cell, prior to fusion of sex cells during fertilisation, while Part 2 shows how the random segregation of chromosomes during meiosis contributes to genetic diversity.

28.7 Investigating linkage and crossing over, using Drosophila

(Investigation)

Mutant forms of *Drosophila* can be used to investigate cases of linkage of genes. Linkage and crossing over are discussed in *Advanced Biology*, pp. 625–9.

■ Aim
To obtain numerically significant evidence of linkage of genes in the inheritance of *Drosophila*.

■ Risk assessment

The risk assessment for Practical 28.4 applies here. Pay particular attention to the precautions needed when using diethyl ether.

■ Method

Linkage of genes

- You are provided with a culture tube containing five to six homozygous normal ('wild-type') virgin females and a similar tube containing five to six homozygous ebony-body, curled-wing mutant males. (If time and resources permit, parent flies for a reciprocal cross will also be provided.)
- The protocols for handing *Drosophila* are detailed in Practical 28.4. Design and carry out a breeding experiment to obtain and count the progeny from an F_1 cross. Using some of the F_1 progeny, make a sibling cross to obtain and count the F_2 progeny.

Sex linkage of genes

- You are provided with a culture tube containing five to six homozygous normal ('wild-type') virgin females and a similar tube containing five to six homozygous white-eye mutant males, together with a culture tube containing five to six homozygous normal ('wild-type') males and a similar tube containing five to six homozygous white-eye mutant virgin females.
- The protocols for handling *Drosophila* are detailed in Practical 28.4. Design and carry out a breeding experiment to obtain and count the progeny from a reciprocal F_1 cross of both sets of parents. Obtain and count the progeny.

NOTE TO TECHNICIAN

Each student group will require:
- the equipment and apparatus detailed for Practical 28.4.

For the study of gene linkage:
- culture tube containing five to six homozygous normal ('wild-type') virgin females and a similar tube containing five to six homozygous ebony-body, curled-wing mutant males (if time and resources permit, parent flies for a reciprocal cross will also be provided).

For the study of sex-linked genes:
- culture tube containing five to six homozygous normal ('wild-type') virgin females and a similar tube containing five to six homozygous white-eye mutant males, together with a culture tube containing five to six homozygous normal ('wild-type') males and a similar tube containing five to six homozygous white-eye mutant virgin females.
Note: segregated males and virgin females, as detailed here, are supplied by laboratory suppliers. They normally require about three weeks notice, however, and may specify a minimum quantity.

■ Data presentation

- Tabulate your data from the 'linkage of genes' cross, F_1 and F_2 generations.
- Tabulate your data from the 'sex linkage of genes' crosses, F_1 generation.

■ Conclusions

- Produce a hypothesis for the reasons for your results from each cross by means of completed proformas I and II (pp. 334 and 336).
- What was the recombinant frequency obtained in the 'linkage of genes' cross (*Advanced Biology*, p. 625)?

■ Evaluation

What does gene mapping of chromosomes involve?

28.8 'Nature versus nurture' in human variation
(Investigation)

Variation in living things may be due to genetic differences ('nature') or it may be due to environment in some way, such as food supply ('nurture') – or to both to varying degrees. Can we tell the difference between nature and nurture components of variation?

■ Aim

To enquire into variation in a human characteristic (such as body height/size) to determine whether differences are largely inherited or due to an environmental factor, such as diet.

■ Risk assessment

Good laboratory practice will be sufficient to take account of any hazards and avoid significant risks.

■ Method

- Measure the height and arm length, and note the sex of as large a sample of young people (17–19 years) as you can contact. You also require a second sample of data from much older adults, such as parents or grandparents. Perhaps the young people who agree to be measured would be able to apply the same measurements to their parents or grandparents? Your samples should include not less than 20 people in both categories, more if possible.
- Height measurements should be taken in bare feet. Arm measurements should be from armpit to fingertip. All measurements should be in centimetres and millimetres.

NOTE TO TECHNICIAN

Each student group requires the use of a metre rule.

■ Data presentation

- Present your data by means of a spreadsheet. Draw up four tables of data with the following columns:
  height; arm length; height/arm length ratio; sex.
- Arrange the data in height order in two groups according to gender.
- Plot scattergrams of height and arm length for both sexes.
- Work out the means of height, arm length and height/arm length for each population (young people, and parents/grandparents), and then for each sex within each population. Means can then be plotted as bar charts.

■ Conclusions

- The scattergram should show the relationship between height and arm length to be linear and, preferably, the spread of the data should not be too wide. (It is worth checking any abnormal plots, because incorrect data may have been entered in error.)

- We must assume that the diet available to male and female participants has been comparable. Any difference in height between males and females in the same population we may attribute to genes (nature).
- Now examine any difference in height between the younger and the older populations. Unless there has been any significant change in the genes (and assuming no significant growth by the 17–19-year-olds before full adult status is achieved), any difference in height between the two populations will be due to environment, such as diet.
- Examine the height distribution of males and females. There should be a certain amount of overlap. What statistical test can be used to determine whether the height data is significantly different?
- Variations in the height/arm length ratio are probably due to genes and, if so, the differences should be of about the same order in both populations.

■ Evaluation

Is this investigation hampered by the relatively small size of the experimental population?

28.9 Resources for learning about post-Mendelian genetics

(Demonstration)

The following resources are available to support learning about issues in post-Mendelian genetics.

ABO Blood Grouping, produced by AVP, is a group of CAL programs that uses graphics and tabulated information to explain and simulate the taking of blood samples, the use of antisera in blood tests, the principles of blood transfusions, the process of agglutination and the genetics of the ABO system. The ABO system is a good example of multiple alleles, complex to understand, yet of great medical importance. Available for Acorn RISC OS, Nimbus 186 and 286 and above, and BBC B and Master 128 microcomputers.

The CAL program *Genetic Mapping*, produced by King's College/AVP, deals with genetic mapping from first principles, starting with its basis in linkage and crossing over. The student specifies a series of genetic crosses, and from the resulting data builds a linkage map for 10 genes of a hypothetical diploid species, using the three points test cross technique. Available from AVP for Acorn RISC OS, IBM PC, Nimbus 186 and 286 and above, and BBC B and Master 128 microcomputers.

Another CAL program, *Crossover*, produced by Netherhall Educational Software and supplied by Cambridge University Press, allows the student to investigate the relationship between gene distance, recombination frequency and crossover frequency. The importance of large samples becomes apparent. Available for BBC B and Master 128 microcomputers.

28.10 Human genetics investigations to avoid

Whilst most individual genes behave according to Mendelian laws, many characteristics in organisms are controlled by two, three or more genes (polygenes), sometimes located on different chromosomes. Control of most characters in humans, for example, is multifactorial. The phenomenon means that often there are no clear-cut Mendelian ratios to be found, and a very large number of variations in phenotype occur.

Another possible cause of confusion is our powerful social or cultural inheritance. We spend so long in growing up, and in being taught and trained, it can at times be hard to tell cultural (that is, environmental) influences from genetic ones.

The following two examples are cases in point. There are many others.

■ Eye colour is not a good example of monohybrid inheritance

The genetics of eye colour is complex and is not fully understood, but it is almost certainly a polygenic trait. Looking carefully at the irises of some people with 'blue eyes', it is possible to see tiny patches of brown pigmentation. It has been noted by geneticists that such people, as parents, may have brown-eyed children. Brown-eyed progeny of blue-eyed parents are fairly common, a genetics phenomenon of which the mechanism is yet to be explained. It is totally misleading to apply Mendel's First Law to human eye colour, *before* we know how many genes are involved.

Reference

M Reiss (1988) 'Brown-eyed children may have blue-eyed parents', *School Science Review* (June 1988) **69**(249), p. 742

■ There is no evidence of a genetic basis for 'tongue rolling'

Tongue rolling is something that many but not all people can do. This does not make 'tongue rolling' a characteristic controlled by a single, dominant allele, however. We know this because members of identical twin pairs may differ in this facility, and because very many people can learn to 'tongue roll'. This facility, if genetically controlled, is likely to have a polygenic basis. But cultural differences, such as early training, may be important factors. Some interesting investigations of the advantages of tongue rolling have been conducted, as described in the reference here.

Reference

J M Patefield and M L Moore (1986) 'The genetic basis of tongue rolling', *J. Biol. Ed.* **20**(4), pp. 255–6

Projects

28.1 Observing genetic principles in cats

The cat is not a suitable organism for breeding experiments in this situation, but the careful observation of variation in the cat population can identify a wealth of characteristics which have a genetical explanation. Discussion with owners and cat breeders may elicit examples of characteristics that illustrate dominance, incomplete dominance, multiple allelism (polygenes), sex linkage and lethality. Other aspects to be observed include characteristics due to X-inactivation and the effect of environment on the phenotype. Photographs or coloured sketches of animals, combined with a rationale for their inheritance, would augment understanding of principles derived from the study of traditional but laboratory-living organisms in controlled experiments. It would make a worthwhile observational project.

References
M Frayne (1983) 'The use of cat genetics in schools', *School Science Review* (December 1983) 65(231), pp. 303–6
J F Kinnear (1986) 'Using the domestic cat in the teaching of genetics', *J. Biol. Ed.* 20(1), pp. 5–11
D J Talbot and C D Talbot (1992) 'Teaching A level genetics; the coat colours of the domestic cat', *School Science Review* (June 1992) 73(265), pp. 29–35
I Gill (1993) 'If only Mendel had owned a cat', *Biol. Sci. Rev.* 5(4), pp. 35–8

28.2 Studies of xanthic forms in guppies

If guppies (*Poecilia reticulata*) are maintained in a tropical fish tank at school, college or home, they can be used in breeding experiments. The fish is hardy and robust, with a short gestation period and numerous offspring. An inherited characteristic that is easily studied is the body colour. Most guppies have a large number of melanophores superficially located in the skin, giving them their traditional grey appearance. Mutants arise which appear yellow or golden because they lack the ability to produce sufficient melanophores to mask colours in the lower layers of the body wall. Test the hypothesis that melanophore production is controlled by a dominant allele.

Reference
C Dodds (1987) 'Genetic studies of xanthic forms of guppies', *School Science Review* (December 1987) 69(217), pp. 293–4

28.3 Studying Mendelian genetics with a harmless, saprotrophic ascomycete fungus

It is relatively easy to culture *Sordaria fimicola* and, using the strain with black ascospores crossed with the strain with off-white ascospores, Mendelian ratios can be obtained. Other possibilities, including linkage and crossing over, are developed in the literature.

Reference
R N Jones and G K Rickards (1991) *Practical Genetics* Chapter 5 'Genetics with *Sordaria*', pp. 104–18. Open University Press

28.4 Studying genetics with a harmless, saprotrophic basidiomycete fungus

It is relatively easy to culture *Coprinus cinereus*, and, with nutritional mutants, the ability of the progeny to survive on different media can be investigated and the results explained. Other possibilities are developed in the literature.

Reference
D Moore and P J Pukkila (1985) '*Coprinus cinereus*; an ideal organism for studies of genetics and developmental biology', *J. Biol. Ed.* 19(1), pp. 31–40

28.5 The genetics of the radish

Although the life cycle of the radish (*Raphanus sativus*) takes several weeks, some of the common commercial varieties show distinctive phenotypes which appear to be controlled by single genes. A study of this sort requires very careful advice, together with some discussion with the seed suppliers, before an investigation is undertaken, because of the time factor.

Reference
G B Ritchie (1978) 'A new look at some genetics of the radish', *School Science Review* (September 1978) 60(210), pp. 77–9

28.6 The inheritance of flower pigments in Antirrhinum

Antirrhinum is a garden plant available in a range of varieties, most with distinctively coloured flowers. The pigments in flowers of different varieties grown from seed can be extracted and analysed by paper chromatography to discover which of the three major pigments of this plant they contain. Can the genotypes of each variety be deduced from the data thus obtained?

Reference
B Harrison and R Strickland (1976) 'Pathways strewn with plant pigments', *New Scientist* (8 July 1976), pp. 70–1

Biological suppliers offer numerous species for various genetics investigations. Most of these can be exploited in longer-term investigations, provided thorough research and careful planning are undertaken, with consultation at an early stage. Organisms include tomato, tobacco and pea (all as seeds), yeasts and the flour beetle (*Tribolium castaneum*), together with *Drosophila* as already described.

Problems and assignments

28.1 The dihybrid cross with maize cobs

The maize cob (*Zea mays*) in Figure 28.9 shows four rows of fruit (rows A to D) in which individual fruits can be identified and counted. You can see that the fruit wall may be coloured or colourless, and the food reserve stored may be predominantly of starch (giving a smooth fruit) or sugar (giving a wrinkled fruit). Examine the photograph carefully, and using the information it contains, and your general knowledge of fruit structure and of genetics, answer the following questions.

1 Draw a longitudinal cross-section of an individual maize fruit to show the position of the endosperm and embryo. Indicate on the drawing the position of the stored food and the coloured wall pigments, when present.

2 Count and record the total number of fruits of the four phenotypes in the rows A to D in Figure 28.9.

3 a Among the alleles for 'coloured' and 'colourless' and 'smooth' and 'wrinkled', which are dominant and which are recessive?

   b Give the reason for your answer.

4 Given a maize fruit that was homozygous for 'coloured fruit wall' and 'starch food store' (smooth fruit) and a maize fruit that was homozygous for 'colourless fruit wall' and 'sugar food store' (wrinkled), what steps would a plant geneticist have to carry out in order ultimately to harvest a maize cob very similar to the one shown here?

5 a Make a copy of Table 28.1, where O = observed number of fruits, and E = expected number.

   b Using the data obtained by counting the fruits in rows A to D, complete column O in the table.

Table 28.1 Question 5b

Phenotypes of grains	O	E	$(O - E)$	$(O - E)^2$	$\dfrac{(O - E)^2}{E}$
Coloured smooth					
Colourless smooth					
Coloured wrinkled					
Colourless wrinkled					
Total =					$\sum =$

   c Calculate the expected number of each phenotype and enter these figures in column E of your table.

   d Calculate the values for $(O - E)$, $(O - E)^2$ and $(O - E)^2/E$, and enter these in your table.

   e Calculate the value of χ^2 from the formula:

$$\chi^2 = \sum \frac{(O - E)^2}{E}$$

6 a How many degrees of freedom are there in this calculation of χ^2?

   b In another experiment, the value for χ^2 for three degrees of freedom was found to lie between probabilities of 0.95 and 0.90. What does this mean?

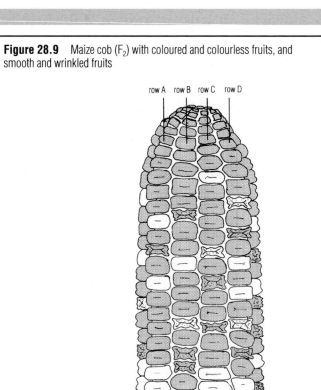

Figure 28.9 Maize cob (F$_2$) with coloured and colourless fruits, and smooth and wrinkled fruits

row A   row B   row C   row D

smooth, coloured fruit

wrinkled, coloured fruit

wrinkled, colourless fruit

smooth, colourless fruit

28.2 Linkage and a linkage map from a Drosophila cross

In a breeding experiment with *Drosophila*, homozygous normal female flies ('wild type', with red eyes and straight wings) were crossed with homozygous mutant male flies with scarlet eyes and curled wings. The progeny of this cross were all of 'normal' phenotype.

When female flies from these progeny were crossed with homozygous mutant male flies with scarlet eyes and curled wings (a test cross), some of the progeny were like the parents, but a few were new combinations of characteristics (recombinant types):

normal (red eye, straight wing)	196
scarlet eye and straight wing	9
red eye and curled wing	11
scarlet eye and curled wing	184

1 a Give the genotype of the parents and their F_1 progeny in conventional notation, where the allele for eye colour is represented by R or r, and the allele for wing shape is represented by S or s.

b From the progeny of this cross, what must we conclude about the location of the genes for scarlet eye and for curled wing on the four pairs of chromosomes in *Drosophila* nuclei?

2 By means of a genetic diagram, explain the outcome of this breeding experiment.

3 a Which of the test cross progeny were recombinant types?

b Why are these progeny described as 'recombinant'?

4 Recombinant frequency (crossover value) is calculated as follows:

$$\frac{\text{number of recombinants}}{\text{total progeny}} \times 100$$

Calculate the recombinant frequency for this cross.

5 The recombinant frequency is said to indicate how far apart the genes are on the chromosome.

a Why is this so?

b What size of recombinant frequencies would you expect from genes that are next door to each other?

c What would be the phenotype ratio of the test cross progeny if the genes were not linked?

6 Draw a simple diagram of the *Drosophila* chromosome involved here, and show the number of map units lying between the genes for curled wing and scarlet eye.

28.3 Mendelian inheritance in humans

Sickle-cell anaemia is an autosomal recessive genetic defect, in which the normal haemoglobin protein A is replaced by haemoglobin S in red cells. Haemoglobin S is less efficient at carrying oxygen and, when deoxygenated, forms long fibres that tend to produce sharp distortions in the red cells.

People who are homozygous for the sickle-cell allele have sickle-cell disease, but this is a rare and serious condition. People with a single allele (heterozygous) for sickle-cell are said to have sickle-cell trait, a disease which may pass unnoticed, and which is rather uncommon in most parts of the world. In some areas of the UK, sickle cell trait is common enough for counselling advice and booklets to be readily available. Ask your librarian or resource staff to collect articles and booklets on sickle-cell counselling.

Figure 28.10 shows the pedigree of a family affected by sickle-cell anaemia. Examine the chart and, using the information given together with your knowledge of human physiology and genetics, answer the following questions.

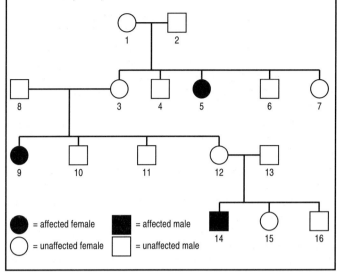

Figure 28.10 Pedigree of a family affected by sickle-cell anaemia (note that some of the 'unaffected' members of the family will be heterozygous for the sickle-cell protein)

1 What is meant by an 'autosomal recessive genetic defect'?

2 Using the symbols Hb^A and Hb^S, give the genotype of a person who is:

a homozygous for normal haemoglobin;

b homozygous for sickle-cell protein;

c heterozygous for sickle-cell protein.

3 a Outline the reasons why being homozygous recessive for sickle-cell anaemia is a serious condition.

b Why is it of no long-term value to treat sickle-cell anaemia by giving a blood transfusion.

4 In the family pedigree:

a who are the grandchildren of individuals 8 and 3?

b which individuals are related to parents 1 and 2 by marriage alone?

c what inherited condition are persons 6 and 16 certain to share?

5 a Which individuals in the pedigree are you certain are heterozygous for sickle-cell anaemia?

b What condition are people who are heterozygous for sickle-cell protein said to have?

c What is the probability that person 7 is heterozygous for sickle-cell anaemia?

6 The malarial parasite lives within human red blood cells for a significant part of its life cycle. In areas where malaria is endemic, sickle-cell trait is a quite common condition.

a How may the malarial parasite, present in red cells, reach another human host?

b What is meant by 'endemic'?

c Outline a reasoned explanation of why people with sickle-cell trait are quite common in the population in areas where malaria is endemic.

28.4 Inheritance of 'white eye' in Drosophila

An uncommon mutant form of *Drosophila*, with white eyes rather than the red ('wild type'), has been isolated from natural populations. This vinegar fly has been used in laboratory breeding experiments, and the outcome depends on whether the male or the female parents carried the mutant allele for eye colour. The results have enabled us to build up a picture of the location of genes on particular chromosomes. Two typical experiments are outlined below.

Experiment 1 involved red-eyed females and white-eyed males as parents, and the progeny were exclusively red-eyed. Sibling crosses of this F₁ generation resulted in an F₂ generation containing three red-eyed flies for every one white-eyed. All the females had red eyes, but some of the males were white-eyed and some red-eyed.

Experiment 2 involved white-eyed female and red-eyed male parents, and here the progeny were red-eyed females and white-eyed males. Sibling crosses of the F₁ generation resulted in an F₂ population of equal numbers of males and females, with both sexes consisting of equal numbers of red-eyed and white-eyed flies.

1 The wild-type parents in both experiments were 'homozygous' for eye colour. What does this mean? How would a geneticist breed flies to be homozygous for eye colour?

2 In breeding experiments with *Drosophila* it is necessary to 'sex' flies. What external features enable the geneticist to tell males and females apart?

3 The XY system of sex determination is characteristic of most vertebrates, and is found in some insects, including *Drosophila*. Construct a genetic diagram to show the segregation of X and Y chromosomes.

4 In setting up a cross with *Drosophila* it is necessary to isolate and use virgin female flies.
   a Why is this the case?
   b How are virgin females obtained from a breeding culture of *Drosophila*?

5 From the outcomes of Experiment 1, can you say which allele for eye colour is dominant? Give the reason for your answer.

6 How is the type of inheritance exhibited in these crosses described by geneticists?

7 Select appropriate symbols and then construct genetic diagrams for the crosses of Experiments 1 and 2, using copies of the proforma for monohybrid crosses (p. 334).

28.5 *Inheritance of the fowl comb*

We learn the principles of genetics by studying characteristics which are controlled by a pair of alleles occupying a particular gene locus. In fact, many characteristics are controlled by two or more genes, often situated on different chromosomes. In addition, the genes may interact.

For example, in the inheritance of the shape of the comb in the domestic fowl, genes at two loci (R/r, P/p), situated on different chromosomes, interact to give rise to four distinct phenotypes. In Figure 28.11, the genotypes that produce the four phenotypes are shown.

A geneticist set up a cross between a homozygous walnut-comb fowl and a single-comb fowl. From the progeny, sibling crosses were set up, and the phenotypes of the progeny of the F₂ generation were analysed and recorded.

1 Using the appropriate genetic symbols, construct a genetic diagram to predict the outcome of these crosses, using the proforma for dihybrid crosses (p. 336).

2 What comb shapes would be formed, and in what proportions, in the F₁ generation?

3 What comb shapes would be formed, and in what proportions, in the F₂ generation?

28.6 *Inheritance in the tomato plant*

Tomato plants typically have an anthocyanin pigment in the vacuoles of the epidermal cells of the stem, giving a purple appearance, but in some plants the pigment is missing and the stem is green. In addition, most tomato plants have 'cut' leaves, but some have leaves of undivided leaflets (known as 'potato' leaf). Figure 28.12 illustrates these contrasting conditions.

A geneticist left a record of an experiment designed to establish whether these phenotypes were inherited, and were controlled by single genes on separate chromosomes. The results of the crosses used are summarised in Table 28.2.

Using the information given in the table, and your knowledge of genetics, answer the following questions.

1 Assume that stem colour (purple or green) is controlled by alleles at a single locus. Say which form is dominant, and give the reasons for your answer.

2 Assume that leaf shape ('cut' or 'potato') is controlled by alleles at a single locus. Say which form is dominant, and give the reasons for your answer.

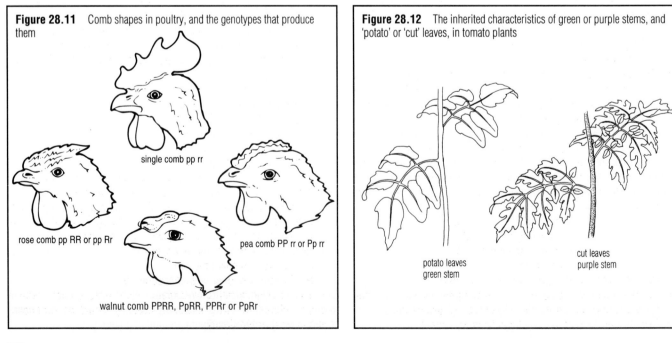

Figure 28.11 Comb shapes in poultry, and the genotypes that produce them

single comb pp rr

rose comb pp RR or pp Rr

pea comb PP rr or Pp rr

walnut comb PPRR, PpRR, PPRr or PpRr

Figure 28.12 The inherited characteristics of green or purple stems, and 'potato' or 'cut' leaves, in tomato plants

potato leaves
green stem

cut leaves
purple stem

Table 28.2 Genetics experiment: phenotypes and numbers of offspring

Parental phenotypes	Offspring: Purple stem, cut leaves	Purple stem, potato leaves	Green stem, cut leaves	Green stem, potato leaves
1 Purple stem/cut leaves × Green stem/potato leaves	345	0	376	0
2 Purple stem/potato leaves × Green stem/cut leaves	61	70	57	66
3 Purple stem/cut leaves × Green stem/cut leaves	691	243	0	0
4 Purple stem/cut leaves × Green stem/cut leaves	321	103	309	108

3 What possible genotypes would produce the following phenotypes?
 a purple stem, cut leaves;
 b purple stem, potato leaves;
 c green stem, cut leaves;
 d green stem, potato leaves.
4 Deduce the genotypes of the parents of crosses 1 to 4. Give your reasons in each case, using the symbols P or p for stem colour, and C or c for leaf shape.

28.7 Inheritance in oilseed rape

Many characteristics are controlled by alleles that are either dominant or recessive. For some characteristics, however, the two alleles do not show complete dominance or recessiveness. This condition may be described as codominance.

In a variety of the oilseed rape plant (*Brassica napus*) the allele for tallness is dominant over the allele for dwarfness. Consequently, some varieties are dwarf compared with the normal tall plant.

Another characteristic of these rape plants, also apparently controlled by a single gene locus, is chlorophyll production, but here the plants are more variable. Whilst many are green, other plants have variegated leaves, and some are totally without chlorophyll. The latter die as young seedlings.

1 Homozygous rape plants, tall and green, were crossed with dwarf plants with variegated leaves. Using suitable symbols for the alleles for height and for chlorophyll production, construct a genetic diagram to show the genotypes and phenotypes of parents and progeny, and the proportions of the genotypes produced.
2 From the progeny were selected tall plants with variegated leaves, and these were grown and allowed to self-pollinate. The progeny of this second generation were kept and grown, and for 100 seeds sown the following numbers of the different phenotypes were obtained:

> tall, green: 19;
> tall, variegated: 38;
> dwarf, variegated: 6;
> dwarf, green: 12.

while 25% of the seedlings died on germinating.
 a Construct a genetic diagram to show the phenotypes and genotypes of the parents and offspring of the (F_2) generations.
 b Explain why 25% of the seedlings failed to survive.

28.8 Incomplete dominance in *Antirrhinum*

We may recognise incomplete dominance, where a heterozygous offspring is distinguishable from both homozygous parents. Flower colour in the garden plant snapdragon (*Antirrhinum*) is an example.

A tall, pink-flowered *Antirrhinum* plant (F_1) was allowed to self-pollinate, and the offspring that were produced are recorded in Table 28.3.

Table 28.3

	Flower colour: red	pink	white
Tall	18	37	16
Dwarf	6	12	7

1 Consider first the origin of the F_1 plants which self-pollinated to produce these offspring. What would be the phenotypes and genotypes of the homozygous parents of tall, pink-flowered plants?
2 Since *Antirrhinum* is capable of self-pollination, what steps would be needed to make a cross between two parent plants?
3 Which of the following offspring would you be certain would breed true?
 a tall, red-flowered plants;
 b dwarf, pink-flowered plants;
 c tall, white-flowered plants;
 d dwarf, white-flowered plants;
 e tall, pink-flowered plants;
 f dwarf, red-flowered plants.
4 **a** If the effect of the presence of an allele for red flowers in *Antirrhinum* is to cause the production of an enzyme that catalyses the conversion of a colourless intermediate to a flower pigment in petals, suggest why the heterozygous plant has pink flowers and the homozygous plant has red flowers.
 b How might your hypothesis be tested:
  i in a research laboratory?
  ii in your school or college laboratory?
5 If a heterozygous tall, pink-flowered plant were crossed with a dwarf, white-flowered plant, what progeny would be produced, and in what proportions?

28.9 Coat colour in mice: an example of epistasis

The condition in which one gene hides the expression of another gene is called 'epistasis'. Fur colour in mice is an example of this phenomenon. Here, two genes at different loci control the colour of the fur. Mice may be agouti (grey) or black, but these coat colours will appear only if accompanied by an allele for coloured fur. The alternative phenotype is albino, which arises in mice homozygous recessive for colour. The genes and alleles may be represented as follows:

- *Gene one* (epistatic gene) determines the presence of colour, where the coloured allele is dominant and the albino gene is recessive. Let C represent the allele for coloured fur, and c the allele for albino fur.
- *Gene two* (hypostatic gene) determines the nature of the colour, where the 'agouti' (grey) allele is dominant and the black allele is recessive. Let A represent the allele for agouti fur, and a the allele for black fur.

In a cross between a black and an albino mouse (parents), the genotypes are as follows:

black	albino
aaCC	AAcc

In this case the progeny (F_1) are all agouti (AaCc).

1 Using the genetic symbols given, and the proforma for a dihybrid cross (p. 336), construct a genetic diagram for the above cross, and work out what will be the expected progeny of the F_2 offspring of a sibling cross between two agouti mice.
2 Summarise the outcome by stating the proportion of agouti, black and albino mice you would expect to be produced.
3 If only one or two pairs of agouti mice are used to produce the F_2 offspring, what limitations might this impose on the experiment?

28.10 ABO blood group

The ABO blood group system is one of several different blood grouping systems in humans that are genetically determined. In the ABO system more than two alleles exist, but only two are present in any particular human. The gene for the ABO system is represented by the symbol I. A person has either two identical alleles (homozygous) or two different alleles (heterozygous). The result is six possible genotypes, but four possible phenotypes:

Genotypes	Phenotypes
$I^A I^A$	A
$I^A I^O$	A
$I^B I^B$	B
$I^B I^O$	B
$I^A I^B$	AB
$I^O I^O$	O

It is straightforward to predict which genotypes and phenotypes are possible in offspring of parents whose ABO blood groups are known. For example, group O parents will have O offspring only. A group O parent and a group AB parent are likely to have equal numbers of offspring of A or B group, and so on.

One busy night in a maternity unit (understaffed, and with the nurses distracted by 'returns' to the hospital administrators, as it happened), the identities of the parents of four babies born were confused.

The children belonged to groups A, B, AB and O.

The parents were as follows:

Mr and Mrs Come	A × B
Mr and Mrs Door	B × O
Mr and Mrs Exit	O × O
Mr and Mrs Fire	AB × O

Explain how you can show which couples are the parents of which children.

28.11 Quick test

1 Distinguish between the following pairs:

  a discontinuous variable and continuous variable;
  b mode and mean;
  c gamete and zygote;
  d monohybrid cross and dihybrid cross;
  e gene and allele;
  f dominant and recessive;
  g genotype and phenotype;
  h homozygous and heterozygous;
  i probability and chance;
  j codominance and incomplete dominance;
  k linkage and crossing over;
  l X and Y chromosomes;
  m multiple alleles and multiple gene action (polygenes);
  n epistasis and pleiotropy;
  o euploidy and aneuploidy.

2 What do you understand by the following?

  a standard deviation;
  b the Law of Segregation;
  c binomial expression;
  d Punnett squares;
  e test cross;
  f null hypothesis;
  g chi-squared test;
  h the chromosome theory;
  i the Law of Independent Assortment;
  j mutation;
  k pedigree chart;
  l sex linkage;
  m gene mapping of chromosomes;
  n autosomal chromosomes;
  o environmental effects on the phenotype.

28.12 Essay assignment

Select one of the following:

- By reference to specific examples, describe the special achievements of Gregor Mendel as a scientist. To what aspects of his approach to investigation may we attribute his particular achievements?

or:

- a Explain what is meant by 'linkage' in the study of inherited characteristics. By means of a specific example, explain how linkage is detected.
  b How are 'gene maps' established, and what value may they have in practical genetics?

29 Applications of genetics

Summary

Early in human history, in the process of breeding domesticated species of plants and animals, people unwittingly began to manipulate the genetic constitution of organisms. Today, a new type of genetic manipulation, genetic engineering or **recombinant DNA technology**, has been developed. In this process genes from one organism are introduced into the genome of an unrelated organism. The result is new varieties, mostly of microorganisms, which are then used in the manufacture of useful substances by **biotechnological processes**, such as fermenter technology.

Recombinant DNA technology exploits bacterial enzymes of a specialised nature, including **restriction enzymes**, which cleave double-stranded DNA into shorter lengths. Cleavage occurs at particular DNA sequences, four to eight bases long. Where the 'cut' is staggered, leaving short, single-stranded DNA exposed, the ends are called **'sticky'**. Then exposed strands of DNA that are complementary (permit pairing of bases) can be joined together, using another enzyme, **ligase**. Genes that have been cut out of a long strand of DNA (from a human chromosome, for example) are transported by attachment to a bacterial plasmid or a virus into the genotype of another organism.

The human gene for **insulin** manufacture has been isolated and transferred via a plasmid into a bacterium, and the engineered bacteria are cultured in fermenters in order to manufacture insulin for the treatment of diabetes. **Transferring genes into eukaryotes** is more difficult, but yeast has been used successfully. The bacterium *Agrobacterium tumifaciens* (a prokaryote), which induces tumour growths in higher plants, has also been used to introduce new genes into its host plant. Engineering of genes into mammals is attempted both by direct injection of cloned genes into mouse egg cells, and by 'adding' a cloned gene to cells (such as liver cells or bone marrow cells) that have been extracted and can be returned to the body to multiply, after being genetically engineered.

Another, more traditional, application of genetics is in **population genetics**. This is concerned with the frequency of phenotypes and genotypes in large populations, and seeks to determine whether the laws of Mendelian inheritance apply to genes in populations. The **Hardy–Weinberg principle** establishes that, in large, randomly mating populations, genes and genotype frequencies normally remain constant. It also permits the detection of disturbances that alter the composition of a gene pool, such as migration, mutation and **selection**.

Artifical selection is the principle in selective breeding by which humans have been able to produce new varieties of plants and animals for use in agricultural production. The process involves the crossing of different varieties, and then selecting the progeny with the special features desired, from which to breed further. Plant and animal breeders may work in laboratories, but are just as likely to be involved in 'field trials' on experimental farms.

Practicals and activities

29.1 Resources for learning recombinant DNA technology

(Demonstration)

Recombinant DNA technology (popularly known as 'genetic engineering') involves the extraction and isolation of DNA, which may be attempted in a school or college laboratory (Practical 9.4, p. 122). Many of the subsequent steps of recombinant DNA technology are too time-consuming, however, or require too specialised resources, to be practised at this level. Nevertheless, the processes involved may need to be understood. Below are reviewed resources for learning that can provide new insights at this level.

Manipulating DNA by Dr E J Wood, University of Leeds, for the Biochemical Society, available from Portland Press (p. 434). This 60-minute video deals with the 'cutting' of DNA by the use of restriction enzymes, electrophoretic separation of DNA fragments on agarose gels, amplification of DNA fragments (such as genes) using the polymerase chain reaction, and cloning, by which fragments of DNA are inserted into a bacterial plasmid and re-inserted inside a bacterium. Thus a manipulated gene is made available for possible exploitation in the commercial production of proteins.

Recombinant DNA Technology – Guidance Notes for A Level Biology no 7, by Dr P Moore for the Biochemical Society, available from Portland Press (p. 434), is a 40-page booklet that deals first with the fundamentals of recombinant DNA technology, explaining how DNA is isolated, the role of restriction endonuclease, separation and identification of DNA fragments, amplification and the location of specific genes. The other major chapter of the booklet reviews the applications of genetic engineering in health, agriculture, food and drink industries, the environment and forensic science. Finally, practical work is outlined, and there is a bibliography.

29.2 Plant protoplasts

(Skills and techniques)

Plant cell walls are rigid structures and, incidentally, effective barriers to the introduction of new genes in the 'genetic engineering' of plants. Plant cell walls can, however, be removed by enzyme action. Once the wall has gone, the naked protoplast can be cultured in an aqueous medium, provided the water potential of the medium is adjusted to that of the cell cytoplasm. Protoplasts may be fused together to make hybrid cells, or new genes may be introduced by means of plasmids from the soil bacterium *Agrobacterium* (*Advanced Biology*, pp. 641–2). Protoplasts may quickly regrow a wall. A whole new plant may be regenerated in this way, by division of this genetically engineered cell.

The cell wall removal technique has also been applied to bacteria and to fungi, for much the same reasons.

■ Aim

To practise plant protoplast technology.

■ Risk assessment

- Take care in the use of the high-speed centrifuge.
- Enzyme preparations are proteins that may cause allergic reaction in susceptible people. Any spilt enzyme solutions should be mopped up immediately, using excess water.
- Otherwise, good laboratory practice will be sufficient to take account of any hazards and avoid significant risks.

■ Method

Equilibration of water potential

In this step, the cells of the lettuce are brought into osmotic equilibrium with 13% sorbitol solution.

1. Prepare the lettuce tissue by cutting leaves into approximately 0.5 cm squares.
2. Place about 20 lettuce leaf squares into 9 cm^3 of 13% sorbitol solution, and incubate this mixture in a water bath at 37 °C for five minutes.

Digestion of cell walls

A mixture of enzymes capable of digesting wall polysaccharides is used to break down the cell walls.

3. Add 0.5 cm^3 of the carbohydrase preparation to the sorbitol/lettuce leaf squares, and maintain the mixture in the water bath for a further 20 minutes. Gently shake the tube to mix the components periodically.

Isolation and examination of protoplasts

Centrifugation is used to isolate naked protoplasts.

4. Pack the nylon gauze provided into the neck of the filter funnel.
5. Stand the funnel in a test tube, retained in the test-tube rack. Pour the digested lettuce leaf mixture into the funnel, and collect the filtrate.
6. Wash free any trapped protoplasts in the residue retained on the nylon gauze (cell wall debris), using 10 cm^3 of 13% sorbitol solution.
7. Divide the filtrate equally between two centrifuge tubes, and place these in the centrifuge. Centrifuge the suspension for five minutes at 2000 rpm.
8. Discard the supernatant liquid from the centrifuge tubes and drain the pellet of protoplast dry of any remaining supernatant liquid.
9. Resuspend the pellet in 0.1 cm^3 of 21% sucrose solution, using a fine paint brush.
10. Mount a small drop of protoplast suspension on a microscope slide and examine it under the microscope, using medium- and high-power magnification.

References

T Storr (1985) *Plant Tissue Culture*. Experiments with Industry series no 13, Association for Science Education

This practical has been adapted from 'Plant protoplast', in:

National Centre for Biotechnology Education (1993) *Practical Biotechnology – a Guide for Schools and Colleges*, pp. 10–11. University of Reading (p. 434)

NOTE TO TECHNICIAN

Each student requires (or requires access to):
- microscope (with medium- and high-power objectives), with bench lamp if necessary;
- fine forceps, fine scissors, tissue papers, microscope slides, coverslips;
- fresh, round, green lettuce (each group requires one leaf);
- 21% sucrose solution (each group requires 0.5 cm^3);
- 20 cm^3 of 13% sorbitol solution (also available from pharmacists as 'sugar for diabetics');
- carbohydrase enzyme mixture Novo *Viscozyme* (each group requires 0.5 cm^3), available from National Centre for Biotechnology Education (p. 434);
- graduated pipettes (1 cm^3 and 10 cm^3) with safety bulb, or disposable plastic syringes (1 cm^3 and 10 cm^3);
- test tube, rack, glass filter funnel;
- strip of nylon gauze, about 10 × 5 cm;
- water bath at 37 °C, containing submerged metal test-tube racks;
- bench centrifuge.

■ Data presentation

- Make a record of the steps in protoplast isolation, noting the exact conditions used.
- Make an annotated sketch of the protoplasts, as viewed under high-power magnification.
- Produce a matrix to record the visible changes to protoplasts in a range of sucrose solutions.

■ Conclusions

- Comment on the ease with which plant cell protoplasts can be isolated and handled, given the careful control of the osmotic environment.
- Why do plant cells require especially careful treatment in this procedure?

■ Evaluation

Why is it unnecessary to take special precautions against contamination by bacteria in this practical technique?

■ Extension

The plasma membrane is partially permeable. Protoplasts placed in an external solution of less-negative water potential (hypotonic solution) therefore become turgid and then burst, whereas in an external solution of more-negative water potential (hypertonic solution) the protoplasts shrink.

Mount drops of protoplast suspension in sucrose solutions of a range of concentrations, from 0.1 to 1.0 mol dm^{-3} sucrose, using microscope slides. Observe the effects on the protoplasts. Remember, the exact concentration of sucrose on the slides will vary, depending on the volume of protoplast suspension used.

29.3 Cloning of plants

(Skills and techniques/Investigation)

Cloning of plants is achieved by a technique called 'tissue culture'. In tissue culture, a few mature cells are taken from a plant, and cultured in such a way that causes division, growth and development to form all the specialised cells of an adult. The discovery that mature, unspecialised cells had this potential (we say they are 'totipotent') has been of great value in research and in agriculture and horticulture. For example, it permits hundreds of genetically identical individuals to be produced from a small part of one plant. It also allows aspects of development to be investigated experimentally.

The technique of tissue culture remains experimental, and the outcome often unpredictable. One requirement is the exclusion of contaminating bacteria and fungi, as far as this proves possible.

This extensive practical has been selected since it permits a significant 'investigation' to be built into an activity which might otherwise only involve the development of a laboratory skill, despite the investment of time and resources.

■ Aim

To develop the technique of plant tissue culture, and to investigate the effects of plant growth regulators on the induction of stem and root *in vitro*.

■ Risk assessment

- Wear eye protection, protective clothing and plastic gloves when working with 70% ethanol and 10% sodium chlorate(I) (hypochlorite) solution for seed-surface sterilisation, and also when handling plant growth regulators in concentrated powder form.
- Otherwise, good laboratory practice will be sufficient to take account of any hazards and avoid significant risks.

■ Method

The technique of tissue culture using *Brassica* sp. seedlings involves three steps:

Germination of surface-sterilised seeds

1 Surface-sterilise about 10 seeds in a small screw-cap bottle, by immersing them in 70% ethanol for three minutes, washing in sterilised water, immersing in 10% sodium chlorate(I) for 15 minutes and, finally, washing in three or four changes of sterilised water.

2 Using Sterile forceps, transfer the seeds to the surface of the sterile germination medium (agar) in a sterilised screw-top jar, and incubate for a week at a room temperature of about 20 °C, with 16 hours' illumination each day.

Isolation of tissue samples

3 When seedlings have grown sufficiently to show the features identified in Figure 29.1, use sterilised dissection tools to remove one seedling at a time, transfer it to a sterile Petri dish, and cut it into cotyledon, shoot apex, hypocotyl (upper, middle and lower parts) and upper root sections.

4 Immediately each part of the seedling ('explant') is isolated, transfer it to the surface of the culture medium in a sterilised, labelled Petri dish. Each Petri dish will accommodate

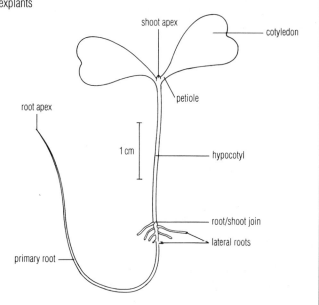

Figure 29.1 A *Brassica* seedling at a stage of growth suitable for taking explants

about 10 explants, except the one designated for cotyledons, which should contain five explants. Use culture medium dishes containing:
- no added plant growth regulator (control);
- added 'auxin';
- added kinetin;
- added auxin and kinetin.

Incubation of the explants

5 Incubate the Petri dishes, lids secured with sticky tape, at about 20 °C in 16 hours' illumination daily for between four and eight weeks.

6 Examine the dishes carefully at intervals, using a hand lens when appropriate. Look for evidence of callus growth, and the appearance of new stem and root growth (Figure 29.2).

Figure 29.2 Hypocotyl and root explants, seven weeks after culture

Alternative approaches

Tissue culture of florets from the 'head' of a cauliflower (*Brassica oleracea* var. *botrytis*), or of cells from cut woody twigs, such as poplar twigs (*Populus* sp.), may be used in place of seedling explants.

References

National Centre for Biotechnology Education (1993) *Practical Biotechnology for Schools and Colleges* pp. 14–15 'Cloned cauliflower', and pp. 12–13 'Poplar tissue culture'. Department of Microbiology, University of Reading

P Freeland (1991) *Microorganisms in Action – Investigations*, 'Micropropagation: softwood cuttings', pp. 63–5. Hodder and Stoughton

T Storey (1985) *Plant Tissue Culture*. Experimenting with Industry no 13, Association for Science Education

M P Fuller and F M Fuller (1995) 'Plant tissue culture using *Brassica* seedlings', *J. Biol. Ed.* 29(1), pp. 53–9

NOTE TO TECHNICIAN

Each student group will require:

- sterilised, clean dissection equipment, including fine scissors, fine forceps;
- access to stocks of *Brassica* seeds, such as cauliflower or similar species;
- small, screw-top bottle;
- 10 cm^3 of 70% ethanol;
- 10 cm^3 of 10% sodium chlorate(I) (hypochlorite) solution;
- supply of sterilised distilled water;
- sterilised screw-top jar (such as a honey jar) containing sterilised germinating medium (25 cm^3 of 0.8% agar), cooled and solidified;
- sterile Petri dish for making explants;
- waterproof marker pen, Sellotape;
- sterilised Petri dishes containing sterile culture medium (see p. 431);
- Bunsen burner, heatproof mat, ethanol, for instrument sterilisation.

■ Data presentation

Set up a matrix to record observations (numerical data, annotated sketches, notes) on the developments observed in explants in the range of Petri dishes with culture media, with or without plant growth regulators.

■ Conclusion

What combination of exogenous plant growth regulators and explants demonstrates totipotency most effectively?

■ Evaluation

Why are 'aseptic techniques' essential to achieve a high level of success with explants of *Brassica* seedlings?

29.4 Resources for learning about genetics

(Demonstration)

The following resources are available to support learning about population genetics.

Genetic Disk, produced by Garland and supplied by AVP (p. 433), is a CAL package in four sections, one of which is concerned with population genetics. This is a simulation based on the Hardy–Weinberg Law, demonstrating the stability of gene pools and gene frequencies in populations where breeding occurs at random. The effects of genetic drift in small populations, and of selection operating against genotypes and phenotypes, are presented. Available for Acorn Archimedes RISC OS, BBC B and Master computers.

The CAL program *Hardy–Weinberg*, from Cambridge University Press (p. 434), allows the effects of changes in genotype percentages and gene frequencies to be followed over generations. The effects of mutation, selection, migration and genetic drift are illustrated. Available for BBC B and Master computers.

A Change of Heart, a 50-minute BBC Video for Education and Training made in 1993, outlines the attempts to rear transgenic pigs for human organ transplants, and examines the ethical dilemmas that this initiative poses. Available for hire from the Video Loans Club, The Wellcome Centre for Medical Science (p. 434).

New Genes for Old (*Antenna*), a 30-minute BBC Video for Education and Training made in 1992, explains how gene therapy is likely to revolutionise certain areas of medicine. It describes the attempts of a team from St Mary's Hospital, London, led by Professor Bob Williamson, to incorporate a gene into human cells, to allow cystic fibrosis sufferers to make the protein their bodies lack. Available for hire from the Video Loans Club, The Wellcome Centre for Medical Science (p. 434).

29.5 Keeping in touch via the Internet

(Demonstration)

Very many fields of modern biology are changing rapidly, but those that have the most immediate, important applications in industry or medicine receive much attention in the media. Biotechnology and the applications of genetics are good examples of this. Here, research teams that develop and apply new ideas and processes vie with each other for recognition of achievement and public awareness of products. This activity generates sources of information, many of which may be excellent resources for learning. Increasingly, these sorts of materials are made available via the World Wide Web of the Internet. You may already be in a position to access these sources.

■ Aim

To introduce the Internet as a resource for learning or updating understanding of the application of genetics (and of biotechnology).

■ Risk assessment

Good laboratory practice will be sufficient to take account of any hazards and avoid significant risks.

■ Method

The Internet is a world wide network linking millions of users' computers via telephone lines, and includes servers which sort, store and distribute information. Each Web server has to be maintained by people who decide what to publish, and who ensure that material is written in a form that servers can understand. The outcome has been an explosion of access to information. Often, this information can be downloaded to your computer, evaluated at leisure, and important sources printed out as a resource for learning.

1 To make use of the Internet the following are essential requirements:
- a personal computer, whether as a 'stand alone' or networked, equipped with a mouse;
- a high-speed modem (a device that allows digital information from a computer to pass along telephone lines), rated at least 28 800 bps;
- a telephone line;
- a link with an Internet service provider, such as BT Campus World;
- appropriate software (such as 'Netscape') that includes a World Wide Web browser.

2 The Internet can be used to provide information in a number of ways. However, there are two main routes: by quoting a URL (Uniform Resource Location) address, or by using a 'search engine'.

3 Relevant examples of direct addresses are:
'Gene Web' (Address =
hhtp://ncet.csv.warwick.ac.uk/www/geneweb/index.html).
Gene Web is a resource for secondary students, schools and colleges. It provides information on genetics checked by scientists working in the relevant fields, is updated and revised regularly, and is interactive in the sense that you may e-mail Gene Web with ideas and suggestions.
This development is sponsored by Biotechnology and Biological Sciences Research Council, ICL Education Systems, Medical Research Council, National Council for Educational Research Technology, Nuffield Foundation, and the Wellcome Trust. It is co-ordinated by Neil Ingram, a teacher at Clifton College, Bristol.
'NCBE resources on the Web' (Address =
http://www.reading.ac.uk/NCBE).
The National Centre for Biotechnology Education (NCBE) materials are now published electronically. Many of the NCBE materials on the Web are Portable Document Format (PDF) files, so that the high quality of the visual presentations are maintained whatever microcomputer you use. These files can be downloaded, too, but a copy of the *Adobe Acrobat®* reader program is needed. This is free of charge, and can be downloaded (**http://www.adobe.com/**).

4 Examples of a 'search engine' operation:
The procedures can be *demonstrated using Netscape* software, **but the process described is not intended to be prescriptive; it is just a guide to getting started.**
In the Windows Program Manager double click on **Depot**. Enter your **User ID**, tab down a line, enter your **Password** and click **OK**.
Click on **Utilities** and on **Internet** from the menu displayed. Netscape Home Page will eventually be displayed. (Avoid searching the Internet during the mid-afternoon because that is when the majority of USA users join the system.)
On the Netscape Home Page click **Directory** and click **Internet Search** from the menu displayed. Eventually various search engines are offered (e.g. **Yahoo, Lycos, WebCrawler**).
For these trial runs, click on **Yahoo**.

a When asked for a search word, type in **GENETICS** and then click on **Search**. Once into a search it is important to keep strictly to your aim. (The matches listed will include 'interest groups', museums or genetics laboratories.) Click **Science: Biology: Genetics**. The range of sites will be limited and focused. Some files can be downloaded to your hard or floppy disk (use **Save As**). Later, when not on-line, they may be edited and printed.
You can log the pathway you have used (go into **Bookmark** to save the address of any page used), or print out a list of the pages you have visited (called a **Go list**).
Use the **'Exit'** button to shut down at the end of your search.

b Alternatively, type **BIOTECHNOLOGY** and then search for **Novo Nordisk**. Novo Nordisk is a large biotechnology company that has a Home Page offering lots of information. For example, click the hyperlink word **Enzyme**, and you will be offered more information.
Select **What is an enzyme?** As this is a long document, download it to a floppy disk (again, use **Save As** in **File Menu**, give the file a title and check it is saved in drive **A**).
Next click on **Pulp and Paper**, and repeat the downloading procedure, using a different file name.
There is information here about the uses of industrial enzymes in paper manufacture, beneficial from the environmental viewpoint, not currently available in most textbooks. Later, use a word processor to print out the files, after you have edited them, to provide specific information for your coursework, long essay or project, perhaps.

NOTE TO TECHNICIAN

The essential equipment (with the exception of a Printer) is listed above.

■ Data presentation

You may choose to print out the sources you have identified, taking care to acknowledge your sources.

■ Conclusion

What have you obtained that was not available to you via 'yesterday's' technology? How can the Internet be best exploited to be useful, once the novelty value has evaporated?

■ Evaluation

You can exchange information via *e-mail*, contacting other schools and colleges around the world. Links may be developed by reference to the Association for Science Education (ASE)/BP 'Science Across the World' project. Funding of links between schools and colleges in Europe may be available from the European Union (via their 'Socrates' programme, for example).

References

P McBride (1995) *The Internet Made Simple*. Made Simple Books
P Moore (Ed) (1995) *Teaching and Learning with the Internet*. British Telecommunications

Projects

Project ideas relating to the applications of genetics are to be found in Chapters 28 and 30.

Problems and assignments

29.1 Recombinant DNA technology

1 Read the following passage on recombinant DNA technology, and make a list of the most appropriate word or words to fill the gaps numbered (i) to (x), to complete the passage.

Today, a type of genetic manipulation known as recombinant DNA technology, or ....(i)...., is in use. The extremely long ....(ii).... of DNA found in a eukaryotic nucleus are functionally divided into shorter lengths, the genes. In recombinant DNA technology, ...(iii).... from one organism are introduced into the genome of an unrelated organism.

The isolation of specific genes during genetic engineering involves forming eukaryotic DNA fragments. These fragments are formed using ....(iv).... enzymes, which make staggered cuts in the DNA within specific ....(v)..... This leaves single-stranded 'sticky ends' at each end. The same enzyme is used to open up a ....(vi)...., which consists of a circular loop of bacterial DNA which acts as a ....(vii).... for the eukaryotic DNA. The complementary sticky ends of the bacterial DNA are joined to the DNA fragment using another enzyme called ....(viii)..... Finally new DNA is introduced into host bacterial cells. The take-up process is achieved by 'zapping' the cells with a ....(ix)...., which causes short-lived holes in the cell membrane that may let the plasmids in. This technique is known as ....(x)..... The engineered cells can then be cloned on an industrial scale, and large amounts of protein harvested.

2 Restriction enzymes cleave DNA at specific sites (that is, at particular base sequences). Two of the restriction enzymes frequently used to cut DNA are known as *Bam*H1 and *Eco*R1. The 'cuts' these enzymes make are staggered, leaving short, single-stranded DNA overhanging at the ends ('sticky ends'). These particular sticky ends are four bases long in the case of *Bam*H1 and two bases long in the case of *Eco*R1.

a Figure 29.3 shows in diagrammatic form strands of the base sequences recognised by each enzyme, that of BamH1 on the left, and that of EcoR1 on the right.
Copy Figure 29.3. Complete the diagram by writing in the base sequence found on the complementary strands.

b BamH1 cuts the sugar–phosphate backbone between two guanine-based nucleotides. EcoR1 cuts the sugar–phosphate backbone between adenine-based nucleotides.

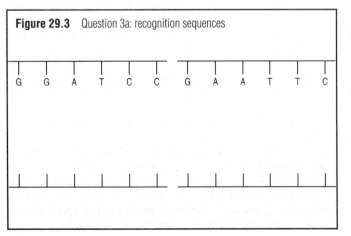

Figure 29.3 Question 3a: recognition sequences

| G | G | A | T | C | C | G | A | A | T | C |

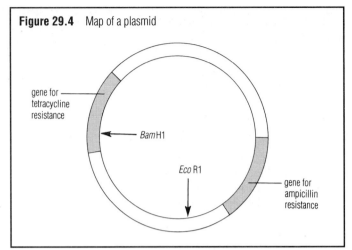

Figure 29.4 Map of a plasmid

gene for tetracycline resistance

*Bam*H1

*Eco*R1

gene for ampicillin resistance

Show on your diagrams the base sequences of the sticky ends produced by these enzymes by marking the cuts by dotted lines.

c Some restriction enzymes cut DNA to produce what are now called 'blunt ends'. Make a diagram of a blunt end cut, showing how it differs from a sticky end cut.

3 Figure 29.4 is a map of a plasmid showing the positions of the recognition sequences of the two restriction enzymes *Bam*H1 and *Eco*R1. The shaded areas represent genes for resistance to specific antibiotics, namely tetracycline and ampicillin.

a In an experiment to use this plasmid as the vector for the human insulin gene, why would the genetic engineer choose *Bam*H1 to cut the plasmid?

b What would be required, in addition to the human gene, to produce a recombinant plasmid?

4 Recombinant plasmids might then be 'zapped' into the bacterium *Escherichia coli*. How does the genetic engineer then isolate bacteria that contain the recombinant plasmid (and therefore the human gene) from other bacteria in the culture? Outline the key process in the separation procedure.

29.2 Insulin by genetic engineering

Study the text and annotated diagram in Panel 29.1, on the genetic engineering of insulin. Then, using the information given and your own understanding of the applications of genetics and human physiology, answer the following questions.

1 a Where in the human body is insulin produced? What triggers its release into the bloodstream?
b What different forms of diabetes occur?
2 In diabetics in which insulin of pig or cattle origin caused the production of antibodies, what was the insulin functioning as? Why was it possible for insulin from another mammal to have such an effect?
3 In very broad terms, what sort of changes would have to be made to pig insulin to cause it to be accepted in a human's body without causing unfavourable reactions?
4 Insulin consists of 'two polypeptide chains linked by disulphide bridges'.
a Explain what this means.
b What are the 'building blocks' of a polypeptide? How are they combined together?
c What constitutes a disulphide bridge and what is it formed from?

Panel 29.1 Insulin by genetic engineering

The daily need for insulin to treat insulin-dependent diabetes is enormous, for more than two million people across the world are afflicted with this disease. Insulin was for many years obtained from pancreases taken from cattle and pigs in slaughterhouses. But insulins from these species are subtly different from human insulin. As a consequence, some patients produce antibodies against the insulin they receive, resulting in the destruction of the hormone in the bloodstream before the body can use it. Two alternative sources of acceptable insulin exist at the moment.

Firstly, a biotechnological firm in Denmark has developed an economical process for the conversion of pig insulin into human insulin, using conventional chemical techniques. The available supply of pig insulin is insufficient to meet all demands, however.

Secondly, an American drug firm has devised a method of producing insulin by recombinant DNA tech-

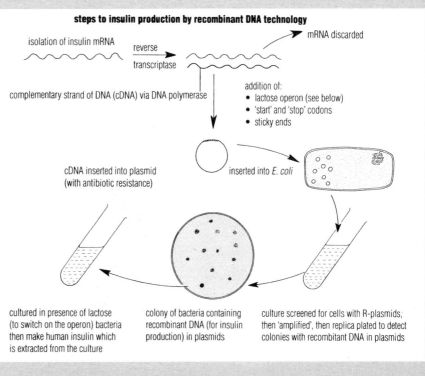

steps to insulin production by recombinant DNA technology

isolation of insulin mRNA

reverse transcriptase

mRNA discarded

complementary strand of DNA (cDNA) via DNA polymerase

addition of:
• lactose operon (see below)
• 'start' and 'stop' codons
• sticky ends

cDNA inserted into plasmid (with antibiotic resistance)

inserted into *E. coli*

cultured in presence of lactose (to switch on the operon) bacteria then make human insulin which is extracted from the culture

colony of bacteria containing recombinant DNA (for insulin production) in plasmids

culture screened for cells with R-plasmids; then 'amplified', then replica plated to detect colonies with recombitant DNA in plasmids

nology (see below). Insulin consists of two polypeptide chains (A and B), linked by disulphide bridges. The polypeptides are 'engineered' separately, and later brought together to make active insulin.

Production of the polypeptides involves exploiting a reverse transcriptase enzyme obtained from a retrovirus.

From: C J Clegg with D G Mackean (1994)
Advanced Biology. *John Murray*

---

5 a What is a retrovirus? To what use is reverse transcriptase put in the virus's life cycle?
  b What do you understand by the 'central dogma' of molecular biology? Why does the existence of reverse transcriptase appear to contradict it?
6 a What does the abbreviation 'mRNA' stand for?
  b From which tissue in the human body would a genetic engineer expect to obtain mRNA that codes for insulin?
7 a What are 'plasmids'? Where do they occur? Why are they especially useful in genetic engineering?
  b Why are plasmids with a gene or genes for antibiotic resistance often selected by genetic engineers for their experiments and procedures?
8 What are the main steps by which complementary DNA (cDNA) may be introduced into an appropriate bacterium, and then used to produce an excess of insulin for use in medicine?

29.3 Transgenic plants

Transgenic plants carry 'foreign' genes and express these genes during their life cycle. The first transgenic plants were produced by using a soil bacterium, called *Agrobacterium tumifaciens*. This bacterium can infect plants that have been injured (perhaps partially grazed by a soil-living slug, for example). The bacterium causes the plant cells around the wound to grow abnormally, forming a tumour

or 'gall'. This occurs because the bacterium contains a plasmid (Ti plasmid) that carries a gene for tumour formation. Further, part of the plasmid becomes incorporated into one of the host plant's chromosomes. Genetic engineers exploit this natural invasion of a host plant to introduce new genes, and then cultivate the transformed plant (Figure 29.5).

Study the illustration and, using the information given and your own understanding of genetic engineering principles, answer the following questions.

1 If undamaged plants are not normally infected by *Agrobacterium tumifaciens*, what may we conclude about the soil bacterium and its natural hosts?
2 What are the specific effects on the host cells of the genes that are naturally introduced from the bacterium, following an infection by *Agrobacterium*?
3 What are the fundamental differences in the genetic material of a prokaryote such as *Agrobacterium* and that of a host plant (eukaryote)?
4 What general properties of plasmids make them particularly useful to the genetic engineer?
5 What are the steps to 'modification' of Ti plasmids in order to achieve genetic engineering of a flowering plant host?
6 The tumour tissue from a plant infected with modified plasmid is cultured to produce a new, transgenic plant. How is this carried out? What substances must be supplied to the cultured tumour cells to induce the production of an independent plant?

Figure 29.5 Production of genetically engineered plants using Ti plasmids

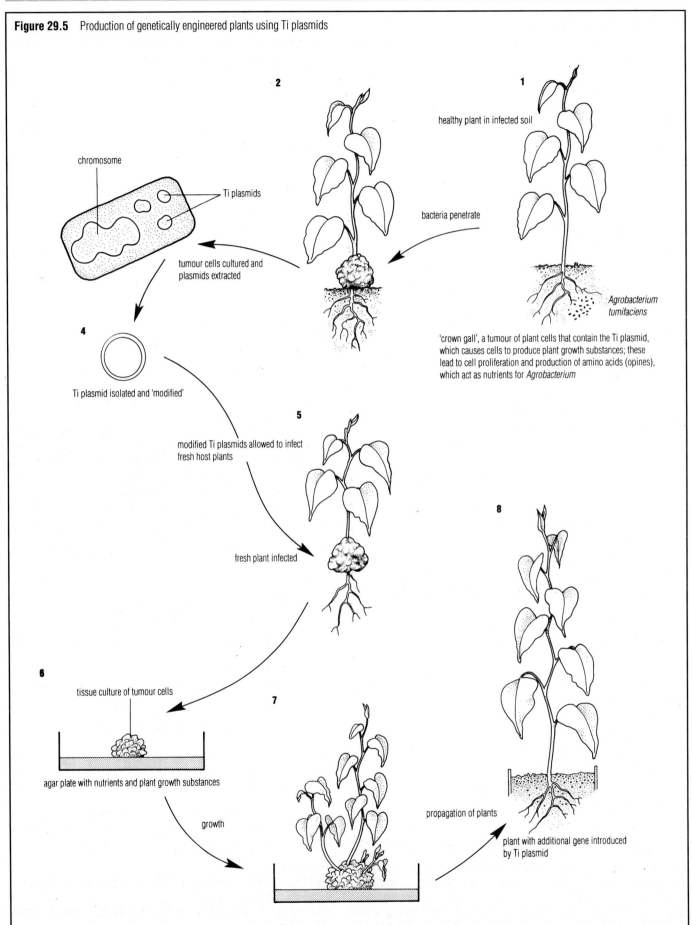

2

chromosome

Ti plasmids

tumour cells cultured and
plasmids extracted

1

healthy plant in infected soil

bacteria penetrate

*Agrobacterium
tumifaciens*

'crown gall', a tumour of plant cells that contain the Ti plasmid,
which causes cells to produce plant growth substances; these
lead to cell proliferation and production of amino acids (opines),
which act as nutrients for *Agrobacterium*

4

Ti plasmid isolated and 'modified'

5

modified Ti plasmids allowed to infect
fresh host plants

fresh plant infected

8

6

tissue culture of tumour cells

agar plate with nutrients and plant growth substances

growth

7

propagation of plants

plant with additional gene introduced
by Ti plasmid

7 This technique has been used to engineer a gene for herbicide resistance into crop plants.

  a How can such a gene be exploited commercially in agriculture and horticulture?

  b What possible hazards may arise from the technique of genetic engineering by this approach?

29.4 Cystic fibrosis

Cystic fibrosis, the most common serious genetic disease among Caucasians, is due to an autosomal recessive allele, and people suffering from the disease are homozygous for the allele. Affected persons produce mucus that is thick and unable to flow, and they suffer with problems in their lungs, in the pancreas and at the gut lining.

A gene on chromosome 7 encodes for a membrane protein of about 1500 amino acid residues. The protein appears to function as a membrane ion channel in epithelial cells, allowing the proper transport of ions and water across membranes. The mutation of this gene which causes cystic fibrosis interferes with the normal functioning of these channels by preventing the protein from binding with ATP.

The mutation appears to occur at a low but steady rate, and very many people in the population are carriers of the mutated gene. The disease occurs among Caucasians at the rate of one affected person per 2000 live births. Most patients can be helped by daily physiotherapy and by other, less frequent treatments, and sufferers survive far longer than in earlier times. The main contribution of the genetic engineer to this problem is to attempt gene therapy, seeking to introduce healthy genes into epithelia where they can have significant effects.

Answer the following questions, on the basis of the above information and on your understanding of applied genetics:

1 What is meant by a 'genetic disease'?

2 a What do you understand by the term 'autosomal recessive allele'?

  b Let a = the cystic fibrosis allele, and A = the normal allele at this locus. Write down the genotypes of:

  i a carrier;

  ii the gametes a carrier produces;

  iii a cystic fibrosis patient;

  iv the gametes the patient produces.

3 Suggest why the disease of cystic fibrosis manifests symptoms:

  a in the lungs;

  b at the gut lining;

  c in the pancreas.

4 Explain why the failure of a membrane protein to bind to ATP may cause failure (non-function) of an ion channel.

5 a If, in the population, 1 in 20 people are heterozygous for cystic fibrosis, what is the probability that any two parents are both heterozygous?

  b The frequency of the cystic fibrosis allele a in Britain is 0.02. What is the expected frequency of people:

  i who are cystic fibrosis sufferers (aa)?

  ii who are unaffected (AA)?

6 The disease is unpleasant, with life-threatening features. Why do genetic diseases of this type not 'die out' quickly?

29.5 Genetic engineering raises ethical issues

The application of genetic engineering processes in medicine, veterinary science and biotechnology seems, on the face of things, to offer us a panacea for many problems associated with health and disease of people and their crops and livestock, and the productivity of the food chain, either immediately, or in the near future. For example:

- human hormones (insulin and growth hormone) derived from transgenic bacteria, and used to treat diabetes and pituitary dwarfism;
- the genetic engineering of crop plants to increase productivity, disease resistance or herbicide resistance;
- human proteins secreted in milk by transgenic sheep, and used to treat the lung disease emphysema;
- farm animals engineered to be more fertile, productive and disease-resistant;
- application of engineered animal hormones (such as bovine somatotrophin) to increase yield;
- human cell culture *in vitro*, for the production of cell products such as vaccines and blood clotting factors;
- human tissue culture for the supply of cells to repair damage (for skin grafting, for example, and in attempts to treat Parkinson's disease by implanting embryonic neural cells in the damaged area of the patient's brain);
- detection of genetic disease early in fetal life, leaving open the possibility of abortion;
- *in vitro* fertilisation and pre-implantation diagnosis of genetic defects;
- correction of genetic disorder by gene therapy, involving the introduction of autosomal genes in the treatment of a life-threatening disease such as cystic fibrosis.

1 From the list above, take two examples of genetic engineering issues with ethical implications. Research these examples to become clear about:

- the problem (for example, disease) or deficiency (for example, food shortage) concerned;
- the type of solution that has been suggested and/or developed.

2 Consider the following reservations held by some people concerning genetic engineering. In your opinion, are they relevant and pertinent points in general (that is, to all genetic engineering) or to one or both of the situations you are addressing?

- the principle that we should not tamper with 'nature' at all;
- the safety of the genetic engineering process, given the possibility of risk to other organisms and/or the environment;
- the possibility of animal suffering, as a result of these applications;
- the 'sanctity' of human life, particularly at the stage when an individual cannot consent.

3 Consider the position of a scientist who takes the research decisions in the issues you are considering, and whose efforts may make a breakthrough. This scientist is almost certainly under many pressures:

- to publish discoveries and establish a personal reputation;
- to sustain the good name of the university laboratory or commercial organisation involved;
- to patent discoveries or claim the commercial rights;
- to keep faith with his or her own values and standards, moral, religious and political.

4 Using a copy of the genetic engineering statements in Figure 29.6, select those relevant to the examples you are researching. Place the statements listed in order of acceptability to you, giving a reason for each.

5 Finally, put together the points you feel cause you to support or oppose the application of genetic engineering in the two examples you have worked on, presenting your points as a wall poster.

References

E Lucassen (1995) 'Teaching the ethics of genetic engineering' *J. Biol. Ed.* **29**(2), pp. 129–38

British Medical Association (1992) *Our Genetic Future.* Oxford University Press

Figure 29.6   Statements of acceptability of genetic engineering

Genetic engineering of microorganisms

It is acceptable to genetically engineer some organisms

It is acceptable to engineer bacteria so that they carry specific genes for use in the laboratory

It is acceptable to engineer bacteria so that they make human proteins for medical use

It is acceptable to release some genetically modified bacteria into the environment

It is acceptable to make genetically engineered bacteria for agricultural use as insecticides and pesticides

It is acceptable to use lipases produced by genetically engineered bacteria in washing powder

It is acceptable to use genetically engineered yeast in the baking of bread, if the consumer is informed

It is acceptable to use genetically engineered yeast in the baking of bread, even if the consumer is not informed

It is acceptable to genetically engineer microorganisms such as bacteria and yeast

It is acceptable to genetically engineer microorganisms, only if it is completely safe to do so

Genetic engineering of plants

It is acceptable to genetically engineer some organisms

It is acceptable to make transgenic plants

It is acceptable to make transgenic plants which are resistant to herbicides, so that more herbicides can be used to eliminate unwanted weeds

It is acceptable to release some transgenic plants into the environment

It is acceptable to make transgenic plants with improved protein content for human or animal consumption

It is acceptable to make transgenic plants which are resistant to destructive pests

It is acceptable to sell genetically engineered vegetables for human consumption without informing the consumer

It is acceptable to sell genetically engineered vegetables for human consumption, if the consumer is informed that the product has been genetically engineered

It is acceptable to make transgenic plants which are more economic because they are easier to ship

It is acceptable to make transgenic plants which make pharmaceuticals for treatment for human disease

Genetic engineering of animals

It is acceptable to genetically engineer some organisms

It is acceptable to genetically engineer animals

It is acceptable to make transgenic sheep that are resistant to attack by blowfly larvae, which burrow into a sheep's skin and can create wounds that leave the animal open to infection

It is acceptable to make transgenic sheep that have more wool than traditional breeds, so that farmers can make the same profit with half as many sheep

It is acceptable to make transgenic sheep that make pharmaceutical proteins in their milk

It is acceptable to make transgenic mice that carry genes causing cancer, in order to study cancer and develop and test cures

It is acceptable to use traditional selective breeding to improve yield of animals, even if it results in crippled broiler chickens and bulls that cannot mate because of their shape

It is acceptable to sell meat from genetically engineered animals for human consumption without informing the consumer

It is acceptable to sell meat from genetically engineered animals for human consumption, if the consumer is informed

It is acceptable to patent transgenic animals

Genetic engineering and human disease

It is acceptable to genetically engineer some organisms

It is acceptable to make transgenic mice which carry genes causing cancer, in order to study cancer and develop and test cures

It is acceptable to correct a faulty gene in the somatic cells of a person suffering from a painful or fatal disease

It is acceptable to put a new gene into an egg or sperm cell which is known to carry a faulty gene

It is acceptable to make transgenic sheep that make pharmaceutical proteins in their milk

It is acceptable to engineer bacteria so that they make human proteins for medical use

It is acceptable for parents to choose to terminate a pregnancy, if prenatal testing indicates the fetus has a genetic defect

It is acceptable to terminate a pregnancy, if prenatal tests indicate that the fetus has some trait (other than disease) which the parents find undesirable

It is acceptable to select for the sex of a fetus, if the fetus is at risk of a sex-linked disease

It is acceptable to carry out pre-implantation diagnosis and to discard any embryos which carry genetic defects

Figure 29.7   Materials for role play about genetic disorders

1	male
CF	CARRIER
DMD	NORMAL
HD	NORMAL

1	female
CF	CARRIER
DMD	NORMAL
HD	NORMAL

2	male
CF	NORMAL
DMD	NORMAL
HD	NORMAL

2	female
CF	NORMAL
DMD	CARRIER
HD	NORMAL

3	male
CF	NORMAL
DMD	NORMAL
HD	AFFECTED

3	female
CF	NORMAL
DMD	NORMAL
HD	NORMAL

Worksheet 2

Having identified the genetic disease in your at-risk family, read the relevant sheet and make yourself aware of the problems. Discuss these with your spouse.

Decision 1   *Will we have any children? Give reasons for your decision.*

_____

_____

If you decided to have children, work out the probability of them suffering from the particular genetic disease.

_____

Decision 2   *Will we have a prenatal diagnosis test? Give reasons.*

To find out the result of the prenatal diagnosis test, ask your teacher, making sure that you identify the possible nature of the disorder.

Decision 3   *Will we abort the fetus? Give reasons.*

_____

_____

Worksheet 1

1   You have selected a male/female card. Don't worry if it is not the correct sex!
On this card information is provided regarding your gene status for three severe diseases – cystic fibrosis, Duchenne muscular dystrophy and Huntington's disease.

2   Look for a partner, that is, someone who has a card of the same colour as yours but of the opposite sex. The two of you are now husband and wife (for the duration of this game!).

3   Compare your card with that of your spouse to find out what combinations of genes occur.

Cystic fibrosis (CF) is an autosomal recessive trait, that is, only children with the homozygous recessive condition will develop the disease.

Q1   What would be the status of parents whose offspring are at risk of developing CF?

_____

Duchenne muscular dystrophy (DMD) is a sex-linked recessive trait, so sufferers are male. No gene for DMD occurs in the Y chromosome.

Q2   What would be the status of parents whose offspring are at risk of developing DMD?

_____

Huntington's disease (HD) is an autosomal dominant trait, the condition only appearing later on in life.

Q3   What would be the status of parents whose offspring are at risk of developing HD?

_____

Q4   Are there any gene combinations between you and your spouse which could cause possible problems? If so, what are they?

_____

Cystic fibrosis

This is a serious genetic disease. It is the most frequent autosomal recessive disorder in white (Caucasian) children. The main symptoms are due to abnormalities of several exocrine secretions.

It mainly affects the lungs and the pancreas, causing recurrent chest infections and poor absorption of food. The thick sticky mucus produced by the bronchi is particularly serious because it is difficult to cough up, so that recurrent chest infections like pneumonia occur. Each bout of infection leaves the lungs slightly more damaged than before so that the child's health deteriorates. Treatment with antibiotics and vigorous chest physiotherapy cannot prevent such episodes but it can help to resolve them.

The pancreas becomes blocked by sticky secretions so that it fails to produce digestive juices in adequate amounts, leading to chronic diarrhoea, poor weight gain and ill-health.

Males are infertile because of abnormal mucous secretions in the vas deferens. The loss of chlorides in the sweat can be severe enough to cause heat prostration in warm weather.

In the UK, cystic fibrosis (CF) affects about one child in every 2000 births. It has been estimated that about one person in 20 is a heterozygote carrier of the CF gene. The risk that a carrier of CF will mate with another carrier is about one in 400. Since children with such recessive traits as CF have normal (heterozygote) parents, usually the only families that can be recognised and studied are those where there is already one affected child.

Even if parents consider themselves unrelated, they may have common ancestry within the past few generations, especially if they are of closely similar ethnic or geographical origin.

No cure for this disease exists at present, although heart/lung transplant operations can be of help. A prenatal diagnosis test is now available.

Duchene muscular dystrophy

Muscular dystrophy covers a group of hereditary disorders in which there is a slow but progressive degeneration of the muscles, usually in the thighs, calves or shoulders. Only two types of muscular dystrophy are sex-linked – Duchenne and Becker. Duchenne muscular dystrophy (DMD) is expressed in early childhood. It affects the young body and is usually noticeable by the time that the child begins to walk. It progresses so that by the time the child is 10 years old he/she is confined to a wheel-chair. Death usually occurs in the teens, so that sufferers don't normally live beyond the age of 20.

This recessive gene is located on the short arm of the X chromosome. The nature of the disease is such that the gene cannot be transmitted by males, since they are affected and often die before reaching reproductive age. It is transmitted by carrier (heterozygote) females who rarely show any symptoms of the disease.

DMD has one of the highest mutation rates measured in humans, being in the range of 1 in 10 000. No cure is available, but prenatal diagnosis and carrier detection are now possible.

Huntington's disease

This genetic disease was first described by Huntington in 1872 in an American of English descent; in fact the gene has spread from north-west Europe throughout the world.

Huntington's disease (HD) is an autosomal dominant trait, the gene being located on the short arm of autosome 4. Very few patients are new mutants since nearly all patients can be shown to have an affected parent – the presence of a family history is actually used as one of the diagnostic criteria.

The presence of the HD gene causes mental deficiency and abnormal jerking movements of the limbs beyond voluntary control (chorea). It begins at between 20 and 40 years of age and progresses to emaciation, exhaustion, dementia and eventually death, which comes as a result of secondary infections, heart failure or pneumonia. It has been called the 'most demonic of diseases' and in the past, many stories of demonic possession and witchcraft may have stemmed from Huntington sufferers' behaviour.

No cure is known, but a prenatal diagnosis test is available.

■ **Extension**

A related issue which raises major ethical issues is the diagnosis and possible treatment of genetic disorders. A 'role play' approach to raise awareness and involve individuals in the development of an informed personal position is outlined in the reference below. Forms of the cards, worksheets and information sheets are given in Figure 29.7.

Note: great sensitivity is needed here. There may be people present whose families have direct experience of these issues.

This exercise involves groups of individuals who receive a 'genetic card' identifying a risk of parenting offspring with one of three genetic disorders, namely cystic fibrosis, Duchenne muscular dystrophy and Huntington's disease. Using colour coding of the cards, 'male' and 'female' cardholders pair up and consider the 'at risk' situation presented to them, with the aid of further information in Worksheet 1. At this stage there are questions of a factual nature to be answered.

Then, difficult decisions about future parenting are presented in Worksheet 2, which supplies additional information in the form of Information sheets 1, 2 or 3, according to the genetic disorder being discussed.

Reference

W Gilbert and L Stefani (1993) 'Genetics – genetic disorders and diagnosis: a role play exercise', *J. Biol. Ed.* **27**(1), pp. 51–7

29.6 Population genetics and the Hardy–Weinberg equation

A breeding population of *Drosophila* was maintained over many generations, secure in a large tank, closed off from predators or other harmful influences. The population consisted of grey-bodied (wild-type) flies and some black-bodied flies. The latter genotype (gg) occurred at a frequency of only 0.09.

1 Assuming random mating occurs without any disturbance to the gene pool, what frequency of GG and Gg genotypes do you predict are present?
2 If this frequency were not found in practice, what processes might possibly be operating to disturb the composition of the gene pool?

29.7 Quick test

1 Distinguish between the following pairs:

  a genotype and genome;
  b restriction endonuclease and ligase;
  c 'blunt ends' and 'sticky ends';
  d a bacterial chromosome and a plasmid;
  e reverse transcriptase and DNA polymerase;
  f R-plasmid and recombinant plasmid;
  g introns and exons;
  h promoter sequence and termination sequence;
  i start and stop signals;
  j protoplast and plant cell;
  k gene therapy and genetic counselling;
  l genotype frequency and allele frequency;
  m mutation and migration;
  n inbreeding and outbreeding;
  o pure lines and hybrids.

2 Explain the importance of the following:

  a recombinant DNA technology;
  b gene probe;
  c plasmid amplification;
  d operon;
  e *Agrobacterium tumifaciens*;
  f genetic disease;
  g genetic fingerprinting;
  h gene pool;
  i Hardy–Weinberg Law;
  j artificial selection.

29.8 Essay assignment

Select one of the following:

• The challenges of genetic engineering are different when applied to prokaryotes and eukaryotes. Explain these differences, and why they arise. Give one example of successful genetic engineering of a prokaryote, and one relating to a eukaryote.

or:

• Gene frequencies of large populations of sexually reproducing organisms do not change, proving that matings occur at random. Explain why this is normally the case. In what circumstances is this statement incorrect?

30 Evolution

Summary

Evolution is our name for the processes that have transformed life on Earth from its earliest beginnings to the vast diversity of fossilised and living forms we know today. The idea of organic evolution has been proposed at various times in human history, but today it is linked to the name of **Charles Darwin** (1805–82), and to his theory of evolution by natural selection. The issue of evolution has at times been controversial, partly because it is impossible to 'observe' evolution directly. Indirect evidence for evolution has to be evaluated, instead.

The evidence for evolution comes from:
- **Biogeography:** the geographic distribution of living organisms. It shows that comparable habitats in different parts of the world are not populated by identical or closely related organisms. Distribution of organisms is **'discontinuous'**, often because species have appeared (evolved) in one area and subsequently dispersed, and flourished in favourable habitats elsewhere. Then organisms living in similar environments have acquired similar structures (**convergence**), although they are unrelated.
- **Palaeontology:** the study of earlier life forms from fossilised remains. The rocks in which fossils occur can often be dated quite precisely. We know when extinct forms lived, so they can be related in time.
- **Comparative anatomy:** the study of structural features of different organisms that are basically similar, and may share a common origin. Examples include the **adaptive radiation** of the pentadactyl limb of vertebrates, and of insect mouthparts.
- **Comparative physiology and biochemistry:** the biochemical analysis of different living things. The degree of difference between related groups (among the primates, for instance) suggests how closely organisms are related.
- **Artificial selection:** the study of domesticated plants and animals that now show marked differences from their wild counterparts. Artificial selection leads to changes in life form within relatively short periods.
- **Systematics:** the study of the classification of living things. The fact that organisms can be placed in groups that are clearly related to differing degrees is evidence for evolution.
- **Computer simulation:** the study of the effects of mutation of the genetic blueprint for 'organisms' on their form in subsequent generations. In this way the effect of genetic change on form is investigated.

There have been alternative theories concerning the mechanism of evolution.

In the **theory of the inheritance of acquired characteristics**, it was claimed that the small changes in individuals, resulting from their adaptation to the environment, have been passed on to their progeny, leading to change and new species with time. This hypothesis does not accord with our understanding of process of heredity.

In the **theory of natural selection**, it is the fact that organisms produce many more offspring than survive, yet the number of individuals of species stays remarkably steady over time, that is significant. There is an obvious 'struggle for existence'. The individuals of one generation are not identical; small changes are manifested, most with a genetic basis (that is, that can be inherited). The variants that have favourable characteristics are more likely to survive, and may pass on their advantageous features through their progeny.

If natural selection is the process by which evolution takes place, then how do new species continue to arise? **Speciation** occurs, for example, when local populations become isolated, and remain so for long periods. Changes in the gene pool arise (for example, by mutation) and are selected for (or against) in succeeding generations.

If organic evolution has occurred then we may anticipate that **life has evolved** from inorganic materials, that cells like those of prokaryotes have been assembled from simpler, self-replicating systems, that eukaryotic cells have evolved from prokaryotic cells, that multicellular plant and animal forms have developed from unicells, that vertebrate animals have evolved from non-vertebrates, and that humans evolved from other primates. Some of these hypotheses have substantial evidence to support them.

Practicals and activities

30.1 Fossil hunting

(Investigation)

When an organism dies its remains are almost always dismembered and eaten by browsers or scavengers, and/or destroyed by weather and by the activities of bacteria. Only rarely does part or all of an organism fall into water and sink into soft mud where decay is delayed. In a few instances such remains may become buried, and some may be gradually infiltrated by minerals that harden both soft tissues and skeletal matter. These remains are the potential fossils – the remains of earlier organisms, preserved in sedimentary rocks. Only a tiny proportion of organisms is fossilised, and very few of these fossils are ever exposed and then discovered. Nevertheless, the fossils that have been found are of great interest. It is one very important way that we know that life forms have changed in geological time.

■ Aim

To learn to observe fossils *in situ*, and to make an appropriate collection of samples, safely and sparingly.

■ Risk assessment

- Never work alone, but always in responsible groups. Leave a record of when and where you will be for others (teachers, tutors or families) to consult if necessary. Report in by phone as soon as possible, if your plans have to be changed.

- Many geologically interesting sites are especially hazardous. Visit only with an adult leader (parent, tutor, teacher or local expert), and always take special care and extra precautions at all times when working near deep or fast-flowing water, at rivers with steep sides, and on seashores where the land slope below cliffs is shallow and the tide comes in quickly. Special care is also needed on exposed rocky faces at cliffs or in quarries or 'cuttings' where there is a danger of falling rock. A hard hat must be worn in these situations, and you must never work immediately below a rock face.
- Do not damage walls, hedges or any type of fence by making holes in them. Close all gates.
- Conserve the countryside. Careless trampling, as well as over-zealous sampling and collecting, can destroy a site very quickly.

■ Method

Selecting sites

- Not all rocks contain fossils. Select suitable sites by consulting geological maps (geographical maps with superimposed details of the rocks forming the land below soil). Such maps normally indicate where fossils are typically found. Local experts, contacted through local natural history societies, may also give guidance and advice.
- Sedimentary rock 'exposures' worth visiting are found at quarries, inland rock outcrops, cliffs at rocky coastline sites, temporary holes and road-building sites, together with mining spoil heaps.
- At any site you propose to visit, check concerning the need for permission both to enter, and to collect there, and apply well in advance.

Equipment for an expedition

- The essential equipment includes the right footwear, outdoor and protective clothing for all possible weather conditions, and adequate food and drink provision.
- Your most important resources are your notebook and pencil, and a hand lens. A camera is extremely useful, if resources run to this. You need to be equipped with a strong bag to carry the tools and implements to be used, depending on the types of rocks and fossils to be found and the samples to be taken. These must be protected in newspaper, held in plastic bags with labels or other identification of the site of collection. Small and delicate samples are best isolated in a small collecting box.
- Geologists normally carry a geological hammer, chisels for removing specimens of hard rock, a strong knife and a small trowel, goggles for eye protection, and strong gloves. A compass/clinometer is essential.

Making observations and taking samples

- The sort of fossils that may be found at any location is best researched beforehand, so you have a clear idea of what to look for. The range of fossils is well illustrated in any good field guide (see below), which will also describe how to isolate a specimen.
- Only collect specimens where they are plentiful. Otherwise, make a record of what you see by a sketch, 'rubbing' or photograph.
- If you find a really large specimen, or one that is contained in a large boulder, seek the help of local experts. Valuable specimens can be ruined in the process of extraction, if tackled in the wrong way.

- Not all fossils have to be chiselled out of rock (see Panel 30.1) although most do.

References

Department of Education and Science (1989) *Safety in Outdoor Education*. HMSO
R Moody (1986) *Fossils; How to Find and Identify over 300 Genera*. Hamlyn

Panel 30.1 Iridescent fossils rise up

These pristine fossils were thrown up by a unique mud "volcano" discovered near Wootton Bassett in Wiltshire. The spring is a 10-metre-wide pool oozing grey mud from layers of Jurassic clay 20 metres below ground. It came to light during a survey by the local council which has asked English Nature to investigate the pool's scientific importance. Neville Hollingworth, secretary of the Natural Environment Research Council's earth sciences committee, says the fossils are the best preserved he has seen. 'You just stand there and up pops an ammonite,' he says. 'What makes the fossils so special,' he says, 'is that they retain their original shells of aragonite, a calcium-based mineral. The outsides also retain their iridescence,' says Hollingworth, 'and on the inside some of the bivalves still have their original organic ligaments.'

From: New Scientist *(7 October 1995), p. 10*

NOTE TO TECHNICIAN

The necessary equipment, maps and resources for a fossil hunt are listed in the 'Method' above. It is possible that some or all of the specialised items may be temporarily borrowed from parents with a geological background and training, or from local experts who are consulted.

■ Data presentation
- The individual notebook may be used to record 'finds' and discoveries by annotated sketches. Accurate map references should be added.
- Fossil samples should be cleaned and exposed; follow the procedures explained in an appropriate field guide. They can be displayed, along with an explanatory note about the organism and the geological period they represent, for the interest of a wider audience.

■ Conclusion
How do the fossils you found relate to what is known about life in the geological period they represent?

■ Evaluation
Do our schemes of classification of living things need to be able to accommodate all previous life forms, if 'classification' is to be truly representative of relationships?

30.2 Natural selection at work

(Investigation)

The land snail *Cepaea nemoralis* is common throughout the UK, with the exception of northern Scotland. The shell is extremely variable in its colour (brown, pink or yellow) and its banding (one to five bands, or bands absent) (Figure 30.1). Typically, the lip of the shell is brown, but in a few variants it is white. The colour and the banding features are both genetically controlled, and the situation is outlined in *Advanced Biology*, p. 631.

Among the many predators of land snails is the song thrush, *Turdus philomelos*. This bird brings the snails it finds to a suitable hard surface (stone, brick or concrete 'anvil'), and there repeatedly and noisily bangs the shell down until it breaks, and the animal within can be eaten. Snail shell fragments accumulate. Throughout spring and summer until early autumn, in gardens, on waste land, beside hedge and in woodland, the song thrush may be heard at work, which may help you find an anvil (Figure 30.2).

■ Aim
To obtain evidence for selective predation of snails, as an example of natural selection in local communities.

■ Risk assessment

- This study involves field observations and the collection of data in the field, probably at some distance from home, school or college. The risk assessment made for such work, described in Practical 3.1 (p. 19), must be consulted now.
- Always discuss and obtain approval for all that you are proposing to do in field studies, with teachers, tutors or supervisors at your school or college. Leave a record of your proposed plans and activities with them, and with a parent, relative or guardian.

■ Method

Range and distribution of Cepaea phenotypes
- Search for snails in contrasting terrestrial habitats, such as woodland, hedgerows, wasteland, gardens and grassland.

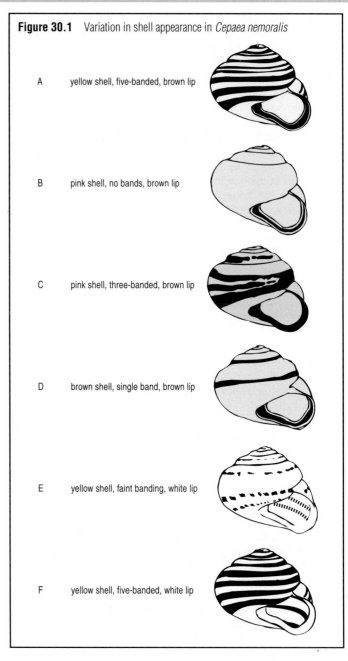

Figure 30.1 Variation in shell appearance in *Cepaea nemoralis*

A   yellow shell, five-banded, brown lip

B   pink shell, no bands, brown lip

C   pink shell, three-banded, brown lip

D   brown shell, single band, brown lip

E   yellow shell, faint banding, white lip

F   yellow shell, five-banded, white lip

Figure 30.2 An 'anvil' of *Turdus philomelos*

Find snails' microhabitats such as leaf litter, around compost heaps, on the undersides of leaves of herbaceous plants and shrubs, in crevices in trunks and walls, and between bricks and under stones.

- Make observations of the snails you can find, carefully noting and recording the phenotype and the precise microhabitat that each is found in.

Is predation selective or random?

- Locate thrushes' 'anvils' in habitats where you have found *Cepaea* to be plentiful.
- At each anvil, assess the numbers of shell fragments that you can ascribe to any one of the given phenotypes of *Cepaea nemoralis*.
- Note that there is a related species, *Cepaea hortensis*. This is almost as widespread in occurrence as *C. nemoralis*, is slightly smaller, and typically has a white lip. These snails are coloured yellow, usually with various forms of banding, highly reminiscent of those on *C. nemoralis*. Your data on predation are inadvertently likely to include members of this second species.
- Collect enough data to have confidence in the significance of the results.

Reference

E B Ford (1973) *Evolution Studied by Observation and Experiment*. Carolina Biology Reader no 55

NOTE TO TECHNICIAN

Each student group will require:
- clip board to record data;
- hand lens;
- plastic box with perforated lid to hold a temporary reference collection of the snail phenotypes. If these are living snails (rather than empty shells), they will need to be returned to their natural habitat quite quickly.

■ Data presentation

- Record your field results on the phenotypes and habitats in the form of a grid.
- Tabulate the data on predation of phenotypes for anvils located in contrasting habitats.

■ Conclusions

- Is there evidence that the colour and visibility of a population of *Cepaea* can be correlated with the predominant background coloration?
- Is there evidence that predation is random, or are certain phenotypes more vulnerable in particular habitats?

■ Evaluation

What statistical test should be applied to numerical data of this type, to increase your confidence?

30.3 Artificial selection in a Brassica species
(Investigation)

The wild plant rock cabbage (*Brassica oleracea*) is common throughout parts of Europe, typically found growing on rocky cliffs, often overlooking the sea. This single species has been genetically manipulated by humans (artificial selection) to produce several, distinctive horticultural varieties, each with heritable characteristics that are markedly different (Figure 30.3). These varieties are interfertile.

■ Aim

To investigate quantitatively the extent of modification of vegetative form brought about by artificial selection.

■ Risk assessment

- Take care when dividing tough, bulky plant material using a sharp knife.
- Otherwise, good laboratory practice will be sufficient to take account of any hazards and avoid significant risks.

■ Method

1 You are provided with a range of most or all of the following vegetable plants: cabbage, cauliflower, kohl rabi, broccoli, brussels sprouts and kale. Examine each to determine which parts of the aerial system (stems, leaves, flower buds, vegetative buds) have most evidently been selected for, during the artificial selection process.
2 Dismember each specimen in turn, separating the stem from vegetative leaves, flower buds and vegetative buds. Weigh and record the masses of all the component parts, using a top-pan balance.
3 You are provided with rooted seedlings of these varieties, germinated and grown for about three weeks, under greenhouse conditions. Examine the aerial systems of the different seedlings. Record your observations by means of annotated sketches.

NOTE TO TECHNICIAN

Each student group requires:
- hand lens, sharp knife, cutting surface, top-pan balance (accurate to 0.1 g);
- healthy, normal examples of 'greengrocer' specimens of the following vegetables: cabbage, kohl rabi, broccoli, brussels sprouts, kale;
- tray or trays containing rooted seedlings of these varieties, germinated and grown for about three weeks under greenhouse conditions.

■ Data presentation

- Record your data on the masses of the component parts of the vegetable varieties as a table (by means of a spreadsheet program, for example).
- Share your data with other student groups, to arrive at a mean value from a group of plants of each variety.
- Present the mean values of stem/leaf/vegetative buds/flower buds as a percentage of the total mass, using pie charts.
- Include your annotated drawings of the three-week seedling stages of these plants.

■ Conclusions

- Do most of the differences in vegetative development in these varieties appear before or after the three-week seedling stage?

Figure 30.3 Domesticated forms of *Brassica oleracea*, and a wild plant of the type from which they were originally bred

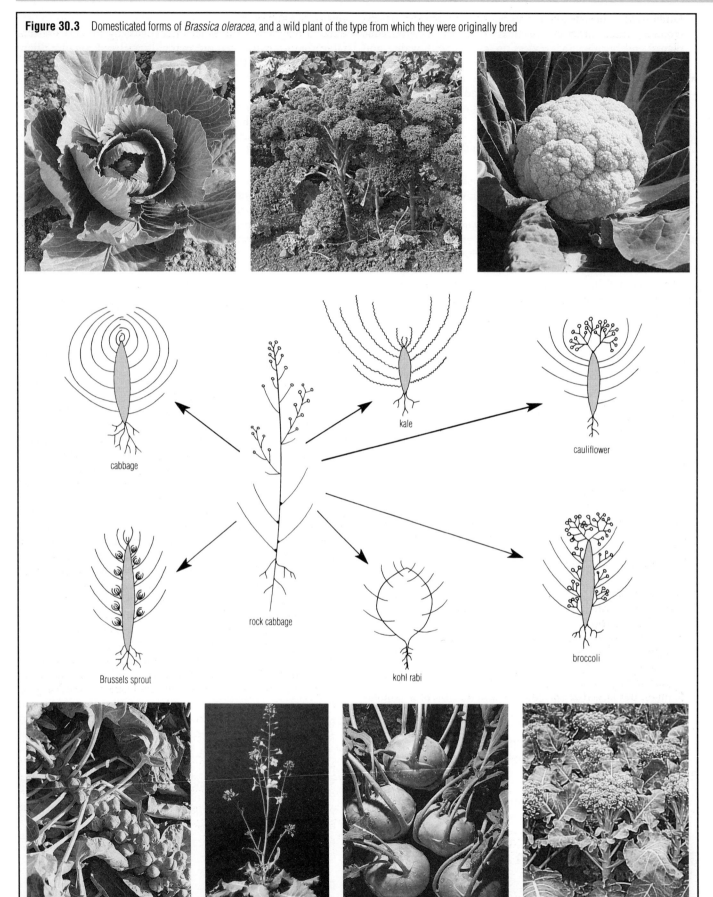

cabbage

kale

cauliflower

rock cabbage

Brussels sprout

kohl rabi

broccoli

- Explain why, despite their pronounced morphological differences, these varieties are held to be all of the same species.

■ Evaluation
Can you research information on when, where and how one or more of these varieties has been developed?

Reference
R N Jones and G K Rickards (1991) *Practical Genetics*. Open University Press

30.4 Evolution of human artefacts: a game
(Demonstration)

The nails, screws, tacks, pins, staples, rivets, fasteners, hook, grip and bolt illustrated in Figure 30.4 have been developed by humans over many years for 'fastening' or 'attaching'. They may be arranged in an 'evolutionary tree', designed to reflect the order in which the changes in structure may have occurred.

■ Aim
To appreciate the principles we may use in the establishment of evolutionary relationships.

■ Risk assessment
Good laboratory practice will be sufficient to take account of any hazards and avoid significant risks.

■ Method
- You are provided *either* with a photocopy of Figure 30.4 on card, cut into pieces to separate the individual drawings, *or* a collection of the 21 objects shown in the illustration. Examine each object carefully. Lay them out on a large sheet of white paper to form a possible evolutionary relationship.
- The smallest, simplest structure may suggest itself as the common ancestor.
- Normally, simpler forms give rise to more complex forms, and smaller forms give rise to larger forms, with occasional, notable exceptions.
- 'Organisms' that resemble each other in many ways may be more closely related than 'organisms' that have little in common.
- Evolution may progress by a large number of small or slight changes, but large (or abrupt) changes may occur from time to time.
- We may expect to discover divergence of closely related forms, but also convergence of distantly related forms. Parallel evolution may also be observed.

Reference
J A Barker (1984) 'Simulating evolution', *J. Biol. Ed.* 18(1), pp. 13–15

NOTE TO TECHNICIAN

Each student group requires:
- *either* a copy of Figure 30.4 on card, cut into pieces to separate the individual drawings, *or* a collection of the 21 objects shown there;
- large piece of white backing paper.

■ Data presentation
Make a diagram (evolutionary tree) showing the relationships you propose; mark the common ancestor, and annotate your flow diagram to identify where you detect divergence, convergence and parallel evolution.

■ Conclusion
If we consider this range of objects as a 'phylum', then can you identify two (or more) orders, and any clear families that have evolved?

■ Evaluation
- If the objects were living organisms, what features other than external morphology would you expect to use in determining evolutionary relationships?
- Several of these objects have very similar functions. Why are these similarities not suitable evidence for a degree of relatedness?

30.5 Resources for learning about evolution
(Demonstration)

The following resources are available to support learning about evolution:

CAL program *Blind Watchmaker*, produced by Software Production Associates and supplied by AVP and Philip Harris (pp. 433–4), is a program by Richard Dawkins of the Zoology Department, University of Oxford, and is introduced in Dawkins's book of the same name, published by Longman. The program demonstrates the way in which complex structures can arise from simpler forms by the accumulation of many small changes. The starting points are 'biomorphs' whose appearance is under the control of a small number of genes, and from which the student may carry out breeding experiments. A minor, random change (a mutation) occurs to one gene controlling the appearance of the biomorphs at every cross. As generations go by, the total of genetic difference from the original ancestors is very great. The progeny that 'breed' for the next generation are selected (by the student), however. Consequently, the cumulative change over the generations is not random. The effects of Darwinian 'natural selection' on variation are demonstrated. Available for IBM/PC clones, Apple Macintosh and Nimbus 186 microcomputers.

Fossil Heroes (*Antenna*) is a teaching video produced by BBC Videos for Education and Training, and was produced as a programme in 1992. It seeks to challenge the tendency to oversimplify the complex interrelationships between species that is sometimes encountered. Nevertheless, the relationship of the human to non-human species is articulated. Available for hire from the Wellcome Centre Video Loans Club (p. 434).

The video *Blind Watchmaker* (*Horizon*), also produced by BBC Videos for Education and Training and produced as a programme in 1987, presents Richard Dawkins asking the question: Did all living things come together by Darwinian natural selection, or was there an intelligent designer-God? Available for hire from the Wellcome Centre Video Loans Club (p. 434).

Figure 30.4 Evolution of human artefacts

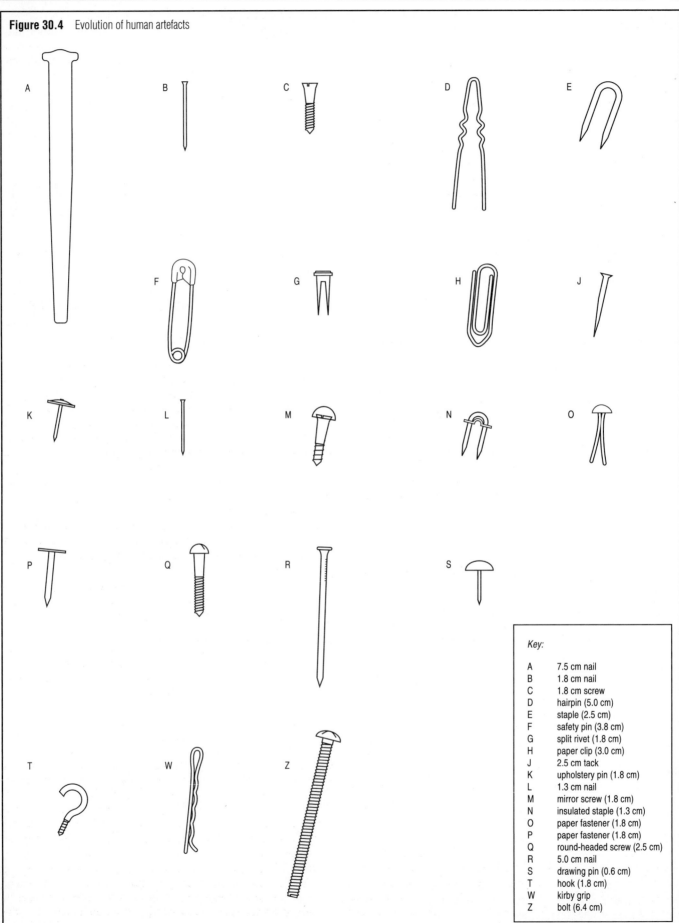

Key:

A   7.5 cm nail
B   1.8 cm nail
C   1.8 cm screw
D   hairpin (5.0 cm)
E   staple (2.5 cm)
F   safety pin (3.8 cm)
G   split rivet (1.8 cm)
H   paper clip (3.0 cm)
J   2.5 cm tack
K   upholstery pin (1.8 cm)
L   1.3 cm nail
M   mirror screw (1.8 cm)
N   insulated staple (1.3 cm)
O   paper fastener (1.8 cm)
P   paper fastener (1.8 cm)
Q   round-headed screw (2.5 cm)
R   5.0 cm nail
S   drawing pin (0.6 cm)
T   hook (1.8 cm)
W   kirby grip
Z   bolt (6.4 cm)

Projects

30.1 Selection pressures on limpets

The common marine limpet (*Patella vulgata*), is a tough-shelled, conical-shaped gastropod (p. 44). Limpets feed on young algae growing on the surface of rocks, and themselves are predated, for example, by dog whelks, which bore holes in the shell and insert their proboscis. The shape of the dome is variable and not entirely genetically determined, being influenced by abiotic factors such as wave action.

Measure the length, width and height of limpets of the lower and upper shore. Enter your data into a spreadsheet program, so that means and standard deviations are calculated automatically. How do limpets in these areas differ in their mean height : length ratio? Are limpets at the top of the shore a different size from those at the bottom of the shore? Are sheltered, upper-shore limpets taller? Are wave-exposed lower-shore limpets flatter?

If selection pressures are at work, then they will select the best-shaped limpet for that environment. Consequently, as the limpets get older, the variation in shape between those in the same area will be reduced. If the standard deviation is reduced as the limpets age, then we may argue that selection pressures are at work. The strength of the stabilising selection pressure can be judged by the degree of reduction.

References

P Openshaw (1984) 'Measuring adaptation and selection pressure', *School Science Review* (March 1984) **65**(232), pp. 508–18

P Openshaw (1985) 'Limpets and field studies: some further notes', *School Science Review* (June 1985) **66**(237), pp. 705–15

30.2 'Visual selection' by wild birds

Conspicuous members of a prey population are vulnerable to predation, and so a selective advantage may be conferred on those that are the same colour as the background. This hypothesis can be tested experimentally, simulating natural selection by using communities of wild birds, with pastry 'prey', created from a mixture of cooking lard, plain flour and edible colouring dyes. The 'prey' may be spread out where birds alone can reach it, set out on trays with different background colours. Species of birds that are commonly, repeatedly and selectively attracted to such food include blackbird (*Turdus merula*), song thrush (*T. philomelos*), starling (*Sturnus vulgaris*), robin (*Erithacus rubecula*), house sparrow (*Passer domesticus*) and blue tit (*Parus caeruleus*). This technique has been developed in various field trials. Consult the literature before planning your project, so as to take advantage of what has been learnt already.

References

J A Allen, K P Anderson and G M Tucker (1990) 'An improved method of demonstrating visual selection by wild birds', *J. Biol. Ed.* **24**(4), pp. 262–6

J A Allen and S R C Ashbourne (1988) 'A method for demonstrating the survival value of cryptic coloration', *School Science Review* (March 1988) **69**(248), pp. 503–5

30.3 Cross-pollination in Primula sp. due to heterostyly

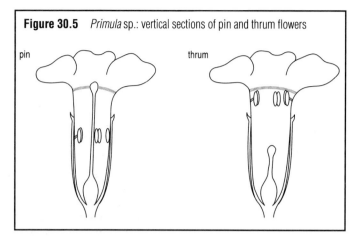

Figure 30.5 *Primula* sp.: vertical sections of pin and thrum flowers

pin

thrum

In many plants there is a genetically controlled system ensuring that pollen from any individual plant will not fertilise ovules on the same plant (a self-incompatibility mechanism). An example of self-incompatibility is found in the 'pin' and 'thrum' flowers of primrose (*Primula vulgaris*) and cowslip (*P. verus*) (Figure 30.5). These distinctive flowers, examples of heterostyly, are borne on different plants. The differences are immediately apparent when an intact flower is viewed from above.

In the pin form of the flower the style is long, and the anthers are attached halfway down the corolla tube. In the thrum form the style is short, and the anthers are attached at the mouth of the corolla tube. This arrangement favours cross-pollination by insects. Furthermore, pin pollen is ineffective on the pin stigma, and thrum pollen is incompatible within the thrum stigma.

All these features are controlled by about seven separate gene loci, very close together, and functioning as a 'super gene', creating a thrum type (dominant) or a pin type (recessive).

Very rarely, however, crossing over does occur within the super gene, creating a plant that has flowers with high anthers and tall stigmas. Such plants are homostylic, and they prove to be self-fertile.

How common is this condition among local populations of *Primula* sp.? What short-term advantages are gained? Is there any evidence that changes in agricultural practices or land use, locally, favour plants that are self-fertile?

30.4 Fast plants, variation and evolution

The cultivation of 'fast plants' (*Brassica rapa* syn. *campestris*) is described and their use in Mendelian genetic experiments outlined on pp. 337–8. In the 'Variation and Evolution' kit available from Philip Harris (p. 434), seeds of both normal-height plants and mutant 'rosette'-type plants are provided. If young plants grown from seeds from a rosette-type plant are treated with gibberellic acid plant growth regulator, they grow to normal height. They then flower in the normal way.

Such GA-treated plants can be crossed with normal-height plants, and the progeny investigated. In one of these parents, 'height' is an acquired characteristic. Will it be inherited in the way Lamarck suggested acquired characteristics could be?

Problems and assignments

30.1 *Selective breeding for creamier milk*

Genetically distinct populations of animals, created by selective breeding over many years, are known as breeds. Two such breeds of cattle are the Red Dane and the Jersey. Figure 30.6 shows data on the range of cream content in milk of herds of cows of these two breeds, and of crosses obtained from them. Using the information given, together with your understanding of the applications of genetics in artificial selection, answer the following questions.

1 **a** What do you understand by artificial selection?
  b What are the similarities and differences between natural selection and artificial selection?
2 A breeder maintains what is called a 'pedigree' herd by breeding only from similar animals, all showing marked features of that breed. This process is also described as 'inbreeding'.
  a In general terms, what effect does inbreeding (selfing in plants, sibling crosses in animals) have on the incidence of heterozygosity in the progeny?
  b For two siblings of genetic constitution Aa, what will be the proportion of heterozygotes in their progeny? What will be the proportion in the next generation, after a further sibling cross of those progeny?
3 In the selective breeding process, what does the geneticist mean by 'hybrid vigour'?
4 **a** What are the possible causes of variation in the average cream content of milk from cows of Red Dane and Jersey breeds?
  b What evidence would you look for to indicate that any of these is an inherited characteristic?
5 Suggest a breeding programme that you would expect both to increase cream content of milk and also to maintain hybrid vigour by avoiding persistent inbreeding, in the future progeny of the Red Dane/Jersey crosses shown in Figure 30.6.

30.2 *Theories of evolution compared*

The influences of religious and social values in Europe about the time of the French Revolution had lasting effects on acceptance of the evolutionary ideas of both Lamarck and Charles Darwin. For example, Lamarck survived in Paris throughout the Revolution. For Darwin, the association of 'evolution' with the philosophy which underpinned that Revolution, delayed the time when it was safe for him to publish the *Origin* without becoming a social outcast. An article that introduces these influences, and explains Lamarck's contribution to evolutionary theory, is:

J Humphries (1995) 'The Laws of Lamarck', *Biologist* **42**(3), pp. 121–5

Charles Darwin (1805–82) was one of two authors of the idea of **evolution by natural selection**. His hypothesis is summarised by these statements and deductions:

- Organisms produce more offspring than survive to adulthood.
- The numbers of individuals of many species remain remarkably constant, so there is a high mortality rate.
- The individuals of a species show variations, and some variants are more successful than others.
- Offspring carry many of their parents' features and characteristics, so later generations are adapted by gradual changes.

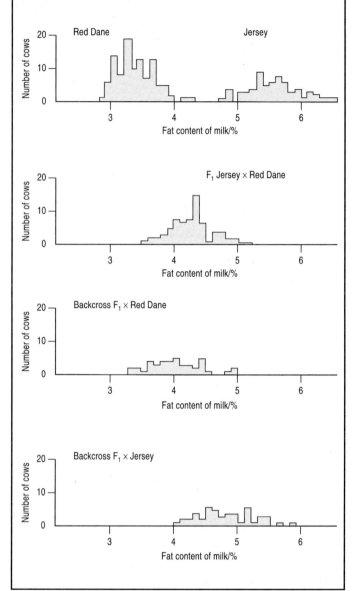

Figure 30.6 Cream content of milk from herds of Red Dane and Jersey cattle, and from certain of their progeny

Jean Baptiste de Lamarck (1744–1829) developed the idea of **evolution by the inheritance of acquired characteristics**. His hypothesis is summarised by these laws:

- Living things tend to increase in size and complexity.
- The development of a structure is in proportion to its use.

Characteristics acquired or developed during the individual's lifetime are passed to its offspring.

The ideas of Darwin are well represented in many sources. You can read an introduction to them in *Advanced Biology*, pp. 11, 652–3 and 662–4. The work of Lamarck is introduced there, too.

1 Compare and contrast these two theories by drawing up a grid, as shown in Table 30.1, to record the significance, if any, that each places on the issues listed.
2 Who else had been, or was, instrumental in developing the ideas of:
  a the inheritance of acquired characteristics?
  b the origin of species by natural selection?

Table 30.1 The mechanism of evolution: comparison of theories

	Inheritance of acquired characteristics	Natural selection
Species change with time – they are not immutable		
How variation in individuals of a species arises		
The significance of random variation among the progeny of each generation		
An inherent tendency of organisms to get larger and more complex		
Inheritance of changes in the body hat arise through hard use		
Consequence of competition between members of the same species		
Inheritance of features of the body that are underused		
The high mortality rate common among offspring		
The observation that certain animal species, having for many thousands of years lived in caves, have become totally blind		
Contribution to the eventual general acceptance of the idea of organic evolution (as opposed to 'special creation')		

30.3 Neo-Darwinism

Many developments in the theory of natural selection have occurred since the rediscovery of Mendel's genetics experiments. The elaborated, modern theory is called 'neo-Darwinism'.

Explain the nature of each of the following concepts, and show how they have influenced our understanding of natural selection:
a random assortment of maternal and paternal homologous chromosomes;
b mutation;
c recombination of segments of maternal and paternal chromosomes during crossing over;
d the difference between genotype and phenotype.

30.4 Human evolution

The theory of natural selection implies that the living world has evolved from non-living material (so all living things are related, however distantly), and that humans are related to other mammals, to all primates, and to the apes in particular.

1 Many important features of human cells are common to the cells of all other living things. Suggest three such features.
2 Humans are 'mammals'. Name four diagnostic features shown by all mammals.
3 Humans are 'primates'.
   a What living animals are thought to be most like the first primates? Which of their bodily features most closely reflect the habitat and way of life of early primates?
   b Name three other groups of primates living wild in tropical regions of the world.
   c Name five diagnostic features shown by all primates.
4 Name two structural features humans typically share with the apes, and two that are found in humans but not in apes.

30.5 Human ancestry

Frequently, articles in the *New Scientist* and similar journals discuss our changing views on human evolution. This area is as much a developing area of biology as, say, cell biology or biotechnology. An interesting and highly readable reference source is:

J Diamond (1991) *The Rise and Fall of the Third Chimpanzee*. Vintage

Read the extract from a *New Scientist* article in Panel 30.2. Then, using your wider reading together with the information given, answer the following questions.

1 Describe the differences between the two family trees. On what evidence is each one based?
2 Which do you think is the more convincing evidence, anatomical similarity or similarity of DNA sequences? Give your reasons.
3 What is the advantage of using mitochondrial DNA to elucidate evolutionary affinities?
4 How do you suppose 'DNA hybridisation' can shed light on evolutionary relationships?

Panel 30.2 The invisible ape

To both the casual zoo-goer and to the expert anatomist it seems obvious that chimpanzees and gorillas are more closely related to each other than either is to humans. They look much more alike. They are hairy, we are smooth. Chimpanzees and gorillas walk on all fours, we walk on two hind limbs. They have short legs and long arms, swing through the trees, and walk on their knuckles. We have long legs and short arms, with hands that are very flexible but do not bear weight. Their brains are small, ours are large. Their canine teeth are large, ours are small; their molars have thin enamel, ours have thick enamel.

For more than a century, these and other similarities convinced comparative anatomists that the two African apes are each other's closest kin. [Nevertheless] scientists are amassing other evidence that splits the two apes and identifies human and chimp as the cosy couple.

In the 1980s, researchers developed advanced techniques such as rapid DNA sequencing. As this decade winds to an end, most analysis of DNA backs the idea of a connection between chimps and humans rather than uniting chimpanzees and gorillas. Three different lines of evidence – nuclear DNA sequencing, mitochondrial DNA sequencing, and DNA hybridisation – consistently support this pairing.

Morris Goodman, Michael Miyamoto, Richard Holmquist and colleagues at Wayne State University, and Shintaroh Ueda and colleagues at the University of Tokyo, have worked out the sequences of portions of the hominoid globin and immunoglobulin genes, respectively. In each case they have found the human and chimpanzee sequences most similar.

The DNA in mitochondria, tiny organelles within a cell, contains only about 15 000 base pairs, contrasted with the 3 billion base pairs in the nucleus. This mitochondrial DNA (mtDNA) apparently evolves five to ten times faster than nuclear DNA. Masami Hasegawa, of the Institute of Statistical Mathematics in Tokyo, and Taka-aki Yaro, at Showa University in Yamanashi, derived a family tree by comparing hominoid mtDNAs. This again puts humans and chimps closest.

From: New Scientist (*3 December 1988*), *pp. 56–9*

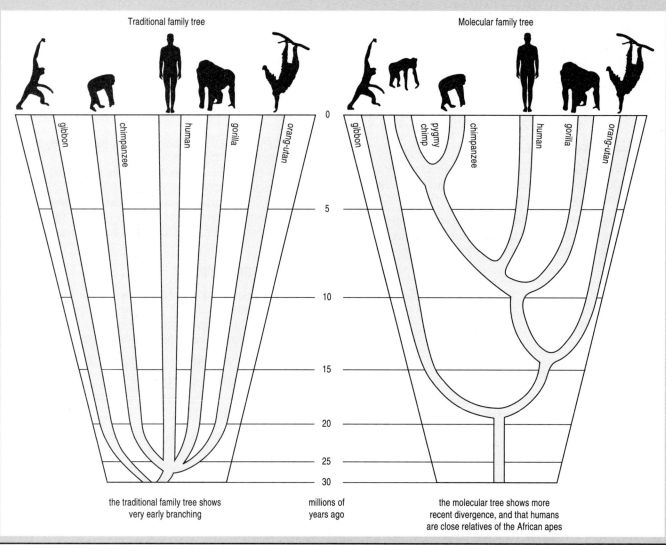

Traditional family tree

gibbon · chimpanzee · human · gorilla · orang-utan

Molecular family tree

gibbon · pygmy chimp · chimpanzee · human · gorilla · orang-utan

millions of years ago

the traditional family tree shows very early branching

the molecular tree shows more recent divergence, and that humans are close relatives of the African apes

30.6 Quick test

1 Distinguish between the following pairs:

a analogous and homologous structures;
b vestigial forms and intermediate forms;
c ontogeny and phylogeny;
d radioactive potassium dating and radioactive carbon dating;
e artificial selection and natural selection;
f germ plasm and soma;
g Charles Darwin and Alfred Russel Wallace;
h George Cuvier and Jean de Lamarck;
i gradual change and punctuated equilibrium;
j founder effect and genetic drift.

2 What do you understand by the following?

a evolutionary convergence;
b adaptive radiation;
c genetic distance between DNAs;
d the immune reaction and evolutionary relationships;
e the law of use and disuse;
f neo-Darwinism;
g types of natural selection;
h the origin of life;
i origin of vertebrates from non-vertebrates;
j hominids.

30.7 Essay assignment

Select one of the following:

• Evolutionary theory is supported by diverse evidence. Outline the nature of evidence from comparative physiology and biochemistry, and also from palaeontology. Show how evidence from both sources supports the concept of organic evolution by natural selection.

or:

• In precisely what ways do the concepts of organic evolution proposed by Lamarck and Charles Darwin differ? Why was it difficult for both workers to obtain evidence in support of their ideas in their lifetimes?

Answers to questions

These 'Answers' relate to the issues raised in the 'Problems and assignments' part of each chapter. Many answers are spelt out in detail, including the questions of a numerical nature. However, the information needed to answer very many of the questions is readily found in the companion book *Advanced Biology*. In these cases, page references to *Advanced Biology* only are given. Occasionally the direction is to a different source, where this is likely to be readily available, and where reference to it will particularly extend understanding.

Section 1

Except where stated, page references are to *Advanced Biology*.

CHAPTER 1

1.1 Characteristics of living things
1 Consist of cells containing DNA and RNA; may be cultured in nutrient broth (i.e. exhibit growth and feeding); reproduce from pre-existing cells; grow by their own biosynthetic machinery; growth involves increasing the amounts of all constituent parts, such as organelles; p. 28 Phylum Bacteria; pp. 554–5 Section 25.3 Bacteria.
2 p. 19 Prokaryotes, eukaryotes and viruses; p. 27 Viruses; pp. 552–3 Section 25.2 Viruses.
3 See Table A1.

1.2 Experimental situation analysis
1 Topsoil; p. 61 Figure 3.30.
2 The water content of soil varies and comparable quantities of soil are needed for a 'fair test'.
3 p. 60 Soil water. So that both samples held their maximum quantity of capillary water and all the water added at the start of the experiment was free to pass through.
4 Qualitative data.
5 Histogram of data (*Study Guide* p. 39, Figure 3.19 Bar graphs, histograms, kite diagrams, scatter graphs, pie charts and rose graphs).
6 Quantitative data
7 p. 59 Table 3.3 A comparison of soil properties.
8 p. 12 Science processes: some important terms.
9 Dependent variable = the volumes of water collected; independent variable = type of soil (sandy and clay).
10 The volume of water used. There is no 'standard' soil type against which clay and sandy soils can be judged.

1.3 Quick test
Chapter 1, pp. 2–17.

1.4 Essay assignment
Chapter 1, pp. 2–17; for the second essay topic, also p. 43 Some practical methods of investigating changes in the soil community of non-vertebrates.

CHAPTER 2

2.1 Living things classified into five kingdoms
1 pp. 18–19 Fundamental differences amongst living things; pp. 149–50 Electron microscopy; p. 164 Section 7.7 Prokaryotic cells.
2 pp. 27–8 Prokaryotes.
3 p. 19 Prokaryotes, eukaryotes and viruses.
4 pp. 30–1 Kingdom Fungi.
5 p. 3 Figure 1.2 Different methods of nutrition; pp. 300–2 Section 14.5 Saprotrophic nutrition.
6, 7 pp. 28–9 Subkingdom Protozoa; pp. 29–30 Subkingdom Algae.
8 p. 28 Eukaryotes; pp. 155–6 The nucleus.
9 pp. 32–4 Kingdom Plantae; pp. 568–9 Types of life cycle.
10 p. 3 Figure 1.2 Different methods of nutrition; pp. 32–4 Kingdom Plantae; pp. 34–41 Kingdom Animalia.
11 Kingdom 1 = Monera (pp. 27–8); Kingdom 2 = Fungi (pp. 30–1); Kingdom 3 = Protoctista (pp. 28–30); Kingdom 4 = Plantae (pp. 32–4); Kingdom 5 = Animalia (pp. 34–41).

2.2 Identification with a key
1, 2
   i = B, pp. 34–5, Cnidaria
   ii = F, p. 35, Platyhelminthes
   iii = E, p. 37, Mollusca
   iv = G, p. 36, Annelida
   v = A, p. 34, Porifera
   vi = C, p. 39, Echinodermata
   vii = H, p. 36, Nematoda
   viii = D, pp. 37–9, Arthropoda.
3 Dichotomous key = A key in which each division is divided into two, often more or less equal subdivisions; see p. 41–2 We can identify using keys; also *Study Guide* Practical 2.2 (p. 10).
   Natural key = A key based on relationships and ancestry (phylogenetic key) pp. 24–5 Why is taxonomy controversial?

Table A1 Contrasting methods of growth

Crystal	Bacterium	Virus
external addition of extra identical molecules	internal addition of molecules	once assembled, virus particles do not grow
	great variety of molecules involved	limited variety of molecules involved
not under any form of internal control	growth internally controlled	coat assembled from many identical protein molecules, formed around viral nucleic acid (DNA or RNA)
dependent entirely on concentration of external solution		
molecules not altered	molecules altered and recombined in different forms	process controlled by viral nucleic acid

2.3 'Design a key' exercise

1 See Table A2.

Table A2 Matrix of characteristics

	A (oak tree)	B (liverwort)	C (flowering plant)	D (fern)
green plant (autotrophic)?	yes	yes	yes	yes
plant sporophyte or gametophyte?	sporophyte	gametophyte	sporophyte	sporophyte
form/habit?	woody tree	leaf-like thallus, at soil level	herbaceous plant of field layer	fern of field layer
anchorage: roots or rhizoids?	root system	rhizoids	root system	rhizome with roots
stem present? woody or herbaceous?	woody stem	none	herbaceous stem	rhizome
water-conducting tissue?	xylem vessels	none	xylem vessels	tracheids
leaves present? annual or persistent?	deciduous leaves	leaf-like thallus persistent	annual leaves	annual leaves
flowers present/absent?	present	absent	present	absent
seed-bearing?	yes	no	yes	no
spores released from sporangia formed on leaves/thallus?	no	yes	no	yes

2

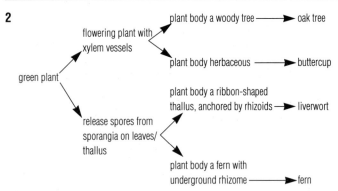

3 The sections are treated on a microscope slide or watch glass with a 1% solution of phloroglucinol in alcohol, acidified with one drop of 0.1 mol dm^{-3} hydrochloric acid, for 1–2 minutes. Lignified tissue will turn bright red. (The chemistry of lignin is discussed on p. 141 <u>Lignin</u>.)

4 A and C (xylem vessels, fibres), and D (tracheids, fibres); pp. 220–2 <u>Sclerenchyma</u>; <u>Xylem</u>; <u>Tracheids</u>.

2.4 Quick test
2.5 Essay assignment
<u>Chapter 2</u>, pp. 18–43.

CHAPTER 3

3.1 Feeding relationships and food webs

1 See Figure A1.

2 p. 46 <u>Interdependence within the ecosystem</u>; <u>Food chains and food webs</u>.

3 Immediately, some (e.g. rabbits) will increase in numbers, but others will decrease when their predators (e.g. tits, shrews) are less predated. In the longer term, new tertiary consumers are likely to restore the status quo.

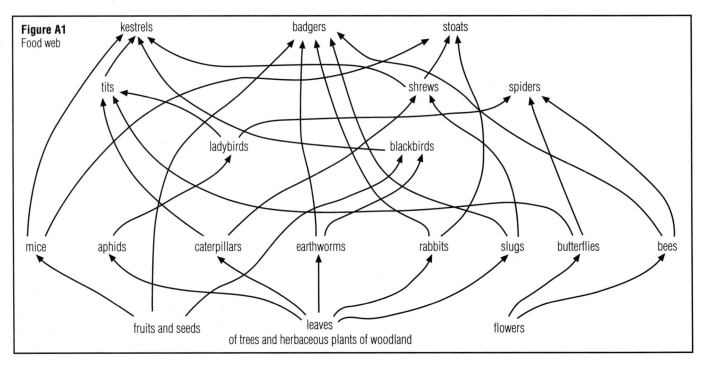

Figure A1 Food web

3.2 The establishment of a thermocline in deep water

1 Graph, with *x*-axis showing depth (0–15 m), and the *y*-axes showing oxygen concentration (0–16 ppm) and temperature (0–25 °C). There will be two curves for temperature (winter and summer) and two for oxygen concentration (winter and summer) against depth; use distinctive symbols (e.g. ○, ●, + and ×) for the four curves.

2 5–11 m.

3 Warm water is less dense than cold water (except just above the freezing point) and therefore occurs above cold water. The layers of cold and warm water do not mix.

The very high specific heat capacity of water means that much heat is required to raise the temperature of water, and also that a mass of water is slow to change temperature. There is little significant heat movement at the interface of hot and cold water.

4 Light intensity is low, due to absorption of light by the water above. Dissolved oxygen is low, due to the low solubility of oxygen in water and slow rate of diffusion, and to oxygen uptake by organisms in surface water.

5 Organic matter such as leaf litter decays anaerobically in deep water, releasing gases such as H_2S. The low oxygen concentration excludes organisms of aerobic decay, and the thermocline reduces mixing and so prevents oxygen from being available at depth.

6 Decay of organic matter at depth is only partial, with many ions locked up in organic matter. The thermocline prevents circulation of ions from the regions of decay to regions where conditions of light and oxygen concentration allow growth to occur (surface water).

3.3 The distribution of organisms on a rocky shore

1 a, b p. 50 <u>Figure 3.10 The subdivisions of the shore imposed by the tides</u>; <u>Figure 3.11 The causes of the tide pattern</u>.

2 Mean tide level.

3 Compared with *Chthamalus stellatus*, *Semibalanus balanoides* is apparently significantly less resistant to desiccation, and/or the higher summer temperatures (or much lower winter temperatures), or is more vulnerable to those predators that have access during periods of exposure.

4 p. 52 <u>Figure 3.14 The resistance to desiccation of four species of brown algae</u>.

5 The lichen cannot survive prolonged submersion in seawater.

6 p. 53 <u>Loss of water by shore animals</u>.

7 p. 72 <u>Section 3.7 Ecological energetics</u>.

8 p. 51 <u>Figure 3.12 Gradation in the physical conditions of the intertidal zone</u>.

9 For example, p. 54 <u>Figure 3.18 A marine/littoral zone food web</u>.

10 p. 52 <u>Adaptation to the conditions of the intertidal zone</u>.

3.4 Succession in sand dune formation

1 Moving sand, high salt concentration, exposure to wind and to salt spray, extremely rapid drainage of rain water.

The areas labelled **1**, **2**, **3** and **4** in Figure 3.22 show progressively more stable soil bound together by plant root systems, a progressively lowered salt concentration, progressively increasing amounts of humus, and increasing retention of rain water in the soil. The sandy soil formed has an acid reaction. Increasing shelter from wind and some shade from direct sunlight is given by larger herbaceous plants, and this supports the presence of larger non-vertebrate and vertebrate animals. Animals deposit excreta which further enhance soil fertility and may contribute to the 'bank' of viable seeds present.

2 The following features are advantageous to plants of these zones, because of the abiotic environments experienced:

a ability to survive regular exposure to salt spray, and occasional immersion in salt water;

b propagation by fast-growing rhizome, growing just below the (moving) sand surface;

c rosette habit with deep roots or creeping stolons or rhizomes, and the presence of water-storage tissue;

d ability to survive in acidic soil conditions and to withstand mild to pronounced water shortages.

3 Animal life present at the initial colonisation phase are passing 'migrant' species, infrequently present, and for very short periods.

4 Mechanical disruption of the stabilising sand dunes (e.g. by the feet of animals) may cause the zonation to break down, and the sand to be blown further inland.

3.5 Diversity in polluted and unpolluted waters

1 a p. 101 <u>Eutrophication</u>.

b Bacterial (and fungal) saprotrophic nutrition and aerobic respiration remove oxygen and suspended solids from the water, and release ions. These in turn are taken up by other organisms. The bacteria support a huge food chain, and the composition of the river is returned to normal (well downstream of the polluted zone).

2 a Ammonia is poisonous to animals if it accumulates in a small volume of water.

b Nitrates start to accumulate downstream, but are taken up (by algae and other green plants).

3 p. 271 <u>The nitrifying bacteria</u>; pp. 336–9 <u>The nitrogen cycle</u>.

4 a As pollutants from detergents, and when released from organic matter by decay.

b pp. 332–5 <u>Section 16.3 Ion uptake in plants</u>.

5 Protozoa are the chief 'predators' of bacteria (and also of 'sewage fungus').

6 Water with minimum of many dissolved ions, and (possibly) suspended organic matter. See p. 100 <u>Contamination of water with inorganic ions</u>; p. 101 <u>Eutrophication</u>.

7 'Sewage fungus', bacteria, protozoa and some algae.

8 Organic matter → saprotrophic bacteria + 'sewage fungus'.
Algae + protozoa → *Daphnia* → *Hydra* → small fish.

9 a Aerate the water by agitating it, or by pumping in air.

b The smell of gases, such as H_2S; death of fish.

10 Enhanced bacterial saprotrophic decay of organic matter, including organisms killed by the heat, leading to a sequence of changes similar to those caused by sewage effluent, but probably much milder.

3.6 Prey–predator relations

1 Graph of data in Table 3.10 (*Study Guide* p. 47).

Graph of data in Table 3.11 (*Study Guide* p. 47) (with numbers of mice and voles in spring and summer combined together).

2, 3 The weevil has an unlimited supply of food, yet the population oscillates in numbers, the oscillations alternating with population 'explosions' by the weevil's parasite, a wasp larva. So an increase of numbers of weevils is not sustained, but is followed by an increase in parasitic wasp numbers. With a reduced population of the host species, the enlarged parasitic wasp population cannot be sustained. A fall in the population of the parasite is followed by an increase in host numbers, and so on.

The weevil investigation was laboratory-based, involving a community of only two populations. The tawny owl has access to many prey species. When wood mice and bank voles have been over-predated (e.g. in 1950 and 1953) and their population numbers are low, the tawny owls can be assumed to have access to other populations of small animals in the wood, and in other habitats further afield. During the period of the experiment (1947–1959) the owl was not significantly short of food sources, and was not especially harmed by human actions (e.g. by pesticides in the environment).

4 Population surveys of all organisms that make up the bulk of the tawny owl diet should confirm that these populations (or at least some of them) are at high levels when the wood mice and bank voles are in short supply.

Tawny owl pellets could be collected and examined to determine the proportion of other prey species in the diet at times when wood mice and bank voles are present in large numbers and small numbers respectively.

3.7 Statistical tests in ecology I

1 For *Ranunculus acris*:

Mode: 25
Median: 25

Calculation of mean and standard deviation for a set of grouped data

See table top right.

$$\text{Mean of data} = \frac{\Sigma fx}{\Sigma f} = \frac{2999}{100} = 29.99$$

$$\text{SD} = \sqrt{\left(\frac{\Sigma fd^2}{\Sigma f - 1}\right)} = \sqrt{\frac{2031}{99}} = \sqrt{20.51} = 4.53$$

Thus the mean of the sample *Ranunculus acris* = 29.99, and the SD = 4.53.

For *Ranunculus repens:*

Mode: 30
Median: 30

Calculation of mean and standard deviation for a set of grouped data

See table bottom right.

$$\text{Mean of data} = \frac{\Sigma fx}{\Sigma f} = \frac{2479}{100} = 24.79$$

$$\text{SD} = \sqrt{\left(\frac{\Sigma fd^2}{\Sigma f - 1}\right)} = \sqrt{\frac{1479}{99}} = \sqrt{14.93} = 3.86$$

Thus the mean of the sample *Ranunculus repens* = 24.79, and the SD = 3.86.

3.8 Statistical tests in ecology II

The null hypothesis (negative hypothesis) assumes there is no difference in size between sun and shade leaves. List the observations (X) for sun (X_A) and shade (X_B) leaves in two columns.

See table on next page.

Standard error of the difference between means of populations A and B can be shown to be:

$$\sqrt{\frac{V_A}{n_A} + \frac{V_B}{n_B}} = \sqrt{\frac{29.54}{12} + \frac{23.33}{12}} = \sqrt{4.41} = 2.09$$

$$t = \frac{\text{difference between means } (\overline{X}_A - \overline{X}_B)}{\text{standard error of the difference between means of populations A and B}}$$

$$= \frac{4.4}{2.09} = 2.10$$

Degrees of freedom $= (n_A - 1) + (n_B - 1) = 11 + 11 = 22$

Now look up the values in the *t*-tables in Appendix 2 on p. 000 of this *Study Guide*.

Look down the 'degrees of freedom' column to the number matching your calculation.

Then move across the table at this level until you reach the column headed $p = 0.05$. This is the level of probability normally used in biological work.

Values obtained in ascending order x	Frequency f	fx	Deviation of x from the mean $(x - \bar{x})[=d]$	d^2	fd^2
17	0				
18	1	18	−12	144	144
19	1	19	−11	121	121
20	1	20	−10	100	100
21	1	21	−9	81	81
22	1	22	−8	64	64
23	3	69	−7	49	147
24	4	96	−6	36	144
25	4	100	−5	25	100
26	5	130	−4	16	80
27	5	135	−3	9	45
28	6	168	−2	4	24
29	8	232	−1	1	8
30	14	420	0	0	0
31	12	372	1	1	12
32	10	320	2	4	40
33	7	231	3	9	63
34	3	102	4	16	48
35	2	70	5	25	50
36	3	108	6	36	108
37	2	74	7	49	98
38	3	114	8	64	192
39	2	78	9	81	162
40	2	80	10	100	200
41	0				
$\Sigma f = 100$		$\Sigma fx = 2999$			$\Sigma fd^2 = 2031$

Values obtained in ascending order x	Frequency f	fx	Deviation of x from the mean $(x - \bar{x})[=d]$	d^2	fd^2
14	0				
15	1	16	−9	81	81
16	1	17	−8	64	64
17	1	36	−7	49	98
18	2	76	−6	36	144
19	4	80	−5	25	100
20	4	168	−4	16	128
21	8	154	−3	9	63
22	7	207	−2	4	36
23	9	240	−1	1	10
24	10	400	0	0	0
25	16	234	1	1	9
26	9	270	2	4	40
27	10	112	3	9	36
28	4	145	4	16	80
29	5	90	5	25	75
30	3	31	6	36	36
31	1	32	7	49	49
32	1	66	8	64	128
33	2	34	9	81	81
34	1	35	10	100	100
35	1	36	11	121	121
36	0				
$\Sigma f = 100$		$\Sigma fx = 2479$			$\Sigma fd^2 = 1479$

Sample 1 Observations (X_A)	Deviation of observation from mean $(X_A - \bar{X}_A)$	Square of deviation $(X_A - \bar{X}_A)^2$	Sample 2 Observations (X_B)	Deviation of observation from mean $(X_B - \bar{X}_B)$	Square of deviation $(X_B - \bar{X}_B)^2$
24	−7.9	62.41	26	−10.3	106.09
26	−5.9	34.81	33	−3.3	10.89
26	−5.9	34.81	34	−2.3	5.29
30	−1.9	3.61	35	−1.3	1.69
31	−0.9	0.81	35	−1.3	1.69
31	−0.9	0.81	36	−0.3	0.09
32	0.1	0.01	36	−0.3	0.09
32	0.1	0.01	36	−0.3	0.09
33	1.1	1.21	37	0.7	0.49
37	5.1	26.01	41	4.7	22.09
38	6.1	37.21	42	5.7	32.49
43	11.1	123.21	45	8.7	75.69

Sum of observations $\sum X_A = 383$	Sum of squares of deviations $\sum(X_A - \bar{X}_A)^2 = 324.92$	Sum of observations $\sum X_B = 436$	Sum of squares of deviations $\sum(X_B - \bar{X}_B)^2 = 256.68$

No of observations $n_A = 12$

Mean of the sample $= \bar{X}_A = \dfrac{\sum X_A}{n_A} = \dfrac{383}{12} = 31.9$

Variance $V_A = \dfrac{\sum(X - \bar{X}_A)^2}{n_A - 1} = \dfrac{324.92}{11} = 29.54$

No of observations $n_B = 12$

Mean of the sample $= \bar{X}_B = \dfrac{\sum X_B}{n_B} = \dfrac{436}{12} = 36.3$

Variance $V_B = \dfrac{\sum(X - \bar{X}_B)^2}{n_B - 1} = \dfrac{256.68}{11} = 23.33$

Write down this value of t:

t for $(n_A - 1) + (n_B - 1)$ degrees of freedom at $p = 0.05$ is 1.71.

t as calculated is 2.10

If the value of t that you calculated exceeds this value of t, the null hypothesis is rejected, and the difference between the two samples is significant. Is the difference significant in this case? ... The difference is significant.

3.9 Statistical tests in ecology III

Step 1 Rank the data of the two samples in increasing order of size:

Site A	9	11	13	21		41	51	64	
Site B				15	25	40		52	66	77

Step 2a For each measurement in sample B, count how many samples in group A are smaller (for measurements that are the same score $\frac{1}{2}$).

Sample B measurements	Number of sample A measurements that are smaller
15	3
25	4
40	4
52	6
66	7
77	7

The total of sample A measurements that are smaller $(U_A) = 31$

Step 2b For each measurement in sample A, count how many samples in group B are smaller.

Sample A measurements	Number of sample B measurements that are smaller
9	0
11	0
13	0
21	1
41	3
51	3
64	4

The total of sample B measurements that are smaller $(U_B) = 11$

Step 3 Check your arithmetic is correct:

$U_A + U_B = n_A \times n_B$ i.e. $31 + 11 = 7 \times 6 \,(= 42)$

where n_A is the number of measurements in sample A, and
n_B is the number of measurements in sample B.

Step 4 Choose the smaller value of U obtained. Look up the critical values of U at the 5% significance level in Table A2.3 on p. 437 of this *Study Guide*. This occurs at the intersection of the values for n_A and n_B. If the smaller calculated value for U is less than or equal to the tabulated value, then the null hypothesis is rejected. If it is greater, the null hypothesis is confirmed. In fact:

smaller value of U calculated $= 11$
tabulated value of U $= 6$

The null hypothesis has been confirmed; there is no statistical significance in the differences in size of the grasshopper populations.

ANSWERS TO QUESTIONS

3.10   Features and characteristics of major biomes
See, as an example, Table A3.

Table A3   Comparing biomes

	Tropical rain forest	Temperate deciduous forest
where they tend to occur	near the Equator in S and Central America, West and Equatorial Africa, S-E Asia, Indonesia and N-E Australia	continental climates with summer rainfall and severe winters, found on all continents
average rainfall	>2000 mm mean annual precipitation	500–750 mm mean annual precipitation
mean temperature	approximately 30 °C	0–20 °C, according to season
typical features of soil	laterite (high iron, high aluminium, low silica, weathering to great depth)	brown earth type (p. 61)
dominant plant species	scattered, very tall trees that emerge above the canopy, trees of a high canopy layer, understorey that becomes dense where there is a break in the canopy; usually no one species is dominant (the species vary with the continent)	e.g. oak (*Quercus*), beech (*Fagus*), ash (*Fraxinus*) (the species vary with the continent)
typical food chain	(in both cases): dead organic matter → decomposers and detritivores → uptake of ions + CO_2 by trees → green leaves of trees → dead organic matter herbivores → carnivores	
characteristic dominant carnivore	giant eagles, tree-living cats	owls, foxes, wolves, badgers
typical influence of humans	(in both cases): deforestation over prolonged periods, turning the land into agricultural arable land and forest margin land e.g. coppice.	

3.11   Quick test
3.12   Essay assignment
Chapter 3, pp. 44–73.

CHAPTER 4

4.1   Human population growth
1 For example, that of Zimbabwe, 1988.
2 Zimbabwe, 1988.
3 **a** 45;
   b 5;
   c between 4 and 5.
4 Application of more effective birth control measures.
5 China.
6 Clean water supply for all; improved diets, especially for the poorest; improved housing; education for the young up to the age of 15, rather than using child labour in industry; improved primary health care for families (mothers and children); more equitable distribution of wealth and resources; reliable and accessible methods of birth control.

4.2   The 'Green Revolution'
1 **a** p. 277 The 'Green Revolution'.
   b Examples include: larger markets for manufactured fertilisers and pesticides; increased profitability; more foods to purchase.
2 Variability within a species due to genetic differences between individuals.
3 Larger leaves means more production by photosynthesis. Less photosynthate wasted on stem production means the potential for larger fruit; shorter-stemmed plants are less likely to be flattened by wind/rain.
4 pp. 650–1 The principles of selective breeding.

5 A range of structural, physiological and biochemical features that confer resistance to harm from long-term exposure to local climatic extremes and to local parasites and predators.
6 **a** These people have access to expensive fertilisers and pesticides to cultivate the new varieties successfully.
   b They cannot afford the input costs of the more productive varieties.

4.3   The world energy crisis
1 p. 78 Alternative sources of energy; p. 95 The control of human population growth; p. 96 The sustainable use of resources.
2, 3 Your list of measures that developed countries need to adopt, and the changes that the individual can make, is likely to include issues of public transport systems and motor cars, diet and preventive medicine, recycling and the waste revolution, leisure activities, and (possibly) the politics of aid and of defence.

4.4   Saving the rain forests
1, 3 p. 78 Deforestation; p. 80 The tropical rain forests; p. 83 Carbon dioxide.
2 p. 81 Figure 4.11 Deforestation of the watershed causes lowland flooding.
3 **a** p. 75 Methods of food production, and the land they support: Slash-and-burn cultivation.
   b pp. 80–1 The tropical rain forests.
4 Size of the human population, combined with general harmful effects of human activities on the living world; demands for land for smallholdings and farming.
5 For examples, see pp. 96–7 Conservation overview.

4.5 Organic farming

1 p. 336 <u>Crop rotation</u>; p. 338 <u>*Rhizobium* in the nodules of leguminous plants</u>.

2 Green plants grown for ploughing in as manure. The most effective such crops are legumes (p. 338 <u>Other steps in the nitrogen cycle</u>; p. 301 <u>Recycling in garden compost</u>).

3 p. 336 <u>Crop rotation</u>.

4 Possibly a higher concentration of combined nitrogen (especially if the 'green manure' crop is *not* a leguminous plant crop).

5 p. 91 <u>Biological control</u>.

6 pp. 104–7 <u>Section 5.3 Biology and agriculture</u>; <u>Figure 5.8 Wheat yields in the United Kingdom, 1948–82</u>.

7 p. 91 <u>Pesticides today</u>.

8 pp. 92–7 <u>Section 4.5 Conservation</u>.

9 pp. 89–91 <u>Pesticides</u>.

10 Information on the potential advantages of organic farming for human health and for the environment.

4.6 Satellite imaging and the productivity of the oceans

1, 2, 5 p. 83 <u>The increasing concentration of greenhouse gases</u> (also explains about ions brought up from the ocean bed by winter storms).

3, 6 pp. 102–3 <u>The world's fishing grounds</u> (also explains about 'upwelling zones').

4 Combine information in p. 243 <u>Figure 12.2 The carbon cycle</u>, and p. 54 <u>Figure 3.18 A marine/littoral zone food web</u>.

4.7 The carbon dioxide question

pp. 82–4 <u>The 'greenhouse effect'</u>.

4.8 The ozone layer: formation and destruction

1 p. 88 <u>Evidence for the destruction of the ozone layer</u>.

2 p. 86 <u>The maintenance of the ozone layer</u>.

3, 4, 5 p. 87 <u>Pollution destroys the ozone layer</u>.

4.9 Quick test
4.10 Essay assignment

<u>Chapter 4</u>, pp. 74–97.

CHAPTER 5

5.1 Designing a desalination plant

A solar still (Figure A2) uses the Sun's energy to distil seawater. The still is cheap to run, but the yield of pure water is low. Periodically the still is closed down and the salt that has accumulated (the other product of the still) is dug out.

5.2 Fertilisers in agriculture

1 Graph.

2 a Nitrate (and ammonium) ions.

　b p. 203 <u>The fate of the proteins formed: The source of amino acids in plants and animals</u>.

　c p. 335 <u>Maintaining soil fertility for commercial crops</u>. Most of the combined nitrogen (protein) of a green plant is in a single enzyme, ribulose bisphosphate carboxylase (p. 269), involved in fixation of CO_2 in photosynthesis.

3 a p. 332 <u>Table 16.1 Macro- and micronutrients of plants</u>.

　b Provides organic matter from which nutrients are released by slow decay. If the 'green manure' involves leguminous plants, combined nitrogen in the soil may be increased (p. 338).

4 a Bacteria and cyanobacteria.

　b p. 338 <u>Other steps in the nitrogen cycle</u>.

5 Organic crops, lacking pesticides, lose more productivity because of the greater impact of diseases and competition with weeds. Similarly, without artificial fertilisers there is more likely to be submaximal availability of soil nutrients.

5.3 Bovine somatotrophin

1 a Lactation = period of milk production.

　b p. 106 <u>Milk production and the milking parlour: The life cycle of the cow</u>.

　c p. 636 <u>Section 29.1 Introduction</u>.

　d Injections made into the tissue fluid below the skin and into the musculature.

2 Higher milk yield per cow; need to milk fewer cows; need to maintain fewer 'followers'.

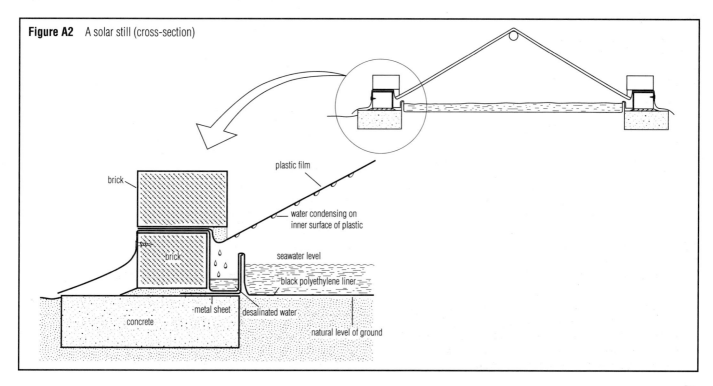

Figure A2 A solar still (cross-section)

brick

plastic film

water condensing on inner surface of plastic

brick

seawater level

black polyethylene liner

metal sheet

desalinated water

concrete

natural level of ground

3 Danger of metabolic and physical strain from greater productivity at the expense of little more feed; possibly a chance of greater vulnerability to disease.

4 Milk is more cheaply and freely available for humans.

Animals' life experience becomes further divorced from that in nature; animals are treated as units of production, entirely subservient to the economic needs of humans; possibility of hormone residues in the milk.

5.4 Pesticides and pollution: a case study

1 p. 98 Groundwater.

2 Into surface waterways, or into soil that drains into aquifers.

3 Because the nervous systems of arthropods also have synapses where neurotransmission can be interrupted.

4 Because these pesticides can penetrate our bodies relatively easily, through the skin and the lungs, for example (p. 89 Pesticides: Recognition of the problems).

5 Initial analysis of carcasses; initial analysis of the product, prior to its marketing.

5.5 Biogas from waste: a design challenge

A suitable design should include temperature regulation (water bath) and temperature-monitoring facilities, a method of topping up with organic matter (suitably shredded), and a method of collecting the 'biogas' effectively and safely. Remember, methane forms explosive mixtures with air.

5.6 Scale-up in biotechnology

Necessary to ensure:

- that the strain is able to carry out the synthesis, i.e. the gene is activated within the yeast's genotype, and the product of the gene is produced in quantity; that the 'engineered' yeast can replicate (bud) efficiently, and is able to grow on the raw material previously used; that the product does leach into the medium and is stable there; that the product can be economically separated from the medium;

- that the laboratory bench performance is maintained in the large-scale operation; that the final-size fermenter functions efficiently regarding (for example) sterilisation of medium and of incoming air, agitation of medium, heat transfer etc.;

- that the planned change of scale is achieved, that the supply and quality of the raw material on which the yeast feeds is maintained, and that inevitable 'teething problems' are anticipated and minimised to reduce loss of production in the early industrial stages.

5.7 Testing for enzymes in 'biological' washing powder

- Enzymes are mostly proteins. Does the washing powder contain protein (test, *Study Guide* pp. 88–9)? How sensitive is the test? Investigate, using different concentrations of protein. Does the test detect protein added to a non-biological washing powder which has previously tested negative for protein?

- How effective is the biological washing powder at digesting (i.e. making soluble and removing from fabric) protein, lipid and starch, at the manufacturers' recommended concentration and temperature? Outline a plan of tests (*Study Guide* pp. 86–9) as a flow diagram, along the lines of *Study Guide* Figure 6.3.

- Compare this activity with the action of a non-biological powder.

5.8 Quick test
5.9 Essay assignment

Chapter 5, pp. 98–115.

Section 2

Except where stated, page references are to *Advanced Biology*.

CHAPTER 6

6.1 Moles in theory and practice

1 a, b p. 121 Moles.

2 $C_6H_{12}O_6$ has a relative atomic mass of 180, so a 0.1 mol dm^{-3} solution contains 18.0 g glucose (accurately weighed) dissolved in distilled water, and made up to one litre (accurately measured).

3 Measure out 25 cm^3 of 0.1 mol dm^{-3} glucose and dilute it with 25 cm^3 of distilled water.

4 a p. 128 Reducing and non-reducing sugars.

  b *Study Guide* pp. 84–6 Practical 6.1 Testing for reducing sugars; Making the test semi-quantitative.

6.2 Water as a biologically important molecule

1, 8 p. 119 Figure 6.2 Hydrogen bonds formed by water molecules.

2, 4, 5, 6 p. 120 The properties of water.

3 p. 123 Figure 6.6 Ionic and covalent bonding.

7 p. 128 Figure 6.13 Disaccharides.

6.3 The structure of proteins

1 p. 129 'Small' molecules *v.* the macromolecules.

2 p. 133 Amino acids; Figure 6.20 The structure of amino acids.

3 p. 135 Figure 6.22 The peptide bond.

4 p. 134 Polypeptides and proteins.

5 See Table A4.

Table A4 Protein structure

Primary structure	linear sequence of amino acid residues (p. 135)
Secondary structure	folding or twisting of protein chain (p. 136)
Tertiary structure	permanent folding of protein into a complex shape (p. 137)
Quaternary structure	aggregation of two or more protein chains (p. 137)

6.4 The chemical composition of living organisms

1 p. 118 The chemical similarity of living things.

2 pp. 118–19 The elements of the chemistry of life.

3 p. 118 Table 6.1 The chemical composition of our bodies, sea-water and the Earth's crust; p. 275 Table 13.3 Minerals required in the human diet; p. 332 Table 16.1 Macro- and micronutrients of plants.

6.5 Quick test
6.6 Essay assignment

Chapter 6, pp. 118–41.

CHAPTER 7

7.1 Studying key figures in early microscopy

For example, see Table A5 on the next page.

7.2 SEM and TEM compared

1 Can be used to examine unstained, living material, e.g. by phase contrast, and also appropriately stained sections to differentiate tissues.

2, 3 pp. 149–50 Electron microscopy.

Table A5

	Marcello Malpighi (1628–1694)	Robert Hooke (1635–1707)	Robert Brown (1773–1855)	Ernst Abbe (1840–1905)
Lived and worked:	Bologna, Italy	Oxford and London	Scotland	Germany
Earned a living as:	professor of medicine and research microscopist	Curator of the Royal Society; expert mechanic; Surveyor of London after the Great Fire	army medical officer and explorer	professor of physics, later as owner of Zeiss factory
Education/training in science in biology	graduated in philosophy and then medicine	science at Oxford	Marischal College Aberdeen, then medicine at Edinburgh	Jena
Theoretical scientist or practical technologist	technically proficient microscopist, working with single-lens microscope	both, but ingenious mechanic first	naturalist collector	academic, and as instrument maker
Major achievements (influential in the development of biology)	observed capillary network of circulation, silkworm as an insect; described stomata, and development of plant embryo	Hooke's law of elasticity, devised an early compound microscope, devised word 'cell' for compartments in plant cork	differences between 'conifers' and flowering plants, cell nucleus, 'Brownian' movement	made instruments with Carl Zeiss: Abbe condenser, achromatic lens

7.3 Magnification and resolution
p. 147 Figure 7.5 The compound microscope.

7.4 Comparing eukaryotic and prokaryotic cells
1 Nucleus, chloroplast, large permanent vacuole, mitochondria.
2 For example, as in p. 144 Figure 7.1 The general features of cells as seen under the light microscope.
3 The mesophyll cell is magnified ×2500. The mean length of three mitochondria in the TEM is 6 mm. The actual mean length is 2.4 μm.
The bacterium is magnified ×10 730. The length of the bacterial cell in the TEM is 70 mm. The actual length is 6.5 μm.
4 p. 165 Table 7.3 The differences between prokaryotic and eukaryotic cells.
5 a, b p. 152 Figure 7.14 The ultrastructure of the eukaryotic cell; Table 7.1 Cell organelles in animal and plant cells.

7.5 The fluid mosaic model of membrane structure
1 p. 155 Fluid mosaic model of membrane structure. An alternative is p. 153 Figure 7.16 (left) The Davison–Danielli model of membrane structure.
2 p. 154 Figure 7.18 The 'fluid mosaic' model of membrane structure.
3 p. 153 The biochemical evidence for membrane structure.
4 p. 233 Figure 11.16 A primary pump for active transport.
5 Annotate *Study Guide* Figure 7.12 as follows. Label the ribosomes attached to the RER 'the site of the synthesis of proteins that are packaged in membrane after formation: such proteins may include hydrolytic enzymes'. Label the lumen of the RER as 'the site where these proteins accumulate'. Label the edges of the RER (where vesicles are pinched off) 'here the proteins are packaged into discrete vesicles for transport about the cell, or for export outside the cell'.
6 p. 479 Figure 21.47 How hormones may act on target cells yet leave other cells unaffected.

7.6 The movement of cilia and flagella
1 p. 161 Flagella and cilia.
2 Flagella *Euglena*, cilia *Paramecium*. Both are illustrated on p. 29.

3 p. 314 Protection of the lungs.
4 An inability to form functioning cilia and flagella anywhere they normally occur within the body.
5 p. 160 Microtubules; p. 161 Figure 7.30 The microtubule in axon transport.

7.7 Electron microscopy and artefacts
1 p. 151 Artefacts in microscopy.
2 pp. 149–50 Preparation of biological materials for the TEM.
3 p. 151 Checking for artefacts.

7.8 Quick test
7.9 Essay assignment
Chapter 7, pp. 142–65.

CHAPTER 8

8.1 Energy and metabolism: sources and fates
1 For example, for grassland: ryegrass; herbivore, rabbit (parasite, liver fluke); carnivore, stoat (parasite, nematode worm); and with a bacterium of the soil microflora that feeds on dead organisms as the decomposer.
2 p. 46 Interdependence within the ecosystem.
3 Lost as heat energy into space: p. 70 Figure 3.47 Pyramid of biomass showing the cycling of materials and the flow of energy.
4 a Photosynthesis; chlorophyll formation; nitrate reduction to form amino acid and glutamic acid.
  b Protein digestion to amino acids; storage of sugars as glycogen; deamination of excess amino acids.
5 a Chemical energy
  b p. 168 Table 8.1 Energy transduction in biology.
6 a, b p. 168 Section 8.2 Energy and metabolism.
7 a Splitting of water at start of light reaction; chemical energy of starch.
  b Movement of leaf parasite (animal) in leaf tissue; chemical energy of glycogen or other reserve carbohydrate.
8 Respiration to sustain the chewing of leaf tissue, swallowing of chewed tissues, digestion, absorption, assimilation; loss of undigested matter.

8.2 Manometry in biochemical investigation

1 a To maintain identical (and constant) temperature conditions in both tubes.

b To absorb CO_2 emitted.

c Control, to show that changes seen are the result of living processes.

2 a Small changes in volume are exaggerated in order to make them easier to detect and measure.

b i With the tap turned down, set the syringe plunger so that its base is level with the highest mark on the syringe.

ii Turn the tap up and move the level marker on the manometer to indicate the liquid level.

iii Start the stopclock, and turn the tap horizontally.

iv Watch the liquid in the manometer and at frequent intervals depress the syringe to return the liquid level to the marker.

v After (say) 5 minutes, depress the plunger to return the liquid level to the marker once more, and record how far the syringe has been depressed. Express the result (volume the syringe has been depressed) in cm^3 oxygen taken up per hour per gram of living material.

vi Treat the 'control' tube (dead seeds) identically. No change in volume is anticipated, however, provided the pressure and temperature remain constant throughout the period of the experiment.

c i Turn the tap down and move the syringe plunger back so its base is level with the highest mark on the syringe.

ii Now repeat the steps in (b) above.

iii Note, when much of the oxygen in the apparatus has been consumed (e.g. when the volume taken up = 6 cm^3 approximately) the air in the apparatus needs renewing by emptying the contents and refilling.

3 a A fall in pressure in the respirometer chamber.

b Carbon dioxide given out is absorbed by soda lime, and nitrogen is an inert gas as far as respiration is concerned.

c It would cause the volume of gas in the respirometer chamber to increase, and also increase the rate of respiration.

8.3 Steps to glycolysis

1 pp. 170–1 Section 8.3 Investigating metabolism.

2 pp. 126–7 Monosaccharides; Figure 6.10 Hexose sugars.

3, 4 p. 171 Figure 8.5 Glycolysis: a metabolic pathway, part of respiration.

5 p. 318 Glycolysis.

6 p. 166 Metabolic pathways; metabolites and intermediates.

7 p. 512 Figure 23.3 Carbohydrate metabolism; a summary.

8 a, b p. 141 Section 6.10 Adenosine triphosphate and nucleotide coenzymes; Figure 6.32 Nucleotide coenzymes involved in metabolism.

c p. 171 Figure 8.5 Glycolysis: a metabolic pathway, part of respiration.

8.4 Investigating catalase activity

1 Graph (x-axis = concentration of hydrogen peroxide, in 'volumes'; y-axis = volume of froth formed).

2 a Set up ten 100 cm^3 graduated measuring cylinders, labelled from 10-volume to 1-volume H_2O_2.

b Using a 100 cm^3 beaker, dilute 30 cm^3 of 20-volume H_2O_2 by addition of 30 cm^3 of distilled water. Mix thoroughly.

c Transfer 10 cm^3 of this 10-volume H_2O_2 solution to the measuring cylinder labelled '10-volume H_2O_2'.

d To the other nine measuring cylinders, transfer 9, 8, 7, 6, 5, 4, 3, 2 and 1 cm^3 of the 10-volume H_2O_2 solution in the beaker to the appropriately labelled measuring cylinder, using the graduated pipette with safety filler.

e To these measuring cylinders add 1, 2, 3, 4, 5, 6, 7, 8 and 9 cm^3 of distilled water respectively, again using the graduated pipette.

3 Avoid any contact between your skin (and especially your eyes), and the hydrogen peroxide solution. Wear safety glasses. Use a safety filler with your pipette for all measurements of volumes of liquids. Clear up spills of hydrogen peroxide with excess water.

4 Investigate the effect of using small pieces of liver that had been heated in boiling water (to inactivate enzymes present) for 5–10 minutes, then cooled before adding to H_2O_2 solution.

5 The amounts of liver used in each test are not identical; the liver samples do not necessarily contain the same amount of enzyme (e.g. if some samples contain more artery and/or vein tissue); the surface areas of the liver samples are not identical.

6 p. 179 Figure 8.16 The effect of substrate concentration on an enzyme-catalysed reaction.

8.5 Quick test
8.6 Essay assignment
Chapter 8, pp. 166–85.

CHAPTER 9

9.1 Mitosis

1 p. 147 Preserved and stained tissues.

2 D, A, C, B.

3 a, b p. 189 Prophase.

4 a Animal cell, see p. 161 Centrioles of the centrosome.

b (i) Centrosome, (ii) centrioles, (iii) spindle fibre (p. 160 Microtubules), (iv) centromere, (v) chromatid.

c p. 189 Prophase.

d Immediately after D (A = very early anaphase).

e Two chromosomes, replicated with chromatids.

5 a Prophase = 70, metaphase = 10, anaphase = 5, telophase = 15.

b Prophase takes the longest and anaphase the least time in the process of nuclear division.

9.2 Mitosis and meiosis compared

1 a p. 187 Mitosis.

b, c p. 186 Figure 9.1 Types of nuclear division.

2 a p. 188 Figure 9.3 Mitosis in cells of the root tip of *Allium* sp. 1. Prophase.

b p. 191 Figure 9.7 Meiosis in an animal cell. 4. Late prophase I.

3 p. 192 Prophase I.

4 p. 192 Figure 9.8 The changes to a homologous pair of chromosomes during meiosis; p. 193 Figure 9.9 The chiasma has a mechanical function in meiosis.

5 a Differences in the genetic information (genes) between two individual cells.

b p. 193 Table 9.2 A comparison of mitosis and meiosis.

9.3 DNA and protein synthesis; transcription and translation

1, 2, 3 pp. 200–1 Section 9.8 The genetic code.

4 G A T C T A A C C.

5 p. 202 Step Two: amino acid activation.

6 mRNA codons:

CUA, CUC, CUG, CUA, GAC, GAU, UGG;

corresponding tRNA anticodons:

GAU, GAG, GAC, GAU, CUG, CUA, ACC.

7 leu–asp–try.

8, 9 pp. 200–1 Section 9.8 The genetic code.

10 p. 157 Ribosomes; pp. 202–3 Section 9.9 Protein synthesis.

9.4 Quick test
9.5 Essay assignment
Chapter 9, pp. 186–205.

CHAPTER 10

10.1 Epithelia
1 pp. 208–9 Section 10.3 Epithelia.
2 a, b, 3 a, b p. 209 Columnar and cubical epithelia.
3 c (i) cilia, (ii) cytoplasm, (iii) nucleus, (iv) basement membrane, (v) goblet cell.
4 a, b p. 209 Stratified epithelium.
5 pp. 208–9 Section 10.3 Epithelia.

10.2 Connective tissue
1 The composition of blood plasma is regulated by the action of the kidneys (p. 387 The nephron). For the origin, composition and functions of plasma, see p. 212 Plasma.
   The origin, composition and functions of the bone matrix are discussed in pp. 210–11 Bone.
2 a, b, c p. 211 Compact bone; Figure 10.10 Compact and spongy bone.
3 a, b, 4 a, b pp. 212–13 Blood cells; Erythrocytes (red blood cells); Leucocytes (white blood cells); Platelets.
4 c Approximately one white cell to 40 red cells. The ratio is atypical (normally 1 : 700).
5 pp. 362–5 Section 17.4 Blood as a transporting medium; pp. 370–1 Immunity and the immune system.

10.3 Muscle
1 pp. 214–15 Section 10.5 Muscle.
2 p. 159 Mitochondria; p. 320 Figure 15.22 The site of tissue respiration.
3 a, b, c, d, 4 a, b, c, 5 a, b pp. 214–15 Section 10.5 Muscle.

10.4 Primary tissues of flowering plants
1 Use the information in p. 413 Figure 19.17 The procambial strand and vascular tissue, and in p. 415 Figure 19.19 Photomicrographs of mature primary growth of the stem and root of *Ranunculus* sp. Alternatively, refer to C J Clegg and Gene Cox (1988), *Anatomy and Activities of Flowering Plants* John Murray, pp. 11, 13, 14 and 15.
2 Fibres, metaxylem, protoxylem.
3 a, b p. 219 Section 10.8 Parenchyma.
4 a, b p. 220 Section 10.9 Collenchyma.
5 a, b p. 220 Section 10.10 Sclerenchyma.
6 a, b p. 223 Section 10.12 Phloem.
7 a, b pp. 220–21 Section 10.10 Sclerenchyma; Section 10.11 Xylem.

10.5 Quick test
10.6 Essay assignment
Chapter 10, pp. 206–23.

CHAPTER 11

11.1 Size, shape and diffusion
1 x-axis = SA/V ratio (0.6, 0.8, 1.0, 1.2, 2.4); y-axis = time for colour change from red to yellow.
2 Inward diffusion of acid, over the entire surface area. In smaller blocks there is a greater surface area per unit of volume.
3 p. 226 Section 11.2 Diffusion.
4 p. 226 Table 11.1 The rate of diffusion.
5 Examples include: producing blocks of precise dimensions; detecting the end-point (colour change) precisely.

11.2 Water potential and the movement of water between cells
1 pp. 228–9 Components of water potential.
2 A = −80; B = −60; C = −70.
3 B → A + C; C → A.
4 a −1000.
b Photosynthetic production of sugars; p. 331 Figure 16.15 The water potential of soil, plant and air.
5 a p. 231 Water relations of animal cells.
b p. 230 Cells and water potential.

11.3 The evidence for active uptake of ions by cells
1 Most cells are in close contact with the bathing solution; conditions are uniform for the experimental cells.
2 Cutting of tissue discs appears to release naturally occurring inhibitors of respiration (it is not due to a shortage of oxygen, for the oxygen-using enzymes are saturated, even at the concentration of oxygen found in bulky storage organs such as the potato).
3 To rule out the effects of unrepresentative discs (e.g. occasional discs containing much vascular tissue and fewer metabolising cells).
4 a p. 332 Table 16.1 Macro- and micronutrients of plants.
b Inhibition of aerobic respiration.
c Aerobic respiration (or one product, ATP) is required for active uptake of ions like phosphate.
5 a Ion uptake is a selective process (e.g. more Na^+ than Cl^-), and is dependent upon metabolic energy (ATP), and therefore occurs faster at 25 °C than 4 °C because the reactions of metabolism are faster at 25 °C than at 4 °C.
b Microorganisms themselves take up ions from the medium for use in metabolism; microorganisms may attack the cells of the tissue discs, altering their metabolism.

11.4 The water potential of cells of an inflorescence stalk
1 So that the physiology of all tissue strips was comparable (e.g. cells had same initial ψ).
2 171 g.
3 Pipette 4 cm^3 of the 0.5 mol dm^{-3} sucrose solution into a beaker, and add 16 cm^3 of distilled water. Mix thoroughly.
4 p. 219 The specialised forms of parenchyma; Epidermis.
5 Curled almost into a ring, exposing more of the inner parenchyma tissue.
6 Loss of most water from the thin-walled parenchyma cells.
7 Equivalent to the water potential of the 0.3 mol dm^{-3} solution, since least change of shape has occurred here.
8 The water potential of the parenchyma of the stalk might be equivalent to that of the 0.5 mol dm^{-3} solution (more solutes would be concentrated in a decreased volume of cell sap).

11.5 Quick test
11.6 Essay assignment
Chapter 11, pp. 224–37.

Section 3

Except where stated, page references are to *Advanced Biology*.

CHAPTER 12

12.1 Carbon dioxide fixation by a green plant crop
1 CO_2 is being given out at this time, due to respiration in the dark.
2 At 7 a.m. and at 11 a.m. (approximately).
3 About 10 a.m. to 12-noon, when net CO_2 fixation was at its maximum.

4 Via stomata, into the sub-stomatal cavity → air spaces around mesophyll cells, dissolves in surface film of moisture on cells' walls, diffuses into chloroplasts, into the stroma (p. 252 Figure 12.18 The functioning leaf).

From respiration in the leaf cells (p. 249 Carbon dioxide).

5 p. 325 Figure 16.2 Transpiration from the aerial system of the flowering plant.

6 p. 338 *Rhizobium* in the nodules of leguminous plants.

12.2 The effect of temperature on photosynthesis at high and low light intensities

1 The oxygen-enriched air produced by the plant in a two-minute period is transferred to the part of the capillary tube with the scale attached, by withdrawing the barrel of the syringe the required distance. The length of the gas bubble is measured, and, with knowledge of the cross-sectional area of the capillary tube, the volume of gas can be calculated.

2 Variations in the temperature of the tube containing the water plant (no water bath in use); effect of water temperature on the solubility of the gases; variations in the performance of the leaf material with time/handling, etc.; variations in barometric pressure during the experiment.

3 Sodium hydrogencarbonate solution ensures a supply of dissolved CO_2; pre-incubation at different temperatures ensures that the photosynthetic cells are at the temperature of the surrounding water when readings were taken.

4 a, b By varying the distance of the light source from the experiment.

Arrange for the light to pass through water in a separate container, to prevent heating up the experimental plant.

5 The light bulb may be low in output of the red and blue parts of the spectrum of white light which are required for photosynthesis (p. 247 Figure 12.9 Chlorophyll: the absorption spectrum and the action spectrum).

6 Graph; x-axis = temperature; y-axis = 'length of bubble' (= rate of photosynthesis). Two distinct curves for the readings at high and low light.

7 There is a marked rise in the rate of gas production between 10 and 20 °C at high light intensity, but a very slight rise at low light intensity.

8 a, b, 10 p. 255 The 'light' and the 'dark' steps.

9 p. 255 Figure 12.22 The effect of temperature.

12.3 Summarising photosynthesis

1 p. 264 A summary of photosynthesis.

2 p. 260 Figure 12.31 The light step of photosynthesis; p. 263 Figure 12.35 The dark step of photosynthesis; or (simplified) p. 264 A summary of photosynthesis.

12.4 The leaf as a factory for photosynthesis

1 The structure of the leaf blade, p. 252 Figure 12.18 The functioning leaf; Table 12.1 The structural adaptations of a green leaf for photosynthesis.

The arrangement of leaf blades on the stems, by growth of the leaf stalks, p. 265 Figure 12.37 Leaf arrangements in which there is a minimum of overlap.

2 a, b p. 329 Air movements; p. 379 Table 18.2 Xeromorphic features: a summary.

3 The shape of the leaf and its vein network, p. 251 Section 12.4 The leaf; its attachment to the stem, p. 484 Figure 22.1 Mechanical stress that organisms resist; the presence of collenchyma below the epidermis, particularly at the mid-rib and the leaf margin, p. 220 Section 10.9 Collenchyma.

4 p. 252 Figure 12.18 The functioning leaf; p. 324 Section 16.2 The movement of water in plants.

5 The air spaces between parenchyma cells of leaf blade (mesophyll), leaf stalk, stem and roots are interconnecting; there are no sealing 'bulkheads' anywhere in the plant. These spaces facilitate diffusion of gases.

6 a Spongy mesophyll.

b A diagrammatic version is shown on p. 260 Figure 12.31 The light step of photosynthesis.

12.5 Photosynthetic productivity in natural and agricultural systems

1 p. 168 Section 8.2 Energy and metabolism.

2 For example, cotton fibres of cellulose from plant cell walls, pp. 162–3 Section 7.5 Cell walls, and p. 437 Figure 20.24 Abscisic acid and fruit fall in the cotton plant. Wool fibres, obtained from the wool of sheep skin. This product (a protein) is formed by sheep from their typical diet of grass.

3 a, b p. 78 Alternative sources of energy.

4 a p. 104 The application of fertiliser.

b p. 335 Maintaining soil fertility for commercial crops; p. 332 Table 16.1 Macro- and micronutrients of plants.

5 Prolonged shortage of water to support plant growth.

6 pp. 114–15 Section 5.6 Biological fuel generation; p. 270 Mimicking photosynthesis.

12.6 'High hopes for C$_4$ plants'

1 a p. 268 Section 12.9 Photosynthesis in C$_4$ plants.

b p. 269 Figure 12.45 Competitive inhibition of RuBP carboxylase by oxygen.

2 a, b, c pp. 268–9 Section 12.9 Photosynthesis in C$_4$ plants; Section 12.10 Photosynthesis and oxygen concentration; photorespiration.

3, 4 pp. 266–7 Plants in arid conditions.

5 Plankton, see p. 83. Figure 4.14 The discovery of extensive seasonal algal blooms by satellite images, and associated text.

6 p. 268 Figure 12.43 C$_4$ plants.

12.7 Designing an investigation

1 Select and prepare suitable lengths of vigorously photosynthesising *Elodea*, placing them in the barrel of a 20 cm^3 syringe as shown. Support the syringe in a well-illuminated and upright position as shown, attach a length of capillary tube to the syringe nozzle, and then fill the barrel with an appropriately diluted sodium hydrogencarbonate solution (keeping your finger over the capillary tube end). Replace the plunger of the syringe and lower it to the 20 cm^3 marker, and then withdraw the syringe up the barrel until the meniscus in the capillary is near the top, as shown in the diagram, marking this position of the meniscus. After 20–30 minutes, measure the distance travelled by the meniscus. Repeat the procedure with different dilutions of sodium hydrogencarbonate solution.

A 0.1 mol dm^{-3} solution of NaHCO$_3$ contains 8.4 g of the solid, dissolved in distilled water and made up to 1 dm^3. The required range of dilutions is made by first mixing equal quantities of the stock solution and distilled water. Then take a measured volume of the diluted solution and dilute it with an equal volume of water, and so on to give, in turn, 0.05, 0.025 and 0.0125 mol dm^{-3} solutions.

2 Differences in the reactions of the *Elodea* in different NaHCO$_3$ solutions; change in rate of photosynthesis in *Elodea* with time; difficulty in reading the position of the meniscus accurately; temperature variations.

12.8 Flow diagram summaries to complete

1 p. 264 A summary of photosynthesis.

a Water; **b** oxygen; **c** ATP; **d** NADP; **e** ribulose bisphosphate; **f** glycerate 3-phosphate; **g** sugars.

2 p. 243 Figure 12.2 The carbon cycle.

a Combustion; **b** respiration; **c** combined carbon of consumers; **d** death; **e** photosynthesis; **f** combined carbon of dead organic matter.

12.9 Quick test
12.10 Essay assignment

Chapter 12, pp. 242–71.

CHAPTER 13

13.1 The Green Revolution re-examined

1 The discovery of archaeological remains (seeds and other plant remains, animal bones) at sites occupied by early human communities (p. 650 Figure 29.19 The Fertile Crescent). Organic remains can be dated quite precisely (p. 656 Figure 30.8 Radiometric dating).

2 They exploit 'genetic diversity' in the use of local (sometimes 'wild') plants as parents for new crop plants.

3 The leaf is a 'factory for photosynthesis' (pp. 251–2 Section 12.4 The leaf), whereas the stem is of limited food value, yet is constructed from products of photosynthesis.

4 They absorb the ions from the soil quickly, and use them effectively in the production of plant materials valuable to the farmer/consumer (p. 335 Maintaining soil fertility for commercial crops).

5 The new varieties are vulnerable to attack by local populations of insects.

6 Breeding of varieties locally, exploiting natural resistance to pests and the ability to grow well in existing regimes of weather (e.g. rainfall) and on fertiliser levels that can be maintained using local herd animals' dung, compost, etc. Farming/crop storage methods that sustain employment for a wide range of local people of all abilities. Cultivation methods based on intermediate technology sustained by the skills of local people, and using available, renewable resources.

13.2 Alcohol, diet and health

1 a i 4 units of beer (4×11.4 g) + 2 units of whisky (2×10 g) = 65.6 g

ii 60% of 80 kg = 48 kg of body fluid (1 kg body fluid = 1 dm^3). Blood alcohol (mg 100 cm^{-3}) = $65.6 \times 1000/48 \times 10$ = 136.66 mg 100 cm^{-3}.

b i Elimination of ethanol in 3 h is 3×21 mg 100 cm^{-3} blood = 63 mg cm^{-3}, leaving 73.66 mg 100 cm^{-3}.

ii Elimination of ethanol in 6 h is 6×21 mg 100 cm^{-3} blood = 126 mg cm^{-3}, leaving 10.66 mg 100 cm^{-3}.

A person may be prosecuted if found to have a blood alcohol level of more than 80 mg 100 cm^{-3} in the UK.

2 a p. 136 Figure 6.24 Cross-linking within a polypeptide; p. 138 Table 6.4 The functions of proteins.

b p. 138 Denaturing of proteins.

3 pp. 454–5 Transmission across the synapse; p. 456 Drugs and the synapse.

4 a, b pp. 131–3 Section 6.7 Lipids; pp. 153–5 The cell surface membrane (plasma membrane).

5 From the existence of the early human communities until relatively recent times – until the development of a supply of uncontaminated drinking water was established, in fact – people often avoided waterborne diseases (unknowingly) by drinking dilute alcoholic drinks, rather than the available water.

13.3 The roles of cholesterol

1 a p. 166 Section 8.1 Metabolism; p. 273 Diet.

b For example:

	metabolites	nutrients
green plants	glycerate 3-phosphate, ribulose bisphosphate	carbon dioxide, water
human	glycogen, urea	proteins, lipids

2 pp. 153–5 The cell surface membrane (plasma membrane).

3 p. 133 Steroids; p. 601 Endocrine control of the menstrual cycle.

4 It is known that the body can manufacture its own supply.

5 pp. 290–1 Absorption of digested food.

6 a pp. 358–9 Atherosclerosis; Figure 17.23 The development of atherosclerosis (plaque = atheroma).

b p. 278 Cholesterol.

7, 8 p. 278 Cholesterol.

13.4 Digestion in the stomach

1, 2, 4 p. 285 Figure 13.17 The human stomach; its wall and glands; p. 284 Gastric juice.

3 a Gastric fistula or pouch.

b Pouch to which the nerve supply is severed.

c Plastic tube sampling, with analysis of stomach contents for pH change and bacterial action.

d Plastic tube sampling with analysis of stomach contents for protein/peptide balance.

e Pouch to which nerves and blood supply are disconnected.

f Protein introduced into a pouch which has nerve supply severed.

5 p. 286 The discovery of stomach function; Figure 13.19 The passage of a 'barium meal'.

13.5 Absorption in the villus

1 a, b p. 288 Figure 13.22 The small intestine: walls and glands; p. 290 Figure 13.23 The structure and function of the villus.

2 p. 135 Figure 6.22 The peptide bond.

3 pp. 284–5 The stomach; p. 291 Absorption of protein.

4 As amino acids, by active transport.

13.6 Quick test
13.7 Essay assignment

Chapter 13, pp. 272–93.

CHAPTER 14

14.1 How do these organisms obtain nutrients?

Autotrophs: **a, f, g** (chemotrophic).

Heterotrophs: holozoic, **d, h, i**; saprotrophic, **b, e**; parasitic, **c, j**.

14.2 The life cycle of a plant parasite

1 p. 24 The five-kingdom scheme of classification.

2 'Body' of mycelium consisting of branching hyphae; production of spores.

3 Feeds on its host plant, causing harm; spends greater part of life cycle attached to host tissues.

4 Weather conditions in Scotland prevent *Phytophthora* infection in potatoes.

5 The 'germination' process of its spores varies according to environmental conditions.

6 p. 305 Virulent and benign parasites.

7, 8 p. 545 Potato blight and the role of fungicides.

9 p. 304 Figure 14.24 Parasitic nutrition of potato blight.

10 Destroy the tubers; 'rest' the ground from potato culture for a period; buy in new seed potatoes for planting on uncontaminated land.

14.3 Quick test
14.4 Essay assignment

Chapter 14, pp. 294–305.

CHAPTER 15

15.1 A simple method of measuring respiration rate

1 It avoids altering the temperature of the respirometer (and therefore the internal pressure).

2 CO_2 absorbent, such as 'soda lime'.

3 They must be kept moist; since their outer surface is permeable they lose water in a dry environment.

4 With the apparatus set up with CO_2 absorbent and containing a weighed sample of maggots, dip the manometer into coloured manometric fluid (e.g. red ink) to introduce a bubble into the manometer capillary tube. Dry off the excess marker fluid. Clamp the apparatus as shown, start the stop-clock, and record the distance moved by the marker in a recorded period. Measure the cross-sectional area of the capillary. Convert the length measurement to a change in volume (oxygen uptake).

5 Lack of a 'thermobarometer' control tube, checking on changes in temperature or pressure during the experiment; lack of a water bath to stabilise the temperature of the respirometer chamber; errors from handling the respirometer in setting it up, causing fluctuations in temperature.

6 Identical apparatus, with soda lime omitted, in order to detect any volume change in the respirometer during an experimental period. For example, if the volume does not change, carbon dioxide output is the same as oxygen intake.

15.2 Measuring respiration by the Warburg manometer

1 a The fresh mass.

b CO_2 absorbent, e.g. KOH solution with a filter paper wick.

c i Adjust screw at base of manometer until liquid level in right arm corresponds to original level. (During the experiment the liquid level in the closed arm has risen with uptake of oxygen by tissue.)

ii Thus the flask volume is kept constant whilst readings are taken.

iii Read the level in the open arm. The height change here is a measure of oxygen taken up in 15 minutes.

d Change in barometric pressure during the experimental period.

A 'control' flask (thermobarometer), identical to the experimental flask except that inert material (e.g. glass beads) of the same volume replaces the living tissue.

2 a The rate of respiration may be regulated by the needs of living tissues for energy; rapidly growing or metabolically active tissues respire more vigorously than metabolically inactive tissues.

b Apical meristem: cell division, cell enlargement, protein synthesis. Mesophyll tissue in the dark: transport of products of photosynthesis into phloem, maintenance of cell's enzymic machinery.

c p. 223 Section 10.12 Phloem; p. 344 The mechanism of phloem transport; p. 221 Section 10.11 Xylem; pp. 324–5 Section 16.2 The movement of water in plants.

d Differences in rate of growth/metabolic activity.

15.3 Measuring oxygen consumption with the respirometer

1 a, b p. 315 Section 15.5 Investigating human breathing; Figure 15.16 Human lung capacity.

2 a Breathing rate should be under unconscious control, and data on breathing may consciously influence the breather's responses.

b Air intake and output are directed via the mouth and spirometer only.

3 a Before.

b The volume of gas in the respirometer chamber would not steadily decrease (CO_2 would take the place of the O_2 absorbed).

4 a Depth and frequency of the volume variations on the chart breathing record.

b Approximately 2.5 dm^3; 22 breaths per 60 s.

5 O_2 consumption in 60 s = 1.32 dm^3.

6 See 'Risk assessment' for Practical 15.4 Investigating human breathing (p. 182 of this *Study Guide*).

15.4 The phases of tissue respiration

pp. 318–19 Section 15.6 Tissue respiration. See Table A6.

15.5 Respiratory quotient of germinating seeds

1 Graph: x-axis = time; y-axis = gas exchange (O_2 uptake and CO_2 output).

Table A6 The phases of tissue respiration

	Glycolysis	Krebs cycle	Electron-transport pathway
involves CO_2 release	no	yes	no
produces ATP	a little	a little	yes
occurs in the cytoplasm (cytosol)	yes	no	no
uses ATP	yes	no	no
occurs in the matrix of mitochondria	no	yes	no
is a series of redox reactions	no	no	yes
involves CO_2 fixation	no	no	no
hexose molecules are the substrate	yes	no	no
involves CoA	no	yes	no
is a cyclic process	no	yes	no
occurs on the cristae of mitochondria	no	no	yes
yields intermediates for cell synthesis reactions	yes	yes	no

Two distinctive curves, and clearly labelled.

2 0.7; 0.8; 0.9.

3 p. 322 Respiratory quotient; p. 323 Figure 15.27 The respiratory quotient (RQ) of germinating seeds.

4 a, b, c p. 404 Fresh mass *v.* dry mass.

5 a, b Different stages in growth and development between early in germination and later, e.g. in the period 0–20 h, the emphasis may be on hydrolytic enzyme formation, food reserve hydrolysis, and transport to growth sites. In the period 30–50 h, additionally, new tissues may be formed, and ion absorption may be occurring, for example.

15.6 Smoking and health

Original material is required here.

15.7 Quick test
15.8 Essay assignment

Chapter 15, pp. 306–23.

CHAPTER 16

16.1 Stomatal numbers and the atmospheric concentration of carbon dioxide

1 p. 252 Figure 12.18 The functioning leaf; p. 326 The role and importance of stomata.

2 a Stomata are open, and a CO_2 concentration gradient is maintained because of the uptake of CO_2 by the mesophyll in the light.

b pp. 226–7 Section 11.2 Diffusion.

3 Decreased numbers of stomata per unit area.

4, 5 Lowered water loss by transpiration, see p. 325 The role of transpiration.

6, 7 pp. 82–3 The concentration of atmospheric carbon dioxide.

8 These leaves would be in comparable conditions during growth, i.e. in full sunlight.

9 Permits direct comparisons of the effects of external conditions.

10 p. 84 The possibility of climate change.

16.2 Deficiency symptoms in plants

1 The inert chips give the experimenter total control over the ions supplied to the plant.

2 p. 334 The process of ion uptake.

3 p. 332 Discovering the mineral nutrient requirements of plants.

4 p. 334 The process of ion uptake.

5, 6 p. 334 Mobilisation and circulation of ions in plants.

7 a p. 332 Table 16.1 Macro- and micronutrients of plants.

b p. 334 Mobilisation and circulation of ions in plants.

8 p. 332 Table 16.1 Macro- and micronutrients of plants; p. 333 Table 16.2 Ion-deficiency symptoms of plants; p. 245 Figure 12.6 The chemistry of chlorophyll pigments.

16.3 Translocation and phloem structure

1 a p. 129 Cellulose; p. 130 Other polysaccharides and polysaccharide derivatives; pp. 162–4 Section 7.5 Cell walls.

b Iodine in potassium iodide gives a yellow coloration to cellulose; chlor-zinc-iodine stain gives a violet coloration to cellulose.

2, 3 a, b p. 223 Section 10.12 Phloem.

4, 5 p. 341 Section 16.6 Movement of elaborated food; Figure 16.32 Sieve tube element with companion cell.

6 a pp. 344–5 The mechanism of phloem transport.

b Cf. pp. 324–5 Section 16.2 The movement of water through plants.

7 p. 343 The use of radiocarbon as a tracer.

8 pp. 344–5 The mechanism of phloem transport.

16.4 Mycorrhizae and the growth of plants

1 p. 294 Figure 14.1 The classification of nutrition; p. 302 Section 14.6 Parasitic nutrition.

2 p. 61 Figure 3.30 Podsol and brown earth soil types.

3 a, b Soil naturally contains a microflora of bacteria and fungi, some of which release ions from dead organic matter in forms that plant roots may absorb.

4, 5 pp. 339–40 Mycorrhizae.

16.5 Quick test
16.6 Essay assignment

Chapter 16, pp. 324–45.

CHAPTER 17

17.1 The structure and functioning of the heart

1 1 = aorta; 2 = anterior vena cava; 3 = pulmonary artery; 4 = right atrium; 5 = semilunar valves; 6 = right atrio-ventricular (tricuspid) valve; 7 = inferior vena cava; 8 = right ventricle; 9 = pulmonary veins; 10 = left atrioventricular (bicuspid) valve; 11 = semilunar valves; 12 = chordae tendinae.

2 p. 350 Section 17.2 The human heart.

3 a, b p. 350 The chambers of the heart.

4 p. 352 The heart as a pump.

5 a Between A and B.

b C.

6 Approximately 80 beats per minute.

7 a pp. 353–4 The control of heartbeat.

b p. 354 Figure 17.14 The regulation of heartbeat.

8 a 1.

b 3.

c 4.

d 5.

9 p. 481 The adrenal medulla.

17.2 Arteries, veins and capillaries

1

	artery	vein
lumen	2660	4000
wall	1170	330

2, 4 pp. 354–5 Section 17.3 Arteries, veins and capillaries.

3 pp. 354–7 The structure of arteries and veins; Figure 17.20 A capillary network, and the origin of a lymph capillary.

5 a In; out; in (-0.2 kPa; $+1.1$ kPa; -1.7 kPa).

b Friction.

c, d p. 357 Tissue fluid; exchange between blood and cells.

17.3 Quick test
17.4 Essay assignment

Chapter 17, pp. 346–75.

CHAPTER 18

18.1 Osmoregulation and excretion crossword

1 = impermeable; 2 = diuresis; 3 = cortex; 4 = juxtamedullary; 5 = distal; 6 = haemodialysis; 7 = ammonia; 8 = contractile vacuole; 9 = excretion; 10 = loop of Henle; 11 = descending limb; 12 = vasa recta; 13 = reabsorption; 14 = Malpighian body; 15 = countercurrent; 16 = guttation; 17 = renal artery; 18 = diffusion; 19 = ultrafiltration; 20 = medulla; 21 = permeability; 22 = uric acid; 23 = osmoregulation; 24 = aldosterone.

18.2 The functioning kidney tubule

1 A = Malpighian body; B = proximal convoluted tubule; C = descending limb; D = ascending limb of loop of Henle; E = distal convoluted tubule; F = collecting duct.

2 4.7 kPa.

3 a, b, c p. 389 Figure 18.17 Re-absorption in the proximal convoluted tubule.

4 pp. 390–1 The role of the loop of Henle.

5 p. 392 Regulation in the distal convoluted tubule; pp. 392–3 Water re-absorption in the collecting duct.

18.3 Halophytes: adaptations and survival

1 pp. 378–9 Halophytes.

2 For example: succulent plant, with water-storage capacity; reduced surface area, with waxy cuticle, restricting water loss by transpiration.

3 a Use large samples of seeds; check they are not in an imposed dormancy state; remove any salt deposits on the outer surface of the seeds by washing; set up tests for percentage germination with samples on filter paper in closed Petri dishes, together with sufficient water or salt solution in contact with each seed.

b Physiological drought due to osmotic loss of water.

c Propagation by vegetative propagation.

d When parts of the rhizome are broken off (tide, animal action) and carried to new sites (tide, animal movement) where they root and grow.

4 a p. 60 Soil air.

b pp. 378–9 Halophytes.

5 From river water and seawater.

18.4 The significance of xeromorphic features in a sand dune species

1 No soil, fast drainage of rain water, salt spray, high wind speeds, lack of shade from sun.

2 a It causes blown sand to accumulate and be held to make the dune.

b Observation of dune structure and sand movement where marram grass is present and absent.

3 Many of the features listed on p. 379 Table 18.2 Xeromorphic features; a summary.

4 a Leaf litter and humus.

b See this *Study Guide*, pp. 22–3.

c About 200 years.

d Because of sand movements, the limited flora and fauna, and the high salt concentration.

5 pp. 266–7 Plants in arid conditions.

18.5 Quick test

18.6 Essay assignment

Chapter 18, pp. 376–97.

Section 4

Except where stated, page references are to *Advanced Biology*.

CHAPTER 19

19.1 Growth of microorganisms

1 See Table A7.

2 Accumulation of dead cells and of waste products of metabolism, e.g. organic acids, CO_2; disappearance of sugar, meat extract and ions.

3 pp. 403–4 Measuring the growth of unicellular organisms. See also Practical 7.3 (p. 98 of this *Study Guide*).

4 $B_t = 5000 \times 2^6$
$= 320\,000$

5 a 352 000.

b Graph: x-axis = time; y-axis = number of cells.

6 a, b p. 407 Figure 19.7 The sigmoid curve of growth; 1 Lag phase, 4 Stationary phase.

7 See the 'Risk assessment' of Practical 7.5 (p. 101 of this *Study Guide*).

8 To test the amount of variation in growth rates in comparable samples, and (via a mean of three flasks) to rule out the likelihood of the result being based on unrepresentative data.

19.2 Analysing growth by means of the Spearman rank correlation coefficient

1 See the scatter diagram in Figure 3.19 (p. 39 of this *Study Guide*).

2 See Table A8.

3 $n(n^2 - 1) = 10(100 - 1) = 990$

4 The Spearman rank correlation coefficient:

$$r_s = 1 - \frac{6\Sigma D^2}{n(n^2 - 1)} = 1 - \frac{6 \times 36}{990} = 0.7818$$

5 Comparing this value of r_s with the critical values for the Spearman rank correlation coefficient in Table A2.4 (p. 437 of this *Study Guide*) for a test with a sample size of $n = 10$, at the 5% significance level:

Critical value of r_s (where $n = 10$) at the 5% significance level = 0.648.

6 The null hypothesis is rejected.

That body mass in the rabbit is directly related to pasture productivity might be confirmed by moving animals to pastures of different qualities to see if the mass of rabbit adjusted (with time) to the new level of food provision.

19.3 Development of the vertebrate embryo

1, 2, 3 p. 419 Fertilisation and cleavage.

4 a Experimental surgical techniques in which groups of cells are transported to a different part of an embryo, and observing subsequent development to be in keeping with their origin, rather than their acquired position; p. 420 Fate maps.

b A 'sense of position' has not yet been acquired (at the eight-cell stage). The notochord may be one of the 'organiser' tissues.

Table A7 Essential nutrients

Nutrient	Source
water	water
carbohydrate (e.g. sugars)	glucose
fatty acids + glycerol	meat extract
amino acids	meat extract
certain growth factors and vitamins	meat extract
ions, e.g. phosphate, potassium	e.g. potassium hydrogenphosphate

Table A8 Analysing growth data

1 Rabbit	2 Body mass/ kg	3	4 Pasture quality/ g m^{-2}	5	6 Difference in ranks (D)	7 D^2
1	1.50	1	12.5	2	−1	1
2	2.00	5	20.0	3	+2	4
3	2.38	9	37.5	9	0	0
4	1.60	2	10.0	1	+1	1
5	2.45	10	35.0	8	+2	4
6	2.20	6	25.0	4	+2	4
7	2.35	8	40.0	10	−2	4
8	2.25	7	30.0	6	+1	1
9	1.95	4	27.5	5	−1	1
10	1.90	3	32.5	7	−4	16

$$\Sigma D^2 = 36$$

c The cells have not started irrevocably on the path to differentiation, i.e. they are still totipotent.

5 p. 420 Gastrulation.

6, 7, 8 p. 420–1 Organogeny, including Figure 19.28 The three germ layers and the tissues formed from them.

9 pp. 502–3 Section 22.5 Fish: locomotion in water; Figure 22.32 Locomotion in the dogfish.

10 Cephalisation, and the development of four limbs.

19.4 Quick test

19.5 Essay assignment

Chapter 19, pp. 402–23.

CHAPTER 20

20.1 The *Avena* curvature test

1, 2 p. 428 Figure 20.9 The coleoptile as an experimental organ; cf. p. 414 Figure 19.18 The pattern of primary growth in stem and root of a dicotyledonous plant.

3 p. 428 Went and the bioassay of auxin.

4 a p. 434 The role of IAA in tropism is controversial.

b p. 434 The status of IAA as a plant growth substance.

5 Physiological regeneration of the coleoptile tip may occur quickly after decapitation (a secondary site of auxin production forms).

6 Agar blocks shrivel up in a dry atmosphere.

7 p. 429 Figure 20.11 The oat coleoptile curvature test for auxin.

8 A series of agar blocks with known, increasing IAA concentration, starting from zero.

9 p. 430 Is 'auxin' indoleacetic acid?

10 p. 436 Plant and animal hormones compared.

20.2 Plant growth regulators interact

1 Graph: *x*-axis = time (hours); *y*-axis = mean gain in length (mm); all four curves distinctive (e.g. using different symbols, say •, ○, ×, +) and clearly labelled.

2 p. 434 <u>The role of IAA in tropism is controversial</u>.

3 As a fair test of the reproducibility of the results, and to mask the effects of one 'freak' or unusual result.

4 p. 414 <u>Origin of leaves and lateral buds</u>.

5 As identical in origin as possible.

6 Plant growth regulators used here are also produced by the plant tissues (i.e. are endogenous).

7 a Between 0 and 18 hours into the experiment.

  b Plant growth regulators may be used up or enzymatically broken down; cut tissue lengths may become deprived of other requirements for growth; there is a limit to cell extension in any one region of the stem.

8 GA and IAA together produce greater extension than either acting alone.

9 p. 439 <u>Table 20.3 The interactions of phytohormones in growth and development</u>.

10 pp. 446–7 <u>Section 20.7 Applications of plant growth substances in industry</u>.

20.3 Herbicides – is there any case for action?

A personal presentation is required, using the information given in the excerpts, in Chapter 4 (pp. 89–91 <u>Pesticides</u>) and pp. 446–7 <u>Section 20.7 Applications of plant growth substances in industry</u>, and your wider reading. (Make clear from the outset the difference between 'pesticides' in general and 'herbicides'.)

20.5 Quick test
20.6 Essay assignment

Chapter 20, pp. 424–7.

CHAPTER 21

21.1 Sequencing activity in a nerve fibre

See Table A9.

Table A9 Activities in a nerve fibre

	Resting potential	Early in action potential	Late in action potential	Absolute refractory period	Relative refractory period
Active transport of K⁺ and Na⁺ (linked)	yes	no	no	no	yes
Facilitated diffusion of K⁺	yes	no	no	no	yes
Facilitated diffusion of Na⁺	yes	no	no	no	yes
Influx of Na⁺ via open channels	no	yes	no	no	no
Outflux of K⁺ via open channels	no	no	yes	no	no
ATP used to maintain resting potential	yes	no	no	no	yes

21.2 The synapse

1 A = axon; B = mitochondrion; C = synaptic vesicle; D = presynaptic membrane; E = synaptic cleft; F = receptor for transmitter substance; G = dendrite.

2 From A to G.

3 p. 159 <u>Mitochondria</u>; p. 320 <u>Figure 15.22 The site of tissue respiration</u>.

4, 5, 6 pp. 454–5 <u>Transmission across the synapse</u>.

7, 8 p. 456 <u>Drugs and the synapse</u>.

9 p. 455 <u>Electrical synapses</u>.

10 c (= 20 nm).

21.3 The retina: structure and function

1 Sensory neurones.

2 p. 464 <u>The role of the brain in vision</u>.

3 Pigment cells of the choroid.

4 p. 462 <u>Section 21.7 Sight</u>.

5 B; p. 216 <u>Figure 10.19 Multipolar, bipolar and unipolar neurones</u>.

6 p. 462 <u>Section 21.7 Sight</u>.

7, 8 p. 464 <u>The light-sensitive cells of the retina</u>.

9 p. 455 <u>The role of the synapse</u>.

10 Light focused on the retina passes through cell bodies, bipolar neurones, and axons linking the retina to the brain before impinging on the photosensitive cells.

21.4 Quick test
21.5 Essay assignment

Chapter 21, pp. 448–83.

CHAPTER 22

22.1 Muscle: structure and function

1 a, b pp. 214–15 <u>Section 10.5 Muscle</u>.

2 pp. 495–6 <u>The physiology of voluntary muscle</u>.

3 a = W; **b** = V; **c** = U; **d** = X.

4 a, b p. 497 <u>Stages in voluntary muscle contraction</u>.

5 See Table A10.

Table A10 Changes in a contracting fibril

	No change	Shorter	Longer
H-zone		yes	
A-band	yes		
I-band	yes		

6 p. 496 <u>Figure 22.21 The structure of a myofibril</u>.

7 p. 497 <u>Figure 22.24 The response of a muscle fibre to a nerve impulse</u>.

8 Respiration within mitochondria in the muscle fibres, and facilitated diffusion.

22.2 Flight

1 Insects, certain extinct reptiles, birds, certain mammals.

2 The information for your table is to be found on the pages listed in Table A11.

Table A11 Flight structures and mechanisms compared

	Insects	Birds
Skeleton	p. 488	p. 504
Flight muscles	p. 489	p. 506
Wing structure	p. 489	pp. 504–5
Body shape	pp. 488–9	pp. 504–5
Supply of oxygen	p. 309	p. 312

22.3 Quick test
22.4 Essay assignment
Chapter 22, pp. 484–509.

CHAPTER 23

23.1 Regulation of blood glucose
1 a pp. 290–1 Absorption of digested food.
  b, c p. 512 Regulation of blood sugar levels.
2 p. 230 Cells and water potential.
3 a p. 482 The pancreas; p. 513 Figure 23.5 The pancreas and hormone production.
  b p. 513 Figure 23.4 The sites and the processes of glucose regulation.
  c 7–8 times; associated with the intake of glucose-releasing foods, most probably.
4 p. 513 Figure 23.4 The sites and the processes of glucose regulation.
5 a Highest after the injection, falling off with time.
  b Variable, but always higher than in a healthy subject; tending to rise towards the end of the 24-hour period.
6 To produce a form of insulin that reduces glucose levels more effectively and for longer periods.
7 p. 513 Figure 23.4 The sites and the processes of glucose regulation.
8 p. 512 Regulation of blood sugar levels.
9 The lipid reserves, prior to mobilisation of the proteins of tissues such as muscle.
10 p. 516 Diabetes mellitus.

23.2 Temperature regulation
1 a Damage to cell proteins of key organs such as heart and brain. Excessive heat cannot be dispersed easily or quickly from a compact organism, and overheating leads to death more quickly than excessive heat loss does.
  b p. 518 Figure 5.23 Mammalian temperature regulation.
2 a The most accessible point in the body nearest the hypothalamus.
  b To know what temperature the 'cold centre' and the 'hot centre' for body temperature regulation are experiencing.
3 a Response to lowered core temperature.
  b p. 518 Figure 5.23 Mammalian temperature regulation.
4 The body remained in a hot environment, but the impulses from skin thermal receptors were ignored in response to impulses from deep thermal receptors.
5 a Initially, via the skin thermal receptors, but ultimately via the deep thermal receptors, if body temperature starts to fall.
  b p. 518 Figure 5.23 Mammalian temperature regulation.

23.3 Quick test
23.4 Essay assignment
Chapter 23, pp. 510–31.

CHAPTER 24

24.1 Food poisoning: the rising risks
1 a Graph: x-axis = time (years); y-axis = number of cases of food poisoning per 100 000 population.
  b Very approximately, between 200 and 250 cases per 100 000 population.

In response to your Minister's questions, your briefing paper will elaborate in appropriate detail on the following points:

2 a 'Better diagnosis' and 'an ageing population (due to rising life expectancy) with a concomitant weakening immune system' are factors in the 'rise' in incidence of food poisoning, but they are not the major causes of the increases. There is an actual rise in the incidence of food poisoning. This is probably largely because of changed eating habits of many people (e.g. greater use of 'convenience' foods, sometimes eaten 'on the move') and because some of this food is occasionally held under conditions where bacteria multiply quickly, at some stage prior to consumption.
  b i Human bacteria which reach the alimentary canal of cattle and sheep (taken in contaminated drinking water) may eventually contaminate meat from them used for human consumption, at the slaughter stage.
    ii Criteria for bacteriological purity of drinking water may help.
  c i Because of the method of filter feeding (pp. 294–5 *Mytilus*; filter feeding by cilia). These molluscs may filter out human pathogens, from sewage, present in the water.
    ii Coastal towns and cities should install complete sewage processing systems (p. 101 Waste water and industrial effluent treatment), and discontinue the daily dumping of raw sewage into the sea.
  d i Yes (p. 635 Gene mutations).
    ii, iii p. 536 How food poisoning occurs.
  e p. 536 How food poisoning occurs.

24.2 Thyroid cancer in the Ukraine
1 a, b, c, 2 a, b p. 479 Figure 21.46 The endocrine system: a summary; pp. 480–1 The thyroid gland.
3 Absorbed into green plants (e.g. agricultural leys), then eaten by cattle, sheep and goats (and wild herbivores such as rabbits or deer), the ^{131}I is then released in the gut of humans by digestion of milk and milk products (e.g. cheese) together with meat and meat products from these animals, and absorbed into the bloodstream, then concentrated in the thyroid gland.
4 See Panel 24.1.
5 Iodine is accumulated in the thyroid and used in the manufacture of hormones. ^{131}I emits β and γ radiation which may trigger mutations (particularly in the chromosomes of any dividing cells).
6 Progressively dispersed more widely in the world's lands, waters and atmosphere, and progressively decays to non-radioactive forms.
7 ^{131}I particularly concentrates in the milk in mammals (e.g. of humans and of cows and goats). In children, milk and milk products make up a large portion of the total diet.
8 The inverse square law applies to radiation.

24.3 Whooping cough and vaccination
1 p. 554 Figure 25.3 The characteristic shapes of bacteria.
2 p. 534 How bacteria cause harm to the body.
3 p. 371 Types of immunity.
4 pp. 547–8 Section 24.12 Preventive medicine.
5 See above.
6 p. 535 The uses of antibiotics.

24.4 Quick test
24.5 Essay assignment
Chapter 24, pp. 532–48.

Section 5

Except where stated, page references are to *Advanced Biology*.

CHAPTER 25

25.1 Viruses
1 a p. 144 Cell size.
  b p. 554 Size, shape and structure of bacterial cells.
2 p. 19 Prokaryotes, eukaryotes and viruses; p. 27 Prokaryotes; p. 28 Eukaryotes.

3 a p. 166 Section 8.1 Metabolism.

b p. 262 The path of carbon in photosynthesis; p. 267 Dark fixation of carbon dioxide.

c p. 27 Phylum Cyanobacteria.

4 a p. 27 Viruses.

b For 'parasite' see Glossary in this *Study Guide*.

5 a, b p. 27 Viruses.

c p. 542 Section 24.9 Bacterial diseases of plants; p. 641 Using *Agrobacterium tumifaciens*.

d pp. 534–7 Section 24.3 Bacterial diseases of animals.

6 p. 535 Bacterial infection and the role of antibiotics.

7 a, b p. 553 Bacteriophages; Figure 25.2 Parasitisation of the host and replication of the phage.

8 p. 553 Retroviruses.

25.2 What science didn't know about disease

1 The life cycles of the known disease-causing agents were understood; the potential vulnerability to modern drugs (antibiotics) and vaccines of these agents had been demonstrated in most cases; some major diseases had already been eradicated (or nearly so).

2 a A pattern of different symptoms characteristic of a particular disease.

b, c p. 374 AIDS, the acquired immune deficiency syndrome.

3 a p. 375 Defence against disease in mammals: a summary.

b p. 374 AIDS, the acquired immune deficiency syndrome.

4 Transfer of body fluids such as blood, via sexual intercourse, infected needles used in intravenous drug-taking, surgery/dentistry or blood transfusion.

5 Presence of HIV antibodies, and the disappearance of T4 cells from blood, together with the destruction of other cells of the immune system, of the lymph nodes and spleen, and of the brain. Vulnerability to a wide spectrum of infections not normally problematical.

6 a, b pp. 370–1 The development of lymphocytes.

7 p. 199 Figure 9.15 The central dogma of molecular biology.

8 Avoidance of accidental transfer of blood from infected to non-infected persons, e.g. in sexual intercourse by the use of condoms, and by the avoidance of re-use of needles by drug addicts. In surgery/dental treatment, by the use of effective protective gloves, and in transfusions, by the screening of blood/blood products to avoid use of infected substances.

9 a, b p. 374 AIDS, the acquired immune deficiency syndrome.

10 Childhood AIDS cases, arising as a result of the mother's HIV infection.

25.3 *Neurospora*: the metabolism of 'wild type' and mutants

1 a p. 200 Section 9.8 The genetic code.

b p. 133 Section 6.8 Proteins p. 138 Table 6.4 The functions of proteins.

2 a, b Glucose (converted to organic acids) and nitrates (reduced to the amino group).

3 a The spore 'germinates', but the fungal colony fails to grow and develop.

b It grows successfully.

4 p. 635 Gene mutations.

5 a e_2 (because M_1 requires citrulline to be present).

b e_3 (because M_2 requires arginine to be present).

c e_1 (because M_3 requires ornithine to be present).

6 a Inability to form an enzyme catalysing the formation of glutamic acid (or of a precursor of this amino acid).

b Culture M_4 on complete medium, and attempt to subculture this mutant on 'minimal medium' augmented with specific intermediates of glutamic acid formation to discover the essential substance that is missing.

25.4 Zygomycete fungi

1 a p. 300 Figure 14.17 Saprotrophic nutrition of the fungi *Mucor* and *Rhizopus*.

b Cytoplasmic streaming, diffusion and active transport (across membranes).

2 a p. 230 Cells and water potential.

b pp. 232–5 Section 11.4 Active transport across membranes.

3 p. 562 Spore production and dispersal.

4 Grow a colony on an appropriate medium in a Petri dish, in the dark apart from a beam of light illuminating part of the mycelium unilaterally. Observe changes in the pattern and direction of subsequent growth of the exposed sporangiophores.

5 a, b p. 563 Figure 25.23 Asexual reproduction in *Mucor*, compared to that in *Rhizopus*.

6 Walls of spores have pigmented substances deposited in them.

7 p. 563 Figure 25.23 Asexual reproduction in *Mucor*, compared to that in *Rhizopus*.

8 p. 562–3 Sexual reproduction.

25.5 Quick test
25.6 Essay assignment
Chapter 25, pp. 552–67.

CHAPTER 26

26.1 The life cycle of a bryophyte

1, 2, 3, 5, 6 Information relating to these questions is given on pp. 569–70 for the liverwort *Pellia*, and on pp. 570–1 for the moss *Funaria*. If other liverworts or mosses are studied, minor differences in the appearance of the gametophytes may be observed.

4 a p. 193 Table 9.2 A comparison of mitosis and meiosis.

b p. 190 Section 9.4 Meiosis.

26.2 Spores in the life of a fern

1 A = transport of water and elaborated foods; B = site of photosynthesis.

2 a, b pp. 573–4 *Dryopteris filix-mas*, the male fern.

c July–August.

3 Mitosis ($\rightarrow$ large numbers of cells); meiosis ($\rightarrow$ haploid nuclei); formation of uninucleate spores (with a protective wall).

4 a, b p. 573 Figure 26.10 *Dryopteris*: spore production and dispersal.

5 a, b p. 573 *Dryopteris filix-mas*, the male fern; p. 574 Figure 26.11 *Dryopteris*: the gametophyte generation.

6 p. 33 Phylum Filicinophyta (ferns).

26.3 Conifers *v.* angiosperms: pointers to success

1 Compile your lists from the following:

Conifers:

strong, woody perennials (trees), able to withstand hostile environmental conditions, and respond and grow under favourable conditions; with robust, efficient, persistent photosynthetic leaves (needles); reproduce by seeds, formed in female cones.

Angiosperms:

p. 585 Section 26.8 The success of the angiosperms.

2 Identify the features from your list that you consider are most important.

26.4 Pine trees and the environment

1 For example, see p. 418 Figure 19.24 Annual growth rings.

2 a See Figure A3 overleaf: approximately 0.6 mm.

b Turgid cells are essential for open stomata (and a supply of CO_2 for photosynthesis), cell growth and enlargement.

3 a 0.85 mm.

b An increase of 40% of industrial areas covered by smoke control orders.

Figure A3 Effect of drought on tree growth

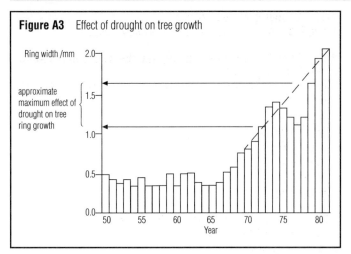

Table A12 Characteristics of flowers

Characteristics	*Ranunculus acris* (buttercup)
Woody or herbaceous plant	herb
Sepals, present or absent	5 present
Petals, present or absent	present
Number of petals	5
Stamens, few or many	many
Carpels, few or many	many
Ovules per carpel, one or many	1
Nectary, present or absent	present
Position of nectary	base of petals

4 a See Practical 4.9 Studying atmospheric dust (pp. 58–9 of this *Study Guide*). Additionally, using folded filter paper discs, wipe the dust from pine needles, using a single consistent wipe. Compare the deposits obtained from this year's needles, and needles from the preceding two years (since pine needles survive on the plant for up to three years). You may choose to compare needles of trees especially exposed to atmospheric pollution (urban trees close to heavy traffic) with pine trees in a country, woodland setting.

b Interfere with light absorption, if sufficiently heavy deposits accumulate; blockage of the stomatal pores.

5 a, b pp. 82–4 <u>The greenhouse effect</u>, or pp. 84–6 <u>Acid rain</u>.

6 Pollutants from motor cars and traffic generally, e.g. hydrocarbon gases, SO_2 and NO_2.

26.5 The features of an inflorescence

1 pp. 577–8 <u>The structure of the flower and inflorescence</u>.

2 a Flower stalk.

b Stem of inflorescence.

3 Racemose inflorescence, e.g. p. 578 <u>Figure 26.18 The flower of Lathyrus odoratus (sweet pea)</u>.

4 C = a developing fruit, formed from a fertilised ovary of a flower.

5 p. 584 <u>The Cruciferae</u>.

6, 7 pp. 577–8 <u>The structure of the flower and inflorescence</u>.

8 B = internode; F = anther; H = stigma; I = style; K = ovule.

26.6 The development of the pollen tube

1 p. 579 <u>Stamens; development of the male gamete</u>.

2 a p. 581 <u>Fertilisation and seed formation</u>; p. 580 <u>Figure 26.22 After pollination . . . .</u>.

b G fuses with D to form the zygote. F fuses with D to form the endosperm.

3 I = 16; F = 16; D = 8; G = 8.

4 a, b p. 582 <u>Fruits and seeds</u>.

5 By osmotic processes, or the absence of an essential metabolite, or the presence of an inhibitor.

26.7 Analysing a flower and designing a key

1 See Table A12.

2 *1* Flowers containing 5 petaloid sepals, but with petals absent *2*
or
Flowers containing 5 green sepals and 5 petaloid petals *3*

2 Woody plant having flowers with many (15 or more) carpels, each containing a single ovule ....
.... *Clematis vitalba* (traveller's joy)

or
Herbaceous plant having flowers with few (5–15) carpels, each containing several ovules..
.... *Caltha palustris* (kingcup)

3 Herbaceous plant having flowers with 5 spurred petals and 5 carpels, each containing several ovules.......................................
.... *Aquilegia vulgaris* (wild columbine)
or
Herbaceous plant, flowers with 5 petals without spurs, and having many ovaries each with a single ovule ....
.... *Ranunculus acris* (buttercup)

26.8 Wind pollination: the 'design' issues

Your proposals will touch on the following issues, and suggest possible solutions:

- *pollen:* ideal shape, size, and surface texture;
- *stamens:* how to efficiently disperse pollen, and when to do so to minimise possible 'losses' of pollen;
- *stigmas:* efficiency at pollen-trapping, favourable environment for effective pollen tube growth, best time of deployment, and how to avoid 'clogging' of stigma with own pollen.

26.9 Quick test
26.10 Essay assignment
<u>Chapter 26</u>, pp. 568–87.

CHAPTER 27

27.1 Gametes and fertilisation

1 a 20 (sperm = 7.25 µm; secondary oocyte = 145 µm).

b p. 597 <u>Figure 27.14 The testis, the site of spermatogenesis</u>; p. 600 <u>Figure 27.18 Secondary oocyte at the time of fertilisation</u>.

2 a, b pp. 602–3 <u>Section 27.9 Fertilisation</u>.

c p. 603 <u>Figure 27.23 The stages of fertilisation</u>.

3 a, b, c pp. 598–9 <u>Egg cell production (oogenesis)</u>.

4 a, b, 5 a, b pp. 602–3 <u>Section 27.9 Fertilisation</u>; <u>Figure 27.23 The stages of fertilisation</u>.

6 p. 159 <u>Mitochondria</u>.

27.2 The cycle of change to follicles

1 Graph: *x*-axis = time (days); *y*-axis = diameter (mm). Points to the curves should be marked distinctively (e.g. ×, ● and ○), and the curves should be clearly labelled.

2 Degeneration of the corpus luteum after about day 28 of the cycle.

3 Shortly after ovulation, approximately day 14–16.

4 p. 600 Figure 27.18 Secondary oocyte at the time of fertilisation.
5, **6** p. 601 Endocrine control of the menstrual cycle.

27.3 The hormones of the menstrual cycle

1 p. 478 Section 21.11 The endocrine system.
2, **3** pp. 600–1 Oestrus and the menstrual cycle; Figure 27.20 The menstrual cycle.
4 a, **b**, **5**, **6**, **7 a**, **b** p. 601 Endocrine control of the menstrual cycle.
8 pp. 604–5 Pregnancy; Figure 27.25 The hormones of pregnancy.

27.4 Oral contraception and hormone changes

1, **2 a**, **b**, **3** p. 602 Oral contraception; the 'pill'.
4 a p. 511 Positive and negative feedback.
b An inappropriate example, perhaps, because it is not a result of natural rhythm arising endogenously, but rather from a conscious act. What do you think?
5 The changes associated with ovulation; see p. 601 Endocrine control of the menstrual cycle.

27.5 The menopause and HRT

1, **2 a**, **b**, **3**, **4**, **6** See Panel 27.1 (p. 330 of this *Study Guide*).
5 Most likely, it is due to the balance of reabsorption and deposition (which go on all the time) being shifted in favour of reabsorption. Calcium can have little effect on this.

27.6 Changing male fertility?

1 a, **b**, **2**, **3** See Panel 27.2 (p. 331 of this *Study Guide*).

27.7 Early human development, and the issues of research on human embryos

Refer to the excerpt of H J Leese's article, in association with your wider reading.

27.8 Quick test
27.9 Essay assignment

Chapter 27, pp. 588–611.

CHAPTER 28

28.1 The dihybrid cross with maize cobs

1 p. 410 Figure 19.12 Seed structure.
2 As counted and recorded from the photograph.
3 a 'Coloured' allele is dominant to 'colourless' allele; 'smooth' allele is dominant to 'wrinkled' allele.
b Because fruits showing 'coloured' and 'smooth' phenotypes predominate.
4 Cross between a plant (P) that is homozygous for coloured, smooth-walled fruit, and a plant that is homozygous for colourless, wrinkled fruit wall. From the progeny (F_1), which will bear coloured, smooth-walled fruit (but will be heterozygous), allow selfing to produce the cob as shown (F_2).

Figure A4 Explanation of a breeding experiment

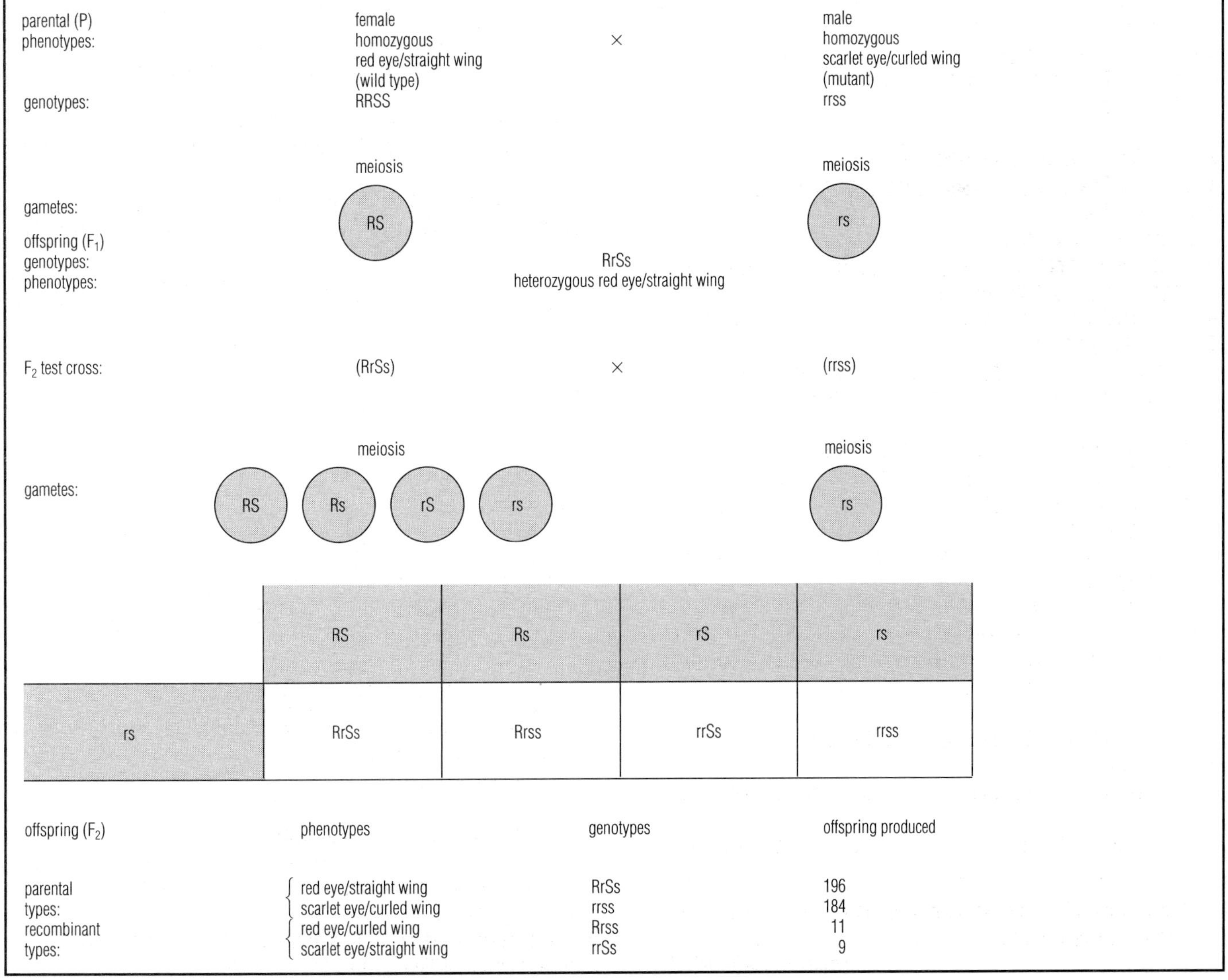
parental (P)
phenotypes:
female
homozygous
red eye/straight wing
(wild type)
×
male
homozygous
scarlet eye/curled wing
(mutant)
genotypes:
RRSS
rrss
meiosis
meiosis
gametes:
RS
rs
offspring (F1)
genotypes:
phenotypes:
RrSs
heterozygous red eye/straight wing
F2 test cross:
(RrSs)
×
(rrss)
meiosis
meiosis
gametes:
RS
Rs
rS
rs
rs
RS
Rs
rS
rs
rs
RrSs
Rrss
rrSs
rrss
offspring (F2)
phenotypes
genotypes
offspring produced
parental types:
red eye/straight wing
RrSs
196
scarlet eye/curled wing
rrss
184
recombinant types:
red eye/curled wing
Rrss
11
scarlet eye/straight wing
rrSs
9

5, **6** Follow the steps given. (The chi-squared test is also shown on p. 346 of this *Study Guide*.)

28.2 Linkage and a linkage map from a *Drosophila* cross

1 a P = (RRSS) × (rrss)
F$_1$ = (RrSs)

b They occur on the same chromosome (i.e. linked).

2, **3 a** See Figure A4 on previous page.

b Recombinations of genes from homologous chromosomes, due to crossing over.

4 $\dfrac{9 + 11}{196 + 9 + 11 + 184} \times 100 = 5\%$

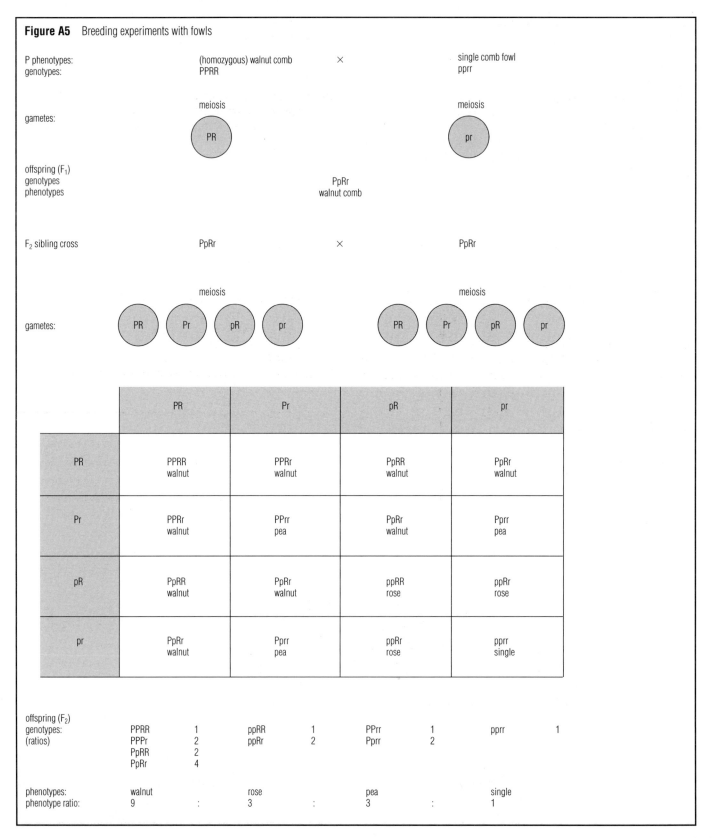

Figure A5 Breeding experiments with fowls

P phenotypes: (homozygous) walnut comb   ×   single comb fowl
genotypes: PPRR   pprr

meiosis   meiosis

gametes: PR   pr

offspring (F$_1$)
genotypes   PpRr
phenotypes   walnut comb

F$_2$ sibling cross   PpRr   ×   PpRr

meiosis   meiosis

gametes: PR   Pr   pR   pr   PR   Pr   pR   pr

	PR	Pr	pR	pr
PR	PPRR walnut	PPRr walnut	PpRR walnut	PpRr walnut
Pr	PPRr walnut	PPrr pea	PpRr walnut	Pprr pea
pR	PpRR walnut	PpRr walnut	ppRR rose	ppRr rose
pr	PpRr walnut	Pprr pea	ppRr rose	pprr single

offspring (F$_2$)
genotypes:

PPRR	1	ppRR	1	PPrr	1	pprr	1
PPPr	2	ppRr	2	Pprr	2		
PpRR	2						
PpRr	4						

phenotypes: walnut   rose   pea   single
phenotype ratio: 9   :   3   :   3   :   1

5 a p. 626 Gene mapping of chromosomes.
  b Nil (or almost nil).
  c 50 : 50.
6

```
------------- R -------------- S ------------ - - - -
            ←------- 5 -------→
```

28.3 Mendelian inheritance in humans

1 p. 644 Genetic diseases of humans.
2 a Hb^AHb^A.
  b Hb^SHb^S.
  c Hb^AHb^S.
3 a p. 204 Sickle-cell anaemia.
  b The lifespan of red cells is about 120 days only. After this they are broken down and replaced by new red cells formed according to the genotype of the individual (i.e. with sickle-cell protein in an individual with sickle-cell anaemia); pp. 212–13 Erythrocytes (red blood cells).
4 a 14, 15 and 16.
  b 8 and 13.
  c Masculinity.
5 a 1 and 2, 3 and 8, 12 and 13.
  b Sickle-cell trait.
  c 0.5 (since one parent must be Hb^AHb^S, and produce 50% of gametes Hb^S).
6 a p. 539 Malaria.
  b See Glossary.
  c The heterozygous condition permits satisfactory transport of oxygen, yet renders the contents of the red cells less accessible to the *Plasmodium* parasite.

28.4 Inheritance of 'white eye' in *Drosophila*

1 p. 616 The chromosome theory; p. 617 Figure 28.8 Genes are located on chromosomes; p. 651 Plant and animal breeding: some common terms (Inbreeding).

2 p. 621 Figure 26.16 *Drosophila melanogaster,* the fruit-fly.
3 p. 627 Figure 28.28 The segregation of X and Y chromosomes: the determination of sex.
4 a, b pp. 621–2 Section 28.4 Illustrating Mendelian ratios in *Drosophila*; also Practical 28.4 pp. 338–41 of this *Study Guide*.
5, 6, 7 pp. 628–30 Sex linkage; Figure 28.29 Reciprocal crosses of white- and red-eyed *Drosophila*.

28.5 Inheritance of the fowl comb

1, 2, 3 See Figure A5.

28.6 Inheritance in the tomato plant

1 Purple stem allele is dominant to green stem allele.
2 Cut leaf allele is dominant to potato leaf allele, because more of the progeny show these phenotypes.
3 a PPCC, PpCC, PPCc, PpCc.
  b PPcc, Ppcc.
  c ppCC, ppCc.
  d ppcc.
4 Cross 1: PpCc × ppcc;
  Cross 2: Ppcc × ppCc;
  Cross 3: PPCc × ppCc;
  Cross 4: PpCc × ppCc.

28.7 Inheritance in oilseed rape

1 See Figure A6, in which
  T = allele for tall (and t = allele for dwarf),
  G = allele for chlorophyll production.
2 a See Figure A7.
  b 'Seedlings' totally without chlorophyll cannot survive once the seed food store is exhausted.

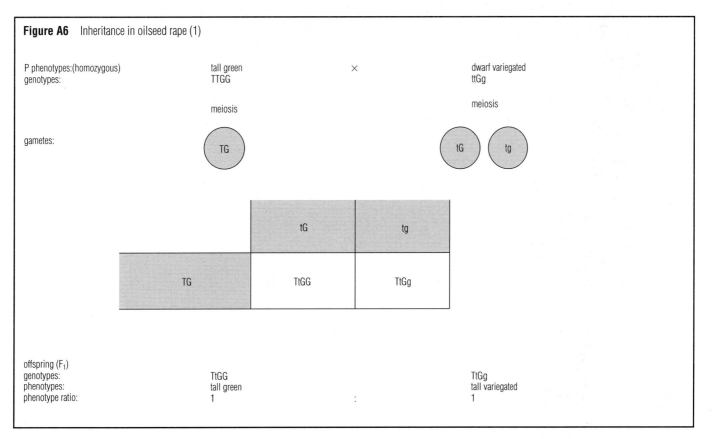

Figure A6   Inheritance in oilseed rape (1)

P phenotypes:(homozygous)   tall green   ×   dwarf variegated
genotypes: TTGG   ttGg

meiosis   meiosis

gametes: TG   tG   tg

	tG	tg
TG	TtGG	TtGg

offspring (F₁)
genotypes: TtGG   TtGg
phenotypes: tall green   tall variegated
phenotype ratio: 1   :   1

28.8 Incomplete dominance in *Antirrhinum*

1 See Figure A8.
2 pp. 614–15 <u>The garden pea plant is self-fertile</u>; <u>Figure 28.4 Cross-pollination of a *Pisum satirum* flower</u>.
3 **d** and **f**.

4 **a** The presence of a single allele for red flower-colour is insufficient to cause production of enough of the specific enzyme to convert all of a pigment precursor into a red pigment. Enough enzyme is produced, however, to convert some of the precursor, so that a pink coloration is created.
b i By investigating the enzymes present in equal amounts of developing 'pink' and 'red' petals.

Figure A7   Inheritance in oilseed rape (2)

F₂ selfed

tall variegated   ×   tall variegated
TtGg   TtGg

meiosis   meiosis

gametes:

(TG) (Tg) (tG) (tg)   (TG) (Tg) (tG) (tg)

	TG	Tg	tG	tg
TG	TTGG	TTGg	TtGG	TtGg
Tg	TTGg	TTgg	TtGg	Ttgg
tG	TtGG	TtGg	ttGG	ttGg
tg	TtGg	Ttgg	ttGg	ttgg

F₂ genotypes:
(ratios)

TTGG 1	TTGg 2	ttGg 2	ttGG 1	TTgg 1
TtGG 2	TtGg 4			Ttgg 2
				ttgg 1

phenotypes:

tall green	tall variegated	dwarf variegated	dwarf green	('albino'; die in germination)

phenotype ratios: 3   :   6   :   2   :   1   :   4

Figure A8   Inheritance of flower colour in *Antirrhinum*

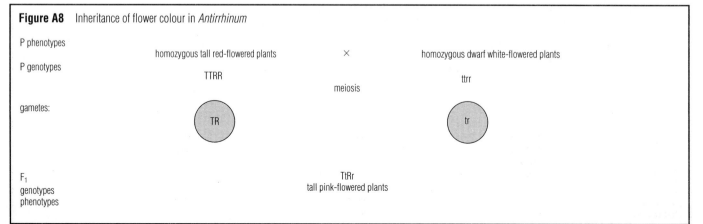

P phenotypes

homozygous tall red-flowered plants   ×   homozygous dwarf white-flowered plants

P genotypes

TTRR   ttrr

meiosis

gametes:

(TR)   (tr)

F₁
genotypes   TtRr
phenotypes   tall pink-flowered plants

ii With difficulty; perhaps by estimating the amount of pigment precursor present in equal amounts of developing 'pink' and 'red' petals, using paper or thin-layer chromatography provided the precursors can be located by spraying with a chemical solution that makes them coloured.

5 25% tall, pink-flowered;
 25% tall, white-flowered;
 25% dwarf, pink-flowered;
 25% dwarf, white-flowered.

28.9 Coat colour in mice: an example of epistasis

1, 2 See Figure A9.

3 There would not have been 16 progeny, and the proportions shown in Figure A9 are most unlikely to be demonstrated without the production of a large number of progeny (i.e. many random matings).

28.10 ABO blood group

The Comes were A × B, which might produce any one of:
 AA × BB = AB group;
 AO × BO = AB or O groups;
 AA × BO = AB or A groups;
 AO × BB = AB or B groups.
So the Comes could be the parents of *any* of the four offspring.

The Doors were B × O, which might produce either of:
 BB × OO = B group
 BO × OO = B or O groups
So the Doors might be the parents of *either* the B group *or* the O group offspring.

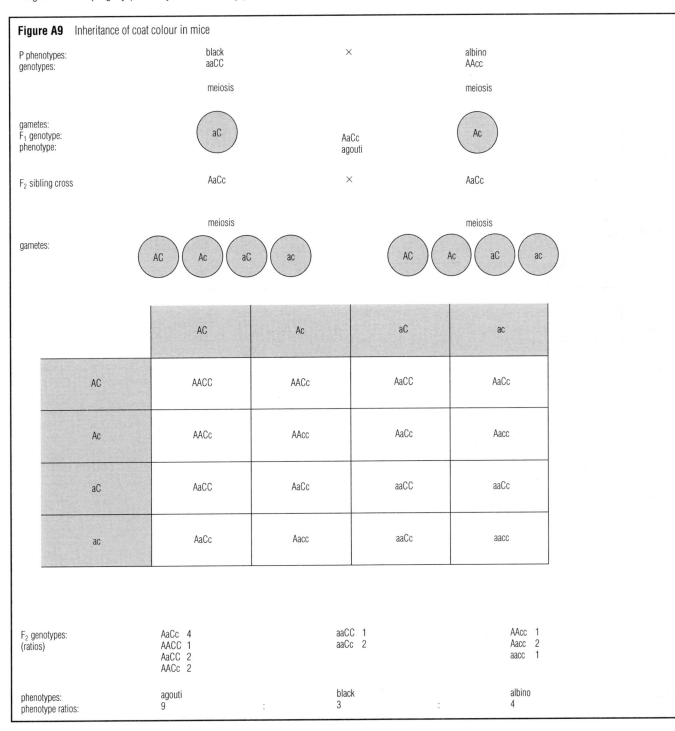

Figure A9 Inheritance of coat colour in mice

	AC	Ac	aC	ac
AC	AACC	AACc	AaCC	AaCc
Ac	AACc	AAcc	AaCc	Aacc
aC	AaCC	AaCc	aaCC	aaCc
ac	AaCc	Aacc	aaCc	aacc

F₂ genotypes: (ratios)

AaCc	4	aaCC	1	AAcc	1
AACC	1	aaCc	2	Aacc	2
AaCC	2			aacc	1
AACc	2				

phenotypes: agouti : black : albino
phenotype ratios: 9 : 3 : 4

The Exits were O × O, which can produce only

00 × 00 = O group

So the *Exits were the parents of the O group offspring* (and therefore the *Doors were the parents of the B group offspring*).

The Fires were AB × O, which might produce:

AB × 00 = A or B groups

So the *Fires were the parents of the A group offspring* (since the Doors are the parents of the B group child).

So, by elimination, the *Comes were the parents of the AB group off-spring*.

28.11   Quick test
28.12   Essay assignment
Chapter 28, pp. 612–35.

CHAPTER 29

29.1   Recombinant DNA technology
1   For the gaps numbered (i) to (x):
  i   genetic engineering;
  ii   double-stranded molecules;
  iii   genes;
  iv   restriction;
  v   base sequences;
  vi   plasmid;
  vii   vector;
  viii   a ligase;
  ix   brief electric shock;
  x   electroporation.
2 **a**, **b**, **c**   p. 636 Section 29.2 Restriction enzymes; p. 637 Figure 29.1 Two types of restriction enzyme; Figure 29.2 The role of ligase.
3 **a**   p. 638 The challenge of gene cloning.
  b and **4**   p. 637 Section 29.3 The making of recombinant DNA.

29.2   Insulin by genetic engineering
1 **a**   p. 512 Regulation of blood sugar levels; p. 513 Figure 23.5 The pancreas and hormone production.
  b   p. 516 Diabetes mellitus.
2   pp. 370–1 Immunity and the immune system.
3   Changes in the amino acid residue sequence to allow the pig insulin protein to be 'recognised' as human, rather than as 'foreign'.
4 **a**, **b**, **c**   pp. 133–6 Section 6.8 Proteins; Figure 6.24 Cross-linking within a polypeptide.
5 **a**   p. 374 AIDS, the acquired immune deficiency syndrome.
  b   p. 199 Figure 9.15 The central dogma of molecular biology.
6 **a**   pp. 202–3 Section 9.9 Protein synthesis.
  b   The islets of Langerhans from the pancreas.
7 **a**, **b**   pp. 637–8 Section 29.3 The making of recombinant DNA; Figure 29.4 Selection and amplification.
8   p. 639 Insulin manufacture.

29.3   Transgenic plants
1   Intact cell walls are an effective barrier to entry of this bacterial pathogen.
2   p. 641 Using *Agrobacterium tumifaciens*.
3   p. 640 Figure 29.8 Transcription in prokaryotes and eukaryotes compared.
4   p. 637 Section 29.3 The making of recombinant DNA.
5   p. 641 Figure 29.9 Production of genetically engineered plants using the Ti plasmid.
6   p. 436 Figure 20.23 Cytokinins, their role in growth and development; p. 437 Roles of cytokinins.

7 **a**   Crop plants 'engineered' to be resistant to a generally effective herbicide will allow the removal of weeds and any other plant competing for the ions in the soil, without harm to the crop itself.
  b   Might the gene for herbicide resistance eventually 'escape' naturally into wild plants, including weed species?

29.4   Cystic fibrosis
1   p. 644 Section 29.6 Genetic diseases.
2 **a**   'Recessive', see p. 616 The chromosome theory; 'autosomal', see p. 627 Sex determination.
  b   Aa; A and a; aa; a and a.
3   The disease is characterised by a thick, 'ropy' mucus which blocks ducts it is meant to lubricate.
  a   p. 314 Protection of the lungs.
  b   p. 280 Saliva; p. 285, description of mucus-secreting cells; p. 288 Villi; p. 289 'Intestinal juice'.
  c   Pancreatic juice is also rich in mucus, and the pancreatic duct becomes blocked.
4   pp. 232–3 How active transport occurs.
5 **a** $\frac{1}{20} \times \frac{1}{20} = \frac{1}{400}$
  or 1 in 400.
  b   p. 649 The Hardy–Weinberg principle.
    i   The frequency of aa = 0.02^2 = 0.0004.
    ii   The frequency of AA = 0.98^2 = 0.9604.
6   p. 645 Will genetic diseases die out?

29.5   Genetic engineering raises ethical issues
A personal response is required here.

29.6   Population genetics and the Hardy–Weinberg equation
1   According to the Hardy–Weinberg principle (p. 649 The Hardy–Weinberg principle):

q^2 = frequency of the homozygous recessive (gg in this case)
   = 0.09.

Therefore q (frequency of the recessive gene g) = $\sqrt{0.09}$ = 0.3.
Now p (frequency of the dominant gene G) = $1 - q$
Therefore p = 0.7.
Frequency of the heterozygote (Gg) = $2pq$ = $2 \times 0.7 \times 0.3$ = 0.42.
Frequency of the homozygous dominant (GG) = p^2 = 0.7^2 = 0.49.
2   Of the possible 'disturbances' (p. 650 Gene frequencies are not always constant), the most likely one to operate in these circumstances is 'mutation'.

29.7   Quick test
29.8   Essay assignment
Chapter 29, pp. 636–51.

CHAPTER 30

30.1   Selective breeding for creamier milk
1 **a**   pp. 650–1 Section 29.12 Artificial selection.
  b   Chief similarity is they both may lead to genetic change and the appearance of new types.
    Chief difference is the selection 'forces', i.e. human *v.* natural forces (e.g. environmental change).

2 **a**, **b**, **3**   p. 651 Plant and animal breeding: some common terms.

4 **a**   Differences in the enzyme 'machinery' by which milk is produced and secreted in the mammary glands of the two varieties.
  b   The fat content of milk from the two varieties is a discontinuous variable (see Figure 30.6 of this *Study Guide*).

5 Select bulls from offspring of high-yielding Red Dane cows, and cross these with high-yielding Jersey cows (and vice versa). Carefully select from the progeny of all these crosses, for further crosses (avoiding sibling crosses, wherever possible).

30.2 Theories of evolution compared
1 See Table A13.
2 a p. 653 An outright evolutionist.
  b p. 663 Natural selection.

30.3 Neo-Darwinism
a, b, c, d p. 664 Neo-Darwinism.
a, c p. 192 Figure 9.8 The changes to a homologous pair of chromosomes during meiosis; p. 193 Table 9.2 A comparison of mitosis and meiosis.
b pp. 633–5 Section 28.13 Mutations.
d pp. 632–3 Section 28.12 Environmental effects on the phenotype.

30.4 Human evolution
1 For example: composition and role of DNA; the structure and functions of cell membranes; the nature and role of ATP; metabolic pathways such as glycolysis and the Krebs cycle (with their enzymes).

2 p. 41 Class Mammalia (mammals).
3 a, b Tree shrews (see p. 674 Figure 30.33 The phylogenetic tree of primates). Tree-climbing, with prehensile hands and feet; insectivorous diet (dentition to accompany this); increasingly forward-facing eyes.
  c p. 673 The characteristics of the primates.
4 Share: skeletal features permitting brachiation and facilitating bipedalism. Humans: head 'balanced' on vertebral column; size of the cerebral hemispheres of brain; little hair; skeletal adaptations for 'power' and 'precision' grip of hands (and for efficient bipedalism).

30.5 Human ancestry
1 Given in the text.
2 DNA sequence, since this underpins (i.e. is the basis of) the differences.
3 Given in the text above.
4 p. 660 Evidence from comparative physiology and biochemistry.

30.6 Quick test
30.7 Essay assignment
Chapter 30, pp. 652–75.

Table A13 Theories of evolution compared

	Inheritance of acquired characteristics	Natural selection
Species change with time – they are not immutable	the main concept of 'evolution'; this idea is central to both theories	
How variation in individuals of a species arises	by a natural tendency for progress, and because changes in the environment produce new habitats	by chance, followed by selective survival of those individuals with advantageous features, given a hostile environment
The significance of random variation among the progeny of each generation	'chance' not seen to operate in the natural world	provides the variety of offspring on which selection operates
An inherent tendency of organisms to get larger and more complex	basis of a natural tendency for change in organs that receive 'hard' use	not stressed by Darwin; dismissed in 'Neo-Darwinism'
Inheritance of changes in the body that arise through continuous use	operates; known as the Law of Use (and Disuse)	recognised as impossible in Neo-Darwinism
Consequence of competition between members of the same species	ignored	acts on 'variations' among offspring, leading to the 'survival of the fittest'
Inheritance of features of the body that are underused	these features will become reduced (Law of Disuse)	underused features may be reduced, but by natural selection
The high mortality rate common among offspring	extinction not believed to occur so mortality rates ignored	the basis of natural selection, leading to 'survival of the fittest'
The observation that certain animal species, having for many thousands of years lived in caves, have become totally blind	an example of the 'Law of Disuse' in operation	an example of a feature without 'selection pressure' operating in its favour, which has become lost
Contribution to the eventual general acceptance of the idea of organic evolution (as opposed to 'special creation')	provided the first systematically argued case for 'evolution' of the living world; laid the foundations for the general acceptance of evolution	provided a mechanistic (rational) explanation of the variety of living things (once modern genetics had uncovered the causes of genetic variation)

Glossary

Entries are *aides-mémoire*, rather than formal definitions. <u>Underlined</u> terms are the subjects of entries in the Glossary.

abiotic factor a non-biological factor (e.g. temperature) that is part of the environment of an organism

abscisic acid a <u>plant growth substance</u> tending to inhibit growth

abscission removal by cutting, e.g. process of separation of deciduous leaf in autumn

absorption spectrum range of a pigment's ability to absorb various wavelengths of light

accessory pigment pigment(s) additional to <u>chlorophyll</u>, present in <u>chloroplasts</u>, absorbing light energy for <u>photosynthesis</u>

acetylcholine a <u>neurotransmitter substance</u>, liberated at <u>synapses</u> in the CNS

'acid rain' the cocktail of chemical pollutants that may occur in the atmosphere

actinomorphic regular (e.g. radially symmetrical) flowers

action potential rapid change in membrane potential of an excitable cell, e.g. a <u>neurone</u>

action spectrum range of wavelengths of light within which a process like <u>photosynthesis</u> takes place

activation energy energy that a <u>substrate</u> molecule must have before it can undergo a chemical change

active site region of <u>enzyme</u> molecule where <u>substrate</u> molecule binds

active transport movement of substances across a membrane involving a <u>carrier protein</u> and energy from <u>respiration</u>

adaptation the process by which an organism becomes fitted to its environment

adaptive radiation descent from a common ancestor, with divergence to occupy different <u>niches</u>

adenine a <u>purine</u> organic base, found in the <u>coenzymes</u> <u>ATP</u> and <u>NADP</u>, and in <u>nucleic acids</u> (DNA and RNA) in which it pairs with thymine

adenosine diphosphate (ADP) a <u>nucleotide</u>, present in every living cell, made of adenosine and two phosphate groups linked in series, and important in energy-transfer reactions of <u>metabolism</u>

adenosine triphosphate (ATP) a <u>nucleotide</u>, present in every living cell, formed in photosynthesis and respiration from <u>ADP</u> and inorganic <u>phosphate (P$_i$)</u>, and functioning in <u>metabolism</u> as a common intermediate between energy-requiring and energy-yielding reactions

adrenaline a <u>hormone</u> secreted by the adrenal medulla (and a <u>neurotransmitter substance</u> secreted by nerve endings of the <u>sympathetic nervous system</u>), having many effects, including speeding of heartbeat, and the breakdown of glycogen to glucose in muscle and liver

aerobic respiration <u>respiration</u> requiring oxygen, involving oxidation of glucose to CO_2 and H_2O

aestivation torpor of animals like the snail, induced by the heat and drought of summer

afferent 'bringing towards', applied e.g. to <u>nerves</u> or blood vessels

agglutinogen cell surface <u>antigen</u>, e.g. ABO antigens of human blood cells

agouti fur colour of a 'grey' mouse, due to hairs that are black with a yellow band

aldose sugar <u>monosaccharide</u> containing an aldehyde group (—CHO);

alimentary canal the gut; a tube running from mouth to anus in vertebrates, where complex food substances are digested and the products of digestion selectively absorbed into the body

allantois a sac-like outgrowth of the <u>embryo</u> of reptiles, birds and mammals

allele an alternative form of a <u>gene</u>, occupying a specific locus on a <u>chromosome</u>

allometric growth when the growth rate of parts/organs is different from the growth rate of the whole organism

allosteric enzyme <u>enzyme</u> susceptible to reversible binding of a small molecule to a part of the protein, inducing change to the shape of the active site of the enzyme

alpha cell (pancreas) glucagon-secreting cells of the <u>islets of Langerhans</u> in the <u>pancreas</u>

alternation of generations the alternation of <u>haploid</u> and <u>diploid</u> stages in the life cycle

altruism behaviour by an organism beneficial to the genetic survival of another related organism at the expense of itself

alveolus air sac in the lung

amino acid building block of <u>proteins</u>, of general formula $RCH(NH_2)COOH$

amniocentesis withdrawal of a small sample of <u>amniotic</u> fluid from around the <u>fetus</u>, 16–20 weeks into <u>gestation</u>, so that fetal cells can be examined cytologically

amnion the innermost of the embryonic membranes in reptiles, birds and mammals

amphoteric having both acidic and basic properties, e.g. <u>amino acids</u>

ampulla a dilated part of one end of each <u>semicircular canal</u> of the inner ear

anabolism the building up of complex molecules from smaller ones, in cellular biochemistry

anaerobic respiration <u>respiration</u> in the absence of oxygen, involving breakdown of glucose to lactic acid or ethanol

analogous structure similar in function but of different evolutionary origin

androecium collective name of <u>stamens</u> (male parts) of a flower

anemophily wind pollination

angiosperm a member of the dominant group of land plants, a seed-bearing plant where the seed is enclosed in a fruit formed from the ovary

animal pole in yolk-laden eggs, the part where the <u>cytoplasm</u> cleaves most rapidly

anion negatively charged <u>ion</u>

anisogamy fusion of <u>gametes</u> that are of different sizes/ shapes

annual plant plant living for a year only

antagonism the effects of (e.g.) a <u>hormone</u> that counteracts the effects of another

antenna one of a pair of jointed 'feelers' on the head of arthropods

anther part of the <u>stamen</u> in flowers, consisting of pollen sacs enclosed in walls that eventually split open, releasing <u>pollen</u>

antheridium an organ of ferns and mosses in which male <u>gametes</u> are formed

antherozoid motile male gamete produced in an <u>antheridium</u>

anthropomorphism the ascription of human emotions to animals

antibiotic <u>organic</u> compounds produced by microorganisms which selectively inhibit or kill other microorganisms

antibody a protein produced by blood <u>plasma</u> cells derived from B <u>lymphocytes</u> when in the presence of a specific antigen, which then binds with the antigen, aiding its destruction

anticodon three consecutive bases in transfer RNA, complementary to a <u>codon</u> on <u>RNA</u>

antidiuretic hormone (ADH) <u>hormone</u> secreted by the <u>pituitary gland</u> that controls the permeability of the walls of the collecting ducts of the kidney

antigen a substance capable of binding specifically to an <u>antibody</u>

antipodal cell a group of three cells in the <u>embryo sac</u>

apical meristem a group of <u>meristematic</u> cells at stem and root tip

apoenzyme <u>protein</u> part of an <u>enzyme</u>, after the removal of the <u>prosthetic group</u>

apoplast collective name for the cell walls of a <u>tissue</u> or plant

appendicular skeleton limb skeleton and girdles

aqueous humour fluid between lens and <u>cornea</u>

archegonium female sex organ of liverworts, mosses and ferns

archenteron embryonic cavity formed at <u>gastrulation</u>

arteriole a very small <u>artery</u>

artery blood vessel that carries blood away from the heart

articulated jointed

artificial classification classifying organisms on the basis of few, self-evident features

artificial selection selective breeding of organisms, carried out deliberately, by humans

ascomycete (ascomycota) major grouping of <u>fungi</u>, the sac fungi, typically forming ascospores in an ascus as a product of sexual reproduction

asexual reproduction <u>reproduction</u> not involving <u>gametes</u> and <u>fertilisation</u>

assimilation uptake of nutrients into cells and tissues

association centre (brain) area of the <u>cerebral cortex</u> where incoming sensory information is integrated

asymmetric carbon atom carbon atom that has four different atoms or groups of atoms attached, forming molecule that can be distinguished from its own mirror image (<u>optical isomerism</u>)

atherosclerosis deposition of plaque (<u>cholesterol</u> derivative) on inner walls of blood vessels

atrioventricular node mass of tissue in the wall of the right <u>atrium</u>, functionally part of the pacemaker mechanism

atrioventricular valve tricuspid or bicuspid valve

atrium (*pl.* **atria**) one of the two upper chambers of the mammalian four-chambered heart

autecology ecology of a single organism

autolysis self-digestion

autonomic nervous system the <u>involuntary nervous system</u>

autotrophic (organism) self-feeding, i.e. able to make its own elaborated foods from simpler substances

auxin <u>plant growth substance</u>, indoleacetic acid

axial skeleton skull and <u>vertebral column</u>

axil angle between leaf and stem (contains a bud)

axon fibre carrying <u>impulses</u> away from the cell body of a <u>neurone</u>

bacillus a rod-shaped bacterium

bacteriophage a <u>virus</u> that parasitises bacteria

baroreceptor a <u>sensory receptor</u> responding to stretch, found in the walls of blood vessels

Barr body the inactivated X <u>chromosome</u>, seen in the nuclei of <u>somatic cells</u> from female mammals

basal body a tiny cylindrical structure in the <u>cytoplasm</u> at the base of a <u>flagellum</u> or <u>cilium</u>, in <u>eukaryotic</u> cells

basal ganglion a mass of <u>grey matter</u> in the <u>cerebral hemispheres</u>, connected with other brain centres involved in motor control

basal metabolism   metabolic activity in organism at rest

basement membrane   the thin fibrous layer separating an epithelium from underlying tissues

basidiomycetes (basidiomycota)   major grouping of fungi, producing basidiospores on the outside of club-shaped basidia, often borne on conspicuous fruiting bodies (mushrooms)

beta cell (pancreas)   insulin-secreting cells of the islets of Langerhans in the pancreas

bicuspid valve   valve between atrium and ventricle on the left side of the mammalian heart

biennial plant   plant living for two years, fruiting in the second year only

bilayer   structure, e.g. membrane, constructed from two layers

bile   an alkaline secretion of liver cells which collects in the gall bladder, and which is discharged into the duodenum periodically

binary fission   the division of a cell into two daughter cells, typically in reproduction of prokaryotes

binomial system   system of double names for organisms, in Latin, the generic name preceding the specific name

bioassay   the use of living organisms or tissues for assay purposes

biodegradation   breakdown of waste materials by living organisms, e.g. bacteria

biodeterioration   decay of economically useful materials brought about by living organisms, e.g. bacteria

biological pest control   control of pests and weeds by other organisms

biomass   total mass (or volume, or energy equivalent) of living organisms in a given area, e.g. a quadrat

biome   a major life-zone over an area of the Earth, characterised by the dominant plant life present

biosphere   the inhabited part of the Earth

biotechnology   the industrial and commercial applications of biology, particularly of microorganisms, enzymology and genetic engineering

biotic factor   the influence of living things on the environment of other living things

biuret test   test for the presence of proteins (peptides), based on the reaction of the peptide linkage

bivalent (chromosomes)   a pair of duplicated chromosomes, held together by chiasmata during meiosis

blastocyst   hollow ball of cells, formed from the morula at the stage of implantation in mammals

blastomere   cells formed by early divisions of a fertilised animal egg cell

blastopore   invagination of part of the wall of the blastula, by which the gut cavity is formed in embryogenesis

blastula   hollow ball of cells, formed early in embryogenesis in many animals, containing a blastocoel (fluid-filled cavity)

blind spot   region of the retina where the optic nerve leaves

body mass index (BMI) the ratio (body mass/kg) : $(\text{height/m})^2$

bolus   chewed food, formed into a ball with saliva

bone marrow tissue   special connective tissue filling the cavity of certain bones

boreal forest   northern coniferous forests (example of a biome)

bovine somatotrophin (BST)   hormone produced by the pituitary gland of the cow, controlling milk production

bract   modified leaf, often scale-like, usually having a protective role

brain   the coordinating centre of the nervous system

breed (animal)   the animal equivalent of a plant variety

bronchiole   small terminal branch of a bronchus

bronchus   a tube connecting the trachea with the lungs

Brunner's gland   gland in the wall of the duodenum that discharges into the lumen

brush border   tiny, finger-like projections (microvilli) on the surface of epithelial cells of the ileum or kidney tubule

buccal cavity   part of the alimentary canal between mouth and pharynx

budding   common method of asexual reproduction

buffer   a solution which minimises change in pH when acid or alkali is added

bundle of His   bundles of long muscle fibres that transmit myogenic excitation throughout the ventricle walls

bundle sheath   layer(s) of parenchyma cells surrounding a vascular bundle

byssus threads   strong threads secreted by certain bivalve molluscs, by which they become attached to the substratum

C_3 pathway   the 'dark reaction' in photosynthesis, producing initially a three-carbon compound, glycerate 3-phosphate

C_4 plants   plants with an additional CO_2 fixation pathway that augments the supply of this raw material of photosynthesis at the chloroplast

caecum   a 'blind' pouch of the gut

Calvin cycle   a cycle of reactions in the stroma of the chloroplast by which some of the product of the 'dark reaction' is re-formed as the acceptor molecule for CO_2 (ribulose bisphosphate)

calyptra   remains of the archegonium wall that surrounds the developing sporophyte (in bryophytes)

calyx   collective name for the sepals of flowers

cambium   meristematic tissue in stem (and roots) from which secondary growth occurs

canaliculus (*pl.* canaliculi)   a tiny channel in the liver lobules, carrying bile

capillary water the bulk of soil water held around particles of soil, available to plants

capitulum disc-shaped head of the flowering stem, carrying many compact, stalkless <u>florets</u>; typical of many Compositae, e.g. dandelion

capsule (in moss/liverwort) the part of the <u>sporophyte</u> generation that contains the <u>haploid</u> spores, from which these spores are released and dispersed

carapace chitinous covering of the 'trunk' in crustaceans

cardiac cycle the stages of the heartbeat, by which the atrial and then the ventricle walls alternately contract (<u>systole</u>), followed by relaxation (<u>diastole</u>)

carnassial teeth shearing teeth of <u>carnivores</u>

carnivore flesh-eating mammal

carotenoids fat-soluble pigments coloured red-yellow to brown, <u>accessory pigments</u> in <u>photosynthesis</u>

carpal bone of the wrist

carpel female reproductive structure of the <u>flower</u>, containing one or more <u>ovules</u>

carrier protein one of the types of protein in <u>plasma membranes</u>, responsible for active transport across the membranes

cartilage firm but plastic skeletal material, e.g. hyaline cartilage over bones at joints

Casparian strip bands of cells with impervious walls, found in the <u>endodermis</u> of plant roots

catabolism the breaking down of complex molecules in the biochemistry of cells

catalyst a substance that alters the rate of a chemical reaction, but remains unchanged at the end

catastrophism the theory that <u>fossils</u> are organisms of earlier creations which suffered mass extinction (and were replaced by freshly created organisms)

cell sap fluid in the <u>vacuoles</u> of plant cells

cellulase <u>enzyme</u> capable of hydrolysing <u>cellulose</u>, the major ingredient of most plant walls

cellulose an unbranched <u>polymer</u> of two or three thousand glucose residues, linked by β-1,4 <u>glycosidic bonds</u>

central dogma the idea that transfer of genetic information from <u>DNA</u> of the chromosome to <u>RNA</u> to <u>protein</u> (<u>amino acid</u> sequence) is irreversible

central nervous system in vertebrates, the brain and spinal cord

centriole one of two <u>organelles</u> that make up the <u>centrosome</u>, found in animal cells outside the <u>nuclear membrane</u>, and involved in <u>nuclear division</u> there

centromere constriction of the <u>chromosome</u>, the region that becomes attached to the <u>spindle</u> fibres in division

centrosome <u>organelle</u> situated near the nucleus in animal cells, involved in the formation of the <u>spindle</u> prior to <u>nuclear division</u>

centrum solid cylinder of bone in a vertebra

cephalisation development of a head at the anterior of an animal

cephalothorax in crustaceans, formed by fusion of head with <u>thorax</u>

circarium larval stage of liver fluke, produced in snail host

cerebellum part of hind-<u>brain</u>, concerned with muscle tone/posture/movement

cerebral cortex superficial layer of <u>grey matter</u> on extension of forebrain, much enlarged in humans and apes

cerebral hemispheres (cerebrum) the bulk of the human <u>brain</u>, formed during development by the outgrowth of part of the forebrain, consisting of densely packed <u>neurones</u> and <u>myelinated nerve fibres</u>

chaeta bristle projecting from body wall in some annelid worms

chemoreceptor a sense organ receiving chemical stimuli

chemosynthesis use of chemical energy from oxidation of inorganic compounds to synthesise organic compounds, typically from CO_2 and H_2O

chemotropism growth response of plant organ due to chemical stimulation

chiasma (*pl.* **chiasmata**) site of crossing over (exchange) of segments of <u>DNA</u> between <u>homologous chromosomes</u>

chitin chemically related to <u>cellulose</u>, a <u>polymer</u> built from glucosamine

chlorenchyma <u>parenchyma</u> cells containing <u>chloroplasts</u>

chlorophyll the main photosynthetic pigment of green plants; occurs in the granal membranes (<u>thylakoid</u> membranes) of the <u>chloroplasts</u>

chloroplast <u>organelle</u> that is site of <u>photosynthesis</u> and contains <u>chlorophyll</u> in grana

cholesterol a <u>lipid</u> of animal <u>plasma membranes</u>, a precursor of the steroid hormones; in humans it is formed in the liver and transported in the blood as <u>lipoprotein</u>

chondrin matrix of <u>cartilage</u>, secreted by cells called chondrocytes

chordae tendinae <u>tendons</u> anchored to heart valves

chordate animal having tubular dorsal <u>nerve cord</u>, a dorsal supporting rod (<u>notochord</u>), a post-anal tail, gill-slits in the throat (<u>visceral clefts</u>), and a closed blood circulation in which blood flows down the body in a dorsal artery and returns in a ventral vein

chorion embryonic membrane, enclosing the <u>amnion</u> and <u>yolk sac</u>

choroid layer containing blood vessels, lying below the <u>retina</u>

chromatid one of two copies of a <u>chromosome</u> after it has replicated

chromatin a nuclear protein material in the <u>nucleus</u> of eukaryotic cells at <u>interphase</u>; forms into chromosomes during <u>mitosis</u> and <u>meiosis</u>

chromoplast similar to a <u>chloroplast</u>, but containing other photosynthetic pigment(s)

chromosome visible in appropriately stained cells at <u>nuclear division</u>, each chromosome consists of a long thread of <u>DNA</u> packaged with <u>protein</u>; chromosomes replicate prior to division, into <u>chromatids</u>, while between divisions the contents of the nucleus appear as granular <u>chromatin</u>

chyme partly digested food as it leaves the stomach

ciliary body contains ring of muscle, regulates the shape of the lens in vertebrate eye

cilium (*pl. cilia*) motile, hair-like outgrowth from surface of certain <u>eukaryotic</u> cells

circadian rhythm behaviour cycle of about 24 hours

citric acid cycle *see* tricarboxylic acid (TCA) cycle

cladism relationship between organisms based on ancestry, shown in a cladogram

cleavage series of divisions by which the <u>zygote</u> is transformed into a ball of cells

climax community the mature (stable) stage of a succession of <u>communities</u>

clitellum swollen part of the body of the earthworm, secretes the cocoon in which fertilised eggs grow

clone a group of genetically identical individuals (or cells)

cnidoblast stinging cells of cnidarians (coelenterates) like *Hydra*

coccus spherical bacterial cell

cochlea part of the inner ear concerned with hearing

codon a group of three consecutive bases in <u>DNA</u> (or <u>RNA</u>), specifying an <u>amino acid</u>

coelom fluid-filled body cavity within the <u>mesoderm</u> of many non-vertebrate and all vertebrate groups

coenocytic fungal (or algal) tissue not divided into individual cells

coenzyme non-protein part of some <u>enzyme</u>s; can become attached to different enzymes

coleoptile protective sheath around germinating <u>plumule</u> of grasses

collenchyma flexible supporting tissue of plants, walls thickened with <u>cellulose</u>

colon part of the <u>gut</u>, preceding the rectum

colostrum first milk secreted by the mother, after birth of young

commensalism a mutually beneficial association between two organisms of different <u>species</u>

community populations of organisms living together in a <u>habitat</u>

companion cell component of <u>phloem</u> tissue, cells lying besides <u>sieve tubes</u>

compensation point the point where <u>respiration</u> and <u>photosynthesis</u> are balanced

condensation reaction formation of larger molecules by the reaction of smaller component molecules, with the loss of water

conditioned reflex a <u>reflex action</u> modified by past experience

cone (retinal cell) a light-sensitive cell in the <u>retina</u>, responsible for colour vision

conjugate protein <u>protein</u> combined with a non-protein part

connective tissue <u>tissues</u> that support, connect and bind, and may be involved in blood and its formation or in food storage

conservation applying the principles of ecology to managing the environment

contractile vacuole a small <u>vesicle</u> in the cytoplasm of many freshwater <u>protozoans</u> that expels excess water from the cell

convergent evolution similarity between organs or organisms due to independent evolution along similar lines, rather than to common ancestry

cork cambium cells below the bark layer that cut off cork cells to the exterior

cornea transparent covering at the front of the eye

corolla collective name for the <u>petals</u> of a flower

corpus luteum glandular mass that develops from an <u>ovarian follicle</u> in mammals, after the <u>ovum</u> is discharged

cotyledon the first leaf (leaves) of a seed plant, found in the embryo

covalent bond bond between atoms in which electrons are shared

cranial nerves nerves arising from the <u>brain</u>

Crassulacean acid metabolism CO_2 fixation into organic acids in the dark, followed by release of the CO_2 for photosynthetic fixation inside the plant, in the light, whilst stomata are closed to reduce water loss (in succulent plants)

cristae folds in the inner membrane of <u>mitochondria</u>

crossing over exchange of genetic material between <u>homologous chromosomes</u> during <u>meiosis</u>

crypt of Lieberkuhn tubular glands at the base of the villi

cuticle (plants) layer of waxy material on the outer wall of the <u>epidermis</u>; (animals) exoskeleton of insects

cyanobacterium photosynthetic <u>prokaryotes</u>

cyclosis circulation of the cytoplasm

cyme <u>inflorescence</u> in which the first flower forms on main stem, and later flowers develop on lateral stems

cytokinesis division of the <u>cytoplasm</u> after the <u>nucleus</u> has divided into two

cytokinin plant growth regulator, derived from the organic base <u>adenine</u>, involved in the breaking of <u>dormancy</u> and in facilitating development

cytology study of cell structure

cytoplasm living part of the cell bound by the <u>plasma membrane</u>, excluding the <u>nucleus</u>

cytoskeleton   microtubule 'framework' to the cytoplasm

cytosol   what remains of cytoplasm when the organelles have been removed

cytostome   region of cell membrane of certain protozoans acting as a 'mouth'

dark reaction (step)   part of photosynthesis, occurring in the stroma of the chloroplasts, and using the products of the light reaction (step) to reduce CO_2 to carbohydrate

data   recorded product of observations and measurements; **qualitative data**   recorded observations not involving measurements; **quantitative data**   recorded precise observations involving measurements

deamination   the removal of the amino ($—NH_2$) group from an amino acid, e.g. as a prelude to formation of urea

deciduous plants   plants that lose leaves at the end of the growing season, e.g. broad-leaved trees

decomposer   organisms (typically microorganisms) that feed on dead plant and animal material, causing matter to be recycled by other living things

degenerate code   describes the triplet code, which contains more 'words' (codons) than there are amino acids to be coded, so most amino acids are coded by more than one codon

deme   a small, isolated breeding population

demersal fish   fish that live at the bottom of the sea (or lake)

denaturation   irreversible changes to the structure of a protein

dendrite   a fine fibrous process on a neurone that receives impulses from other neurones

dendrochronology   study of the age of trunks (and timber) by counting and analysing the rings of annual growth

dendrogram   a branching diagram, designed to show the relationship between organisms

dental formula   system of recording the numbers of each type of a mammal's teeth, in half the upper and lower jaws, expressed as a fraction

dentine   hard, bone-like material, making up the interior of the vertebrate tooth

depolarisation (of axon)   a temporary and local reversal of the resting potential difference of the membrane that occurs when an impulse is transmitted along the axon

desertification   the conversion of marginal cultivated land into desert, caused either by climate change or by overgrazing or inferior cultivation

desmosome   point of strong attachment of a cell membrane, e.g. to another cell

detrital chain   a food chain based on dead plant matter

detritivore   an organism that feeds on detritus (dead organic matter)

dextrorotatory   effect of an optical isomer, rotating the plane of polarised light to the right

dialysis   separation of large and small molecules in solution/suspension by the inability of the former to pass through a selectively permeable membrane

diaphragm   a sheet of tissues, largely muscle, separating thorax from abdomen in mammals

diastema   gap in the jaw between canine and premolar teeth, common in many herbivores

diastole   relaxation phase in the cardiac cycle

dichotomous key   one in which a group of organisms is progressively divided into equal-sized groups of smaller size

dicotyledon   an angiosperm having two seed leaves (cotyledons) in the seed

dihybrid cross   one in which the inheritance of two pairs of contrasting characters (controlled by genes on separate chromosomes) is observed

diploblastic body   body of two layers, e.g. ectoderm and endoderm of Cnidaria (coelenterates)

diploid cell   cell having nuclei containing two sets of chromosomes

directional selection   selection favouring one extreme of the inherited variability of a population

disaccharide   a sugar that is a condensation product of two monosaccharides, e.g. maltose

disruptive selection   selection favouring more than one phenotype within a population

distal   far apart, or far from the midline of a structure

disulphide bond   S—S bond between two sulphur-containing amino acid (residues) in a polypeptide/protein chain

diuresis   increased secretion of urine

division of labour   the carrying out of specialised functions by different types of cell in a multicellular organism

DNA   a form of nucleic acid found in the nucleus, consisting of two complementary chains of deoxyribonucleotide subunits, containing the bases adenine, thymine, guanine and cytosine

dormancy   resting condition with reduced metabolic activity which may be imposed on seeds, for example, or which may arise from internal factors (innate)

double bond   a covalent bond involving the sharing of four electrons (rather than two)

double circulation   in which the blood passes twice through the heart (pulmonary circulation, then systemic circulation) in any one complete circuit of the body

double fertilisation   a feature of flowering plants in which two male nuclei enter the embryo sac, and one fuses with the egg cell and another fuses with the endosperm nucleus

duodenum   the first part of the intestine after the stomach

ecosystem   a natural unit of living (biotic) components and non-living (abiotic) components, e.g. temperate deciduous forest

ectoderm   outer layer of an embryo of vertebrates, e.g. layer giving rise to epidermis and nervous system

ectotrophic   literally, 'feeding on the outside'; applied to the external mantle of mycorrhizal fungus (typically) found around many tree roots

edaphic factor   factor influenced by the soil

effector   an organ or cell that responds to a stimulus by doing something, e.g. a muscle contracting, a gland secreting

efferent   'coming away from', e.g. a nerve carrying impulses away from the central nervous system

egestion   disposal of undigested solid from the body, e.g. defecation

egg cell   an alternative name for an ovum

elator   cell in spore capsule of liverworts which aids spore dispersal

electron microscope (EM)   microscope in which a beam of electrons replaces light, and the powers of magnification and resolution are correspondingly much greater

electron-transport system   carriers that transfer electrons along a chain of redox reactions, permitting ATP synthesis in the process

electroporation   a technique for infiltrating DNA into a cell, through short-lived holes in the plasma membrane

embolism   a blood clot blocking a blood vessel

embryo   the earliest stages in development of a new animal or plant, from a fertilised ovum, entirely dependent on nutrients supplied by the parent

embryo sac   occurs in the ovule of flowering plants, and contains the egg cell and endosperm nucleus

emersion   being above the water (e.g. tide) level

emulsify   to break fats and oils into very tiny droplets

endemic disease   disease present within a localised area or particular to a particular group of people

endemic species   species restricted to a particular region

endergonic reaction   metabolic reaction requiring energy input

endocrine glands   the hormone-producing glands that release secretions directly into the body fluids

endocytosis   uptake of fluid/tiny particles into vacuoles in the cytoplasm, carried out at the plasma membrane

endoderm   inner layer, e.g. in vertebrate embryo, giving rise to the gut

endodermis   layer of cells surrounding the pericycle, around the stele in plant roots

endogenous rhythm   a rhythm originating within an organism that persists despite external changes

endolymph   fluid of the semicircular canals and cochlea of the ear

endonucleases   see restriction enzymes

endoplasmic reticulum (ER)   system of branching membranes in the cytoplasm of eukaryotic cells, existing as rough ER (with ribosomes) or as smooth ER (without ribosomes)

endoskeleton   an internal skeletal system

endosperm   the stored food reserves within the seed of flowering plants

endospore   a thick-walled protected spore formed within a sex organ or sporangium

endothelium   a single layer of cells lining blood vessels and other fluid-filled cavities

endothermic   generating body heat metabolically

endothermic reaction   chemical reaction that requires heat energy

endotrophic   term applied to mycorrhizal fungi that are found within tree roots, penetrating the host cells

enteron   gut

entomophily   pollination by insects

enzyme   substances, mainly proteins (a very few are RNA), that function as biological catalysts

eosinophil   a type of white blood cell

epicotyl   stem of the embryo plant, occurring above the attachment of the cotyledons

epidermis   outer layer(s) of cells

epigeal germination   germination in which cotyledons are carried above the ground

epiglottis   flap of cartilage that closes off the trachea when food is swallowed

epiphyte   plant living on the surface of other plants

epistasis   the masking of the effect of one gene by another

epithelium   sheet of cells bound strongly together, covering internal and external surfaces of multicellular organisms

erythrocyte   red blood cell

ester   organic compound formed by a condensation reaction between an organic acid and an alcohol

etiolation   the condition of plants when grown in the dark

eukaryotic (cells)   cells with a 'good' nucleus, e.g. animal, plant, fungal and protoctistan cells

euploidy   a polyploid with a chromosome number an exact multiple of the haploid chromosome number

euryhaline (fish)   living in seawater

eutherian mammals   true ('good') mammals, i.e. not the monotremes or marsupials

exergonic reaction   metabolic reaction releasing energy

exine   outer layer of pollen grain wall

exocrine gland   gland whose secretion is released via a duct

exocytosis   secretion of liquids and suspensions of very fine particles across the membrane of eukaryotic cells

exogenous rhythm   a rhythm originating outside the cell or organism

exoskeleton   skeleton secreted external to the epidermis of the body

exothermic reaction   chemical reaction that releases energy as heat

expiratory   emitting air during breathing

explant   fragments of tissue taken to culture and grow new individuals

extensor muscle   a muscle that extends or straightens a limb

F_1 generation   first filial generation, i.e. arising by crossing parents (P); when selfed or crossed via sibling crosses, produces the F_2 generation

facilitated diffusion   diffusion across a membrane facilitated by molecules in the membrane (without the expenditure of metabolic energy)

facultative   having the capacity to do something, if necessary or if the opportunity arises, e.g. be anaerobic, or be a parasite

false fruit   fruits formed with other parts of the flower, additional to the fertilised ovary, e.g. from receptacle

fermentation   anaerobic breakdown of glucose, with end-products ethanol and CO_2, or lactic acid

fertilisation   the fusion of male and female gametes to form a zygote

fetus   a mammalian embryo, after the stage at which it becomes recognisable

field capacity   describes a soil holding its maximum capacity of capillary water

field layer   the layer of herbaceous plants in a forest or wood

filter feeding   feeding on tiny organisms which are strained from the surrounding medium

fimbrium   thin, short filament protruding from some bacteria, involved in attachment

fission (of a cell)   division of a unicellular organism into two (or more) parts

flaccid   state of a tissue with insufficient water, as in wilting leaves

flagellum   a long thin structure, occurring singly or in groups on some cells and tissues, and used to propel unicellular organisms, and to move liquids past anchored cells; flagella of prokaryotes and eukaryotes are of different internal structure

flame cells   system of cells for osmoregulation, found in flatworms (Platyhelminthes)

flexor muscle   a muscle that on contraction flexes or bends a limb (or part of a limb)

floret   one of many flowers crowded together on a compressed inflorescence, e.g. those on the capitulum of the dandelion

flower   develops from the tip of a shoot, with parts (e.g. sepals, petals) that are modified leaves, surrounding the male (stamens) and female (carpels) reproductive organs

fluid feeder   animal feeding holozoically by the taking in of fluids or very soft tissues

fluid mosaic model   the accepted view of the structure of the plasma membrane, of a phospholipid bilayer with proteins embedded but free to move about

fluorescence   the absorption of light by a pigment and its re-emission as light of longer wavelength

food chain   a sequence of organisms within a habitat in which each is the food of the next, starting with a primary producer which is photosynthetic

food web   interconnected food chains

founder effect   genetic difference that develops between original breeding population and a small isolated interbreeding group of these organisms

fovea   small region of the retina with greatest resolution

free energy   when molecules are broken, that part of the potential chemical energy in the molecules that is available to do useful work

freeze-etching   the shadowing of a surface of freeze-dried tissue or cells after the organelles have been exposed, for examination of structure in the electron microscope

frequency   commonness of an occurrence

frond   leaf of a fern or thallus of a seaweed

fruit   structure formed from the ovary after fertilisation, as the ovule(s) develops into seed(s)

functional group   the chemically active part of an organic molecule

fungus   heterotrophic, non-motile, largely multicellular eukaryotic organism with 'plant' body a mycelium of hyphae with cell walls of chitin; fungi constitute a separate kingdom

funiculus   stalk of ovule, attaching it to ovary wall

furanose   a five-atom ring structure found in some monosaccharides

gall bladder   sac associated with the liver that stores bile

gamete   sex cell, e.g. ovum, sperm

gametophyte   haploid, gamete-forming phase in a plant life cycle showing alternation of generations

ganglion   part of a nervous system, consisting of cell bodies

gap junction   a tiny space between the plasma membranes of adjacent cells

gaseous exchange   exchange of respiratory gases (O_2, CO_2) between cells/organisms and the environment

gastric   relating to the stomach

gastrula   an early embryonic stage, cup- or sphere-shaped, that develops from the blastula (hollow ball of cells) by intucking (invagination) of cells

gastrulation   early stage in embryology, involving cell movements, forming the gut and laying down the primary layers (ectoderm, mesoderm, endoderm)

gene   a basic unit of inheritance by which inherited characteristics are transferred from parents to offspring, consisting of a length of DNA on a chromosome

gene pool   all the genes (and their alleles) present in a breeding population

gene probe   an artificially prepared sequence of DNA made radioactive with carbon-14, coding for a particular amino acid residue sequence

gene therapy   various mechanisms by which corrected copies of genes are introduced into a patient with a genetic disease

generative layer   layer of cells that divide, cutting off cells for a particular role

generator potential   localised depolarisation of a membrane of a sensory cell

genetic code   the order of bases in DNA (of a chromosome) that determines the sequence of amino acids in a protein

genetic counselling   genetic advice to potential parents on the risks of having children with an inherited disease

genetic drift   random genetic changes in an isolated gene pool, not due to natural selection

genetic engineering   when genes from one organism are introduced into the genome of an unrelated organism

genome   the genetic complement (genes) of an organism or of an individual cell

genotype   the genetic constitution of an organism

genus   a group of similar and closely related species

geotropism   a tropic response (tropism) by plants to gravity

germination   the resumption of growth by an embryonic plant in seed or fruit, at the expense of stored food

gestation   time between fertilisation and birth in a viviparous animal

gill   organ for gaseous exchange found in many species of aquatic animals

gland   cells or tissues adapted for secretion

glial cells   *see* neuroglial cells

global village   the concept that through modern communication and transport systems the whole world human population has become a single community

global warming   the hypothesis that the world climate is warming due to rising levels of atmospheric CO_2, a 'greenhouse' gas

glomerulus   network of capillaries surrounded by the renal capsule, which together make up the Malpighian body of a nephron

glottis   the opening of the trachea in the throat

glycocalyx   long carbohydrate molecules attached to membrane proteins and membrane lipids

glycogen   a much-branched polymer of glucose; the storage carbohydrate of many animals

glycogenesis   the synthesis of glycogen from glucose (the reverse is glycogenolysis)

glycolysis   the first stage of tissue respiration in which glucose is broken down to pyruvic acid, without use of oxygen

glycoprotein   compound of protein and polysaccharide, such as those found in the plasma membrane

glycosidic bond   a type of chemical linkage between monosaccharide residues in polysaccharides

goblet cell   mucus-secreting cell of an epithelium

Golgi apparatus   a stack of flattened membranes in the cytoplasm, the site of synthesis of biochemicals

gonad   an organ in which gametes are formed

gonadotrophic hormones   follicle-stimulating hormone (FSH) and luteinising hormone (LH), secreted by the anterior pituitary gland, which stimulate gonad function

granum (*pl. grana*)   stacked discs of membranes found within the chloroplast, containing the photosynthetic pigments, and the site of the light step of photosynthesis

grey matter   regions of the brain and spinal cord consisting largely of nerve cell bodies

growth   more or less irreversible increase in size and amount of dry matter, classified as limited (as in an annual plant) or unlimited (as in a sponge colony)

gut   the alimentary canal

gynoecium   the female reproductive organs of a flower

habitat   the locality or surroundings in which an organism lives

habituation   adjustment by which contact with the same stimulus produces a diminished effect

haemocoel   a cavity filled with blood, which bathes the body organs

haemodialysis   artificial kidney function, carried out by a dialysis machine

haemoglobin   a conjugated protein, found in red cells, effective at carrying oxygen from regions of high partial pressure (e.g. lungs) to regions of low partial pressure of oxygen (e.g. respiring tissues)

half-life   the time taken for the ionising radiation emitted by a sample of a radioactive isotope to fall to half its present level

hallucinogen   a drug, like cannabis, capable of causing hallucinations

halophyte   a plant adapted to survive at abnormally high salt levels, e.g. a seashore or saltmarsh plant

haplodiplontic   a life cycle with haploid and diploid stages

haploid (cell)   cell having one set of chromosomes, the basic set

haplontic   when the body cells (somatic cells) are haploid

haustorium   an outgrowth from a parasitic organism, e.g. a parasitic fungus, through which nutrients are absorbed

Haversian canal   the arrangement of bone cells and canaliculi in compact (hard) bone

heliotropism   'suntracking' by the aerial parts of mature plants, particularly the leaves

hepatic   associated with the liver

herb layer   layer of herbaceous plants (mainly perennials) growing in woodland

herbaceous   non-woody

herbicide   pesticide toxic to plants

herbivore   a holozoic animal that feeds exclusively on plants

hermaphrodite   organism with both male and female reproductive systems

heterodont dentition   teeth differentiated for different purposes

heterogamous   fusion of unlike gametes

heterogamy   the condition of being heterogamous

heteromorphic alternation   having different forms at different times, e.g. haploid and diploid generations that are morphologically different

heterosporous   plants producing two kinds of spores

heterothallic   cells (or mycelia), e.g. of fungi, that may undergo sexual reproduction with members of a different physiological strain

heterotroph   an organism incapable of synthesising its own elaborated nutrients

heterozygous   a diploid organism that has inherited different alleles from each parent

hexose   a monosaccharide containing six carbon atoms, e.g. glucose, fructose

hibernation   passing the unfavourable season in a resting state of sleep

histology   the study of the structure of tissues

histone   basic protein (rich in the amino acids arginine and lysine) that forms the scaffolding of chromosomes

holdfast   attachment organ of many algae, particularly the larger seaweeds

holometabolous   insects that undergo full metamorphosis

holozoic   ingesting complex food material and digesting it

homeostasis   maintenance of a constant internal environment

homodont dentition   having teeth all of one type

homoiotherm   organism that maintains a constant body temperature

homologous chromosomes   chromosomes in a diploid cell which contain the same sequence of genes, but are derived from different parents

homologous series   organic chemicals that are of such similar structure that they can be arranged in an ordered series, each one differing from the preceding one by the addition of a —CH$_2$— group

homologous structures   structures that are similar owing to common ancestry

homosporous   plants producing only one type of spore

homozygous   a diploid organism that has inherited the same alleles (for any particular gene) from both parents

horizon   a layer in the soil showing particular characteristics

hormone   a substance, formed by an endocrine gland and transported in the blood all over the body, but producing a specific physiological response in target organs or tissues

host   an organism in or on which a parasite spends all or part of its life cycle

humus   complex organic matter, the end-product of the breakdown of the remains of plants and animals, which colours the soil

hybrid   an individual produced from a cross between two genetically unlike parents

hybrid vigour   an individual that is heterozygous at many gene loci, and often more vigorous or healthy, or more fertile, as a result

hybridoma   an artificially produced hybrid cell culture, used to produce monoclonal antibodies

hydathode   an epidermal structure that may secrete water

hydrocarbon chain   a linear arrangement of carbon atoms combined together and with hydrogen atoms, forming a hydrophobic 'tail' to many large organic molecules

hydrogen bond   a weak bond caused by electrostatic attraction between a positively charged part of one molecule and a negatively charged part of another

hydrolysis   a reaction in which hydrogen and hydroxide ions from water are added to a large molecule causing it to split into smaller molecules

hydrophilic   'water-loving'

hydrophobic   'water-hating'

hydrophyte   an aquatic plant

hydroponics   cultivation of plants in dilute culture solution, in place of soil

hydrosere   a plant succession that originated from open water

hydrostatic pressure   mechanical pressure exerted on or by liquid (e.g. water), known as pressure potential

hyperglycaemia   excess glucose in the blood

hyperthyroidism   over-activity of the thyroid gland

hypertonic solution   one with a more negative water potential than that of a cell solution

hypha   the tubular 'plant' body of a fungus; in certain species it is divided by cross-walls into either multicellular or unicellular compartments

hypocotyl   the part of the stem below the point of attachment of the cotyledons in an embryonic plant

hypogeal germination   germination in which the cotyledons remain below ground

hypoglycaemia   very low levels of blood glucose

hypothalamus   part of floor of the rear of the forebrain, a control centre for the autonomic nervous system, and source of 'releasing factors' for hormones of the pituitary gland

hypothesis   a tentative (and testable) explanation of an observed phenomenon or event

hypothyroidism   under-activity of the thyroid gland

hypotonic solution   one with a less negative water potential than that of a cell solution

ileum   part of the gut where digestion is completed and absorption occurs; the second part of the small intestine

imbibition   passive uptake of water

immunisation   the injection of a specific antigen, derived from a pathogen, to confer immunity against a disease (e.g. inoculation/vaccination)

immunity   resistance to the onset of a disease after infection by the causative agent

immunoglobin   proteins synthesised by the B lymphocytes of the immune system

immunology   study of the immune system

immunosuppressant   a substance causing temporary suppression of the immune response

implantation   embedding of the blastocyst (developed from the fertilised ovum) in the uterus wall

imprinting   process occurring soon after birth, causing young birds to follow their mother

impulse   *see* action potential

in situ   in the original place (in the body or organism)

in vitro   biological processes occurring in cell extracts (literally 'in glass')

in vivo   biological processes occurring in a living organism (literally 'in life')

inbreeding   when gametes of closely related individuals fuse, leading to progeny that are homozygous for some or many alleles

incubation period   period between infection by a causative agent and the appearance of the symptoms of a disease

incus   tiny anvil-shaped bone, the middle ossicle of the middle ear in mammals

induction process   (in science processes) the theory that scientific 'facts' are based on the accumulation of data, followed by the formulation and testing of a hypothesis (F Bacon, 1561–1626)
 (in metabolism) specific synthesis of protein/enzyme in response to the presence of a particular substrate molecule

indusium   an outgrowth of the epidermis of a fern leaf, covering sporangia

industrial melanism   an increasing proportion of a darkened (melanic) form of an organism, associated with industrial pollution by soot

infectious disease   capable of being transmitted from one organism to another

inference   a tentative conclusion, drawn from a series of observations

inflorescence   groups of flowers arranged on a stem

inhibitor (enzyme)   a substance which slows or blocks enzyme action; a competitive inhibitor binds to the active site, and a non-competitive inhibitor binds to another part of the enzyme

inhibitory synapse   synapse at which arrival of an impulse blocks forward transmissions of impulses in the post-synaptic membrane

innate behaviour   behaviour that does not need to be learnt

inner cell mass   thickening of the inner wall of the mammalian blastocyst, composed of cells that become the embryo

innervation   nerve supply

inspiratory capacity   amount of air that can be drawn into the lungs

integument   wall or coat of the ovule

intelligence   the ability to learn by reasoning and to solve problems not previously experienced

intercalary meristem   meristem between regions of mature tissues

interferon   proteins formed by vertebrate cells in response to virus infections

intermediate   metabolites formed as components of a metabolic pathway

internode   stem between two nodes

interphase   the period between nuclear divisions when the nucleus controls and directs the activity of the cell

interspecific competition   competition between organisms of different species

interstitial fluid   body fluid between the cells

intestine   part of the gut

intine   the inner wall of the pollen grain

intracellular   within/inside a cell

intracellular enzymes   enzymes operating inside the cell

intraspecific competition   competition between organisms of the same species

intrinsic factor   a factor originating and operating within an organism or cell

intron   a non-coding nucleotide sequence of the DNA of chromosomes, present in eukaryotic chromosomes

invagination   the intucking of a surface or wall

involucre   a circle of bracts (scale-like leaves) at the base of a flower

ion   charged particle formed by transfer of electron(s) from one atom to another

ionic bonding   electrostatic forces between the <u>ions</u> in an ionic crystal

ionophore   a molecule in a <u>lipid</u> bilayer that increases the permeability of the <u>plasma membrane</u> to ions

iris   circular disc of tissue, in front of the lens of the eye, containing circular and radial muscles

irreversible inhibitor   <u>inhibitor</u> that binds tightly and permanently to an <u>enzyme</u>, destroying its catalytic properties

islets of Langerhans   groups of <u>endocrine</u> cells in the <u>pancreas</u>

isoelectric point   the pH at which molecules of an <u>amphoteric</u> substance (e.g. an <u>amino acid</u>) carry no charge

isogamy   union of male and female <u>gametes</u> that are of the same size

isolating mechanism   mechanism that prevents breeding between two distinctive <u>populations</u>

isomers   chemical compounds having the same chemical formula but different structural formulae

isometric growth   the growth of an organ at the same rate as the rest of the organism

isotonic   being of the same osmotic concentration, and therefore of the same <u>water potential</u>

isotopes   different forms of an element, chemically identical but with slightly different physical properties, based on differences in atomic mass (due to different numbers of neutrons in the nucleus)

joule   the SI unit of energy

keratin   a fibrous <u>protein</u>, found in horn, hair and nails, and in the upper layer of skin

ketose   a <u>monosaccharide</u> containing a ketone functional group ($>C=O$)

kin selection   <u>selection</u> operating on social insects, such as ants and bees, of closely related individuals

kinesis   random movements maintained by motile organisms until more favourable conditions are reached

kinetic energy   energy in movement

kingdom   the largest and most inclusive group in <u>taxonomy</u>

Krantz anatomy   type of leaf anatomy in <u>C_4 plants</u>

Krebs cycle   part of tissue respiration, the <u>tricarboxylic acid (TCA) cycle</u>

labium   the lower 'lip' in insects

labrum   anterior 'lip' in arthropods

lactation   secretion of milk in mammary glands

lacuna   a cavity, as in the <u>Haversian canals</u> in compact bone

laevorotatory   the rotation of polarised light to the left by an <u>optical isomer</u>

lamella   thin plate, as in spongy bone, or in the 'gills' of fungi

lamina   the blade of a leaf

larva   an independent juvenile stage in the life cycle, distinctly different from the adult form into which it changes by <u>metamorphosis</u>

leaching   washing out of soluble ions and nutrients by water draining through soil

leaf mosaic   arrangement of leaves that minimises overlap of leaf blades

learned behaviour   in animals, behaviour that is consistently modified as a result of experiences

lemma   lower of two <u>bracts</u> in a grass floret

lenticel   pore in the bark of a tree that permits <u>gaseous exchange</u>

leucocyte   white blood cell

leucoplast   colourless <u>plastid</u>

Leydig cells   <u>endocrine</u> cells in the <u>testis</u> that secrete <u>testosterone</u>

lichen   permanent, mutualistic associations between certain fungi and algae, forming organisms found encrusting walls, tree-trunks and rocks

ligament   strong fibrous cord or capsule of slightly elastic fibres, connecting movable bones

light reaction (step)   step in <u>photosynthesis</u> occurring in <u>grana</u> of <u>chloroplasts</u>, in which water is split and <u>ATP</u> and <u>NADPH$_2$</u> are regenerated

lignin   complex chemical impregnating the walls of <u>xylem</u> vessels, fibres and <u>tracheids</u>, imparting great strength

lipid   diverse group of <u>organic</u> chemicals essential to living things, insoluble in water but soluble in organic solvents (e.g. ether, alcohol), such as lipid of the <u>plasma membrane</u>

lipoprotein   a complex of <u>lipid</u> and <u>protein</u> of various types which are classified according to density (very-low-density, low-density and high-density lipoproteins)

littoral zone   seashore

liver lobule   polygonal block of liver cells, a functional unit within the liver structure

locus   a position on a chromosome

lodicule   small structures at base of <u>carpels</u> in grass flowers

loop of Henle   loop of mammalian kidney tubule, passing from cortex to medulla and back, important in the processes of concentration of urine

lumen   internal space of a tube (e.g. gut, artery) or sac-shaped structure

lymph   fluid derived from <u>plasma</u> of blood, bathing all tissue spaces, draining back into the <u>lymphatic system</u>

lymph node   tiny swelling in the <u>lymphatic system</u>, part of the body's defences against disease

lymphatic system   network of fine capillaries throughout the body of vertebrates, draining <u>lymph</u> and returning it to the blood circulation

lymphocyte   type of white blood cell

lysis   breakdown, typically of cells

lysosome   membrane-bound vesicles, common in the cytoplasm, containing digestive enzymes

maceration   process of chemically softening (woody) tissues so that cells and vessels fall apart

macromere   larger cell of early embryo (morula) where there is unevenly distributed yolk

macromolecule   very large organic molecule (r.m.m. > 10 000), e.g. protein, nucleic acid or polysaccharide

macronucleus   larger of two types of nucleus found in ciliate protozoa such as *Paramecium*

macronutrients   ions required in relatively large amounts by organisms

macrophagous feeders   animals feeding on relatively large masses of food

malleus   tiny bone, the outer ossicle of the middle ear in mammals, connecting eardrum and incus

Malpighian body   glomerulus and renal capsule of mammalian nephron

Malpighian tubule   excretory tubule in the posterior part of the gut of an insect

mandible   in vertebrates, the lower jaw; in arthropods, paired, biting mouthparts

mantle   soft tissue underlying the shell in a mollusc

mastication   chewing of food to small pieces

matrix   ground substance of connective tissue or bone; the innermost part of a mitochondrion

maxilla   in vertebrates, the upper jaw; in arthropods, paired appendages posterior to the mandible

mechanoreceptor   a sensory receptor sensitive to mechanical stimuli

medullary rays   sheets of parenchyma cells extending through secondary xylem and phloem

medusa   one of two forms in which cnidarians (coelenterates) of the hydroid and jellyfish type exist

meiosis   nuclear division, in which the daughter cells contain half the number of chromosomes of the parent cell

melanic   pigmented

membraneous labyrinth   the semicircular canals, cochlea and associated structures of the inner ear

menopause   cessation of ovulation and menstruation in women

menstrual cycle   monthly cycle of ovulation and menstruation in human females

meristem   plant tissue capable of giving rise to new cells and tissues

mesentery   connective tissue holding body organs (e.g. gut) in position

mesoderm   layer of embryonic cells in gastrula, giving rise to muscle, blood, etc.

mesogloea   non-cellular layer between outer and inner body wall layers in Cnidaria (coelenterates)

mesophyll   parenchyma containing chloroplasts

mesophyte   plant thriving in temperate climate in presence of moderate amounts of water

mesosome   an invagination of the plasma membrane of a bacterium

messenger RNA (mRNA)   single-strand RNA that is formed by the process of transcription of the genetic code in the nucleus, and then moves to ribosomes in the cytoplasm

metabolic pathway   sequence of enzyme-catalysed biochemical reactions in cells and tissues

metabolic water   water released within the body by oxidation, typically of dietary lipids

metabolism   integrated network of all the biochemical reactions of life

metabolite   a chemical substance involved in metabolism

metacercaria   a stage in the life cycle of a liver fluke

metamorphosis   change in form and structure of the body between larval and adult forms, e.g. as in many insects

metaphase   stage in nuclear division (mitosis and meiosis) in which chromosomes become arranged at the equator of the spindle

metaphloem   later-formed primary phloem

metaxylem   later-formed primary xylem

Michaelis constant   a measure of the affinity of an enzyme for its substrate (and a highly significant parameter where two enzymes 'compete' for the same substrate molecule)

microfilament   a protein microfibre in cytoplasm, part of the cytoskeleton

microhabitat   the environment immediately surrounding an organism; particularly applied to tiny organisms

micromere   smaller cell of early embryo (morula) where there is unevenly distributed yolk

micronucleus   smaller of two types of nucleus found in ciliate protozoa (e.g. *Paramecium*)

micronutrients   ions required in relatively small amounts by organisms

microphagous feeders   animals that feed on minute organisms, e.g. filter feeders

micropyle   a small hole in the seed coat, site of passage of the pollen tube into an ovule, prior to fertilisation

microtubule   hollow protein tube in cytoplasm, a component of eukaryotic cilia and flagella, and of the spindle

microvilli   tiny projections of the plasma membrane, making up a 'brush border'

micturition   urination

middle lamella a layer of <u>pectins</u> between the walls of adjacent cells

miracidium ciliated larval stage in life cycle of e.g. liver flukes

mitochondrion <u>organelle</u> in eukaryotic cells, site of the <u>tricarboxylic acid (TCA) cycle</u> and the <u>electron-transport pathway</u>

mitosis <u>nuclear division</u> in which the daughter cells have the same number of <u>chromosomes</u> as the parent cell

mitral valve left <u>atrio-ventricular valve</u>

mode the most frequently occurring value in a distribution

monoclonal antibodies <u>antibodies</u> produced by a single clone of B <u>lymphocytes</u>, consisting of a population of identical antibody molecules

monocotyledons class of angiosperms having embryos with single <u>cotyledons</u>

monocyte large phagocytic white blood cell

monohybrid cross a cross (breeding experiment) involving one pair of contrasting characters exhibited by <u>homozygous</u> parents

monophyletic a group (e.g. a <u>phylum</u>) of organisms derived from a common ancestor

monosaccharide the simplest type of carbohydrate (all monosaccharides are <u>reducing sugars</u>)

morphogenesis the development of shape and form

morphology form and structure of an organism

morula early <u>embryo</u>, in the form of a solid ball of cells

motile capable of moving about

motor area areas of the <u>brain</u> where muscular activity is initiated and coordinated

motor end plate the point of termination of an <u>axon</u> in a voluntary muscle fibre

motor neurone nerve cell that carries impulses away from the <u>central nervous system</u> to an <u>effector</u> (e.g. muscle, gland)

moult periodic shedding of outer layers, e.g. of the <u>exoskeleton</u> of an insect larva

mucilage mixture of various <u>polysaccharides</u> that becomes slippery when wet

mucosa the inner lining of the <u>gut</u>

mucus a watery solution of <u>glycoprotein</u> with protective/lubrication functions

muscle spindle sensory <u>receptor</u> in muscle, responding to 'stretch' stimuli

muscularis mucosa smooth muscle fibres in sub-mucosa of gut wall

mutagen an agent that causes <u>mutation</u>

mutant organism with altered genetic material (abruptly altered by a <u>mutation</u>)

mutation a change in the amount or the chemical structure (i.e. base sequence) of <u>DNA</u> of a <u>chromosome</u>

mutualism a case of <u>symbiosis</u> in which both organisms benefit from the association

mycelium a mass or network of <u>hyphae</u>

mycology the study of <u>fungi</u>

mycorrhiza a mutualistic association between plant roots and <u>fungi</u>, either with the <u>mycelium</u> restricted to the exterior of the root and its cells (<u>ectotrophic</u>), or involving a closer association between hyphae and root cell contents (<u>endotrophic</u>)

myelin sheath an insulating sheath enclosing nerve fibres, formed by the wrapping around of the cell bodies of <u>Schwann cells</u>

myelinated nerve fibre nerve fibre 'insulated' by a lipid sheath formed from membranes of <u>Schwann cells</u> (neuroglial cells)

myofibril contractile <u>protein</u> filament from which muscle is composed

myogenic originating in the muscle e.g. heart muscle generates the basic heart beat

myotome block of later-formed <u>embryo</u> tissue that develops into muscle tissue

nasty/nastic movements a plant growth movement in which the direction of the response is not determined by the direction of the <u>stimulus</u>

natural classification classification of organisms by finding as many common features as possible, and therefore likely to reflect evolutionary relationships

natural selection <u>selection</u> by which evolutionary change comes about

necrotrophic fungi parasitic fungi capable of subsequently living off dead <u>host</u> plant tissue

nectary group of cells secreting nectar (dilute sugar solution) in a flower

nematoblast a cell from which a <u>nematocyst</u> develops

nematocyst stinging cell of cnidarians (coelenterates), e.g. *Hydra*

Neolithic Revolution the period of human development involving the establishment of settled agriculture, and including the breeding and cultivation of crop plants and herd animals

nephridiopore external opening of a <u>nephridium</u> (excretory organ) in non-vertebrates

nephridium excretory organ of certain non-vertebrates

nephron the functional unit of a vertebrate kidney

nephrostome opening of nephridial tubule into body cavity

nerve bundle of many nerve fibres (axons), connecting the central <u>nervous system</u> with parts of the body

nerve cord in non-vertebrates, a bundle of nerve fibres and/or nerve <u>ganglia</u> running along the length of the body

nervous system   organised system of neurones which generate and conduct impulses

neural plate   band of ectoderm along the mid-dorsal line of the chordate embryo, from which the neural tube develops

neural tube   tube that forms by invagination of the neural plate in the chordate embryo, from which brain and spinal cord develop

neuroglial cells (glial cells)   cells other than neurones that make up the nervous system

neurone   nerve cell

neurosis   an irrational fear or anxiety

neurotransmitter substance   chemical released at the pre-synaptic membrane of an axon, on arrival of an impulse, which transmits the impulse across the synapse

neutrophil   a type of white blood cell

niche   both the habitat an organism occupies and the mode of nutrition employed

node   point on a plant stem where leaves arise

node of Ranvier   junction in the myelin sheaths around a myelinated nerve fibre

noradrenaline   neurotransmitter substance in the sympathetic nervous system

notochord   slim rod of cells along the dorsal midline in the embryo of chordates, which appears to be the 'organiser' for the neural tube

nucellus   in the ovule, tissue that persists around the embryo sac

nuclear division   the first step in the division of a cell, when the contents of the nucleus are subdivided by mitosis or meiosis

nuclear membrane   double membrane surrounding the eukaryotic nucleus

nuclear pore   organised gap in the nuclear membrane, exit point for mRNA

nucleic acid   polynucleotide chain of one of two types, DNA (deoxyribonucleic acid) or RNA (ribonucleic acid)

nucleolus   compact region of nucleus where RNA is synthesised

nucleoside   organic base (adenine, guanine, cytosine, thymine or uracil) combined with a pentose sugar (ribose or deoxyribose)

nucleosome   repeating structural unit of chromatin, consisting of DNA wound around a protein core

nucleotide   phosphate ester of a nucleoside, i.e. an organic base combined with a pentose sugar and phosphate (P_i)

nucleus   largest organelle of eukaryotic cells, controls and directs the activity of the cell

numerical taxonomy   system using a very large number of phenetic characteristics to classify organisms into groups

nutation   spiralling growth movements of the stem tip of plants, pronounced in climbing plants

nutrients   substances required as food or in nutrition

nutrition   the process by which an organism acquires from its environment the matter and energy it requires

nymphs   the juvenile, intermediate forms of insects in which the larvae are similar to the adult and the changes at each moult are small.

obesity   condition of being seriously overweight (body mass index >30)

obligate anaerobe   restricted to living in the absence of air (oxygen)

obligate parasite   restricted to living as a parasite

obligatory   binding or compulsory (lifestyle)

ocellus   simple eye, found in many non-vertebrates

odontoblast   cell that secretes dentine of tooth

oedema   swelling of tissue due to accumulation of tissue fluid

oestrous cycle   reproductive cycle in female mammal in the absence of pregnancy

oestrus   period of fertility (immediately after ovulation) during the oestrous cycle

olfactory   relating to the sense of smell

ommatidium   individual light-sensitive unit of the compound eye of an insect

omnivore   an animal that eats both plant and animal food

oncogene   a cancer-initiating gene

oocyte   a female sex cell in the process of a meiotic division to become an ovum

oogamy   union of unlike gametes, i.e. large ovum and tiny sperm

operant conditioning   use of rewards and punishments to reinforce behaviour

operculum   lid or cover, as in non-vertebrate eggs

opsonin   type of antibody that attacks bacteria and viruses, facilitating their ingestion by phagocytic cells

optical isomer   one of two forms of an organic compound that contains an asymmetric carbon atom, and so can exist in distinct mirror-image forms, which rotate the plane of polarised light in opposite directions

order   a group of related families

organ   a part of an organism, consisting of a collection of tissues, having a definite form and structure, and performing one or more specialised functions

organ of Corti   structure running the length of the mammalian cochlea, concerned with sound transduction

organelle   a unit of cell substructure

organic (compounds)   compounds of carbon (except CO, CO_2 and carbonates)

organism   a living thing

organogeny the formation of organs during embryo development

ornithine cycle the cycle of biochemical reactions by which urea is formed

osmoreceptor sense cells/organ stimulated by changes in water potential

osmoregulation regulation of the water potential of body fluids by the adjustment of water and/or salt content

osmosis diffusion of free water molecules from a region where they are more concentrated to a region where they are less concentrated

ossicle a small bone

osteoblast still-dividing cells that secrete the ground substance (matrix) of bone

osteocyte no-longer-dividing cells that secrete the ground substance (matrix) of bone

otolithic membrane dense deposits in parts of the semicircular canals of the inner ear, aiding the detection of body movements

out-breeding crosses (breeding) of unrelated organisms, which increases heterozygosity

ovarian cycle the monthly sequence of changes that occur to ovarian follicles leading to ovulation and the formation of a corpus luteum

ovarian follicle spherical structures found in the mammalian ovary, containing a developing ovum with liquid surrounded by numerous follicle cells, and from which a secondary oocyte is released at ovulation

ovary female reproductive organ in which the female gametes are formed

oviparity the laying of eggs

ovoviviparity the formation of eggs that hatch within the maternal body

ovulation shedding of ova from the ovary

ovule in the flower, the structure in an ovary which, after fertilisation, grows into the seed

ovum a female gamete

oxygen dissociation curve a graph of percentage saturation (with oxygen) of haemoglobin against concentration of available oxygen

oxyntic cells cells in the gastric glands secreting hydrochloric acid

pacemaker the origin of the myogenic heartbeat, known as the sinoatrial node

Pacinian corpuscle sensory receptor in the dermis of the skin and around the joints

paedogenesis reproduction in larval stages

palaeontology the study of fossils

palea the upper of two bracts surrounding the floret of a grass

pancreas an exocrine gland discharging pancreatic juice into the duodenum, and containing endocrine glands (islets of Langerhans)

paradigm a generally accepted view or model, underlying theoretical explanations

paraphysis sterile, hair-like structures in capsule of moss or liverwort

parasite an organism that lives on or in another organism (its host) for most of its life cycle, deriving nutrients from its host

parasympathetic nervous system part of the involuntary nervous system, having effects that are antagonistic to those of the sympathetic nervous system

parenchyma living cells, forming the greater part of cortex and pith in primary plant growth

parthenocarpy fruit development without fertilised seeds

parthenogenesis reproduction from a female gamete without fertilisation by a male gamete

pathogen a disease-causing microorganism

pectins chemically complex, gelatinous polysaccharides, built from sugar-acid residues, important in plant wall chemistry and wall function

pedicel a short stalk

pedology soil science

pelagic fish fish living below the surface of, or in the mid-layers of the sea

pellicle a flexible outer covering

pentadactyl limb limb terminating in five digits

pentose a five-carbon monosaccharide sugar

peptide a chain of up to 20 amino acid residues, linked by peptide linkages

peptide linkage a covalent bonding of the α-amino group of one amino acid to the carboxyl group of another, with the loss of a molecule of water

perception the mental interpretation of sense data (i.e. occurring in the brain)

perennation the preservation of the plant during the unfavourable season

perennial plant a plant that persists for several years

perianth a collective name for the sepals and petals of flowers

pericardium a tough membrane surrounding and containing the heart

pericycle a ring of cells around the central stele in roots

perilymph fluid of inner ear, separating membraneous labyrinth from the bone

periodontal fibres fibres holding teeth in their sockets

peripheral nervous system in vertebrates, neurones that convey sensory information to the central nervous system, and neurones that convey impulses to muscles and glands (effector organs)

peristalsis wave of muscular contractions passing down the gut wall

peristome ring of 'teeth' around the opening of the capsule of a moss

peroxisome vesicles in cytoplasm (e.g. in liver cells) with single membrane and containing catalase/peroxidase

pesticide a chemical that is used to kill 'pests'

petal modified leaf, often brightly coloured, collectively forming the corolla of flowers

petiole leaf stalk

phagocytic cells cells that ingest bacteria etc., e.g. certain leucocytes

phagosome phagocytic vacuole

pharyngeal cleft *see* visceral cleft

pharynx an anterior part of the alimentary canal, immediately following the buccal cavity

phellogen cork cambium

phenetic resemblance resemblances based upon appearances (the phenotype)

phenotype the appearances (structural, biochemical, etc.) of an organism

pheromone volatile chemical signal ('hormone') released into the air

phloem tissue that conducts elaborated food in plant stems

phosphate (Pi) phosphate ions, as involved in metabolism

phosphodiester bond covalent bond between oxygen and phosphorus atoms, linking nucleotide residues in a polynucleotide

phospholipid compound formed from a triacylglycerol in which one of the fatty acid groups is replaced by an ionised phosphate group

photomorphogenesis effects of light on plant growth

photonasty a nastic response to light

photoperiodism daylength control of flowering in plants

photophosphorylation the formation of ATP, using light energy (in the light step, in the grana)

photorespiration in the 'dark step' of photosynthesis, when oxygen replaces CO_2 at the active site of ribulose bisphosphate carboxylase, and the products are only *one* molecule of glycerate 3-phosphate plus a molecule of a two-carbon compound, glycolate

photosynthesis the production of sugar from CO_2 and H_2O, occurring in chloroplasts and using light energy, and producing O_2 as a waste product

phototropism a tropic response of plants to light

phyllotaxy the arrangement of leaves on a stem

phylogenetic classification a classification based upon evolutionary relationships (rather than on appearances)

phylogeny the evolutionary history of a group of organisms

phylum organisms constructed on a similar general plan, usually thought to be evolutionarily related

physiology the study of the functioning of organisms

phytoplankton photosynthetic plankton, including unicellular algae and cyanobacteria

pileus the characteristic 'umbrella-shaped' cap of a mushroom

pilus alternative name for a fimbrium

pineal gland an outgrowth of the forebrain with an endocrine function associated with detection/response to diurnal and seasonal change

pinnate highly divided structure, with many lateral processes (e.g. the bracken leaf)

pinnule a branch of the compound pinnate leaf of a fern

pinocytosis uptake of a droplet of liquid into a cell involving invagination of the plasma membrane

pith the central region of a herbaceous plant stem, typically occupied by large parenchyma cells

pituitary gland the 'master' endocrine gland, attached to the underside of the brain

placenta maternal and fetal tissue in the wall of the uterus, site of all exchanges of metabolites and waste products between fetal and maternal blood systems

plagiotropism growth at an angle to the stimulus of gravity, shown by lateral roots and stems

plankton very small, aquatic (marine or freshwater) plants and animals, many of them unicellular, that live at or near the water's surface

plant growth seedlings undergo primary growth to form the herbaceous tissues; woody plants go on to form large amounts of secondary tissues (mostly xylem and phloem), often with an external cork layer, the bark

plant growth substance substances produced by plants in relatively small amounts, which interact to control growth and development

plaque a troublesome deposit, e.g. on the surface of teeth, or in the internal surface of blood vessels

plasma the liquid part of blood

plasma membrane the membrane (plasmalemma) of lipid and protein that encloses the cytoplasm (described in terms of the fluid mosaic model)

plasmid a small circular length of DNA that is independent of the chromosome in bacteria (R plasmids contain genes for resistance to antibiotic)

plasmodesma cytoplasmic connection between plant cells, passing through the walls at simple pits

plasmolysis withdrawal of water from a plant cell by osmosis ('incipient plasmolysis' is established when about 50% of cells show some shrinkage of cytoplasm away from the walls)

plastid an organelle containing pigments, e.g. a chloroplast

platelets tiny cell fragments that lack a nucleus, found in the blood and involved in the blood-clotting mechanism

pleiotropy   multiple effects of a single gene

pleural   related to the lung; the pleural membrane lines the outside of the lungs and the inside of the thorax cavity and contains the pleural fluid

pleuron   side plates of the arthropod external skeleton

plexus   a network of vessels, capillaries or nerves

plumule   the embryonic shoot in a seed

pneumostome   a gaseous exchange aperture in slugs and snails

poikilotherm (animal)   'cold-blooded' organism, i.e. one that does not maintain a constant body temperature

polar bodies   the smaller products of the first and second meiotic division of human oocytes, the chief product being the ovum

polarimeter   instrument that measures the angle of rotation of polarised light

polarise   the setting up of an electrical potential difference, e.g. across a membrane

polarised light   light of which the rays vibrate in one plane only

pollen   microspore produced in anthers (and male cones), containing male gamete(s)

pollen tube   tube that grows out of a pollen grain attached to a stigma, and down through the style tissue to the embryo sac

polymer   large organic molecule made up of repeating subunits (monomers)

polymorphism   the existence within a species of different forms of individual

polynucleotide   a long, unbranched chain of nucleotides, as found in DNA and RNA

polyp   sedentary form of cnidarian (coelenterate) animal; one of the two forms in which these animals exist

polypeptide   a chain of amino acid residues linked by peptide linkages

polyphyletic   a taxonomic grouping (such as a phylum) having several different evolutionary origins, rather than a single ancestral type

polyploidy   having more than two sets of chromosomes per cell

polysaccharides   carbohydrates with very high molecular mass, formed by condensation of vast numbers of monosaccharide units, with the removal of water

polysome   an aggregation of ribosomes along a strand of messenger RNA

pons   structure connecting two sides or parts of the brain

population   the individuals of one species in a habitat

portal vein   vein beginning and ending in a capillary network (rather than at the heart)

postsynaptic neurone   neurone 'downstream' of a synapse

potential difference   separation of electrical charge within or across a structure, e.g. a membrane

potential energy   stored energy

predator   an organism that catches and kills other animals to eat

pressure potential   hydrostatic pressure, perhaps generated osmotically

presynaptic membrane   membrane of the tip of an axon at the point of the synapse

presynaptic neurone   neurone 'upstream' of a synapse

prey–predator relationship   the interrelationship of population sizes due to predation of one species (the predator) upon another (the prey)

primordium   the original form of a structure, as it develops

proboscis   a projection from the head, used for feeding

procambial strand   meristematic tissue from which the vascular bundles develop

producer   an autotrophic organism

productivity   the amount of biomass fixed by primary producers (photosynthetically)

progeny   offspring

proglottid   segment of an adult tapeworm

prokaryote   tiny unicellular organism without a true nucleus (with a ring of RNA or DNA as a chromosome), e.g. bacteria and cyanobacteria

proleg   an unjointed abdominal appendage, seen in larvae of butterflies

prophase   first stage in nuclear division, mitotic or meiotic

proprioceptor   an internal sensory receptor

prosthetic group   a non-protein substance, bound to a protein as part of an enzyme, often forming part of the active site, and able to bind to other proteins

protandry   in hermaphrodite flowers, where the stamens mature first

protein   a long sequence of amino acid residues combined together (primary structure), which take up a particular shape (secondary and tertiary structure)

prothallus   the gametophyte of a fern, as it grows from a dispersed spore

protobiont   the postulated forerunners of cells, product of an 'RNA-world'

protochordate   animal almost intermediate between non-vertebrates and the simplest chordates

Protoctista   kingdom of the eukaryotes consisting of single-celled organisms and multicellular organisms related to them (e.g. protozoa, algae)

protogyny   in hermaphrodite flowers, where the carpels mature first

protonema   the gametophyte of a moss or liverwort, as it grows from a dispersed spore

protophloem the first-formed phloem

protoplast the living contents of a plant cell, contained by the cell wall

protoxylem the first-formed xylem

protozoan a single-celled 'animal', belonging to a sub-kingdom, the Protozoa, of the phylum Protoctista

proximal nearest to (the body)

pseudopodium a temporary extension of the body of an amoeboid cell, by which movement or feeding may occur

pulmonary circulation the circulation to the lungs in vertebrates having a double circulation

pulmonary ventilation rate breathing rate

pulse a wave of increased pressure in the arterial circulation, generated by the heartbeat

pulvinus swelling at junction of leaf and stem, playing a part in leaf movements

pump proteins in plasma membranes that use energy directly to carry substances across (primary pump), or which work indirectly from metabolic energy (secondary pump)

pupil central aperture in the iris through which light enters

pure breeding homozygous, at least for the gene(s) specified

pure line generations of an organism that have arisen from a single homozygous ancestor

Purkinje fibres type of neurone found in the cerebellum

pyloric sphincter a circular muscle at the opening of stomach to duodenum

pyranose a monosaccharide in the form of a six-membered ring

pyrenoid a body in a chloroplast where starch formation occurs

pyruvic acid a three-carbon organic acid, $CH_3COCOOH$, product of glycolysis

quadrat a sampling area enclosed within a frame

raceme an inflorescence in which the lowest (first-formed) flowers open first

radical a short-lived intermediate product of a reaction, formed when a covalent bond breaks, with one of the two bonding electrons going to each atom

radicle developing root of the embryonic plant

radioactive dating using the proportions of different isotopes in the remains (often fossilised) of biological material in order to estimate when the original organism was alive

radula a rasping organ of gastropod molluscs (e.g. slugs and snails), used in feeding

ray initials a type of cell in the vascular cambium that gives rise to medullary rays during growth of secondary tissues

reaction centre protein–pigment complexes in the grana of chloroplasts, sites of the photochemical reactions of photosynthesis

receptacle the swollen tip of a flowering stem, where the flower parts are attached

receptor a sense organ

recessive allele allele not expressed in the phenotype

reciprocal cross cross between the same pair of genotypes in which the sources of the gametes (male v. female) is reversed

recombinant a chromosome (or cell, or organism) in which the genetic information has been rearranged

recombinant DNA DNA which has been artificially changed, involving joining together genes from different sources, typically from different species

recycling of nutrients the process by which the materials from dead organisms are broken down and made available for re-use in the biosphere

Red Data Book an internationally produced record of actions for endangered species

redia a larval stage of the liver fluke, found in certain snails

redox reaction reaction in which reduction and oxidation happen simultaneously

reducing sugar monosaccharide sugar with either an aldehyde (—CHO) or ketone ($>$CO) group, able to reduce Cu^{2+} ions to Cu^+ ions, causing a brick-red precipitate of copper(I) oxide to be formed

reductive division meiosis, in which the chromosome number of a diploid cell is halved

reference collection a sample of organisms which have been accurately identified and labelled, and are used to check the identity of later samples

reflex action a response automatically elicited by a stimulus

reflex arc a functional unit in the nervous system, consisting of sensory receptor, sensory neurone, possibly relay neurones, motor neurone and effector (e.g. muscle or gland)

refractory period the period after excitation of a neurone, when a repetition of the stimulus fails to induce the same response, divided into periods known as absolute and relative

relative atomic mass the ratio of the mass of an atom of an element to the mass of a carbon atom

releaser a stimulus that triggers an innate behavioural response

renal capsule the cup-shaped closed end of a nephron, which with the glomerulus constitutes a Malpighian body

renewable energy energy that comes from exploiting wave power, wind power, tidal power, solar energy, hydroelectric power or 'biological sources' such as biomass

replication duplication of DNA by making a copy of an existing molecule; in semiconservative replication, each strand of an existing DNA double helix acts as the template for the synthesis of a new strand

replicative division   mitosis

reproduction   formation of new individual by sexual or asexual means

residual volume   volume of air remaining in the lungs, after maximum expiration

respiration   the cellular process by which sugars and other substances are broken down to release chemical energy for other cellular processes

respiratory centre   region of the medulla oblongata (in the brain) concerned with the involuntary control of breathing

respiratory pigment   substances such as haemoglobin, which associate with oxygen

respiratory quotient   ratio of the volume of CO_2 produced to the volume of O_2 used in respiration

respiratory surface   a surface adapted for gaseous exchange

respirometer   apparatus for the measurement of respiratory gaseous exchange

resting potential   the potential difference across the membrane of a neurone when not being stimulated

restriction enzymes   enzymes, also known as endonucleases, that cut lengths of nucleic acid at specific sequences of bases

resuscitation   artificial ventilation of a patient's lung to restart breathing

reticular activating system   neurones in the midbrain that arouse the brain and maintain consciousness

reticulate vessel   xylem vessel with a network of lignin thickening in lateral walls

retina   the light-sensitive layer at the back of the eye

retrovirus   viruses that, on arrival in a host cell, have their own RNA copied into DNA which then attaches to the host DNA for a period

rhizoid   a filamentous outgrowth from a liverwort or moss gametophyte

rhizome   a thick, horizontal stem, typically found growing underground

ribosome   non-membraneous organelle, site of protein synthesis

ribulose bisphosphate   the five-carbon acceptor molecule for CO_2, in the dark step of photosynthesis

RNA (ribonucleic acid)   a form of nucleic acid containing the pentose sugar ribose, found in nucleus and cytoplasm of eukaryotic cells (and commonly the only nucleic acid of prokaryotes), containing the organic bases adenine, guanine, uracil and cytosine

rod cell   one of two types of light-sensitive cell in the retina, responsible for non-colour vision

root cap   cap of protective tissue at the root tip

root pressure   a positive hydrostatic pressure in xylem

roughage   indigestable matter (such as cellulose fibres) in our diet

sacculus   part of the membraneous labyrinth of the inner ear, concerned with posture

saliva   secretion produced by salivary glands

salt gland   in marine birds, organ positioned near the eye, for excretion of excess sodium chloride

saltatory conduction   impulse conduction 'in jumps', between nodes of Ranvier

saprotroph   organism that feeds on dead organic matter (i.e. saprotrophic nutrition)

sarcolemma   membraneous sheath around a muscle fibre

sarcomere   a unit of a skeletal (voluntary) muscle fibre, between two Z-discs

sarcoplasm   cytoplasm around the myofibrils of a muscle fibre

sarcoplasmic reticulum   network of membranes around the myofibrils of a muscle fibre

saturated fat   a fat having fully hydrogenated carbon backbone, i.e. with no double bonds present

Schwann cell   type of neuroglial (glial) cell which forms the sheath around nerve fibres

sclera   the opaque, fibrous coat of the eyeball

sclerenchyma   plant tissue with thickened, lignified wall, the fibres (and sclereids)

scolex   the 'anchorage' unit at the anterior of a tapeworm, with suckers and hooks

secondary sexual characteristics   sexual characteristics that develop under the influence of sex hormones (androgens and oestrogens)

secondary succession   a plant succession on soil already formed, from which the original community has been abruptly removed

secretion   material produced and released from glandular cells

sedentary   animal living attached to the substratum

seed   structure formed from a fertilised ovule, containing an embryonic plant and food store

segmentation   body plan built upon a repeating series of similar segments, e.g. as in annelids

selection   differential survivability or reproductive potential of different organisms of a breeding population; *see also* directional, disruptive, kin, natural, sexual and stabilising selection

selfing   self-pollination or self-fertilisation

self-pollination   transfer of pollen from the anther to the stigma of the same plant (normally the same flower)

semicircular canals   system of semicircular tubes of the inner ear, set at right angles to each other, concerned with body position and balance

semilunar valves   half-moon-shaped valves, preventing backflow in lymph vessels, veins and the heart

seminiferous tubules   elongated tubes in the <u>testis</u>, the site of <u>sperm</u> production

sense organ   an organ of cells sensitive to external stimuli

sensory area   an area of the <u>cerebral cortex</u> of the brain receiving impulses from the sense organs of the body

sensory neurone   nerve cell carrying impulses from a sense organ or receptor to the <u>central nervous system</u>

sensory receptor   a structure specialised to respond to stimulation by the production of an <u>action potential</u> (impulse)

sepal   the outermost parts of a flower, usually green, protective and <u>bract</u>-like

seral stage   stage in a seral succession, the whole <u>succession</u> being known as a sere

serosa   connective layer lining body cavities and organs, e.g. gut

sessile   attached directly, without a stalk, e.g. of flowers to a main stem

seta   bristle of annelid; stalk of a moss or liverwort <u>capsule</u>

sex chromosome   a <u>chromosome</u> which determines sex rather than other body (<u>somatic</u>) characteristics

sexual reproduction   reproduction involving the production and fusion of <u>gametes</u>

sexual selection   <u>selection</u> due to the struggle between individuals of one sex (usually males)

shrub layer   the low-level (below trees) woody <u>perennials</u> growing in a forest or wood, normally most numerous in 'clearings', e.g. where a full-grown tree has died

siblings   offspring of the same parent

sieve tube   a <u>phloem</u> element, accompanied by a companion cell, and having perforated end walls, known as sieve plates

silage   animal winter feed derived from grass, cut and then preserved by fermentation with the exclusion of air

simple sugar   <u>monosaccharide sugar</u>, e.g. triose sugar (three-carbon), pentose sugar (five-carbon), or hexose sugar (six-carbon)

single-access key   contrasting or mutually exclusive characteristics are used to divide the group of organisms into progressively smaller groupings until individual organisms (<u>species</u>) can be identified

sinoatrial node   cells in the wall of the right <u>atrium</u> in which the heartbeat is initiated, also known as the <u>pacemaker</u>

sinus   a cavity or space

sinusoid   a minute, blood-filled space

solar energy   electromagnetic radiation derived from the fusion of hydrogen atoms of the Sun, reaching Earth from space

solute potential   the <u>water potential</u> of a solution, determined by the amount of dissolved substance

somatic cell (soma)   body cell, i.e. not a cell producing <u>gametes</u> (sex cells)

somite   one of a number of segments in which the <u>mesoderm</u> of a developing animal <u>embryo</u> is divided

sorus   cluster of fern <u>sporangia</u>, typically covered by an <u>indusium</u>

specialisation   adaptation for a particular mode of life or function

speciation   the evolution of new <u>species</u>

species   a group of individuals of common ancestry that closely resemble each other and that are normally capable of interbreeding to produce fertile offspring

spermatocyte   cell formed in <u>seminiferous tubules</u> of <u>testis</u>; develops into sperm

spermatophore   sperms enclosed in a capsule for insertion into the female genital opening in many insect species

sperms   motile male <u>gametes</u> of animals

spindle   structure formed from <u>microtubules</u>, guiding the movements of <u>chromosomes</u> in <u>mitosis</u> and <u>meiosis</u>

spiracle   hole in the side of an insect (thorax and abdomen) by which the tracheal respiratory system connects with the atmosphere

spiral vessel   <u>protoxylem</u> vessel with spirally arranged <u>lignin</u> thickening in lateral walls

spirochaete   spirally shaped bacterium

spirometer   apparatus for measurements of lung capacity and breathing rates

splash zone   uppermost region of the shore habitat

sporangiophore   an aerial hypha in 'pin moulds' (e.g. *Mucor*) on which a <u>sporangium</u> forms

sporangium   a container of <u>spores</u>, found in some fungi, and in ferns and other plants

spore   a small (usually unicellular) reproductive structure from which a new organism arises

sporocyst   a larval stage of the liver fluke, formed in the secondary host (a snail)

sporophyll   a leaf of a fern bearing a <u>sporangium</u>

sporophyte   the diploid phase in the <u>alternation of generations</u> in plants

standing crop   the <u>biomass</u> of a particular area under study

stabilising   <u>selection</u> favouring the existing mean of a <u>population</u>, leading to a reduction in variation

stamen   male reproductive organ of the flower, consisting of filament and anther, containing pollen sacs where pollen is formed and released

stapes   tiny stirrup-shaped bone, the inner <u>ossicle</u> of the middle ear in mammals, connecting <u>incus</u> and oval window

statolith   large starch grain in cells near stem and root apex that may change position when a plant is moved

stele   central <u>vascular tissue</u> of a root

steroid   organic molecule formed from a complex ring of carbon atoms, of which <u>cholesterol</u> is a typical example

stigma part of the carpel receptive to pollen

stimulus a change detected by the body that leads to a response

stipe stalk of a mushroom

stoma (*pl.* **stomata**) pore in the epidermis, surrounded by two guard cells

stomium group of thin-walled cells in the wall of a fern sporangium

stretch receptor sensory receptor in muscles

strobilus cone of conifers and related plants (perhaps a forerunner of the flower)

stroma the membraneous matrix of the chloroplast, site of the dark reaction in photosynthesis

structural isomers compounds with the same molecular formula but with atoms linked together in different sequences

style in a carpel, linking stigma to ovary

suberin a waxy material found in the walls of cork (bark) cells

sublittoral zone the lowest part of the shore, almost always submerged by the tide

submersion covered by (sea)water

substrate a molecule that is the starting point for a biochemical reaction, forming a complex with a specific enzyme

subthreshold stimulus a stimulus not strong enough to trigger an action potential

succession the sequences of different communities developing in a given habitat over a period of time

succulent plant a plant with much 'fleshy' tissue

sugars compounds of general formula $C_x(H_2O)_y$, where x is approximately equal to y, and containing an aldehyde or a ketone group; compound sugars are composed of monosaccharide sugars condensed together; simple sugars are monosaccharides

summation combined effect of many nerve impulses; spatial summation concerns many impulses arriving from different axons; temporal summation concerns many impulses arriving via a single axon

suspensory ligament attaches lens to ciliary body in the vertebrate eye

symbiosis literally 'living together', covering parasitism, commensalism and mutualism

sympathetic nervous system part of the involuntary nervous system, having effects that are antagonistic to those of the parasympathetic nervous system

symplast the pathway (e.g. of water) through the living contents of plant cells

synapse the connection between two nerve cells, functionally a tiny gap, the synaptic cleft, traversed by transmitter substances

synaptic knob the terminal swelling of a presynaptic neurone

syncytium a multinucleate structure, not divided into cells

synecology ecology of a community

synergid cell cells found within the embryo sac, beside the egg cell

synergism acting together, producing a larger effect than when acting separately

syngamy fusion of two cells that are structurally similar

synovial fluid secreted by the synovial membrane at joints, having a lubricating role

systematics the study of the diversity of living things

systemic circulation the blood circulation to the body (not the pulmonary circulation)

systemic pesticide pesticide that is absorbed and carried throughout the organism

systole contraction phases in the cardiac cycle

tapetum nutritive tissue inside the anther, supplying developing pollen grains

target organ organ on which a hormone acts (although broadcast to all organs)

taste bud sense organ found chiefly on the upper surface of the tongue

taxis response by a motile organism (or gamete) where the direction of the response is determined by the direction of the stimulus

taxon a classificatory grouping

taxonomy the science of classification

tectorial membrane a flap of tissue running the length of the cochlea

teleology explaining a biological process in terms of its outcomes (implying 'purpose')

teleost a bony fish

telophase a phase in nuclear division, when the daughter nuclei form

template DNA the DNA of the chromosome, copied to make mRNA

tendon fibrous connective tissue connecting a muscle to bone

tentacle flexible structure found at anterior of some non-vertebrates, typically a feeding or sensory structure

tergum dorsal part of a segment in the exoskeleton of an arthropod

terminal bud bud at the apex of the stem

testa seed coat

testis male reproductive organ, producing sperms

testosterone a steroid hormone, the main sex hormone of male mammals

tetrad a group of four

thalamus   region of forebrain where many sensory pathways converge

thallus   a plant body not differentiated into stem and leaf

theca   a protective covering, e.g. around ovarian follicle

thermogenesis   generation of heat by metabolism

thermonasty   nastic response to change in temperature

thigmotropism   tropic response to contact/touch

thorax   in mammals, the upper part of the body separated from the abdomen; in insects, the region between the head and the abdomen

threshold of stimulation   the level of stimulation required to trigger an action potential (impulse)

thrombocyte   component of blood, also known as a platelet

thrombosis   blood clot formation, leading to blockage of a blood vessel

thylakoid   membrane system of a chloroplast

thyroid gland   an endocrine gland found in the neck of vertebrates, site of production of thyroxine and other hormones influencing the rate of metabolism

tidal volume   volume of air normally exchanged in breathing

tight junction   point where plasma membranes of adjacent cells are sealed together

tissue   collection of cells of similar structure and function

tissue fluid   liquid bathing cells, formed from blood plasma minus proteins

tissue respiration   biochemical steps by which energy is released, typically from sugars

tonoplast   membrane separating cytoplasm from vacuole

tooth bud   stage in the formation of a tooth, e.g. of permanent set

topographic factor   factor influencing distribution of organisms relating to the lie of the land

toxic   poisonous

toxin   poisonous protein from a bacterium

toxoid   an inactivated toxin

trabeculae   cross-barred sheets or strands of bone, making spongy bone structure

trachea   (in vertebrates) windpipe; (in insects) an air-filled tube

tracheal system   system of tubes by which air is passed to tissues (in an insect's body)

tracheids   fibre-like water-conducting cells of some plants

tracheole   branch of a trachea in insects

tracheophyte   general name for 'higher' plants with water-conducting tracheids/xylem

trait   a tendency or characteristic

transcription   the 'conversion' of the DNA sequence of bases into mRNA

transducer organelle   one in which energy is converted (transduction), e.g. the chloroplast

transect   an arbitrary line through a habitat, selected to sample the community

transfer cell   parenchyma cell surrounding phloem in a leaf, with in-growths of cell wall

transfer RNA (tRNA)   short length of specific RNA that combines with specific amino acids prior to protein synthesis

transitional epithelium   epithelium occurring as lining to bladder

translation   decoding of the information of mRNA into protein (amino acid sequence)

translocation   transport of elaborated food via the phloem

transmitter substances   substances released into the synaptic cleft on arrival of an impulse at the presynaptic membrane that conduct the 'signal' across the synapse

transpiration   loss of water vapour from the aerial parts of plants

triacylglycerols   the components of fats and oils

tricarboxylic acid (TCA) cycle   the steps in tissue respiration in which pyruvic acid is broken down to carbon dioxide, and hydrogen is removed for subsequent oxidation

trichocyst   tiny structure in membrane of ciliates (e.g. *Paramecium*)

tricuspid valve   right atrioventricular valve

triose   a three-carbon monosaccharide

tripeptide   a peptide of three amino acid residues

triploblastic   body wall of three (embryonic) layers

trophic level   a 'level' in a food chain, determined by the method or type of nutrition

trophoblast   outer layer of cells of the early embryo stage known as a morula (ball of cells)

tropism   a growth response of plants in which the direction of growth is determined by the direction of the stimulus

true fruit   fruit formed from the fertilised ovary only

tumour   abnormal proliferation of cells, either benign (if self-limiting) or malignant (if invasive)

tunica   body wall or outer covering

turgid   having high internal pressure

tympanic canal   lower compartment of cochlea

typhlosole   longitudinal fold of the gut, projecting into the lumen, as seen in earthworm.

ultrafiltration   filtration, e.g. through the tiny pores in the capillaries of the glomerulus; only the smallest molecules pass through

ultrasonography   use of high-frequency, inaudible sound waves to build a picture of internal structure

ultrastructure   fine structure of cells, revealed by electron microscopy

uniformitarianism   the 'timeless' geological cycle, a theory of Charles Lyell (1797–1875)

unisexual   of one or other sex

unit membrane   (earlier) view of plasma membrane constructed of static lipid bilayer coated by protein on both sides

unlimited growth   growth in organisms like the oak, continuing year after year throughout life

unsaturated fat   lipid with double bond(s) in the hydrocarbon chain

upwelling zone   region of ocean where winds cause water from depths to come to surface

urea NH_2CONH_2, formed from amino groups 'deaminated' from excess amino acid

ureotelic excretion   urea-excreting

ureter   tube from kidney to bladder

urethra   tube from bladder to exterior

uric acid   an insoluble purine, formed from the breakdown of nucleic acids and proteins

uricotelic excretion   uric acid excreting

urine   an excretory fluid produced by the kidneys, consisting largely of a dilute solution of urea

uterine cycle   roughly 28-day cycle of changes to the wall of the uterus

uterus   the organ in which the embryo develops in female mammals

utriculus   part of the membraneous labyrinth of the inner ear

vaccination   conferring immunity from a disease by injecting an antigen (of attenuated microorganisms or inactivated component) so that body generates antibodies prior to potential infections

vacuole   fluid-filled space in the cytoplasm, especially large and permanent in plant cells

vagus nerve   tenth cranial nerve, supplying many internal organs, including the heart

valve (diatom)   part of the cell wall of a 'pill box' type of structure

valves   structures found in the heart, in veins and in the lymphatic vessels that permit flow in one direction only

variety   a taxonomic group below the species level

vasa recta   capillary loops supplying the loops of Henle

vascular bundle   strands of xylem and phloem (often with fibres) separated by cambium; the site of water and elaborated food movements up and down the stem

vascular tissue   xylem and phloem of plants

vasoconstriction   constriction of blood supply to capillaries (of skin)

vasodilation   dilation of blood supply to capillaries (of skin)

vector   an organism that transmits a disease-causing organism; a device for transferring genes during genetic engineering

vegetal pole   part of a fertile ovum with yolk, where cleavage is delayed

vegetative cell   cell where reproduction does not occur

vein   (in animals) blood vessel that returns blood to the heart

ventral   the underside

ventricle   chamber, either of the centre of the brain, or of the heart

venule   branch of a vein

vernalisation   exposure of seeds or buds to low temperature as a prerequisite for growth

vertebrate   animal with a vertebral column

vesicle   membrane-bound sac in cells

vestibular apparatus   the semicircular canals and utriculus of the inner ear, concerned with balance

vestibular canal   upper compartment of the cochlea

vestigial   small, imperfectly developed structure

virus   minute, intracellular parasite, consisting of protein and nucleic acid

visceral cleft   gill slit

vital capacity   the total possible change in lung volume

vitalism theory   idea that organic compounds can only be produced in living cells

vitreous humour   clear jelly of inner eye

viviparity   producing live young

water potential   the tendency of water molecules to enter or leave a solution by osmosis

water table   level of ground water in the soil

wax   complex form of lipid

weathering   breakdown of rock

whey   liquor from milk when the proteins have precipitated with much of the butter fat

white matter   nerve fibres wrapped in their myelin sheaths

xeromorphic   modified to withstand drought

xerophyte   plant showing modifications to withstand drought

xerosere   succession of plants starting from dry terrain

xylem   water-conducting vessels of plants

yolk   food store of an egg cell, rich in proteins and lipids

yolk sac   membranous sac with numerous blood vessels, developed by vertebrate embryos around the yolk (e.g. in birds and reptiles) or as a component of the placenta (in mammals)

zonation naturally occurring distribution of organisms in zones

zoonosis disease of animals that can be distributed to humans

zwitterion amphoteric <u>amino acid</u> at its <u>isoelectric point</u>

zygomorphic irregularly shaped (flowers)

zygospore thick-walled spores formed by <u>sexual reproduction</u>

zygote product of the fusion of <u>gamete</u>s

zymogenic cells cells of <u>gastric</u> glands, secreting pepsinogen

Appendix 1
Notes on equipment and materials

Apparatus (to be made/modified)

Manometer (for Practical 15.1, p. 178)

Cut 40 cm capillary tubing (1 mm bore and 5–6 mm diameter) and flame-polish each end. Make a U-bend 6.5 cm from one end and fit the barrel of a 2 cm³ plastic syringe to the short arm (see Figure 15.1). Use 5–6 mm delivery tubing for the other tubes. Cut rings from 5 mm bore rubber tubing to make the adjustable markers.

Polystyrene discs (for Practical 23.6, p. 270)

Use a small electrical soldering iron to cut two discs of about 10 cm diameter from a piece of dense expanded polystyrene about 2 cm thick, from discarded packaging (this should be done in a fume cupboard or well-ventilated room). Use a 12 mm cork-borer to cut 20 holes in each disc. Make a recess, about 1 cm deep, in one of the discs by heating a suitably sized tin can and pushing it into the base of the disc to melt the polystyrene. Cut two rectangles of nylon fabric from tights or stockings, such that they can be stretched to fit over the top and bottom of each disc; secure the fabric to the base of each disc with a strong elastic band, pulling the fabric very taut in disc A so that woodlice cannot move from one hole to another (see Figure 23.2).

Potometer (for Practical 16.1, p. 193)

Make from a 30 cm length of capillary tubing (bore 0.5–1 mm, 4–5 mm outside diameter), flame-polished at each end. Stick a 20 cm strip of 'Scalafix' transparent scale (if possible, varnish to prevent the scale peeling off in water); alternatively, fix a ruler securely to the capillary tube using elastic bands. Attach a 25 mm length of pressure tubing (3 mm bore) to the top of the capillary tube and fit the tapered arm of a three-way tap into the tubing. Cut or file away the lip of the vertical arm so that a 35 mm length of the same pressure tubing can be fitted to it. Fit a 2 cm³ plastic syringe to the side-arm (cf. Figure 16.1).

T-maze (for Practical 23.8, p. 272)

Cut this from Perspex sheet 5–6 mm thick, with a lid to fit. Scratch the pattern of the maze on to the Perspex and then cut out with a band saw, smoothing the sides of the channels with a file. Make the channel width 7.5 mm for woodlice and 15 mm for seaslaters; make A–C 50 mm, D–H 100 mm, B–M 200 mm (see Figure 23.3).

Buffer solutions

Ethanoate buffer (pH 4.7)

Prepare by mixing equal volumes of 0.1 mol dm⁻³ sodium ethanoate and 0.1 mol dm⁻³ ethanoic acid.

Required for Practical 8.5 (p. 111); 50 cm³ per student group.

Citrate-phosphate buffer (pH range 2.2–8.0)

Prepare 100 cm³ from stock solutions of 0.2 mol dm⁻³ Na_2HPO_4 and 0.1 mol dm⁻³ citric acid as follows:

pH	phosphate	citric acid
2.2	2.0	98.0
3.0	20.5	79.5
4.0	38.5	61.5
5.0	51.5	48.5
5.6	58.0	42.0
6.0	63.2	36.8
7.0	82.4	17.6
7.6	93.6	6.4
8.0	97.2	2.8

Required for Practical 8.4 (p. 110): 20 cm³ of each in the range pH 2.2–8.0 per student group.

Required for Practical 13.6 (p. 166): 100 cm³ of buffer at pH 2, 3, 4, 5, 6 and 8 per student group.

Phosphate buffer (pH range 5.0–8.0)

Prepare 100 cm³ from stock solutions of 0.15 mol dm⁻³ K_2HPO_4 and 0.15 mol dm⁻³ KH_2PO_4 as follows:

pH	K_2HPO_4	KH_2PO_4
5.0	2.0	98.0
5.5	6.0	94.0
6.0	17.0	83.0
6.5	38.0	62.0
7.0	67.0	33.0
7.5	86.0	14.0
8.0	95.0	5.0

Required for Practical 8.3 (p. 109), 20 cm³ of phosphate buffer pH 7.0 per student group.

Required for Practical 8.6 (p. 111), 30 cm³ of phosphate buffer pH 7.0 per student group.

Required for Practical 8.9 (p. 114), 100 cm³ of phosphate buffer pH 6.0 per student group.

Required for Practical 12.4 (p. 145), 100 cm³ of phosphate buffer pH 6.5 per student group (to which is added 6 g of glucose and 0.01 g potassium chloride).

Chromatography solvents

Butan-1-ol : glacial acetic acid : water

For Practical 8.8 (p. 113), prepare using 4 parts butan-1-ol : 1 part glacial acetic (ethanoic) acid : 1 part water; 60 cm³ required per student group.

Petroleum ether : propanone

For Practical 12.2 (p. 141), prepare using 9 parts petroleum ether (b.p. 100–120 °C) : 1 part 90% aqueous propanone (acetone); 30 cm³ required per student group.

Propan-2-ol : ethanoic acid : water

For Practical 12.6 (p. 147), prepare using 15 parts propan-2-ol : 5 parts glacial acetic (ethanoic) acid : 5 parts water; 50 cm³ required per student group.

Computer software

ABO Blood Grouping, from AVP (pp. 207 and 344)

Analyse Your Diet, from Garland (p. 156)

Animal Physiology Pack, from AVP (p. 267)

Bacterial Growth 2, produced by Mike Tait of Aberdeen University, from Scotcal Software (p. 289)

Behaviour, from AVP (p. 273)

Blind Watchmaker produced by Software Production Associates, from AVP or Philip Harris (p. 369)

Blood – a 'Sheffield BioScience Physiology Program/Philip Harris Ltd' (p. 207)

Crossover, produced by Netherhall Educational Software, from Cambridge University Press (p. 344)

Data Disk Plus, from Philip Harris (pp. 108 and 184)

Ecology Disk, from Garland, available from AVP (p. 40)

Ecology Pack, from King's College, available from AVP (p. 40)

Female Reproductive Cycle, Fertilisation and Early Pregnancy, produced by Garland, available from AVP (p. 326)

Flora, produced by Flora Project Team, University of Plymouth, (p. 11)

Food and Lifestyle, from Nutrition and Education Department, Milk Marketing Board for England and Wales (p. 157)

Genetic Mapping, produced by King's College/AVP, from AVP (p. 344)

Genetics Disk, produced by Garland, from AVP (p. 342)

Heredity Pack, produced by King's College/AVP, from AVP (p. 342)

Histology without Tears, from Dr J Bagust (p. 433)

Human Reproductive Cycle, produced by King's College/AVP, from AVP (p. 326)

Insulin, from AVP or Cambridge University Press (p. 257)

Investigating Plant Science (CD ROM), produced by ATTICA Cybernetics, 'Plants for Schools' and Homerton College, available from the IT Unit, Homerton College, Cambridge CB2 2PH (p. 434)

Menstruation and Pregnancy, produced by Netherhall Educational Software, from Cambridge University Press (p. 326)

Microdiet, from Longman (p. 156)

Nerve, from AVP (p. 247)

Nerve Physiology, from Sheffield Bioscience Physiology Program/Philip Harris (p. 247)

Nervous System, from CUP Microsoftware (p. 247)

Nutrition 2.0, by KimTec UK (p. 434)

Photosynthesis Parts 1 and 2, from Bio-Animate Productions, Canada (p. 148)

Plant Biology, from Garland, available from AVP (p. 433)

The Biology Explorer – Genetics, from Philip Harris (p. 148)

Understanding Nutrient Requirements, Diet and Menus Planner and *The Foods You Eat* by DAB Computing (all from Dr David A Bender, p. 156)

Video Rat Stack (with videodisc), by Megan Quentin-Baxter and David Dewhurst, Sheffield BioScience Programs (pp. 162, 165, 248 and 325)

Culture solutions

Water culture solutions (plants)

complete:

$CaSO_4.2H_2O$	0.25 g
$Ca(H_2PO_4)_2.H_2O$	0.25 g
$MgSO_4.7H_2O$	0.25 g
NaCl	0.08 g
KNO_3	0.70 g
$FeCl_3.6H_2O$	0.005 g,

all dissolved in distilled water and made up to 1 dm^3;

minus calcium: replace calcium sulphate in complete solution with 0.20 g of K_2SO_4, and the calcium dihydrogenphosphate with 0.71 g $Na_2HPO_4.12H_2O$

minus iron: omit the iron(III) chloride

minus nitrogen: replace potassium nitrate with 0.52 g KCl

minus phosphorus: replace calcium dihydrogenphosphate with 0.16 g $CaNO_3$

minus potassium: replace potassium nitrate with 0.59 g $NaNO_3$

minus sulphur: replace calcium sulphate with 0.16 g $CaCl_2$, and magnesium sulphate with 0.21 g $MgCl_2$

Required for Practical 16.3 (p. 195), 100 cm^3 of each solution per student group.

Required for Practical 25.7 (p. 290), 200 cm^3 of the complete solution per student group. **Also required**, a concentrated liquid plant fertiliser (such as Tomorite or Baby Bio), to be applied in various aqueous dilutions.

Ringer's solution

This is 'physiological' (saline) solution, adjusted to have the same water potential as the animal tissues it is used to bathe. The composition of Ringer's solution for the tissues or organs of various laboratory animals can be found in zoological or physiological laboratory manuals.

For practical purposes at this level it is ideally replaced by a 50% (v/v) aqueous solution of propane-1,2,3-triol (glycerol or glycerin) solution. Required for Practical 8.7 (p. 113), approximately 25 cm^3 per student group.

Enzyme preparations

amylase, 5% solution (p. 110)

carbohydrase Novo *Viscozyme* from National Centre for Biotechnology Education (p. 434)

cellulose powder (p. 73)

invertase solution: prepare by mixing 5 cm^3 invertase concentrate with 95 cm^3 buffer solution (p. 111)

lactase (Novo Lactozym) from NCBE (p. 434)

lipase solution, 5% (p. 108)

pectinase powder (p. 73)

pepsin solution, 1% (p. 166)

trypsin solution, 1% (p. 166)

urease solution

 5%: prepare by shaking 5 g urease active meal (BDH) with 100 g distilled water for several minutes; allow to settle and decant off the liquid layer (p. 108)

 10% solution (p. 77)

'Fast plants' for Project 19.1 (p. 231) and Practicals 26.7 and 28.3 (pp. 309–10 and 337–8), from Science and Plants for Schools (SAPS) or Philip Harris.

Fruits and seeds for use in Practical 26.9 (p. 311)

Dispersal by animals, internally: blackberry *Rubus fruticosus*, apple *Malus* sp., plum *Prunus domestica*.

Dispersal by animals, externally: burdock *Actium lappa*, cleavers *Galium* sp.

Dispersal by water: coconut (with fibrous husk) *Cocos nucifera*, water lily *Nymphaea alba*.

Dispersal by explosive propulsion: shepherd's purse *Capsella bursa-pastoris*, broom *Cytisus scoparius*, violet *Viola* sp.

Dispersal by wind: poppy *Papaver rhoeas*, snapdragon *Antirrhinum* sp., rose bay willow herb *Chamaerion angustifolium*, clematis *Clematis vitalba*, dandelion *Taraxacum officinale*, thistle *Cirsium* sp., sycamore *Acer pseudoplatanus*, lime *Tilia vulgaris*, ash *Fraxinus excelsior*, birch *Betula pubescens*.

Dispersal by other methods: acorn *Quercus* sp., hazel *Corylus avellana*.

Kidney, corrosion preparation for Practical 18.3 (p. 213)

Inject the renal artery with coloured latex (obtained via Philip Harris) using a 10 cm^3 syringe attached to a glass catheter pulled from a piece of softened delivery tube. Ligature the artery and immerse the kidney in 5% formalin for several days. Immerse portions of the injected kidney in dilute sodium hydroxide solution until the tissues are soft enough to be washed away. The latex casts that are left can be stored in water or 30% aqueous alcohol.

Media

Malt agar* (sterilised)

Required for Project 25.4 (p. 296).

Nutrient agar* (sterilised)

Required for Practical 5.2 (p. 69): 100 cm^3 in a plugged labelled flask per student group.

Required for Practical 25.1 (p. 284): 15 cm^3 in a sterilised McCartney bottle per student group.

Required for Practical 25.3 (p. 288): 15 cm^3 in a sterilised McCartney bottle per student group.

Required for Practical 25.4 (p. 288): as two plates in sterile Petri dishes per student group.

Dextrose peptone agar* (DPA)

Required for Practical 5.2 (p. 69): 100 cm³ in a plugged labelled flask.

*The formulation and preparation of these microbiology media are detailed in:

J I Williams and M Shaw (1982) *Microorganisms 2nd edn*, Bell & Hyman, p. 121–2.

Both can be obtained in powder or tablet form from the following suppliers, however, and many people find using these sources economical of time and materials: Difco Laboratories, Oxoid Ltd, and Philip Harris Ltd.

Starch/agar/iodine plates for investigating insect amylase activity

Prepare by mixing 200 mg soluble starch with water, and make up to 100 cm³. Heat to boiling, then turn off the heat and add 2 g agar. Cool to 50–60 °C, pour into Petri dishes to a depth of 0.5–0.7 cm, and add two drops of iodine solution, stirring to achieve even colour throughout the agar.

Required for Practical 13.5 (p. 164): one Petri dish per student group.

Yeast culture medium (detailed on p. 75)

Required for Practical 5.7 (p. 74): 1–2 litres per student group.

Drosophila culture medium

Prepare as detailed in:

R N Jones and G K Richards (1991) *Practical Genetics*. Open University Press, pp. 48–83.

Alternatively, it can be purchased in powder form from biological supply houses and reconstituted by addition of water.

Required for Practical 28.4 (p. 338): six culture bottles or tubes (or more, according to crosses planned) per student group.

Microorganism cultures

Amoeba and *Paramecium* (p. 264)

Chlorella culture (p. 290).

Cultures of *Escherichia coli*, *Bacillus subtilis* or *Micrococcus luteus* (pp. 284 and 288).

Vorticella culture: once *Vorticella* has been obtained from a pond it can be cultured in the laboratory in a tank or large jar of pond water with some duckweed, by adding one or two boiled wheat grains from time to time; if glass slides are suspended in the culture, *Vorticella* may become attached to them, and in this case the first part of the students' 'method' will have to be modified (p. 294).

Yeast suspension, 1% (p. 110).

Microscopy: checklist of errors and faults

Some common problems that may arise in optical microscopy, <u>with quite straightforward solutions</u>:

Dark-rimmed circles present around or in object (image):

- air bubble(s) trapped when coverslip was lowered. A few may be useful for initial focusing, but bubbles within specimen sections are disastrous. Take more care when lowering coverslips (pp. 2–3, Figure 1.1).

Dirty particles present (slightly out of focus):

- dirt on the slide (lower surface) or coverslip (upper surface). Clean slide with lens tissue (with temporary mounts, clean slides and coverslips before use),
- dirt on eyepiece (moves when eyepiece is rotated) or objective. Clean very carefully with lens tissue.

Foggy appearance to image:

- The surface of the lamp (a 'pearl' light bulb) is in focus. Slightly defocus the condenser (pp. 94–96). A similar solution is required if lettering (e.g. '60 watt') is superimposed on image.

Illumination uneven:

- either the lamp or the condenser mirror may be displaced to one side. Re-align, checking the illumination as you do so,
- the filter ring may be partly displaced across the light path. This is easily

done when you reach to adjust the iris diaphragm of the condenser. Swing the filter ring in (or out),

- objective lens may not have been fully 'clicked' into position. Rotate objective turret until desired objective clicks firmly in position.

Image traversed by blurred lines:

- the specimen is at the edge of the coverslip (or the coverslip is cracked at the point of examination). Move the slide so as to examine a different part of the specimen, well clear of any edges of the coverslip.

Image far too bright to examine:

- the iris diaphragm is far too open and needs adjustment. It is most likely to need adjustment each time you switch from medium to high power, and back again.

Image far too dark:

- the iris diaphram is closed down too much and needs adjustment. It is most likely to need adjustment each time you switch from medium to higher power, and back again.

Image has bright outlines on a dark background ('darkground' illumination):

- the lamp is directed onto the upper surface of the stage and is illuminating your slide from above or the side. Meanwhile little light is entering via the condenser. This an unsatisfactory form of 'darkground' illumination (p. 96). Set up correct ('brightfield') illumination (pp. 94–6).

Image will not focus sharply:

- the objective is dirty. Clean very carefully with lens tissue. Take care the objective does not come in contact with stains or mounting liquids at any time,
- the prepared slide is upside down on the stage. Invert and refocus,
- if the image will not remain in focus and slowly goes blurred, the focus mechanism is faulty. The microscope needs attention ('servicing') by a skilled service technician.

Plant growth regulator solution for Practicals 20.1, 20.2 and 29.3 (pp. 236, 237 and 353)

Either kinetin 4 g dm⁻³ (prepared by dissolving 0.08 g kinetin in a few drops of 0.5 mol dm⁻³ HCl, and making up to 20 cm³) *or* 'auxin' as indole-3-butyric acid (IBA) 2 g dm⁻³ (prepared by dissolving 0.04 g IBA in a few drops of 0.5 mol dm⁻³ NaOH, and making up to 20 cm³).

Pollen germination medium

1 (for Practical 26.6, p. 308): Dissolve 5 g sucrose, 0.01 g boric acid (or sodium borate) and 2 g agar in distilled water and make up to 100 cm³. Warm to about 50 °C, dispense into small bottles containing 20 cm³. Hold at 45 °C in a water bath prior to use. Each student group requires 20 cm³.

2 (for Practical 26.7, p. 309): 0.417 g calcium nitrate, 0.200 g boric acid, 0.101 g potassium nitrate, 0.217 g magnesium sulphate ($MgSO_4.7H_2O$) and 3.5 cm³ of 1 mol dm⁻³ ammonium hydroxide, make up to one litre. Sugar solution medium: 1.2 mol dm⁻³ sucrose (41 g sugar in 100 cm³ distilled water). For the practical, mix equal volumes of these two solutions. The pH should be 8.8: vary the quantity of ammonium hydroxide in the pollen germination medium to adjust the pH.

Prepared slides

Many of these slides are offered as suggestions. Attention is drawn (by 'e.g.') to the numerous cases where alternative slides are suitable.

Practical 1.1 (p. 2)

Obelia, stained whole mount of colony, showing hydranths and blastostyles dicotyledonous plant stem, TS, e.g. buttercup (*Ranunculus*) mammalian stomach wall, VS, stained.

Practical 7.1 (p. 94)

any section of specimen, animal or plant, stained to show good colour contrast of tissues.

Practical 7.4 (p. 100)

A selection of slides of contrasting structures to measure, e.g.:

mammalian lung, TS, thin section, plastic-embedded

Zea mays, TS and LS of stem

human blood smear, stained

Lilium anthers in TS, at second division of meiosis, and tetrads of pollen grains

mammalian small intestine, VS, stained for epithelial cells and goblet cells

Fagus (beech), TS, sun and shade leaves

Amoeba proteus, stained specimen

Ranunculus (buttercup), TS, mature root, with pronounced stele with metaxylem

human scalp, VS, showing hair insertion.

Practical 10.1 (p. 126) *e.g. (alternatives)*

for squamous/pavement epithelium:

mammalian kidney, showing surface of Bowman's capsule

mammalian peritoneum of gut cavity

mammalian oesophagus, TS, stained

human buccal smear, stained

columnar epithelium:

mammalian gall bladder

mammalian small intestine, thin section, stained

mammalian duodenum, TS Brunner's glands, stained

mammalian rectum, TS, stained

mammalian kidney, VS, stained

mammalian trachea, TS, stained

mammalian oviduct, TS, stained

cubical epithelium:

mammalian thyroid gland, section, stained

mammalian kidney, VS, stained

stratified epithelium:

mammalian vagina, TS, stained

human skin, plantar, VS, stained.

Practical 10.2 (p. 127)

e.g.: dicotyledonous stem (*Helianthus annuus*), TS and LS, stained.

Practical 13.3 (p. 162)

mammalian small intesine, TS, stained

mammalian small intestine, LS, injected to show capillaries in villi

mammalian pancreas, thin section/plastic-embedded, showing islets of Langerhans and exocrine acini.

Practical 17.1 (p. 205)

human blood smear, stained

e.g.: *Rona* blood smear or bird blood smear

Practical 18.1 (p. 212)

Ammophila arenaria, TS of leaf, stained.

Practical 19.3 (p. 226)

dicotyledonous stem apex in LS, stained, e.g. *Vicia* or *Helianthus*, or *Curcubita*.

Practical 21.1 (p. 246)

mammalian spinal cord/peripheral nerve in section, e.g.:

vertebral column, TS, showing spinal cord, ganglion and peripheral nerve

mammalian spinal cord, TS, stained

peripheral nerve, TS, stained

peripheral nerve, LS, stained.

Practical 21.6 (p. 251)

vertebrate embryo showing developing eye, e.g.:

chick embryo, 72 hour, TS, optic cup.

Practical 21.10 (p. 256)

pituitary gland, VLS, stained

thyroid gland, section, stained

adrenal gland, TS, cortex and medulla, stained.

Practical 22.2 (p. 261)

compact bone, TS, stained

hyaline cartilage, section, stained

striated muscle, teased, stained

effector nerve ending on voluntary muscle, stained

smooth muscle, stained

cardiac muscle, stained.

Practical 22.4 (p. 262)

Lumbricus, TS, intestinal region, showing insertions of chaetae

Lumbricus, LS, anterior of body.

Practical 23.1 (p. 266)

liver, section, preferably pig

mammalian pancreas, thin section/plastic-embedded, showing islets of Langerhans and exocrine acini.

Practical 23.3 (p. 267)

human skin, VS, pigmented, showing general structure

human scalp, VS, showing hair insertion.

Practical 24.1 (p. 277)

e.g.:

Fasciola hepatica, whole mount, stained

Taenia sp., scolex and proglottids.

Practical 24.2 (p. 278)

Phytophthora, whole mount, showing spore production.

Practical 25.8 (p. 291)

Spirogyra, whole mount, showing conjugation stages.

Practical 25.9 (p. 292)

e.g.:

Fucus serratus, *vesiculosus* or *spiralis*, VS fertile conceptacles.

Practical 25.11 (p. 294)

e.g.:

Mucor, whole mount, with sporangia

Mucor, whole mount, with zygospores.

Practical 26.1 (p. 301)

e.g.:

Pellia epiphylla, VS, with archegonia

Pellia epiphylla, VS, with antheridia

Pellia epiphylla, VS, with sporophyte plant.

Practical 26.5 (p. 307)

Lilium regale, anthers, TS, showing various stages in meiosis.

Practical 27.4 (p. 325)

mammalian ovary, thin section, stained

mammalian ovary, thin section, pregnant, showing corpus luteum, stained

mammalian testis, TS, showing spermatogenesis, stained

human spermatozoa, smear.

Reagents

albumen suspension: prepare by crushing sufficient commercial albumen flake to make an adequate volume of 1% solution; allow to dissolve in cold distilled water with gentle stirring; then heat to 90 °C and filter through glass fibre or a 'Scotchbrite' pad to remove the larger particles (p. 166)

amino acids (for Practical 8.8, p. 113)

aspartic acid solution: prepare by dissolving 10 mg in 10 cm^3 water

leucine solution: prepare by dissolving 10 mg in 10 cm^3 water lysine solution: prepare by dissolving 10 mg in 10 cm^3 water

ATP (available as ampoules each containing 1 cm^3)

bile salts solution, 3%

calcium chloride solution, 0.1 mol dm^{-3}

DCPIP solution
> 0.01%: prepare by dissolving 0.1 g DCPIP in distilled water and making up to 100 cm^3: dilute one part with nine parts water
> 0.1%

ethanoic acid, 0.1 mol dm^{-3} solution

glucose 1-phosphate solution, 3% w/v

glycerol
> 30% solution
> 50% solution
> 85.5%, 70.35%, 50.15% solutions

hydrochloric acid, 0.1 mol dm^{-3}

hydrogen peroxide solution, 20-volume

malonic acid, 0.01 mol dm^{-3} solution: prepare by dissolving 0.10 g malonic acid in distilled water, make up to 100 cm^3

nitric acid, 0.1 mol dm^{-3}

potassium dihydrogenphosphate solution, 0.2 mol dm^{-3}

potassium hydroxide solution, 2 mol dm^{-3}

pyrogallol solution, 2% w/v

resorcinol solution, 10% in propanone

silver nitrate, 0.01 mol dm^{-3} solution: prepare by dissolving 0.17 g AgNO$_3$ in distilled water, make up to 100 cm^3

sodium carbonate solution, 0.1 mol dm^{-3}

sodium chlorate(I) (hypochlorite) solution
> 1%
> 10%

sodium chloride solution (0.5 mol dm^{-3})

sodium hydrogencarbonate solution, 1 mol (84 g) dm^{-3}

sodium hydroxide solution, 0.1 mol dm^{-3}

sodium metabisulphate(IV) solution, 10%

sodium succinate solution, 0.125 mol dm^{-3}: prepare by dissolving 1.75 g sodium succinate in distilled water, make up to 100 cm^3

sorbitol solution, 13%

starch solution, 1%
> sugars
> > glucose solution
> > > 1%
> > > 3% w/v
> > lactose solution, 5%
> > maltose solution, 5%
> > sucrose solution
> > > 0.2 mol dm^{-3}
> > > 0.2–1 mol dm^{-3}
> > > 0.4 mol dm^{-3}: prepare by dissolving 13.68 g sucrose in distilled water and making up to 100 cm^3
> > > 0.5 mol dm^{-3}
> > > 2%
> > > 5%
> > > 10%
> > > 21%

unknown solutions for Practical 6.4 (p. 88):

Solution A: prepare by breaking a hen's egg and collecting the egg-white in a 250 cm^3 beaker; fill the beaker slowly with 1% sodium chloride solution, without mixing; gently stir for 1–2 minutes, then allow to stand for 1–2 minutes; decant into flask labelled 'Solution A'

Solution B: prepare by adding 0.5 g of casein to 50 cm^3 of distilled water at 40 °C; add 10 cm^3 of 1 mol dm^{-3} sodium hydroxide, stir gently until the casein dissolves; add 10 cm^3 of 1.0 mol dm^{-3} ethanoic acid solution and make up to 100 cm^3 with distilled water; place in a flask labelled 'Solution B'

Solution C: allow about 10 g of wheat flour to stand overnight in 100 cm^3 of distilled water in a large beaker; decant off the liquid through a filter paper and place the almost clear filtrate in a flask labelled 'Solution C'

Solution D: stand 20 g of lentils in 100 cm^3 of water overnight in a large crystallising dish; decant off the fluid without disturbing the solid material; filter this solution and place the filtrate in a flask labelled 'Solution D'

Solution E: prepare a 1% (w/v) solution of starch by boiling 1 g of starch powder in 10 cm^3 of distilled water; place the cooled solution in a flask labelled 'Solution E'

urea
> 0.1 mol dm^{-3}, 0.5 mol dm^{-3}, 2.0 mol dm^{-3} solutions
> 1% solution

Seedlings

Oat seedlings (for Practical 20.1, p. 236)
These should be grown in the dark and if possible should stay in these conditions until the students begin using them. They should have coleoptiles that are 15 mm long or more, but which have not been broken by the growth of the first leaf. Fresh oat seed sown in moist peat, kept in warm conditions, can reach this stage of development in four to six days, but it is best to sow a batch early and a batch late to ensure suitable material for the day it is needed.

Pea seedlings (for Practical 20.4, p. 238)
Soak peas for 24 hours, drain off the water and leave in a closed container for a day or two or until the radicles emerge. Select seeds that are germinating and roll them up in a tube of blotting paper or kitchen towel, with radicles pointing downwards. Put the roll in a plastic bag and leave for two or three days until the radicles are about 20 mm long. Then put the rolls in the refrigerator until needed. Choose seedlings with more or less straight radicles.

Wheat seedlings (for Practical 20.3, p. 238)
Six or seven days before the practical, soak wheat grains for 24 hours in water. Drain off the water, but leave the seeds in a closed container for another day or two. Select grains showing signs of germination and place them 'cleft' side down on moistened cotton wool squares in Petri dishes, allowing about 20 per dish. Leave the seeds in darkness to germinate, and when the coleoptiles reach a height of 20–30 mm transfer the dishes to the refrigerator until needed. Make foil caps for the coleoptiles by rolling thin aluminium foil on the end of a cocktail stick to make tubes about 10 mm long. Pinch the tops to make a 'handling tag', leaving a 5 mm tube to go over the coleoptiles.

Silicone rubber (Lastic), from Claudius Ash (for Practical 18.3, p. 213)

Stains
Required in labelled dropping bottles:

aceto-orcein, for Practicals 9.1 and 9.2 (pp. 120 and 121)

bacterial stains:
> crystal violet (2% w/v crystal violet in 20% v/v ethanol/water)
> nigrosin (10% w/v in water)

for Practicals 5.1 and 7.5 (pp. 67 and 101)

methylene blue, for Practicals 5.7 and 7.4 (pp. 74 and 100)

toluidine blue, for Practicals 10.2, 12.1, 18.1 and 19.4 (pp. 127, 140, 212 and 227)

methyl green pyronin, for Practical 26.6 (p. 308).

Suppliers
Association for the Study of Animal Behaviour, c/o Biology Department, Homerton College, Cambridge CB2 2PH (01223 411141)

AVP, School Hill Centre, Chepstow, Gwent NP6 5HP (01291 625439)

Dr J Bagust, Department of Physiology and Pharmacology, Medical Science Building, University of Southampton, Southampton SO16 7PX

BDH (Merk Ltd), Broom Road, Poole, Dorset BH15 1TD (01202 669700)

Dr David A Bender, Department of Biochemistry, University College, London WC1E 6BT

Biochemical Society, 59 Portland Place, London W1N 3AJ (0171 580 5530)

Blades Biological, Cowden, Edenbridge, Kent TN8 7DX (01342 850242)

Boulton–Hawker Films Ltd, Hadleigh, Ipswich, Suffolk IP7 5BG (01473 822235)

Class Productions, 34 Wycombe Gardens, London NW11 8AL

CUP Microsoftware, The Edinburgh Building, Shaftesbury Road, Cambridge CB2 2RU (01223 312393)

Data Harvest Group Ltd, Woburn Lodge, Waterloo Road, Linslade, Leighton Buzzard, Bedfordshire LU7 7NR (01525 373666)

Difco Laboratories, PO Box 290, Central Avenue, West Molesey, Surrey (0181 979 9951)

Educational Media Film & Video Ltd, 235 Imperial Drive, Rayners Lane, Harrow, Middlesex HA2 7HE (0181 868 1908)

Griffin and George, Bishops Meadow Road, Loughborough, Leicestershire, LE11 0RG (01509 231166)

Homerton College, Cambridge CB3 2PH (01223 411141)

Insect Lore – Europe, Suite 6, Linford Forum, Linford Wood, Milton Keynes MK14 6LY (01908 200794)

Irwin-Desman, Eurocrown House, 23 Grafton Road, Croydon, Surrey, CR9 3AZ (0181 686 6441)

Kim Tec UK, Fairways House, 8 Highland Road, Wimborne, Dorset BH21 2QN

Longman Logotron, 124 Cambridge Science Park, Milton Road, Cambridge CB2 4ZS (01223 425558)

National Centre for Biotechnology Education (NCBE), University of Reading, Whiteknights, Reading RG6 2AJ (01734 873743)

NES Arnold Scientific, Ludlow Hill Road, West Bridgeford, Nottingham NG15 8ES (0115 945 2200)

Oxoid (Unipath) Ltd, Wade Road, Basingstoke, Hampshire RG24 8PW (01256 841144)

Philip Harris Education, Lynn Lane, Shenstone, Lichfield, Staffordshire WS14 0EE (01543 480077)

Portland Press, Commerce Way, Colchester CO2 8HP (01206 796351)

School Science Service, Brunel University, Uxbridge UB8 3PH (01895 251496)

Science and Plants for Schools (SAPS), Homerton College, Hills Road, Cambridge CB2 2PH (01223 411141)

Scotcal Software, 34a Watson Street, Aberdeen AB2 4QL (01224 620040)

Unilab Ltd, The Science Park, Hutton Street, Blackburn BB1 3BT (01254 681222)

Wellcome Centre Video Loans Club, The Wellcome Centre for Medical Sciences, 210 Euston Road, London NW1 2BE (0171 611 8246)

Tests (and the reagents required)

Benedict's solution, qualitative test for sugars (reducing and non-reducing) (Practical 6.1, p. 84).

Biuret test: test for —CONH— group, as in peptide links in soluble proteins/peptides.
Reagents: 10% sodium hydroxide solution, 0.5% copper(II) sulphate solution.

Cellulose test, using iodine in I_2/KI solution (see 'Starch test', below). This stains cellulose yellow.
Alternatively, Schultze's solution (chlor-zinc-iodine), obtained from biological suppliers, stains cellulose purple. Care – corrosive.

Haemotoxylin (Ehrlich), general stain for animal histology, obtained from biological suppliers in 30% ethanol. Tissue sample, in 30% ethanol, transferred to haemotoxylin until dark blue (about three minutes). Tissue 'blued' in top water, examining under medium power, until nuclei are dark blue and cytoplasm is light blue or colourless.

Lignin test, using a few drops of phloroglucinol, followed by a drop of concentrated hydrochloric acid. This stains lignin in the walls of fibres, tracheids and xylem vessels red (Practical 19.4, p. 227).

Lipids test, based on their insolubility in water (Practical 6.3, p. 87).

Maltose test, using iodine in I_2/KI solution (see 'Starch test', below). This stains maltose red.

Millon's reagent (if allowed to be used in your laboratory) tests for insoluble protein. Use 3 cm^3 of the suspension, add six drops of Millon's reagent and boil. A brick-red precipitate forms in the presence of protein.

Ninhydrin spray, test for amino acids. Made by dissolving 0.2 g of ninhydrin in 200 cm^3 propanone (Practical 8.8, p. 113).

Reducing sugar
a Using Diastix (Practical 5.8, p. 67).
b See 'Benedict's solution', above.

Resazurin test, uses a 0.005% resazurin solution, as test for bacterial activity (Practical 5.6, p. 65).

Starch test, using iodine in I_2/KI solution: dissolve potassium iodide (2 g) in as little distilled water as possible, and then add iodine (1 g). Make up to 100 cm^3 with distilled water. The solution stains starch blue-black (Practicals 7.4 and 12.5, pp. 100 and 146, etc.).

Sudan III test for oils; the dye is used in powder form (Practical 6.3, p. 57).

Viability of yeast cells, a drop of yeast culture plus a tiny drop of 0.1% methylene blue (redox indicator), examined on a slide under a coverslip. Living cells decolorise, dead cells stain blue (Practical 5.7, p. 67).

Tissue culture medium for Practical 29.3 (p. 353)
Make up using Murashie & Skoog salts 4.4 g, sucrose 30 g, agar 8 g, in 500 cm^3 distilled water plus 1 cm^3 plant growth regulator solution (q.v.) per litre of medium, followed by adjustment of pH to 5.8 by adding either HCl or NaOH.

Videotapes

Antibiotics: The Mould, the Myth and the Microbes (BBC *Horizon* production), from Wellcome Centre Video Loans Club

Blind Watchmaker (a BBC *Horizon* production), BBC Videos for Education and training, from Wellcome Centre Video Loans Club

Fossil Heroes (*Antenna* production from BBC Videos Education and Training), available for hire from the Wellcome Centre Video Loans Club

Homeostasis: Maintaining the Body's Internal Environment, from Boulton–Hawker Films

Hormones and the Endocrine System, produced by Human Relations Media Inc., USA, from Boulton–Hawker Films

Manipulating DNA by Dr E J Wood, University of Leeds, for the Biochemical Society, from Portland Press

Meiosis: Key to Genetic Diversity, produced by Human Relations Media Inc., USA, from Boulton–Hawker Films or Class Productions

Monera: Bacteria and Cyanobacteria, from Boulton–Hawker Films

Sexual Reproduction in Animals, BBC Enterprises, from Class Productions

Stimulus/Response, from Association for the Study of Animal Behaviour

The Architecture of Cells: Special Structure, Special Function, from Boulton–Hawker Films

The Biochemical Basis of Biology: Cell Structure and Energy Production, produced by Dr E M Evans and Dr E J Wood (including teacher's notes)

The Immune Response and Immunization, from Boulton-Hawker Films

Vertebrate Dissection Guides – The Rat by the TV Centre, University of Portsmouth in association with the Institute of Biology

Appendix 2
Experimental design and the evaluation of data

How does science 'work'? How does new knowledge about living things and of the workings of the living world come about?

These are interesting and important questions in their own right, and they are quite challenging to answer fully. Biology certainly involves the processes of asking questions, thinking up possible explanations, and the eventual formulation of hypotheses. Then the testing of hypotheses involves making observations, and the planning and conducting of experiments.

But there is no such thing as *the* scientific method. Rather, developments in scientific understanding are based on:

- accurate observation and carefully devised experiments;
- collection of numerical data that is then handled mathematically, allowing distinctions to be made between alternative explanations (hypotheses);
- examination and re-interpretation of existing data;
- the devising of new ways of looking at familiar things, leading to new explanations that can be tested;
- creativity and imagination in our approaches to existing explanations and theories.

Since the time available for experimentation is always limited, how are you to make the best use of your time? The short answer must be 'by planning carefully' (particularly longer-term investigations and projects). To do so, follow these points.

1 Acquire a realistic view of science

Read, for example, Sections 1.5, 1.6 and 1.7, 'Biology as a science', 'The processes of practical science' and 'Modern biology' in *Advanced Biology*, pp. 9–15.

2 Carefully select an issue to study

Ideas that really interest you may originate from 'investigation' practicals or longer-term project ideas in the main text of this *Study Guide*, of from your wider reading and study, or through a hobby interest in natural history or in science and technology. Perhaps a project will grow out of an introductory small-scale investigation, undertaken near the start of your present course (see Practical 1.2 A small-scale scientific investigation, pp. 3–4 of this *Study Guide*).

Check that your ideas are feasible by talking to science tutors and teachers, giving as much detail as you can at this stage of what you think the study may involve. Then listen to their points and views, and reassess your plans realistically.

3 Design your study

Formulate a testable hypothesis, and select appropriate data collection methods. Design aspects are discussed in detail in 'Data handling: Planning data collection' in this *Study Guide*, p. 38, and in:

C Barnard, F Gilbert and P McGregor (1993) *Asking Questions in Biology*. Longman.

Appropriate practical experimental methods are described in detail in this *Study Guide*. Access them via the Index (pp. 441–450). Further information on ecological techniques is available in:

G Williams (1987) *Techniques and Fieldwork in Ecology*. Bell & Hyman.

Further advanced information on laboratory experimentation is available in:

A Jones, R Reed and J Weyers (1994) *Practical Skill in Biology*. Longman.

4 Recording and presenting your data

The emphasis here is on obtaining the maximum significant information from your results, and on communicating the data effectively. These issues are discussed in 'Data handling: Recording data' and 'Presenting data' in this *Study Guide*, pp. 33–4. Further discussion is presented in:

J W Garvin and J D Boyd (1990) *Skill in Advanced Biology 2: Observing, Recording and Interpreting*. Stanley Thornes.

5 Examining the data

Exploring data, making statistical checks on their validity and drawing conclusions is the next step. These issues are discussed in 'Data handling: Exploring data' and 'Statistical checks on data' in this *Study Guide*, p. 34, where there is guidance to aid you in the selection of appropriate statistical tests. A dichotomous key to commonly used statistical tests is given at the back of:

N Chalmers and P Parker (1989) *The OU Project Guide; Fieldwork and Statistics for Ecological Projects* (2nd edn). Open University Press/Field Studies Council.

The statistical tables you may need to refer to are reproduced on pages 436–7.

6 Evaluation

At the end of your study you must be able to criticise your methods constructively and be able to suggest what sort of further work would be worthwhile to undertake, if the time were available.

The *t* test

Reject the null hypothesis if your value of *t* is larger than the value tabulated in Table A2.1 at the 5% significance level, for the calculated number of degrees of freedom.

The chi-squared test

Reject the null hypothesis if your value of χ^2 is bigger than the value tabulated in Table A2.2 at the 5% significance level, for the calculated number of degrees of freedom.

The Mann–Whitney *U* test

Reject the null hypothesis at the 5% level if your value of *U* is less than or equal to the value tabulated in Table A2.3.

The Spearman rank correlation coefficient

Reject the null hypothesis if your value of r_s is greater than or equal to the value tabulated in Table A2.4 at the chosen significance level, for the calculated degrees of freedom, for your number of pairs, *n*.

Table A2.1 Table of t distribution

Degrees of freedom	Significance level 5%
1	12.706
2	4.303
3	3.182
4	2.776
5	2.571
6	2.447
7	2.365
8	2.306
9	2.262
10	2.228
11	2.201
12	2.179
13	2.160
14	2.145
15	2.131
16	2.120
17	2.110
18	2.101
19	2.093
20	2.086
21	2.080
22	2.074
23	2.069
24	2.064
25	2.060
26	2.056
27	2.052
28	2.048
29	2.043
30	2.042
40	2.021
60	2.000
120	1.980
∞	1.960

Table A2.2 Table of χ^2 distribution

Degrees of freedom	Significance level 5%
1	3.841
2	5.991
3	7.815
4	9.488
5	1.070
6	12.592
7	14.067
8	15.507
9	16.919
10	18.307
11	19.675
12	21.026
13	22.362
14	23.685
15	24.996
16	26.296
17	27.587
18	28.869
19	30.144
20	31.410
21	32.671
22	33.924
23	35.172
24	36.415
25	37.652
26	38.885
27	40.113
28	41.337
29	42.557
30	43.773

Table A2.3 Critical values of U

n_1/n_2	1	2	3	4	5	6	7	8	9	10	11	12	13	14	15	16	17	18	19	20
1	–	–	–	–	–	–	–	–	–	–	–	–	–	–	–	–	–	–	–	–
2	–	–	–	–	–	–	–	0	0	0	0	1	1	1	1	1	2	2	2	2
3	–	–	–	–	0	1	1	2	2	3	3	4	4	5	5	6	6	7	7	8
4	–	–	–	0	1	2	3	4	4	5	6	7	8	9	10	11	11	12	13	13
5	–	–	0	1	2	3	5	6	7	8	9	11	12	13	14	15	17	18	19	20
6	–	–	1	2	3	5	6	8	10	11	13	14	16	17	19	21	22	24	25	27
7	–	–	1	3	5	6	8	10	12	14	16	18	20	22	24	26	28	30	32	34
8	–	0	2	4	6	8	10	13	15	17	19	22	24	26	29	31	34	36	38	41
9	–	0	2	4	7	10	12	15	17	20	23	26	28	31	34	37	39	42	45	48
10	–	0	3	5	8	11	14	17	20	23	26	29	33	36	39	42	45	48	52	55
11	–	0	3	6	9	13	16	19	23	26	30	33	37	40	44	47	51	55	58	62
12	–	1	4	7	11	14	18	22	26	29	33	37	41	45	49	53	57	61	65	69
13	–	1	4	8	12	16	20	24	28	33	37	41	45	50	54	59	63	67	72	76
14	–	1	5	9	13	17	22	26	31	36	40	45	50	55	59	64	67	74	78	83
15	–	1	5	10	14	19	24	29	34	39	44	49	54	59	64	70	75	80	85	90
16	–	1	6	11	15	21	26	31	37	42	47	53	59	64	70	75	81	86	92	98
17	–	2	6	11	17	22	28	34	39	45	51	57	63	67	75	81	87	93	99	105
18	–	2	7	12	18	24	30	36	42	48	55	61	67	74	80	86	93	99	106	112
19	–	2	7	13	19	25	32	38	45	52	58	65	72	78	85	92	99	106	113	119
20	–	2	8	13	20	27	34	41	48	55	62	69	76	83	90	98	105	112	119	127

Dashes indicate no decision possible at the stated level of significance.

Table A2.4 Table of critical values of r_s

Number of pairs, n	Significance level		
	5%	2%	1%
5	1.000	1.000	–
6	0.886	0.943	1.000
7	0.786	0.893	0.929
8	0.738	0.833	0.881
9	0.683	0.783	0.833
10	0.648	0.746	0.794
12	0.591	0.712	0.777
14	0.544	0.645	0.715
16	0.506	0.601	0.665
18	0.475	0.564	0.625
20	0.450	0.534	0.591
22	0.428	0.508	0.562
24	0.409	0.485	0.537
26	0.392	0.465	0.515
28	0.377	0.448	0.496
30	0.364	0.432	0.478

Appendix 3
Study techniques, revision and examinations

What will you get from your biology course?

The general aims of Advanced level (and other 16+) biology courses can be listed something like this:

- to qualify you for further study (possibly at degree or diploma level, should you choose this), and for worthwhile employment;
- to sustain and develop your interest and enjoyment in living things and in the natural world;
- to develop your understanding of a range of biological concepts and principles (for example, structure in relation to function, diversity of living things and their interactions) and their significance, and how to explain related but unfamiliar phenomena, using concepts and principles;
- to enable you to practise the range of practical skills needed for biological investigations and experimental design, normally carried out in laboratory work and in field studies, and develop the ability to present, analyse and critically interpret the resulting data;
- to enhance your respect for living things and their environment, now and in the future, and heighten your awareness of how finite resources and fragile habitats may be conserved;
- to establish some of the personal, social, environmental, economic and technological consequences of biological understanding, and the potential significance of biology for employment and production;
- to facilitate your development of information technology and communication skills in a wide variety of forms in the collection, selection and use of information in problem solving in scientific contexts.

What will *you* have to invest for this outcome?

What your course actually does for you is partly (at least) up to you. For example,

- how you manage your time and studying,
- how you undertake practical work and investigations,
- your attitude to living things and to investigating environmental implications,

may all influence what you can achieve.

An appropriate, committed contribution by you will tend to help others, as well as yourself. To get your approach 'just right' may take some organising and careful thought. It is well worth doing these early on. When you've got it together, practise it!

Study techniques
Studying for understanding

In studying biology at this level you have to understand and apply information, rather than merely learn and recall facts. For example, you need to be able to work out and understand the principles behind a particular situation or example; when you encounter a new situation or case, you will have to work out what is going on from basic principles that you previously understood in a different context. This means that when you meet new principles and concepts you should try to understand them, and not rote-learn them. If you find problems with this, ask lots of questions. Your textbook, too, should help both by explaining and by suggesting alternative sources to use.

Relating issues to your world and your interests

Most, if not all, of the biological topics you study have some direct consequence or application for you and your environment. Think these out, bear them in mind, and make your new learning apply to the situations you already understand. In learning for GCSE science, teachers will often stress the significance of what is studied, right at the start of the topic. Continue to do this yourself, and work it out with peers and teachers if it is not immediately apparent. Be aware of the significance of what you learn, from the outset.

Developing skills

Throughout your course you are developing and extending your personal skills. You are steadily getting better at understanding, presenting and explaining, questioning, analysing, interpreting and applying ideas and principles. This goes on, almost in the background, whilst you learn new topics in biology, and as you develop your practical biology skills and techniques. These developments grow out of all sorts of almost mundane skills, including the following.

Practical work skills   Biological knowledge arises from practical observation and experiment; practical work and the outcome of enquiries based on it are the foundations of biology. The skills you must deliberately practise and develop include observing, measuring, manipulating apparatus and equipment, recording qualitative and quantitative results and observations, analysing data, designing experiments and investigations, and reporting (communication skills of many types).

Reading skills   Effective 'reading for a purpose' is best achieved as follows:

- quickly scan through the source to assess its direction and value to you;
- then read it again carefully, highlighting or noting down the key words and phrases;
- decide if the source is really useful to you; if so,
- make concise notes of the key points, recording these in your own words;
- finally, scan through again, to make certain you have overlooked nothing important.

The technique of reading for understanding is illustrated in Problem 1.1, p. 4 of this *Study Guide*.

Note taking   Here you need to practise at working quickly and neatly, distinguishing between key points or principles, and examples or applications.

Make distinctions by subheadings, keeping the bulk of what you note and record very concise. Use abbreviations for terms that occur repeatedly. Labelled and annotated diagrams may often be worth more than a written description.

Expect to revisit the topic when you learn more, when you come across a new source, or when you learn about another application or development. Since you may expect to add repeatedly to important topics, the ways in which you organise your notes must be flexible, perhaps by using ring files with dividers for major topics.

Team work (work in a self-help group)   A self-help group consists of two or more students who are studying the same course, who maintain informal but regular contacts (meetings or by telephone) because they find they can give each other assistance to solve study problems more quickly. A 'confusion' to one student is often clearly understood by another. Teaching each other helps to sort out other ideas and principles.

There is often a lot of mutual benefit to be had from self-help. The dangers here arise if the group spends too much time chatting (if so, revert to a formal agenda, or a list of points where help is needed, at the outset), or if there are problems that no one can solve (if so, it's back to the teacher).

Time management

Perhaps for the first time, you now have unsupervised study time during the working day. Time is immensely precious to us all, and accordingly we can become very discouraged when we find we have wasted it. To make a success of study time, it may help to plan how you use it, but only if you do not end up worrying over whether you are keeping to your plans!

Planning simply involves the identification and recording of the tasks arising from your course that you have to complete independently, using a diary, perhaps on a weekly or daily basis. Tasks will include formal assessment items (such as essays), background study and wider reading, revision or checking of classroom notes, and possibly tasks associated with an independent longer-term project. To locate exactly when a task has to be completed, plan backwards from when the work must be submitted, or when it is needed for some other purpose, or when the next input on the topic will come. Keep a check on your recognition of tasks. Are you getting your essential activities properly identified, allowing sufficient (but not too much) time for them, and generally making your deadlines?

Overall, you will find it easiest to stick to regular patterns of study time, wider reading and background research, liberally scattered with relaxation time and time for other unrelated interests.

School or college studies; course work assessment

Formal studies usually centre around listening (and questioning) and note-taking at lectures or classroom teaching sessions, and the conduct and recording of practical and fieldwork studies, working individually or in small groups. As a follow-up, you need to check through your notes regularly and promptly, making certain that you understood what you wrote, and that it will be intelligible to you when next you read it. Practicals need writing up at the time, but checking and correctly filing subsequently, for later assessments.

Course work assignments normally consist of essays, or notes for peer-group presentations, or records of group visits to off-school sites in industry, at a museum or elsewhere in the local environment.

When preparing to *write an essay* (or any other written record):

1 Check that you understand what is required. Read the title or instructions very carefully, underlining (highlighting) key words. Remember what the following commonly used commands actually demand from you:
   - *describe* requires a clear statement of the points in the right order;
   - *explain* requires you to 'describe' *and* give reasons;
   - *outline* requires a brief statement of the essential features;
   - *discuss* involves you in making points for and against something;
   - *compare* requires recognition of similarities *and* differences;
   - *contrast* expects you to write about the essential differences;
   - *suggest* is an invitation to speculate on causes or reasons;
   - *devise* demands that you design a credible solution to a (practical) issue;
   - *annotate* means you should write notes, usually relating to structures in a diagram;
   - *list*: compile a list of the essentials, with some explanatory expansion, showing you understand.
2 Prepare your background information for the essay or report.
3 Write a plan of the whole, so that you have identified the points in the introduction, the points you will expand upon, and the conclusion or summary to make.
4 Then write it at one sitting, keeping to a time allocation as far as possible (this skill develops with experience, if you work at it consciously).
5 Read what you have written very carefully afterwards, and preferably later, when you can return to it afresh. Make any necessary improvements before you submit it.
6 When it is marked, carefully check out the response your effort has received, particularly where criticisms are made. Painful though it may be, we all learn much more from our mistakes (or when we get lost) than when life is plain sailing!

Independent work; structured private study

When you have checked that your notes are complete, written up your practicals, and completed your wider reading, what is there to be done, other than 'revision'? The answer is: lots!

Look up the 'Problems and Assignments' activities in the relevant chapter of this book. You will find items that may help you to review and apply the information you have gained. You can use these to structure your private study in a way that will enhance your understanding (and prepare you for Advanced level examination issues).

Having your own copy of the Examination Board's syllabus (or your 'scheme of work', see Introduction, p. vii) to hand, and consulting it periodically, is a good way of keeping your independent studies focused wisely.

Revision

You will need a schedule of revision so that you can cover the course work topics you have studied several times before you are examined on them. Do this for your 'mock' exams first, and then revise your schedule in the light of this experience. It is most important you revise topics thoroughly, more than once. (You may need to be selective about the topics you revise, but you must take advice from teachers and tutors on this very important issue, first.)

In addition, focus on the exam papers themselves. Look at past papers very carefully, so that you are thoroughly familiar with the types of question you will have to answer and with the time that is allowed for each type of question. Note also the parts of the syllabus that each paper is concerned with, especially if you are working to either a modular or a core and 'options' syllabus.

Examinations
Coping with exam stress

Many of us suffer anxiety about revision and exams, although not everyone does! Being anxious is not related to our abilities, but the nervousness felt *may* affect performance in exams (and in revision work too). People seem to divide according to whether:
   - they have little or no 'adrenaline' in the situation, and are too relaxed to make the necessary preparations;
   - they are sufficiently anxious to develop strategies to cope, prepare and perform to do themselves justice;
   - they are initially far too anxious to develop true and realistic confidence in their own abilities.

Clearly, we can all benefit from help and guidance and regular practice with formal testing, but people that are *too* confident and those that are *too* anxious need to recognise they are 'special cases' in these matters.

1 Seek support and guidance early on. Anxiety will be a big problem if not identified and addressed long before 'final examinations'.
2 Work to identifying exactly what triggers or causes the condition. When you experience feelings of panic and a 'blank' mind, or muscle tension and tense breathing, what approaches or routines help as tension-reducing techniques?
3 Build up a record of the growing numbers of times and situations when the problem was largely overcome. Practise simple routines that reduce tension, even if they seem only slightly effective.
4 Make a practice of appropriately 'psyching-up' for small challenges, so as to become realistically convinced the task can be done. You need to acquire good experiences of success on an increasing number of occasions.

Just as with other aspects of study at this level, success never comes overnight, but rather by patient application of effort and analysis. Avoid 'perfectionism' if you can. Merely aim to do a reasonably competent job at all times, and allow yourself to get on with it!

Success with the different types of examination questions

Before you review the range of test items, the issue of examination *timing* can be identified as the over-riding issue for success. Only if you handle your timing successfully can you do justice to yourself and the paper. But you will be required to apply your timing routine just at that moment when anxiety can be greatest – when you have sat down for the 'big' exam, and are reading *the* paper for the first time. Be forewarned, so you can cope.

1 Set aside time to read the whole paper, including the instructions, really carefully.

2 When you have identified the question you will answer, write down the start and finish time for each.

3 Stick to your timing rigidly. Don't spend ages on just one or two questions, leaving others unanswered or skimped. The bulk of the marks for each question or task are what you must have to get the 'result'. If you struggle over a few questions in detail and do not deliver something on all the questions you have to answer, you are courting disaster. But remember, you have got to organise yourself on this vital point at a time of tension and stress. So be clear about the timing approach beforehand. Then do not let yourself 'escape' from the demands of timing under stress.

Multiple choice questions   There are different types of multiple choice question. For example:

Question 1   If radioactive carbon dioxide is made available to a green leaf in the light, we can obtain extra proof that during photosynthesis sugar and starch are built up. Which *one* of the following statements is *untrue*?

A Radioactive carbon dioxide gets into the leaf by the same pathway as unlabelled carbon dioxide.

B Radioactivity can be detected in a leaf by subsequently pressing a detached leaf against photographic film in the dark.

C Film exposed to radioactivity in a living leaf will show a dark image of the radioactive area in the leaf when the film is developed.

D With time the radioactivity in a living leaf will also appear in many sugars, in amino acids, in proteins and in new cell walls.

E In this experiment a plant must be destarched if newly formed, radioactive starch is to be detected at the end of the experiment.

Question 2   Which of the following cellular processes are directly dependent upon metabolic energy?

A entry of water into a cell by osmosis;

B removal of water from *Amoeba* via a contractile vacuole;

C diffusion of oxygen into a red blood cell;

D uptake of ions across the plasma membrane, from a very dilute solution;

E passage of the action potential along an axon plasma membrane;

F re-establishment of the resting potential in a depolarised membrane.

Make sure that you read and understand the precise instructions you are given in the general introduction to multiple choice questions before you start to choose your answer(s), so that you know whether you are looking for one right answer, one wrong answer or the possibility of several suitable examples of a principle.

Remember that all multiple choice questions contain one or many 'distractors' – statements that are not true, but are *almost* credible. On no account be casual or careless in reading them, before you decide. For example, in Question 1 only E is untrue; in Question 2, B, D and F all require direct involvement of ATP.

Structured short answer questions   There are very many examples of structured short answer questions in this book. For example, Problem 7.4 (p. 104), Problem 8.4 (p. 118), Problem 11.1 (p. 136), Problem 12.1 (p. 150), Problem 15.1 (p. 189), Problem 17.1 (p. 209), Problem 20.2 (p. 243), Problem 23.1 (p. 275) and Problem 25.3 (p. 299). Once you are familiar with this type of question you will be able to recognise others.

Questions like these are extremely common in Advanced level papers today. They are popular with examiners because they enable a wide range of syllabus topics to be covered in total. Also, in structured short answer questions, candidates get excellent guidance as to the length and importance of the answer required, both from the space set aside for the answer, and from the breakdown of total marks available for the answer to each part.

Good short answer questions allow fairly simple 'recall' issues of a basic nature to be asked first, allowing candidates to 'get started'. The use of 'data' or an experimental situation in the questions allows other aspects of learning and understanding to be tested. Issues like experimental method and experimental design may come up. Alternatively, issues of error or safety in practical work may be touched on. Because the questions give information too, candidates may be required to apply this information to solve another problem, or explain the significance of results in some other way. The testing of a range of the different skills of knowing and using biological knowledge makes structured short answer questions valuable. You can have confidence that your abilities across a broad front are being recognised and credited. With these questions, if you have done the work, you should get a result you deserve.

It's really worth practising structured short answer questions on topics in your syllabus, just as soon as you have finished studying the topic. Good structured short answer questions aid understanding, as well as testing candidates fairly.

Numerical questions   Numerical questions of various types may arise. For example, you may be required to summarise numerical results in graphs, or make simple calculations, such as of an arithmetic mean. You may be required to compare data or comment on its significance, by application of a (named) statistical test. Experience of these procedures will arise from your practical work, and you will develop the skills of manipulating data practically. They will also arise in doing selected problems in the *Study Guide*. For example, the common statistical tests are used in Problems 3.7 (p. 47), 3.8 (p. 48), 3.9 (p. 50), 19.2 (p. 223), and 28.1 (p. 346). Probability calculations are practised in Problem 29.4 (p. 359). Once again, familiarity and experience should develop your skills of data handling.

Essay questions   We develop the skills of essay writing in the process of course work. The ability to write a concise, logical presentation on an issue of importance is a highly marketable skill. Many people sustain themselves financially with the pen and the word processor. This might come to apply to you, too!

Examples of appropriate essay titles are given at the end of every Chapter of the *Study Guide*. You are likely to be required to answer some of these, or similar essay questions, as part of course work. The essential steps are spelt out in 'When preparing to *write an essay* . . .', above. Once again, familiarity and experience should develop your skills of essay writing.

Index

Index

Index